URBAN HEART.
CUBAN SOUL.

PRIVATE STOCK
RING GAUGE 43
5¹/₂" LENGTH

NUMBER 35
RING GAUGE 35
4¹/₂" LENGTH

SLIM PANATELLAS
RING GAUGE 26
4³/₈" LENGTH

SMALL CIGARS
RING GAUGE 21
3¹/₂" LENGTH

A REVOLUTION IN TASTE

SOBRANIE
CUBAN
LEAF CIGARS

TEN SMALL CIGARS
Made exclusively from tobacco of
100% Cuban origin.

TOBACCO SERIOUSLY DAMAGES HEALTH

SMOKING CAUSES HEART DISEASE
Chief Medical Officers' Warning

Dinner gongs

Where are London's best new restaurants, bars and cafés? Every year *Time Out* hosts the **Time Out Eating & Drinking Awards** to highlight them. *Guy Dimond* witnessed the feast of talent.

It's not just the big and the bold that *Time Out* celebrates – both in this Guide, in the weekly *Time Out* magazine and at the annual Eating & Drinking Awards ceremony, *Time Out* champions fabulous neighbourhood restaurants, the best bargain meals, gastropubs, and those little places that enrich eating and drinking in London but that you're unlikely to read about anywhere else.

How the Awards work
On page 31 we ask you to nominate your favourite bars, pubs and restaurants in eight categories designed to reflect the diversity of dining and drinking places in London. The latest restaurants, the best interior design, the best venues for family meals, the bars where the drinks are great and the staff attitude-free – we recognise and reward them all. Based on your suggestions, we draw up a shortlist of six places in each category, and then our judges – all expert reviewers for the *Time Out Eating & Drinking Guide* – eat and drink their way anonymously round all of them. Our reviewers drop by just like anyone else, pay just like anyone else, and leave unrecognised. (Unlike most other critics our reviewers do not attend launch parties and do not accept PR invitations.) We then inform you of our experiences – which are just the same as yours would be, unlike the kid-glove treatment that certain critics inevitably receive.

In Year 2000, the *Time Out* Eating & Drinking Awards were the usual star-studded event, compered by Richard Wilson and with awards presented by Graham Norton, Jane Asher, Al Murray, Wayne Hemingway, Kim Wilde, Tara Palmer-Tomkinson, Alan Davies and Paul and Stacey Young. The venue was the fabulous Great Eastern Hotel, Sir Terence Conran's hotel and restaurant complex – and of course Sir Terence was on hand and presented an award too.

CANARY WHARF - NOT JUST AN OFFICE ENVIRONMENT

FREE WEEKEND PARKING

3 HOURS FREE PARKING WHEN YOU SPEND £5 OR MORE AT CANARY WHARF. PRESENT YOUR CAR PARKING TICKET
TO THE RETAILER FOR STAMPING. AFTER 3 HOURS, DISCOUNTED RATES APPLY.

FOR MORE RETAIL INFORMATION CALL CANARY WHARF GROUP PLC ON 020 7418 2042

We're glad to welcome...

some of the more notable new places we've been delighted to welcome since the last edition of the Time Out Eating & Drinking Guide.

In chronological order

The Great Eastern Hotel
Schnecke
St Martins Lane
Soviet Canteen
Al Duca
Quilon
Riso
Busaba Eathai
Monte's
Zeta
The Salusbury
The Pool
Black Truffle
Rosmarino
25 Canonbury Lane
China House and The Orient
Quiet Revolution
K-10
The New End
Zander
Kennington Lane
Il Forno
The Belvedere
The Light
Elbow Room, N1
Spoon+ at Sanderson
Tate Modern
Cotto
1 Blossom Street
Potemkin
Smiths of Smithfield
Admiralty
Incognico
Alloro
High Holborn

Sadly missed

We'll especially miss these landmark caffs and restaurants, which have shut down since the last Guide was published.

Alfredo's *Essex Road, N1.*
Islington's finest greasy spoon kicked the bucket – after 80 years of fry-ups.
The Canteen *Chelsea Harbour, SW10.*
Lack of business forced the closure of this fine dining establishment; the owners blamed the landlord.
Crowbar Coffee *W1, N1 and EC1.*
These stylish coffee bars predated the Starbucks invasion.
The Good Cook *Powis Square, W11.*
Allegra McEvedy moved from Notting Hill to Kensington to a tent in the park... but where is she now?
Hodja Nasreddin *Newington Green Road, N1.*
The Turkish bazaar has pulled its tent-door shut for the last time.
Mandeer *Bloomsbury Way, WC1.*
The 'Ayurvedic' Indian vegetarian restaurant survived only a couple of years after its enforced move from Hanway Street (where it had prospered since 1961, serving George Harrison among others).
Maremma *Theberton Street, N1.*
Islington's *Time Out* Award winner for the most child-friendly restaurant in 2000.
The Market Café *Fournier Street, E1.*
For the past 30 years this caff was a fixture – not least with artists Gilbert and George, who ate breakfast and lunch there for much of that time.
The Tibetan Restaurant *Irving Street, WC2.*
Now there's nowhere to get a yak milk tea anywhere near Leicester Square.
Upper Street Fish Shop *Upper Street, N1.*
After 20 years of serving some of the best fish and chips in London to appreciative Islington dwellers, Olga and Alan Conway decided it was time to call it a day. The site is being taken over by Nando's at the end of October 2000.
Venus Kebab House *Charlotte Street, W1.*
One of Charlotte Street's Cypriot eateries that introduced al fresco dining to a wary British public.

The Winners

First row Duke of Cambridge (Best Gastropub), Dick Bradsell (Special Award for Outstanding Achievement, as bar consultant over the last two decades).
Second row Isola (Best Interior Design).

Open season

Guy Dimond on this year's highlights and forthcoming openings.

As the Guide went to press there were scores of new openings we were unable to include, with scores more scheduled for the next few months. Dates are approximate (you know what builders are like), and so are other details (ditto restaurateurs).

September 2000

L'Anis
1 Kensington High Street, W8 (020 7795 6533).
The team behind Frith Street has moved west into the former bank that was the Good Cook during the summer of 2000.

Bear on the Square
2 St John's Square, EC1 (020 7608 2117).
More pub than gastro-pub this time, from the award-winning Geronimo Inns.

Christopher's
101 Buckingham Palace Road, SW1 (020 7834 9494).
Branch of the American restaurant (see p21 **The Americas**) in the Thistle Hotel, Victoria Station.

Living Room
443 Coldharbour Lane,SW9.
New, more sophisticated branch of Brixton's Dogstar.

Perc%nto
16-28 Ludgate Hill, EC4.
City Italian from the Etrusca Group.

Public Life
Commercial Street, E1 (020 7375 2425).
Cyber café in a former public toilet.

Pug
66-68 Chiswick High Road, W4 (020 8987 9988).
Chiswick nosh.

Six-13
19 Wigmore Street, W1 (020 7629 6135).

A kosher restaurant that promises high-end, interesting fusion food.

Souk
165 Clapham High Street, SW4 (020 7622 4004).
North African-themed eaterie from Lee Chapman, former footballer and the man behind Teatro in the West End.

Tokyo City
46 Gresham Street, EC2 (020 7726 0308).
City Japanese restaurant.

Zero Degrees
29-31 Montpelier Vale, SE3 (020 8852 5619).
Great new microbrewery and pizza joint facing Blackheath.

October 2000

Bush Bar & Grill
45A Goldhawk Road, W14
A style bar and restaurant comes to Shepherd's Bush.

Cargo
Rivington Street, EC2.
Second bar from Shoreditch's Cantaloupe (see p209 **Bars**).

Carluccio's Caffè
Fenwick, 63 New Bond Street, W1.
A second branch is opening inside Fenwick's store (see also p199 **Cafés**).

Hakkassan
8 Hanway Place, W1.
Asian cooking from Wagamama's founder.

Lemon Thyme
190 Castelnau, SW13 (020 8748 3437). Another Red Pepper Group restaurant (see p189 **Pizza & Pasta**), close to Hammersmith Bridge.

?
92 Kensington Park Road, W11 (020 7581 4045).
Where Leith's used to be, now bought by the hotel group that runs the Charlotte Street hotel – the name is undecided.

Opium
A big new bar planned for Covent Garden.

Perzzomolo
142 Wandsworth Bridge Road, SW6.
An A-Z Group restaurant, so you can expect high standards and Italian cooking.

10 Covent Garden
Great Queen Street, WC2 (www.10-coventgarden.co.uk).
A vast new bar from the 10 Room (see p222) crowd.

November 2000

The Cinnamon Club
Old Westminster Library, SW1.
Smart Indian restaurant fronted by Iqbal Wahhab, former editor of *Tandoori* magazine.

Itsu
103 Wardour Street, W1.
A second branch of Brompton Cross's Award-winning Asian conveyor-belt restaurant (see p149 **Oriental**).

Spiga Chelsea
312 King's Road, SW6.
A branch of Soho's popular Spiga restaurant (see p104 **Italian**), on the site where Café Milan used to be.

2001 and beyond...

Providores
Marylebone, W1.
Kiwi-style café-bar from Peter Gordon and Anna Hansen, formerly of the Sugar Club.

Temple
9 Conduit Street, W1.
French restaurant next door to, and run by, Momo (see p144 **North African**).

The White House
65 Clapham Park Road,SW4.
A restaurant, bar and private members' club.

Third row Schnecke (Best Bargain Meal), The Real Greek (Best New Restaurant).
Fourth row Lab (Best Bar), Maremma (*Kids Out* Best Family Restaurant).
Fifth row Tas (Best Vegetarian Meal), Luca (Best Local Restaurant).

Where to...

...do brunch
see also **Cafés, Brasseries**
Aurora (Sat)
The Avenue (Sun)
Bank (Sat, Sun)
Beach Blanket Babylon (Sat, Sun)
Bluebird (Sat, Sun)
Boisdale (Sat, Sun)
Butlers Wharf Chop House (Sat, Sun)
Cactus Blue (Sat, Sun)
Canyon (Sat, Sun)
Christopher's (Sat, Sun)
Crescent (Sun)
Coyote Café (Sat, Sun)
Dakota (Sat, Sun)
Frocks (Sat, Sun)
Giraffe (daily)
Honest Cabbage (Sat, Sun)
Idaho (Sat, Sun)
Indigo (Sat, Sun)
Joe Allen (Sat, Sun)
Kavanagh's (Sun)
Lawn (Sat, Sun)
Lola's (Sat, Sun)
Mash (Sat, Sun)
Maxwells (daily)
Medicine Bar (Sat, Sun)
Montana (Sat, Sun)
New Restaurant at the V&A (Sun)
The Park (Sat, Sun)
PJ's Grill (daily)
Smith's (Sat, Sun)
Vong (Sat, Sun)
Windows (Sun)

...eat Sunday lunch
Butler's Wharf Chop House
Coq d'Argent
Cucina
Greenhouse
Gresslin's
Jack's Place (Sept-Easter)
Quality Chop House
Putney Bridge

Monsieur Max
Redmond's
Rhodes on the Square
Rules
Stepping Stone
Tate Gallery Restaurant
La Ventura

...eat at any time (24 hours)
1997
Anadolu Lokantasi
Brick Lane Beigel Bake
Café Boheme (Fri-Sat)
The Knosherie
Old Compton Café
Tinseltown
Vingt-Quatre

...eat late
See also **Chinese, Middle Eastern, Portuguese, Spanish, Turkish**
Aka
Al's Bar Café
Balans
Café du Jardin
Le Caprice
Circus
Coast
Häagen-Dazs on the Square
Hard Rock
Incognico
The Ivy
Kensington Place
Lahore Kebab House
Little Italy
Mash
Mezzo/Mezzonine
Pharmacy
Quo Vadis
Randall & Aubin
RYO
Satsuma
Smollensky's on the Strand

Souk
Teatro
Villandry
Yo! Sushi/Yo! Below

...take the kids
See also **Cafés, Brasseries, Fish & Chips, Pizza & Pasta**
Babe Ruth's
Banners
Bel & the Dragon
Bread & Roses
Café Pacifico
The Depot
Ed's Easy Diner
Häagen-Dazs
Hard Rock Café
Hotel du Vin
Lawn
Marine Ices
Maxwells
Planet Hollywood
Rainforest Café
RK Stanleys
Smollensky's on the Strand
Sticky Fingers
TGI Fridays
Tootsies
Wintons Soda Fountain
Yellow River Café

...take teenagers
See also **Pizza & Pasta**
Arkansas Café
Belgo Centraal
Busaba Eathai
Café Med
Café Pacifico
Capital Radio Café
Dish Dash
Hard Rock Café
Havana
Noho
Oriental City Food Court
Planet Hollywood

Satsuma
Sausage & Mash Café
Soho Spice
Sound
Tiger Lil's
Wagamama
Wintons Soda Fountain
Wok Wok
Yo! Sushi

...take the grandparents
Al Bustan
American Bar, The Savoy
L'Aventure
Bistrot 190
Boisdale
Brady's
Builders Arms
Butlers Wharf Chop House
Chez Moi
L'Estaminet
Frederick's
Goring Hotel
Greenhouse
Greens
Hotel du Vin
Ibla
Jin Kichi
The Library, The Lanesborough
Launceston Place
Lundum's
Mr Chow
North Sea Fish Restaurant
Passione
Pied à Terre
Prospect Grill
Redmond's
Rules
Savoy Grill
Shepherd's
Stephen Bull
Tate Gallery Restaurant
Vasco & Piero's Pavilion
Veronica's

ABSOLUT SQUEEZE.

ABSOLUT CITRON IS NATURALLY FLAVOURED WITH ORANGE, GRAPEFRUIT, LEMON AND LIME.
YOU'D BE HARD PRESSED TO FIND A PURER VODKA. ENJOY ICE COLD.

Silks & Spice
Thai-Malaysian restaurant

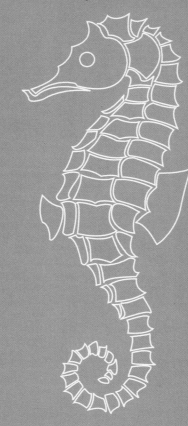

information line on: 020 7278 0999
or visit our website at:
www.silksandspice.com

Clerkenwell City

Temple Court 11
Queen Victoria St, London EC4N 4UJ
Tel: 020 7248 7878 fax: 020 7248 9595
open mon-tue 11am-11pm
wed-fri 11am-2am

42 Northampton Rd, London EC1R 0HU
Tel: 020 7278 9983 Fax: 020 7713 6783
open mon-fri 11am-11pm

Camden

28 Chalk Farm Rd, London NW1 8AF
Tel: 020 7267 5751 Fax: 020 7482 0271
open mon-thu 12pm-11pm
fri-sat 12pm-11.30pm
sun 11.30am-10.30pm

Foley

23 Foley St, London W1P 7LA
Tel: 020 7636 2718 Fax: 020 7323 1927
open mon-fri 12pm-11pm
sat 5.30pm-11pm
sun 11.30am-10.30pm

Chiswick

95 Chiswick High Rd, London W4 2EF
Tel: 020 8995 7991 Fax: 020 8994 7773
open mon-thu 12-3pm/5-11pm
fri 12-3pm/5pm-11.30pm
sat 12-11.30pm   sun 12pm-10.30pm

Chelsea

561 Kings Rd, London SW6 2EB
Tel: 020 7736 2333 Fax: 020 7736 0899
open mon-sat 12pm-11pm
sun 12pm-10.30pm

little plates from £2.90
big bowls from £5.20

highlights from our menu...

roast duck ramen
egg noodles with roast duck
in 5 spice soup

salmon red curry
pan fried salmon fillet in red
curry sauce, with steamed rice
and papaya salad

squid sambal tumis
baby squid in very hot chilli
paste of tomatoes, chillies and
lemon grass, with steamed rice
and papaya salad

won ton noodles
with shredded chicken and shitake,
charsiu and prawn won ton soup

laksa
egg noodles with fishcakes, prawns,
baby squid and crabsticks ini mild
curry and coconut soup

udon hokkien noodles
thick udon noodles with chicken,
fishcake and baby squid in thick gravy

ekachai
oriental dining room

9-10 arcade
liverpool street
london EC2M 7PN
tel: 020 7626 1155
fax: 020 7626 1145

opening time:
mon - fri 11am - 10pm
sat - sun closed

...dine alone

See also **Cafés, Fish & Chips**
Café Delancy
Café Flo
Café Rouge
Chez Gérard
Dôme
Food for Thought
Laxeiro
Moshi Moshi Sushi
Nicole's
Oriel
Pizza Express
RK Stanleys
Table Café
Itsu
Star Café
Wagamama
World Food Café

...take a date

Bibendum
Le Caprice
Chez Bruce
Claridge's Bar
Club Gascon
Criterion
Dakota
French House Dining Room
Grano
Isola
The Ivy
Julie's Wine Bar
Lickfold Inn
Mango Room
Momo
Odette's
Orrery
Sugar Club
Quo Vadis
Trader Vic's
Veerswamy
Vong
Zafferano

...go with a crowd

All Bar One
Babe Ruth's
Bah Humbug
Bar Lorca
Café Fish
Café Latino
Café Pacifico
Cubana
Czech Club
Down Mexico Way

The Finca
Havana
Jamies
Karahi King
Mash
Mezzo
New World
Ognisko Polskie
Rodizio Rico
Satay Bar
Schnecke
Si Señor
Solly's
Souk
Texas Embassy Cantina
Viet Hoa

...enjoy the view

Aquarium
Baradero
The Belvedere
Blue Print Café
The Bridge
Butlers Wharf Chop House
Cantina del Ponte
Coq d'Argent
The Depot
Fifth Floor
Four Regions
Lotus Chinese Floating Restaurant
Mem Saheb on Thames
Nipa
L'Odéon
Oxo Tower
The People's Palace
Le Pont de la Tour
Putney Bridge
Ransome's Dock
San Miguel's on the River
Seven
Shakespeare's Globe
Tate Modern
The Tenth
Vertigo 42
Whistable Oyster Fishery Company
Windows

...go back in time

See also **Pie & Mash** (in **Budget**), **Fish & Chips**
Bar Italia
Bleeding Heart
Borough Café
Connaught
El Vino
Fortnum & Mason

Gambardella
Goring Hotel
India Club
The Ivy
Jerusalem Tavern
Julie's Wine Bar
The Lamb
Maggie Jones
C Notarianni & Sons
Perdoni's
Quality Chop House
The Ritz
Regent Milk Bar
Rules
Simpson's-in-the-Strand
Sweetings
Victory Café

...eat outdoors

See also **Cafés** (especially Park Cafés)
Bleeding Heart
Blue Print Café
Canyon
Dakota
El Parador
Engineer
Golders Hill Park Refreshment House
Idaho
Jason's
1 Blossom Street
Orrery
Oshobasho Café
Le Pont de la Tour
Room at the Halcyon
The Ship
Sun & Doves
Truckles of Pied Bull Yard

...eat meat

Arkansas Café
B&K Salt Beef Bar
Butlers Wharf Chop House
Chez Gérard
Christopher's
City Rhodes
Dorchester Grill Room
El Gaucho
Gaucho Grill
Greenhouse
The Guinea
The Ivy
Jack's Place
Lindsay House
Mangal
Maroush
La Pampa Grill

Popeseye Steak House
Quality Chop House
Rhodes in the Square
RK Stanleys
Rodizio Rico
Rôtisserie Jules
The Rôtisserie
Rules
Savoy Grill
The Ship
Simpson's-in-the-Strand
Smith's of Smithfield
Springbok Café
St John
Wiltons

...raid the bar

Boisdale (whiskey)
Belgo chain & Bierdrome (Belgian beer)
Cactus Blue (tequila)
Dovetail (Belgian beer)
Freedom Brewing Company (micro-brewery)
La Perla (tequila)
Mash (micro-brewery)
Mulligan's (whiskey)
Navajo Joe (tequila)
Na Zdrowie The Polish Bar (Polish vodka)
Tsar's Bar (vodka)
Wenlock Arms (cider)

...find the buzz

See also **Bars**
Asia de Cuba
Bank
Bar Italia
Belgo chain
Cicada
Cubana
Dakota
The Eagle
Great Eastern Dining Room
The Ivy
Joe Allen
Kensington Place
Little Italy
Mash
Momo
Moro
Osteria Basilico
Quaglino's
Sakoni
Smith's of Smithfield
Souk
Spoon+ at Sanderson
Tuba
Yo! Sushi

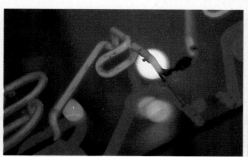

A FRESH APPROACH TO PASTA

SPAGHETTI HOUSE

LONDON is a city full of wonderful, varied and excellent restaurants, sometimes they are not easy to find, so to help you we would like to suggest some of our excellent restaurants.

Spaghetti House Restaurants have been serving high quality Italian food and wine to Londoners and visitors for over 45 years.

Our friendly and efficient staff will make all your friends feel at home when visiting a Spaghetti House Restaurant.

Find them in Theatreland, close to West End cinemas, theatres, galleries and the best shopping areas in town.

LONDON RESTAURANTS

Oxford Street and Shopping
74 Duke Street W1
☎ 020 7629 6097
⊖ BOND STREET

British Museum
20 Sicilian Avenue WC1
☎ 020 7405 5215
⊖ HOLBORN

Theatreland and Covent Garden
24 Cranbourn Street WC2
☎ 020 7836 8168

30 St Martin's Lane WC2
☎ 020 7836 1626
⊖ LEICESTER SQUARE

Buckingham Palace & Victoria Theatres
3 Bressenden Place SW1
☎ 020 7834 5650
⊖ VICTORIA

Harrods and Knightsbridge Shopping
77 Knightsbridge SW1
☎ 020 7235 8141
⊖ KNIGHTSBRIDGE

SPAGHETTI HOUSE

24 Cranbourn Street London WC2H 7AA   Tel: 020 7395 0390   Fax: 020 7395 0391
www.spaghetti-house.co.uk

Fax-a-Menu service

✳✳✳

Unable to decide what to eat and where to go? What better way to help you decide than to look at the menu first? That's precisely where our Fax-a-Menu service is invaluable. If you have access to a fax machine, simply phone the number below from any telephone or telephone on a fax machine and follow the instructions to receive a copy of the menu from any of the restaurants listed.

09063 655 556

1001	Atlantic Bar & Grill	**1018**	Incognico	**1036**	Rasa W1
1002	Bam-Bou	**1019**	Isola	**1037**	The Real Greek
1003	Bank	**1020**	The Ivy	**1038**	Rhodes in the Square
1004	Belair House	**1021**	Lola's		
1005	The Belvedere	**1022**	Mandalay	**1039**	The River Café
1006	Bluebird	**1023**	Mash	**1040**	The Room at the Halcyon
1007	Boisdale	**1024**	Mezzo		
1008	Café Fish	**1025**	Mezzonine	**1041**	J. Sheekey
1009	Café Spice Namaste	**1026**	Mirabelle	**1042**	Sofra
1010	Le Caprice	**1027**	Osteria d'Isola	**1043**	Soho Spice
1011	Chez Moi	**1028**	Oxo Tower	**1044**	Stephen Bull
1012	Cheznico	**1029**	Ozer	**1045**	Tamarind
1013	Club Gascon	**1030**	Pharmacy	**1046**	Teatro
1014	Coq d'Argent	**1031**	Quaglino's	**1047**	The Sugar Club
1015	Ebury Wine Bar & Restaurant	**1032**	Quality Chop House	**1048**	Vong
		1033	Ransome's Dock	**1049**	Zaika
1016	Florians	**1034**	Rasa	**1050**	Zander
1017	French House Dining Room	**1035**	Rasa Samudra		

STOP PRESS...

We may be adding further restaurants to this list throughout the year. For a full list of menus available, please follow the instructions above and then use the code 1000.

ring ring ring ring, ring ring ring ring,
ring ring ring ring, ring ring ring ring,
ring ring ring ring, ring ring ring ring,
ring ring ring ring, ring ring ring ring,
ring ring ring ring, ring ring ring ring,
ring ring ring ring, ring ring ring ring,
ring ring ring ring, ring ring ring ring,
ring ring ring ring, ring ring ring ring,
ring ring ring ring, ring ring ring ring,
ring ring ring ring, ring ring...

hang up!
and
click

book2eat.com

New Year,
St. Valentine's day,
Birthdays, Easter,
Anniversaries,
Mother's Day, Office
Parties, Christmas…
An occasion for a lot of fun or an
occasion for a lot to organise? Both.
Organising can be fun: book2eat
helps you build up the excitement for
that special day.
No more rude receptionists, busy
phones or annoying answering
machines. With book2eat.com you
can see which restaurants are available and check their websites to
make sure they suit the occasion.
Take your time to value the opportuni-
ties, have fun! Make a special list in
'mybook2eat' or take advantage of
one of the many promotions - the
choice is yours!

london's live, online restaurant reservation service

The Restaurants

African & Caribbean

There's a considerable overlap in ingredients and cooking styles between the African and Caribbean cultures, yet in London it is the sheer diversity of restaurants dedicated to these cuisines that is most striking. Contrast, for instance, **Mandola**'s delicately flavoured Middle Eastern-influenced Sudanese dishes with the robust, chilli-hot Nigerian cooking at **Obalende Suya**.

The capital's African dining scene is now dominated by Ethiopian and Eritrean restaurants such as **Lalibela** and **Asmara**, serving traditional, richly spiced stews (wot) eaten with injera bread and served with warm hospitality. These places successfully perform the balancing act of offering authentic food for their own communities and providing an accessible experience for newcomers to the cuisine. The emergence of elegant **Mekasha** shows how quickly this cuisine is moving upmarket.

The more established of London's Caribbean restaurants are also becoming increasingly sophisticated affairs, as witnessed by smooth operations such as the **Brixtonian Havana Club** and **Jamaica Blue**. The seemingly automatic association of Caribbean food with rum cocktails and a party atmosphere means that restaurants such as **BB's** and the **Mango Room** have successfully carved out niches as feel-good party venues.

From our experience it is always worth phoning ahead to double-check opening hours. Similarly, most of these restaurants are distinctly laid-back and not designed for those eating in a hurry. Instead, come here for a relaxed and mellow dining experience.

African

Central

Covent Garden WC2

Calabash
The Africa Centre, 38 King Street, WC2 (020 7836 1976). Covent Garden tube.
Bar **Open** 5.30-11pm Mon-Sat.
Restaurant **Lunch served** 12.30-2.30pm Mon-Fri. **Dinner served** 6-10.30pm Mon-Sat.
Main courses £12-£15. **Service** 10%.
Credit DC, MC, £TC, V.
Just a short stroll from the mayhem of Covent Garden, it's possible to dine on pan-African cuisine in sedate, discreetly positioned surroundings. A long-established institution, Calabash is located in the basement of the Africa Centre. The journey from the street, down the stairs and through a gloomy corridor ends in a rather murky subterranean dining room. The anonymous décor and a large TV in a corner near the bar create a sense of airport lounge limbo, which was compounded on our visit by the fact that only one other group of lunchtime diners was present. Background African music and a courteous waiter did, however, brighten the surroundings a little. There's an extensive, reasonably priced menu offering dishes from all over Africa (vegetarians are especially well catered for). Our starters – a hot tomato salad, garnished with green chillies, and fried plantain with a powerfully hot dipping sauce – were simple and unpretentious. The main courses came in generous portions but were a bit bland: groundnut stew with chicken (strictly for peanut lovers), and the Calabash special (a vegetarian assortment of beans, plantain, sweet potato and salad). Eba,

the most intriguing side dish, consisted of mashed cassava with a distinctive sour flavour. Desserts proved to be Middle Eastern-influenced syrup pastries, but the Abyssinian coffee arrived according to tradition, accompanied by incense.
Babies and children welcome. Book weekends. Entertainment: African bands 9pm-3am Fri (ground floor of Africa Centre). Takeaway service. Map 14/7L.

West

Notting Hill W11

Mandola
139-141 Westbourne Grove, W11 (020 7229 4734). Notting Hill Gate tube/23 bus. **Meals served** noon-11.30pm Mon-Sat; noon-10.30pm Sun. **Main courses** £6-£9.50. **Unlicensed.** **Corkage** £1. **Credit** MC, £TC, V.
Much expanded from its original cramped premises, this pleasant Sudanese restaurant now extends over three rooms, attractively decorated in bright, warm colours punctuated by woven straw baskets and pictures. On our weekday lunchtime visit, however, it was empty, apart from friends of the owner chatting in the entrance room – a great shame, as the cooking is as good as ever and the service is friendly (if a little timid). The meal got off to a flying start, with generous portions of mish (smooth, tangy sheep's milk yoghurt flavoured with spices) and aswad salat (a fried aubergine salad in a subtle sweet and sour dressing) served with pitta. All the while, sounds of frying and clanking pots and pans emanated from the kitchen, providing resounding evidence of freshly cooked food. Next, we feasted on tender, juicy lamb kustaletta (tiny fried chops of flavourful meat, medium cooked as requested), samak magli (pieces of delicately flavoured tilapia fish in a light batter) and adas (lentils in a tomato sauce flavoured with crunchy caramelised garlic). Portions were so generous that we had to pass on date mousse for dessert (a Mandola speciality), opting instead for fragrant mint tea. The BYO policy (with an off-licence next door) makes this very good value dining indeed.
Babies and children welcome. Takeaway service. Map 11/6A.

South

Battersea SW11

Zula
62 Lavender Hill, SW11 (020 7223 4618). Clapham Junction rail/77, 137 bus. **Meals served** 6pm-midnight daily. **Main courses** £4-£8. **Credit** MC, V.
This friendly, intimate restaurant on a busy stretch of road mainly caters to a local Eritrean community. The frilly décor brings to mind an old-fashioned French restaurant, but the menu is unmistakably Eritrean. The manager very helpfully came to our table to explain the dishes. Skipping the likes of houmous and fish salad, we headed straight for the mains. They arrived with a huge communal platter of injera, allowing us to dip into different dishes, scooping up portions with strips of bread. The definite highlight was the silsi assa, pieces of very fresh fish in a subtly spiced sauce that far exceeded the humble menu description of 'fish curry'. Awaze kilwa (fried strips of beef in a fiercely hot chilli sauce) and nay tsom (an assortment of vegetable dishes including spinach, cabbage, potato and carrot) offered an interesting range of flavours and textures. The traditional coffee, served with fragrant incense and a bowl of freshly made popcorn, was worth the considerable wait. But then, judging by the crowd of smartly dressed young Eritreans who were arriving as we were heading home, it was just the beginning of a long night.
Babies and children welcome; high chairs. Tables outdoors (2, pavement). Takeaway service. Vegetarian menu.

Brixton SW9

Asmara
386 Coldharbour Lane, SW9 (020 7737 4144). Brixton tube/rail. **Dinner served** 5pm-12.30am daily. **Main courses** £3.80-£7.50. **Credit** AmEx, MC, V.
Among the pubs and clubs of Coldharbour Lane, Asmara is a peaceful haven for Brixton diners. The pink-sponged walls, chandeliers and embroidered white drapes give this intimate restaurant a dainty feel. Diners can choose between conventional tables and chairs or traditional low wicker seats. Despite a concession to conservative palates (in the form of chicken and chips), the order of the day here is Eritrean home-cooking with plenty of injera to mop it up, all lovingly prepared by a motherly figure in the back kitchen. We started with zelzil tibssi – tender pieces of lamb, flavoured with onion and green chilli – served sizzling in a clay dish. Alicha derho was a tasty creation of chicken and hard-boiled egg in a richly spiced sauce, while well-judged green spinach, flavoured with chilli and garlic, was particularly impressive. Foul midemas, a version of the Middle Eastern classic f'ul medames, was roughly crushed broad bean purée, flavoured with spices and tomatoes: extremely moreish. The meal concluded with a pleasant ceremony in which roasting coffee beans are paraded around the restaurant before being whisked back into the kitchen. When the brew arrives it is accompanied by burning frankincense and a large bowl of popcorn.
Babies and children welcome. Takeaway service. Map 18.

Streatham SW16

Trini's
13 High Parade, Streatham High Road, SW16 (020 8696 9669). Brixton tube/rail/Streatham Hill rail/57, 118, 133, 159 bus. **Meals served** 2-11pm Mon, Thur-Sat; 5-11pm Tue, Wed, Sun. **Main courses** £6-£10. **Credit** MC, V.
Behind a deceptively small, nondescript façade, via a bar area, is this large, bright Trinidadian restaurant. Yellow walls (complete with wall sculptures of nubile dancing figures) and a steel-drum soundtrack evoke a relaxed, party atmosphere. Trini's pulls in a multiracial crowd which included, on our Sunday evening visit, several families with young children in tow. The bargain-priced menu (no dish costs more than £3) offers a canter through Trinidadian classics such as goat curry and the intriguingly named Bus Up Shot Roti. Our harassed but friendly waitress was happy to describe the dishes to us. Once ordered, the food arrived promptly. Coo-coo (baked cornmeal) and salt-fish were both tasty dishes, but the callaloo was particularly good: a moreish concoction of callaloo greens flavoured with coconut milk and garlic. Only the huge portion of barbecue chicken in an overly sweet sticky sauce disappointed. The steady stream of diners showed the appeal of good, down-to-earth cooking at rock-bottom prices.
Babies and children welcome; high chairs. Booking advisable. No smoking. Takeaway service.

North

Islington N1

Merkato
193A Caledonian Road, N1 (020 7837 1838). King's Cross tube/rail. **Meals served** noon-midnight daily. **Main courses** £5-£8. **Set meal** £19 (for two). **Credit** MC, V.
Housed in a former pub, this Ethiopian restaurant offers a pleasant haven on a rather bleak stretch of Caledonian Road. Despite the incongruous mix of vestigial pub Tudor and Ethiopian pictures and artefacts, the genuine warmth and enthusiasm of the staff made us feel instantly at home. First impressions of the cooking were not quite as reassuring, though. Given the large choice on the menu, the speed with which our food arrived was disconcerting and the meagreness of the portions (although partly compensated for by generous quantities of injera) was also a surprise. But any misgivings vanished with the first mouthfuls of rich, tasty doro wot, and azipha (a lentil dish dressed in an intriguingly fiery sauce with a mustard bite). More delicate flavours also shone through in spinach wot and fragrant kinche (cereal grains). In no time at all, as we settled down to the final ceremony of frankincense, roasted coffee and pistachio-studded baklava, the restaurant was brimming with a lively, appreciative Ethiopian crowd.
Babies and children welcome; high chairs. No-smoking tables. Takeaway service.

Kentish Town NW5

Lalibela
137 Fortress Road, NW5 (020 7284 0600). Kentish Town tube/rail. **Meals served** 7-10.30pm Mon-Sat. **No credit cards.**
From the unprepossessing entrance on a busy main road to the plastic brickwork in the downstairs bar, it soon becomes apparent that Lalibela is not gunning for any design awards. But once you're safely installed in the upstairs dining room (with its infinitely preferable woven fabric wall coverings), even the uncomfortable ordeal of stowing your legs under the traditional low wooden seats seems bearable. A lively mix of Ethiopian and other diners injected the necessary brio while we pondered the lengthy menu. Crisp lamb samosas and shrimp on sugarcane were our first choices. Next up, main courses arrived with a foundation of injera and a friendly demonstration from the waitress on how to position each dish within easy scooping and dunking range of the bread supply. Fried spinach with lamb had a distinctive herbal overtone, while doro wot had a richly spiced sauce. Side dishes of shembera wot (small, chewy balls of chickpea flour in a thick sauce) and bamiya (okra in tomato sauce) delivered a colourful assortment of distinctive flavours. Despite the brisk trade, service was attentive – our waitress even found time to show us the coffee beans roasting in their pan before reappearing in a cloud of frankincense smoke with a flask of Ethiopia's finest.
Babies and children welcome.

Swiss Cottage NW6

Mekasha
75 Fairfax Road, NW6 (020 7625 8964). Swiss Cottage tube. **Lunch served** noon-3.30pm Tue-Sun. **Dinner served** 6-11.30pm daily. **Minimum** £10. **Main courses** £3-£7. **Service** 10%. **Credit** DC, MC, V.
Tucked away in a discreet Swiss Cottage side-street, this is London's most upmarket Ethiopian restaurant. A restful colour scheme of white and dark purple walls and dark wood sets off the carefully chosen selection of Ethiopian fine art and ceramics. Staunch traditionalists and Ethiopian locals favour the small back room, with its traditional messob (low wicker tables), but less supple visitors might want to stick with the western-style tables in the main restaurant. Wherever you end up, though, the seductively written, short menu offers the same choice of traditional dishes, which arrive at the table in colourful woven containers. The charming owner is keen to explain the intricacies of the cuisine. Even if fans of traditional injera are disappointed by the Mekasha version, which is made from self-raising flour and lacks the customary sour tang, the rest of the menu leaves no room for complaints. Doro wot featured a tasty piece of chicken that easily came off the bone. The rich sauce had a delicate cinnamon flavour. Awaze merek (a chilli lamb dish) provided a satisfying kick, while ataket (fried mixed vegetables) was a simple but likeable dish. Coffee, served in a beautiful flask and drunk from tiny cups, provided a suitably civilised ending.
Babies and children welcome. Separate room for parties, seats 12. Tables outdoors (2, pavement). Takeaway service.

Caribbean

Central

Mayfair W1

Jamaica Blue
18 Maddox Street, W1 (020 7408 2272/www.jamaicablue.co.uk). Oxford Circus tube. **Meals served** 8am-10pm Mon-Thur; 8am-11pm Fri; 9am-11pm Sat; noon-10pm Sun. **Main courses** £3.95-£5.95. **Unlicensed.** **Credit** AmEx, DC, MC, V.
This spacious coffee bar, which sports a bright combination of fresh white walls and wooden flooring, now offers self-service meals. For anyone who missed the restaurant's name, Jamaican landscapes on the wall, books on Jamaican culture by the gas fire at the back, and the practically mandatory Bob Marley soundtrack are additional reminders of its roots. Some Jamaican enthusiasts like to come here, but the menu – targeting office workers looking to grab a quick soup or salad – failed to deliver much bite. Callaloo quiche was too bland to rise above the merely adequate, and jerk chicken, despite looking authentically blackened, lacked

Zula.
See page 18.

any real flavour. Kiwi smoothies were also uninspiring. Things picked up near the end, though, with good coffees (imaginatively termed 'reggaeccino' and 'dreadlatte') and an even better, sinfully rich coffee cheesecake; alternatively, try the fruit ice-creams served in the fruits' skins. The feeling that the whole operation is running on Caribbean time makes Jamaican Blue a laid-back novelty in the frantic environs of Regent Street.
Babies and children welcome; games. Entertainment: music, poetry, literature, discussion forum (phone for details). Takeaway service. Map 2/6H.

West

Ealing W13

BB's
3 Chignell Place, off Uxbridge Road, W13 (020 8840 8322). Ealing Broadway tube/rail/West Ealing rail. **Lunch served** 11.30am-2.20pm Mon-Fri. **Dinner served** 6.30-11.30pm Mon-Fri; 6.30pm-12.30am Sat. **Main courses** £9.50-£12.95. **Service** 12% for parties of six or more. **Credit** LV, MC, £TC, V.
'BB's is the Caribbean' is one of many graffiti messages scrawled on the walls of this popular feel-good restaurant, and even on a weekday night there was enough carnival spirit to support the claim. A throbbing sound system keeps the party alive (and drowns out any musical interference from the Velvet Lounge nightclub overhead), while Brian Benjamin, the Grenadian chef-patron, dishes out banter, cocktails and huge portions of food. We kicked off with crabbacks (a rich stuffed crab dish) and, a Caribbean classic, ackee and saltfish. Next came goat curry (tender meat but the sauce had a slightly gritty curry powder texture) and king prawns Seroste, a generous portion of king prawns in a rich, creamy tomato sauce. Side dishes were excellent, from tasty

rice and peas to deep-fried sliced pumpkin. It was only sheer gluttony that egged us on to the own-made coconut and mango ice-cream, and brown maiden (dark chocolate cake). Beers, vintage rums and colourful cocktails take precedence over the minimal wine list; teetotallers should be prepared for mind-bogglingly bitter maudy, scarlet sorrel or thick, sweet peanut punch.
Babies and children welcome; high chairs. Book dinner Thur-Sat. Entertainment: limbo dancing 9.30pm Fri, Sat. No-smoking tables.

South West

East Sheen SW15

The Melting Pot
180 Upper Richmond Road, SW15 (020 8408 4833). Mortlake rail/33, 209, 337, R69 bus. **Lunch served** noon-4pm Thur-Sat. **Dinner served** 6-11pm Mon-Sat. **Main courses** £8.75-£11.95. **Set lunch** £9.95 two courses. **Credit** DC, JCB, MC, V.
Sedate East Sheen is the somewhat unlikely home to this upmarket Caribbean restaurant. Apricot-coloured walls, bright modern paintings and huge potted plants make an attractive, if unexciting interior resembling that of a neighbourhood pasta joint. By night it might foster romance; on a Friday lunchtime, we dined alone and the restaurant had a forlorn feel. The menu, from Martinique-born and French-trained chef, Pierre Renaudeau, offers a cross-Caribbean medley of dishes. There's a strong seafood element and a distinct French influence. It's immediately clear this isn't the usual takeaway-standard Caribbean food. A jambalaya was way too posh, a timbale of rice and crab risotto, perfectly cooked and surrounded by a freshly made seafood sauce. On another occasion, however, a starter of vivaneau au escabeche (marinated red snapper) was way too vinegary. Slow casseroling tenderised a curry goat main course, the dark

meat tasting like lamb and strongly spiced, yet without the searing heat of pepper sauce (ask the friendly waitress if you want added fieriness). Brandade of cod looked like apple crumble, but under the breadcrumbs was the smoothest purée of salt-cod and breadfruit. Caramelised mango pancake and a lovely West Indian bread pudding rounded off our meal. Though food doesn't always live up to expectations, the Melting Pot is worth a trip if you want to discover how good Caribbean food can be when it's done with care and precision. Best come at night.
Babies and children welcome; high chairs; toys. Entertainment: jazz Thur evening. No-smoking tables. Tables outdoors (2, pavement).

South

Brixton SW2, SW9

Bamboula
12 Acre Lane, SW2 (020 7737 6633). Brixton tube/rail. **Meals served** 11am-11pm Mon-Fri; noon-11pm Sat. **Main courses** £2.20-£4.90 lunch, £5.80-£7 dinner **Set Meal** (5-8.15pm) £10 three courses. **Credit** MC, V.
Packed with sun-kissed vitality, Bamboula is a bouncing confection of bright yellow walls, rattan roofing, bamboo bar, and tables sporting jaunty banana leaf motifs – all set to rolling reggae rhythms. The informal restaurant

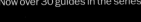
specialises in jerk chicken, offering portions from a quarter to a whole bird. The large helpings and reasonable prices seemed more impressive still when our order arrived – a satisfyingly blackened dish with spicy jerk flavours infused into the flesh. A side portion of freshly fried plantain was equally appetising, but watery callaloo and the accompanying festival (more of a deep-fried fritter) were an anticlimax. Caribbean fruitcake with rum cream – tiny spiced fruitcake with a generous portion of delicious tipsy cream – makes for a splendid finale.
Babies and children admitted. Book dinner Fri, Sat. Separate room for parties, seats 32. Tables outdoors (4, pavement). Takeaway service; delivery service. **Map 18.**

Brixtonian Havana Club
11 Beehive Place, SW9 (020 7924 9262). Brixton tube/rail.
Bar **Open** noon-2am daily.
Restaurant **Lunch served** noon-3pm daily.
Dinner served 7-10.30pm Mon-Thur, Sun; 7-11pm Fri, Sat. **Main courses** £13.
Both **Credit** MC, £TC, V.
Despite its out-of-the-way location down a tiny sidestreet, the bright blue façade of the Brixtonian continues to lure punters. Salsa rhythms rattle down the narrow staircase that leads to the restaurant, which shares its breezy loft space with a busy bar specialising in rum cocktails. We dutifully sampled a Cuban Mojito – a particularly refreshing concoction of crushed mint, white rum and lime juice – before settling down with the menu (a monthly snapshot of evolved Caribbean cooking). The pleasant but ultimately forgettable first course consisted of pawpaw baked with ginger (the fruit merely covered in a layer of finely chopped stem ginger) and a very peppery chicken and split pea broth. Main course saltfish and potato pie was a finely balanced, tasty collection of generous pieces of moist saltfish flavoured with thyme, while duck with orange plant sauce turned out to be a smallish portion of tender duck breast in an enjoyable, sweet orange sauce. Guava roly poly with rhum sauce suffered from a batter that was too doughy and undercooked to do justice to the fragrant filling. Plenty of smiles from the staff, and a lively bar give an upbeat feel to the place.
Dress: smart casual. Entertainment: jazz musicians 8pm Wed; gospel music lunch Sun. Tables outdoors (20, terrace). **Map 18.**

North

Camden Town & Chalk Farm NW1

Mango Room
10 Kentish Town Road, NW1 (020 7482 5065). Camden Town tube. **Lunch served** noon-3pm Tue-Sun. **Dinner served** 6pm-midnight daily. **Main courses** £8.50-£11. **Service** 12½%. **Credit** MC, V.
A bright turquoise exterior announces this popular local. Inside, wooden floors and orange walls adorned with bright oil paintings take on a softer hue in the evenings, when a mix of candlelight and luminous stars on the ceiling cast a romantic spell. A daytime visit found us perusing the short lunch menu, opting for starters of saltfish fritters with apple sauce, and ebony wings. Though prettily presented, the fritters were quite stodgy and lacked a saltfish flavour, and the chicken wings (marinated in chilli, soy sauce and garlic) were missing that vital chilli kick. Things took a definite upturn with main courses, as a vast portion of goat curry, boasting tender chunks of meat in a deliciously rich gravy, arrived alongside an equally substantial and flavourful helping of jerk chicken. Extras of rice and peas, starchy plantain, lip-smacking sweet potato and delicately curried spiced roti maintained high standards in a performance that ended with a scrumptious banana crème brûlée.
Babies and children welcome; high chairs. Booking advisable. Entertainment: jazz Mon, Sun. Takeaway service. **Map 10.**

Menu

African

Aloco: fried plantain with a hot tomato sauce.
Berbere: an Ethiopian seasoning of paprika, chilli, cinnamon and other spices.
Cassava (manioc, yuca): a coarse root that is boiled and pounded to make bread and various other farinaceous dishes. There are bitter and sweet varieties (the former is poisonous until cooked).
Egusi: ground melon seeds, added to stews and soups.
Fufu: a stiff pudding of maize or **cassava** (qv) flour, or pounded **yam** (qv).
Gari: Solid, heavy pudding made from ground fermented **cassava** (qv), served with thick soups.
Ground rice: stiff rice pudding served to accompany soup.
Jollof rice: a kind of hot, spicy risotto, with tomatoes, onions and (usually) chicken.
Injera: a spongy, flannel-like bread that doubles as an eating implement.
Kelewele: fried plantain, also called **do-do.**
Ogbono: large seed similar to **egusi** (qv). Although it doesn't thicken as much, it is used in much the same way.
Pepper soup: a light, peppery soup made with either fish or meat.
Suya: a spicy Nigerian meat kebab.
Tuo (tuwo): a stiff rice pudding sometimes served as rice balls to accompany soup.
Ugali: a Tanzanian stew served with maize porridge. Goat is traditionally used, but in Britain, lamb may be substituted.
Wot: a thick, dark sauce made from slowly cooked onions, garlic, butter and spices – it is an essential component in the aromatic stews of East Africa. Doro wot, a stew containing chicken and hard-boiled eggs, is particularly common.
Waakye: a dish of rice and black-eyed beans mixed with meat or chicken in gravy.
Waatse: rice and black-eyed beans cooked together.

Caribbean

Ackee: a red-skinned fruit with yellow flesh that tastes remarkably like scrambled eggs when cooked; traditionally served in a Jamaican dish of salt-cod, onion and peppers.
Breadfruit: introduced from West Africa in 1792 by Captain Bligh, this football-sized fruit has sweet, creamy flesh that is like a cross between sweet potato and chestnuts. Eaten as a vegetable.
Callaloo: the spinach-like leaves of either taro or malanga, often used as a base for a thick soup flavoured with pork or crabmeat.
Coo-coo: a polenta-like cake of cornmeal and okra.
Festival: deep-fried, slightly sweet dumpling often served with fried fish.
Foo-foo: a Barbadian dish of pounded plantains, rolled into balls with seasoning, served hot.
Curried (curry) goat: more usually lamb in London; the meat is marinated and slow-cooked until tender.
Escovitch fish: fish fried or grilled and then pickled in a tangy sauce.
Jerk chicken or pork: the meat is marinated in chilli and hot spices and slowly roasted or barbecued.
Peas or beans: interchangeable name for black-eyed beans, black beans, green peas and red kidney beans.
Pepperpot: traditionally a stew of meat and casserep (a juice obtained from cassava; in London it's more likely to be a meat or vegetable stew with cassava.
Plantain: a variety of banana that is cooked and used in much the same way as potato.
Roti: the Indian bread, usually filled with curried fish, meat or vegetables.
Saltfish: salt-cod, classically combined with **ackee** or **callaloo** (qv).
Soursop: a dark green, slightly spiny fruit; the pulp can be made into a refreshing drink.
Sweet potato: most varieties of this tuberous root have a sweetish taste, although some are drier.
Yam: a large tuber, with a yellow or whitish flesh and a slightly nutty flavour; may be cooked like a potato.

The Americas

North American

City E1

Arkansas Café ★ ★
Unit 12, 107B Commercial Street, Old Spitalfields Market, E1 (020 7377 6999). Aldgate East tube/Liverpool Street tube/rail. **Lunch served** noon-2.30pm Mon-Fri; noon-4pm Sun. **Dinner served** by arrangement. **Main courses** £3.50-£12.50. **Credit** DC, LV, MC, V.
Bubba, an affable American who claims he once played Cowboys and Indians with President Clinton, presides over the grill at this no-frills barbecue. The seating area is a collection of ancient, rusty chairs and an old church pew, and you have to eat with plastic cutlery, but this is all part of the experience – just imagine you're in a trailer park instead of Spitalfields market. The food is basic but terrific. Tender char-grilled Irish steak had great just-off-the-grill flavour and came with a selection of wholesome salads, potato and coleslaw. This is carnivore country, but the one meatless option, a moist, char-grilled veggie burger, tasted delicious doused with Bubba's perfectly tangy barbecue sauce. Note, though, that the café is not equipped for deep-frying, so you won't get any fries, and on our visit, the desserts – chocolate Alabama fudge cake and New York-style lemon cheesecake – lacked the home-made quality of the rest of the meal. There's a small selection of mainly New World wines, but how could you drink anything but beer with this authentic Yankee grub? For parties of 25 to 50 people, Bubba will even barbecue a half or whole pig (evenings only, with several days' notice).
Babies and children welcome. Booking advisable, no bookings accepted Sun. Separate room for parties, seats 50. No-smoking tables. Tables outdoors (30, terrace inside market). Takeaway service. **Map 4/5R**.

Covent Garden WC2

Christopher's
18 Wellington Street, WC2 (020 7240 4222). Covent Garden tube/Charing Cross tube/rail. **Bar Open** 11.30am-11pm Mon-Sat. *Restaurants* **Brunch served** 11.30am-4.30pm Sat, Sun. **Lunch served** noon-3pm Mon-Fri. **Dinner served** 5-11.45pm Mon-Sat. **Main courses** £11.50-£28. **Pre-theatre menu** (5-7pm Mon-Sat) £14.50 two courses, £17.50 three courses. *Both* **Service** 12½%. **Credit** AmEx, DC, MC, £$TC, V.
It is hard to put your finger on the exact moment when a restaurant starts to feel tired, but it's always a bad sign when the waiters can't recommend any of the dishes because they are not allowed to eat the food. It seems the accountants have gone into Christopher's as surely as the sparkle has gone out of it, despite the grand, spiralling staircase and the lofty dining rooms. The food, too, was showing signs of neglect. Salad of oven-roast tomatoes, braised artichoke and bocconcini (small mozzarella balls) came straight from the fridge ('here's one I dried out earlier'); crisp nut polenta with Gorgonzola, pears and mixed leaves was a better bet, though not spectacular. Fish is still impressive, as in buttermilk fried sole with lemon mash and dill butter: a delicious combination of crunchy battered flesh sitting on creamy potato. However, summer pudding with lemon sorbet was not a good combination, and suffered from a paucity of fruit; cappuccino brownie was more successful. Service verges on the harassed and the bill for two (with a bottle of excellent Vasse Felix semillon-sauvignon 1998 at £27) came to £114 – £30 too much for a meal of this quality.
Babies and children admitted. Booking advisable. Dress: smart casual. Separate room for parties, seats 50. **Map 14/7L**.
For branch see index.

Joe Allen
13 Exeter Street, WC2 (020 7836 0651/020 7497 2148). Covent Garden or Embankment tube/Charing Cross tube/rail. **Brunch served** 11.30am-4pm Sat, Sun. **Meals served** noon-12.45am Mon-Fri; 11.30am-12.45am Sat; 11.30am-11.30pm Sun. **Main courses** £7.50-£14.50. **Set brunch** £14.50 two courses, £16.50 three courses, incl drink. **Set lunch** £12 two courses, £14 three courses, incl coffee. **Pre-theatre menu** (5-6.45pm Mon-Fri) £13 two courses, £15 three courses. **Credit** AmEx, MC, £TC, V.
One of Theatreland's perennial success stories, this lively basement restaurant continues to lure a steady stream of punters below street level. Appropriate to its location, the scene can seem quite stagy, but it works. There's a pianist (of course), there's plenty of exposed brickwork, as well as photos and posters from screen and stage, and there's candlelight (each of the little tables has its own flickering flame). The fast, friendly and flamboyant staff have also been perfectly cast to cope with a heavy traffic of pre- and post-show audiences. The daily menu combines the likes of decent own-made soups and fresh, inventive salads with sassily updated American classics. We started with a crisp, nourishing salad of baby spinach, Asian slaw, marinated feta and crunchy roast peanuts. Main courses were comforting and well-balanced dishes: golden pieces of chicken accompanied by a deliciously rich pile of onions, sun-dried tomatoes and new potatoes; crispy leg of confit duck came with a creamy herb mash and a pleasingly sharp green peppercorn sauce. Desserts are less inspiring (brownies, pies and the like) but satisfying all the same. The wine list is suitably wide-ranging and accessibly priced.
Babies and children admitted. Booking advisable. Entertainment: pianist 9pm-1am Mon-Sat. No-smoking tables. **Map 14/7L**.

Maxwell's
8-9 James Street, WC2 (020 7836 0303). Covent Garden tube/Charing Cross tube/rail. **Bar Open** noon-11pm Mon-Sat; noon-10.30pm Sun. *Restaurant* **Brunch served** 9.30am-12.30pm, **meals served** noon-midnight, daily. **Main courses** £5-£15. **Set lunch** £5 two courses, £12 three courses. **Minimum** £7 when busy. **Service** 10% for parties of five or more. *Both* **Credit** AmEx, DC, JCB, MC, £TC, V.
On weekend nights, this Covent Garden stalwart seems to serve primarily as a filling station for scantily clad clubbers plus a smattering of family groups. Chart hits play at ear-splitting volume and beepers are handed out at the door, so that you know when a table becomes free. A neon Stars and Stripes on the ceiling is one of the few decorative tributes to the American theme, but the menu has all the usual US suspects – burgers, barbecues, steaks and Tex-Mex tortillas. Our meal started with a tasty, if somewhat over-powering quesadilla – a toasted tortilla filled with cheese, chillies and (a bit too much) onion. The more mildly spiced Louisiana crab cakes are fine as long as you like dark crab meat. Mains were mediocre. The veggie burger, made of mushroom, onion and rice, had a pleasant, herby flavour, but a dry, stodgy consistency. Barbecued chicken with grainy fries wasn't much better. The evening improved with the arrival of a huge chocolate fudge brownie sundae – nicely moist and drizzled with a rich chocolate sauce – for sweet-tooths only. A convenient pit stop, but you don't have to look far to find better food.
Babies and children welcome; children's menu; high chairs; nappy-changing facilities; toys. No-smoking tables. Tables outdoors (6, pavement). **Map 14/6L**.
For branch see index.

Navajo Joe
34 King Street, WC2 (020 7240 4008). Covent Garden tube. **Bar Open** noon-11pm daily. *Restaurant* **Meals served** noon-midnight Mon-Sat; noon-11.30pm Sun. **Main courses** £7.95-£13.95. **Set lunch** £8.95 two courses. **Pre-theatre menu** (5.30-7.30pm Mon-Fri) £8.95 two courses. **Service** 12½%. *Both* **Credit** AmEx, DC, JCB, MC, £TC, V.

Prospect Grill. *See page 23.*

This busy Covent Garden bar-restaurant is the bigger, brasher sister of Chelsea's Cactus Blue and shares its updated Tex-Mex decor: massive modern paintings of Native Americans, and seating upholstered in Navajo blankets. The long marble bar, stacked with tequilas and mezcals, dominates the ground floor, where carousing office workers and some head-throbbing techno create a mood not exactly suited to an intimate meal. Battered jalapeños stuffed with cream cheese had a nice kick and came with a sweet-spicy red pepper conserve. Louisiana crab cakes were milder with a good chunky consistency, but arrived lukewarm, while the fancy-sounding roast fennel and pesto aïoli tasted much like tartare sauce. Chicken fajitas were impressively presented in two tiers – a pan of sizzling sliced chicken, peppers and onion underneath; tortillas and condiments on top – but the chicken lacked spice and the guacamole tasted processed. Shrimp tacos were also a mixed success: the shrimps were fat and juicy, but had very tough shells and were swamped by onions and peppers. The dish sat rather oddly on a bed of thick-cut chips. The highlight of the meal came at the end: light, creamy white chocolate cheesecake, perfectly offset by a tangy raspberry coulis.
Babies and children welcome; children's menu. Book dinner. Separate room for parties, seats 50. **Map 14/7L.**

PJ's Grill

30 Wellington Street, WC2 (020 7240 7529). Covent Garden or Embankment tube/Charing Cross tube/rail. **Brunch served** noon-4pm daily. **Meals served** noon-1am Mon-Sat; noon-4pm Sun. **Main courses** £8.50-£14. **Pre-theatre menu** (5-7.30pm Mon-Sat) £8.95 two courses. **Service** 12½%. **Credit** AmEx, DC, JCB, MC, £TC, V.
Located in the middle of theatreland, PJ's Grill is apt to send tourists home confirmed in their prejudice that food in Britain is depressingly overpriced and uninspired. Front-of-house staff try hard to please, but the kitchen can only tread a well-worn path to steak and chips, sausage and mash or char-grilled chicken. Accordingly, a 7oz fillet steak was perfectly nice and perfectly pink, despite its oddly sweet pepper sauce, dark brown sautéed potatoes and pricey side dish of tomato and red onion slices. A salad of asparagus and feta was really a heap of rocket garnished with some asparagus spears, but it was saved by fresh broad beans and peas, and would have gone down a treat without its ocean of mayonnaise. Bread and butter pudding with marmalade cream had a solid consistency and proved to be a good choice, whereas baked lemon tart with lime sorbet featured dodgy lemon pie filling and tough, soggy pastry. The wine list comprises off-licence favourites at around £4 a glass. The only real surprise is the number of theatrical somebodies who have their names engraved on the brass plaques that are dotted about the place – as if they had once enjoyed a decent meal here. We've had better reports of the new branch in Hampstead – so maybe all the effort is in that direction at the moment.
Babies and children welcome (entertainment noon-4pm Sun); children's menu; high chairs; toys. Booking advisable. Entertainment: jazz pianist 10.30pm-1am Thur-Sat; 12.30-3.30pm Sun. **Map 14/6L.**
For branches see index.

Prospect Grill ★

4-6 Garrick Street, WC2 (020 7379 0412). Covent Garden or Leicester Square tube. **Lunch served** 11.45am-3.30pm, **dinner served** 5.45pm-midnight Mon-Fri. **Meals served** 11.45am-midnight Sat. **Main courses** £9.95-£15.95. **Credit** AmEx, MC, V.
Claret walls and chocolate leather banquettes give the Prospect Grill an air of sophistication, while hinting at the laid-back style of a New York grill. You won't find any short-order cooks sweating the burners here, though: this is a rare example of grilling as an art form, with delicious accompaniments and decent wine (Tyrell's Long Flat chardonnay) to match. Even asparagus with shaved Parmesan had benefited from grilling, its flavour intensified, its cell structure still solid. Grilled swordfish steak, apt to be a dry disaster, was a lemony revelation, with coriander salsa and faultless chips. Roasts were also excellent: roasted pepper with tomatoes, basil and mozzarella made a fresh, not too sweet combination. Roast rosemary and lemon chicken tasted all the better for us knowing its free-range pedigree, although the gratin dauphinois beneath it was the real show-stopper. Decent desserts – from chocolate brownie with vanilla ice-cream and fudge sauce, to mixed berries with mascarpone or summer fruit crumble – cater to all tastes. In an area renowned for tourist tat, Prospect Grill is an oasis of good food, sweet-natured service and fair prices.
Babies and children welcome; high chairs. **Map 14/7L.**

TGI Friday's

6 Bedford Street, WC2 (020 7379 0585). Covent Garden or Embankment tube/Charing Cross tube/rail.
Bar **Open** noon-11pm Mon-Fri; 11am-11pm Sat; 11am-10.30pm Sun.
Restaurant **Meals served** noon-11.30pm Mon-Sat; 11am-10.30pm Sun. **Main courses** £6.75-£15.25.
Both **Credit** AmEx, MC, £TC, V.
You have to pity the staff here in their ridiculous uniforms of red and white striped shirts, plastered with badges and crowned with silly hats. Their humiliating attire doesn't prevent them from being friendly and efficient, though, and the interior of wood, stained glass and sundry American relics is easy on the eye. The menu delivers average food, ranging from kid-friendly burgers to adult options such as the 'Jack Daniels grill' selection. We shared a generous plate of starters: buffalo wings were moist and meaty; crispy fried mozzarella came with fresh-tasting habanera sauce. Potato skins, however, were greasy and held only a smattering of bitty bacon and cheese. Burgers are served cooked through; ours was a bit dry, though the onion, mushroom and cheese topping provided a moist counterpoint. Salmon with Jack Daniels glaze was rare enough to be succulent, the veg nicely al dente but the sauce verged on the sickly. Desserts such as popcorn brownie sundae with Ben & Jerry's Phish Food ice-cream and toffee popcorn will launch kids into a sugar-fuelled delirium, leaving adults no choice but to hit the ten-page list of speciality cocktails.
Babies and children welcome; children's menu (dinner); face-painting (noon-4pm Sat, Sun); high chairs; toys. No-smoking tables. Takeaway service. **Map 14/7L.**
For branches see index.

Leicester Square W1

Planet Hollywood

Trocadero, 13 Coventry Street, W1 (020 7287 1000/www.planethollywood.com). Piccadilly Circus tube. **Meals served** noon-1am Mon-Sat; noon-11.30pm Sun. **Main courses** £6.50-£16.95. **Service** 12½%. **Credit** AmEx, DC, LV, MC, £$TC, V.
Planet Hollywood seems to have recovered from its recent financial difficulties and the London branch was certainly busy on a Thursday night, with a cordoned-off queue seducing packs of teenagers and tourists with quasi-celebrity mystique. Nothing prepares the uninitiated for the spectacle that is the dining room, with its palm trees, Hollywood Hills tableaux peopled with cardboard celebs, and an unappetising near-naked life-size Sly Stallone suspended from the ceiling. The food is enjoyable, though. Texas nachos was a massive platter of tortilla chips that remained crisp despite their burden of melted Jalapeño Jack cheese, chopped tomato, chillies and strips of chicken. Blackened shrimps were sizeable, succulent, covered in spicy Cajun seasoning and served with a cooling mustard dip. The classic burger was also a winner – firm and tender with a crisp salad garnish. Fries were perfectly spindly; the coleslaw fresh and chunky. Portobello mushroom fajita was a flavour-packed if pricey vegetarian option – foil-wrapped pancakes served with sizzling marinated mushrooms, onions, peppers and portions of guacamole, salsa and grated cheese. For dessert, a rich brownie (swirled with chocolate and caramel sauces and topped with two flavours of ice-cream) proved suitably indulgent. Cocktails continue the cinematic theme, and include Indecent Proposal, a potent Margarita made with Cuervo Gold tequila.
Babies and children welcome; children's menu; high chairs; nappy-changing facilities. Bookings not accepted Sat. No-smoking tables. Separate room for parties, seats 90. **Map 14/7K.**

Mayfair W1

Hard Rock Café

150 Old Park Lane, W1 (020 7629 0382/www.hardrock.com). Hyde Park Corner tube. **Meals served** 11.30am-12.30am Mon-Thur, Sun; 11.30am-1am Fri, Sat. **Main courses** £7.95-£14.95. **Minimum** main course when busy. **Service** 12½% on bills over £30. **Credit** AmEx, MC, £$TC, V.
Tablefuls of rainbow-haired teenagers and an ever-present queue out front prove that though it's been going since 1971, the Hard Rock still rocks. With its low ceilings and battered booths, the basement is not as airy as the ground floor, and you have to shout over music ranging from the Beatles to Nirvana. Service, from waitresses in white mini-dresses, is laid-back yet efficient and, on the whole, the food lives up to the legend. The 'pig sandwich' made of shredded pork, hickory-smoked for at least ten hours, then 'hand-pulled' was incredibly tender with a lovely smoky-bacon flavour, but the sauce-saturated bun disintegrated. The accompanying barbecue beans were delicious, too. Onion rings – big, juicy and crisply coated – came with a tasty barbecue dip. Vegetarians have limited options (even the pastas contain meat), but the veggie burger was one of the best we've tasted. Hefty desserts have a homely wholesomeness: cheesecake, with a traditional Graham-Cracker crumb base, tasted fresh though slightly grainy, while the chocolate chip pie was a rich take on pecan, packed with melting morsels. If you can stomach the theme-merchandise madness, Hard Rock Café is a fun place to pig-out on great American nosh.
Babies and children welcome; children's menu; high chairs; toys. Bookings accepted for parties of ten or more only. No-smoking tables. Separate room for parties, seats 110. Tables outdoors (10, pavement). Takeaway service. **Map 6/8G.**

Havana

17 Hanover Square, W1 (020 7629 2552). Oxford Circus tube. **Open** 5pm-3am Mon-Wed; noon-3am Thur-Sat; 5pm-1am Sun. **Meals served** 5pm-2am Mon-Wed; noon-2am Thur-Sat; 5pm-midnight Sun. **Admission** £3 after 10pm Mon, 11pm Tue, 9-11pm Wed; £5 after 11pm Wed, Thur, 9-11pm; Fri, Sat; £10 after 10pm Fri, Sat. **Main courses** £6.25-£9.95. **Credit** AmEx, DC, JCB, MC, V.
More salsa club than restaurant, Havana has DJs spinning Latin sounds every night and there are even dance classes some evenings. The rough, brightly painted plaster walls, mosaic-topped cocktail tables and animal-print booths create an air of ersatz Cuban glamour, while the dining area (tucked behind the bar) is shielded from the sweat and seduction of the dancefloor. After all this, the quality of the cooking is a surprise. We kicked off with two enjoyable tapas: plump Louisiana hot chicken wings doused in a piquant sauce, and spicy crab rolls accompanied by a fiery fruit salsa. A thick fillet of ranch-style marinated steak came medium-rare as ordered, with light and crispy fries. It was tender enough but lacked any real flavour. A second main course of tuna steak was undeniably huge but it didn't taste particularly fresh and its accompanying mango and melon salsa was ferociously hot. The only dessert offered, a thickly iced chocolate cake with ice-cream, was nothing more than a massive sugar injection. The waitress was overworked yet charming with it, but at the bar we were forced to wait 15 minutes to order a drink while the barman downed shots with punters.
Booking essential weekends. Dress: smart casual; no trainers. Entertainment: Latin bands, disco, dance groups, dance classes (phone for details). **Map 2/6H.**
For branch see index.

Piccadilly W1

Cheers

72 Regent Street, W1 (020 7494 3322). Piccadilly Circus tube.
Bar **Open** noon-3am Mon-Sat; noon-10.30pm Sun.
Restaurant **Meals served** noon-10.30pm daily. **Main courses** £6.95-£12.90. **Minimum** £6. **Set lunch** £5.95 noon-7pm. **Service** 12½% for parties of six or more.
Both **Credit** AmEx, DC, MC, £TC, V.
Fans of the Bostonian bar sitcom might get a kick out of this theme pub-cum-restaurant. The square wooden bar at the back is a reproduction of the TV set, while shutters, baseball memorabilia and bottles of Samuel Adams conjure up the feel of a Beantown boozer. The food, however, is not so authentic. What Cheers calls Boston clam chowder simply isn't (although it is quite a tasty tarragon and dill flavoured clam bisque). Deep-fried potato skins filled with bacon, cheese and salsa, surrounding a pool of guacamole were let down by ingredients that tasted processed. A meltingly good rack of barbecued ribs, straddling a bowl of Boston baked beans (a spiced-up relation of Heinz), temporarily raised our spirits, only for things to take a dive again when a rather mushy, disappointing veggie burger arrived with pub-standard chips. To finish, a stodgy white sponge couldn't live up to its moniker of Boston cream pie. The raucous music was only overcome by the shouted conversations of a young crowd at one of the tables, and by a hair-raising bell that was rung each time the bar staff got a tip. Don't come here expecting intimate dining at low decibels – or fabulous food for that matter.
Babies and children welcome (restaurant); children's menu; crayons; high chairs; toys. Bookings not accepted dinner Fri, Sat. Dress: smart casual. Entertainment: TV (three large screens). No-smoking tables. **Map 13/7J.**

Soho W1

Blues Bistro & Bar

42-43 Dean Street, W1 (020 7494 1966/ www.bluesbistro.com). Leicester Square, Piccadilly Circus or Tottenham Court Road tube.
Bar **Open** noon-midnight Mon-Thur; noon-1am Fri; 5pm-1am Sat.
Bistro **Meals served** noon-11.30pm Mon-Thur; noon-12.30am Fri; 6pm-12.30am Sat; 6-11pm Sun. **Main courses** £7.25-£20. **Set lunch** (Mon-Fri) £12 two courses, £14 three courses. **Set dinner** (6-11pm Mon, Tue, Sun) £10 three courses. **Service** 12½% for parties of five or more.
Both **Credit** AmEx, MC, V.
Beating off the Dean Street competition on Monday, Tuesday and Sunday evenings with the 'tenner menu' (three courses for £10), Blues Bistro is looking sharp. This menu offers straight-forward but carefully cooked food, as in chicken with braised savoy cabbage and shallots in a strongly reduced sauce. Otherwise, the à la carte majors on European favourites, with the occasional nod towards American cuisine (maybe New York strip-loin or Maryland chicken). The list of middle-of-the-road wines takes a back seat. We opted for roast fillet of sea bass and marinated baby squid: a huge portion of fish sitting on a few morsels of artichoke, innocently dressed in lemon and black pepper. Although the bill rises as side dishes accumulate (ours were sea-salted new potatoes and creamy, dense spinach), there is still a sense of value for money and competence in the kitchen. We've no complaints about the service either, which was universally friendly. From a long list of desserts, fruit trifle contained a pleasingly fresh, thick layer of fruit packed in jelly. The contemporary disdain for textiles in the decor makes for harsh acoustics; you may leave with Blues ringing in your ears.
Babies and children welcome; children's menu; high chairs. Booking advisable. Entertainment: jazz 11pm-1am Fri, Sat. Separate room for parties, seats 45. Takeaway service.
Map 13/6K.

Ed's Easy Diner

Old Compton Street, W1 (020 7287 1951). Leicester Square or Tottenham Court Road tube. **Meals served** 11.30am-midnight Mon-Thur, Sun; 11.30am-1am Fri, Sat. **Main courses** £3.95-£5.50. **Minimum** £3.60 (6pm-midnight Fri-Sun). **Credit** MC, TC, V.
Ed's replica 1950s diner has enough stainless steel and red leatherette to make you wonder when Michael J Fox will roll through the door on his skateboard. Burgers and fries dominate the menu (supplemented by hot dogs, sandwiches and salads), while the sounds of Roy Orbison & Co ring out. The 5oz ground Irish steak patties are served five ways, while vegetarians have three meatless options (Quorn, spicy bean, or potato and vegetable). Big Bubbas burger (topped with bacon and cheese, at a very un-retro £5) came cooked through, rather than medium-rare as requested. It was still moist and tasty, though, even if it lacked any memorable qualities. French fries, which were on the dry side and preter-naturally yellow, would probably benefit from one of the five toppings (gravy or chilli cheese, say). Shakes, served in a stainless-steel pitcher, were creamy, thick and generous enough to share, but the brownies tasted synthetic. Counterside seating, friendly staff and fun music create an air of camaraderie that is rare in London. As a quick and easy pit stop (particularly with kids), Ed's beats McDonald's hands down.
Babies and children welcome; children's menu; crayons. Takeaway service; delivery service (noon-6pm). **Map 13/6K.**
For branches see index.

Strand WC2

Smollensky's on the Strand

105 Strand, WC2 (020 7497 2101/ www.smollenskys.co.uk). Embankment tube/ Charing Cross tube/rail.
Bar **Open** noon-11pm Mon-Wed; noon-12.30am Thur-Sat; noon-10.30pm Sun.
Restaurant **Meals served** noon-midnight Mon-Wed; noon-12.30am Thur-Sat. **Lunch served** noon-5.30pm, **dinner served** 6.30-10.30pm Sun. **Main courses** £6.85-£19.95. **Set lunch/pre-theatre menu** £12 two courses, £14 three courses. **Service** 15% for parties of nine or more.
Both **Credit** AmEx, DC, MC, £TC, V.
Saturday night and this basement bar and restaurant was crammed to its faux-deco edges with birthday parties and hen nights. A resident Billy Joel-style pianist, followed by a disco after 10pm, keeps the show going while the kitchen turns out some quality dishes. Classic Caesar salad, for example, was crisp and tasty, but potato

Cactus Blue

skins were slightly singed and the sour cream filling was cooked to a custard. What really impressed, though, was a main course of rare, tender rump of lamb with herby cornbread coating, complemented by a creamy leek sauce and sweet potato wedges. An overcooked grilled Pacific swordfish couldn't compete, though peach relish was a nice touch. French fries were excellent (thin and crisp with their skins still intact) and the diet-busting desserts demanded to be demolished. Grandma Smollensky's peanut butter cheesecake may sound like the worst kind of American excess, but it was a subtle, smooth delight. White chocolate fudge brownie smothered in hot chocolate sauce also got the moist factor just right. House wine ventures south of the border with a delightful Valdivieso Chilean sauvignon blanc. *Babies and children welcome; children's menu; entertainment (noon-3pm Sat, Sun); high chairs; toys. Booking advisable. Entertainment: pianist 7pm-close Mon-Sat; DJ 10pm-close Thur-Sat; jazz 8-10.30pm Sun (£4.50 cover). No-smoking tables.* **Map 14/7L.**

West

Chiswick W4

Coyote Café
2 Fauconberg Road, W4 (020 8742 8545). Chiswick Park tube/Gunnersbury tube/rail. Brunch served 11am-3pm Sat, Sun. Lunch served 11am-3pm Mon-Fri. Dinner served 5-11pm Mon-Sat; 5-10.30pm Sun. Main courses £7.95-£11.95. Service 12½% for parties of six or more. Credit AmEx, MC, V.
The simple surroundings of this little local – terracotta walls decorated with Navajo blankets and chilli-heat charts – don't prepare you for the top-notch nosh. On a busy night, service may be slow as the few staff are rushed off their feet, but the wait is well worth it. Everything we had was freshly prepared and delicious. Spinach enchilada with tequila lime olive oil was a substantial tortilla full of lightly cooked spinach, generously topped with melted Cheddar and Red Leicester. Two

chunky Gulf Coast crab cakes were enhanced by a coriander-spiked tomato sauce. The blackened rib-eye steak was cooked exactly as ordered – a perfectly tender medium rare, served with a smoky chipotle gravy and a haystack of fries. Although the dish was massive, we couldn't help clearing our plates. The fish special, wild sea trout, was also expertly cooked, coming off the bone in moist flakes. It was glazed with a subtle tomato-based sauce and served with spiced vegetable-laced rice and gourmet leaf salad. Banoffi pie was a joyful union of ripe bananas, melting toffee and cream on a light biscuit base. Frozen Margaritas are a speciality here – perhaps one reason the bar was hopping.
Babies and children welcome (until 8pm); children's menu. Book dinner. Tables outdoors (7, pavement).

Holland Park W11

Tootsies
120 Holland Park Avenue, W11 (020 7229 8567). Holland Park tube. Meals served summer 9am-11.30pm Mon-Sat; winter 9am-11pm Mon-Sat; 9am-11pm Sun. Main courses £5.50-£9.75. Service 12½%. Credit AmEx, MC, £TC, V.
Open frontages in summer and cosy, family-friendly interiors in winter make this London-wide chain a perennial magnet for fans of the chips-with-everything fodder so beloved of North America. The Holland Park branch is no exception, drawing a well-heeled crowd of all ages for steak and fries, bangers and mash or late breakfast. Most come for a burger, however – and who can blame them? The Tootsies burger costs £7.75 and comes cooked to order with bacon, cheese, tomato, lettuce, mayonnaise and chips. Portions are authentically huge. Diners are invited to design their own burgers with such additions as Mexican hot sauce or Thai green curry. A side dish of smoked cheese and spinach parcels was a tasty surprise, while deep-fried potato skins with sour cream and chives were a more ordinary (though still delicious) way to pile on the pounds. Salmon fish cakes were typically high on potato and low on fish, but not unpleasant and came with all the

trimmings. Sticky, dark chocolate cake had a treacly consistency that was hard to resist, especially with its corollaries (custard, cream or ice-cream). Wines are high-street favourites.
Babies and children welcome; children's menu; crayons; high chairs. Bookings not accepted. No-smoking tables. Tables outdoors (4, pavement). Takeaway service. **Map 11/7Az.** **For branches see index.**

Kensington W8

Sticky Fingers
1A Phillimore Gardens, W8 (020 7938 5338). High Street Kensington tube. Bar Open noon-8pm Mon-Sat. Restaurant Meals served noon-11pm Mon-Thur, Sun; noon-11.30pm Fri, Sat. Main courses £5.95-£15.95. Both Credit AmEx, DC, MC, V.
The bar of this loud, jolly, uncomplicated burger restaurant is practically wallpapered with gold discs awarded to The Rolling Stones – Bill Wyman part-owns the joint. Some thought has gone into a menu that tries to please all comers, even if the execution is patchy. We started with chunky, under-spiced and over-salted guacamole served with a mountain of corn chips. Another popular starter, barbecued spare ribs, appeared to be a vast wall of meat, but was thin on flesh, though the marinade was mercifully less honeyed than usual. The obligatory char-grilled burger is made with good beef, it arrives in a bun with relish on the side, a small salad of fresh leaves and excellent golden fries. The 'New York Strip' surf and turf is a 10oz sirloin, grilled to a turn and topped with (overcooked) prawns, plus 'homefries' – alarmingly dark wedges of potato – and the house salad. After all this, few diners order dessert, apart from the many youngsters entitled to ice-cream as part of the children's menu. On Sunday lunchtimes there's face-painting, balloons, crayons, and competitions. Cocktails are pricey (£4.95), wine is cheap and dull, but pitchers of beer are a safe bet. You're supposed to buy a T-shirt on the way out.
Babies and children welcome; children's menu; entertainment (magician or face-painting 1-3pm Sun); high chairs. Bookings not accepted dinner Fri, Sat. Takeaway service. **Map 5/9A.**

Westbourne Grove W11

Dakota ★
127 Ledbury Road, W11 (020 7792 9191). Notting Hill tube/52 bus. Bar Open 7-11pm Mon-Sat; 11am-3.30pm Sun. Restaurant Brunch served noon-3.30pm Sat; 11am-3.30pm Sun. Lunch served noon-3.30pm Mon-Fri. Dinner served 7-11pm Mon-Sat; 7-10.30pm Sun. Main courses £10-£16. Both Credit AmEx, JCB, MC, £TC, V.
More West 11 than Wild West, Dakota's hip Notting Hill credentials shine through in its mock Mediterranean terrace and slick interior divided by timber screens. Despite its name, the restaurant specialises in Californian cuisine. An intriguing starter of blackberry-tea-smoked duck breast salad, with purple plums and walnuts, was a brilliant success – the meat juicy and perfumed, the walnuts marinated, the plums tart and fresh. Equally good were crispy Gulf prawns coated with a gossamer tempura batter and served with crunchy vegetable 'slaw spiced with ginger and chilli. Main-course pan-seared lamb fillet came up deliciously pink, as requested, with a pretty and pungent assortment of lentil, broad bean and mint salsas. Pea and Taleggio risotto cakes were also mouthwateringly appealing and contrasted well with a slightly sour pea-shoot salad and corn and sweet-pepper relish. Staff are friendly, portions are enormous and there are frequent wine promotions. More than just a component in the highly successful Hertford group (**Canyon, Montana** etc), Dakota is a perfect neighbourhood restaurant.
Babies and children welcome; children's menu; high chairs. Booking advisable. Tables outdoors (20, terrace). **Map 11/A5.** **For branch (Utah) see index.**

South West

Chelsea SW3

Big Easy
332-334 King's Road, SW3 (020 7352 4071). Sloane Square tube then 11, 19, 22 bus. Bar Open noon-11pm Mon-Sat; noon-10.30pm Sun. Main courses £3.95-£14.95.

Restaurant **Meals served** noon-midnight Mon-Sat; noon-11pm Sun. **Main courses** £5.95-£14.95. **Set lunch** (Mon-Fri noon-4pm) £5.95 two courses. **Service** 12½%.
Both **Credit** AmEx, MC, V.
'An American restaurant and proud of it,' proclaims the sign above the door. Clapboard walls, US flags and an impressive collection of baseball caps prove the point. Country music and a generation-spanning crowd out for a good ol' time keep the mood upbeat, as do the friendly waiting staff. Food arrived so fast it aroused suspicion but, in fact, was pretty good. Tender baby back ribs came smothered in a rich, smoky barbecue sauce. Texas torpedoes (deep-fried jalapeño peppers stuffed with cream cheese) were mild, fluffy on the inside, crisp on the outside, and came with a decent salsa. Lobster and crab bake for two is a huge pan of seafood, new potatoes and sweetcorn, served with a marinara or creamy garlic sauce. At £14.95 each, it isn't cheap, but you do get a whole lobster and a mountain of mussels. Some of the shellfish (especially the jumbo shrimp) was dry, suggesting reheating, but the lobster was succulent and the Alaskan snow crab legs were particularly fresh tasting. On a Saturday night, most desserts were sold out, so we settled for an adequate lemon tart. The New World rules the wine list, but with this food you might prefer a pitcher of Big Easy Brew lager.
Babies and children welcome; children's menu; crayons; high chairs; nappy-changing facilities; under-10s accompanied by adults eat free. Bookings not accepted after 7pm Fri, Sat except for parties of 10 or more. Disabled: toilet. Entertainment: country, blues and jazz music from 9pm daily. No-smoking tables. Tables outdoors (4, pavement). Takeaway service. **Map 5/12D.**

Cactus Blue
86 Fulham Road, SW3 (020 7823 7858). South Kensington tube.
Bar **Open** 5.30-11pm Mon-Fri; noon-11pm Sat; noon-10.30pm Sun.
Restaurant **Brunch served** noon-4pm Sat, Sun. **Dinner served** 5.30-11.45pm Mon-Sat; 5.30-11pm Sun. **Main courses** £9.95-£13.95. **Service** 12½%.
Both **Credit** AmEx, MC, £TC, V.
With its terracotta walls, Navajo-blanket banquettes and massive paintings of buffaloes and Native Americans, Cactus Blue offers a more sophisticated take on the Tex Mex theme (although it does have a vast selection of tequilas). A steer's skull takes pride of place in the cosy back restaurant, while the gallery above the lively bar is open for dining on busy nights. We shared a sampler of starters, including succulent chilli-rubbed tiger prawns (with just a hint of smoky heat) and an authentic coriander-laced guacamole, refreshingly served with root vegetable crisps instead of corn chips. An excellent main course of roast vegetable chimichanga looked as exciting as it tasted – a potato pancake encircling chunks of courgette and aubergine, served on a bed of spinach and black bean 'houmous', with a riot of zesty tomato sauce, avocado cream and coriander pesto. Less impressive was overcooked yellowfin tuna, which failed to be revived by a bland salsa rossa. A sizeable round chocolate banana brownie was deliciously moist and shot through with sweet, melting fruit, while crisp shortbread stacked with cream and strawberries was lighter but equally tasty. Upbeat music and a laid-back buzz make this a fun place for decent food and a bit of Margarita-fuelled mayhem.
Babies and children welcome. Booking advisable dinner. Dress: smart casual. No-smoking tables. Separate room for parties, seats 60. Tables outdoors (4, pavement). **Map 12/11D.**

Fulham SW6

Montana
125-129 Dawes Road, SW6 (020 7385 9500/ www.montanafood.co.uk). Fulham Broadway tube.
Bar **Open** 6.30-11pm Mon-Sat; noon-10.30pm Sun.
Restaurant **Brunch served** noon-4pm Sat, Sun. **Dinner served** 7-11pm Mon-Thur; 7-11.30pm Fri, Sat; 7-10.30pm Sun. **Main courses** £10-£16. **Service** 12½%.
Both **Credit** AmEx, MC, £TC, V.
Cowskin cubbyhole, rag-rolled walls, bare floorboards and chocolate-brown ceiling – the epitome of south-west American chic? We don't think so. The original branch of the Idaho-Canyon-Dakota-Montana chain is looking more than a little tired. It now serves an identical menu to its sister establishments, out of a less competent kitchen. Here, for example, chilled smoked tomato and orange soup was too powerfully flavoured – it was like drinking a bowl

of hot barbecue sauce. Crispy Gulf prawns with gingered vegetable 'slaw was nice, but not properly heated through. Pan-roasted monkfish had an interesting coating and came with excellent samphire and a citrus pepper salsa, but was so thick that eating it seemed hard work. Pan-seared lamb fillet was the highlight of the meal, its lentil salsa sprinkled with broad beans and mint; but greasy summer vegetables and rocket salad left us cold. A slice of lemon and lime chiffon cake was dry, so once its accompanying coconut sorbet had gone, eating it was a chore. Own-made ice-creams were also a letdown. We enjoyed the jazz piano/flute duo, but if you don't like music while you eat, head elsewhere.
Babies and children admitted. Booking essential. Entertainment: jazz pianist from 8.30pm daily, from 1-4pm Sat, Sun. **Map 6.** For branch (**Utah**) see index.

Canyon. *See page 27.*

Catford SE6

Buzz Brasserie
195 Rushey Green, SE6 (020 8697 5433). Catford or Catford Bridge rail. **Lunch served** noon-3pm Tue-Fri. **Dinner served** 7pm-12.30am Tue-Sun. **Main courses** £5.50-£10.95. **House wine** £7 bottle, £2.30 glass. **Mineral water** £1 bottle. **Credit** AmEx, DC, MC, JCB, V.
There's usually something lively going on at this small restaurant on Catford's main drag (salsa, karaoke, cocktails, jazz and the like), but on the quiet Wednesday night we visited, a mellow soul recording was providing a romantic groove for just a few couples. American and West Indian

dishes (including goat curry) sit side by side on the menu. A pastel colour scheme reinforces the Caribbean mood. Louisiana sweetcorn fritters (lightly battered baby corn) weren't at all greasy and came with a well-spiced salsa. Tender New Orleans Creole chicken satay was complemented by a sweet and sour sauce bulked out with chunks of veg. A slim Cajun tuna steak served with spicy tomato-based sauce and moulded couscous remained succulent despite being cooked through, though its presentation and flavour were more reminiscent of the islands than the bayous. Despite a rich gravy, the lean 'steak rum Creole' was disappointingly bland and conspicuously lacking in rum. We finished with some good own-baked desserts, including apple and ginger surprise (a traditional pie with a kick) and a dense, spicy and not too sweet carrot cake.
Babies and children welcome; children's menu. Entertainment: salsa (incl lessons) from 7.30pm Tue; jazz alternate Fri, Sat (phone for details). Tables outdoors (3, pavement). Takeaway service.

South Woodford E18

Yellow Book Californian Café
190 George Lane, E18 (020 8989 3999). South Woodford tube. **Lunch served** noon-2.30pm Tue-Sat. **Dinner served** 6.30-11pm Mon-Thur; 6.30-11.30pm Fri, Sat. **Meals served** noon-10.30pm Sun. **Main courses** £6-£13.95. **Minimum** £10 when busy. **Credit** MC, £TC, V.
A Californian restaurant in suburban Essex may sound improbable, but the Yellow Book was awash with well-heeled locals on a Thursday night. The decor is tastefully eclectic, if slightly dated: trompe l'oeil pillars, Mexican-style hand-painted chairs and a conservatory full of old books. In true Californian style, the menu is a magma of ethnic influences. Huge char-grilled prawns, served in their shells, were moist, meaty and perfectly offset by a soy, honey and ginger dip. Another starter of quesadilla had a wonderful filling of salmon, goat's cheese and spinach, but the cooking process seemed to have vulcanised the tortilla. Pizzas cooked in a wood-burning oven are a speciality – a faultlessly crisp base deliciously topped with artichokes, spinach and green olives. Pan-seared calf's liver was expertly cooked, served on a bed of bubble and squeak, but could have done with a bit more of the wine-laced gravy. Alabama soft rock pie turned out to be a wickedly indulgent chocolate mousse studded with marshmallows on a biscuit base. There's a good choice of cocktails as well as wines; a decent-sized bar at the front completes the relaxed West Coast picture.
Babies and children welcome; high chairs. Bookings not accepted at weekends. Tables outdoors (20, patio).

Highgate N6

Idaho
13 North Hill, N6 (020 8341 6633/ www.montana.plc.uk). Highgate tube.
Bar **Open** 6.30pm-midnight Mon-Sat; 6.30-11pm Sun.
Restaurant **Brunch served** 12.30-3.30pm Sat; 11.30am-4pm Sun. **Dinner served** 6.30pm-midnight Mon-Sat; 6.30-10.30pm Sun. **Main courses** £12-£16. **Set meal** £12.95 two courses. **Service** 12½%.
Both **Credit** AmEx, MC, £TC, V.
Idaho is a bit of a departure for Highgate, but the locals have taken to it – booking is essential and waiting in the bar not unheard of. The look of the place is starkly modern, softened by curves. Upstairs there's a 'like it or loath it' super-enlarged American landscape photo and a huge note-hung lampshade. The main attraction, though, is a diverting menu of uncommon ingredients. It includes starters such as roast corn fritters with baby leaves and sweet pasilla (chilli) sauce; corn blini with tequila-cured salmon, horseradish cream and cucumber salsa; and half a dozen oysters with an inspired Granny Smith and shallot relish. Less exciting, but not without interest, are mains like braised lamb shank with cracked wheat and herb salad with mint pesto; or rigatoni with iron-bark pumpkin, roast red onion and pine nuts; or Caesar salad. The latter was, surprisingly, the most successful dish, the lamb being too fatty and the pasta tasty but lukewarm. Even a trio of sorbets was inventive, with grape, cranberry and passion fruit replacing more ordinary flavours. The waiters are friendly and efficient – in stark contrast to the front of

Sally's Diner

house staff – and there's a certain hard, noisy edge to the atmosphere, unlike the other links in the chain (Montana, Canyon, Dakota, and Utah – the latest addition, in Wimbledon), which might not make it everyone's cup of tea.
Babies and children admitted; high chairs. Booking essential Thur-Sun. Disabled: toilet. Entertainment: jazz pianist daily from 8.30pm, lunchtime Sun. Separate room for parties (seats 15). Tables outdoors (terrace, 25).
For branch (Utah) see index.

Islington N1

Santa Fe

75 Upper Street, N1 (020 7288 2288). Angel tube/19, 30, 73 bus.
Bar **Open** noon-10.30pm Mon-Sat; noon-10.30pm Sun.
Restaurant **Meals served** noon-10.30pm Mon-Sat; noon-10pm Sun. **Main courses** £4.95-£10.50 (lunch), £5.75-£12.95 (dinner). **Service** 12½% for parties of six or more.
Both **Credit** AmEx, JCB, MC, £TC, V.
The capacious interior at Santa Fe incorporates separate smoking and non-smoking dining areas, a bar, cosy pod-like booths and, at the back, a border-town shrine of jewellery and chillies through to the novelty toilets. Loud, determinedly feel-good music and a youngish crowd provide the noise, while friendly, accommodating staff keep the cogs turning. Unfortunately, the menu, which even has its own glossary, just doesn't deliver. A shared starter (the Santa Fe sampler) was nice enough – shrimps spiked with lime and chilli were particularly tasty – but there wasn't enough of it. Another starter of char-grilled salmon wrap tasted like tinned salmon mush dotted with large capers, while a main-course pot roast had also fallen victim to portion control – tiny quantities of bland beef in an indifferent sauce. A side dish of calabacitas was a suspiciously perfect dice of carrots, corn, peas and courgettes and lacked any real flavour, whereas a solid, sweet-tasting corn pudding would have made a great accompaniment to a really spicy stew. At least chocolate brownie with cinnamon ice-cream was good. Santa Fe has what it takes to be a better than average Tex Mex restaurant, but it's currently slipping into Upper Street mediocrity.
Babies and children welcome; children's menu; high chairs; nappy-changing facilities; toys. Disabled: toilet. No-smoking tables. Separate rooms for parties, seating 25 and 50.
Map 16/20.

King's Cross NW1

Sally's Diner ★

2 Pancras Road, NW1 (020 7713 8474/ 8462/www.sallysdiner.co.uk). King's Cross tube/rail. **Meals served** 7am-10pm Mon-Fri; 9am-10pm Sat. **Main courses** £3.75-£13.75. **Unlicensed. Credit** £TC.
On a positive note, Sally's is a fun, witty take on classic roadside Americana. It's a bright and spacious venue, with smart chrome panelling and lurid neon signs; chilli comes in a bowl, coffee comes in mugs and the frantic short-order cooks still find time to wisecrack to the waitresses. Sounds like a winner? Not quite. If this was a proper blue-collar, 'eat all you can for a few bucks' chow-down, we would happily overlook the artery-furring blandness of the cooking, but this is King's Cross and these are London restaurant prices (main courses prices level out at £13.75). There are Caesar salads and club sandwiches galore but we opted for a more genteel-sounding starter of crab cake, mixed leaves and home-made sauce. This was dry, small, singed and tasteless. Main courses read like the contents of the Simpsons' fridge – meatloaf, burgers, fried chicken, hot dogs and so on. A steak arrived under two enormous slabs of butter that rapidly dissolved into a slick of grease, wilting the accompanying fries into limp submission. Dessert was a microwaved brownie. The limited wine list matches every bottle with a dish on the menu (even the apple pie). We preferred a bottle of San Fran's own Anchor Steam beer – that, at least, was delicious.
Babies and children welcome; high chairs. Disabled: toilet. No-smoking tables. Tables outdoors (25, courtyard). Takeaway service. Vegetarian menu. **Map 3/3L.**

North West

West Hampstead NW3

Babe Ruth's

O_2 Complex, Finchley Road, NW3 (020 7433 3388/www.baberuths.com). Finchley Road tube.
Bar **Open** noon-11pm Mon-Sat; noon-10.30pm Sun.
Restaurant **Meals served** noon-11.30pm Mon-Sat; noon-11pm Sun. **Main courses** £6.99-£15.99. **Service** 12½% for parties of six or more.
Both **Credit** AmEx, MC, £TC, V.
One of several American-style chains in the cavernous O_2 complex, the Babe Ruth's restaurant has the feel of a chic airport lounge, with floor-to-ceiling windows, blue leatherette booths and overhead TVs. Sport is the theme, but the arcade games and glassed-off basketball hoop are discreetly tucked away from the dining area. The menu ranges from sandwiches to sophisticated-sounding mains, but the kitchen didn't deliver. Monterey Jack and spinach dip was tangy and creamy, but accompanying deep-fried Parmesan flatbread made this a fat-saturated starter. Thai sticks – tender spiced chicken served with a coconut and coriander dip – went down better. Fatty blackened swordfish came with insipid fresh tomato and red onion salsa, burnt and sticky black beans, dry jasmine rice and bland guacamole. By comparison, the slow-cooked lamb shank with mash was very pleasant comfort food, if less ambitious. Desserts came in large portions and were extremely sweet: toffee and banana pie was an elegant interpretation of banoffi, while a chocolate brownie was moreishly rich but unusually moist. Babe Ruth's is an ideal place to bring the kids for a pre-movie bite, but for a decent meal adults should stick to the simpler dishes on offer.
Babies and children welcome; children's menu; crayons; high chairs. Book dinner. Entertainment: bouncy castle; face painting 1-4pm Sun; interactive games machines; mini-basketball court. Disabled: toilet. No-smoking tables. Separate room for parties, seats 50.
For branch see index.

Outer London

Richmond, Surrey

Canyon

Riverside, near Richmond Bridge, Richmond, Surrey (020 8948 2944/www.montana.plc.uk). Richmond tube/rail. **Brunch served** 11am-4pm Sat, Sun. **Lunch served** noon-3.30pm Mon-Fri. **Dinner served** 7-11pm daily. **Main courses** £9-£16. **Service** 12½%. **Credit** AmEx, MC, £TC, V.
This white ranch-style building, with its floor-to-ceiling windows, terrace and cacti, ought to overlook the Pacific. Even so, Canyon's riverside location, relaxed modern mood and excellent brunch make it a pleasant spot. Tasty chocolate and apricot bread preceded our brunch, which began in earnest with smoked haddock hash (which looked like fish cakes to us) with a well-poached egg and nearly faultless (slightly over-seasoned) hollandaise. Char-grilled 10oz Iowa rib-eye steak was next, arriving without its advertised egg at first, but the meat was succulent, cooked exactly as ordered and had bags of flavour. Barbecue sauce (from a choice of three) added an extra nip of roast pasilla chilli. Caesar salad was crisp, richly dressed and generously topped with Parmesan and fresh anchovies. Only dessert failed to live up to expectations. We could taste none of the promised bourbon in the chocolate sauce that topped an exceedingly moist brownie, while apple pie hid beneath a spongy crust. The wine list favours California. In true US style, Canyon manages to be both fashionable and family-friendly.
Babies and children admitted; high chairs. Disabled: toilet. Booking advisable; essential weekends. Tables outdoors (18, courtyard; 18, terrace).
For branch (Utah) see index.

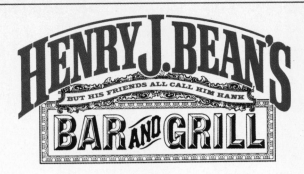

Latin American

Argentinian

Central

Piccadilly W1

The Gaucho Grill ★
19 Swallow Street, W1 (020 7734 4040). Piccadilly Circus tube.
Bar **Open** noon-3pm, 5-11pm, Mon-Fri; noon-11pm Sat; noon-10.30pm Sun.
Restaurant **Lunch served** noon-3pm, **dinner served** 5-11pm Mon-Fri. **Meals served** noon-midnight Sat; noon-10.30pm Sun. **Main courses** £7.50-£32.50. **Service** 10% for parties of eight or more.
Both **Credit** AmEx, DC, MC, £TC, V.
This smart, adult-oriented cellar restaurant has a decadent, clandestine feel. Its candlelit brick-walled, labyrinthine vaults, and its cowhide-upholstered seating make it a popular spot for late-night lovers. Appropriately, then, the meat-and butter-heavy menu makes no concessions to virtuousness. Steaks are the attraction. The bife de lomo fillet steak was gorgeous – melt-in-the-mouth – you'd be hard-pressed to find better in London. Choose your accompanying sauces for £1; we chose rich, buttery béarnaise. Catch of the day was, perhaps inevitably for this place, a rich, meaty tuna steak with salsa sauce. It was offset well by a peppery, mustardy green salad. Every dish we tried had been stripped down to the bare essentials, emphasising the high-quality ingredients and precision cooking. The desserts, however, almost defeated us. The sweetness of the flan con dulce de leche would be enough to see off a hundred diabetics, although the chocolate tart (a creamy truffle chocolate set on to a layer of chocolate sponge) was just right. With its classy Argentinian wine list and highly professional service, the Gaucho Grill is a rare treat.
Babies and children welcome; high chairs. Booking advisable. **Map 13/7J.**
For branch see index.

South West

Fulham SW10

El Gaucho
88 Ifield Road, SW10 (020 7823 3333). West Brompton tube/14 bus. **Dinner served** 6.30-11pm daily. **Main courses** £5.40-£17.90. **No credit cards.**
Still packing them in since moving further into Fulham (the Chelsea branch is only open at lunch now), El Gaucho is probably the best value of London's Argentinian steak specialists – the steaks tend to be very large, free from gristle, and of high quality. But be warned: dishes are very literal versions of their description on the menu. A starter of grilled provolone was just that, a whole round of cheese with nothing added, and as such impossible to eat after a couple of bites. Bife de lomo, a fillet steak, was a little bloody for a medium-rare, but velvet-smooth. However, a dish of glazed vegetables consisting of corn on the cob, carrots and runner beans was excruciatingly dull; not even the hottest of mustards could release it from its prison of gastronomic tedium. French fries cooked Provençal style (with garlic and parsley) provided limited respite. The look of the place fits in well with the no-nonsense food: cow hides hang on the walls, leather saddles straddle the banisters. The friendly Argentinian waitresses and the little wooden tables at the back are the greatest assets – apart from the very good steak, of course.
Babies and children admitted. Bookings accepted before 8pm only.
For branch see index.

South

Battersea SW11

La Pampa Grill
60 Battersea Rise, SW11 (020 7924 4774). Clapham Junction rail. **Dinner served** 6-midnight Mon-Sat; 6-11pm Sun. **Main courses** £7.95-£15.50. **Service** 10% for parties of seven or more. **Credit** MC, £TC, V.
If you don't fancy a steak, don't bother coming here: this popular restaurant is a shrine to the manliest meat of them all. Most of the menu is taken up by a series of Argentinian beef steaks (the fried egg on top is optional), although there are a few simple chicken dishes as well. Sirloin steak was of the highest quality, but was requested rare and came well-done; the fact that it arrived about a minute after being ordered suggests that it wasn't cooked specifically for us. The vegetarian dish, unsurprisingly, was very much an afterthought: courgettes, aubergines, carrots and onions, thrown together without as much as a sauce to enliven them. Panqueques con dulce de leche, an Argentinian speciality, couldn't have been much worse: cheap ice-cream melting inside a rubbery, overcooked pancake, with runny dulce de leche gluing the whole thing together. But the place was packed, there's a good Argentinian wine list (Terralis Sangiovese, £14.80), and the heavy wooden interior and relaxed staff do create a welcoming ambience, so perhaps we were just unlucky.
Booking advisable. Separate room for parties, seats 24.

Brazilian

Central

Covent Garden WC2

Copacabana
186 Drury Lane, WC2 (020 7404 7808). Covent Garden or Holborn tube. **Meals served** 9am-6pm Mon-Sat. **Main course** £5.50. **Unlicensed. Corkage** no charge. **No credit cards.**
This daytime café, long-standing but with a new name (it was Hammock Café), has a light, airy, and slightly stark feel to it. The floor is tiled, the walls are painted in bright yellows and reds, and the distance between tables is a refreshing change for central London, but the place needs a hot day to come into its own. The simple menu is based on that of a Brazilian worker's café, so the national dish, feijoada – black beans and pork with rice and ground cassava – is always served. The food served at Copacabana is robust, healthy and authentic (the place was full of Brazilians on our visit). The other regular dish, fish in coconut sauce, was not available, so we tried a tasty salt-cod fish cake instead, and a slightly dry spinach calzone from a range of pastries. Vitamina (fresh fruit juice with guaraná) is worth a try as well, but the main reason for coming here is the feijoada.
Babies and children admitted. Separate room for parties, seats 30. Takeaway service.
Map 14/6L.

Euston NW1

Terra Brasil
36-38 Chalton Street, NW1 (020 7388 6554). Euston tube/rail. **Lunch served** noon-2.30pm Mon-Fri. **Dinner served** 7-10.30pm Fri-Sat. **Main courses** £3.95-£4.95. **Set buffet** £5, £7. **No credit cards.**
In the no-man's land between Euston and King's Cross, this quietly excellent little place operates a pay-by-weight system (£1.50 per 100g). With its bright yellow walls, tiled tables and books on Brazil, it feels more like a community centre than a restaurant. The opening hours are pretty weird, too, so phone to check before travelling far. The owners are a very friendly couple who may well start chatting to you before your meal is finished; they will guide you through the buffet, which includes national favourites like feijoada (beans and pork stew), shrimp stew with pumpkins, chicken with coconut, ground cassava and various salads. A plateful will typically add up to around £6, making it very good value. We augmented our buffet with delicious desserts: coconut milk set in a mousse with prune juice, and a passion fruit fool. Then we finished off with a spice-laced hot chocolate – all very Latin American and rarely seen over here. There's a big fish stew on Wednesday evenings that, on the evidence of our visit, could well be worth making a beeline for.
Babies and children admitted. Entertainment: Brazilian guitarist occasionally (phone for details). No smoking. Tables outdoors (5, pavement). Takeaway service.
Map 3/3K.

West

Hammersmith W6

Paulo's
30 Greyhound Road, W6 (020 7385 9264). Hammersmith tube/11, 74, 220 bus.
Lunch served noon-3pm Tue-Sat; 1-3.30pm Sun. **Dinner served** 7.30-10.30pm Tue-Sat. **Set buffet lunch** £8.50. **Set buffet dinner** £8.50 Tue; £10.50 Wed-Sat. **Service** 10% for parties. **Credit** MC, £TC, V.
Hidden down a quiet residential street, this family-run restaurant is worth seeking out for an authentic Brazilian experience. There's no menu for main courses, just a buffet with dishes such as prawn stew, red bean stew, chicken breasts, beef casserole, cassava, okra, various salads and the hottest chilli sauce known to man. The vivacious Brazilian owner claims to have lost a finger after having erroneously dipped it into his own vicious concoction. Some of the dishes were delicious, some were lacklustre, but the mood of the place is so friendly and relaxed that you can't help but enjoy yourself. There are also a few starters (prawn croquettes and crab Brazilian-style on our visit), but you don't really need them as well as the buffet. In fact, you're better off saving room for desserts such as quinlim, a sublime coconut flan. Bear in mind that staff also mix a mean Caipirinha (the national tipple of lime and cachaça rum).
Babies and children welcome. Booking advisable; essential Fri, Sat. Tables outdoors (6, garden). Takeaway service.

Westbourne Grove W2

Rodizio Rico
111 Westbourne Grove, W2 (020 7792 4035). Bayswater or Notting Hill Gate tube. **Lunch served** 12.30-4.30pm Sat. **Dinner served** 6.30-11.30pm Mon-Sat. **Meals served** 1-11.30pm Sun. **Set buffet meal** £10 (vegetarian), £16.90. **Service** 10%.
Credit MC, £TC, V.
It doesn't get more authentic than this huge Brazilian steakhouse. An enormous grill takes centre stage, where a moustachioed chef lays what look like whole cows and pigs over the roaring flames. Waiters patrol the brick-walled restaurant with metre-long skewers, stopping to carve slices of every conceivable type of meat straight on to your plate. There's no menu, just a meat or vegetarian option. The first step is to take what you want from the buffet: red beans and rice, fried plantain, cassava, salsa, cauliflower cheese, various salads and so on. Then sit down and wait; the skewer-bearers will come to you. Surprisingly, vegetarians are very well catered for, with vegetable grills as ubiquitous as the meat. The secret is to make this long, heavy meal stretch over a couple of hours or more; you'll never feel you're outstaying your welcome. House wines, like the Argentinian rioja, will arrive at your table almost as fast as you; you pay for what you open, but waiters will take orders for other wines and beers. Desserts include Brazilian faves like crème caramel flan and coconut cake. You won't feel like eating, or moving for that matter, ever again.
Babies and children welcome; high chairs. Booking advisable; essential dinner. No-smoking tables. Separate room for parties, seats 55. Tables outdoors (6, pavement).
Map 11/6B.

North

Archway N19

Sabor do Brasil
36 Highgate Hill, N19 (020 7263 9066). Archway tube. **Lunch served** by appointment Tue-Sun. **Dinner served** 7-11.45pm Tue-Sun. **Closed** Aug. **Main courses** £3.50-£10.50. **Set buffet dinner** £9.50. **Cover** £1 Wed. **Credit** £TC.
Very much a family affair, this small, friendly restaurant is run by an affable mama who potters out of the kitchen occasionally to make sure her guests are enjoying themselves. For the rest of the time, it's up to the good-natured, if linguistically challenged, Brazilian waiters to look after you. Starters tend to be quite rich: prawns fried in garlic were tasty but oily; ainpim frito (fried cassava) was both simpler and lighter. Dried salt-cod baked Brazilian-style was a piquant main course, with a generous, tender fish steak brought alive by dried spices and onions. Pork in tarragon with rice was a little heavy for the season (it's a substantial winter dish but too much for summer). If you can, try and save room for the house favourite, manjar branco (coconut milk blancmange), which is exotic and absolutely delicious. Sabor do Brasil is one of those rare places that are so endearing you simply can't help but leave in a good mood. There's a band every Wednesday night, too.
Babies and children welcome; high chairs. Booking advisable; essential Fri, Sat. Entertainment: Latin jazz 8-11pm Wed (phone for details). Separate room for parties, seats 38.

Colombian

North West

Kilburn NW6

Doña Olga
Latin American House, Kingsgate Place, NW6 (020 7624 3831). Kilburn Park tube/16, 28, 32, 98, 189 bus. **Meals served** 11am-10pm Tue-Sun. **Main courses** £7.50-£9.50. **Set meal** (noon-3pm) £12 three courses, (7-10pm) £10 three courses. **Credit** MC, V.
Hidden down a bin-lined alley, looking like the back room of a shop, with just one waiter (who speaks pidgin English), Doña Olga doesn't sound like much on paper, but this tiny restaurant is a real find. It serves authentic Colombian home-cooking to Kilburn's small Latin American community. The blackboard menu features robust but exotic dishes such as plantain fried with cheese and flour, and sacorho (a traditional chicken, cassava and potato soup). Mojava frita, a whole red snapper with crushed plantain, fried cassava and salad, was superb – the fresh snapper was grilled in fiery spices and came with a very hot green salsa to liven up the Colombian vegetables. Soft beef in aromatic sauce with rice and crushed plantain was also very good: simple ingredients kept wholesome and unspoilt, cooked in a time-honoured way. The size of main courses makes desserts an unlikely proposition, but you'd be mad to miss the milkshakes – guanabana's name gives it away, but lupo, described simply as a 'tropical favourite' remained a delicious mystery. We tried to find out what was in it from the silent waiter, but to no avail.
Babies and children welcome; high chairs. Separate room for parties, seats 50. Takeaway service.

Cuban

South

Waterloo SE1

Cubana
48 Lower Marsh, SE1 (020 7928 8778/ www.cubana.co.uk). Waterloo tube/rail.
Bar **Open** 10am-midnight Mon-Sat.
Restaurant **Meals served** noon-11.30pm Mon-Sat. **Main courses** £4.95-£9.45. **Set lunch** £5.95 two courses, £7.95 three courses.
Both **Credit** AmEx, DC, JCB, MC, £TC, V.
Selling itself on the island's turbulent history, this colourful, loud and bustling restaurant has AK47s hanging from the ceiling, paintings of Castro and other revolutionaries on the walls, and a giant mural of a Cuban beauty covering its façade. Two cocktail bars also draw in crowds of local workers. A starter of ceviche (fresh raw tuna marinated in lemon and olive oil with garlic and peppers) was refreshingly zesty, but tortilla with Cuban vegetables and mint was overcooked and oily. The mains were similarly patchy. Char-grilled snapper in a tangerine sweet-sour sauce with rice and black beans had a good mix of flavours, but the fish was unremarkable; coconut rice with char-grilled sweet potatoes, plantain and black beans in a tomato salsa was dry and lacklustre (the dish had a thrown-together feel about it). Fruit salad with coconut provided welcome freshness, but a crêpe with mango was rather heavy. Culinary glitches aside, Cubana is still fun and good value. But be warned: a single loo in a place so big and so popular can become very busy.
Babies and children welcome. Booking advisable. Tables outdoors. **Map 7/9N.**

North

Islington N1

Cuba Libre
72 Upper Street, N1 (020 7354 9998). Angel tube.
Bar **Open** 10am-2am Mon-Sat; 10am-11pm Sun.
Restaurant **Breakfast served** 10am-noon daily. **Meals served** noon-11.30pm Mon-Sat; noon-10.30pm Sun. **Main courses** £8.50-£11.75. **Set lunch** (noon-5pm Mon-Fri) £5 two courses. **Set meal** (5pm-midnight Mon-Thur; noon-5pm Sat; noon-10.30pm Sun) £10 two courses.
Both **Service** 12½%. **Credit** MC, £TC, V.
The capital's first Cuban restaurant is still going strong, offering north Londoners a dash of Latin colour. It's like being inside a Cuban courtyard, with a colonial mural, brightly painted glass windows, palm trees and papier mâché models of Fidel

Castro and friends guarding over the whole affair from the top of a wall. A starter of cassava chips came with a fresh coriander dip; and a truly tropical Cuban salad was made up of avocado, plantain, banana and pineapple, all held together by a hollowed-out pineapple. The main courses weren't so good: both cod fish cakes and casseroled meatballs with grilled peppers, rice, black beans and fried plantain looked and tasted like they had been left on hotplates. Better were pudín diplomático (crème caramel on a sponge base) and arroz con leche (rice pudding spiced up with cinnamon and nutmeg). As Cuba Libre is constantly catering for huge parties, standards are variable, but the potential for a decent meal is there. *Booking advisable Fri, Sat. Entertainment: late-night dancing in bar. Tables outdoors (8, pavement).* **Map 16/2O.**

Mexican & Tex-Mex

Central

Covent Garden WC2

Café Pacifico
5 Langley Street, WC2 (020 7379 7728/ www.cafepacifico-laperla.com). Covent Garden or Leicester Square tube. **Meals served** noon-11.45pm Mon-Sat; noon-10.45pm Sun. **Main courses** £3-£5.10 (lunch), £6.50-£13.25 (dinner). **Service** 12½%. **Credit** AmEx, JCB, MC, £TC, V.
This hardy Covent Garden perennial needs a nice balmy evening to do it justice. Its façade opens up on to the street, and the tiled floors, swishing fans and raised platforms (separated by wood-framed glass) have the feel of a tropical bar. Perhaps that's why Café Pacifico is a favourite destination for drunken office parties, hen nights, and other large groups ordering one fresh fruit Margarita after another. The long menu updates Mexican standards, with a 'modern Mexican lite' section that includes cross-cultural pollinations such as swordfish with strawberry salsa, and wild mushroom fajitas with sun-dried tomato salsa and crème fraîche. We went trad with enchiladas san blas (soft tortillas with cod, crab, prawns, cheese, onions, avocado and salad), which (despite being drowned in cheese) tasted like authentic Mexican beach-restaurant food. Another main, lobster and papaya quesadillas (pan-fried tortillas with lobster, papaya, chillies, feta, roasted peppers and a mango cream sauce) was tasty and unusual, but contained virtually no lobster. No marks for finesse, then, but that isn't really the point of this boozy, late-night hangout.
Babies and children welcome; children's menu; crayons; high chairs; toys. Bookings not accepted dinner Thur-Sat. **Map 14/6L.**

La Perla
28 Maiden Lane, WC2 (020 7240 7400). Covent Garden or Embankment tube/Charing Cross tube/rail. **Meals served** noon-11.45pm Mon-Sat; 4-10.30pm Sun. **Main courses** £7.25-£12.50. **Credit** AmEx, MC, £TC, V.
This fish-based Mexican restaurant is an exception to the tourist trap norm of Covent Garden. The decor is clichéd Americana: tin plates and photos of big fish abound, and a mural of a mermaid looks like the jacket design of a John Steinbeck novel. We kicked off with delicious quesadillas filled with lime-marinated fish and a proper spicy salsa, and the best nachos rancheros (with beans, melted cheese, ranchera sauce and salad) this side of Tijuana. Mains were even better. Catch of the day, swordfish steak grilled with lemon and served with herb-roasted potatoes and vegetables, tasted deliciously fresh. Quesade grande (tortillas filled with tender shredded beef, good refried beans and salsa vegetables) was packed with clear, strong flavours. Unlike more dive-like Mexican joints, La Perla doesn't sell itself as a party venue either; it's a quiet place that takes real care in its cooking. Well worth checking out.
Babies and children admitted (restaurant only). Book dinner. **Map 14/7L.**

Piccadilly W1

Down Mexico Way
25 Swallow Street, W1 (020 7437 9895/ www.downmexway.com). Piccadilly Circus tube. *Bar* **Open** 5pm-3am Mon-Sat. *Restaurant* **Meals served** noon-midnight Mon-Sat; noon-10.30pm Sun. **Main courses** £9-£13.50. **Service** 12½%. *Both* **Credit** AmEx, DC, MC, £TC, V.
In a grand, colonial-style ballroom down a small Piccadilly sidestreet is London's smartest Mexican restaurant – Down Mexico Way. It's an opulently tiled, surprisingly large hideaway,

Cubana.
See page 29.

replete with an impressive domed ceiling with huge tropical plants hanging down. After-work parties and expense-account businessmen seem to be regulars. You'll have to shout to make yourself heard (particularly when the professional salsa dancers do their nightly floor-show). The menu aims for a more sophisticated take on the standard Mexican fare. The quesadilla de pato tropicala, tacos with blueberry, cheese, duck, mango and peppers, didn't quite come off, though, as the blueberries and cheese were nowhere to be seen and the domineering peppers were slimy. Crab tostadas were better but could have done with more lime and salsa. Things picked up with the mains: a delicious fajita with

char-grilled salmon, onions and red and green peppers came with a properly chunky guacamole and fresh, authentic salsa; a nicely simple tuna steak with avocado and peach salsa tasted very fresh, too. Chocolate a la mexicana (bitter chocolate mousse with coffee), and a tequila cassata gave the meal a nicely decadent ending. This is an accomplished restaurant with a brave cook, although not all the experiments come off.
Babies and children admitted (restaurant only); high chairs. Booking advisable; essential dinner Fri, Sat. Entertainment: Mexican music and dancers (7pm, 10pm, Wed-Sat). Separate room for parties, seats 25. **Map 13/7J.**

Soho W1

Sí Señor
2 St Anne's Court, off Dean Street, W1 (020 7494 4632). Leicester Square or Tottenham Court Road tube. *Bar* **Open** noon-11pm daily. *Restaurant* **Lunch served** noon-5pm, **dinner served** 5pm-midnight daily. **Main courses** £2.80-£12.50. **Set meal** £5.50. *Both* **Credit** AmEx, DC, MC, £TC, V.
London's biggest cantina has forsaken the ponchos and sombreros for a more authentic Mexico City look: Day of the Dead skeletons and papier mâché pinatas hang from the rafters, with

Time Out

Eating & Drinking Awards 2001

How it works

The *Time Out Eating and Drinking* Awards were the first to involve you, the readers, in the selection process and they remain the most democratic of their type. They're designed to be won by places that have given most pleasure to you and us – and that doesn't mean the most exclusive, expensive or obvious choices.

Each year you help us to choose eight places worthy of receiving one of these coveted awards. Here's what you do.

There are eight categories, designed to represent the diversity of great eating and drinking venues in London. We'd like you to nominate your favourite place(s) in one or more categories. Then our panel of judges – reviewers with an unrivalled knowledge of the range of places to eat in London – draws up a shortlist of six restaurants in each category. We visit all of these 48 restaurants anonymously, and also ask in *Time Out* magazine and on timeout.com for your views on the finalists. These are then taken into consideration as the final verdict is reached. That way, the Awards represent your and our experiences of London restaurants. Help us make the right choices.

Independent views

We're unbiased, independent, anonymous, and we pay our own way.

The *Time Out* Eating & Drinking Guide is the biggest and best-selling restaurant guide in London. Hundreds of restaurants are reviewed and the Guide is fully updated each year. No other guide covers London (and a few places outside) as widely and wisely and in as much depth as we do. Our specialist reviewers, experts in each cuisine, compare and contrast restaurants in a way no other guide even attempts. Who else can claim Chinese, Japanese, Korean, Polish, Spanish and Thai speakers visiting restaurants in each of these categories?

THE AWARDS

1. PERRIER BEST BAR
Be it born-again pub, West End cocktail bar or Shoreditch style bar, great bars come in many shapes and disguises. We and our sponsor Perrier want you to get your drinking caps on and tell us which places have the most refreshing range of drinks, poured by the most knowledgeable bar staff in attitude-free surroundings.

2. BEST LOCAL RESTAURANT
We've noticed a shift away from the West End in the last year. Where once you had to visit Zone 1 to find stylish surroundings, professional staff and excellent food, now many of London's best finds are in Zone 2, 3 or beyond. Do you have somewhere nearby with personal service, friendly owners and above all, great food that's worth recommending as an example of a neighbourhood restaurant? It should be a restaurant that makes your corner of the capital the envy of others. Share your local knowledge.

3. *KIDS OUT* BEST FAMILY RESTAURANT
Sometimes a balloon and a lollipop aren't enough – especially if you're a grown-up. Which restaurants cater as well for the adults as the kids, but still keep children amused and well-fed? Which places are genuinely child-friendly, have good facilities (high chairs, toys, special menus) and staff who welcome family groups without rolling their eyes? Tell us the best (and the worst).

4. BEST ORGANIC MEAL
Only a year ago we would have had difficulty putting together a shortlist of organic eateries. But now, several of London's best restaurants are showing their true colours – Lindsay House, Sugar Club, St John, and the River Café are just some of the top places that have always favoured organic ingredients, they just weren't making a fuss about it. There are also the newer wholly organic eateries such as Sauce, The Crown in Victoria Park, and The Source, with new places opening every month. Which one do you feel good about?

5. BEST HOTEL RESTAURANT
The past year has seen the transformation of Londoners' perceptions of hotel restaurants. Such venues are no longer the domain of wealthy tourists; Londoners now flock to the fashionable bars and restaurants in new-wave hotels. The long-established hotels haven't been caught napping, either, as many of them are lowering their prices and investing in the finest chefs and surroundings. Which one would you go to for a special treat?

6. BEST GASTROPUB
The London boozer has been transformed. Many pubs now serve restaurant-quality food in friendly, simply furnished surroundings, with as good a choice of wines as beers. You can just eat or just drink, and meet friends who might do one but not the other. Tell us your favourite.

7. BEST INTERIOR DESIGN
London restaurants are as much about theatre as eating and drinking, as many successful restaurateurs realise. Some cafés, restaurants and bars have taken this to new heights, with lavishly designed interiors that become the draw in themselves. Which interior has blown you away? Which one do you take your out-of-town friends to see? It doesn't have to be a big West End venue, but it must be somewhere that has captured the zeitgeist of modern dining and drinking, and must have opened in 2000 or early 2001.

8. BEST NEW RESTAURANT
Every year dozens of new restaurants appear, but only a few will make a lasting contribution to eating out in London. Which of this year's crop (having opened in 2000 or early 2001) will prove to be more than a flash in the pan, long after the initial hype has died down? Tell us about the newcomer you think should win this prestigious Award.

SPECIAL AWARD
We've introduced one more Award, a free-form category for outstanding achievement. The winner could be a person, a product, a trend-setter, a team, a campaign – even a dream that came true. The aim is to acknowledge the less obvious contenders, or deserving examples of achievement within the eating-out scene who slip through the net. If there's anyone or anything you would like to nominate, let us know.

NOMINATION FORM
for the 2001 *Time Out* Eating & Drinking Awards

Category
_____

Restaurant
_____

Address
_____
_____
_____
_____

Reason for nomination
_____
_____
_____
_____
_____

Your name
_____

Your daytime telephone no
_____

Your address
_____
_____
_____
_____

Conditions: Nominate only one restaurant per form. To make nominations in more than one category, photocopy this page and return completed forms to: Sarah Guy, *Time Out*, Universal House, 251 Tottenham Court Road, London W1P 0AB by 1 Feb 2001.

colourful, cartoon-style paintings of wrestlers, old señors and young señoritas on the walls. In the evenings the place is office-party central, and as darkness falls and the music gets louder, all diners have the right to demand that their waiters break out some dance moves (the waitresses are excused). It's a fun place, in other words, but the food suffers as a result. A guacamole starter with tortilla chips was of the mass-produced, not freshly made variety, while a main-course conchita pibil taco – glazed pork with achiote (annatto seed) and orange juice served with rice and pinto beans – sort of collapsed in on itself, as if it had given up the will to exist. Potato and cheese enchilada was equally squidgy, its tasteless ingredients blending into a mush. The buffet might be a better bet, as it typically features refried beans, chicken wings, rice with sweetcorn, tortillas and various salads. But to come here for the food – rather than beer by the yard and Margaritas by the two-litre jug – is to miss the point.
Babies and children welcome; children's menu; crayons; high chairs. Book dinner Thur-Sat. No-smoking tables. Takeaway service. **Map 13/6K.**

Trafalgar Square SW1

Texas Embassy Cantina
1 Cockspur Street, SW1 (020 7925 0077). Charing Cross tube/rail. **Meals served** noon-11pm Mon-Wed; noon-midnight Thur-Sat; noon-10.30pm Sun. **Main courses** £7.25-£16.95. **Service** 12½% for parties of six or more. **Credit** AmEx, DC, MC, £TC, V.
This is a massive, family-style, Tex-Mex chow-down centre. The large, airy room is filled with stripped wooden tables, fairy lights, big plants and sombreros, plus eager-to-please, mostly foreign staff doing their best to make you feel welcome. The complimentary salsa was surprisingly good (although even the hot version is still quite mild), and a starter of nachos with refried beans, Cheddar cheese, sour cream, guacamole and jalapeños was a meal in itself. Red snapper fajita was a bit dry and overcooked, but was nicely seasoned. We ignored the Texas favourites (basically the staples of any American roadside diner) and went for a Monterey – two beef enchiladas with carne sauce, a soft beef taco and a crispy beef taco, all smothered in cheap barbecue sauce. Desserts are sticky American favourites; pecan pie, for instance, was tasty and enormous. A further plus – staff serve a decent Margarita.
Babies and children welcome; children's menu; crayons; high chairs. Booking advisable. Disabled: toilet. Separate room for parties, seats 120. Tables outdoors (8, pavement). **Map 13/7K.**

South

Battersea SW11

El Gran Taco
43 St John's Hill, SW11 (020 7585 3050). Clapham Junction rail/77 bus. **Dinner served** 6-11.30pm Mon-Sat; 6-10.30pm Sun. **Main courses** £3.25-£8.95. **Set dinner** £12, £15, three courses. **Credit** AmEx, MC, £TC, V.
This cavernous cantina goes for the traditional approach: long wooden tables, Aztec wall hangings, fairy lights, mescal and tequila galore and Santana on the stereo. The friendly Mexican owner sticks to the tried and tested flour-based favourites upon which Mexico has survived for centuries. We went for a burro (the same as a burrito but bigger), in which soft tortillas were filled with spicy chilli vegetables and good refried beans. Next, Monterey especial consisted of two rather greasy tacos with chilli, two taquitos (smaller tacos filled with chicken that was in dire need of some kind of sauce) and a tasty and wholesome frijolito (refried beans in a taco with sour cream). A side dish of calamares was spoilt by heavy, greasy batter, while a dessert of pan dulce, a banana and cinnamon cake, was stodgy but hit the spot. It all adds up to a fairly unhealthy night out, particularly if you go for bizarre cocktails like Submarino (a shot glass of tequila submerged into half a pint of beer), but it's a lot of fun and leans more towards the authentic than theme joint.
Babies and children welcome; high chairs. Booking advisable Fri, Sat. Separate room for parties, seats 50. Takeaway service.

Clapham SW4

Café Sol
56 Clapham High Street, SW4 (020 7498 9319). Clapham Common or Clapham North tube. **Meals served** noon-midnight Mon-Thur, Sun; noon-1am Fri, Sat. **Main courses** £5.95-£9.95. **Credit** AmEx, DC, MC, £TC, V.
Cafe Sol's reputation has grown so much among young Claphamites that this enormous place is now packed most nights with a partying crowd, usually more intent on downing jugs of Margarita than sampling fine food. This is just as well – more Tex than Mex, typical dishes here are 'swamp thing' (alligator with Cajun dip) and seafood fajitas, with more traditional Mexican favourites like enchiladas and beef chilli-stuffed tortillas. The mass-market attitude of the place was evident in a rather weedy salsa. A generous blackened tuna steak cooked in black pepper and a simple tomato sauce was satisfying enough, but enchiladas were a typically dried-up fast-food mess of refried beans, rice covered in melted Cheddar, cheap salsa vegetable filling and tacos. The Margaritas are produced by a Slush Puppy-style machine. With frantic waiters, tables jammed close together, and familiar salsa classics blaring out of the stereo, this is certainly not the place for a romantic dinner, but hey, the party people love it.
Babies and children welcome; high chairs. Book dinner Fri, Sat. Tables outdoors (4, pavement). Takeaway service.

North

Belsize Park NW3

Cactus ★
85A Haverstock Hill, NW3 (020 7722 4112/ www.cactusrestaurant.co.uk). Belsize Park or Chalk Farm tube. **Dinner served** 6pm-midnight Mon-Sat; 6-11pm Sun. **Set buffet** £4.88. **Service** 10%. **Credit** MC, £TC, V.
It's easy to miss this fun, laid-back place. A mere doorway on Haverstock Hill announces it, but go downstairs and you'll find a cavernous basement filled with every type of pinata, sombrero and Mexican plant imaginable. There's no menu, just a buffet that stretches beyond the usual tacos and burritos to include the likes of refried beans, chicken wings, vegetable stew, beef chimichangas and various salads. No ingredient is too expensive but, at the same time, standards are much higher than with most buffet food – there's no sense that corners have been cut. Waitresses come round to take your orders for drinks, which include an electric-blue tequila and a mighty litre bottle of San Miguel that seemed the popular choice on our trip. Cactus is an ideal place for big groups, yet it's also a place to escape to for a couple of hours. There is no rush at all; nobody seems to mind if you take as much time as you like.
Babies and children welcome (6-7pm). Booking essential. Separate room for parties, seats 50.

Camden Town & Chalk Farm NW1

Camden Cantina
34 Chalk Farm Road, NW1 (020 7267 2780). Chalk Farm tube. **Dinner served** 5.30-10.45pm Mon, Tue. **Meals served** 11.30am-10.45pm Wed-Sat; 11.30am-9pm Sun. **Main courses** £6.95-£8.95. **Credit** AmEx, MC, £TC, V.
Unsurprisingly, given its location, this cheaply knocked-up bar-restaurant serves food designed for the palates of students and young tourists on a tight budget. Camden Cantina occupies a long dark room containing bits of old furniture; various enamel signs decorate the walls, with trashy Mexican ephemera filling the gaps. Outside, the garden looks as if it belongs to a pub. Staff are very friendly, though, and happy to keep the jugs of Margarita or San Miguel flowing. The menu offers standard, messy Mexican food. Enchiladas with guacamole, sour cream, spicy enchilada sauce and melted cheese had that thrown-together, overcooked taste; distinguishing one ingredient from another was an impossibility. The rich mole di pollo (chicken strips in a dark, spicy, savoury chocolate-based sauce) is a Mexican staple not seen much on these shores and had a little more style. Come here expecting an inexpensive refuelling point that offers a refuge from the weekend hordes at the market and you won't be disappointed.
Babies and children welcome; high chairs. Booking advisable Fri, Sat. Tables outdoors (10, garden). **Map 10.**

Finsbury Park N4

Exquisite
167 Blackstock Road, N4 (020 7359 9529). Arsenal tube/19 bus. **Meals served** 4.30-11pm Mon-Sat; noon-10.30pm Sun. **Main courses** £4.20-£9.60. **Set meal** half-price menu (4.30-7pm Mon-Sat; noon-7pm Sun). **Service** 12½% for parties of six or more. **No credit cards.**
This small local restaurant has built up a loyal young clientele. The staff are friendly and the decor simple – stone walls painted with flowery murals and adorned with Aztec wall hangings in the glow of candlelight. The food, however, is not an attraction. The guacamole, that great leveller of Mexican restaurants, was puréed and tasted like it had been mixed with salad cream to make it go further. Similarly, the salsa was far too weak. Main courses were no better: burritos contained mixed bean salad, seemingly from a tin (rather than refried beans and chilli), with a few artichokes and some salsa, sour cream and bottled chillies thrown in for good measure. Enchiladas (savoury tortillas with more of the dreaded guacamole, plus mixed salad, asparagus and cheese) were equally unpalatable. A dessert of mango fool was no more than whipped cream and sugar with the odd bit of insipid mango. Despite low prices and a pleasant atmosphere, Exquisite has a lot to sort out before it can live up to its name.
Babies and children admitted. Takeaway service.

Kentish Town NW5

Zuni
134 Fortess Road, NW5 (020 7428 0803). Kentish Town tube/rail. **Dinner served** 7-10.30pm Tue-Sat. **Main courses** £8-£11. **Credit** MC, V.
This new addition to London's Tex-Mex restaurant scene is a breath of fresh air – rather than going for the maracas-shaking party atmosphere that means cheap jugs of Margaritas and lousy burritos, this is a much more civilised, but still down-to-earth affair, serving adventurous but authentic takes on classic Mexican staples. Cactus quesadilla, a dish rarely seen here but as common as, well, cacti in Mexico, was light and refreshing (cactus tastes rather like asparagus), while guacamole was own-made and chunky. Chicken enchilada had large strips of chicken, Monterey Jack cheese, refried beans and chilli in a corn tostada, and tasted fresh and zesty. A crab tostada would have done any of Mexico's finest beach restaurants proud: a generous amount of crab with lots of fresh coriander, sour cream and refried beans. Some own-made, creamy lemon ice-cream finished us off nicely. The American owner has created a pleasant atmosphere, too: desert colours, Mexican and American Indian prints, quiet country and western music. Despite keeping the prices on a par with many inferior Mexican places, Zuni has created a real slice of quality.
Babies and children welcome; children's menu.

Pan-American

South

Camberwell SE5

Chibchas
119 Grove Lane, SE5 (020 7733 7927). Denmark Hill rail/40, 176, 185 bus. **Dinner served** 6-11pm daily. **Tapas** £3-£5.20. **Credit** MC, V.
Chibchas is resolutely a neighbourhood tapas bar. It deservedly attracts a loyal local crowd who help create a laid-back, very south London atmosphere; you can either pop in for a drink or sit down to a full meal. Furnishings are bright orange, with adornments of Aztec wall hangings. There's a conservatory at the back and a space for tables outside. We gave full marks for the tapas, too: tender cod in coriander (with the added punch of hot peppers); spicy Colombian sausage; plantain Inca (with guacamole and melted Cheddar: an unusual combination of flavours that worked well); tortilla with avocado salad; and a hearty plate of rice and red beans. Everything tasted home-made and the portions were generous. Desserts aren't so interesting; banana cake and chocolate cake were unremarkable. The wine list is a compilation of inexpensive Chilean standards (Artis chardonnay, £10.50). The name comes from a Colombian tribe that died out after its forest home was destroyed by developers early in the 20th century.
Babies and children welcome; high chairs. Booking advisable Fri, Sat. Tables outdoors (11, garden; 4, forecourt).

South East

Borough SE1

El Vergel ★
8 Lant Street, SE1 (020 7357 0057). Borough tube. **Meals served** 8.30am-3pm Mon-Fri. **Main courses** £3.50-£5.50. **No credit cards.**
So what makes a successful Latin-American sandwich bar? In El Vergel's case, location certainly isn't a factor (it is hidden down a tiny Borough sidestreet), but the food is so good that people come from far and wide – this small café is absolutely thriving at lunchtimes. A big group of frantic staff copes admirably with the large takeaway trade, as well as the rapid turnover of hungry punters seated around the table at the back. El Vergel is one of the few places in London where you'll find a proper Mexican torta: a heavy bread roll typically filled with chicken, refried beans, guacamole, cheese and salsa sauce. The tacos are unusually healthy, too. A soft tortilla filled with refried beans, feta cheese, coriander, guacamole and spring onion was light and fresh – not qualities usually associated with Mexico's most famous snack. Latin-American breakfasts are a new venture: scrambled eggs with mild salsa sauce, chorizo, beans, bread and tea or coffee. All the usual café standards are served too, but it'd be a shame to miss out on such excellent cooking.
Babies and children welcome. No smoking. Tables outdoors (10, pavement). Takeaway service; delivery service. **Map 8/9P.**

North

Islington N1

La Piragua
176 Upper Street, N1 (020 7354 2843). Angel tube/Highbury & Islington tube/rail/ 4, 19, 30, 43 bus. **Meals served** noon-midnight daily. **Main courses** £5.50-£9.90. **No credit cards.**
Unlike the many flashy restaurants that have taken over Upper Street, this café-style venue is resolutely earthy. Checked tablecloths, folk paintings, yellow walls and Latin music make a change from sleek design and banging house music. The unpretentious cooking is also a welcome breath of fresh air. Starters of empanadas (fried corn with spicy beef) and prawns in garlic were lip-smacking dishes. Main-course chicken in broth with plantain, cassava, rice and salad was a delicious, heavy stew for which the word 'hearty' was invented, while grilled swordfish marinated canyon-style with salad and sautéd potatoes was enlivened by a sauce concocted from the cooking juices. The problem with all this Latin authenticity, however, is that it can weigh heavy on European stomachs – a dessert of fried plantain in molasses defeated us. La Piragua is a popular, bustling place, with brisk but friendly service; the presence of large families of bona fide Latinos can only be a good sign.
Babies and children welcome before 7pm; high chairs. Booking advisable dinner. Tables outdoors (2, pavement). Takeaway service. **Map 16/1O.**

Peruvian

South East

Tower Bridge SE1

Fina Estampa
150 Tooley Street, SE1 (020 7403 1342). Tower Hill tube/London Bridge tube/rail/ Tower Gateway DLR. **Lunch served** noon-2.30pm, **dinner served** 6.30-10.30pm Mon-Sat. **Main courses** £7.95-£14.95. **Cover** 10% (optional). **Credit** AmEx, DC, JCB, MC, £TC, V.
London's only Peruvian restaurant is a smart, rather traditional place, with liveried staff, stiff napkins, Peruvian oil paintings and high prices distinguishing it from the laid-back style of most Latin-American restaurants. We started with ceviche (the South American dish of raw white fish marinated in lemon and lime, onions and fresh coriander) which was deliciously tangy. Papas a la huancaina, a national dish of new potatoes in a fromage frais and mild yellow chilli sauce, was another tastebud pleaser. Main course carapulcra was an unusual dish of dried potatoes in a rich Inca-style spicy sauce, with pork and chicken served with cassava and parsley rice. Sudado do camerónes (king prawns with lots of onions, red peppers and fresh herbs) was tasty and richly oily, but rather insubstantial for the price. However, this is a wildly different cuisine from the flour and cassava staples that most Latin-American food is based around, and worth seeking out. The wine list is pricey, too, but there's a good Peruvian chardonnay at £14.95.
Babies and children admitted. Booking essential. Dress: smart casual. Entertainment: musicians (dinner Mon). Separate room for parties, seats 60. Takeaway service. **Map 8/8Q.**

British

Central

Bloomsbury WC2

Alfred
245 Shaftesbury Avenue, WC2 (020 7240 2566). Tottenham Court Road tube. **Lunch served** noon-3.30pm Mon-Fri. **Dinner served** 6-11.30pm Mon-Sat. **Main courses** £10.75-£14.25. **Set meals** £13.90 two courses, £17 three courses. **Service** 12½% for parties of six or more. **Credit** AmEx, DC, JCB, LV, MC, £TC, V.
If you're lucky, you'll be seated in the small, intimate annex round a bend from the main dining room, which doesn't suffer (as much) from the terrible acoustics that plague the rest of Alfred when busy. All the same, this is a smart restaurant in a great location, with double-aspect views of the more bustling streets of Bloomsbury. Local advertising folk enjoy the dark maroon and duck-egg blue colouring, seated on leather benches and simple wooden chairs. Service was pleasant enough, but slow and nonchalant. Food, however heavy, was good. The set menu is a bargain, with a choice of three starters, four mains and three desserts. We enjoyed Glamorgan patties: a huge cake made of potatoes, leeks and cheese, topped with salsa and served with a creamy chive sauce. A lighter option was flattened corn-fed chicken breasts with almond rice. A plate of fine cured salmon was chosen from the à la carte, served with a potato and egg salad. Delicious cod and salmon fish cakes (also on the set menu) looked just like the Glamorgan patties. Kill yourself off with a black cherry syllabub served with three chocolate-dipped shortbreads. A crisp refreshing house white (South African, Silver Lining chenin blanc, 1999) was a light choice for what had been a weighty, but enjoyable lunch.
Babies and children welcome; high chairs. Booking advisable weekends. Separate room for parties, seats 20. Tables outdoors (7, pavement). **Map 14/5L.**

City EC4

City Rhodes
1 New Street Square, EC4 (020 7583 1313). Chancery Lane tube/Blackfriars tube/rail. **Lunch served** noon-2.30pm, **dinner served** 6-9pm Mon-Fri. **Main courses** £16-£24. **Service** 12½%. **Credit** AmEx, DC, MC, V.
Despite being housed in a less than graceful building (an ugly office block), opposite another ugly office block, City Rhodes has managed to muster some grace from its surroundings. Sweeping stairs lead you up from a shapely lobby to a wide, low-ceilinged room, where modernist paintings and minimalist style create an environment of simple elegance. Frequented for the most part by City brokers and their clients, the restaurant is busier at lunchtime than in the evenings. Lobster, sea bass and foie gras feature among the first courses; a crisp asparagus with an exquisite truffle dressing was a promising start. The mains were a choice of fish, meat and game. Caramelised pork and confit of bacon came with a pea purée and sage cream, and was as tender as it was sweet; pan-fried sea bream with fresh herb and oyster tartare wasn't too dry, and was supported by a creamy, rich mash. Although the glorious artworks that were the puddings seemed an anticlimax, and the uniformity of the clientele made for a somewhat dull atmosphere, a meal at City Rhodes won't disappoint. You might even want to buy a book by the spiky-haired chef who founded the restaurant – copies are for sale in the foyer.
Babies and children admitted. Booking essential lunch. Disabled: toilet. Dress: smart casual. Separate room for parties, seats 12. **Map 15/6N.**

Clerkenwell & Farringdon EC1

Quality Chop House ★
94 Farringdon Road, EC1 (020 7837 5093/020 7833 3748). Farringdon tube/rail/19, 38, 55, 63, 341 bus. **Lunch served** noon-3pm Mon-Fri; noon-4pm Sun. **Dinner served** 6.30-11.30pm Mon-Sat; 7-11.30pm Sun. **Main courses** £6.75-£22. **Credit** MC, £TC, V.
You'll be struck by the juxtapositions at the QCH. All the charm of an old-style café is complemented with quality details found in the highest class of restaurant. Condiments such as HP sauce, Heinz tomato ketchup and Sarson's vinegar sit proudly beside the narrow booth tables (laid with paper napkins); bottles of Schweppes are lined up next to the Gaggia machine. Staff, on the other hand, are dressed in starched linen and the atmosphere is like that of an old-fashioned, formal and discreet bistro. Jellied eels and sevruga caviar have similar billing on the menu, and there's much in between. What might appear as simple caff food (eggs, bacon and chips; fish pie; black pudding), is presented beautifully and bursts with fine flavours. Fresh anchovy on tomatoes had a light, herby dressing, and an asparagus dish was served with a very generous portion of Pecorino and a delicate vinaigrette. Smoked haddock was exceedingly tender, smoked gently with no artificial colouring, and served on a bed of nutty lentil salad. Grilled rump steak and chips was perfectly cooked. Crème brûlée was robust and delicious; the burned sugar topping took a little hammering to give way to a rich and solid vanilla cream. Nothing could be more fitting than the Quality Chop House name, and its claim to produce 'progressive working-class' cuisine. One of a kind.
Babies and children welcome. Booking advisable. No-smoking tables. **Map 15/4N.**

St John ★
26 St John Street, EC1 (020 7251 0848/4998/www.stjohnrestaurant.co.uk). Farringdon tube/rail.
Bar Open 11am-11pm Mon-Fri; 6-11pm Sat. **Main courses** £3-£10.
Restaurant **Lunch served** noon-3pm Mon-Fri. **Dinner served** 6-11pm Mon-Sat. **Main courses** £9-£16. **Service** 12½% for parties of six or more.
Both **Credit** AmEx, DC, JCB, MC, £TC, V.
Painted brilliant white, with no adornment, this large warehouse space near to Smithfield meat market is not decorated to everyone's taste. The restaurant espouses an equally uncompromising approach to its cooking. St John is big on offal and traditional, sometimes obscure, British ingredients. We started with razor clams – rubbery things cooked deliciously in parsley and shallots – and an elegant dish of cured sea trout with cucumber salad. While macho City types at a nearby table tried to outdo each other with orders of pig's head, conger eel and the like, we opted for more straightforward dishes for our main course: leg of lamb, and plaice and samphire. Both were cooked to perfection, of the finest provenance, and tasted, somehow, home-cooked. As did our desserts: a refreshing elderflower jelly with gooseberries and shortbread, and an extraordinarily good chocolate mousse cake, served with cherry

Rules.
See page 34.

ice-cream. After polishing off a bottle of Côtes de Roussillon from the interesting, idiosyncratic wine list, we left with the happy feeling that this was British restaurant cooking as it should be.
Babies and children welcome; high chair. Booking advisable, essential dinner Thur-Sat. Separate room for parties, seats 18. **Map 15/50.**

Top Floor at Smiths ★
Smiths of Smithfield, 67-77 Charterhouse Street, EC1 (020 7236 6666). Farringdon tube/rail. **Lunch served** noon-3pm Mon-Fri; noon-4pm Sun. **Dinner served** 6-11pm Mon-Sat; 6-10.30pm Sun. **Main courses** £16-£26. **Credit**.
Top Floor is the long-awaited dining room perched at the top of the great new drinking and dining warehouse, Smiths of Smithfield (*see also p131* **Modern European**). From the tables on the fourth floor's open terrace there are fine views over the roofs. Top Floor does some bloody good steaks. So it should: it overlooks Smithfield Meat Market. Starters might be seared scallops with skordalia or beef ravioli with braised shallots and Parmesan. We headed straight for the 'fine meat, available grilled or pan-fried'. A 14oz Islay sirloin, aged 30 days, costs a staggering '25½ pounds'. It was excellent, perfectly tender and cooked rare as requested then 'rested' before being served with a béarnaise sauce. It was also absurdly large. Smaller portions, like the 10oz Galloway rump (18½ pounds), might have been a more sensible choice. Side dishes (veg, salad, chips) cost an extra 2½ pounds. If steak's really not your thing, there are also appealing fish and vegetarian options, plus pork chops, chicken breast and the like, also mostly organic and additive-free where possible; there is a commendable commitment to high-quality ingredients. Overall pricing at Top Floor is on the high side for essentially plain cooking – but this is edge-of-City, and most of our fellow diners (besuited, well-fed types) didn't appear to mind. Go when you fancy a steak and a treat.
Booking advisable.
Map 15/50.

Covent Garden WC2

Rules ★
35 Maiden Lane, WC2 (020 7836 5314/ www.rules.co.uk). Covent Garden or Embankment tube/Charing Cross tube/rail. **Meals served** noon-11.30pm Mon-Sat; noon-10.30pm Sun. **Main courses** £16-£19.95. **Set meal** (3-5pm Mon-Fri) £19.95 two courses. **Credit** AmEx, DC, MC, £TC, V.
Rules is popular, and busy. So busy, in fact, that we had to wait 45 minutes for our reservation, and another half hour for the food to arrive. But London's oldest restaurant (founded 1798) is popular because it's so reliably good. A central bar area is surrounded by tables in and out of alcoves. Couples, family reunions and theatre-goers chat merrily beneath stuffed animals, sculptures and paintings. We settled below a sublime cupola in one corner. The menu is always much the same: over half a dozen each of game (fallow or red deer, venison, rabbit); fresh and sea water fish (poached salmon, grilled sole, fish pie); or simple meat dishes (prime Aberdeen Angus beef in a pie, a suet pudding, or a mixed grill). The 24oz roast rib of beef, with spinach and Yorkshire pudding (for two) was almost enough for three – a rack of meat, a pile of spinach, and a huge Yorkshire pudding that might have escaped from Woody Allen's *Sleeper*. Creamy dauphinoise and sweet shallots boosted the tender beef. We've had fine Dover sole and venison here before, and always enjoy the anticipation of pudding. The rich list contains a dozen teasers, from a light raspberry syllabub to sticky toffee pudding with butterscotch and vanilla custard. There's an energy to Rules that belies its slightly misty-eyed, traditional appearance, and the kitchen invariably hits the spot.
Babies and children admitted; high chairs. Booking advisable Thur-Sat one week in advance. No smoking. Separate rooms for parties, seating 12, 16, 18, and 24. **Map 14/7L.**

Fitzrovia W1

RK Stanleys
6 Little Portland Street, W1 (020 7462 0099). Oxford Circus tube.
Bar **Open** noon-11pm Mon-Sat.
Restaurant **Lunch served** noon-3.30pm, **dinner served** 6-11.30pm Mon-Sat. **Main courses** £7.25-£11.95. **Service** 12½%. *Both* **Credit** AmEx, MC, V.
Its slickly designed interior is a clever, modern take on the classic American diner, with high-backed booths, a long bar and dramatic lighting, but RK Stanleys promises more than it delivers. The menu is short and straightforward. There was nothing too disastrous about our starters: fried whitebait and a plate of (hard-edged) smoked haddock with poached egg and mustard leaves. Sausages are what draw customers here, but a main course Simple Stanley comprised an undercooked livery grey sausage, mash with a hard crust and a thin, sweet orange gloop of a gravy. A plate of bratwurst choucroûte suffered from similar shortcomings. Two unspectacular tarts – treacle and chocolate – did nothing to alleviate the disappointment. Neither did the inattentive service, although the excellent selection of English beers and ciders (we chose a bottle of 'Pig' rye lager and another of Weston's Old Rosie scrumpy) was a mitigating factor. RK Stanleys is a great, potentially franchisable, concept: pity it has been realised in such lacklustre fashion.
Babies and children welcome; high chairs. Booking advisable dinner. No-smoking tables. **Map 13/5J.**

Mayfair W1

Dorchester Grill Room
The Dorchester, 53 Park Lane, W1 (020 7317 6336/www.dorchesterhotel.com). Hyde Park Corner or Marble Arch tube. **Breakfast served** 7-11am Mon-Sat; 7.30-11am Sun. **Lunch served** 12.30-2.30pm daily. **Dinner served** 6-11pm Mon-Sat; 7-10.30pm Sun. **Main courses** £22-£40. **Set lunch** £32.50 three courses incl coffee. **Set dinner** £39.50 three courses incl coffee. **Credit** AmEx, DC, JCB, MC, TC, V.
It's a grand affair in the Grill Room at the Dorchester. Large windows throw light on the tapestries above the doorways, and gold leaf and flamboyant lights add sparkle from the lofty ceiling. A mixture of residents, tourists and business types dots the room, a few of them hidden in alcoves. Slick waiters float through, serving your every need, including, if you wish, a tour of the kitchen – an opportunity, perhaps, to dip your finger into potted shrimps, or the cream of wild mushroom and quail, or a spoonful of the refreshing, tangy chilled gazpacho. But return to give the mains a proper sitting. The Grill Room Classics are a familiar quartet: roast Angus beef, Dover sole with brown butter capers, trad steak and kidney pie, and roasted rack of lamb. Other mains are available (escalope of sea bass, escalope of salmon), but despite the display and effort, the quality of the food doesn't quite match the spin. The pot-roasted chicken with bubble and squeak and shallot 'confit' was fine, but only fine; sea bass on roasted aubergine purée was too salty. The breads are always an assortment of delights, and our high hopes were realised with the sweet trolley. However, there is a slightly anti-climactic aftertaste to a visit to the Dorchester Grill Room. Perhaps with its new chef, Henry Brosi, the taste will change.
Babies and children welcome; high chairs. Booking advisable; essential weekends one week in advance. Dress: smart casual. Vegetarian menu. **Map 2/7G.**

The Guinea Grill
30 Bruton Place, W1 (020 7499 1210). Bond Street, Green Park or Oxford Circus tube.
Pub **Open** 11am-11pm Mon-Fri; 6.30-11pm Sat.
Restaurant **Lunch served** 12.30-2.30pm Mon-Fri. **Dinner served** 6.30-11pm Mon-Sat. **Main courses** £10.50-£27. **Set lunch** £17.50 two courses. **Cover** £1. **Service** 12½%. **Credit** AmEx, DC, JCB, MC, £TC, V.
The Guinea Grill occupies various small, timber-beamed rooms at the back of a quaint old pub in Mayfair. Given this and the fact that steak features heavily on the menu, it was no surprise on our visit to find we were the only non-Americans within earshot. A selection of prime Aberdeen rump, sirloin and fillet aside, the Guinea's great signature dish is the steak and kidney pie. In 1997 it won the national pie championship for the third time. The rest of the menu contains the usual gastropub staples: plenty of pan-fried chicken and goat's cheese. Starters – Caesar salad, and salmon and asparagus with a potato galette – were decidedly unspectacular. The steak and kidney pie was pretty fine, though, with a thick, suet-heavy top and rich, rich filling. This was followed by (unripe) strawberries and cream and summer pudding with a ludicrously over-sweet coulis. You might blame the location, but though we chose one of the cheaper New World bottles from an expensive wine list, our meal for two came to just under £100. A lot of money to spend in a pub.
Booking essential. Children admitted. Separate room for parties, seats 30. **Map 2/7H.**

Piccadilly W1

Fortnum & Mason
181 Piccadilly, W1 (020 7734 8040). Green Park or Piccadilly Circus tube.
Fountain (ext 492) **Open** 8.30am-8pm Mon-Sat. **Breakfast served** 8.30-11.30am, **lunch served** 11.30am-3pm, **ice-cream tea served** 3-6pm, **afternoon tea served** 3-5.30pm, **dinner served** 5.30-8pm Mon-Sat. **Main courses** £7.95-£19.50. **Set afternoon tea** £11.95.
St James's (ext 241) **Open** 10am-6.30pm Mon-Sat. **Breakfast and morning coffee served** 10am-noon, **lunch served** noon-2.30pm, **afternoon tea served** 3-5.45pm Mon-Sat. **Main courses** £13.95. **Set lunch** £11.95 one course incl glass of wine, £16.95 two courses, £19.95 three courses. **Cover** £1 (lunch).
Both **Credit** AmEx, DC, JCB, MC, TC, V.
There's a complete contrast to the two eateries at this quintessentially English establishment. Pass by the frilly-topped jars of jam and chutney to the fourth-floor St James's Restaurant, or continue to the back for the Fountain. Whenever we've visited the St James's it hasn't exactly brimmed with activity. It's a large, sprawling room surrounded by maritime prints and portraits, and endless white-clothed tables. In this slightly austere environment, a menu called a Taste of the West sets the tone for the target customer: the well-heeled, well-aged tourist. It's quite a stiff deal – fillet of mackerel, or an adequate pan-fried supreme of chicken, or a more adventurous Harbourne and Keen's Cheddar-stuffed flat mushrooms, plus a glass of wine, cider or fruit juice – for £11.95. Downstairs offers a much brighter experience. The Fountain, an ornate summery room with shades of the colonial East in the decor, specialises in the English tea tradition. There are savouries, cakes, scones, and ice-creams to die for: Dusty Road, Maple Dipper, and, of course, the Knickerbocker Glory. Diners are more varied – tourists, couples, old and young, and those aunts still taking tea with their niece, 40 years on. Once seated, however, it can be a touch less relaxing than the setting deserves. There's a sense of urgency to the service, and with queueing people sometimes leering at your table, this isn't the place for hours of chat over pots of tea. But that doesn't mean to say The Fountain isn't worth just the one-pot visit.
Babies and children welcome; children's menu (Fountain); high chairs. Bookings accepted for dinner Mon-Fri only. Dress: smart casual. Entertainment: pianist 3.15-5.15pm (St James's). No-smoking tables (Fountain). **Map 13/7J.**

Pimlico SW1

Chimes of Pimlico
26 Churton Street, SW1 (020 7821 7456). Pimlico tube.
Bar **Open** noon-3pm, 5.30-11pm daily.
Restaurant **Lunch served** noon-2.30pm, **dinner served** 6-10.15pm daily. **Main courses** £5.25-£10.45. **Set dinner** £11.45 two courses, £13.95 three courses. **Credit** AmEx, LV, MC, £TC, V.
It's lovely walking into this Pimlico local on a lunchtime visit, as the back area is lit up with natural daylight from the skylights. Ivy, chunky furniture and strategically placed country-life bits and bobs add to the natural feel of the place, positioning it somewhere between country pub and local tea shop. And with a menu whose opening page features two quotes: one about cider, the other about pies, you know what to expect. The pies are particularly good (the fidget had big lumps of succulent flaky gammon, and a lovely golden crusty pastry). Meat is a strong point, but stay well away from the salads. Even though the oak-smoked chicken was delicious, its accompaniment of shredded lettuce, slices of tomato and cucumber and a quarter of lemon (with no sight of a dressing) made the dish too expensive at £7.95. Service is so relaxed it barely existed on our visit. Empty tables seemed to hold more interest to staff than our empty plates and pressing schedules. Chimes is great for a quiet, uninterrupted chat, but if you're wanting to get back to the office after a swift lunch, forget it.
Babies and children welcome. Booking advisable. Separate room for parties, seats 40. Tables outdoors (2, pavement). **Map 6/11J.**

Rhodes in the Square ★
Dolphin Square, Chichester Street, SW1 (020 7798 6767). Pimlico tube. **Lunch served** noon-2pm Tue-Fri. **Dinner served** 7-10pm Tue-Sat. **Set lunch** £10.50 one course, £16.50 two courses, £19.50 three courses. **Set dinner** £12.50 one course, £25.50 two courses, £31 three courses. **Service** 12½%. **Credit** AmEx, DC, MC, £TC, V.
Gary Rhodes' Pimlico restaurant is now three years old. From a standard hotel lobby you enter what might once have been an art deco disco (if such things existed). The bulk of the tables are in a sunken area in the centre. The decor is deep blue in colour, with op-art canvases on the walls and black thrones as chairs. There's no natural light, which on a dank spring evening can be cosy, but is less appealing for a summer lunch. Once your eyes grow accustomed to the lighting, however, you sense a pleasant warmth in the surroundings. Such warmth was sustained on our visit by the short, but stylish menu. Risotto of duck confit and prunes was finished with a sesame oil dressing; and game terrine had been given some zip by the Cumberland sauce. Our spirits continued to improve with the mains – a sweet and juicy honey-glazed and lemon-roasted chicken; and bone marrow and anchovy-flavoured lamb, served with a subtle artichoke and mushroom duxelle – an indication of the interesting combinations favoured by the kitchen. Given the additional benefits of fine desserts (the iced pear parfait with sweet kirsch cherries was, well, parfait) and fine wines from the lengthy, if pricey, list, we reckoned that sacrificing natural light to this midnight-blue lagoon was, after all, a worthwhile experience.
Babies and children welcome; high chairs. Booking advisable. Dress: smart casual. **Map 6/12J.**

Soho W1

Lindsay House
21 Romilly Street, W1 (020 7439 0450). Leicester Square or Piccadilly Circus tube. **Lunch served** noon-2.30pm Mon-Fri. **Dinner served** 6-11pm Mon-Sat. **Main courses** £16-£22 lunch. **Set lunch** £23 three courses. **Set dinner** £43 three courses. **Service** 12½%. **Credit** AmEx, DC, MC, TC, V.
Stepping into Lindsay House is like walking into a private supper party – you even have to ring the bell to be let into this quiet, sparsely furnished little warren of rooms. But Richard Corrigan's intelligent, precisely executed cooking definitely belongs in a top-class restaurant. An amusette of tomato consommé, which arrived shortly after the wine list, was packed with clean seasonal flavours. Starters were similarly impressive: gazpacho of English crayfish was beautifully presented and garden-fresh; marinated sea bream was tender and sharp, with the accompanying tomato tart and artichoke salad in silky contrast. Main courses were a more mixed success. Roast pigeon, sautéed foie gras and shallot purée was an incredibly rich dish and not improved by the fact that the pigeon was served extremely rare. Much better was a second dish of beautifully tender saddle of rabbit, which came with a deeply satisfying layer of black pudding and mustard jus. An assiette of raspberries (including a heavenly champagne jelly containing a single plump berry) was a much more light-hearted end to the meal. The wine list is voluminous and contains some real treasures, particularly among the burgundies. The staff are knowledgeable and amiable enough, as long as they remember that topping up people's wine every few seconds is not going to make them drink faster; it's just going to piss them off.
Booking essential. Dress: smart casual. Separate rooms for parties, seating 8, 20 and 40. **Map 13/6K.**
For branches (The House, English Garden) see index.

St James's SW1

Wiltons
55 Jermyn Street, SW1 (020 7629 9955). Green Park or Piccadilly Circus tube. **Lunch served** 12.30-2.30pm Mon-Fri, Sun. **Dinner served** 6.30-10.30pm Mon-Fri; 6.30-10pm Sun. **Main courses** £14.80-£29.50. **Set Sunday lunch** £19.75 three courses. **Cover** £1.50. **Credit** AmEx, DC, JCB, MC, £TC, V.
Hidden away on Jermyn Street lies this traditionalists' gem: a smooth, smart and polished affair that can trace its lineage back to a shellfishmongery that first opened in 1742. An expanded corridor holding a bar laden with seafood platters opens out to the restaurant proper, where yellow walls bear heavily gilded oils and nostalgic prints of an illustrious past, plus the occasional stuffed angling trophy. Apt really, as fish is the speciality here – that is, when it isn't game. The à la carte is a banquet of choice: baby lobster from the cold buffet, whitebait, marinated salmon, or maybe just a mixed herb omelette. For your main course, Dover sole can be grilled, baked, fried, meunière, Colbert or Walewska. We opted for lightly grilled plaice, and baked sole with chive and lemon dressing (a perfectly moist sole fillet served with melting creamed potatoes). Puddings should not

Rhodes in the Square

be passed over either. They include an exquisite iced Grand Marnier soufflé, strawberry terrine with a soft melon sorbet, and sherry trifle: not cheap, but not bad either. Business diners, and the occasional family get-togethers, sit in the alcoves and enjoy their meals with hearty cheer, while being served with sometimes stern efficiency. While we've had some not so good times here (yes, it is dreadfully formal, slightly stuffy and sharp on the wallet), Wilton's can offer a pleasant, efficient and tasty experience, too.
Booking advisable; essential Mon-Thur. Dress: jacket and tie; no jeans or trainers. Separate room for parties, seats 18. **Map 13/7J.**

Strand WC2

The Savoy Grill

The Savoy Hotel, Strand, WC2 (020 7420 2065). Covent Garden or Embankment tube/ Charing Cross tube/rail. **Lunch served** 12.30-2.30pm Mon-Fri. **Dinner served** 6-11.15pm Mon-Sat. **Closed** Aug. **Main courses** £17.50-£21 lunch, £19-£24 dinner. **Set dinner** (6-7pm Mon-Sat) £20 two courses. **Credit** AmEx, DC, JCB, MC, TC, V.

The Grill Room's atmosphere is resolutely old-fashioned – somewhere between a gentlemen's club and an ocean liner. Discreet, dickie-bowed waiters push impressive silver trollies of daily roasts and sturdy desserts around the low-lit, wood-panelled room. Food fashions haven't entirely passed this place by, but you are probably better off sticking to the classics. Such advice was certainly worth taking as regards our starters: a time-honoured dish of dressed crab was superior to a less traditional, tapenade-heavy roasted scallop salad. Main courses came from the grill: an overcooked Dover sole at a whopping £26; and a gut-busting mixed grill (caff fare with top-class ingredients). The wine list is very traditional, prices are high, and culinary fireworks are few indeed, but the Grill Room is great for people watching (African royalty, old men and their 'nieces') and retains a reassuring, timeless charm.
Children over 12 years admitted. Booking advisable; essential lunch. Dress: jacket and tie; no denim or trainers. **Map 14/7L.**

Simpson's-in-the-Strand

100 Strand, WC2 (020 7836 9112). Embankment tube/Charing Cross tube/rail. **Breakfast served** 7.15-10.15am Mon-Fri. **Lunch served** 12.15-2.30pm daily. **Dinner served** 5.30-10.45pm Mon-Sat; (Grand Divan) 6-9pm Sun. **Main courses** £14.50-£22.95. **Minimum** £9.50 breakfast. **Set breakfasts** £14.50, £16.95. **Set meals** (lunch, 5.30-7pm Mon-Sat) £15.50 two courses, £18.75 three courses. **Set Sunday meal** £23 three courses. **Credit** AmEx, DC, JCB, MC, TC, V.

Sunday at Simpson's is quite different from the rest of the week. Then, this stuffy 152-year-old establishment loosens its tie a little and promotes an all-day set menu and a relaxed dress code. The staff's attire still resembles penguin suits, and, of course, the wood-panelled and chandelier-lit decor remains grand in a rather oppressive way, but you do get to sample some excellent food at a fair price. Roasts have the starring role (as in the week); there's a choice of beef, lamb or turkey. Beef was brought on a trolley, with the choice of medium or rare, then three very generous slices were laid on our plate. This succulent meat – combined with a huge Yorkshire pud, ferocious horseradish and extras of spinach, roast potatoes and perfectly cooked beans and asparagus – was exceptional. No corners were cut, and quantities were huge. Salmon fillet was just as good: a lovely melting piece of fish with a buttery sauce. A starter of potted shrimps was tasty but overly buttery, and we weren't impressed with duck and pork terrine (which resembled luncheon meat and was served with sliced processed bread). Neal's Yard cheeses made a great third course, as did plum and almond crumble with clotted cream. All this was accompanied by an excellent house claret (Comte de Morancy). Simpson's is due for a makeover; it's a pretentious, fuddy-duddy place. But for Sunday roast it has few equals.
Babies and children admitted. Booking advisable; essential weekends. Disabled: toilet. Dress: smart; jacket and tie; no jeans or trainers (Grand Divan). No-smoking tables (Simply Simpson's). Separate rooms for parties, seating 50 and 150. **Map 14/7L.**

Victoria SW1

Boisdale

15 Eccleston Street, SW1 (020 7730 6922/www.boisdale.co.uk). Victoria tube/rail.
Bar **Open** noon-1am Mon-Fri; 7pm-1am Sat. **Main courses** £5.50-£12.90.
Restaurant **Lunch served** noon-2.30pm Mon-Fri. **Dinner served** 7-10.30pm Mon-Sat. **Main courses** £10.50-£24.90. **Set meals** £14.90, £17.45, two courses. **Service** 12½%.
Both **Credit** AmEx, DC, MC, £TC, V.

Boisdale has expanded, almost doubling its size, a reflection of the growing popularity of this Franco-Scottish, cigar-and-whisky bar-restaurant. The back bar is still a cosy arsenal for the impressive dram and stogie stock, and the front still a homely restaurant. But alongside the central covered patio is a huge rectangular room, done out in the trademark deep red and with a long bar at the end. Unfortunately the space still seems insufficient, as our promise of a seat (over the phone) was a false one. On another attempt, having booked well in advance, we found ourselves set tightly to the wall, with a small, narrow table further constricting us. The rib-eye was disappointing, too – a pity, as Boisdale's has long been a favourite, and the kitchen, while not spectacular in its produce, is reliable. We struck it lucky third time. Seated in the extension, an altogether more airy place, we could have gone native and tried roast McSween's haggis with mash and neeps, or the cod, smoked haddock and Orkney salmon. Instead we stuck with the trusty gourmet sausages and creamy mashed potato, and a soft calf's liver and bacon that came with a rich, sweet, slightly honeyed sauce. We toasted our restored faith with a cranachan for dessert, a golden mix of raspberry, cream and whisky.
Babies and children admitted. Booking essential. Dress: smart casual. Entertainment: jazz musicians from 10pm Mon-Sat. Separate room for parties, seats 22. Tables outdoors (7, garden). **Map 6/10H.**

The Goring Hotel

15 Beeston Place, Grosvenor Gardens, SW1 (020 7396 9000/www.goringhotel.co.uk). Victoria tube/rail.
Bar **Open** 8am-midnight daily.
Restaurant **Breakfast served** 7-10am Mon-Fri; 7.30-10.30am Sat, Sun. **Lunch served** 12.30-2.30pm Mon-Fri, Sun. **Dinner served** 6-10pm daily. **Set lunch** £25 two courses, £29 three courses. **Set dinner** £37 three courses. **Credit** AmEx, DC, JCB, MC, £TC, V.

This traditional, grand hotel dining room, a stone's throw from Buckingham Palace, was very quiet on a Saturday night, save for the tinkling of a piano and the yah-yahing of a few American tourists. Once we were ensconced in throne-like chairs, a black-and-white army of waiters presented us with a not particularly amusing amuse bouche and a menu chock-full of delicious-sounding roasts. A starter of terrine of ham was accompanied by superb piccalilli, but a smoked duck breast salad was too heavy on the truffle oil. The evening's star turn proved to be a plate of immaculately cooked best end of lamb with brioche crust. Fish cake in lobster sauce was excessively rich; the next table's handsome Dover sole looked a better choice. At the Goring, the three-course menu (there is no à la carte) is rounded off with a choice of reliable trolley desserts: fig tart, sorbet, crème brûlée, that kind of thing. Competent cooking in impressively posh surroundings.
Babies and children welcome; high chairs. Book lunch. Disabled: toilet. Dress: smart casual. Entertainment: pianist 7-10pm nightly. No-smoking tables (bar). Separate rooms for parties (3), seating 4-50. **Map 6/10H.**

Westminster SW1

Shepherd's

Marsham Court, Marsham Street, SW1 (020 7834 9552). Pimlico or Westminster tube. **Lunch served** 12.30-2.45pm, **dinner served** 6.30-11pm Mon-Fri. **Main courses** £17.25. **Set meal** £23.95 two courses, £25.50 three courses. **Service** 12½%. **Credit** AmEx, DC, JCB, MC, £TC, V.

Tucked away in the very heart of Westminster, Shepherd's has become a veritable parliamentary institution despite its tender years (founded 1993). The low-ceilinged room, decorated by prints, cartoons and mirrors, has tables hidden behind partitions and around the side of pillars: ideal for the politicking that MPs, journalists and civil servants indulge in here. It's busiest at lunchtime and early evening. Staff serve reliable and fairly traditional fare with quiet efficiency. There are over a dozen dishes to choose from – both starters and mains – and all are along safe British lines. Pan-fried lambs' kidneys, jellied eels and a smooth chicken liver pâté with a sweet Cumberland sauce are staples among the starters. The main courses include pies such as steak and kidney, or chicken and mushroom; or monkfish wrapped in bacon and spinach roasted with ratatouille. We opted for roast rib of beef and Yorkshire pudding from the trolley: several slices of beef and a huge puff of pudding swimming in thick, if slightly bland gravy. We capped our lunch with warm glazed chocolate cake with cherries, and an Eton Mess (something that's not exactly unheard of in Westminster).
Babies and children welcome. Booking advisable. Dress: smart casual. No smoking Separate room for parties, seats 32. **Map 7/10K.**

West

Kensington W8

Maggie Jones's

6 Old Court Place, Kensington Church Street, W8 (020 7937 6462). High Street Kensington tube. **Lunch served** 12.30-2.30pm daily. **Dinner served** 6.30-11pm Mon-Sat; 6.30-10.30pm Sun. **Main courses** £4.95-£8.95 lunch, £9.95-£18 dinner. **Cover** £1 (dinner). **Service** 12½%. **Credit** AmEx, DC, JCB, MC, £TC, V.

Now in its 38th year, Maggie Jones's remains a delightful spot. Unabashed, it has recreated a Welsh farmhouse in Kensington – right down to the scrubbed wooden tables, wooden floors, wooden chairs and (somewhat dusty) plethora of dried flowers, cartwheels, horse harnesses and other artefacts festooned from the ceiling. It's an obvious draw for tourists, but locals, too (especially those with children) come for the good-value no-nonsense, rustic cooking. Portions may catch you unawares: after a starter of 'tart of the day' (a huge wedge of eggy spinach quiche with an odd, but pleasant topping of flaked almonds) we felt daunted at the thought of further courses. Some ingredients used (artichoke hearts, crab) may turn out to be canned, but you can't help but admire the cauliflower cheese smothered in strongly flavoured Cheddar sauce; or onion soup with its coarse-cut onions. Wild boar sausages with mash arrived in the creaking dumb waiter with smooth, creamy potatoes and good, if homogeneous sausages; rocket salad contained proper peppery leaves weighed down by a good heap of sautéed oyster mushrooms and thick slices of Parmesan. Puddings are listed with specials on a blackboard. Burnt cream had a caramelised surface solid as a frozen lake, with very sweet custard below; bread and butter pudding suffered from dry slices on top but was otherwise a fair example. Service is provided by a close-knit team of good-humoured Aussies, who clearly like the place and the people who patronise it.
Babies and children welcome; high chair. Booking advisable, essential dinner.
Map 11/8B.

Olympia W14

Popeseye Steak House

108 Blythe Road, W14 (020 7610 4578). Olympia tube/rail. **Dinner served** 7-10.30pm Mon-Sat. **Main courses** £7.95-£29.95. **Service** 12½%. **Credit** TC.

Popeseye is carnivore heaven. No fiddly starters, just main course steak: rump, sirloin or fillet in a variety of sizes from 6oz up and flame-grilled to order. Chips are served on the side and there are a variety of mustards, béarnaise sauce and ketchup. Side salad is the only other distraction from the meat on the plate. We chose 8oz fillets. As you would hope in a specialist establishment, both were perfect thick lumps of prime meat, cooked exactly as we had ordered. Popeseye offers a great selection of red wines, including some fairly expensive French numbers and a good house red by the glass. White wine drinkers get just two choices available by the bottle. Puddings are simple: sticky toffeee pudding was good, but not the best we've had; rhubarb crumble was OK, but a little sharp and the unadvertised ginger was a little overpowering. Be warned that Popeseye doesn't take credit cards, so take plenty of cash as, at £64 for two with puddings and two glasses of wine, it's not quite as cheap as the simple surroundings might suggest.
Babies and children admitted. Booking advisable.
For branch see index.

Shepherd's Bush W14

Wilson's
236 Blythe Road, corner of Shepherd's Bush Road, W14 (020 7603 7267). Goldhawk Road or Shepherd's Bush tube. **Lunch served** 12.30-2.30pm Mon-Fri; *Sept-Easter* 12.30-2.30pm Sun. **Dinner served** 7.30-10.30pm Mon-Sat. **Service** 12½%. **Credit** JCB, MC, £TC, V.
The restaurant was closed for refurbishment as this guide went to press, but we can predict with a fair degree of confidence that when it does reopen it will continue to serve excellent Scottish-themed food and drink (and music) to a highly appreciative mixture of local diners and other regulars. Assuming an unchanged menu, Wilson's features dishes such as Finnan haddock pudding with spinach and bacon salad, haggis with mash, neeps and a dram, salmon fish cakes, pork and herb sausages and one or two vegetarian options. Among our favourite puddings are lemon and lime posset and athol brose (like a sort of sweet porridge with whisky). For the discerning Scotch drinker, there is a range of whiskies; there's also a short but well-chosen wine list and a choice of two or three beers. Affable owner Bob Wilson and his staff have always provided a warm welcome and reliable service, and we've never had a bad meal here. If you're lucky, towards the end of the evening, a bekilted Mr Wilson will take up his bagpipes and really blow the cobwebs away. *Booking advisable.*

Westbourne Grove W2

Veronica's ★
3 Hereford Road, W2 (020 7229 5079/1210). Bayswater or Queensway tube. **Lunch served** noon-2.30pm Mon-Fri. **Dinner served** 6-11.30pm Mon-Sat. **Main courses** £10.50-£17.50. **Set meal** £13.50 two courses, £17.50 three courses. **Service** 10%. **Credit** AmEx, DC, JCB, MC, £TC, V.
In celebration of the millennium year, Veronica's aimed to explore the last 1,000 years of cooking. As a restaurant that usually takes influences from the past 700 years, it has had a lot of practice. The menu, with its little historical note at the foot of each dish, makes interesting reading (and is also annotated with symbols indicating whether dishes are low fat, high fibre, vegetarian or vegan). Most dishes have a base in history, but then are jazzed up with more modern ingredients. For instance, the menu informs us that mushrooms and beetroot were 'probably' a popular combo in Roman London, and are 'enlivened' by the addition of goat's cheese and rocket. But when eating such superb flavour combinations, who are we to complain? There's a lot of marinated meats, hence the generally high intensity of flavours. A dish of raw tuna seemed seared, and came with equally piquant ginger, cinnamon and coriander-flavoured beans. A 'halibut duo' was equally good: a flaky, tender piece of fish with the pungent addition of lemon, saffron and dill-marinaded halibut as its crown, plus an orange butter sauce said to have been described in Pepys's diaries. In summer, prime dining is outside. Then you can watch the glow of the warm, buzzing interior, while enjoying a quieter side of Notting Hill. The historical theme even reaches to the cocktail list; try the 1920s champagne cocktail with a sugar cube soaked in Angostura Bitters.
Babies and children admitted. Booking advisable, essential weekends. Separate room for parties, seats 40. Tables outdoors (4, patio). **11/6B.**

Chelsea SW3

Foxtrot Oscar
79 Royal Hospital Road, SW3 (020 7352 7179). Sloane Square tube/11, 239 bus. **Lunch served** 12.30-2.30pm Mon-Fri; 12.30-3.30pm Sat, Sun. **Dinner served** 7-11pm Mon-Sat; 7-10pm Sun. **Main courses** £6.50-£12.95. **Service** 12½% for parties of five or more. **Credit** AmEx, DC, MC, £TC, V.
The local Sloane set love this tiny brasserie-style restaurant. Its informal seating and blackboard 'meat and two veg' menu makes for a relaxed atmosphere where they can guffaw with the next table while quaffing the semi-decent house red wine. There's no pretence here: staff are very matter of fact, and little care seems to be taken over the food's presentation. Unfortunately, on the occasion of our last visit, scant attention was also paid to the execution of the food. Both sirloin steak and salmon had to be sent back: the sirloin was so overcooked it resembled shoe

© Dennis Gilbert / View

leather; the salmon, in contrast, was raw, cold and covered in a glutinous hollandaise sauce. Second time around produced a more successful result, but the dishes were incredibly basic when you consider £10.95 (£9.25 for the salmon) buys you a piece of meat and that's all. Any extras come with a price tag (spinach and bacon salad, £3.50; chips, £1.60). We did, however have a lovely pudding. Banoffi pie (recommended by the waitress) was sweet, creamy, crunchy perfection.
Babies and children welcome. Booking essential. Separate room for parties, seats 35. Takeaway service. **Map 6/12F.**
For branches see index.

Battersea SW11

Buchan's
62-64 Battersea Bridge Road, SW11 (020 7228 0888). Bus 19, 319. *Bar* **Open** noon-3pm, 5.30-11pm, Mon-Sat; noon-3pm, 7-10.30pm Sun. **Main courses** £7.95-£8.95. *Restaurant* **Lunch served** noon-2.45pm daily. **Dinner served** 7-10.45pm Mon-Sat; 7-10pm Sun. **Main courses** £10.95-£16.50. **Set lunch** (Mon-Sat) £9.50 two courses. **Set dinner** (Mon, Sun) £8.95 two courses. **Service** 12½%. *Both* AmEx, DC, MC, £TC, V.
It's the diversity of the eating arrangements that makes this Battersea restaurant such an attractive spot. The front is a buzzing and boisterous brasserie (try the bar menu if your appetite only goes as far as a salad or burger), the back is starched and serious, and on warmer months there's café-style seating outside. That's not to say the young regulars (aged 20-40) don't make use of the more formal area. The main menu is a treat, including a batch of modern British dishes (including some Scottish-themed recipes – along with 39 malt whiskies at the bar), and a handful of interesting global choices (miso soup with tiger prawns and noodles; asparagus ravioli with goat's cheese and rocket pesto). We ignored the more exotic choices, with pleasing results. Kedgeree was fishy and buttery; guinea fowl was tender and worked wonders with the accompanying fennel and bed of plum tart. Aberdeen Angus fillet steak was beautifully rare,

Butlers Wharf Chop House

Central & East European

Central European

Lucky London has venues that offer the complete 'mittel European' experience – authentic regional transplants where you'll find the full complement of vernacular style and accessories. **Jägerhütte** and **Tiroler Hut** even provide musicians, so you can eat to the national beat. These restaurants tend to celebrate culinary tradition rather than innovation, but that's not necessarily a bad thing.

Austrian

Tiroler Hut

27 Westbourne Grove, W2 (020 7727 3981). Bayswater tube. **Dinner served** 6.30pm-12.30am Mon-Sat; 6.30-11.30pm Sun. **Main courses** £8.20-£15.50. **Cover** £1. **Service** 10%. **Credit** AmEx, MC, £TC, V.
Imagine our delight: Monday night is Gypsy music night, and quite by chance we'd decided on a Monday visit. Unfortunately the cow bell show wasn't on, but the evocative Gypsy musicians included a violinist, an electronic organist housed in the mini 'barnyard' enclosure, and an accordionist. Everyone, except us, seemed to know everyone else. Furnishings ape those of a Tyrolean-style mountain inn, with a faux window providing a picture postcard view of an Austrian valley. Crudités in a sundae glass were a nice welcoming gesture, but there was no dip. Mushroom salad (£5.50, with or without bacon) had good, fresh ingredients – mushrooms that were still warm from the pan; crunchy walnut segments creating contrast; perfectly nice vinaigrette – if rudimentary presentation. Liver dumpling soup boasted a meaty, rounded flavour and an equally spherical dumpling that retained its firmness. One of three main-course vegetarian options, gemuse strudel, didn't amuse, having a heavy, deep-fried, breaded nature. Its filling, a medley of vegetables diluted with rice, delivered a generic (rather than an individual) vegetable flavour. A generous roast knuckle of pork tumbled off the bone as it should, while red cabbage tasted better than it looked, with the dumpling being nicely stodgy. Cheesecake had a mousse-like texture, and creamy, cheesy flavour, marred only by a swirl of aerosol cream bearing a glacé cherry implant.
Children welcome. Book weekends. Entertainment: accordionist 8pm-1am nightly. **Map 11/6B**.

German

Jägerhütte

36 Queensway, W2 (020 7229 7941). Bayswater or Queensway tube. **Open** 11.30am-midnight daily. **Lunch served** noon-5pm, **dinner served** 6pm-midnight daily. **Mains** £7.25-£12.95. **Service** 10%. **Cover** £1. **Credit** AmEx, DC, JCB, LV, MC, £TC, V.
Piped accordion music precedes the live accordion and electronic-organ music, which creates a bit of fun at Jägerhütte for its core consumer group of tourists. Germans and Austrians in particular seem to feel at home among furnishings that resemble those of a hunting lodge: antler chandeliers, table mats depicting hunting scenes, a cuckoo clock. Reasonable goulash soup had a spicy, meaty flavour and no shortage of vegetables. Wiener schnitzel was adequate, but no more than that, as was the wiener holstein (crowned by a fried egg and anchovies). Potato salad had undercooked spuds, but a reasonable dressing. At least the excellent wheat beer won't let you down. Quite dense, dry, and with a dull chocolate flavour, sachertorte had been dressed up with some squirty cream, crowned by a glacé cherry. It seemed appropriate.
Babies and children welcome; high chair. Entertainment: Gypsy music from 7.30pm Tue-Sun. Tables outdoors (6, pavement). Takeaway service. Vegetarian menu. **Map 11/7C.**

Swiss

Marché ★

Portland House, Bressenden Place, SW1 (020 7630 1733/www.commoevenpick.com). Victoria tube/rail. **Open** 7.30am-11pm Mon-Sat; 11am-9pm Sun. **Meals served** 11am-11pm Mon-Sat; 11am-9pm Sun. **Main courses** £5.10-£9.95. **Credit** AmEx, DC, MC, £TC, V.
Abba in the background produced a retro note at Marché, while murals in the themed basement dining areas struck a surreal note: a wisteria-framed terrace overlooks an idyllic 'lake' in one. A 'ship' is a bar, and you choose dishes (cooked to order) from 'market stalls'. It's all explained on arrival by helpful staff, but choosing from more than one stall, and even eating with just one friend doing the same, means either hanging around, or remembering and coordinating the culinary pick-up – not something you want to think about when dining out. Salads (coleslaw, beansprout and spinach with Parmesan) were fine, as was roasted salmon. Rösti with smoked salmon was one of the Swiss dishes offered: well prepared with a crisp surface and tender potato. There's also a good range of Swiss ice-creams. Tourists abound here, not necessarily all disgorged from a coach tour. On Sundays, newspapers are provided.
Babies and children welcome; high chairs. Disabled: toilet. Entertainment: musicians 7-11pm Tue, Fri, Sat. No-smoking tables. Separate rooms for parties, seating 60 and 100. Takeaway service. **Map 6/9J**.

St Moritz

161 Wardour Street, W1 (020 7734 3324). Oxford Circus, Piccadilly Circus or Tottenham Court Road tube. **Lunch served** noon-3pm Mon-Fri. **Dinner served** 6-11.30pm Mon-Sat. **Main courses** £7.95-£14.50. **Service** 12½%. **Credit** AmEx, DC, MC, £TC, V.
For a modified Swiss chalet experience, St Moritz's cosy ground-floor dining room is ideal. The other option is an authentic 'mountain-top retreat' on the first floor, with brick walls, timber beams and all the national trimmings. Making a strategic decision to steer clear of fondues (there are several options for a minimum of two people, top price – £14.90 per person – being fondue chinoise, with strips of beef), we enjoyed going off-piste. Pizokel was a great starter: Swiss pasta (resembling plump fusilli) tasting freshly made and perfectly cooked. It came with a hearty, creamy sauce featuring al dente cabbage that harmonised well with the bacon and sbrinz. Thinly sliced air-dried cured beef was moist and big on flavour. Next, veal bratwurst with onion sauce and rösti was OK, while veal cordon bleu was tremendous (both in size and flavour): chunky, tender meat encasing plenty of ham and Swiss cheese. Though sorely tempted by the carrot cake (which originated from Berne) on the impressive dessert trolley, we couldn't eat any more.
Babies and children admitted. Book dinner. Separate room for parties, seats 28. Vegetarian dishes. **Map 13/6K.**

East European

London's East European venues can be divided into two genres: either those stuck in a post-war timewarp, preserving their original decor and culinary perspective, or the modern pioneers that come clad in contemporary furnishings, and hope to generate a more mainstream appeal by adapting recipes to the modern palate.

A prime example of the former sub-division is **Daquise**, the first post-war emigré outpost in London (and indeed Britain), that has waved goodbye to many other contenders during a long and still-popular reign. Clubs such as the **Ognisko** and **Czech & Slovak House**

---

its reduced pepper sauce rich and spicy; and monkfish was big and beautiful, complemented by a bed of Caesar-style salad. Unfortunately we had no space to sample the delectable selection of puddings (curd cheese cake with Greek yoghurt and honey, banana tatin with chocolate ice-cream and butterscotch sauce), but sweets were served with both the coffee and the bill. Service was friendly, charming and attentive.
Babies and children welcome; high chairs. Booking advisable Wed-Sat. Separate room for parties, seats 50. Tables outside (4, pavement). **Map 5/13E.**

Jack's Place

12 York Road, SW11 (020 7228 8519/ 1442). Clapham Junction rail. **Lunch served** Sept-Easter noon-4pm Sun. **Dinner served** 6-11pm Tue-Sat. **Main courses** £8.50-£18.50. **Set Sunday lunch** (*Sept-Easter*) £14.50 three courses. **Service** 10%. **Credit** MC, V.
Not much changes at Jack's Place. The traffic still speeds by along the drab York Road, the American visitors and local couples still get a hearty welcome from Jack, and the interior remains a duster's nightmare. Hats of all shapes and eras frame the door, clumps of ties hang from the ceilings with the lights, and the walls are chock a block with photos, flags and scarves, many along the 'Jack with…', or 'Jack adores…' theme (US presidents, UK royalty, Chelsea FC). Red and white checked table cloths, and a menu that hasn't changed a great deal over the years complete the setting. But there hasn't really been the need to vary the cuisine. Twenty starters offering plenty of choice (rollmops, jellied eels, garlic prawns), mains including steak au poivre, mignon, or chasseur and duck à l'Orange (Jack's fresh orange and brandy sauce), and a selection of 'Arfters' mean that, vegetarians excepted, there's something for everyone here. And the quality is good, if not spectacular. Melon boat starter was fresh and ample; the entrecote au poivre was tender, and came with a selection of five al dente vegetables, a rich pepper sauce and a pile of crisp roast potatoes. A wholesome warm chocolate fudge cake and cream rounded off an unpretentious and highly accomplished meal. Indeed, the only drawback was having to leave the cosy restaurant to brave the urban sprawl beyond the door.
Babies and children admitted. Booking essential, lunch; advisable, dinner. Separate room for parties, seats 16.

South East

Tower Bridge SE1

Butlers Wharf Chop House

Butlers Wharf Building, 36E Shad Thames, SE1 (020 7403 3403). Tower Hill tube/London Bridge tube/rail/Tower Gateway DLR/47, 78, 142, 188 bus.
Bar **Open** noon-3pm, 6-11pm Mon-Sat; noon-3pm Sun. **Brunch served** noon-3pm Sat, Sun. **Main courses** £6.75-£22. **Set brunch** (Sat, Sun) £13.95 two courses, £16.95 three courses, incl drink. **Set meal** (noon-3pm, 6-11pm Mon-Fri; 6-11pm Sat) £8 two courses, £10 three courses.
Restaurant **Lunch served** noon-3pm Mon-Fri, Sun. **Dinner served** 6-11pm Mon-Sat. **Main courses** £12-£30. **Set lunch** £19.75 two courses, £23.75 three courses.
Both **Service** 12½%. **Credit** AmEx, DC, JCB, MC, £TC, V.
The spectacular setting remains unchanged here, but the output from the kitchen is becoming unpredictable. In the past, this Conran product has delighted us with some rewarding meals, but this year's wasn't one of them. The beautifully lit Tower Bridge shone for us, and the polite, efficient and friendly staff passed between the wood-panelled benches and pine chairs with aplomb. Maybe it was because we didn't get to sit out on the terrace in the summer's balm, but the food didn't seem to live up to the setting. Perhaps we should have opted for roast saddle of lamb, champ and sherry; or red wine-poached plaice with dill potatoes – both successes in the past. Instead we had a rather plain half-lobster mayonnaise starter, followed by excessively salty salmon fish cakes. Furthermore, pork fillet was ample but too dry and not as tender as those we've eaten here before. Nevertheless, the mash was as creamy as ever; the bread basket was a happy collection of walnut, onion and raisin varieties; and desserts – a rich and cloying sticky toffee pudding, and a glazed caramel cream – were a dream. However, for such an alluring setting and such amenable service, it's a shame that the kitchen can be so off-key. Perhaps the chefs, like us, spent too long looking at the view.
Babies and children welcome; high chairs. Booking advisable. Dress: smart casual. Tables outdoors (12, terrace). **Map 8/8R.**

also serve up tradition, catering for an emigré market though welcoming all.

Modern Polish Cooking (a movement that is firmly established in Poland) is still restricted to a minority, led by the likes of **Wódka**. Modern Russian is similarly restricted to a splinter group of restaurants such as **Potemkin** and **Soviet Canteen**. The break-up of the former Soviet Union has also seen greater ethnic diversity manifesting itself, with Georgian and Armenian contenders bolstering the line-up. Greater social diversity has resulted in the first Tsarist restaurant, **Firebird**, pioneering the haute cuisine sector. Yet, for the serfs among us, there are still plenty of good-value, bargain eateries on the Eastern European circuit.

St Moritz.
See page 37.

Armenian

Jacob's ★

20 Gloucester Road, SW7 (020 7581 9292). Gloucester Road tube. **Meals served** 8am-10pm Mon-Sat; 8am-5pm Sun. **Main courses** £5-£7. **Credit** AmEx, MC, £TC, V.

Jacob's certainly puts the Ah! into Armenian. The choice of food is both enticing and unusual. Dishes are displayed in cabinets by the entrance (which staff deliver to your table), so you don't need to know the name of anything. The waiters are happy to talk you through the eclectic range and point out all the Armenian dishes. These include ikra, a smoked aubergine and tomato purée that's subtly smoky and creamy. We also tried dolma, an excellent cabbage roll garnished by a cooked prune, with al dente, full-flavoured cabbage and a meaty filling bearing only trace-elements of rice. Spinach and coriander 'Armenian tortilla' was a winner, while tabouleh showcased parsley in every fresh mouthful. Someone in the kitchen has a masterful way with leeks. Cold leeks were perfectly cooked examples in a lemony, olive oil dressing; and tasty poached chicken came stuffed with a medley of vegetables wrapped in leeks. The dining areas include a conservatory-style room with sienna walls, sideboard and chandelier; and a refectory table surrounded by shelves bearing interesting items. Either way it's like eating in a friend's rustic-chic kitchen/diner. A meal well worth a bill of £34 for two (including several drinks).

Babies and children welcome; high chairs. No-smoking tables. Separate room for parties, seats 25. Tables outdoors (5, conservatory; 2, pavement). Takeaway service. Vegetarian dishes. **Map 5/9C.**

Czech

Czech & Slovak House

74 West End Lane, NW6 (020 7372 5251). West Hampstead tube/rail.
Bar **Open** 6-11pm Tue-Fri; noon-11pm Sat; noon-10.30pm Sun.
Restaurant **Lunch served** noon-3pm Sat, Sun. **Dinner served** 6-9pm Tue-Sun. **Main courses** £6.20-£8.70.
Both **No credit cards.**

Among the many attractions of this club is the superb waiter who acts like a host, explaining everything in an enticing manner. The bar has a studenty feel and includes photos of Prague and an al fresco terrace. The Edwardian-style dining room, with fresh carnations on each table, has pictures of the Queen and Vaclav Havel forming an entente cordiale. Downsides of the club (the brown swirly carpet, for instance) are minor and easily overlooked. Chicken soup was heavy on the noodles, and included carrots and shredded chicken (not all lean). A good sprinkling of salt improved it. Tla cenko was an enjoyable, thinly sliced, fresh and flavourful brawn with onions. Potato salad comprised tender, slightly nutty potato chunks laced with diced carrots and peas in a light, creamy dressing – very nice indeed. Equally good was svickova, thinly sliced marinated beef with some wonderfully rounded flavours. It came in a full-bodied creamy sauce that also contained chewy bread dumplings (with a dense, buttery flavour): perfect for mopping up. Spinach was a finely chopped purée effectively spiked with fried garlic. To finish, we bought the waiter's pitch for the cheesecake, served hot. He was right.

Babies and children welcome; high chairs. Booking advisable. Separate room for parties, seats 21. Tables outdoors (6, patio). Takeaway service.

Georgian

Little Georgia ★

2 Broadway Market, E8 (020 7249 9070). Bethnal Green tube/rail/London Fields rail/26, 48, 55, 106, 236 bus. **Lunch served** 1-3pm Sun. **Dinner served** 6.30-10pm Tue-Thur; 6.30-10.30pm Fri, Sat. **Main courses** £7.50-£9.50. **Credit** MC, £TC, V.

Successfully transcending its pub-conversion origins, with sienna-coloured walls above tongue-and-groove panelling, Little Georgia has the air of a delightful neighbourhood restaurant. Further decoration is provided by velvet drapes and some restrained ethnic adornments: a wall-hanging, amphoras, small hand-mills grouped with walnuts (a culinary symbol of Georgia). The food is sublime. Hachapuri was a triumph, with creamy, grainy cheese encased by flaky pastry. The flavour and texture of Russian salad was enlivened by gherkins and fresh dill, while beetroot phalli (with fresh pomegranate seeds) had a pleasing, slightly rasping garlic flavour. We couldn't wait for round two. Roast duck arrived juicy, gamy and lean with a real depth of flavour. Meatballs were firm and rounded (in flavour as well as texture); the accompanying stewed peppers added some spice. Friendly and attentive service also helped to make the evening both relaxing and indulgent.

Babies and children welcome. Booking advisable Fri, Sat. Entertainment: occasional pianist and guitarist (phone for details). Tables outdoors (5, pavement). Vegetarian dishes.

Tbilisi

91 Holloway Road, N7 (020 7607 2536). Highbury & Islington tube/rail. **Dinner served** 6.30-11pm daily. **Main courses** £4.95-£7. **Credit** AmEx, MC, V.

Tbilisi's decor is full of contradictions. Neo-Victorian and Edwardian gentility comes in the form of wall lamps and dainty/naff china and glasses, while in contrast there's some funky modernistic light fittings, suburban lounge wallpaper and ethnic wall-hangings. The food also spans a range of quality. Chihirtma soup made a good sweet-sour start, with wonderfully fresh dill and subtle buttery chicken. Starters are available in mini 'set menus': we chose a trio of beetroot phalli (fresh beetroot, tangily spiked with garlic and garnished with pomegranate seeds), an equally meritorious spinach phalli, and hachapuri (a merely mediocre cheesebread). The main course of Georgian pork barbecue meat was tender, not too smoky, and was balanced by a tomato passata. Chicken satsivee had only the most subtle chicken flavour, and not much evidence of walnut either, while the accompanying 'Georgian polenta' was too bland to be of interest. We finished on a high point: ice-cream, and a nice walnut sponge cake with creamy walnut filling.

Babies and children admitted. Booking advisable Fri, Sat. Entertainment: occasional Georgian music (phone for details). Separate rooms for parties, seating 22 and 28. Takeaway service.

Hungarian

Gay Hussar

2 Greek Street, W1 (020 7437 0973/ www.gayhussar.co.uk). Tottenham Court Road tube. **Lunch served** 12.15-2.30pm, **dinner served** 5.30-10.45pm Mon-Sat. **Main courses** £11.50-£16.50. **Set lunch** £15 two courses, £18 three courses. **Service** 12½%. **Credit** AmEx, DC, JCB, MC, £TC, V.

Fast approaching its fiftieth anniversary, this renowned Soho landmark has recently been spruced up. However, the essential bohemian appeal of the place – somewhere between that of a gentlemen's reading room and a club dining room – has been heightened rather than compromised. Books on the shelves are now arranged rather than merely stacked, with new upholstery freshening the seating areas. Neatly aligned rows of black and white photographs are another innovation. Tables for two tucked away by the entrance are the best for privacy, while also enabling all-round observation. The three-course set lunch seemed the best way to tackle the menu. Goose and duck pâté had a slightly crumbly texture and a rounded creaminess. It made a great start to the meal, as did the selection of Hungarian salami (tender and juicy but also faintly spicy, accompanied by fresh, crunchy dill cucumber). Next came generous amounts of roast duck with lovely crisp skin and juicy, tender meat, served with al dente red cabbage and tender Hungarian potatoes (cooked in a good meat stock and sprinkled with sesame seeds). Hungarian potatoes also accompanied another main: duck liver Hungarian-style, fried with onions and made mildly spicy through restrained use of paprika. The third courses maintained the high standards: walnut pancake was nicely rich and alcoholic, with a walnut and raisin stuffing and chocolate sauce; Liptauer (very savoury fresh white cheese) was garnished with chopped spring onion and a hint of paprika, giving a fine creamy flavour.

Babies and children welcome. Booking advisable dinner. Dress: smart casual, no shorts. No-smoking tables. Separate rooms for parties, seating 12 and 20. **Map 13/6K.**

The Old Europeans

106 High Road, N2 (020 8883 3964/ www.oldeuropeans.com). East Finchley tube/ 102, 263 bus. **Meals served** noon-11pm Tue-Sat; noon-10pm Sun. **Main courses** £7.25-£10.25. **Minimum** £10 dinner Thur-Sat. **Set lunch** (noon-4pm) £5.50 two courses. **Credit** MC, V.

Strings of dried peppers in the window, and a couple of mannequins attired in folk costume, create a guard of honour by the entrance to this 'hunting lodge'. Pictures of folk scenes and several maps of Hungary enable you to plan a travelling itinerary. The meal started well, with an excellent goose liver pâté that had plenty of refreshing salad garnish, and a beefsteak tartare with subtle but effective seasoning. To follow, chicken in butter was juicy, tender and encased in a crisp batter. Its accompaniments were delicious, too: a dollop of crème fraîche; nutty, tender potato croquettes; and extra onions as requested (nicely fried). The low point of our visit turned out to be an oily goulash soup (served as a main course) with more vegetables than meat; much of it was left uneaten. Noticing this, a waiter simply stated that the dish was supposed to be that way. Beigli made an ideal conclusion to the meal; filled with poppyseeds it resembled a dense roulade cake. Palinka (fruit eau-de-vie) comes in a range of fruit flavours here and is an apt digestif.

Babies and children welcome; high chairs. Book dinner. Entertainment: Hungarian Gypsy music 8-11pm Thur (£2 cover). No-smoking tables. Tables outdoors (5, garden). Takeaway service. Vegetarian dishes.

Menu

Dishes followed by (Cz) indicate a Czech dish; (H): Hungarian; (P): Polish; (R): Russian; (Uk): Ukrainian. Others have no particular affiliation.

Bigos (P): hunter's stew made with sauerkraut, various meats and sausage, mushrooms and juniper.
Blini: yeast-leavened pancake made from buckwheat flour, traditionally served smothered in butter and sour cream.
Borscht: classic beetroot soup. There are many varieties: Ukrainian borscht is thick with vegetables; the Polish version (**barszcz**) is clear. There are also white and green types. Often garnished with sour cream, boiled egg or little dumplings.
Caviar: fish roe. Most highly prized is that of the sturgeon (beluga, oscietra and sevruga, in descending order of expense), though keta or salmon caviar is underrated.
Chlodnik (P): cold beetroot soup, shocking pink, served with sour cream.
Galabki, **golabki** or **golubtsy**: cabbage parcels, usually stuffed with rice or kasha (qv) and sometimes meat.
Golonka (P): pork knuckle, often cooked in beer.
Goulash (H): rich beef soup.
Kasha or **kasza**: buckwheat, delicious plain roasted, light and fluffy with a nutty flavour.
Kaszanka (P): blood sausage made with buckwheat.
Knedliky (Cz): bread dumplings.
Kolduny (P): small meat-filled dumplings (scaled-down pierogi, qv) often served in beetroot soup.
Kotlet schabowy (P): breaded pork chops.
Koulebiaka, kulebiak or **Coulebiac** (R): layered salmon or sturgeon pie with eggs, dill, rice and mushrooms.
Latke: grated potato pancakes fried until golden and crisp.
Makowiec (P): poppyseed cake.
Mizeria: (cucumber salad (very thinly sliced and dressed with soured cream).
Nalesniki (P): cream cheese pancakes.
Paczki (P): doughnuts, often filled with plum jam.
Pelmeni (R): Siberian-style ravioli dumplings.
Pierogi (P): ravioli-style dumplings. Typical fillings are sauerkraut and mushroom, curd cheese or fruit (cherries, apples).
Pirogi (large) or **pirozhki** (small) (R): filled pies made with yeasty dough.
Sashlik: Caucasian spit-roasted meat (usually lamb).
Shchi (R): soup made from sauerkraut.
Stroganoff (R): beef slices in a rich, sour cream and mushroom sauce.
Surowka (P): raw shredded vegetable salad.
Ushka or **uszka**: small ear-shaped dumplings served in soup.
Vareniki (Uk): Ukrainian pierogi (qv).
Zakuski (R) or **zakaski** (P): hors d'oeuvres, traditionally covering a whole table. The many dishes can include: pickles, marinated vegetables and fish, herring, smoked eel, aspic, mushrooms, radishes with butter, salads and caviar.
Zrazy (P): beef rolls stuffed with bacon, pickled cucumber and mustard; the Polish version of beef olives.
Zurek (P): sour rye soup.

Polish

Polanka

258 King Street, W6 (020 8741 8268). Ravenscourt Park tube. **Lunch served** 10am-3pm, **dinner served** 6-10pm Mon-Sat. **Meals served** 11am-8pm Sun. **Main courses** £3-£7.50. **Unlicensed. Corkage** £1 wine, £5 spirits. **Credit** £TC.

Formerly known as Adam i Agusia, Polanka has recently had a furnishing upgrade. The gallery of Polish thespians has been replaced by floral pictures on a freshly painted yellow wall. Fake ivy adds greenery, while a fake fuchsia bush and fake sunflowers on the table provide more colour. A giant teddy stands cheerfully by the art nouveau piano. All this is an improvement (honestly), but the food on our visit was mediocre. A pungent zurek, bulked out with potato chunks and hard-boiled egg, was at least generous. Lukewarm pierogi had a firm but ultimately yielding texture, with the cheese filling of the same (OK) standard as the meat; the sauerkraut filling took pole position. A combination of surowki (raw vegetable combinations) and salad was poor: limp lettuce, overcooked red cabbage and an adequate carrot and sauerkraut number – not good value at £4. Background music was provided by Capital Radio. Service, however, was friendly and prompt. The restaurant lies behind a deli section where you can also eat, sitting at patio furniture.

Babies and children welcome; high chairs. Entertainment: bands Sat, Sun. No-smoking tables. Separate room for parties, seats 36. Takeaway service. Vegetarian dishes.

Anthony's ★

54 Porchester Road, W2 (020 7243 8743). Royal Oak tube. **Dinner served** 6pm-midnight Mon-Sat. **Main courses** £7.50-£13.80. **Cover** 60p. **Credit** MC, £TC, V.

Among Anthony's interesting Euro-Med menu are some Eastern Euro triumphs. Barszcz showed what beetroot is capable of in the right hands, reflecting good stock and a dill garnish; al dente uszka retained fresh mushroom flavours. Herrings were delightfully presented: small slices dressed in soured cream, onion and dill, around an elegant salad garnish, with fresh bread provided. Next, grated potato pancake arrived with a side pot of soured cream. Its crisp surface and faintly nutty flavour guaranteed it had been freshly prepared. Wiener schnitzel (highly popular in Poland, which has adopted the dish as its own) featured nice thick meat with a crisp surface and a rich meaty flavour. Accompanying vegetables were another highlight: buttery carrots in sesame seeds and dill, chopped cabbage and mushrooms. A finale of own-made ice-cream and light but chunky pancakes with stewed apples and cream meant we smiled all the way home. Decor here is a combination of retro elements (Edwardian inlaid mirror, Cubist painting) within a modern white space. It works very well. The proprietress, an excellent hostess, is an added attraction, as was a bill of just £36 for two.

Babies and children welcome. Entertainment: disco 10.30pm-1am Thur-Sat (basement). **Map 11/5C.**

L'Autre

5B Shepherd Street, W1 (020 7499 4680). Green Park tube. **Lunch served** noon-2.30pm Mon-Sat. **Dinner served** 5.30-11pm daily. **Main courses** £7.50-£12.95. **Service** 10%. **Credit** AmEx, MC, V.

First impressions of L'Autre seem contradictory: a French name, decor combining sombreros with displays of Polish vodka – all in an endearing faux-Tudor and Edwardian wine bar setting. The menu also spans Polish and Mexican dishes (an entirely economic decision, as a previous Mexican chef built up a Mexican clientele, so his Polish successor had to provide continuity while adding his own native cuisine). Barszcz with pirozhki combined sweet and savoury flavours and came garnished with dill; a separate pot of soured cream was provided for DIY mixing. The pirozhki had a pleasingly chewy texture. Kotlet schabowy, featuring tender pork and crispy breadcrumbs, was all the better for its generous proportions. Golonka was equally generous, with tender meat falling off the bone at the gentlest prod. Accompaniments to both main courses were a crisp sauerkraut salad, nice red cabbage and buttery mashed potatoes (with a good stock flavour) garnished with dill. The friendly staff greet regulars by name.

Book dinner. Children admitted. Tables outdoors (3, pavement). **Map 6/8H.**

Café Grove

65 The Grove, W5 (020 8810 0364). Ealing Broadway tube/rail. **Open** 11am-11pm daily. **Main courses** £3.50-£7.50. **Credit** AmEx, DC, MC, £TC, V.

Vivid Wedgwood-blue walls are the backdrop for exhibitions of modern art (for sale) at Café Grove. Corrugated-metal sheets provide a rippling ceiling, and scaffolding acts as a banister on the staircases. Varnished floorboards, marble-topped tables and a cottagey patio garden lend this early 19th-century building an air of tradition. There are plenty of Euro-Mediterranean dishes on the menu, including salad niçoise, feta salad and tuna salad. The Polish element is provided by a line-up of greatest hits. Zurek had a rounded flavour, with diced bacon and mushroom joining the usual cast of hard-boiled egg and potato chunks. Mixed pierogi filled with meat and mushrooms were well-prepared, and had the option of being drizzled with melted butter or fried lardons. The accompanying garnish (lettuce, tomato, cucumber and sweetcorn dressed in vinaigrette) was substantial enough to be a side salad. The cheesecake, however, was too buttery and sweaty. Other Polish dishes include bigos, golabki, and blinis with herring or smoked salmon.

Babies and children welcome. Book Sat, Sun. Separate room for parties, seats 30. Tables outdoors (2, pavement). Takeaway service.

Café Wanda

153 Clapham High Street, SW4 (020 7738 8760). Clapham Common tube. **Meals served** noon-11pm Mon-Thur; 10am-midnight Fri-Sun. **Main courses** £4.15-£9.85. **Set lunches** £5.85 two courses, £7.95 three courses incl coffee. **Set teas** £6.95. **Set dinner** £11.95 three courses. **Credit** DC, MC, £TC, V.

Effective decor – a mustard and olive-green colour scheme, green tablecloths, a medley of dried flowers and potted plants, and interesting framed photographs – helps you forget that Café Wanda occupies what is essentially a long oblong room. Piano music on Saturday night adds a party atmosphere, while Wanda, the proprietress, also generates good humour. Golabki featured al dente cabbage filled with tender rice and well-seasoned meat, accompanied by a great tomato sauce and buttery mashed potatoes. Goat's cheese salad hadn't been grilled enough. No problem: it got an extra session under the heat. Except that it still wasn't great, being essentially hot cheese on toasted bread with sliced tomatoes and greenery – still, we weren't charged for it, and were also offered complimentary mineral water, which more than settled the account. Blinis were quite bready and came piled with soured cream, smoked salmon, a nice chopped cucumber garnish and salad leaves. A sauceboat of good mustardy vinaigrette was supplied for DIY dressing. Decent, dense, creamy cheesecake topped with almonds was a fine way to finish. The total bill for two (minus the cost of the salad) came to only £25.60.

Babies and children welcome. Book Thur-Sat. Entertainment: pianist 8.30pm-midnight Wed-Sat. Tables outdoors (5, pavement). Takeaway service. Vegetarian menu.

Daquise

20 Thurloe Street, SW7 (020 7589 6117). South Kensington tube. **Meals served** 11.30am-11pm daily. **Main courses** £4.80-£10.50. **Set lunch** (noon-3pm Mon-Fri) £6.80 two courses incl glass of wine, coffee. **Credit** MC, £TC, V.

Britain's first Polish café (established back in 1947), Daquise has a unique atmosphere. The endearingly déshabillé decor remains unchanged (though it is occasionally refreshed), so the large collage of the royal wedding coach containing Charles and Diana still takes pride of place, alongside folk art motifs. We love it. The food's not bad, either. Chlodnik had a creamy, yoghurty, home-made flavour that was animated by spring onion, diced cucumber and dill, yet still managed to keep its beetroot identity. A slightly sweet barszcz had body and al dente uszka filled with appealing chopped mushrooms. Main course pork schnitzel featured a thick slice of meat clothed in crispy breadcrumbs – not the lightest example, but heartily rewarding. Hungarian pancake was also an enjoyable, robust number. It was served calzone-style, folded over the goulash and stewed pepper filling, and garnished with a dollop of soured cream. Hot grated beetroot was as it should be, while refreshing cucumber slices in the mizeria were only slightly marred by traces of bitter cucumber juice within the soured cream dressing. To finish, eggy pancakes had a rich cream filling and came dusted with icing sugar: a satisfying package. The bill for two came to just £31.60 including drinks. Service ranges from aloofness to warmth.

Babies and children welcome. Book dinner. No-smoking tables. Separate room for parties, seats 30. Takeaway service. **Map 12/10E.**

Lowiczanka Polish Cultural Centre

238-246 King Street, W6 (020 8741 3225). Ravenscourt Park tube.
Coffee shop **Open** 9.30am-9pm daily.
Bar/restaurant **Lunch served** 12.30-3pm daily. **Dinner served** 6.30-11pm Mon-Thur, Sun; 7pm-midnight Fri, Sat. **Main courses** £5.90-£10.50. **Set lunch** £7 three courses. **Credit** AmEx, MC, £TC, V.

We've enjoyed several meals at the Cultural Centre's first-floor restaurant in the past, yet on a recent busy Sunday night, we received three courses of seemingly mass-produced food that lacked the usual attention to detail. At least sorrel soup made a nice start: creamy, buttery flavours counterbalancing the tangy leaf. Golonka was a little dry, however. Spinach crêpe with dill sauce was OK, as were golabki, though neither measured up to the wild boar pâté and curd cheese pierogi that were highlights of previous trips. Seromakowiec, a combined cheese cake/poppyseed cake was great, but walnut cake had too buttery a filling with the level of alcohol going over the limit. There's plenty of alcohol in liquid form, with a good choice of Polish vodka (£1.50) and Polish beer (£2.50). Lowiczanka's pleasantly conservative decor transcends the ugliness of this 1960s building, which also houses a ground-floor café (an inexpensive option) and a travel agent (who can make all the arrangements to fly you eastwards to sample the real thing).

Babies and children welcome; high chairs. Book lunch Sun, dinner Sat. Disabled: toilet. Dress: smart casual (restaurant). Entertainment: Gypsy band (£1.90 cover) 8.30pm-midnight Fri, Sat; 7-10pm Sun. Separate rooms for parties, seating 40, 60 and 200. Tables outdoors (6, patio). Takeaway service (coffee shop).

Na Zdrowie The Polish Bar

11 Little Turnstile, WC1 (020 7831 9679). Holborn tube. **Meals served** noon-9pm Mon-Fri. **Dinner served** 6-9pm Sat. **Main courses** £3.95-£5.95. **Credit** MC, £TC, V.

What a difference a year makes. Where students once hung out in a funky bedsit setting, young groomed suits now perch on orange stools, surrounded by contemporary decor. Silvery walls and woodwork are accessorised with metalwork cut-outs of the Polish eagle (as much a style statement as a national emblem); one wall has a crazy-paving effect of irregular pieces of mirror. A laid-back beat certainly suits the uptempo crowd. The food doesn't show any such signs of a makeover – but, to be fair, this is really a bar, not a restaurant. Barszcz was a fair rendition and came with slightly overcooked uszka. Requesting the 'cocktail version' of placki ziemniaczane, we were surprised to get sliced potato pancakes on cocktail sticks, with a choice of dips: either a decent mushroom sauce or soured cream. Although on the oily side, they were freshly made and did taste of potatoes. Among the mixed selection of pierogi, cabbage were easily the best, with meat reasonable and cheese bland. More importantly, there's a choice of six Polish lagers (from £2.40) and around 45 Polish vodkas (from £1.80) – including gems like Zubrowka and rarities such as Siwucha.

Tables outdoors (3, pavement). Bookings not accepted. Takeaway service. Vegetarian dishes. **Map 14/5L.**

Ognisko Polskie

55 Prince's Gate, Exhibition Road, SW7 (020 7589 4635). South Kensington tube.
Bar **Open** noon-11pm daily. **Bar snacks** £1.20-£4.90.
Restaurant **Lunch served** 12.30-3pm, **dinner served** 6.30-11pm daily. **Main courses** £7.90-£13.90. **Set meal** £8.50 three courses.
Both **Credit** AmEx, DC, MC, £TC, V.

Located within the Polish equivalent of a club on the Mall, Ognisko Polskie now has a new colour scheme: a subtle range of pinks, picked up by the pink tablecloths and napkins. The dining room retains a pleasing club-like atmosphere; only Poles and those in the know frequent it. Portraits of English aristos and eminent emigré Poles combine with the pillars and chandelier to give a delightfully ancestral feel. Creamy chlodnik was full of beetroot flavour and contained fresh hard-boiled egg segments; avocado with prawns and chilli sauce was fine, too. Fresh, nutty rye bread came with butter garnished with flat-leaf parsley. A well-prepared kotlet schabowy featured plenty of pork with deliciously savoury white cabbage on the side, while a side dish of red cabbage had a hint of apple. Lean and tender duck with a well-balanced orange sauce was another success, along with the side dish of spinach laced with mushrooms, and a combination dish of mange-tout, broccoli and courgettes. Crème brûlée with Grand Marnier made an indulgent conclusion; our other choice for dessert, excellent cheesecake, came topped with chocolate and almonds for a subtle extra.

Babies and children admitted. Booking advisable. Dress: smart casual. Separate rooms for parties, seating 35 and 120. Tables outdoors (10, terrace). **Map 12/9D.**

Patio ★

5 Goldhawk Road, W12 (020 8743 5194). Goldhawk Road or Shepherd's Bush tube/49, 94, 220, 273 bus. **Lunch served** noon-3pm Mon-Fri. **Dinner served** 6-11.30pm daily. **Main courses** £4.50-£10. **Set meal** £10.90 three courses incl shot of vodka. **Credit** AmEx, DC, JCB, MC, £TC, V.

Balloons on the walls of this welcoming, comfortable 'lounge/diner' imply that a party is about to begin. The quality of the food and the value for money certainly provide reasons to celebrate. We sampled the particularly well-priced set menu. Wonderful blinis had a spongy, almost doughnut-like texture beneath a crisp surface. The topping was thickly sliced smoked salmon, and a soured cream garnish agreeably sharpened by chopped onion. Next, golabki had a good cabbage-meat interplay of flavours, and came with a smooth tomato and red pepper sauce – even better for its sprinkling of dill. Four accompanying salads included two based on sauerkraut, one pepped up with chilli, as well as beetroot salad and an enjoyable platter of roast potatoes. This bargain-priced set menu doesn't preclude the kind of extras that come as standard in more expensive places; a pre-dessert palate-cleanser of melon and orange slices was accompanied by pieces of caramel sponge cake dipped in desiccated coconut. Dessert was a high-quality cheesecake, lightly grainy with a hint of soured cream, plus the excellent addition of 'fortified' sultanas that seemed to have spent quite a spell in brandy.

Babies and children welcome; half-price children's portions. Book dinner Fri, Sat. Entertainment: Gypsy band Fri, Sat. No-smoking tables. Separate room for parties, seats 50. Vegetarian dishes.

Polish White Eagle Club

211 Balham High Road, SW17 (020 8672 1723). Tooting Bec tube/Balham tube/rail/49, 155, 181, 319 bus.
Bar **Open** noon-3pm, 6-11pm Mon, Sat; 6-11pm Tue-Fri; 11am-10.30pm Sun.
Restaurant **Lunch served** 12.30-3pm Mon, Tue. **Dinner served** 6-10pm Thur-Sun. **Main courses** £3.70-£7.50. **Set lunch** £5.50 two courses incl coffee. **No credit cards.**

The White Eagle Club's dining room has a faux-Edwardian style, with velvety embossed wallpaper and floral pictures in gilt frames. It is accessed through the club's pub-style bar and was full of a range of ages and types the night we went. Friendly service got our meal off to a nice start. Mushroom soup was fine, having a lightly spicy fungous flavour. The herring came entombed in soured cream, featuring a cucumber twist in the middle and a strategically placed tomato wedge at either end. The most successful filling of the mixed pierogi was mushroom, with meat and cheese close behind; all came garnished with fried breadcrumbs. A good palate-cleansing surowka combined sauerkraut with gherkins and carrots. For dessert, fluffy, creamy cheesecake was enlivened by a lemon zing; lemon tea (served in a glass) makes an ideal accompaniment. The food might not be top-notch, but is perfectly adequate – and great value.

No-smoking tables. Separate rooms for parties, seating 30 and 120.

Wódka

12 St Alban's Grove, W8 (020 7937 6513/ www.wodka.co.uk). Gloucester Road or High Street Kensington tube. **Lunch served** 12.30-2.30pm Mon-Fri. **Dinner served** 7-11.15pm daily. **Main courses** £8.90-£13.90. **Set lunch** £10.90 two courses, £13.50 three courses. **Credit** AmEx, DC, MC, TC, V.

Fresh crushed raspberries with vodka and soda (£4.50) was an ideal aperitif for an accomplished meal here. Wódka delivers traditional Polish dishes with a progressive slant. Gilded blinis provided cushions for generous amounts of thickly sliced smoked salmon, heightened by soured cream laced with chopped shallots. Wild mushroom soup had a highly desirable texture of mushroom segments, plus creamy hints and full-bodied stock. Medallions of venison were nicely pink beneath a seared surface, and came with cherries and poached pears (just sweet enough for a balancing act). Side orders were far from being sidelines, as mizeria spiked with spring onion was refreshingly creamy; buckwheat salad (with mint and shallots) had depth of flavour; and

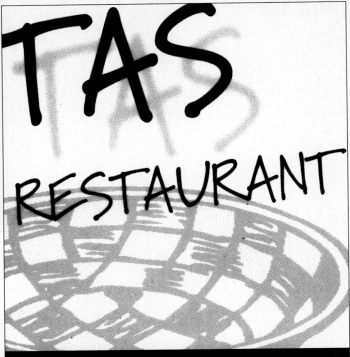

al dente red cabbage offered just the right degree of sweetness. Another main course, salt beef, was firm but tender, and its horseradish sauce produced tears of joy. The accompanying leniwe (similar to gnocchi) were as soft and yielding as they should be. A silvery skyscape ceiling, period wooden panelling and art deco tiles animate Wódka's series of minimalist-style rooms, as do the magnificent fresh flower arrangements.
Babies and children welcome. Booking advisable; essential dinner Thur-Sat. Separate room for parties, seats 30. Takeaway service. **Map 5/9C**.

Russian

Borshtch 'n' Tears
45-46 Beauchamp Place, SW3. (020 7589 5003). Knightsbridge tube/14, 74, C1 bus. **Open** 6pm-2am daily. **Set dinner** £17.50 three courses incl shot of vodka. **Credit** AmEx, JCB, MC, V.
It's easy to assume Borshtch 'n' Tears has become an anachronism – after all, the place has been around for ages. Far from it, though: we had a great dinner. A red and black colour scheme (with hints of Byzantine motifs) makes for a darkened, twilight setting that tempers the rather raffish but endearing atmosphere. Russian icons are kept to a minimum; a large hammer and sickle flag provides some post-communist chic. Music (every night) from an accomplished guitar/violin combo, spans every nuance from tragic romance to exuberant and passionate romance. Spicy beef pelmeni were well-cooked and arrived garnished with soured cream. The pirozhki were good, too, their flaky pastry benefiting from yet more soured cream. Fresh, light blinis came crowned with smoked salmon. Crispy chicken Kiev delivered a proportional degree of garlic, while stroganoff was tender and creamy. Note that stag parties frequent the place at the weekends, so go in the week for peace and quiet.
Babies and children welcome; high chairs. Tables outdoors (2, pavement). Takeaway service. **Map 12/9F**.

Erebuni ★
London Guards Hotel, 36-37 Lancaster Gate, W2 (020 7402 6067). Lancaster Gate tube. **Dinner served** 7pm-midnight Mon-Sat. **Service** 10%. **Credit** MC, V.
Featuring the Edwardian appeal of the hotel in which it is located, this basement restaurant also has a light Russian accent in the form of postmodern folk paintings, discreetly positioned Babushka dolls, and Russian disco music in the background – not to mention the customers. We were surrounded by Russians: always a good endorsement. The food didn't disappoint. A pancake-style meat blini balanced spicy, tender meat with a soured cream garnish. Hachapuri was a version of Georgian cheese bread: light, flaky pastry filled with tangy cheese, arriving in a dish straight from the oven. Juicy gryby maryovane (prime mushrooms in a good briny marinade) arrived with an effective red onion garnish. Emanbajady was a fine version of the Turkish imam bayildi: aubergine with lightly char-grilled, mildly spicy pepper. Pelmeni had a perfect chewy consistency, with soured cream lifting the fillings (spicy meat, and curd cheese with mashed potato). Great golubtsy (al dente cabbage wrapped around a meaty filling) was paired with excellent tomato sauce, while ischkhan (rainbow trout in Armenian sauce) was delightfully spicy, and arrived with tender potatoes and peppers. Finishing on Armenian baklava was indulgent but not cloying (a considerable achievement). We also enjoyed Napoleon, a millefeuille with ethereally light, flaky pastry and creamy filling.
Babies and children admitted. Book Fri, Sat. Dress: no jeans or trainers. Takeaway service. Vegetarian dishes. **Map 1/6D**.

Firebird
23 Conduit Street, W1 (020 7493 7000/ 7088). Oxford Circus tube. **Lunch served** 12.30-2.45pm, **dinner served** 7.15-10.45pm Mon-Sat. **Main courses** £17-£25. **Set lunch** £15 two courses, £18.95 three courses. **Service** 12½%. **Credit** AmEx, JCB, MC, V.
London's first haute cuisine Tsarist restaurant. Firebird's furnishings seem as much haute bourgeois as imperial to us, though it reminded one regular visitor to Russia of current restaurants in that country, which link modernity to the Tsarist past. Whatever the verdict, the red and green colour scheme, swagged curtains, gilded highlights and combination of oil paintings of flamboyant characters and photographs of the estate back home, create an authentic setting. Buttery, creamy sorrel soup didn't lose sight of its namesake, with rounded sorrel and spinach flavours, while langoustine

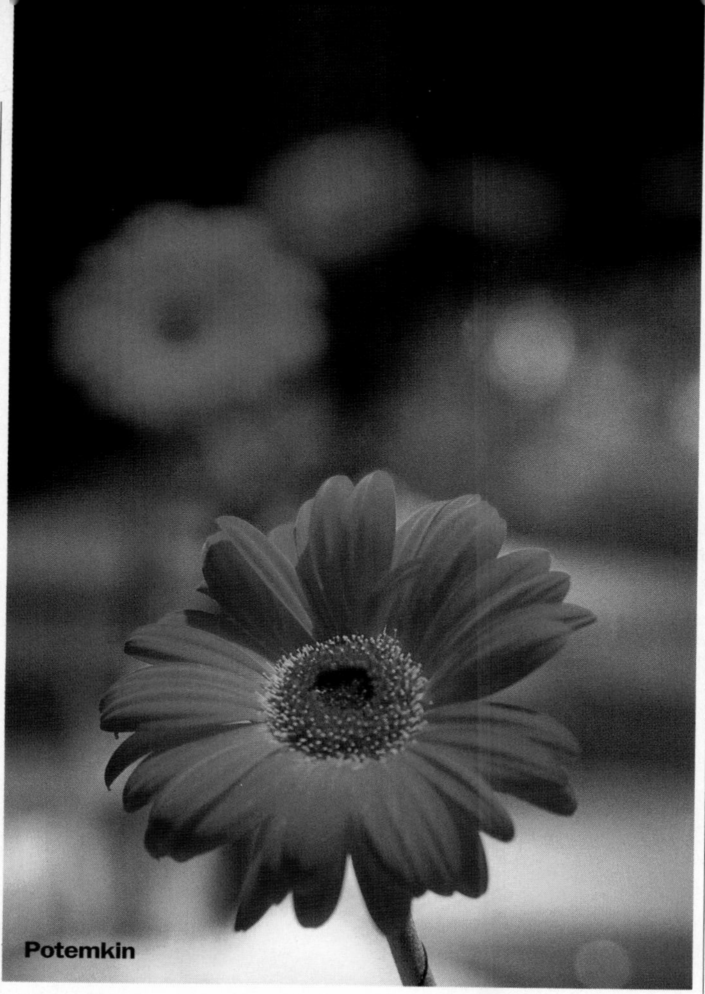
Potemkin

tart boasted ultra-light pastry and delicious langoustine. Quail Kiersky was a superb scaled-down version of chicken Kiev, with gamy, tender meat enlivened by superior garlic butter. Perfectly cooked Ukrainian pechenya zayach meant rabbit with a marvellous gamy flavour, full-flavoured cabbage, and a generous helping of mushrooms in an accompanying cream sauce, not to mention a terrific potato cake. For afters, rice pudding with an occasional burst of mint was inspired, while chocolate bolshoi was ultra-rich and came with a successful caramelised walnut ice-cream. Staff were very attentive and most courteous. Details such as the jug of hot milk with coffee, and the extensive tea menu, also speak of Fire Bird's pedigree. Dining here may require a Tsarist budget, but it will certainly provide a memorable experience.
Children admitted. Disabled: toilet. Entertainment: Pianist Thur-Sat dinner. No-smoking tables. Separate room for parties, seats 14. **Map 13/6J**.

Kozachok
10 Red Lion Street, Richmond, Surrey (020 8948 2366). Richmond tube/rail. **Dinner served** 6.30-11.15pm Tue-Sat. **Main courses** £8.50-£9.75. **Minimum** £8.50. **Service** 12½%. **Credit** AmEx, JCB, MC, £TC, V.
A Gypsy shawl draped over a loudspeaker at Kozachok provided a great example of how to create an atmosphere with imagination rather than heavy financial investment. The effect was enhanced on our visit by a Ukrainian version of Shirley Bassey belting out emotive numbers from beyond the shawl. The same ethos applies to much of the decoration here: a mirror painted with dancing Cossacks, and murals of folk scenes and an Orthodox church. It's fun without being over the top. Great value vodka (£2 for 25ml, £2.50 for 50ml) includes the deliciously wheaty Sibirskaya, and the over-proof but fruity Krepkaya (56% abv). A pleasurable meal began with a sensational blini, which had a soufflé-like texture beneath a crisp, gilded surface, layered with shredded smoked salmon and soured cream. Taras bulba pâté with rye bread was full-bodied and (to its credit) uncompromisingly ethnic. Next, steak was well cooked, and came with wonderfully soft mini potato dumplings. Good stuffed cabbage had the emphasis on tender meat rather than rice, and the tomato sauce was as traditional as it was enjoyable. To finish, we tucked into blinchiki, a delightfully light pancake with cinnamon apple and a creamy custard.
Babies and children welcome. Booking advisable, essential Thur-Sat. Entertainment: traditional Russian music occasionally (phone for details).

Luba's Place ★
164 Essex Road, N1 (020 7704 2775). Essex Road rail/38, 56, 73 bus. **Meals served** 6pm-midnight Tue-Sun. **Main courses** £4.45-£7.95. **Credit** MC, V.
Electronic Russian disco provides the warm-up before the musicians take over at Luba's. The colour scheme here is a vivid blend of orange above the dado, purple below, with accessories such as an imposing painting of a religious procession (in full serf mode), and crooked venetian blinds (not that the view on to Essex Road needs to be encouraged). Blinis exhibit both Russian and Mediterranean touches: herring, or avocado salsa sauce with cheese. We tried the smoked salmon, and the veggie version (broccoli, cauliflower, spinach, carrot and cheese); both came on rather rudimentary pancakes. Pelmeni had a good beefy filling, and despite no sign of cream, the beef stroganoff was OK. Russian vodka at £1.75 for 1¼oz is worth trying, with the choice including gems like Wyborowa, Sibirskaya and Moskovskaya. Our bill arrived in a lacquered Russian box, which also contained some native chocolates that sweetened our exit.
Babies and children welcome. Book weekends. Entertainment: Russian sax and violin Wed, Fri, Sat. Takeaway service. Vegetarian dishes.

Nikita's
65 Ifield Road, SW10 (020 7352 6326). Earl's Court tube/14, 31, 74 bus. **Dinner served** 7.30-11.30pm Mon-Sat. **Main courses** £8.50-£14.95. **Set meals** £18.50-£30.50 four courses incl coffee. **Cover** £1.50. **Credit** AmEx, JCB, MC, V.
A long-established fixture on the Russian circuit, Nikita's has friendly, attentive staff. They easily manage to handle the over-excited Sloanes who love having a session here. The tiny bar, a shrine to vodka, is a little too tiny for aperitifs so we went straight to a table in the candelit, dark red basement, where walls are hung with prints of Russian aristos. Background music is a mix of downbeat and uptempo numbers. The food was upbeat and served at a good tempo. Euro rather than Eastern-Euro pirozhki comprised good flaky pastry filled with blue Stilton and spinach, or spicy lamb and soured cream – but the flavours worked. Blinis with smoked sturgeon were deliciously puffy, while the rarity of this fish (not to mention the degree of flavour and the generous slices) made the dish a real treat. Fresh rye bread scored more points. Lean, tender duck breast with peppers and pepper vodka delivered balanced pepperiness. Steak tartare was well-seasoned and although finely textured retained a nice chunkiness. Side dishes were equally good: buckwheat laced with mushrooms; and green salad with the unexpected addition of broccoli florets and a superior vinaigrette. To finish, syrniki was an alcoholic filling of cream cheese and raisins within a light pancake dusted with icing sugar, enhanced by caramel sauce.
Babies and children admitted until 9pm Mon-Thur. Booking essential Thur-Sat. Dress: smart casual. Entertainment: Gypsy music 8.30-11.30pm Fri, Sat. Separate rooms for parties, both seating 6. Takeaway service. Vegetarian dishes. **Map 5/12C**.

Potemkin
144 Clerkenwell Road, EC1 (020 7278 6661). Farringdon tube/rail.
Bar **Open** 11am-11pm Mon-Fri; 6-11pm Sat.
Restaurant **Meals served** 11am-11pm Mon-Sat. **Main courses** £5.50-£18.50.
Both **Credit** AmEx, JCB, MC, V.
An attractively modern ground-floor bar that also serves food is the 'economy' option at this new venue, but we went straight to 'club class', in the basement restaurant. Here the decor is not so minimal as to exclude flamboyant streaks such as oversized purple banquettes extending up the wall, or the telling use of Russian objets d'art. Indeed, everything has been chosen on the basis of stylistic impact: chunky but angular vodka carafes, elegant vodka glasses on a stem, salt and pepper pots like rounds of mozzarella. Culinary presentation was equally artistic. The caviar platter (£15) comprised gilded blinis with a selection of caviar. We also chose stolichny salad kouritza, which comes with or without chicken (we had with: a superior version of a familiar classic). Next, pan-fried sturgeon, the most expensive dish at £18.50, was cooked very rare (as per the Siberian school, the kindly waiter informed us) resulting in an ultra-delicate flavour, but still too undercooked for our taste. Stroganoff à la Potemkin meant nicely flavoured meat covered by a pile of inauthentic straw chips (a concession to the British palate, apparently). Nevertheless, two sensational, ultra-indulgent puddings, shok vostorg (chocolate sponge mousse) and mishka kasalape (toffee cake), sent us away on a real high.
Babies and children admitted. Dress: smart. No-smoking tables. **Map 15/4N**.

Rasputin
265 High Street, W3 (020 8993 5802). Acton Town tube. **Meals served** 11am-midnight daily. **Main courses** £7.50-£12. **Service** 10%. **Cover** £1. **Credit** MC, V.
Some very nice touches – a platter of pickled vegetable crudités on customers' arrival, butter flowers garnished with flat-leaf parsley, the 'ice bowl' on which plates of blinis are served, not to mention the fun proprietress – tend to overshadow the food at Rasputin, which is enjoyable rather than a culinary highlight. Lacy buckwheat pancakes with smoked salmon, Ukrainian borscht (with more vegetables than its Eastern European relatives) and pierogi with cheese, were all fine, as were the main courses of grated potato pancakes, and beef stroganoff (despite an absence of cream). Accompanying vegetables were red cabbage, broccoli and sautéed potatoes. A dessert of generously proportioned charlotte Russe seemed more like an apricot soufflé with aerosol cream highlights. Decor is pleasant, resembling that of a high street wine bar, circa 1975, though there's plenty of dark red Tsarist touches as well.
Babies and children welcome. Booking advisable. Separate room for parties, seats 35.

Soviet Canteen
430 King's Road, SW10 (020 7795 1556). Sloane Square tube/19, 22, 49 bus. **Dinner served** 6.30-11pm Mon-Sat; 6.30-10.30pm Sun. **Main courses** £7.50-£12.95. **Set meals** £9.95 two courses, £12.95 three courses. **Credit** AmEx, DC, JCB, MC, V.
It's a catchy name, but this sterling establishment is characterised just as much by non-Soviet and non-Canteen elements: linen napkins, polka-dot upholstery. The menu thrives on its Russian roots. Wild mushroom and truffle relish (presented in a small pot with fresh, springy walnut bread) made

Firebird.
See page 41.

Chinese

A couple of years ago, a trainee chef at China's most prestigious cooking school told this writer that he disliked western food. When questioned further, he explained that he had once eaten fried chicken and mashed potatoes at an American fast-food outlet and had found it really disgusting. On the basis of this one unhappy experience he was apparently willing to write off as worthless the great cuisines of the entire western world. This may seem outrageous and even hilarious, but it's really no different from the common western perception that Chinese food is cheap and junky. Like the Chinese, whose first experience of western food may well be something in a polystyrene box, many British people associate Chinese cooking with the ghastly takeaway fare which has had such an indelible effect on the national psyche.

So, let's get some things straight. China has one of the world's most ancient, most diverse and most sophisticated cuisines. Chinese poets and philosophers have mused for centuries on the pleasures of eating, and Chinese cooks have developed a culinary tradition that not only prizes colour, fragrance and flavour, but that also does things with texture that European cooks cannot even imagine. And Chinese cooking isn't just about stir-frying, but involves a vast range of cooking methods, many of which simply cannot be expressed in English. If Chinese cooking in London seems dull and monotonous, something is clearly getting lost in translation…

One of the main problems is that Chinese restaurant food seems to be caught in a deadlock of mutual misunderstanding between Chinese restaurateurs and the customers they serve. Many restaurateurs seem to think that they are catering for the British of the 1960s, for whom even spaghetti was outlandish. Restaurants have an irritating habit of keeping their more interesting dishes on Chinese-language menus, which are beyond the reach of most of their customers, and waiters often try to bulldoze unwary Europeans into ordering set menus that no Chinese would ever order. British customers are also to blame for their unwillingness to shed their narrow stereotypes of Chinese food. To make matters worse, there's a shortage of well-trained Chinese chefs in London, since they can often earn far greater salaries in Hong Kong or Taiwan.

There's also the MSG problem which tends to sully the reputation of Chinese cookery. MSG, or monosodium glutamate, has been widely used in China for the last few decades. It is basically a 'flavour enhancer', but many downmarket Chinese cooks use it as a substitute for proper stocks and sauces. For Chinese people, MSG doesn't have junk food connotations and is treated like any other cooking ingredient; for the British, however, it's always been associated with fast food and artificial flavours. Fortunately, some Chinese restaurateurs are beginning to cotton onto the fact that the use of MSG does them a great disservice in British eyes, and a growing number are rejecting it (the new Chinese chef's school at Westminster College has banished MSG from the cooking curriculum).

To make the most of London's Chinese cooking, the first rule is to avoid the set menus, which are almost always a western parody of Chinese food. Don't worry too much about starters, which are often the least interesting items on the menu, but bear in mind that steamed scallops or cold marinated meats make a pleasant alternative to deep-fried snacks. Then order one main dish for every person in your party, plus one or two extra. Try to mix contrasting ingredients, flavours and cooking methods: a lazy hot-pot to balance a swift stir-fry, a whole steamed fish to offset the richness of a piece of fat roast duck. Fill up with simple steamed rice, which absorbs the flavours of the other dishes and won't leave you feeling that you've overeaten. Keep an eye on what Chinese people are eating at other tables; they may be tucking into seasonal delicacies or enticing dishes from the Chinese menu. And pay serious attention to the specials lists in more adventurous restaurants like **Four Seasons**, **Magic Wok** and **Mr Kong**. These offer the kind of dishes that may revolutionise your view of Chinese cooking.

So where does *Time Out* eat Chinese for pleasure? For dim sum, the best places are **Royal China** (Queensway), the **Golden Dragon** and **New World**. For a special dinner with a group, we like to splash out in the **Mandarin Kitchen** or the grander **Royal China** in Queensway, but for intimate dining and interesting food we head to the **Yming** in Greek Street. **Four Seasons**, **Golden Harvest**, **Magic Wok**, **New Mayflower** and sometimes **Mr Kong** are favourites for a delicious and inexpensive meal, while **Canton** in Newport Place is perfect for a quick plateful of roast duck and rice.

Central

Bloomsbury WC1

Poons
50 Woburn Place, WC1 (020 7580 1188). Russell Square tube. **Meals served** noon-11.30pm daily. **Main courses** £4.60-£13. **Minimum** £5. **Set meals** £9.50-£25 per person (minimum two). **Credit** AmEx, MC, V.
Entering this restaurant is like walking into a 1970s television series. The decor is almost indescribably awful, with enormous brass-lined portholes, a yellow ceramic floor, pink linen and smart but ugly furniture (surely it must be time for a refit?). Nonetheless, the selection of dishes listed on the scuffed menu cards is unusual and appealing, and the cooking can be excellent. Our last visit was a somewhat surreal experience. A starter of minced wind-dried duck with lettuce leaves was delicious, but contained virtually no duck: instead it was made almost entirely with pork. When we complained, the waiters didn't seem to understand that there was a problem. We also ordered a steamed sea bass with mandarin peel, and they gave us a sea bass with ginger and spring onion instead. When quizzed, a waiter said with some embarrassment that they had run out of mandarin peel. As it happens, the fish was so superbly cooked and seasoned that we enjoyed it anyway. Overall, a good meal, but one marred by the staff's unprofessionalism.
Babies and children welcome; high chairs. Booking advisable. **Map 3/4L**.
For branches see index.

---

an ideal welcome to the place. 'Ultra borscht' teamed al dente beetroot chunks with grated beetroot and meaty sliced sausage, giving a full-bodied, sweet-savoury balance; dill and soured cream garnish was a nice touch. 'Decadence zakuski' comprised smoked salmon, smoked sturgeon and keta salmon caviar, with chive sour cream on rounds of fresh rye bread – excellent. 'Roll your own' salmon blini (with thick-cut smoked salmon and soured cream) was good, too, self-assembly heightening the tasty experience. We had no complaints, either, about meaty sausages with mustard sauce and creamy mashed potatoes; and full-flavoured mushroom bitki were winning patties. Side dishes (including kasza with mushroom sauce, al dente cauliflower, and a superb piquant dressing for the green salad) kept up the standard. Ice-cream made a light, creamy conclusion to what was a highly satisfactory meal.
Babies and children welcome. Separate rooms for parties, seating 5 and 8. Takeaway service. **Map 5/12D**.

Trojka
101 Regent's Park Road, NW1 (020 7483 3765). Chalk Farm tube. **Open** 9am-11pm, **meals served** noon-10.30pm, daily. **Main courses** £5.50-£8.50. **Set lunch** (noon-4pm) £6.95 two courses. **Corkage** £3 wine. **Credit** MC, £TC, V.
Attracting a wide range of Euro and Eastern-Euro couples, friends and families, Trojka is an enjoyable, subtly themed affair, as bohemian as Russian. A vibrant colour scheme of lilac below the dado, and lemon-yellow above, provides the backdrop for attractive Russian landscape paintings in antique gilded frames, plus some delightfully kitsch reinterpretations of Russian folk art. One of our starters, however, was an Italian, rather than a Russian, cliché: Trojka mozzarella, avocado and tomato salad featured an unripe avocado as its most memorable component. A sweet borscht was an adequate rendition. To follow, coulebiac was fine, though the accompanying tomato sauce added quite an Italian accent; buckwheat was a better example of the vernacular. Pelmeni had a decent, meaty filling, while a good helping of salt beef was nice, if a little dry. Puddings were unexceptional: a cream cheese pancake seemed a bit heavy, and had a gooey filling; apple charlotte was no more than average.
Babies and children welcome; high chairs. Book dinner Fri-Sun. Entertainment: Russian music 8-10pm Fri, Sat (£1 cover). No-smoking tables. Tables outdoors (3, pavement). Takeaway service. **Map 10**.

Tsar's Bar
Langham Hilton Hotel, 1C Portland Place, W1 (020 7636 1000). Oxford Circus tube. **Open** noon-11pm Mon-Fri; 6-11pm Sat. **Lunch served** noon-2.30pm Mon-Fri. **Dinner served** 6-10.45pm Mon-Sat. **Main courses** £11-£17.50. **Credit** AmEx, DC, JCB, MC, £TC, V.
The attractively panelled Tsar's Bar is lined with oil paintings evoking a nostalgic view of Russian country life (idyllic landscapes and dachas) and city life (elegant street scenes and stylish interiors). As a vodka hub, the bar has a range of bottles that includes some of the finest Polish, Russian and Finnish clear and flavoured styles, not to mention kosher vodka (from £5.50 for 50ml). Many typical Russian dishes are on the menu. Borscht exhibited the classic combination of meaty, beetroot and slightly sweet flavours, but the accompanying buckwheat was slightly overcooked. Pirozhki arrived in the form of a single pie with a lightly singed lid and tough pastry, so a replacement was requested – no problem. No.2 was much better, though the filling was more rice than salmon, but at least the accompanying coleslaw was lifted by the addition of horseradish. Kotlet pozharski was well prepared, with nice mushrooms, though the buttery noodles were a bit limp. Our other main course, pelmeni, had been overcooked, with the filling so firm it resembled meatballs. To finish, a cappuccino cost an excessive £3.50. Service was not always very friendly or efficient; we seemed to be on a time-share scheme between three waiters.
Babies and children admitted. Booking advisable dinner Fri, Sat. Disabled: toilet in hotel. Dress: smart. No smoking. Separate room for parties, seats 60. **Map 2/5H**.

Sheng's Tea House ★
68 Millman Street, WC1 (020 7405 3697). Russell Square or Holborn tube/38 bus. **Lunch served** 11.30am-3pm Mon-Sat. **Dinner served** 5.30-10.30pm. **Main courses** £6-£7.50. **Credit** JCB, MC, V.
This delightful restaurant is run by a garrulous husband-and-wife team; he's Malaysian Chinese, she's Marseillaise. The dining area is nicely decked out with Chinese calligraphy and plenty of red, and there's been traditional Chinese music playing on each of our visits. The food has no pretension to be haute cuisine, but the short menu offers a decent selection of cheerful, home-style dishes. Our starter of squid was succulent and well cooked, with a tasty scattering of garlic and red chillies (although its bed of seaweed turned out to be a few stray wisps), and the pot-sticker dumplings were pleasant if a little bland. A laksa noodle dish was tasty and lovely to look at; a melee of prawns, deep-fried beancurd and squid with snaking vermicelli in a sunset-coloured soup, it was velvety with coconut milk and curry spices. A plateful of fried ho fun (flat rice noodles) with chicken was pretty nice, too, and we approved of the juicy pak choy stir-fried with ginger and garlic. We lunched at an outside table on a glorious summer's day, and almost forgot we were in London.
Babies and children admitted. Disabled: toilet. Takeaway service (free delivery). Vegetarian menu. **Map 3/4M**.

Chinatown W1, WC2

1997 ★
19 Wardour Street, W1 (020 7734 2868). Leicester Square tube. **Meals served** 24 hours daily. **Main courses** £2.20-£28. **Set meals** £9.80-£12.50 (minimum two) per person. **Credit** MC, £TC, V.
This eccentric, informal restaurant is popular among London's young Chinese because of its cheap, simple food and irreverent decor. Poster portraits of Karl Marx, Chairman Mao and Deng Xiaoping hang on the walls, and a free jukebox spills out the melodies of Cantonese pop. The tables are inlaid with mother-of-pearl, and someone has clearly had fun choosing the teapots and other details. The menu is short but we've had some good food here, including fried beancurd with slivers of pork and vegetables. The glossy, chestnut-coloured ducks and barbecued pork hanging over the central counter can be sliced to request, and there's also a number of one-dish dumpling and noodle meals. Staff are generally friendly.
Babies and children admitted. Takeaway service. **Map 13/7K**.

Aroma
118 Shaftesbury Avenue, W1 (020 7437 0377). Leicester Square tube. **Meals served** noon-11.30pm Mon-Sat; noon-10.30pm Sun. **Main courses** £6.20-£28. **Minimum** 7-10pm £9. Set meals £9-£21.20. **Service** 12½%. **Credit** AmEx, DC, JCB, MC, TC, V.
The Aroma restaurants have their fans: this Shaftesbury Avenue branch has won the praise of several food critics. We've always been baffled by this acclaim. The menu is full of promise, but the cooking isn't even the best in Shaftesbury Avenue, let alone in London; we've eaten relentlessly average meals here on a number of occasions. On our last visit the 'numbing-and-hot' jellyfish came soused in an unappealing pickled chilli dressing, while the northern-style grilled prawns, clothed in a robe of soft beaten egg, were succulent in texture but had little flavour. Braised grouper was overwhelmed by its punchy sweet-and-sour sauce, and Chinese broccoli with ginger was lacking in wok fragrance. We can, however, recommend the cold meat platter, which is usually excellent. The restaurant itself is bright and cheery, with yellow walls and tropical fish tanks. Fake flowers and foliage, a display of prestigious liquor bottles and plinky muzak create a cheesy atmosphere, but the staff are friendly and helpful, which helps to explain why the place is always packed.
Babies and children welcome; high chairs. Takeaway service. **Map 13/6K**.
For branch see index.

Canton ★
11 Newport Place, WC2 (020 7437 6220). Leicester Square or Picadilly Circus tube. **Open** noon-midnight daily. **Main courses** £5.20-£9. **Set meal** £12.50 per person. **Credit** AmEx, DC, JCB, MC, £TC, V.
The delicious barbecued pork and roast duck sold in this tiny caff make it a good bet for a takeaway, but it's also great fun for a swift sit-in meal. The rice and noodle-based dishes are tasty and filling, and there's a long menu of other foods for those who desire them. The cooking is nothing special, but this isn't really a foodie restaurant; more a place to fill up when you're out on the town. When we last dropped in we tried beancurd in a spicy sauce – a colourful tumble of ingredients flavoured with pickled chillies – and a simple but nourishing fish and beancurd soup. Sadly, the Chinese broccoli we ordered came with a toxic-tasting oyster sauce, so we scarcely touched it. Service is bustly and led by the friendly and flamboyant Harry and Louis, who seem to be on first-name terms with many of their customers. The cramped space and jovial atmosphere mean you may end up sharing a table, flirting, and even talking to your neighbours (radical stuff in London!).
Babies and children admitted. Separate room for parties, seats 22. Takeaway service. Vegetarian menu. **Map 13/6K**.

China City
White Bear Yard, 25A Lisle Street, WC2 (020 7734 3388). Leicester Square tube. **Meals served** noon-11.45pm Mon-Sat; 11.30am-11.15pm Sun. **Dim sum** noon-5pm Mon-Sat; 11.30am-5pm Sun. **Main courses** , £8.50-£20, £1.70-£3.50 dim sum. **Minimum** £10 per head. **Set meals** £8.50-£20, per person (minimum two). **Service** 10%. **Credit** AmEx, MC, £TC, V.
China City is an oasis of calm amid the hurly-burly of the rest of Chinatown. Set back from the street, it lies behind a small courtyard with flowering pot plants dotted around a gently-flowing fountain. Inside, three pleasant dining floors are pastel-painted and hung with Chinese art. The place is often abuzz with Cantonese chatter, but it's not intimidatingly Chinese, and staff can be delightful. The dumplings may lack the subtlety of Chinatown's finest, but they are fresh, tasty and generously sized. Prawn cheung fun had a good, slithery texture, with nice plump prawns, and roast duck rolls were lip-smackingly good (tender duck, juicy mushrooms and vermicelli cradled in a rice pasta sheet). 'Ningbo-style' dumplings from the specials menu were intriguingly textured, with skins of puckered wheaten pastry. In the past, steamed lotus with bamboo web, a sweet, chilled soup afloat with diaphanous white wood ear fungus, lacy bamboo pith fungus and lotus seeds has also been a good bet.
Babies and children welcome; high chairs. Book Fri, Sat. No-smoking tables. Separate rooms for parties, seating 10-45. Takeaway service. **Map 13/7K**.

Chuen Cheng Ku
17 Wardour Street, W1 (020 7437 1398/020 7734 3509). Leicester Square or Piccadilly Circus tube. **Meals served** 11am-11.45pm Mon-Sat; 11am-11.15pm Sun. **Dim sum** 11am-5.45pm daily. **Main courses** £5.50-£9.50, £1.80 dim sum. **Set meals** £26 per person (minimum two). **Credit** AmEx, DC, JCB, MC, £TC, V.
Gone are the days when you had to queue for a table in this enormous restaurant. The dim sum buzz has moved elsewhere, but the illustrated menus are still a boon for novices, and prices are among the cheapest in Chinatown. Like the New World restaurant round the corner, CCK uses the trolley system, so you can order whatever takes your fancy as it glides past in a trail of steam. Waitresses will rustle up a bowl of noodles as you watch, or sauté a slab of turnip paste on a mobile hot-plate. Dumplings tend to be on the stodgy side, but are often tasty. Favourites include steamed scallop dumplings interwoven with the taste of Chinese mushrooms, and char siu cheung fun generously packed with fragments of barbecued pork. The green peppers stuffed with a mixture of minced prawn and pork were succulent and gently crunchy, and the deep-fried prawn dumplings were crisp, if a little ungainly. The dining rooms have a slightly jaded look, with their patterned wallpaper and chandeliers, but staff are usually friendly.
Babies and children welcome; high chairs. Booking advisable. No-smoking tables. Separate rooms for parties, seating 42, 60, 100 and 180. Takeaway service. Vegetarian menu. **Map 13/7K**.

Fung Shing
15 Lisle Street, WC2 (020 7437 1539). Leicester Square or Piccadilly Circus tube. **Meals served** noon-11.30pm daily. **Main courses** £5.95-£60. **Minimum** £8.50 after 6.30pm. **Set meals** £25-£30. **Service** 10%. **Credit** AmEx, DC, MC, £TC, V.
The walls of Fung Shing are hung with culinary awards, but the place is still riding on the reputation of the late Chef Fu, who took the place to legendary gastronomic heights in the 1980s. These days the quality of the cooking is erratic, and the restaurant isn't much patronised by Chinese. The interesting menu features a number of extravagant traditional dishes involving dried seafood. In the past we've enjoyed a delicate 'shark's fin in basket', one of Mr Fu's prize-winning creations. On our last visit, however, the food wasn't so impressive. 'Chilli fish' came in a fruity sweet-and-sour sauce which was gently laced with chilli: the sweet and sour notes were unduly aggressive. Fish maw with crab meat was an example of the mild, gelatinous comfort food loved by the Cantonese; texturally interesting but somewhat bland. Our best dish was the delicious Bechalan water spinach, a Southeast Asian-inspired concoction involving plenty of garlic and little salted fish. The back dining room is delightful, with its yellow paint and high ceiling; the front part of the restaurant pleasant but ordinary. Staff are charming, helpful and chatty.
Babies and children welcome; high chairs. Book dinner. Separate rooms for parties, seating 30 and 50. Takeaway service. **Map 13/7K**.

Golden Dragon ★
28-29 Gerrard Street, W1 (020 7734 2763). Leicester Square or Piccadilly Circus tube. **Meals served** noon-11.30pm Mon-Thur; noon-midnight Fri, Sat; 11am-11pm Sun. **Dim sum** noon-5pm Mon-Sat; 11am-5pm Sun. **Main courses** £6-£20, £1.80-£3.50 dim sum. **Minimum** £10. **Set meals** £10 per person (minimum two)-£20 per person (minimum five). **Service** 10%. **Credit** AmEx, DC, MC, £TC, V.
Still Chinatown's premier dim sum restaurant, the Golden Dragon serves reliably excellent snacks in the noisy, bustling atmosphere much loved by Chinese diners-out. Waiters charge around bearing tottering towers of bamboo steamers; dumplings and other delicacies are invariably dainty and freshly cooked. Dishes from the main menu are also of a high standard. We savoured a hot-pot of buttery-fleshed aubergines and minced pork, infused with the strong taste of smoked fish, and a huge platter laden with roast duck braised with beancurd, fragrant mushrooms and pak choy. Pea shoots, stir-fried with garlic, were superbly juicy and tender, and the only disappointment was a plateful of unexceptional steamed scallops. The two dining rooms are smartly Chinese, with plenty of red and gold, and carved golden dragons curling up the pillars: perfect for a celebratory lunch. Service is mostly efficient, although cracks sometimes appear under the pressures of the weekend feeding frenzy. Midweek the restaurant is more serene.
Babies and children admitted. Booking advisable. Separate rooms for parties, seating 10 and 40. Takeaway service. Vegetarian set meal. **Map 13/7K**.

Golden Harvest ★
17 Lisle Street, WC2 (020 7287 3822). Leicester Square or Piccadilly Circus tube. **Meals served** noon-2.45am daily. **Main courses** £3.95-£40. **Minimum** £5 from 5pm. **Set meals** £6.95-£25. **Service** 10%. **Credit** MC, V.
The food in this unpretentious restaurant has a clarity and freshness that makes it one of our favourites in Chinatown. The seafood steam-pot (which is not on the English-language menu) is an exceptional dish, featuring a vast platter piled high with fruits of the sea – a whole lobster, oysters, languid wreaths of squid, king prawns and arctic clams – as well as chunks of shuddering beancurd, skeins of beanthread noodles, raw sliced meats and crunchy green leaves. All you need to do is pluck morsels from this ravishing array and cook them in the soup that is left simmering in the centre of the table. The sheer sensuousness of this dish makes it perfect for an evening of seduction. Also highly recommended are fried lamb with sweet basil and aubergine, which never fails to satisfy, and the marvellous baked clams in black bean sauce. More everyday dishes like chicken with cashew nuts and sizzling beef are decently cooked but dull by comparison. Keep an eye on what Chinese customers are ordering and you might catch seasonal specials such as a New Year's salad involving raw salmon and a rainbow of pickled vegetables, drizzled with sesame seeds and a sweet plum sauce.
Babies and children welcome; high chairs. Booking advisable. Takeaway service. **Map 13/7K**.

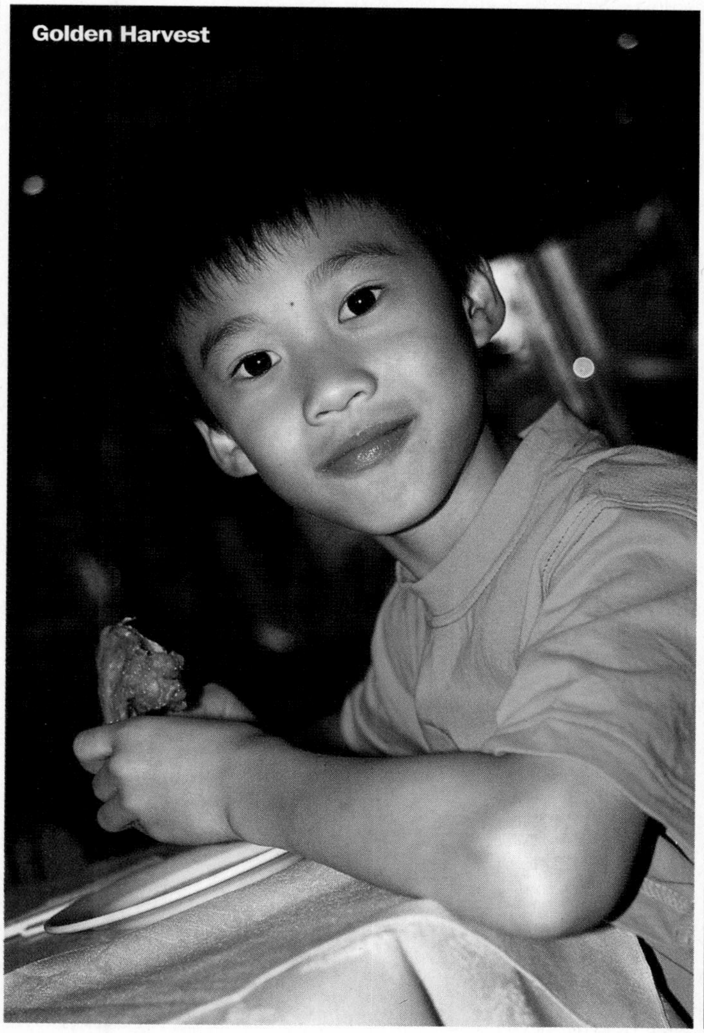
Golden Harvest

Harbour City

46 Gerrard Street, W1 (020 7439 7859/ 020 7287 1526). Leicester Square or Piccadilly Circus tube. **Meals served** noon-11.30pm Mon-Thur; noon-midnight Fri, Sat; 10.30am-10.30pm Sun. **Dim sum** noon-5pm Mon-Sat; **Main courses** £5.50-£20, £1.80-£2.50 dim sum. **Set meals** £12.50-£25 per person (minimum two). **Service** 10%. **Credit** AmEx, DC, JCB, MC, £TC, V.

A good middle-of-the-road Cantonese restaurant, Harbour City is best known for its dim sum, but the main dinner dishes can also impress. We liked both the cold qing ping chicken (from the Chinese menu), with its firm, moist and almost crisp flesh, served with a garlic and vinegar dip, and a fine rendition of stuffed beancurd, pepper and aubergines. The peppers were delectably al dente, the aubergines deliciously browned, and everything was piled up enticingly in a light black bean sauce, with a splash of green coriander on top. The beef with pickled vegetables was an unusual dish, with a nice strain of sourness from the mustard greens, although the meat was rather tough. The dining rooms, on three floors, are clean and spruce; the second floor, in particular, has plenty of windows and is very congenial for a dim sum lunch. Waiting staff can be dour, but tend to warm up if you express a spirit of gastronomic adventure.
Babies and children welcome; high chairs. Book weekends. Separate room for parties, seats 40-80. Takeaway service. Vegetarian menu. **Map 13/7K.**

Hing Loon

25 Lisle Street, WC2 (020 7437 3602/ 020 7287 0419). Leicester Square or Piccadilly Circus tube. **Meals served** noon-11.30pm daily. **Main courses** £3.60-£15. **Set meals** £5.80, £7.50, £9.50, per person (minimum two). **Unlicensed. Corkage** no charge. **Credit** AmEx, MC, £TC, V.

This tiny, cramped restaurant is ideal for a swift, cheap meal on your way to somewhere else. Food tends to arrive with preternatural speed, and is simple but decently cooked. Our advice is to order the simple one-dish meals, based on rice, noodles or congee with all kinds of toppings, or the dishes on the short specials menu, which include some unusual treats like stir-fried water spinach with fermented beancurd, bitter melon with beef, and five-spiced duck's kidneys (delicious; try them). The rest of the menu includes lurid sweet-and-sours and other very standard Chinese restaurant fare. There's little room in the microscopic downstairs dining room; upstairs is brighter and more relaxed. Staff at Hing Loon are invariably friendly and efficient.
Babies and children admitted. Bookings not accepted dinner Fri, Sat. Takeaway service. **Map 13/7K.**

Hong Kong

6-7 Lisle Street, WC2 (020 7287 0352). Leicester Square or Piccadilly Circus tube. **Meals served** noon-11.30pm Mon-Sat. **Dim sum** noon-5pm daily. **Main courses** £4.50-£8.80, £1.80-£2 dim sum. **Set meals** £10-£14 per person (minimum two). **Service** 10%. **Credit** AmEx, MC, V.

One of Chinatown's better dim sum specialists, Hong Kong can also seduce with its main-menu cooking, if you manage to order it. On our last visit we asked for more information about a couple of dishes and a surly waiter tried to bulldoze us into taking a boring set menu. We persisted, and when he saw we were serious he mellowed and became smiley and helpful. The highlight of our meal was a stunningly good chiu chow mandarin duck: sumptuously moist, replete with flavour and served with a vinegar dip that was a sublime and wholly successful contrast to the richness of the meat: one of the best dishes we've tasted in Chinatown. The barbecued pork in honey sauce was also exceptionally fine. A chef's special starter of raw surf clams with jellyfish was less inspiring, but the clams in chilli and black bean sauce and a steamed sea bass were suitably fresh and tasty. We always like to sit in the bustling ground-floor dining room; the basement is far less agreeable.
Babies and children welcome; high chairs. Booking advisable. Separate room for parties, seats 25. Takeaway service. **Map 13/7K.**

Jade Garden

15 Wardour Street, W1 (020 7437 5065). Leicester Square or Piccadilly Circus tube. **Meals served** noon-midnight daily. **Dim sum** noon-4.30pm Mon-Sat; 11am-4.30pm Sun. **Main courses** £7-£19, £1.70-£3 dim sum. **Set meals** £11.50-£21.00 per person (minimum two). **Service** 10%. **Credit** AmEx, DC, MC, £TC, V.

This chirpy Wardour Street restaurant scores on atmosphere, with its bright front dining room, lovely mezzanine floor, and posters of Shanghai cigarette girls smiling down from the walls. The illustrated menu is enticing, but we've found the dim sum here consistently mediocre, despite its popularity among the Cantonese. The cooks obviously have a penchant for the chemical paintbox: some of our vegetable garnishes were an alarming purple, and the deep-fried squid was too yellow to be true. We do like the comforting chicken congee (rice porridge), though, with its scattering of green spring onion. Duck and preserved vegetable dumplings are also pleasant enough, but scallop and lobster dumplings, like the dried scallop dumplings, were over elaborate and lacking in flavour. Prawns in the gently slithery cheung fun were also disappointingly bland. The main menu gallivants proudly over an unusual range of seafood, with several concoctions involving shark's fin and other exotica, and the range of interesting teas is a treat. Service is generally friendly and efficient.
Babies and children welcome; high chairs. Booking advisable. Separate room for parties, seats 60. Takeaway service. **Map 13/7K.**

Jen

7 Gerrard Street, W1 (020 7287 8193). Leicester Square or Piccadilly Circus tube. **Meals served** noon-3am daily. **Main courses** £5.50-£9. **Minimum** £8.50 after 7pm. **Set lunches** (noon-5pm) £4.50-£7. **Set meals** £9-£18 per person (minimum two). **Service** 10%. **Credit** AmEx, MC, £TC, V.

One of the newer restaurants in Chinatown, Jen lures potential customers with a mouthwatering display of roasted ducks and barbecued pork. The menu is unusually inventive, featuring many weird and wonderful Chinese ingredients; there's even a whole section devoted to frog's legs. Highlights include the double-boiled soups, which can be exceptionally rich and satisfying; two different versions are offered each day. We lapped up a delicate, soothing brew of abalone, fish maw, chicken claws, Chinese mushrooms, fish lips and herbs. We also enjoyed the chicken steamed in a lotus leaf with Chinese dates, wolfberries and morsels of intensely flavoured Yunnan ham, served attractively in a bamboo steamer. The stewed spare ribs in honey vinegar sauce, first deep-fried and then braised in a dark, treacly liquid with lashings of onion and whole garlic, was a hearty home-style dish. A stir-fry of fresh and pickled mustard greens with minced pork was rather carelessly thrown together and undercooked, although the juices were delicious. The restaurant is simply but attractively furnished. We had great fun chatting to our waiter, who seemed to take a pleasure in his work.
Babies and children welcome; high chairs. Booking advisable. Separate room for parties, seats 13, 15. Takeaway service. **Map 13/6K.**

Joy King Lau

3 Leicester Street, WC2 (020 7437 1133/ 1132). Leicester Square or Piccadilly Circus tube. **Meals served** noon-11.30pm Mon-Sat; 11am-10.30pm Sun. **Dim sum** noon-5.45pm Mon-Sat, 11am-4.45pm Sun. **Main courses** £5.50-£8.50, £1.80-£2.50 dim sum. **Set meals** £8.50 per person (minimum two)-£35 per person (minimum eight). **Credit** AmEx, DC, JCB, MC, £TC, V.

This discreet, elegant restaurant draws Cantonese lunchers away from the bustle of Lisle and Gerrard streets. The main dining rooms are attractively fitted out with mirrors, latticework panels and East Asian art, with a plainer fourth floor providing overflow space on busy Sunday afternoons. The dim sum is generally fresh and tasty, although standards sometimes slip. We relished the contrasting textures of the chiu chow fun quor, steamed rice dumplings stuffed with a mixture of pork, shrimps, peanuts and crunchy vegetables, and also enjoyed the sweet succulence of the prawn and scallop dumplings. The turnip paste and the cheung fun were a little stodgy, but the Chinese mushroom dumplings were made with moist, crisp prawns, each topped with a luscious mushroom 'hat'. The prawns in rice paper were on the greasy side, but had a delicious, well-seasoned filling. Drop in at weekend lunchtimes to enjoy the Chinese family atmosphere here.
Babies and children welcome; high chairs. Book weekends. Separate rooms for parties (three), seating 10-60. Takeaway service. **Map 13/7K.**

Mr Kong ★

21 Lisle Street, WC2 (020 7437 7341/9679). Leicester Square or Piccadilly Circus tube. **Meals served** noon-2.45am daily. **Main courses** £6-£26. **Minimum** £7 after 5pm. **Set meals** £9.30- per person (minimum two)-£25 per person (minimum four). **Credit** AmEx, DC, JCB, MC, £TC, V.

Mr Kong's is a prime example of the 'one restaurant, two systems' phenomenon in the Chinese catering trade. The same kitchen turns out two entirely different styles of cooking: standard Chinese restaurant fare for British customers and tourists, and delicious, unusual Cantonese dishes for Chinese customers. Some of the good dishes appear on the main menu, but our advice to curious Europeans is to stick more-or-less entirely to the specials menu if you want to make the most of Mr Kong. We were bowled over by a hot-pot of stewed lamb belly with Chinese herbs: the meat was simply melting off the bone, into a sumptuously rich stock scattered with wolfberries, Chinese dates and various medicinal roots. The dish was served with a light, fresh dip of vinegar, chilli and coriander, which cut perfectly the richness of the meat. Another dish we have enjoyed on many occasions is the baby squid with shrimp paste, which has an unusual and delicious flavour. The dining rooms are somewhat cramped, but bright and cheery, and staff are uncommonly friendly and co-operative for Chinatown.
Babies and children welcome; high chairs. Book dinner Fri, Sat. Separate room for parties, seats 20. Takeaway service. **Map 13/7K.**

New Diamond

23 Lisle Street, WC2 (020 7437 2517/7221). Leicester Square or Piccadilly Circus tube. **Meals served** noon-3am daily. **Main courses** £5.50-£22. **Minimum** £8. **Set meals** £10.50-£16 per person (minimum two). **Credit** AmEx, DC, MC, £TC, V.

In the past this tiny restaurant has wowed us with its subtle sauces and graceful use of cooking heat. On our last visit the food wasn't quite as fine, although we heartily enjoyed some dishes. The spicy salted squid was wonderfully succulent and seasoned perfectly, and a duck and yam hot-pot came in a dark, mellow sauce, aroused by hints of mandarin peel. A sea bass was nicely done, but someone seemed to have burnt the garlic in our pipa beancurd, which was pleasingly textured but a little bitter. A simple stir-fry of peashoots was lacking in flavour, and a touch underdone. The English-language menu is unusually challenging, with Chinese folk dishes like fish head hot-pot and at least one concoction involving the webbed feet of ducks. The dining room is narrow and a bit of a tight squeeze, but pleasant enough, and the staff are most helpful.
Babies and children welcome; high chairs. Booking advisable. Takeaway service. **Map 13/7K.**

New Hoo Wah

37-38 Gerrard Street, W1 (020 7434 0521). Leicester Square or Piccadilly Circus tube. **Meals served** noon-11.30pm Mon-Thur; noon-11.45pm Fri, Sat; 11am-10.30pm Sun. **Main courses** £6-£16, £1.70-£3.50 dim sum (noon-5pm daily). **Set meals** £9.50-£20 per person (minimum two). **Service** 10%. **Credit** AmEx, DC, MC, £TC, V.

This imposing dim sum specialist has the kind of large, festive dining room which Cantonese people adore, and offers an unusually large range of lunchtime titbits. Despite the imaginative menu, however, the quality of the food is fairly shaky. Pan-fried dumplings with diced shrimp and chive were attractive and tasty, but had rather tough skins; beancurd rolls with needle mushrooms, by contrast, fell apart as we tried to eat them. The Shanghai-style steamed meat buns were lacking in their vital juiciness, although we enjoyed the chilli oil dumplings. In the past we've found the staff here pleasant and co-operative, but on our last visit the waiters were negligent and positively unfriendly; an off day we hope.
Babies and children welcome; high chairs. Booking advisable. Separate room for parties, seats 40. Takeaway service. **Map 13/6K.**

New Mayflower

68-70 Shaftesbury Avenue, W1 (020 7734 9207). Piccadilly Circus tube. **Meals served** 5pm-4am daily. **Main courses** £5.90-£24.

Chinese regional cookery

One of the most amazing things about Chinese food is its regional diversity. In southern China in particular, almost every county town has its own speciality, whether it's a local wild vegetable or a certain kind of dumpling. Over the years, a number of distinct regional cuisines have also emerged. Broadly speaking, there is fresh Cantonese cooking in the south; spicy, intensely flavoured cooking in Sichuan and Hunan in the south-west; sweeter, oilier cooking in the eastern coastal areas and Shanghai; and northern cookery which is usually typified by the use of certain ingredients like lamb and spring onions, and by certain famous dishes like Peking duck and Mongolian hot-pot, rather than any dominant flavouring style.

Sadly, very little of this regional diversity is reflected in London's restaurant culture. Most of the more established Chinese immigrants are Cantonese people who came to the UK via Hong Kong, so there's an inevitable southern bias in the capital's cooking skills. You'll certainly find a few famous regional dishes on London restaurant menus, such as Sichuanese ma po beancurd and Peking duck: most of them, however, are not only tailored to western palates, but also cooked according to the taste preferences of the Cantonese themselves, with their traditional dislike of spicy food. Extravagant promises of Sichuanese or Shanghainese cuisine are usually just examples of canny marketing by Cantonese restaurateurs eager to persuade you that they have something different to sell. Even **Mao Tai**, which calls itself a Sichuanese restaurant and has a menu dominated by famous Sichuan dishes, offers little in the way of genuine Sichuanese food.

The only restaurant that makes a real attempt to specialise in western Chinese cooking is **Hunan** in Pimlico, where we've enjoyed some good spicy dishes. **Kai** in Mayfair also offers one or two good renditions of classic Sichuan fare. Eastern Chinese food is almost impossible to find in London, although a few Shanghainese snacks like steamed xiao long bao (siu loon bao) dumplings have become part of the Cantonese dim sum tradition.

Wheat rather than rice is the staple food of the northern Chinese, with steamed bread, noodles and dumplings dominating the local diet. The culinary influence of the Mongolian herders to the north is felt in the use of lamb in stir-fries and in the famous Mongolian hot-pot, which consists of wafer-thin slices of raw lamb, beanthread noodles and other foods which are all cooked in a simmering pot on the table. The **Golden Harvest** in Lisle Street offers a fabulous Cantonese seafood version of this dish. Beijing's most famous delicacy is, of course, Peking duck, which is traditionally wind-dried and then roasted to caramelised perfection in a hanging oven. If you go to specialist duck restaurants in Beijing, you will first be served the crisp, fatty duck skin with pancakes, fresh spring onions and cucumbers and a sweet fermented paste; then the flesh, stir-fried with beansprouts, and finally a milky soup made from the carcass of the duck. In London, several restaurants will make you a Peking duck if you give them 24 hours' notice (to allow them to marinate and wind-dry it); we can vouch for the version offered by **North China** in Ealing. Otherwise, you will have to be content with crispy aromatic duck, a Sichuanese treat which London restaurants now serve in the Peking style.

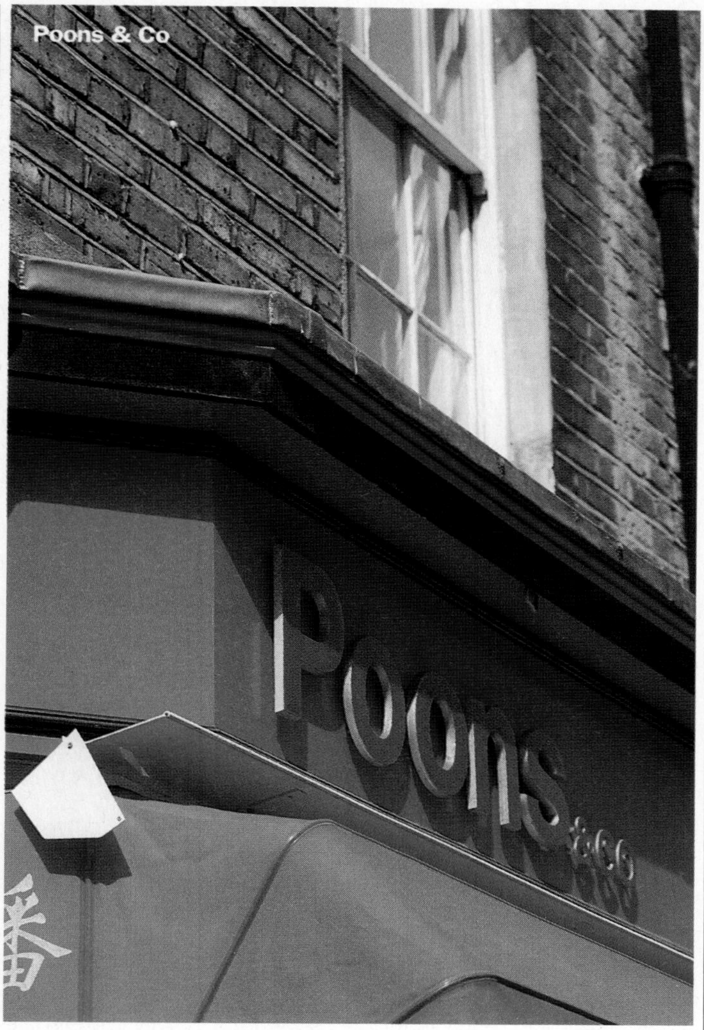

Poons & Co

Minimum £8. **Set dinners** £11, £13, per person (minimum two). **Service** 10%. **Credit** AmEx, MC, V.
This noisy, crowded restaurant may not offer Chinatown's most luxurious dining, but the food is reliably good. The place is also worth bearing in mind if you find yourself hungry at an unlikely hour, because it's open daily until 4am. Over the past few months, we've tucked into a scrumptious mixed seafood with salt and chilli, and a rich, buttery rendition of fish-fragrant aubergines. The belly pork with yam – a slow-cooked traditional dish from the Chinese menu – is mellow and comforting, and there's also a mean stir-fry of spinach with fermented beancurd. Everything is served in hearty portions. Many interesting dishes are left untranslated on the Chinese menu, so it's worth keeping an eye on what Chinese customers nearby are ordering. Staff can be brusque, but tend to be friendly if you express an interest in the food.
Babies and children welcome; high chairs. Booking essential 7-10.30pm. Takeaway service. **Map 13/7K.**

New World

1 Gerrard Place, W1 (020 7734 0396). Leicester Square or Piccadilly Circus tube.
Meals served 11am-11.45pm Mon-Thur; 11am-12.15am Fri, Sat; 11am-11pm Sun. **Dim sum** 11am-6pm daily. **Main courses** £4.35-£8.80, £1.70-£3.50 dim sum. **Set meals** £7.50 per person pre-theatre menu, £26 per person (minimum five). **Credit** AmEx, DC, JCB, MC, £TC, V.
There's something captivating about the sheer scale of the New World, with its three dining floors, 700 covers and flamboyant red-and-gold chinoiserie. At lunchtime on Sundays the place is usually packed with Chinese families, but it's so enormous that you never have to queue for long. Dim sum are dispensed from circulating trolleys, which sometimes makes it hard to concentrate on your own table as your eyes and nose follow the trail of some enticing dumpling. On our last visit the food was impressive. We caught the taro croquettes fresh from the kitchen, their hot, crisp flesh encasing a creamy pork filling. Beancurd rolls stuffed with pork were juicy and delicious, and the deep-fried prawn balls encased in ribbony strips of noodle were an unusual treat. One of the weekend specials, mussels in black bean sauce, looked wonderful but tasted of little: the only real disappointment in a satisfying meal. Go with a large group of friends and you're bound to have a lazy, greedy, delightful time at no great expense.
Babies and children welcome; high chairs. Bookings not accepted Sun. Separate rooms for parties, seating 10-200. Takeaway service. **Map 13/6K.**

Poons & Co

26-27 Lisle Street, WC2 (020 7437 4549). Leicester Square or Piccadilly Circus tube.
Meals served noon-11.30pm daily. **Main courses** £2.60-£8.20. **Set meals** £7.50-£17.50 per person (minimum two). **Credit** AmEx, DC, JCB, MC, V.
This unassuming caff in Lisle Street is one of Chinatown's earliest Chinese restaurants, and still going strong. Sometimes the cooking is nothing to write home about, but on our last visit they surprised us with the magnificence of our simple meal. A large pot of steamed rice topped with the house speciality, wind-dried meats, was delectable, with mellow, treacly sausages and dark, smoky duck. The steamed minced pork (a typical Cantonese dish which Europeans rarely try) was succulent and perfectly seasoned, and came topped with green spring onions and a tranche of punchy smoked fish. Most delicious of all was a halved aubergine, which had been briefly deep-fried and then steamed into melting, buttery submission. This home-style Cantonese lunch was a rare treat in London, and much nicer than the day-glo sweet-and-sours which most Europeans order in Chinese restaurants. Service at Poons & Co can be brisk and impatient; tables are cramped and decor is functional, but if they feed us like this, we'll be back for more…
Babies and children admitted. Booking advisable Fri, Sat. Separate rooms for parties, seats 25. Takeaway service. Vegetarian menu. **Map 13/7K.**
For branches see index.

Royal Dragon

30 Gerrard Street, W1 (0207 734 0935). Leicester Square or Piccadilly Circus tube.
Meals served noon-3am Mon-Sat; 11am-3am Sun. **Dim sum** noon-5pm. **Main courses** £5.80-£7.50, £1.70-£3.70 dim sum. **Set meals** £9.80 four courses, £23 (mininum two). **Service** 10%. **Credit** AmEx, JCB, MC, £TC, V.
This cosy restaurant may not have the pzazz of the neighbouring Golden Dragon, but on our last visit the dim sum were impressive. Our steamed scallop dumplings were delicate and thinly wrapped, with a subtle, juicy filling, and the creamy turnip paste was exemplary. Some Shanghainese xiao long bao from the Chinese specials menu were pleasantly moist and savoury, and we loved the crisp wrappers and plump prawny stuffing of our beancurd skin rolls. The restaurant is larger than it appears from outside, but a little cramped nonetheless. Fresh, bright walls and understated decor make the most of the limited space. Staff on our visit were pleasant and friendly, and allowed us to enjoy a relaxed lunch over the Sunday papers.
Babies and children welcome; high chairs. Separate room for parties, seating 15, 30. Takeaway service. Vegetarian menu.
Map 13/7K.

Wong Kei ★

41-43 Wardour Street, W1 (020 7437 8408/3071). Leicester Square or Piccadilly Circus tube. **Meals served** noon-11.30pm daily. **Main courses** £4.80-£7.80. **Set meal** £6.50 per person (minimum two). **No cheques or credit cards.**
Regulars adore this cavernous restaurant, with its cheap, no-frills Cantonese food and notoriously surly waiters. One veteran customer claims that it's the Chinese equivalent of McDonalds, with cooking that has been 'exactly the same for the last ten years.' Others wax lyrical about the brisk, buzzy atmosphere and cheap prices, and some people even claim to appreciate the food. The bargain meals which tend to attract students and other budget eaters are the one-plate rice and noodle dishes, some of them topped with the roast duck and barbecued pork hanging by the entrance. Our rice noodles (chow ho fun) were soggy and stuck together in a heavy mass, but at least the beef in the black bean topping was tender. A bowlful of congee with sliced pork was plain and comforting if slightly oversalted. Other dishes tend to be heavy and hearty, with a certain murkiness in the sauces. In case you were wondering, most of the items listed in Chinese characters at the end of the menu involve offal products such as pig's intestines and tripe. Waiting staff are not as spectacularly rude as legend suggests, but will still chivvy you through your meal and cram you onto tables with other diners, even if the place is half-empty.
Babies and children admitted. Takeaway service. **Map 13/7K.**

City EC3

Imperial City

Royal Exchange, Cornhill, EC3 (020 7626 3437). Monument tube/Bank tube/DLR.
Meals served 11.30am-9pm Mon-Fri. **Main courses** £4.95-£11.90. **Set meals** £15.99, £19.99, £25.99, per person (minimum two). **Service** 12½%. **Credit** AmEx, DC, JCB, MC, TC, V.
This attractive restaurant in the vaulted cellars of the old Royal Exchange is popular with City types, so it's generally filled with suits, including a few Chinese faces. Bonsai trees are scattered around and water tumbles over a small rockery at one end of the restaurant. Clever touches of chinoiserie include a golden dragon snaking along a large pipe attached to the ceiling, and little bamboo seedlings on every table. The menu includes some interesting dishes, but the food is unexceptional and tailored to western tastes. We enjoyed starters of crisp spring rolls filled with a mix of vermicelli, slivered carrot and wood ear fungus, and tender monkfish in a ginger sauce, but main courses were dull and meanly portioned. The fresh prawns came in a cloyingly sweet spicy sauce, and the imperial stuffed chicken was disappointingly bland. The wine list is good – one advantage of a restaurant aimed at non-Chinese customers – and service was better than on our last visit, but still suffered from a lack of co-ordination.
Babies and children admitted. Book lunch. Dress: smart casual. Separate room for parties, seats 16. Takeaway service. **Map 4/6Q.**

Poons in the City

2 Minster Pavement, Minster Court, Mincing Lane, EC3 (020 7626 0126). Monument tube.
Meals served 11.30am-10.30pm Mon-Fri. **Main courses** £4.80-£8.60 incl £1.60 cover. **Set meals** (restaurant) £14.50-£30.80 per person (minimum two). **Credit** AmEx, DC, MC, £TC, V.
There's something charmingly surreal about this oasis of Old World chinoiserie tucked in the basement of one of the City's most futuristic buildings. Up above, a vast edifice of pink stone and glass towers into the sky; while down below it's all antique furniture inlaid with mother-of-pearl and waitresses decked out in silken qi pao. The main dining area is particularly elegant, with displays of Chinese ceramics and interesting pictures on the walls, and there are a couple of private rooms available for larger parties. Sadly, the food is resolutely mediocre; on our last visit, nothing was really bad, but nothing danced either. We began with a starter of roast duck, soya chicken and barbecued pork, which was pleasant but a little insipid. Later, a stir-fry of scallops in black bean sauce was very pedestrian; the scallops had been sliced up to make them go further, which of course deprived them of much of their texture. Lotus-leaf rice, mixed up with shrimps, pork, peas and egg, was served rather inelegantly in a pyrex dish, and a red-braised beancurd was unmemorable. Our waitresses, however, were very friendly and helpful.
Babies and children admitted. Book lunch. Disabled: toilet. Separate rooms for parties, seating 12-26. Tables outdoors (5, garden). Takeaway service. **Map 4/7R.**

Knightsbridge SW1

Mr Chow

151 Knightsbridge, SW1 (020 7589 7347). Knightsbridge tube. **Lunch served** 12.30-3pm, **dinner served** 7pm-midnight daily. **Set meals** £24 two courses, £28 three courses incl £1 cover. **Service** 12½%. **Credit** AmEx, DC, JCB, MC, £TC, V.
This sleek Knightsbridge restaurant has a certain eternal quality. It was set up in 1968, when Michael Chow decided to create a restaurant that married the best of East and West: Chinese savoury dishes with French puddings and Italian waiters. It proved so successful that little has changed, except perhaps for the funky modern art, which currently includes a few silver Peking ducks suspended from a rail. The menu is simple, elegant and interesting, and the food can be excellent. On our last visit the chef was playing a little too freely with the salt, but we did enjoy a dexterously cooked smoked chicken, and the With Three stir-fry, in which chicken, prawns and scallops had been heated to velvety, succulent perfection. Lamb with spring onions was pleasant enough, but lacking in flavour and the pak choy was dull and watery. The wine list is a serious one, as you'd expect of a restaurant with branches in Los Angeles and New York, and the downstairs dining room is smart but intimate, with dark mirrored panels, traditional Chinese chairs and sensitive lighting. Service is usually superb, although last time around our Italian waiter was a little bit gruff.
Babies and children admitted. Booking advisable. Dress: smart casual. Separate rooms for parties, seating 10, 30 and 75. **Map 12/9F.**

Veg Veg

8 Egerton Garden Mews, SW3 (020 7584 7007). Knightsbridge or South Kensington tube. **Meals served** 12.30-10pm daily. **Main courses** £5-£25. **No credit cards.**
This cosy basement restaurant specialises in Chinese Buddhist cookery (fo zhai cai), which often involves the recreation of traditional meat and fish dishes using purely vegetarian ingredients and not a little ingenuity. The fun lies in the fact that the menu looks like a standard Chinese restaurant menu, but the crispy duck with pancakes is actually deep-fried beancurd, and the beef is made from soya protein. On our last visit we quite enjoyed the vegetarian dim sum, which were dumplings stuffed with beanthread noodles, mushrooms and other nice titbits, although they were undersalted and crying out for a strong-tasting dip. A hot and sour soup was good and peppery, and the crispy veg duck with pancakes was delicious. The restaurant itself is attractively furnished, with a wooden floor, red tablecloths and arty Chinese decorations.
Babies and children admitted. No smoking. Separate room for parties, seats 20. Takeaway service. **Map 12/10E.**

SHANGHAI

EXPERIENCE THE DIFFERENCE

A modernised quality Chinese restaurant in an 18th Century listed building, specialising in Shanghai Cuisine

Enjoy our exquisite chef's regional specialities and be pampered and doted on by our friendly and courteous staff...
...or extend your evening fun with our advanced sound and vision karaoke system in our party rooms.

"...Shanghai is the local Chinese of your dreams ...visit it even if you don't live nearby"
-Time Out

"...the best Chinese food I've had in a long time..."
-Sunday Times

"...it is certainly worth the journey because I cannot remember when I have enjoyed a Chinese meal so thoroughly..."
-What's On

"...We tried various dishes described as Shanghai-style and were not disappointed..."
-Evening Standard

Opening Hours
Mon to Fri: 12noon-3.00pm
5pm-11.00pm
Sat & Sun: 12noon-11.00pm

41 Kingsland High St. Dalston, London, E8 2JS

Tel: 020 7254 2878 or 020 7254 9322
Fax: 020 7249 9271

WENG WAH HOUSE
Karaoke • Chinese Restaurant

COME FOR A PLEASANT SURPRISE

- Friendly atmosphere
- Authentic Oriental recipe
- 60 seated ground floor
- 70 seated party level
- Unique karaoke experience
- Children welcome

Relax and enjoy your meal in a warm modern setting, with authentic oriental cuisine, or celebrate your special occasion in our party floor equipped with state of the art karaoke system. Music ranging from the latest chart toppers to all time classics.

"...we had a smashing time...cost wasn't extortionate for the area..."
Time Out

"...I think we've found the premier North West London karaoke room..."
What's On

Opening times
Mon to Fri: 12.30-2.45pm & 6.00pm-11.30pm
Sat: 12.30 - midnight   Sun: 12.30-11.15pm
open all day Bank Holiday Mondays 12.30pm-11.30pm
240 Haverstock Hill Belsize Park London NW3 28E
Tel: 020 7794 5123/431 4502 Fax: 020 7431 8620

Also at :

SEE WOO BUFFET
7-13 Station Road,
Edgware, Middlesex,
HA8 7RY
Tel: 020 8952 7666
Fax: 020 8951 4467

HAINANESE BUFFET
63 Golders Green Road,
Golders Green, London,
NW11 8EL
Tel: 020 8455 0704
Fax: 020 8455 7954

Marylebone W1

Royal China

40 Baker Street, W1 (020 7487 4688). Baker Street tube. **Meals served** noon-11pm Mon-Thur; noon-11.30pm Fri, Sat; 11am-10pm Sun. **Main courses** £8-£30, £3-£5 dim sum, **Minimum** dinner £10. **Set meals** £25 per person (minimum two). **Service** 12½%. **Credit** AmEx, MC, £TC, V.

With its plateglass windows facing onto the roaring traffic of Baker Street, this branch of Royal China doesn't have quite the air of grandeur of its Queensway and St John's Wood siblings, but our recent visit showed the dim sum to be just as excellent. Scallop dumplings were dainty and succulent, and roast pork puffs melted delightfully in our mouths. The triangular steamed dumplings filled with shredded duck and preserved vegetables (a chef's special) were similarly fine, and we relished the spicy chicken's feet, which had been steamed in a dark, sweet sauce with chilli and black beans. Sadly, another chef's special, the fresh ground sweetened walnut cream, was (as usual) unavailable. Staff were helpful and unusually laid-back; no one seemed to mind that we lingered for hours over a mid-week lunch.

Babies and children welcome; high chairs. Booking advisable. Separate room for parties, seats 14. Takeaway service. **Map 2/5G.**

Mayfair W1

Kai ★

65 South Audley Street, W1 (020 7493 8988/1456/www.kaimayfair.co.uk). Hyde Park Corner or Marble Arch tube. **Lunch served** noon-2.30pm Mon-Fri, 12.30-3pm Sun. **Dinner served** 6.30-11pm Mon-Fri, 6.30-10.30pm Sun. **Main courses** £8-£45. **Credit** AmEx, DC, JCB, MC, £TC, V.

An exceptionally smart Chinese restaurant in the heart of Mayfair, Kai has been in business for more than 20 years. The current menu is a fascinating read, with well-researched information about Chinese eating traditions at the foot of every page. The food is also unusually good, particularly for a restaurant which caters for a mainly non-Chinese clientele. Stir-fried spicy aubergines were delicious: rich, buttery strips of aubergine in a dense red sauce of pickled chillies, ginger and garlic. Another Sichuan-inspired dish, kung po scallops, was also excellent, and more authentic than most (it even used dried chillies as the Sichuanese do). Clay-pot duck was another hit, with tender, bronzed meat and a bed of glassy noodles that had absorbed all the tempting savours of the sauce. The spinach with red beancurd was a little slushy, though the flavour was good (water spinach would have been more interesting). The meal drew to a delightful close with a complimentary treat involving truffles and dry ice, and a beautiful teapot filled with aromatic iron Buddha tea (tie guan yin). Service is slick and pleasant; decor impeccable and the atmosphere cool but intimate.

Babies and children admitted. Dress: smart casual. Separate room for parties, seating 6, 10. **Map 2/7G.**

Oriental ★

The Dorchester Hotel, 55 Park Lane, W1 (020 7317 6328). Green Park, Hyde Park Corner or Marble Arch tube. **Lunch served** noon-2.30pm Mon-Fri. **Dinner served** 7-11pm Mon-Sat. **Main courses** £17.50-£60. **Set lunches** £25 (dim sum) incl glass of wine. **Set meals** £43-£95 per person. **Credit** AmEx, DC, JCB, MC, TC, V.

Hidden in the heart of the lovely old Dorchester Hotel, the Oriental is London's grandest and most expensive Chinese restaurant. The sheer opulence and idiosyncratic decoration of the three private dining rooms, decorated in Thai, Chinese and Indian styles, make them fit for an emperor, while the main dining area is also delightful, if more understated. The kitchen is well run (do take them up on their offer of a post-prandial tour), and the cooking is taken seriously. No MSG is allowed, so the flavours of sauces come from a rich stock base, without that artificial kick. Some of the cooking has left us in raptures; we won't forget a mesmerising soup of filleted Dover sole with beancurd and spinach, the steamed scallops served with a delicious own-made chilli sauce, or the sensational stir-fried beef with lemongrass and lashings of black pepper. Less interesting dishes still show a high degree of skill with the wok. Waiting staff are cordial, efficient and well informed, as you'd hope in such a place.

Booking essential lunch; advisable dinner. Dress: smart; no jeans or trainers. Separate rooms for parties, seating 6, 10 and 16. Vegetarian menu. **Map 2/7G.**

Zen Central

20-22 Queen Street, W1 (020 7629 8103). Green Park tube. **Lunch served** 12.30-2.45pm daily. **Dinner served** 6.30-11.15pm Mon-Sat; 6.15-11pm Sun. **Main courses** £4-£35 incl £1 cover. **Set dinners** £35-£55 per person (minimum four). **Service** 15%. **Credit** DC, JCB, MC, £TC, V.

Zen Central serves Chinese food in elegant, minimalist surroundings. The menu waxes lyrical about the excellence of genuine Chinese cooking, but we were surprised by the mediocrity of the food. None of it was really bad, but there wasn't a single dish which actually impressed either: shocking at these Mayfair prices. We chose two dumpling starters; Peking ravioli in chilli sauce were bland and lacked vitality, while the deep-fried prawn cakes, served with sweet vinegar, were similarly uninteresting. Main courses failed to raise a murmur of approval. The kung po mixed seafood consisted of battered, deep-fried prawns, squid and scallops served in a very average orange sweet-sour sauce, and the sea-spice aubergines were watery and dull. Even a steamed sea bass, which should be a safe bet in a high-class restaurant, failed to satisfy. Service was friendly, but there were some curious slip-ups considering the 15% service charge; our prawn cakes were placed on plates sullied with the soy sauce dip of the previous dumplings, and a dish bearing someone else's fishbone was held over our table while our plates were cleared away. The dining room itself is pleasant enough, though, with white ceilings, mirrored walls and chrome and black leather chairs.

Babies and children welcome; high chairs. Booking advisable. Separate room for parties, seats 21. Takeaway service. **Map 2/7H.**

For branches see index.

Piccadilly W1

China House

160 Piccadilly, W1 (020 7499 6996/ www.chinahouse.co.uk). Green Park tube. **Meals served** noon-11.30pm daily. **Dim sum** noon-5pm Sat, Sun. **Main courses** £6.50-£7.50, £3.30 dim sum. **Credit** AmEx, JCB, MC, £TC, V.

Situated in the old Barclays Bank on Piccadilly, an extraordinary 1919 listed building, this noodle restaurant cannot fail to make an impression. The white vaulted ceiling rises high above and great cast-iron chandeliers shed their light on the diners below. The food, however, is decent but run-of-the-mill. A starter of deep-fried squid rolls was served with a traffic-light of red, yellow and green dips, which seemed more gimmicky than appropriate. Soi gau (juicy boiled dumplings with silky skins) were more satisfying, with a good slosh of crushed garlic, chilli oil and soy sauce. The meat and seafood on the China House special dry noodles were fresh, delicious and well cooked, but the noodles were greasy and a tad overdone. Seafood soup noodles were more successful, with a generous scattering of mussels and prawns. But in a place like this, the dramatic location seems to be at least as important as the food.

Babies and children welcome; high chairs. Disabled: toilet. Entertainment; clowns and face-painting (weekends). No-smoking tables. Vegetarian menu. **Map 13/7J.**

Orient

160 Piccadilly, W1 (020 7499 6888/7779/ www.chinahouse.co.uk). Green Park tube. **Lunch served** noon-2.30pm Mon-Fri. **Dinner served** 6-11.30pm Mon-Sat. **Main courses** £12-£27.50, £3.30 dim sum (per portion). **Set lunch** £19.50 per person. **Credit** AmEx, JCB, MC,£TC, V.

A tiny, claustrophobic capsule of a lift takes you shooting up above the vaulted ceiling of **China House** (*see above*) to the more ambitious (and expensive) Orient restaurant. The T-shaped dining room is plain but pleasing, with cool, minimalist lines, evocative lighting and Japanese-style table settings. Waiters are friendly and well informed. The menu is unabashed fusion food, in which traditional Chinese dishes are interwoven with Mediterranean and South-east Asian influences, but is no less tasty for its departure from strict Chinese cuisine. Shark's fin soup – a pretty bowlful of seafood slivers topped with pale yellow fronds of gelatinous fin – was soothing and superbly seasoned; seared mahi-mahi was perfectly cooked and sumptuously tasty, with a subtle soy-based dressing; and Hunanese spiced lamb was succulent in a curried sauce laced with fresh red chillies. That said, portions are modest and prices astronomical, so if you're not an expense-account diner you might prefer to eat elsewhere.

Babies and children admitted. No-smoking tables. Separate room for parties, seats 25. Vegetarian menu. **Map 13/7J.**

Soho W1

YMing ★

35-36 Greek Street, W1 (020 7734 2721). Leicester Square or Tottenham Court Road tube. **Meals served** noon-11.45pm Mon-Sat. **Main courses** £5-£10. **Set meal** £15, £20. **Service** 10%. **Credit** AmEx, DC, JCB, MC, £TC, V.

YMing is one of the few London restaurants to offer well-cooked and interesting Chinese food in European-style surroundings, so it's a good bet for foodies who feel intimidated by the frenzy of Chinatown. Some concessions are made to western tastes, but the menu is adventurous and the chef shows an unusual command of huo hou (the control of heat which is fundamental to successful Chinese cooking). Our starter of salt-and-pepper mushrooms was magnificent: juicy chunks of fungus expertly fried and then tossed with a fragrant chilli-and-garlic salsa. Yunnan prawns with red beancurd were underseasoned, but well-cooked and juicy. A main dish called ta t'sai mi, apparently based on an 18th-century imperial recipe, offered ultra-succulent lamb with onion in a pleasant hoisin sauce. We also liked the aubergine parcels filled with a slice of bacon, deep-fried in batter and then topped with a suggestion of black bean sauce and a scattering of green spring onion. The dining area is quiet and comfortable – perfect for a dinner date with someone you really want to talk to – while downstairs, a dramatic purple dining room is available for private hire. Service is polite, but pleasantly informal.

Babies and children admitted. Book weekends. No-smoking tables. Separate rooms for parties, seating 15, 18 and 30. Tables outdoors (4, pavement). Takeaway service. **Map 13/6K.**

Victoria SW1

Hunan ★

51 Pimlico Road, SW1 (020 7730 5712). Sloane Square tube. **Lunch served** noon-2.30pm, **dinner served** 6-11pm Mon-Sat. **Main courses** £5.50-£200 incl 80p cover. **Set meals** £25-£200 per person (minimum two). **Service** 12½%. **Credit** AmEx, MC, £TC, V.

Hunan is the name of a central Chinese province, famed (like Sichuan) for its spicy and fragrant food. This restaurant, run by the charismatic Mr Peng, is the only one in London to genuinely specialise in this type of cooking (though it also offers other regional dishes). On our last visit we asked Mr Peng to arrange a menu for us (for the fixed price of £25), and most of the dishes he came up with were extremely good. Minced chicken with carrot and peanuts was deliciously spicy, and set off perfectly by the crisp lettuce leaf wrappers. Fried green beans were expertly cooked in a light tempura-style batter and tossed with fresh red chilli and garlic. We also enjoyed the delicate spinach dumplings and tiny parcels of salmon, wrapped in monkfish and tied with strands of spring onion. Our main criticism was that the menu hadn't been well planned: the overemphasis on ruddy, spicy dishes and complex flavours left us crying out for the kind of simple vegetable dishes or clear soup with which western Chinese cooks would normally accompany such a meal. Service was also somewhat chaotic, with long gaps between some courses, but Hunan's dining room was as comfortable as ever.

Booking necessary. No-smoking tables. Separate room for parties, seats 20. Vegetarian menu. **Map 611G.**

Jenny Lo's Tea House

14 Eccleston Street, SW1 (020 7259 0399). Victoria tube/rail. **Lunch served** 11.30am-3pm Mon-Fri; noon-3pm Sat. **Dinner served** 6-10pm Mon-Sat. **Main courses** £5-£7.50. **Minimum** £4.75. **Credit** £TC.

This friendly noodle shop is one of London's more congenial Chinese restaurants. The dining area is colourful and idiosyncratic, and waiting staff are always helpful. On our last visit we enjoyed our chunky guo tie dumplings, stuffed with pork and served with the traditional vinegar dip, some crisp, juicy spring rolls and a side-dish of French beans cooked with garlic and dark soy sauce. A bowlful of cha shao soup noodles was simple and nourishing. Our experiences of the main dishes served with rice have been less happy (gloopy sauces and an uncertain grasp of flavour), but the noodle and side dishes are fine for a swift, healthy meal. Everything has a home-cooked air, and food is served in rustic earthenware dishes. A selection of Chinese teas, some of them therapeutic, is an unusual and welcome touch.

Babies and children welcome. Bookings not accepted. Takeaway service (local delivery). **Map 6/10H.**

Ken Lo's Memories of China

67-69 Ebury Street, SW1 (020 7730 7734). Sloane Square tube/Victoria tube/rail. **Lunch served** noon-2.30pm Mon-Sat. **Dinner served** 7-11pm Mon-Sat; 7-10.30pm Sun. **Main courses** £4.50-£27. **Set lunches** £22-£27.50 per person (minimum two). **Set dinners** £24.50-£40 per person (minimum two). **Service** 12½%. **Cover** £1.25. **Credit** AmEx, DC, JCB, MC, £TC, V.

Most Chinese restaurants aimed mainly at non-Chinese customers are sloppy in their culinary standards, so Memories is unusual in providing reliably decent Chinese food. Service is what you'd hope for in an upmarket restaurant, and the dining area has a delightful buzz. Latticework screens loosely divide the room, and the whitewashed walls are painted attractively with Chinese characters in a variety of calligraphic styles. On our last visit we broke with our golden rule and ordered a set menu, because it looked unusually promising and offered good value in an expensive restaurant. Lobster was juicy and fresh and Mongolian lamb in lettuce leaves was well cooked, if slightly light on flavour. Sichuan fish fillet was an interesting and well-executed dish, with tender fish flesh, wood ear mushrooms and water chestnuts in a gently spicy, red-peppery sauce. Scallops and prawns with Chinese vegetables were competently done, and the staff were happy to oblige us with steamed rice served in an attractive copper pot, instead of the fried rice offered on the menu. In fact, the only off-note was a Sichuan beef dish; the beef slivers were too crispy and were draped in an excessively sweet sauce.

Babies and children admitted. Booking advisable, essential weekends. Separate room for parties, seats 20. Takeaway service. **Map 6/10H.**

For branch see index.

West

Bayswater W2

Magic Wok

100 Queensway, W2 (020 7792 9767). Bayswater or Queensway tube. **Meals served** noon-11pm daily. **Main courses** £5-£12.50. **Set meals** £10.50-£24 per person (minimum two). **Service** 12½%. **Credit** AmEx, DC, MC, £TC, V.

We still recommend the specials menu at the Magic Wok, one of London's more daring Cantonese restaurants. In the simply adorned but bright and clean dining area you'll get the chance to try some of the dishes that are normally kept secret from Europeans: preserved eggs, fat belly pork and intriguing texture foods. Standards are generally high, although on our last visit the cooking and the service were both somewhat slapdash. Deep-fried baby squid was well-seasoned, but a tad overdone. Braised winter melon with dried scallops failed to arrive with our other dishes and after a reminder we were served a hastily cobbled-together dish that was nothing like the glorious creation we had savoured on a previous visit. Still, the belly pork was rich and soothing, with peppy pickled vegetables, and the steamed rice was perfectly cooked. Maybe Magic Wok was just short-staffed that evening; on the basis of other visits, we'll happily give it the benefit of the doubt.

Babies and children admitted. Book dinner. Separate room for parties, seats 30. Takeaway service. **Map 11/6C.**

Mandarin Kitchen ★

14-16 Queensway, W2 (020 7727 9012). Bayswater or Queensway tube. **Meals served** noon-11.30pm daily. **Main courses** £5.90-£25. **Set meal** £10.90 per person-£30 (minimum two). **Credit** AmEx, DC, JCB, MC, £TC, V.

Even if you book a table for dinner at the Mandarin Kitchen, you will often have to wait for ages, perching on a banquette in the cramped entrance. Frankly, however, even if the staff tied us up and beat us, we'd probably put up with it for the sake of a plateful of their Scottish lobster, nestling on a bed of succulent noodles, fragrant with ginger and green onions. The steamed sea bass, steamed scallops and deep-fried baby squid all tend to be excellent, too, which is why London's Cantonese flock here for seafood feasts. This kind of dining doesn't come cheap – the seasonal price of a lobster or whole fish alone is usually around £25 – but it's just too tantalising to come here for a modest dinner and watch (and smell) the ceaseless procession of lobsters sailing past your nose to other, more fortunate tables. Don't expect glitzy decor or deferential waiters – the dining room is pretty

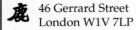

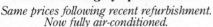

unexceptional and the staff are often aloof – but once your dishes have arrived, you are likely to forget such secondary considerations.
Babies and children welcome; high chair. Booking essential dinner. Takeaway service. Vegetarian menu. **Map 11/7C.**

Four Seasons ★
84 Queensway, W2 (020 7229 4320). Bayswater or Queensway tube. **Meals served** noon-11.30pm Mon-Sat; noon-11pm Sun. **Main courses** £4.30-£25. **Set meals** £17 per person (minimum two). **Service** 12½%. **Credit** AmEx, MC, £TC, V.
This modest restaurant in Queensway is always a good bet for a hearty and delicious Cantonese meal, although you may have to queue for a table. The mouthwatering specials list is always our point of departure. Here you'll find the kinds of dishes most restaurants confine to their Chinese-language menus: bitter melon, duck's feet and sea cucumber; sumptuous slow-cooked hot-pots; unusual fungi. On our last visit the lotus leaf steamed chicken with Chinese sausages and mushrooms was lavishly proportioned and magnificently tasty, while the seafood hot-pot with bamboo pith fungus was fresh and bursting with flavour. The other must-order is the chestnut-brown, moist and succulent Cantonese roast duck, which attracts Chinese customers from all over London. Staff tend to play hard-to-get with the tables, even if you have a reservation, but are friendly once you're seated. The dining area has been spruced up recently, and is always abuzz with Chinese chatter.
Takeaway service. **Map 11/6C.**

Royal China ★
13 Queensway, W2 (020 7221 2535). Bayswater tube. **Meals served** noon-11pm Mon-Thur; noon-11.30pm Fri, Sat; 11am-10pm Sun. **Dim sum** noon-5pm daily. **Main courses** £6-£9, £9-£10 dim sum. **Set meals** £25, £32, per person (minimum two). **Service** 12½%. **Credit** AmEx, DC, JCB, MC, V.
No one disputes that the dim sum at this branch of Royal China are the best in London, and there are long queues to prove it at every weekend lunchtime. The steamed dumplings are impeccable, with fillings that allow you to distinguish the taste and texture of every separate ingredient. Deep-fried snacks are uncommonly delicate, and the roast pork puffs and cheung fun are particularly fine. What's less well known is the high quality of the rest of the food, which shows a mastery of subtle flavours and cooking temperatures. A spicy duck starter was a delectable variation on the smoked chicken theme: small pieces of duck lightly dusted in starch, deep-fried and served with a slightly sour chilli dip. Steamed scallops were fleshy and magnificently tender. We also loved an innovative version of Sichuanese dry-fried beans, which used olives instead of the authentic pickled mustard leaves. The kitchen also specialises in grandiose Cantonese cooking, typified by succulent seafood cradled in a taro basket (a dish on the Chinese menu recommended by our waitress). Our only complaint about the dinner experience was the brutal efficiency of the staff, who seemed intent on hurrying us through our meal.
Babies and children welcome; high chairs. Booking advisable; essential weekends. Separate room for parties, seats 40. Takeaway service. **Map 11/7C.**

Ealing W3

North China
305 Uxbridge Road, W3 (020 8992 9183). Acton Town or Ealing Common tube/207 bus. **Lunch served** noon-2.30pm daily. **Dinner served** 6-11.30pm Mon-Thur, Sun; 6pm-midnight Fri, Sat. **Main courses** £3.80-£22.50. **Set meals** £13.50, £14.50, £16.50, per person (minimum two). **Credit** AmEx, DC, MC, £TC, V.
It's still worth a trip to Ealing for the exceptional Peking duck at North China (24-hours' notice required, serves four greedy people). The crisp, fatty duck skin and tender meat is served with freshly made Mandarin pancakes that are quite different in taste and texture from the papery discs offered elsewhere. The whole bronzed bird is brought to the table for your delectation before being whisked back to the kitchen for slicing. Later, you will be offered the remaining slivers of duck flesh stir-fried with beansprouts and finally a milky duck soup. Other dishes can be excellent, although mediocrity sometimes creeps in. On our last visit a cold mixed meat starter offered an unusual glimpse of northern Chinese eating habits, with slices of beef, pork, char siu

Four Seasons

(barbecued pork) and a couple of vegetables fanned out prettily around a pile of tasty pickles. Fish in wine sauce was an excellent dish of beautifully tender pieces of sole in a sweet, mellow sauce, but duck with beansprouts was underdone and rather unfragrant. Grilled Peking prawns, too, were almost tasteless. Staff are particularly pleasant, and will do their best to accommodate unusual off-menu requests (some notice may be required).
Children admitted. Booking advisable weekends. Separate room for parties, seats 36. Takeaway service.

Westbourne Grove W2

Lee Fook
98 Westbourne Grove, W2 (020 7727 0099). Bayswater or Notting Hill Gate tube/7 bus. **Meals served** noon-11.15pm Mon-Sat; noon-10.45pm Sun. **Main courses** £20. **Minimum** £9 after 7pm. **Set meals** £13.50-£19.50 per person (minimum two). **Credit** DC, MC, £TC, V.
A recent meal at Lee Fook left us happy and satisfied, not to mention extremely full. The steamed scallops were exemplary, and a crab with ginger and spring onion was so juicy and bursting with flavour that we devoured every last morsel. The house special soup was a gentle melange of wonton wrappers, straw mushrooms, shrimps, wispy crab meat and bamboo shoot; it was eloquent with flavour and had a pleasing texture. Pipa beancurd was a little bland, but came in a smokily fragrant sauce, while belly pork hot-pot was superbly succulent and set off by the pleasant sharpness of pickled mustard greens. The menu roves across the regions of China in search of culinary inspiration, although the main focus of the cooking is Cantonese. The dining room is understated and elegant, and the service efficient, if rather cold at times. Staff will select dishes for you on request, and create a meal that far exceeds the standard set menu fare. A pleasant closing touch was the choice of teas for a post-prandial brew.
Babies and children welcome; high chairs. Booking advisable. Takeaway service. **Map 11/6B.**

South West

Parsons Green SW6

Mao Tai
58 New King's Road, SW6 (020 7731 2520). Parsons Green tube/22 bus. **Lunch served** noon-3pm Mon-Fri; 12.30-3pm Sat, Sun. **Dinner served** 7-11.30pm Mon-Sat; 7-11pm Sun. **Main courses** £5.50-£22.50. **Set meal** £23.70 per person (minimum two). **Credit** AmEx, DC, JCB, MC, £TC, V.
Mao Tai is one of London's more glamorous Chinese restaurants. Many critics rave about the food here, but we've never understood their fascination. True, the menu is unusual in offering mainly Sichuanese dishes, but as is the case with most of London's supposedly regional Chinese restaurants, the actual cooking is Cantonese in style. (The sweet, vinegary pickled vegetables dispensed as a pre-dinner nibble are a dead giveaway; in Sichuan the pickles are salty and eaten at the end of the meal.) A soup of pork shreds with Sichuan pickled mustard was a respectable rendition of a simple home-style dish, but the ganshow monkfish, named after Sichuan's famous dry-braising cooking method, wasn't dry-braised at all, but deep-fried and draped in a sweet-and-sour sauce. Such quibbles of definition aside, the food is competent but unexceptional. Sea-spice aubergine was fairly tasty and we quite enjoyed the dainty grilled pork dumplings, but our best dish was a beautifully stir-fried spinach. Fulhamites may enjoy the sophisticated atmosphere, excellent service and highly original decor, but we doubt that many Chinese would be prepared to pay these hefty prices for what is actually very ordinary restaurant fare.
Babies and children admitted. Booking advisable. Separate room for parties, seats 28. Takeaway service.

Putney SW15

Royal China ★
3 Chelverton Road, SW15 (020 8788 0907). East Putney tube/Putney rail/14, 37, 74 bus. **Lunch served** noon-3.30pm Mon-Sat; noon-4.30pm Sun. **Dinner served** 6.30-11pm Mon-Thur; 6.30-11.30pm Fri, Sat; 6.30-10.30pm Sun. **Main courses** £10-£20. **Set meals** £23, £26, per person (minimum two). **Credit** AmEx, DC.
Every time we visit this place (once part of the Royal China chain, now an independent concern), we're amazed by the sheer excellence of the dim sum. It's not only exceptional for a suburban Chinese restaurant, but also better than much of what's on offer in Chinatown. This fact is clearly well known among London's Chinese community, who seem to make up most of the customers. On a recent visit we were thrilled by the plump, juicy pork and chive dumplings, and the delicious turnip paste, which was languid on the tongue and generously studded with meat. The prawn cheung fun, which we can never resist, anywhere, was exemplary, and its sauce was perfectly seasoned. We also enjoyed an offbeat treat of cold chicken's feet marinated in a gently spicy sweet-sour sauce. The location of the restaurant seems unlikely (it's in a building labelled 'The Putney and Wimbledon Synagogue'), but once inside, you'll find the ambience seductive. The dark walls are decorated in trademark Royal China gold and silver, lighting is sensitive, and the sun drifts in through Venetian blinds. Staff were a bit vague, but very friendly on our visit.
Babies and children admitted. Book dinner. Takeaway service; delivery service.

South Kensington SW5

Mr Wing
242-244 Old Brompton Road, SW5 (020 7370 4450). Earl's Court or South Kensington tube. **Meals served** 12.30-11.30pm daily. **Main courses** £6.95-£13.95 incl £1 cover. **Set meals** £29.95-£54.95 per person (minimum two). **Credit** AmEx, DC, MC, £TC, V.
This slick Kensington restaurant has a green, jungly intensity, with plenty of thick foliage and low, romantic lighting. A Chinese lion peers out from a waterfall by the door and downstairs an entire wall is aswim with tropical fish shimmering under ultraviolet light. Waiters are friendly, but highly professional, and the place has a festive, funky atmosphere. The enticing menu includes a good range of Chinese regional dishes with a few Southeast Asian touches. On our last visit we enjoyed some plump, juicy prawn patties served with a fresh, sour dip, and some fried french beans in a pleasant garlicky sauce. The highlight of our meal, though, was a magnificent Mongolian lamb: juicy, flavoursome meat fried to the perfection, and complemented beautifully by some crisp lettuce leaves. Stuffed beancurd boxes were less successful: a bland and unhappy marriage of textures and flavours. In general then, the food is nice enough, but not as good as it can be in Chinatown.
Babies and children admitted. Booking advisable Thur-Sat. Entertainment: jazz musicians 8.15pm-midnight Thur-Sat. Takeaway service. **Map 5/11B.**

South

Waterloo SE1

Four Regions
County Hall, Riverside Building, Westminster Bridge Road, SE1 (020 7928 0988). Westminster tube/Waterloo tube/rail. **Lunch served** noon-3pm, **dinner served** 6-11.30pm daily. **Main courses** £6-£11. **Set meals** £20-£32 per person (minimum two). **Service** 12½%. **Credit** JCB, MC, V.
You can hardly beat the location of this restaurant, with its riverside terrace and spectacular views of Big Ben and the Palace of Westminster. Underneath is the London Aquarium, and the Millennium Eye is now right next door. The cooking, however, is not as sensational as the setting, although it usually passes muster. Our steamed scallops were good and tender, with a well-seasoned soy and chilli sauce; a helping of crispy duck was also perfectly fine. An ostentatious dish of Dover sole, partly stir-fried, partly deep-fried, was nice enough, but an aubergine and minced pork hot-pot was

Local Friends. *See page 52.*

bafflingly tasteless, with bland meat and limp, greasy strips of aubergine. Service was pleasant, but erratic and uncoordinated. The dining room is dignified, with blond wood panelling and red silk drapes; chinoiserie is limited to a few stone lions and other decorations.
Booking advisable. Children admitted. Separate room for parties, seats min 50-200. Tables outdoors (16, terrace). Takeaway service. Vegetarian set meal. **Map 7/9M.**
For branch see index.

East

Docklands E14

Lotus Chinese Floating Restaurant
38 Limeharbour, Inner Millwall Dock, E14 (020 7515 6445). Crossharbour DLR. **Meals served** noon-11pm Mon-Sat; noon-10.30pm Sun. **Set meals** £17.50-£33 per person. **Minimum** £10. **Credit** AmEx, DC, MC, V.
The Lotus has an unlikely location, moored to the bank of Millwall Dock, behind the vast, warehouse-like London Arena. At night, however, the glow of the fairy lights and the Chinese-style architecture make it warm and welcoming. Picture windows look out over the still waters of the dock, and Canary Wharf looms in the distance. The menu is unusually seductive for a Chinese restaurant, with flowery descriptions of many of the dishes, and cooking can be good on occasion. We particularly liked the delicately aromatic scallops steamed in lotus leaves, and the 'snowballs', globes of prawn meat encrusted in tiny croutons and deep-fried for an interesting variation on the usual Chinese repertoire of fried starters. Other dishes disappointed. 'Welcome of spring' turned out to be meanly stuffed spring rolls; Cantonese roast duck was dry and chewy; and the shredded pork with Chinese pickles 'for the more adventurous' was a run-of-the-mill stir-fry. Despite the inconsistency of the food, however, the efficient service and picturesque setting make for a pleasant evening.
Babies and children welcome; high chairs. Booking advisable. Separate room for parties, seats 200. Takeaway service.

Limehouse E14

Old Friends
659 Commercial Road, E14 (020 7790 5027). Limehouse DLR/5, 15, 40 bus. **Meals served** noon-11pm Mon-Thur, Sun; noon-11.30pm Fri,

Sat. **Main courses** £3.80-£6.50. **Set meals** £14 (vegetarian) per person (minimum two)-£20 per person (minimum six). **Service** 10%. **Credit** AmEx, DC, JCB, MC, V.
One of a mere couple of Chinese restaurants left in Limehouse, London's original Chinatown, Old Friends caters mainly to a Docklands crowd. The place has a slightly dated, dingy feel and the menu is uninspiring, with a very clichéd selection of dishes, but on our visit the staff were delightfully friendly and the cooking was better than we were expecting. A dish of stir-fried monkfish was fresh and succulent; sizzling prawns were fairly tasty; and simple stir-fried broccoli was well executed. The barbecued pork, however, was dry and leathery, and the crispy duck was very crudely seasoned. The atmosphere is surprisingly soothing and peaceful, considering the roar of traffic on Commercial Road outside, but we do wish they'd switch off that ghastly muzak.
Babies and children welcome; high chair. Book dinner Fri, Sat. Separate room for parties, seats 30. Takeaway service.

Tai Pan
665 Commercial Road, E14 (020 7791 0118). Limehouse DLR. **Meals served** noon-11.15pm Mon-Thur, Sun; noon-11.45pm Fri, Sat. **Main courses** £3.10-£8.40. **Minimum** £10. **Set lunch** £12.50 adults, £6.50 under-7s. **Set meals** £14 per person (minimum two). **Credit** AmEx, DC, MC, V.
This convivial Limehouse restaurant has a family atmosphere and smiling, helpful waiters. The menu offers few surprises, but the cooking is above average, and is clearly popular with the locals. Moreover, Tai Pan also offers the curious Limehouse speciality, jar jow. This is a mixture of finely chopped barbecued pork, shrimps and crunchy vegetables, served up in a cloyingly sweet sauce, designed by the original Limehouse restaurateurs to appeal to British tastes. The fact that it seems so tacky these days is an indication of how much British appreciation of Chinese food has improved over the last decade (even if there is still a long way to go). Other dishes were more appealing. Deep-fried prawns were beautifully crispy, while mixed seafood was cooked with crunchy vegetables in a light black bean sauce. Large groups of diners all around us were happily tucking into great platters of the usual deep-fried starters: spare ribs, crispy seaweed et al.
Babies and children welcome; high chairs. Booking advisable. Separate room for parties, seats 50. Takeaway service; delivery service.

North East

Dalston E8

Shanghai
41 Kingsland High Street, E8 (020 7254 2878). Dalston Kingsland rail. **Lunch served** noon-3pm, **dinner served** 5-11pm Mon-Fri. **Meals served** noon-11pm Sat, Sun. **Main courses** £4.20-£18. **Set meals** £12 (vegetarian), £15, £17, per person (minimum two). **Credit** MC, £TC, V.
This quirky place has an originality and zest lacking in most neighbourhood Chinese restaurants. It occupies the listed premises of a former eel and pie shop, complete with wooden pews and tiled walls. Little brass eels still decorate the mirrors, and there is an eel mosaic on the floor. The cooking, which is nominally focused on Shanghainese cuisine, is hit and miss; some of the dishes are takeaway-mediocre, while others can be fresh-tasting and delicious. The highlight of the menu is undoubtedly the dumplings, which are made on the premises and often excellent. Shanghainese ravioli were slippery and succulent and served in a daringly spicy sauce. Steamed chicken dumplings were delectable and we also enjoyed the Shanghai spring onion cakes, with their crisp, short pastry wrappers and juicy spring onion filling. The restaurant (which is much larger than it appears from outside) is attractively decorated, and service is always friendly. There's also a private karaoke room, which is sometimes really rocking at weekends.
Babies and children welcome; high chairs. Booking advisable. Disabled: toilet. Separate rooms for parties, seating 50 and 60. Takeaway service.

North

Camden Town & Chalk Farm NW1

Feng Shang
Cumberland Basin, Prince Albert Road, NW1 (020 7485 8137). Camden Town tube/24, 31, 168, 274 bus. **Lunch served** noon-2pm, **dinner served** 6-11pm Mon-Fri. **Meals served** noon-11pm Sat, Sun. **Main courses** £8-£9. **Minimum** £12. Set meals £16-£26.50 per person (minimum two). **Service** 10%. **Credit** AmEx, MC, £TC, V.

There's a thrill about a visit to Feng Shang. The restaurant occupies a Chinese-style houseboat tethered to the bank of the Regent's Canal and is reached via a high drawbridge. The menu is also adventurous, with several unusual regional dishes, but the cooking tends to be a little heavy-handed. Our summery starters were disappointing: the braised beef slices dry and not particularly tasty; the prawns and scallops with mango wasted in their prawn cocktail sauce. Sichuanese roast duck, though, was fun and different: chunks of duck draped in a peanut sauce and eaten with Sichuan-style steamed buns, rather than the ubiquitous Mandarin pancakes. This was followed by a less-than-fresh-tasting white fish, served in an insipid wine sauce, and twice-cooked pork, in which the sliced meat was unforgivably tough and chewy. Fried beans with garlic and soy sauce, however, were nicely done. The dining rooms are light, bright and peaceful, with a few golden wood-carved panels on the walls and decent linen. Deferential, attentive service is an added bonus.
Babies and children admitted. Book dinner. Separate deck for parties, seats 90. Takeaway service.

The New Cultural Revolution ★
43 Parkway, NW1 (020 7267 2700). Camden Town tube. **Lunch served** noon-3pm daily. **Dinner served** 6-11pm daily. **Main courses** £4.90-£7.50. **Set meal** £12.50. **Credit** AmEx, JCB, MC, £TC, V.
Despite its name, this small Camden eaterie is not related to the slick New Culture Revolution chain. It's a cosy place, simply decked-out, and popular with its regulars. A few modern paintings hang on the walls and some dishes are served in delightful china bowls. The main attractions are the dumpling and noodle dishes, but there are also a few starters and side orders on offer, and some dishes served with rice. Grilled king prawns were fresh and sumptuously garlicky, with a gentle chilli kick; a soup of chicken, mushrooms and seaweed was bland but refreshing. The pork pan-fried dumplings (guo tie or 'pot-stickers') were unusually juicy and flavoursome, but sadly, a bowlful of chilli and lemongrass seafood noodles was little better than takeaway fare: plenty of prawns and mussels in an unappealing gloopy sauce. It is worth noting that none of the food served here contains GM ingredients, peanuts or MSG.
Babies and children welcome; high chairs. Booking advisable dinner. No-smoking tables. Separate room for parties, seats 20. Takeaway service. **Map 10.**

Islington N1

New Culture Revolution ★

42 Duncan Street, N1 (020 7833 9083). Angel tube/19, 38, 73 bus. **Lunch served** noon-3pm Mon-Fri. **Dinner served** 6-11pm Mon-Fri, 1-11pm Sat, Sun. **Main courses** £4.50-£6.50. **Credit** AmEx, DC, JCB, MC, £TC, V.

The restaurants in the New Culture Revolution chain appear to have been highly successful in introducing the British public to a Chinese version of the Wagamama dumpling-and-noodle formula. All offer short, clean-cut menus filled with the obligatory waffle about balanced eating and healthy living, and the cooking does not use MSG or any other artificial additives. Meals are served in clean-cut minimalist spaces, with blond wood tables and quotations by Chinese philosophers hanging on the walls. While we applaud New Culture Revolution's efforts to remind people that Chinese food isn't just about rich banquet cookery, we do wish it would pay more attention to the flavour of the dishes. Wok-fried vegetables were almost unbelievably tasteless; the garlic was still raw and someone had forgotten the salt. Some guo-tei (pot-sticker dumplings) were freshly made and well cooked, but similarly bland. The food at other branches has generally given us the same impression. This kind of plain, healthy food is appealing, but with a bit more effort to conquer the basics of Chinese cooking (that is, stocks, marinades and frying garlic to extract its fragrance) it could be extraordinarily delicious.

Babies and children admitted. No-smoking tables. Takeaway service. Vegetarian menu.
Map 16/2O.
For branches see index.

Swiss Cottage NW3

Green Cottage

9 New College Parade, Finchley Road, NW3 (020 7722 5305/7892). Finchley Road or Swiss Cottage tube. **Meals served** noon-11.30pm daily. **Main courses** £5.20-£17. **Set meals** £12.50-£15 per person (minimum two). **Service** 10%. **Credit** (on bills over £10) AmEx, MC, £TC, V.

It may look like a well-worn local standby – and so it is – but as many of Green Cottage's locals are discerning Cantonese, the food here is proper Chinese and reliably executed. Best are the roast meats, though as the chap who inhabits the roasts counter by the window had gone home, we ordered our belly pork in a hot-pot, steamed with preserved vegetables. The rich, dark, salty flavours and gorgeously tender fat needed a helping of steamed rice for balance, and we needed a few slurps of uncommonly good house white (Opal Ridge semillon chardonnay) for nirvana. Another main-course dish, stir-fried scallops with vegetables, matched yielding sliced seafood with crunchy broccoli to fine effect. Fish-flavoured aubergine (from a vegetarian list of rare abundance, including zhai duckling made of sheets of beancurd) chucked chilli heat and pleasing slitheriness into the equation. We'd had a fair wait for these dishes – after a tantalisingly fine starter of al dente grilled dumplings brimming with fresh-from-wok flavour – but service was otherwise kind and patient, staff humouring two young children in our party. We could pardon the knobbly cream wallpaper, the cramped tables (on both the first floor and ground), the tired linen foliage and even the open credit-card slip.

Babies and children welcome. Booking essential weekends. Separate room for parties, seats 30. Takeaway service.

Harvest

7 New College Parade, Finchley Road, NW3 (020 7722 8474). Finchley Road tube/ 13, 82, 113 bus. **Meals served** noon-11pm Mon-Sat; noon-10.30pm Sun. **Dim sum** noon-4.30pm daily. **Average** £4.80-£6.50, £1.80-£2.60 dim sum. **Set meals** £11 (vegetarian)-£18 per person (minimum two). **Service** 10%. **Credit** AmEx, DC, MC, £TC, V.

Yes, Harvest is a welcome and friendly outpost for dim sum and proper Chinese food, but a measure of inelegance had crept into the cooking last time we visited for a feast of lunchtime snacks. Cantonese mini pork dumplings had thick, stodgy pastry and bland fillings, while fried ho fun noodles with mixed meat in XO sauce produced a welter of congealed pasta strewn with off-cuts. In contrast, preserved egg and sliced pork congee was a comforting dish of rice porridge suffused with the flavour of fresh ginger and with the gelatinous egg adding piquancy. Grilled cheung fun with XO sauce was good, too, the intense, hot sauce and dried shrimps tempered by the slithery pasta. Deep-fried squid with coriander cake produced an unexpected, but welcome, helping of crisp battered squid tentacles (and no cake), while coconut custard buns made for a sweet, if heavy finale. Chicken with walnuts in champagne sauce, and duck with yam in red beancurd sauce in hot-pot are two of the more interesting dishes from the long full menu. With wooden ceiling, blue carpets and white walls decorated with photos of Chinese artefacts, this restaurant is a comfortable little local, and a shelter from the traffic of the Finchley Road.

Babies and children welcome; high chairs. Booking advisable, essential Sat. No-smoking tables. Separate room for parties, seats 20. Takeaway service.

North West

Belsize Park NW3

Weng Wah House

240 Haverstock Hill, NW3 (020 7794 5123). Belsize Park or Chalk Farm tube/ 168, 268, C11 bus. **Lunch served** 12.30-2.45pm, **dinner served** 6-11.30pm Mon-Fri. **Meals served** 12.30pm-midnight Sat; 12.30-11.15pm Sun. **Main courses** £5.80-£8.90. **Set lunch** £4.95 two courses. **Set meals** £15.50-£17.30 per person (minimum two), £15 Sun. **Credit** MC, £TC, V.

For long, Weng Wah has teetered on the balance between offering proper Chinese food to savants, and showy stir-fries to the well-heeled but ill-informed. You can find both on the menu, which is huge. A similar approach can be discerned in the service. Sharp and on-the-ball, to begin with, it slid into smarminess. We chose from both wings of the menu: crowd-pleasing starters, more authentic mains. Mixed starters for two produced an abundance of deep-fried things, from the prosaic (seaweed) to the more complex (springy fish cakes), via interlopers like satay. Apart from the satay sauce, no dips (red vinegar, chilli sauce) were provided: most un-Chinese. Next, steamed pork with three types of egg was a diverting savoury custard; spinach with chilli and preserved beancurd had been rightly, lightly boiled, but was timid with the pungent old-Camembert-flavoured beancurd; monkfish with asparagus in XO sauce exhibited decent main ingredients but also held back on the fiercely flavoured sauce. Furnishings here have a veneer of seemliness (both ground floor and first – with its big round banquet table – are spacious and sensitively lit, and crisp napery clothes the tables). But then there's the chairs resembling those of a doctor's waiting room; the water-feature that seems merely to indicate a leaky roof; and the tacky Athena-style pictures of oriental nudes. We've had good meals at Weng Wah House, but this time around we felt a little let down.

Babies and children welcome; children's menu; high chairs. Book dinner Fri, Sat. No-smoking tables. Separate room for parties, seats 70. Takeaway service (15% discount before 7.30pm).

Golders Green NW11

Local Friends

28 North End Road, NW11 (020 8455 9258). Golders Green tube/13, 82, 83, 102, 210, 226, 268, 328 bus. **Meals served** noon-11pm, **dim sum** noon-4.30pm daily. **Main courses** £4.50-£16, £2-£5 dim sum. **Set meals** £10.50-£18 per person (minimum two). **Service** 10%. **Credit** AmEx, MC, £TC, V.

We had two surprises upon entering this modest old venue for a late dim sum. First, the place was half-full at 3pm on a Tuesday (with local Japanese, Chinese, and a scattering of European tourists creating a pleasing multi-phonic hum). Second, the dim sum were better than many we've eaten in Chinatown. Best was first. Monk's vegetable cheung fun – from an uncommonly plentiful and varied vegetarian dim sum list – featured tiny shards of crunchy mooli and carrot, and slippery slivers of mushroom within the

Dim sum

If you haven't yet tried dim sum, you're missing one of London's most extraordinary gastronomic bargains, not to mention the simplest and most delightful means of initiation into the pleasures of Chinese food. The Cantonese term 'dim sum' (dian xin in Mandarin Chinese) means something like 'touch the heart' or 'little pieces so dear to the heart', and it refers to the vast selection of dumplings and other enticing snacks which southern Chinese people like to eat for breakfast. Traditional teahouses in Hong Kong and Guangdong start serving them early in the morning with pots of tea, as part of the eating ritual fondly known as 'yum cha' ('drink tea'). And in Chinese communities abroad, many Cantonese families like to make a dim sum feast the centrepoint of a weekend get-together.

The meal consists of a series of tiny dishes, each bearing just two or three dumplings, perhaps, or a tiny helping of steamed meat or seafood. You can order as many or as few as you please, and if you want to fill up with something more substantial, you can always add a plateful of fried noodles or a dish or two from the main menu. Most dim sum restaurants also offer cold meats such as roast duck and steamed chicken. Many of the snacks will appeal to children, and to adults who are unfamiliar with Chinese food. But they are also a fantastic way of dipping your toes into the wilder waters of Chinese cooking without spending too much money: how about a mouthful of tender chicken feet in black bean sauce, or even a few spicy duck's tongues?

Weekend dim sum lunches are noisy, informal occasions, and perfect for parents with small children, since any tantrums tend to get drowned out in the general hubbub. The only people who definitely won't enjoy this kind of eating are strict vegetarians, as most of the snacks contain pork or seafood.

In Hong Kong, dim sum are often served from heated trolleys stacked with miniature bamboo steamers or pretty little plates. Two London restaurants, **Chuen Cheng Ku** and **New World**, do them this way. This has the advantage of allowing dim sum novices to see exactly what's on offer: just ask the waitress to lift the lid on a few bamboo steamers and see what looks tempting. Other restaurants serve them à la carte, which means they are cooked to order and usually fresh and piping hot. Several restaurants (including the **Jade Garden**, **Chuen Cheng Ku** and **New World**) have illustrated menus which are a useful guide for the uninitiated.

How to eat dim sum

The first thing to remember is that dim sum remains a daytime ritual: most London restaurants start serving the snacks an hour or so before noon, and go on until four or five in the afternoon, when the rice-based evening menus take over. When restaurants offer dim sum on their main menus, they are just referring to a few lonely dumplings offered as starters, and not to the snack-fest described above.

Dim sum specialists always list the snacks on separate lunch menus, which are roughly divided by cooking method, with separate sections for steamed dumplings, fried dumplings, sweetmeats and cheung fun (*see below*). You should try to order a variety of different types of food, with plenty of light, steamed dumplings to counterbalance the heavier, deep-fried snacks. A pair of dainty eaters may find they're content after half-a-dozen little snacks, but *Time Out*'s greedy reviewers generally order at least eight or nine. If you are going with a large group, it's best to order multiples of everything, or at least of the more popular delicacies. Do bear in mind that if you stay away from the more expensive cold meats, you can order a vast selection of snacks without risking bankuptcy (most dishes cost between £1.70 and £2.50).

The traditional accompaniment to all this food is Chinese tea: some places offer a selection of different leaves, with dark, intriguingly musty bo-lay (pu'er in Mandarin Chinese) a favourite alternative to the ubiquitous jasmine blossom. Waiters should keep your teapot filled throughout your meal – just leave the lid tilted at an angle or upside-down if you want to signal that you need a top-up.

The best dim sum in London are served at **Royal China**'s Bayswater branch; other top venues are the Royal Chinas in Baker Street, St John's Wood and Putney, and the **Golden Dragon** in Chinatown. Other *Time Out* favourites include **Hong Kong** and the **New World** in Gerrard Place. Do be warned that you may have to queue at weekends, especially at Royal China in Queensway. Beyond Chinatown and Bayswater, dim sum are harder to come by: specialists include **Local Friends** in Golders Green, **Golden Palace** in Harrow and **Harvest** in Swiss Cottage.

The dim sum menu

The following is a guide to some of the more common dim sum delicacies. Please note that spelling may vary according to the method of transliteration used.

Char siu bao: fluffy steamed bun stuffed with barbecued pork in a sweet-savoury sauce.

Char siu puff pastry or **roast pork puff**: triangular puff-pastry snack, filled with barbecued pork, scattered with sesame seeds and roasted in an oven.

Cheung fun: slithery sheets of steamed rice pasta wrapped around fat prawns, tasty roast pork or other meats and splashed with a sweet soy-based sauce. At its best, it's meltingly delicious, although some non-Chinese dislike its texture.

Chiu Chow fun gwor: soft steamed dumpling with a wheat-starch wrapper, filled with pork, vegetables and peanuts. Chiu Chow is a regional Chinese cooking style that is popular in Hong Kong.

Har gau: steamed minced prawn dumpling with a translucent wheat-starch wrapper.

Nor mai gai or **glutinous rice in lotus leaf**: lotus leaf parcel enclosing a filling of moist, sticky rice with pork, mushrooms and other bits and pieces; steamed until the rice is permeated with the fragrance of the leaf. A good way of filling up during a dim sum meal.

Paper-wrapped prawns: tissue-thin rice paper enclosing plump prawn meat, sometimes scattered with sesame seeds; deep-fried.

Scallop dumpling: delicate steamed dumpling with a wheat-starch wrapper and a seafood filling: the proportion of scallop varies with the quality of the restaurant.

Shark's fin dumpling: small steamed dumpling with a wheaten wrapper pinched into a frilly cockscomb on top; filled with minced prawn and pork and, if you're lucky, tiny fronds of shark's fin.

Siu loon bao: little round dumpling with a wheaten wrapper pinched into a little whirl on top, stuffed with minced pork: a Shanghai speciality.

Siu mai: little gathered dumpling with an open top, a wheatflour wrapper and a minced pork filling. They are traditionally topped with orange-coloured crab roe, although minced carrot and other substitutes are often used.

Taro croquette or **yam croquette**: egg-shaped, deep-fried dumpling with a frizzy, melt-in-your-mouth outer layer; made of mashed taro with a savoury minced pork filling.

Turnip paste: heavy slab of creamy paste made with glutinous rice and white oriental radishes, studded with fragments of wind-dried pork, sausage and shrimps and sauteed to a golden brown on either side.

Royal China

freshest, most slithery pasta. Another meat-free choice, vegetable and peanut dumpling, was almost as accomplished. Squid in curry sauce provided some contrasting coarseness: thick yielding rings with a garlicky, chilli-hot coating. Deeply comforting steamed custard buns rounded off a simple yet gratifying lunch. A list of congees (rice porridge) and noodles (soft white noodles with shredded pork and dried scallop, say) provides plenty of noontide fillers, while the full menu includes several Chinatown pairings (fried pork chops with chilli and salt) among the ubiquitous stir-fries. The friendly couple who run the place greeted locals with warmth, and allowed us time to sip tea and study the pictures of old China that partly draw attention away from the off-white walls and a carpet that has seen long service.
Babies and children welcome; high chairs. Book weekends. Separate room for parties, seats 50. Takeaway service.

Hendon NW4

Kaifeng
51 Church Road, NW4 (020 8203 7888). Hendon Central tube/113,143, 186, 326 bus. **Lunch served** noon-2.30pm Mon-Thur, Sun. **Dinner served** 6-10.30pm Mon-Thur, Sun; one hour after sunset-11pm Sat. **Main courses** £5.95-£17.95. **Set meals** from £24 per person. **Service** 15%. **Credit** AmEx, DC, JCB, MC, £TC, V.
London's only kosher Chinese restaurant performs a useful service in the Jewish heartland of Hendon, yet has little else to recommend it. Almost everything except the floor is wood-panelled, with red curtains, pink tablecloths and artificial flowers adding embellishment. Split-level dining areas and various partitions create a series of intimate spaces. Shilly-shallying over the menu was prevented by a stern silk-clad Chinese waitress of military mien. We were only partially calmed by a glass of Israeli peach nectar (perhaps we should have tried the Rabbi's Ruin cocktail), and our dismay was renewed with a starter of fried dumplings. Six weighty parcels arrived: very oily, with a hard crisp base and virtually flavourless meat filling (was it lamb or beef?). Next, drunken fish in kosher wine had good fresh slices of sole ruined by a sickly-sweet sauce, while mixed vegetables in coconut cream came doused in an indistinctive gloop. The only

pleasing dish was Kaifeng fried noodles with meats: thick al dente noodles nicely coated in sesame oil, with tender slices of fried lamb, chunks of chicken breast, and more lamb that successfully aped char siu. Yes, there's skill involved in bypassing shellfish and pork, but the cooking here mimics that of countless Sino-suburban restaurants (rather than genuine Chinese cuisine); it's expensive (jasmine tea at £1.95), and the service is cynical (open credit-card slips, despite the service charge). Blame the lack of competition.
Babies and children welcome; high chairs. Booking necessary. Kosher supervised (Beth Din). Takeaway service.

Mill Hill NW7

Good Earth
143-145 The Broadway, Mill Hill Circus, NW7 (020 8959 7011). Colindale or Edgware tube/Mill Hill rail. **Lunch served** noon-2.15pm Mon-Sat; 12.30-2.30pm Sun. **Dinner served** 6-11.15pm Mon-Sat; 6-10.30pm Sun. **Main courses** £7.80-£18.80. **Minimum** £10. **Set meals** £21.90-£29.80 per person (minimum two). **Credit** AmEx, JCB, MC, £TC, V.
To its constituency of well-shod locals – some of them African Asian, none of them Chinese – Good Earth offers refinement, a spacious refuge from the roar of the A1 outside, and reassuringly high prices (that discourage takeaway *hoi polloi*). In truth, it's a fair example of London's Sino-suburban genre with a notable vegetarian menu that includes mock chicken (made from wheat gluten), and courgettes stuffed with chopped vegetables and nuts. There's also a batch of Thai food, and the odd dish rarely seen this far from Chinatown (such as shredded duck with jellyfish). We were seated at a small table (most are big and round) and took in the tasteful surroundings and expensive fittings. Our meal, though not bad, exhibited some of the traits sadly typical of such suburban restaurants. Five-spice mussels arrived with a preponderance of some barely cooked onions and leeks, masses of salt and nicely crunchy deep-fried peppercorns. The bivalves were shell-less, abundant and clothed in light crisp batter, but were so small their flavour was masked. To follow, springy prawn

patties had that freshly fried zing and came atop a mound of crunchy mangetout, but dry-fried french beans (a spicy Sichuan dish) looked wizened and the advertised chopped meat and dry shrimps were indiscernible. The ice-cream served at Good Earth was low-grade vanilla with a green smudge of crème de menthe. Service came from plentiful, prompt waiters sporting flamboyant bow ties. Bet they don't eat the food.
Babies and children welcome; high chairs. Booking advisable; essential weekends. Separate room for parties, seats 30. Takeaway service.
For branches see index.

St John's Wood NW8

Royal China
68 Queens Grove, NW8 (020 7586 4280). St John's Wood tube. **Open** noon-11pm Mon-Thur, noon-11.30pm Fri, Sat; 11am-10pm Sun. **Main courses** £6-£20. **Set dinner** £25-£32 three courses. **Service** 12½%. **Credit** AmEx, DC, MC, £TC, V.
This youngest branch of the Royal China chain has a more intimate feel than its Bayswater and Baker Street siblings, with a small, beautiful dining room and bright gilded walls. We haven't found the dim sum to be as consistently excellent as it is at the Royal China Bayswater branch (which is a class apart), but it's still pretty good. On our most recent visit, the chicken and mushroom buns were lacking in juiciness and the prawn cheung fun was a little plain, but these were minor quibbles, since we loved both the deliciously dark and sweet roast pork puffs, wrapped in feather-light pastry, and the unusual soup of mung beans and seaweed, with its intriguing tangerine peel flavour. The steamed scallop and pork and radish dumplings were also typically fine examples. The restaurant was sparkling with chatter on a sunny Sunday, and tables filled and re-filled in swift succession. The lunchtime bustle rendered the briskly efficient staff somewhat impatient; it's best go in the evenings for a more relaxed but equally tasty dining experience.
Babies and children welcome; high chairs. Booking advisable; essential weekends. Separate room for parties, seats 12, 20. Takeaway service.

Harrow, Middlesex

Golden Palace ★
146-150 Station Road, Harrow, Middx (020 8863 2333). Harrow-on-the-Hill tube/rail. **Meals served** noon-11.30pm Mon-Sat; 11am-10.30pm Sun. **Dim sum** noon-5pm Mon-Sat; 11am-5pm Sun. **Main courses** £3.50-£9.50, £2-£3.50 dim sum. **Set meals** £17 (vegetarian)-£22.50, per person (minimum two). **Service** 10%. **Credit** AmEx, DC, MC, V.
At each successive visit we're astonished by the variety and the quality of Golden Palace's dim sum. More adventurous concoctions appear every year, drawing from traditional, modern and pan-oriental influences. Few Chinatown venues could compete. First to arrive were three baked custard-filled buns coated in honey: so moist, so crisp we ate them before the savouries. Even better were the curried cuttlefish: supremely succulent, glistening little chaps that outshone their tame sauce. Fish balls with choi were prosaically named delights, too, the three delicate cakes eggy and crisp outside and springy within, the slight pungency of dried fish counterbalanced by quarters of lime. The dish described as 'grilled chicken lemongrass flavour' had precious little lemongrass, but the bite-sized portions were juicy. Cheung fun, congees, noodles and glutinous rice are there to fill up (and thrill) dim sum diners, while the capacious main menu has luxury seafood, and a few hot-pots alongside a myriad stir-fries. Patient, helpful waitresses; a card on each table depicting the snacks; and a spacious, serene interior (spotlit tables, starched tablelinen; grey walls) – all allow you to concentrate on the food. Slips aren't unknown here: there was the bone in the four-treasures roll (yam, chicken and mushroom wrapped in beancurd skin) slip; and there was the open credit card slip (after a service charge had been levied). But we'd still slip down to Golden Palace at the faintest excuse – as do many local Chinese.
Babies and children welcome; high chairs. Booking advisable. Disabled: toilet. No-smoking tables. Separate room for parties, seats 60. Tables outdoors (10, pavement). Takeaway service.

Fish

Recent reports about dangerously depleted fish stocks (cod is now an endangered species), dying fishing communities and the environmental drawbacks of fish farming have thrust fish into the headlines. Yet such gloomy news doesn't seem to have affected our consumption of marine life, which continues to grow (especially in the case of salmon and prawns) – despite fish being markedly more expensive than meat.

Consumers may be fussier about the geographical origin of what they are eating (many restaurants now stipulate which part of the world their fish and shellfish come from), but they seem less concerned by farming methods. This state of affairs may change, however, if the public's love affair with organic food continues. We've already noticed a couple of restaurants specifying 'hand-caught langoustine' and 'wild' rather than farmed fish, and the occasional menu claiming environmentally responsible sourcing.

Certainly, the wave of new or expanded fish restaurants shows that fish continues its fashionable surge. Last year's arrival, **fish!** in Borough market, was an instant hit, and has traded on its success, spawning new branches. Chez Gérard's **Livebait** chain is also flourishing, with a new branch in Notting Hill to add to Covent Garden and its original outpost in Waterloo. Modish newcomers aside, upmarket **J Sheekey** continues to be a winner, while Scottish stalwart **Loch Fyne**'s takeover of a rather dismal fish restaurant in Twickenham and the arrival of **Creelers** in Chelsea bring a welcome Caledonian slant to London's piscine scene. Traditional **Rudland & Stubbs** in Farringdon and eccentric **Sweetings** in the City also prove there is still a place for fish restaurants of the old school.

Central

City EC2, EC4

Fishmarket
Great Eastern Hotel, 40 Liverpool Street, EC2 (020 7618 7200/www.fish-market.co.uk). **Lunch served** noon-2.30pm, **dinner served** 6-10.30pm daily. **Main courses** £10.50-£25. **Credit** AmEx, DC, JCB, MC, V.
Terence Conran may have gone one restaurant too far in his most recent hotel venture, also the home of three other restaurants. There's nothing much wrong with it, but that's faint praise for such a high-profile, highly priced operation. The main thing lacking is a buzz, in fact any atmosphere at all beyond the echo of your own conversation around the high ceilings and, on our evening visit, largely empty tables. At lunch the place is busier, with well-padded business eaters well suited to the formal decor and service. There are two very different rooms, both dominated by a bar whose ocean mosaic decoration is the main modern accent in otherwise gorgeously Victorian surroundings. The menu is short and simple, yet ranges widely in price and formality, reflecting Fishmarket's hotel role. The cooking is good without being breathtaking. Oysters (Cuan, Loch Fyne, fine de claires) were fine, yet Thai fish cakes were only so-so. A big, well-presented smoked salmon and potato cake lacked the promised horseradish bite in its crème fraîche accompaniment. Mains were better: skate on olive mash with red wine jus; and unpretentious salmon and smoked-haddock fish cakes. We drank a Clare Valley riesling, from a wine list specialising in champagnes. By the time we ordered dessert (a rich lemon tart with fab fromage blanc ice-cream), the staff had started to put barstools up on the bar. We knew how they felt.
Babies and children welcome; high chairs. Disabled: toilet. **Map 4/6R.**

Sweetings
39 Queen Victoria Street, EC4 (020 7248 3062). Cannon Street tube/rail. **Lunch served** 11.30am-3pm Mon-Fri. **Main courses** £8-£19.50. **Credit** £TC.
We're glad to see that this much-loved bastion of City tradition still preserves its quirky characteristics and unpretentious, friendly atmosphere. Occupying a small, two-level corner site, it boasts nicotine-yellow walls decorated with old prints and photos, and a mosaic floor dating back to the 1880s (when the premises housed a fishmonger). Seating is on stools at high counters, behind which servers take orders, supply cutlery, drinks and sliced bread and butter, and pass the time of day with the largely male, City-worker clientele. There are also a couple of tables in the cramped and noisier back room. Sweetings' eccentricities mean it's only open at lunchtime, you can't book, or use credit cards as payment, and staff don't serve tea or coffee. Don't expect a quiet or leisurely meal: an air of organised chaos prevails, with white-aproned waiters delivering dishes in quick-fire succession against a background of clattering dumb waiters and wine-fuelled chatter. The menu offers old-fashioned, unfussy fare with the likes of potted shrimps, lobster bisque and dressed crab for starters, and plainly cooked fish (skate and John Dory among them) for mains. Other dishes include salmon fish cakes, smoked haddock and poached eggs, and a decent fish pie. Vegetables – peas, spinach, french beans, excellent chips – cost extra. There's a good choice of wine and, for afters, the likes of syrup sponge and other school-dinner favourites. The food is not spectacular, but Sweetings is nonetheless an experience that everyone should try at least once.
Bookings not accepted. Dress: smart casual. **Map 4/6P.**

Clerkenwell & Farringdon EC1

Rudland & Stubbs
35-37 Greenhill Rents, Cowcross Street, EC1 (020 7253 0148). Farringdon tube/rail. **Lunch served** noon-2.45pm Mon-Fri. **Dinner served** 6-10.45pm Mon-Fri; 7-10.45pm Sat. **Main courses** £8.25-£20. **Service** 10%. **Credit** AmEx, MC, £TC, V.
With its cream-tiled, dark-wood fish-shop decor (it's actually an old sausage factory) and varied menu, Rudland & Stubbs is a slightly more sedate version of Livebait and its ilk. It has now bedded in nicely, as an unassuming local restaurant that can be trusted both for its assurances of freshness and for the quality of its specials – in food and wine. The menu is long, with sections for starters, shellfish, plain-served fish and some standard, but more elaborate, fish dishes (phone in advance if you want meat). There's also a long list of daily specials (starters and mains). Predictably, the latter provides the best dishes: blinis with caviar, fish soup and a stargazy pie (mixed fish pie with a langoustine peering out of its crust) from the main menu could have been better, but the chef's recommendation of Cornish hake with a saffron sauce, and a special of roast cod with firm yet juicy fat flakes were both excellent, as was a bumper summer pudding. In the evening, Rudland & Stubbs is quiet, bar a jazz soundtrack; at lunch, it's busier (and louder) with City overflow.
Babies and children welcome. Book lunch. Vegetarian dishes (on request). **Map 15/5O.**

Stream Bubble & Shell
50-52 Long Lane, Smithfield, EC1 (020 7796 0070). Farringdon tube/rail. **Open** noon-midnight Mon-Fri; 6pm-midnight Sat. **Main courses** £5.50-£15. **Credit** AmEx, DC, JCB, MC, £TC, V.
Yet another over-designed style-bar/restaurant, Stream at least tries to do something different by serving seafood and all the trimmings at middle-market prices. The menu's short, with a handful of mod-Med starters, four 'large plates' (two fishy, one meaty, one veggie) and a longer seafood list – oysters, prawns, langoustines, crab, lobster, shellfish and platters. Everything we sampled was fresh and fine (with the exception of some rubbery, over-large Mediterranean prawns), thoughtfully served (pretty ribbons on the lemon muslins, finger and discard bowls), and the service was solicitous, almost to a fault. And there's the rub. Stream tries

Sweetings

a bit too hard. With the industrial/leather decor and endless fashionable touches, the cute Japanese vending machines in the basement (in case you'd forgotten to bring your own nodding dog) and the all-black staff uniforms, there's not much room left for any atmosphere. When we visited (a Monday night), the place was nearly empty. But it packs out later in the week, and we'd still recommend it for a stacked seafood platter at a decent price: for two, £23.50 with crab, £29.50 with lobster.
Babies and children admitted. Vegetarian menu. **Map 15/5O.**

Fitzrovia W1

Back to Basics

21A Foley Street, W1 (020 7436 2181/ www.backtobasics.uk.com). Goodge Street tube. **Lunch served** noon-3pm, **dinner served** 6-10pm Mon-Fri. **Main courses** £7.95-£15.25. **Credit** AmEx, DC, MC, £TC, V.

Much loved by a relaxed, unassuming crowd for its distinctly non-corporate character, Back to Basics is a good local restaurant that just happens to be in the centre of town (with prices to match). The street-corner location means it's light and bright (and crowded) at lunchtime; at night, jewel-coloured lighting illuminates the small and otherwise simply decorated room. Two huge blackboards list the day's fish. There are other dishes on the menu, mainly meaty and none too interesting (sausage platters and vegetables in filo pastry, for instance); fish are conspicuously the chef's forte. Starters are a simple list of preserved varieties (pickled herring, gravadlax); mains change with the catch and are far from fancy themselves, for example mackerel with tomato sauce and salade niçoise. We've never had anything other than perfectly fresh fish here, perfectly cooked, but occasionally the accompaniments are a little ordinary. Faultless baked cod flaked randomly into its base of unadorned chunks of sun-dried tomato and feta; a hefty, succulent tuna steak was well teamed with sautéed leaves and melted goat's cheese, but the chickpea stew was a little raw. Desserts – we had bread and butter pudding with whisky sauce and a continental-style (and size) apple pie – are safe rather than scene-stealing. Still, the charming service and short, nicely judged wine list ensure that you leave in no mood to quibble.
Babies and children welcome. Book lunch. Tables outdoors (20, pavement). Takeaway service. **Map 2/5J.**

Leicester Square W1, WC2

Café Fish

36-40 Rupert Street, W1 (020 7287 8989). Leicester Square, Piccadilly Circus or Tottenham Court Road tube.
Bar **Open** noon-11pm Mon-Sat; noon-10.30pm Sun.
Canteen **Meals served** noon-10.30pm Mon-Sat; noon-10pm Sun. **Main courses** £7.50-£16.
Restaurant **Lunch served** noon-3pm daily. **Dinner served** 5.30-11.30pm Mon-Sat; 5.30-10.30pm Sun. **Main courses** £9.80-£21.95. **Cover** £1.50. **Service** 12½%.
All **Credit** AmEx, DC, JCB, MC, £TC, V.

Café Fish, with its tiled and mirrored decor, is divided into first-floor restaurant and a ground-floor canteen, which has hunky pine benches and a metal bar. We'd recommend sitting downstairs, if necessary at one of the overflow restaurant tables. The food is inconsistent, but the cover charge is worth it for the tasty fish pâté served with toast. Next, oysters were great (if a little too cold), and attractively served; fish soup was initially disappointing for its blandness but grew on us in a silky kind of way. For mains, we had an expertly cooked sea bream with a caper sauce that cut through the natural grease. Scallops, with roes, were very good, but the accompanying stir-fried veg were more braised and nothing special. A monkfish and salmon kebab with couscous was dull on all fronts, and undercooked to boot. Desserts varied too, with the nadir a flaccid ginger and caramel cheesecake. Great service and a bill we'd expected to be higher, combined with a buzzy atmosphere, mitigated the disappointment of the variable menu – it was actually a great evening, and food was only ever the half of it here.
Babies and children admitted. Booking advisable. Disabled: toilet. No-smoking tables (restaurant). Vegetarian dish. **Map 13/7K.**

Manzi's

1-2 Leicester Street, WC2 (020 7734 0224). Leicester Square tube. **Lunch served** noon-2.45pm Mon-Sat. **Dinner served** 5.30-11.45pm Mon-Sat; 6-10.45pm Sun. **Main courses** £10.50-£26. **Set dinner** (5.30-7.30pm Mon-Sat) £13.95 three courses. **Credit** AmEx, JCB, MC, £TC, V.

This Italian-run restaurant and hotel has served Soho for more than 70 years and resolutely refuses to move with the times. The decor has a certain kitsch appeal if you like engraved and painted wall mirrors, dreadful ceiling murals and red and white checked tablecloths. White-jacketed waiters move through the cramped room with a world-weary air. However, Manzi's is undeniably popular with a mix of businessmen, middle-aged couples and tourists too nervous to stray far from Leicester Square. The long menu will please traditionalists with the likes of smoked eel, cod's roe and potted shrimps for starters and grilled or fried fish for mains, along with some fancier dishes and daily specials. Presentation is plain and quality variable. A starter of avocado with crab produced a sliced-up avocado, a pile of cold, tasteless crab and a few lettuce leaves: not a bargain at £7.95. Yet the rock oysters were fresh and delicious. Best stick to simple dishes: a large grilled lemon sole was perfectly cooked, although swordfish steak was dry and chewy. Vegetables – including broccoli, spinach, mushy peas, mash and great chips – cost an extra £1.50 each. A dessert of white chocolate cheesecake was a marvel of synthetic flavours, sporting an alarmingly scarlet topping and swirls of chocolate sauce that tasted straight from a bottle. The wine list is nothing special but at least the house wine costs less than a tenner a bottle.
Babies and children welcome. Book dinner. Separate room for parties, seats 50. Vegetarian dish. **Map 13/7K.**

J Sheekey ★

28-32 St Martin's Court, WC2 (020 7240 2565). Leicester Square tube. **Lunch served** noon-3pm Mon-Sat; noon-3.30pm Sun. **Dinner served** 5.30pm-midnight daily. **Main courses** £9.80-£27.50. **Set lunch** (Sat, Sun) £10.75 two courses, £14.50 three courses. **Cover** £1.50. **Credit** AmEx, DC, MC, TC, V.

If you can't get into the Ivy, try Sheekey's, which is under the same ownership and offers a similarly civilised and upmarket dining experience. A series of small interconnected wood-panelled rooms, decorated with photos of film stars and decent modern art, provides an intimate atmosphere. Bustling black-jacketed waiters, who flourish such theatrical dishes as salt-baked sea bass (a whole fish encrusted in salt), add a touch of flamboyance. The menu lives up to the surroundings. Starters include shellfish, crab, Irish and French oysters, caviar and rarely seen seasonal ingredients such as razor clams and samphire. We enjoyed herring roe on toast with capers, but found even upmarket jellied eels an acquired taste. There are a dozen or so main dishes, as well as a small selection of plain fish (grilled or steamed) and a handful of specials. Herbs are used generously, with a thick herby crust surrounding perfectly cooked cod; sorrel sauce served with the salmon fish cake on spinach (an Ivy favourite); and chervil sauce accompanying roast turbot (from the specials). Vegetables – from mushy peas to roasted cauliflower mash – cost extra. Top-quality ingredients, inventive combinations and elegant presentation add up to a memorable meal. Leave room for afters: in addition to a heavenly summer pudding (in season), there's a series of fantastic chocolate desserts and spotted dick. One of London's best fish restaurants.
Babies and children welcome; toys. Booking advisable. Vegetarian dishes. **Map 14/7K.**

St James's W1, SW1

Caviar House

161 Piccadilly, W1 (020 7409 0445/www.caviarhouse.com). Green Park tube. **Open** noon-10pm Mon-Fri; noon-7pm Sat. **Lunch served** noon-3pm, **dinner served** 7-10pm Mon-Fri. **Meals served** noon-7pm Sat. **Main courses** £14.50-£18.50 (caviar from £52-£735). **Set menu** (Mon-Fri) £22.50 two courses, £24.50 three courses; (Sat) £65 three courses. **Credit** AmEx, DC, MC, £TC, V.

This small, elegant restaurant – all blue and white, with linen tablecloths and big blue-glass plates – is a showcase for the Caviar House shop next door, which sells caviar, caviar apparatus, foie gras and high-priced wine, mainly to tourists. It's best to visit at lunchtime, as the place doesn't feel like a restaurant when the shop is closed. And best go in the week, because the Saturday set menu is much more expensive (£65 for 30g of sevruga, smoked-salmon platter and dessert) – and staff don't always change the printed menu in the window. Otherwise, you have a choice of seven Iranian caviars, in 30g or 50g portions, served with mini blinis and new potatoes and costing £45-£199. There are also various plates of smoked salmon (Russian and Scottish), foie gras and a few other dishes, such as salad of half a Maine lobster with black truffle dressing. Presentation is perfect: sjomga salmon salad on a bed of rocket had twists of exquisite smoked fish arranged like petals of a flower. Even if you avoid the caviar, it's not cheap: with a glass of Sancerre, a wonderfully intense lemon tart for dessert, an espresso and service, the bill topped £30 for one. The extras are good though: bread comes with four pots containing olive oil, salmon pâté, herbed sea salt and butter, and you get petits fours with the coffee. Staff are charming, service is polished.
Babies and children admitted. Book lunch Mon-Fri. Dress: smart casual. **Map 13/7J.**

Creelers

Greens

36 Duke Street St James', SW1 (020 7930 4566). Green Park or Piccadilly Circus tube.
Sept-Apr **Lunch served** 11.30am-3pm, **dinner served** 5.30-11pm Sun. *May-Aug* **Lunch served** 11.30am-3pm, **dinner served** 5.30-11pm Mon-Sat. **Main courses** £10.50-£37. **Cover** £2. **Credit** AmEx, DC, JCB, MC, £TC, V.

Posh, discreet and surprisingly mellow, Greens is the kind of restaurant well-fed business folk choose, especially if they've a taste for privacy. Tables are sheltered by dark-wood panelling, the high windows are opaque, opulent (sometimes over-pongy) flower arrangements shield you from the outside world, and no music interrupts your cosy chat. Dapper, jovial staff do a fine job of dancing attendance, when you want to attract them. The menu covers shellfish (rather plainly served), fish and more standard classics, in safe but interesting presentations. A seared tuna starter was exquisite, its guacamole and wasabi accompaniments melding nicely; lobster salad was unfussy and of a good quality. The impetus was lost with the mains, where a school dinner ethos came too much to the fore. Encased in yellow breadcrumbs, outsized salmon fish cakes were a bit Bird's Eye in appearance; inside they were fish-stuffed but bland. A smoked haddock pie wasn't much better than the TV-dinner version. Treacle tart, on the other hand, could have done with more home-made oomph; though a sharp, intense raspberry sorbet was spot on. Side dishes were good throughout. Green's is a bit of an institution, yet we've often found its quality slightly variable – though not to such a degree that the pleasant environment has failed to compensate.
Babies and children admitted. Booking advisable. Dress: smart casual. Separate room for parties, seats 36. **Map 13/7J.**

Soho W1

Zilli Fish

36-40 Brewer Street, W1 (020 7734 8649). Piccadilly Circus tube. **Meals served** noon-11.30pm Mon-Sat; noon-10.30pm Sun. **Main courses** £15.90-£26. **Credit** AmEx, DC, JCB, MC, V.

Zilli continues to attract a youngish, well-off media crowd, somewhat to our perplexity. Presumably they come for the Soho location (easily appreciated through big windows), the buzzy drinking-club feel, and because they chalk their large bills through to expenses – since the self-financed non-regular swiftly notices that the food and particularly the service isn't up there with the prices. We were frequently ignored and left with empty wine glasses and dirty plates. The menu is long and ranges from antipasti (oysters 'at your own risk', char-grilled squid with chilli jam), through pastas (some non-fish sauces) and a meat dish, to 'What we are famous for' (spaghettini with lobster, wild salmon stuffed with crab and spinach, grilled swordfish on Caesar salad). Scallops were properly served with roes attached, and a lobster pasta was good (as you'd expect given Zilli's Italian heritage), but fish dishes and desserts (we had tiramisù and mango brûlée) were just OK. If this is your clubhouse, enjoy; if not, you might feel you don't belong. However, it sounds as if we're in the minority, as Zilli is forever packed, and a new branch has recently opened in west London.
Babies and children welcome. Booking advisable. Tables outdoors (7, pavement). Vegetarian dishes. **Map 13/7J.**
For branch see index.

West

Holland Park W11

Offshore

148 Holland Park Avenue, W11 (020 7221 6090). Holland Park tube/94 bus. **Lunch served** noon-3pm Mon-Fri. **Dinner served** 6-11.30pm Mon-Sat. **Main courses** £9.75-£19.50. **Set lunch** £12.95 two courses, £15 three courses, both incl coffee. **Credit** AmEx, DC, MC, V.

The inventive and distinctive menu at this Mauritian-accented French restaurant is unlike that of any other fish restaurant in London, mixing the likes of lemongrass, tamarind and chilli with more conventional flavours. There are a dozen or so appetisers and mains (including a couple of meat dishes and a vegetarian option), plus a few daily specials. Starters include fish soup, crab salad and tuna three ways – seared sashimi, balsamic ceviche and wasabi tartare – all fantastically fresh and tender. For mains, spicy grilled brill (a special) came with tagliatelle and a lemongrass-tinged sauce, and was nicely piquant (although noodles might have been preferable as an accompaniment). Mauritian fish curry was an unusual, delicate and delicious combination of snapper and halibut with aubergine, served with rice and a side dish of pickled tomatoes and cucumbers. Vegetables – including spicy spinach, new potatoes, noodles, rice and Mister Ho's aubergine fondue – cost extra. For puds, raspberry and passion-fruit mousse was a sight to behold, artfully arranged with triangular chocolate and biscuit wafers; it tasted as good as it looked. The pretty split-level room has plenty of fishy artworks (even fish-patterned loo paper), soft lighting and a hushed atmosphere. If anything, it's a bit too formal, and the mainly French staff were over-attentive, but this was probably due to the lack of customers: Offshore is very quiet midweek, which it doesn't deserve.
Babies and children welcome. Booking advisable. No-smoking tables. Separate room for parties, seats 20-40. Tables outdoors (2, pavement). Vegetarian menu. **Map 11/8Az.**

Maida Vale W9

Jason's

Jason's Wharf, opposite 60 Blomfield Road, W9 (020 7286 6752). Warwick Avenue tube. **Breakfast served** 9.30-11.30am, **lunch served** 12.30-3pm, **tea served** 3-5pm, daily. **Dinner served** 6.30-10.30pm Mon-Sat. **Main courses** £12.95-£29.95. **Set lunch** £17.95 two courses. **Set dinner** £21.95 two courses, £37.50 four courses. **Credit** AmEx, DC, JCB, MC, V.

Jason's makes the most of its Little Venice setting, with an attractive, woody interior filled with light, and two pretty canal boats that can be hired for parties or functions. The best tables (which you need to book) are outside next to Regent's Canal. The food, unfortunately, doesn't live up to the location – or the prices. There's an à la carte menu, divided into starters, shellfish and fish, plus a few meat dishes, as well as chef's platters of mixed shellfish and fish (minimum two) and daily specials. For starters, scallops with mushrooms were big and juicy; the cloying quality of grilled goat's cheese was offset by a raspberry vinaigrette; mussels (a special) were a little dry but came with a delicious spicy sauce of tomato, onion and ginger. The emphasis on rich, heavy food continued with main courses. Dover sole (also a special) – a delicate fish best served plainly – came in a buttery almond sauce. Monkfish, covered with crabmeat and a cheese sauce, was absurdly rich (though enjoyable). Even the side dish of new potatoes was swimming in butter. Good grilled prawns came with a heavily prawn-flavoured tomato sauce (described simply as 'herbs and garlic'). Desserts were equally hit and miss: a rather leathery crêpe with a pleasant orange sabayon cream filling; and a hefty banana and almond tart. Still, staff are friendly and the mainly French wine list, though uninspired, is dependable.
Babies and children admitted (daytime only). Book dinner. Disabled: toilet. Dress: smart casual. Separate boats for parties, seating 28 and 36. Tables outdoors (10, canal-side terrace). Vegetarian dishes. **Map 1/4D.**

South West

Chelsea SW3

Creelers

3 Bray Place, SW3 (020 7838 0788). Sloane Square tube. **Lunch served** noon-2.30pm, **dinner served** 6-10.30pm Tue-Sun. **Set lunch** (Mon-Sat) £12 two courses, £15 three courses. **Main courses** £11.95-£17.50. **Credit** AmEx, MC, V.

You can smell it coming in alluring fashion from a block away – which is appropriate, since the focus here is on the first-rate food. The decor is inoffensively, comfortably pastel, the table settings discreetly tasteful and the service quiet, expert and agreeable. Creelers came down from Arran and Edinburgh in late 1999 to purvey its largely Scottish seafood prepared to contemporary standards, and we're glad it did. On one visit we enjoyed most dishes but had cause to question the freshness of some ingredients, yet on a re-check were more impressed. Scallops were small and juicy, wild salmon with asparagus on a bed of spring onion mash was generous and delicious, and cod provençale, though over-salted, was a quality act. First-rate Neal's Yard Dairy cheeses and sweet but moreish rice pudding with summer fruit and coconut caramel made a good finale. Even the wine had a Scottish connection: a Bordeaux rosé put together by a Scottish vigneron. The surroundings might be simple, but the location draws the lairds and ladies of Chelsea – tending towards the smart and middle-aged. A shame, since Creelers deserves a wide audience, though by necessity a rich one.
Babies and children welcome. No-smoking tables. Separate room for parties, seats 30. **Map 12/11F.**

Earl's Court SW5

Lou Pescadou

241 Old Brompton Road, SW5 (020 7370 1057). Earl's Court tube. **Lunch served** noon-3pm, **dinner served** 7pm-midnight daily. **Main courses** £10.80-£23.80. **Set lunch** (Mon-Fri) £9.90 three courses incl cover. **Set meal** (Sat, Sun) £13.50 three courses. **Service** 15%. **Cover** £1.50. **Credit** AmEx, DC, MC, £TC, V.

It seems things have changed at Lou Pescadou. In the past we've had problems with everything from the decor to the staff to the clientele, but not this time. The staff's English is a little better, and on a recent night they were joyous verging on silly. Lights were muted, the atmosphere laid-back but elegant and the tiny back patio under the stars the best place to be. The £1.50 cover charge remains, as does the 15% service charge, but the food was well-prepared, seasoned with a restrained touch and served in huge portions. Appetisers outshine main courses, which tend to be plain, well-cooked dishes. Menu highlights include an enormous bowl of mussels, served steaming in a rich cream and garlic sauce that clung to each mollusc. Tomato, mozzarella and avocado salad was fresh, and dazzling to look at. Among the main courses, top choices are the sea bass, which was grilled until its skin was crisp, the flesh steeped with the sweet taste of fennel. It came with a small bowl of slightly overcooked and under-seasoned courgettes, and a bowl of equally bland boiled potatoes. Sirloin steak, served with a mass of fries, was a large, tender cut on a tangy bed of creamy peppercorn sauce. Desserts are largely traditional French sweets like apple and pear tart, and ice-creams. We particularly relished the frothy, rich, retro-pud of chocolate mousse.
Babies and children welcome; children's menu £5.50. Booking essential. Tables outdoors (7, terrace). **Map 5/11B.**
For branch (The Stratford) see index.

Fulham SW6

Fishnets

Chelsea Village, Stamford Bridge, Fulham Road, SW6 (020 7565 1430). Fulham Broadway tube. **Lunch served** noon-2.30pm Tue-Sat. **Dinner served** 6-10pm Mon-Sat. **Main courses** £7-£14.50. **Service** 12½%. **Credit** AmEx, DC, MC, V.

Part of Chelsea FC's Chelsea Village complex, Fishnets exudes an air of bland corporate hospitality. It was empty bar a group of besuited businessmen on the night we visited, and staff obviously didn't have enough to do; we were asked by three separate waiters if we wanted a pre-dinner drink. The room has a rather gloomy wood and maroon colour scheme, and is half-heartedly decorated with nautical artefacts. It lacks any individuality, and feels like a hotel restaurant (which is really what it is). Yet this isn't a stuffy place. As with fish!, the menu is written on paper placemats and offers a variety of fish grilled, steamed or roasted, with a choice of sauces, plus fish 'n' chips – but there's none of the elan of fish!. Prices are good (sea bass for £10.50, oysters for £1.35 a throw, and veg side orders at £1.50 each), but this is no compensation for lack of quality. For starters, grilled sardines were rather dry, and seafood chowder bland. Side dishes of soggy broccoli and greasy mash did little to enliven a small and overcooked portion of sea bass. The tuna niçoise was a winner, though, with large,

succulent slabs of fish. Puds, such as ice-cream and crème brûlée, are standard in style and flavour, but the wine list is better than you might expect, given the rest of the fare. Overall, a bit of an own goal for Chelsea.
Babies and children welcome; high chairs.
Booking advisable. Tables outdoors (8, patio).
Takeaway service (match days). **Map 5/13B.**

South Kensington SW3, SW7

Bibendum Oyster Bar
Michelin House, 81 Fulham Road, SW3 (020 7581 5817). South Kensington tube. **Meals served** noon-11pm Mon-Fri; 12.30-11pm Sat; 12.30-10.30pm Sun. **Main courses** £14.50-£24.50. **Service** 12½%. **Credit** AmEx, DC, MC, £TC, V.
A charming place to while away a leisurely lunch, the oyster bar is located just off the beautiful foyer of the Michelin building. You can sit in the bright, airy bar (decorated with black and white photos), but nicer are the tables in the foyer itself, surrounded by fabulous tiled pictures of cars. Oysters are a speciality, of course – six very fresh Irish, Scottish and French rocks cost £7.50 – and there are also clams, crabs, langoustines, a grand seafood plateau (minimum two people), salads and a handful of larger dishes, as well as a daily-changing specials menu of fish and meat dishes, all served cold. Portions are more suited to casual snacking than a full-blown meal, but ingredients are first-class and presentation is elegant. Brown shrimp salad with french beans and fennel came with a tangy tarragon dressing, while slivers of pink veal contrasted well with a rich, dark lentil salad and parsley-heavy salsa verde. For dessert, a special of intensely flavoured passion-fruit sorbet was more successful than crème brûlée. Staff are attentive and eager to please, and the mainly white wine list is admirable, with six champagnes available by the half-bottle and four house wines by the glass, bottle and 450ml 'pot'. Outside, there's a coffee counter and a fish stall, where you can stock up on shellfish as you leave.
Babies and children welcome; high chairs.
Booking essential. Vegetarian menu. **Map 12/10E.**

Downstairs at One Ninety
190 Queens Gate, SW7 (020 7581 5666). Gloucester Road tube.
Bar **Open** 11am-1am daily.
Restaurant **Dinner served** 6-11pm Mon-Sat. **Main courses** £10-£13.95. **Set dinner** £21 two courses, £25 three courses. **Service** 12½%. **Credit** AmEx, DC, JCB, MC, V.
With its splendid wooden panelling, cosy red velvet bucket seats and sparkling table settings, Downstairs at One Ninety has the feel of a dining room in a stately home. But with wine coolers placed strategically over the frayed areas of an aging white carpet, the grandeur is fading. The same could be said of the food, from an inventive, internationally inspired menu that has been far better delivered on previous visits. Ceviche of red snapper cocktail, from a starter list bristling with intercontinental ingredients, was dull, though pertly served in a Martini glass. The shikado box, containing six mini-portions of daily changing dishes, was pretty patchy, veering from lacklustre lobster to a fine red Thai mussel stew via an average prawn fajita. A main course of swordfish with pineapple, red pepper salsa and aubergine was ordinary. Desserts were similarly hit and miss: a definite hit for a tower of intense chocolate mousse and shortbread; a miss for an uninspired orange tart. Though the food was slightly disappointing, the meal could still have been successful had there been any atmosphere. But with our table the only one occupied for the bulk of Friday evening, and the service therefore a little stilted, we didn't even get that. We turned to the well-judged wine list for consolation, with a good bottle of New World riesling.
Babies and children admitted. Booking advisable. Dress: smart casual. Separate room for parties, seats 24. Vegetarian dishes. **Map 12/9D.**

Poissonnerie de l'Avenue
82 Sloane Avenue, SW3 (020 7589 2457). South Kensington tube. **Lunch served** noon-3pm, **dinner served** 7-11.30pm Mon-Sat. **Main courses** £12.50-£34. **Set lunches** £10.95 one course, £14.95 two courses, £18.95 three courses. **Cover** £1.50. **Service** 15%. **Credit** AmEx, DC, JCB, MC, £TC, V.
You'd better dress up smart for a visit to the Poissonnerie or you'll feel out of place among the immaculately groomed, middle-aged locals who pack the place on a midweek night. The design is as old-fashioned as the customers – acres of white tablecloths, Old Master-style oil paintings on panelled walls, carnations in silver vases. The cooking, too, matches the clientele,

being rich but unadventurous, poised but predictable. The lengthy menu contains a mixed bag of starters (£6.50-£12.50): fresh, if slightly tasteless prawns; a palatable fish soup (with an odd-tasting rouille); and an overly rich crab and spinach tart with cheese sauce. For mains, scallops (with Creole rice and butter sauce) were fat and very fresh, but fillets of sole with asparagus tips and prawns in a light white wine sauce wasn't so successful; the sole was undercooked, the sauce was a hollandaise and the asparagus was more stalks than tips. Best stick to the simpler dishes, such as grilled Dover sole, which was cooked to perfection. Side dishes were disappointing: soggy spinach, watery puréed carrots; only the celeriac chips had any flavour. Still, the mainly French wine list is well-chosen, and the service is generally polished (although the formal, black-waistcoated waiters can be offhand; one said he couldn't provide a particular aperitif, then walked off before we could ask for an alternative). Expect to pay SW7 prices. An eggcup-sized 'chocolate pot' cost a laughable £6 – but the set lunch menus are more reasonable.
Babies and children admitted (lunch). Book dinner. Dress: smart casual. Separate room for parties, seats 20. Vegetarian menu. **Map 12/10E.**

South

Clapham SW4

Moxon's ★
14 Clapham Park Road, SW4 (020 7627 2468). Clapham Common tube. **Dinner served** 6.30-11pm Mon-Sat. **Main courses** £9.95-£15.95. **Set menu** £12.50 two courses 6.30-7.30pm. **Service** 10% for parties of eight or more. **Credit** MC, V.
Moxon's low-key but stylish surroundings let the food do the talking. Fishing print textiles and select pieces of modern art provide simple decoration, while smiling staff provide professional service with a personal touch. The food is a delight. Succulent seared diver scallops on a bed of sautéed cabbage were flavoured with a frothy Thai-inspired coconut and lemongrass broth. Skate and leek terrine with chardonnay vinaigrette had an interesting combination of delicate flavours but was rather over-chilled. Next we reluctantly decided against sea bass with confit of potatoes and mussels in a saffron broth, choosing instead a perfect black bream fillet, served on a colourful, flavour-packed bed of roast beetroot, olives, green beans and tomatoes. Equally excellent was an extraordinarily thick piece of sole (more a platform heel than a flip-flop) that came with creamy broad bean and lemon thyme risotto and a zingy sprinkling of red peppercorns. For dessert we shared the day's special, an ambrosial pancake stuffed with apple purée and served with Calvados cream. Within days of eating here we were told Robin Moxon plans to revamp this excellent local restaurant; here's hoping the exemplary food doesn't suffer.
Babies and children welcome. Booking advisable. Vegetarian dishes.

Kennington SE11

The Lobster Pot
3 Kennington Lane, SE11 (020 7582 5556). Kennington tube/Elephant & Castle tube/rail. **Lunch served** noon-2.30pm, **dinner served** 7-11pm Tue-Sat. **Main courses** £5.80-£18.50. **Minimum** (8-10pm) £20. **Set lunch** £10 two courses, £13.50 three courses. **Set dinner** £19.50 three courses. **Set meal** £39.50 eight-course surprise menu. **Credit** AmEx, DC, JCB, LV, MC, TC, V.
Marooned on a traffic-locked corner, the Lobster Pot asserts its maritime credentials with an insistence that would be laughable were it not for the excellent fish cooking that backs it up. Seagulls shriek at the door, staff are decked out in striped Breton shirts, and fishing tackle decorates the small, wooden-clad dining room, whose portholes look into a murky aquarium. We started with perfectly cooked prawn brochetta, an enticing smokiness shining through its accompanying smoked salmon sauce. A Breton soupe de poissons was tasty and substantial, coming with an authentic, punchy rouille – but the kitchen needed two attempts to heat it properly. Next, Dover sole, although expertly filleted and cooked, didn't live up to the promise of the starters. Marlin in Cajun spices was better (meaty and well spiced) but the choice of vegetables with it was disappointing. However, a sublime melt-in-the-mouth tarte tatin ensured the meal finished on a high note. The restaurant was reassuringly busy for a weekday evening; service

Bibendum Oyster Bar

was smiley and attentive. Neat touches included a plate of amuses gueules (olives wrapped in fresh anchovies) with aperitifs, and a sardine tin full of mints with coffee. Despite its kitsch setting, the Lobster Pot is no budget option – our bill with drinks came to just over £100 for two – but the quality of food is high.
Booking advisable. Children welcome. Dress: smart casual. Vegetarian dishes (on request).

Waterloo SE1

Livebait ★
41-45 The Cut, SE1 (020 7928 7211). Southwark or Waterloo tube/rail. **Lunch served** noon-3pm, **dinner served** 5.30-11.30pm Mon-Sat. **Main courses** £15-£17. **Set meal** (lunch Mon-Fri; 5.30-7pm, 10-11.30pm, Mon-Sat) £12.50 two courses, £15.50 three courses. **Credit** AmEx, DC, MC, JCB, £TC, V.
Undiminished by takeover (by Chez Gerard), diffusion (more branches) and cookbook celebrity, the original Livebait continues to flourish. The trademark strengths that fuelled its success remain: impeccably fresh seafood; a simple, flexible and interesting menu; a pleasant, unimposing environment; and engaged and intelligent service. Livebait Waterloo has three dining rooms: all white-tiled and big-windowed and with a kitchen or bar focus. All but the smoking room have cosy green diner booths. The menu changes monthly. A meal kicks off with free prawns, then might progress to either short lists of seafood (oysters, whelks and the like) and starters, such as honey roasted squid, and Thai crab cakes (luscious, but oddly textured). Mains either mix and match fish with cooking styles and accompaniments, or are more creative dishes such as coriander tempura of skate and crevette, or a cod on lentil curry that fair pulsed with flavours. The details are spot on: interesting breads (baked in-house), a short specials board presented at table, and a good-value set menu – useful, since despite the informal atmosphere, Livebait is far from cheap.
Babies and children admitted. Booking essential one week in advance. Disabled: toilet. Vegetarian dishes (on request). **Map 7/8N.**
For branches see index.

Borough SE1

fish! ★
Cathedral Street, SE1 (020 7234 3333). London Bridge tube/rail. **Lunch served** 11.30am-2.45pm Mon-Sat; noon-3.30pm Sun. **Dinner served** 5.30-10.30pm Mon-Sat. **Main courses** £8.90-£15.50. **Service** 12%. **Credit** AmEx, DC, MC, V.
You'll have to learn to love that exclamation mark, because though fish! is about being perky and in your face, it's also about great seafood and a good time. So good, in fact, that it has expanded into new branches in and out of London: but that was always the plan, presumably, since everything from the menu/tablemat and staff tunics to the environmental policies and groovy website always looked ripe for replication. We've always enjoyed eating here. There are a few gripes – tables too close together, relentlessly buoyant staff, the odd disappointing dish – but prices are fine and the formula convenient. The menu is split between smaller dishes (some for omnivores), and a 'choose your own' section, whereby the diner picks one of the available fish and then has it either steamed or grilled and served with salsa, hollandaise, herb butter, olive oil dressing or red wine fish gravy. Elsewhere on the menu, oysters for a quid each did the job well; devilled whitebait and fish pie were a little bland; and the fruit salad was lovely. The under-arch, market location and attention-seeking glass and metal design add a sense of occasion. fish! aims to recapture fish for the working (well, OK, largely middle) classes: and it succeeds.
Babies and children welcome; colouring books; high-chairs. Disabled: toilet. **Map 8/8P.**
For branches see index.

Tower Bridge E1

Aquarium
Ivory House, St Katharine-by-the-Tower, E1 (020 7480 6116). Tower Hill tube/DLR. **Brunch served** noon-3pm Sat, Sun. **Lunch served** noon-3pm Mon-Fri. **Dinner served** 6.30-11pm Mon-Sat. **Main courses** £13-£23. **Set meal** £14.50 two courses, £17.50 three courses. **Credit** AmEx, DC, MC, V.
Overlooking touristy but pretty St Katharine's Dock with its speedboats and high-masted yachts, Aquarium is popular, especially in the week, with City workers, rich tourists and boating types. Its simple blue and white decor is attractive, although

the white-draped ceiling is claustrophobically low. The fresh-faced staff are attentive and friendly. The eclectic and expensive menu reads well but doesn't always live up to expectations. For starters, there's plenty of plain shellfish, including excellent Irish rock oysters (£1.30 a go), crab and lobster, as well as more creative dishes. No complaints about starters of plump seared scallops with noodles in a chilli and honey broth (a scary £11.50), and a hefty slice of seared gravadlax with smoked cod's roe (a more reasonable £7.50). The fashion of combining meat and fish is evident in a couple of dishes, including a main of red mullet with potato and chorizo millefeuille and cauliflower purée; the mullet was perfect but the chorizo almost invisible. Good but not great roast cod came perched on a prawn and thyme mash that turned out to be a curious hard-crusted cylinder with very liquidy mash inside. Portions aren't big and you can't order extra veg. Desserts were similarly half-successful: we liked the light raspberry omelette, but crème brûlée was nothing special. The wine list is absurdly high-priced (the cheapest bottle is £19) and filter coffee for £3.50 a shot is just a joke.
Babies and children welcome; high chairs. Booking advisable. Separate room for parties, seats 150. Tables outdoors (14, patio). Vegetarian dishes. **Map 8/8S.**

Richmond, Surrey

Ocean
100 Kew Road, Richmond, Surrey (020 8948 8008). Richmond tube/rail/27, 65, R68 bus. **Meals served** noon-10.30pm Sun. **Dinner served** 6-11pm Mon-Sat. **Main courses** £8-£15.50. **Credit** AmEx, MC, V.
The split-level interior is stylishly decorated in a modern, Conran kind of way. The menu is reassuringly brief and reassuringly expensive (though not overpriced), and tends towards the modern (sushi, seared tuna), but with enough to satisfy traditionalists (dressed crab, fish pie). Our dishes were mostly good. A starter of eel was smoked and firm-fleshed, quite unlike the Cockney way of eating it. Salt and pepper shrimp is originally a Chinese dish, and this was a good version – though the batter was uncannily similar to the beer batter used for the deep-fried cod and chips. Said cod had signs of being frozen (the flesh was soft and mushy, not firm and distinct), but it tasted fine, served on a mound of mushed garden peas, an interesting interpretation of mushy peas. Our other main, pan-roasted sword-fish, accompanied by broad bean risotto, was delicious and fresh. There's outdoor seating along this entire restaurant row, yet plenty of traffic noise, too – still that's a small complaint for a local that deserves a warm welcome.
Babies and children admitted.

Twickenham, Middlesex

Loch Fyne Restaurant at the Fisherman's Hut
175 Hampton Road, Twickenham, Middx (020 8255 6222/www.loch-fyne.com). Fulwell, Strawberry Hill or Twickenham rail. **Meals served** 9am-10pm Mon-Sat; 10am-10.30pm Sun. **Set lunch** (Mon-Fri) £9.95 two courses. **Main courses** £4.95-£34.95. **Credit** AmEx, DC, MC, £TC, V.
Loch Fyne is a distinct improvement on the Fisherman's Hut, which occupied the building before. The tacky fishy decor and the gloomy pub area have vanished; now it's all light-wood flooring and furniture, and cream walls. The food is better, too. The place is an offshoot of the famous Loch Fyne oyster farm and restaurant in Argyll, so oysters, as you might expect, are a speciality – and good value, at £5.95 for six. The menu is nominally divided into starters and mains, but you're free to choose what you want, in any order. There's a definite Scottish slant, resulting in such dishes as Bradan Rost (salmon roasted in a smoke kiln, served hot with a whisky and horseradish sauce: a definite winner), Glen Fyne Scotch rib-eye steak, and Scottish farmhouse cheeses. Top marks go to the creamy peppered mackerel pâté, served with oatcakes, but smoked haddock chowder lacked flavour, and langoustine salad was spoiled by being drowned in an overpowering Thousand Island-style dressing. Fruit crumble was melt-in-your-mouth gorgeous – and large enough for two. Service was a little offhand, but excusable considering how busy the restaurant was. The majority of the shellfish and smoked fish comes from Loch Fyne itself and, admirably, the restaurant makes a point of using wild, free-range or sustainably resourced ingredients.
Babies and children admitted; high chairs. Book weekends. No-smoking tables. Tables outdoors (10, patio). Vegetarian dishes.

French

Central

Barbican EC1

Simply Nico
*7 Goswell Road, EC1 (020 7336 7677).
Barbican tube/4 bus.*
Bar **Open** noon-11pm Mon-Fri; 6-11pm Sat.
Restaurant **Breakfast served** 7-9.30am,
lunch served noon-2.30pm Mon-Fri. **Dinner
served** 6-10.30pm Mon-Sat. **Main courses**
£9.50-£15.90. **Set lunch** £15 three courses,
£25 three courses. **Pre-theatre menu** (6-8pm
Mon-Sat) £12.50 two courses.
Both **Credit** AmEx, DC, MC, £TC, V.
Well-known Matisse prints, lemon paintwork and
attractive frosted glass (to obscure the mock-
Tudor Barbican flats opposite) give Simply Nico
the feel of a hotel dining room; which, in a way,
it is. Thus, it caters to all tastes and thrills none
(note that Nico Ladenis is no longer connected to
the chain that bears his name). We went on a
Saturday night and the blandness had edged over
into disengagement. There was no fish for the
'fish of the day' slot, there were no sorbets and
the waiter positively sniffed when we asked
whether there were any rosés on the wine list.
Soup of the day, gazpacho (£5.50), had been
liquidised into homogeneity and so had none of
the essential crunchy bits, nor much of a
Mediterranean kick. Our other choice – deep-fried
nutty goat's cheese salad, pickled onions and
confit tomatoes – was fine, but costly at £7.90.
Next, calf's liver with balsamic jus and celeriac
mash was pretty bland, while the salmon fish
cake, spinach and sorrel sauce was heavy and
dry. For dessert (all around £5), fruit platter was
refreshing but lacked zip. Other choices included
tiramisu with hazelnut croccante, and dark
chocolate mousse. A restaurant in need of an
injection of enthusiasm.
*Babies and children admitted. Book lunch.
Dress: smart casual. Separate rooms for
parties, seating 6-40.* **Map 15/5O.**
For branches see index.

Belgravia SW1

La Poule au Pot
*231 Ebury Street, SW1 (020 7730 7763).
Sloane Square tube/Victoria tube/rail.* **Lunch
served** 12.30-2.30pm daily. **Dinner served**
7-11.15pm Mon-Sat; 7-10.30pm Sun. **Main
courses** £12.50-£19. **Set lunch** £16 three
courses. **Service** 12½%. **Credit** AmEx, DC,
LV, MC, £TC, V.
Nostalgia is just what it used to be at La Poule au
Pot. Immensely popular with its largely middle-
aged francophile clientele, this long-established
favourite is equally appealing in summer and
winter. A terrace at the front provides alfresco
dining in the warmer months, while the rambling,
wooden-floored, candle-lit interior is enveloping
romantic in colder weather. Usually, the casual
bonhomie of the determinedly French staff adds
to the feeling of well-being and mitigates what is,
frankly, an overpriced if enjoyable glad-to-be-trad
menu. Soupe à l'oignon was overwhelmed by the
cheesy raft floating on its surface; better was a
superbly earthy campagne terrine flecked with
creamy foie gras (though outrageously priced at
£13). To follow, a classic gigot d'agneau with
flageolets was all it should have been, but magret
de canard with lime overdosed on citric flavours.
The chips are good, and come à l'anglaise,
wrapped in paper. A light chocolate mousse and
a reasonable cheese selection provided a
satisfactory finale. The wines rarely stray beyond
Burgundy and Bordeaux and offer few surprises
(and few under £20). Despite these reservations,
you have to be unusually curmudgeonly (or
budget-minded) not to warm to La Poule au Pot.
*Babies and children welcome. Booking advisable.
Separate room for parties, seats 15. Tables
outdoors (10, pavement terrace).* **Map 6/11G.**

Roussillon
*16 St Barnabas Street, SW1 (020 7730 5550).
Sloane Square tube.* **Lunch served**
noon-2.15pm Mon-Fri. **Dinner served**
6.30-10.45pm Mon-Sat. **Set lunch** £15 two

courses, £18 three courses. **Set dinner** £25
two courses, £29.50 three courses. **Set meals**
£29 six courses (Garden menu), £40 seven
courses. **Service** 12½%. **Credit** AmEx, DC,
JCB, LV, MC, £TC, V.
Despite being an upmarket French restaurant,
Roussillon takes special care of vegetarians, even
down to providing a regularly changing six-
course 'Garden' menu. Expect dishes like broad
beans in herb consommé, wild garlic potato
purée, a stir-fry of early spring vegetables in a
balsamic vinegar dressing, and white gnocchi of
ricotta with sautéed chanterelle and chervil. This
range and quality earned Roussillon a place in
the six finalists for Best Vegetarian Meal in the
Time Out Eating & Drinking Awards 1999 and
2000. Fish eaters are well catered for with the
'Sea' menu, featuring such delights as grilled cut
of turbot with fondant cos lettuce and simple fish
bone reduction or John Dory cooked in leaves, figs
and spicy aubergine. Meat-eaters needn't panic,
either, as the 'Land' menu has plenty of meaty
choices; get your tongue around the fussily
worded grilled dynamic Shedbush Farm lamb
rubbed with fresh mint, fennel and flowering
chive gratin, herb and olive oil, or pigeon and foie
gras from the grill with fondant potatoes. The
restaurant's two rooms look something like the
interior of a smart French country home,
decorated with modern paintings and plenty of
pastel shades. Despite the high standards of
service and cooking, the atmosphere at Roussillon
is unstuffy and ebullient.
*Booking advisable. No-smoking tables. Separate
room for parties, seating 30.* **Map 6/11G.**

City EC2, EC3

1 Lombard Street
*1 Lombard Street, EC3 (020 7929 6611/
www.1lombardstreet.com). Bank tube/DLR
exit 7.*
Bar **Open** 11am-11pm Mon-Fri.
Brasserie & restaurant **Lunch served** noon-
3pm, **dinner served** 6-10pm Mon-Fri. **Main
courses** £9.75-£26.50 brasserie; £24.50-
£29.50 restaurant. **Service** 12½%.
Both **Credit** AmEx, DC, JCB, MC, £TC, V.
This restaurant is as smart and assured as its
predominantly pin-striped clientele. There's a
formal, expensive restaurant on the premises, but
we ate in the main brasserie, an impressively clean,
slightly austere space, dominated by a central
circular bar and flanked by tables laden with crisp
white cloths and intimate banquette seating. There
are plenty of interesting, neatly assembled dishes
on the menu, as well as the more predictable
selections of caviar and other high-finance fodder.
We opted for one of the chef's recommendations,
gazpacho, which was a light and refreshing
starter; casserole of mussels and clams, however,
arrived in a disappointingly flavourless, brackish
marinière broth. Our main course, coq au vin
bourguignon, proved to be an infinitely more
enjoyable, robust rendition of a classic French
dish. Coriander, lemon and lime leaf risotto was
more delicate, although it had been artfully souped
up with a sharp ginger jus and perfectly cooked
prawns. We finished with a cleansing terrine of
summer berries. The extensive (and expensive)
wine list and the ceremonious service, like
everything else here, are geared towards City suits.
*Babies and children welcome. Booking essential
lunch; advisable dinner. Separate room for
parties, seats 40.* **Map 4/6Q.**

Le Coq d'Argent
*No.1 Poultry, EC2 (020 7395 5000/5050/
www.conran.com). Bank tube/DLR.*
Bar **Open** 11.30am-11pm Mon-Fri; 6.30-11pm
Sat. **Main courses** £10.50-£16.50.
Restaurant **Breakfast served** 7.30-10am
Mon-Fri. **Lunch served** 11.30am-3pm Mon-
Fri; noon-3pm Sun. **Dinner served** 6-10pm
Mon-Fri; 6.30-10pm Sat. **Main courses** £10.50-
£21. **Service** 12½%.
Both **Credit** AmEx, DC, JCB, MC, V.
To call his City restaurant the 'Silver Cock' may
seem to chime with Sir Terence Conran's
awesome self-image, but we prefer to assume that
the name comes from the address (No.1 Poultry)
rather than from an incipient mid-life crisis.

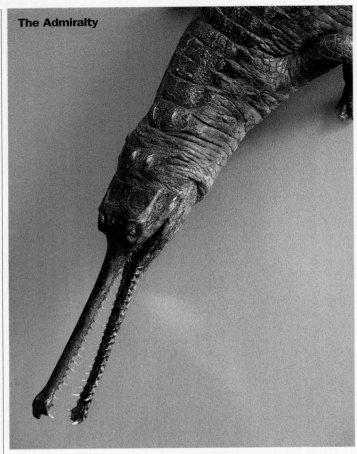

The Admiralty

Certainly the title does little justice to the menu, which is fresh and French, but (discounting the numerous pages of wines, spirits, cocktails and cigars) dominated by seafood. You could start with half a dozen rock oysters and follow with lobster, langoustine or (as we did) a plateau de fruits de mer. The ruggedly authentic petit plateau costs £18 and is crowded with half a crab, oysters, winkles, clams, prawns and other alarming things in shells. Vegetarians are also well served: a starter of gazpacho was a little over-spiced, but roast peppers with mozzarella and anchovies was beautifully accomplished and a main course of marinated vegetables with houmous and chive oil was colourful and crisp. We chose to sit outside on the bar side of the rooftop (covered) terrace, which boasts a seafood beach hut, heaters and a view of the City rooftops. The main restaurant is just as bright, but the menu's longer and the atmosphere a nudge more formal. Service is out of the Conran school of casual professionalism. A golden egg.
Babies and children admitted. Booking essential; bookings not accepted for bar or terrace. Disabled: toilet. Tables outdoors (60, restaurant terrace; 150, bar terrace). **Map 4/6P**.

Clerkenwell & Farringdon EC1

Café du Marché
22 Charterhouse Square, Charterhouse Mews, EC1 (020 7608 1609). Barbican tube/ Farringdon tube/rail. **Lunch served** noon-2.30pm Mon-Fri. **Dinner served** 6-10pm Mon-Sat. **Set meal** £24.95 three courses. **Service** 15%. **Credit** MC, £$TC, V.
Despite its location, tucked behind the tidy urban greenery of Charterhouse Square, Café du Marché oozes rustic charm. Solid beams, exposed brickwork and simple furnishings extend over two floors, with a pianist providing subdued spells of dinner jazz. The menu is written entirely in French, but don't rely on the staff for explanations: they seemed to know less than us. A more serious glitch in staff-customer relations came when our waiter tipped a brimming glass of wine all over us, and then legged it into the kitchen, never to be seen again. But not even wine-sodden trousers could spoil our enjoyment of the food. A starter of cotriade was the kind of hearty stew of fish, shellfish and chunky potatoes that trawlermen daydream about. Coarse rabbit terrine with a fabulously tart apple compote was equally satisfying. Mains were just as gutsy; navarin of spring lamb was meltingly tender in its ragout of seasonal veg, while chicken breast with morels, perhaps a little too rich for a main course, was still very tasty. Naturally, we had to skip pudding. Worth a visit, but arrive with a healthy appetite (and a pair of waterproof trousers).
Booking essential lunch. Entertainment: jazz duo 8-11pm Mon-Sat. Separate rooms for parties, seating 30 and 65. **Map 15/50**.

Chez Gérard
84-86 Rosebery Avenue, EC1 (020 7833 1515/ www.santeonline.co.uk). Angel tube/19, 38, 55, 341 bus. **Open** 11.45am-11pm Mon-Fri; 5.30-11pm Sat. **Brunch served** noon-3.30pm Sun. **Lunch served** 11.45am-3pm Mon-Fri. **Dinner served** 5.30-11pm Mon-Sat. **Main courses** £4.95-£8.95 café, £9.70-£20 restaurant. **Set lunch & pre-theatre menu** £12.50 two courses. **Set meal** £15.95 three courses. **Cover charge** £1 restaurant. **Service** 12½%. **Credit** AmEx, DC, MC, £TC, V.
Another year passes and the grill-meisters at Chez Gérard are still wooing London diners with the simple pleasures of perfectly cooked steaks and unfussy French food. The decor, too, remains the same: high ceilings, large windows, railway carriage-style seating around the edges and a glittering bar. Steaks are the undoubted speciality but the lengthy menu has a number of viable alternatives up its sleeve. We began with fish soup with rouille and croutons. The soup itself was fine (not too salty and obviously freshly made) but the rouille was an insipid substitute for the real thing, lacking that distinctive rust colour and devoid of any trace of chilli. When the 9oz fillet steak arrived, though, we remembered what we'd come for; thick, juicy and perfectly rare, it was surrounded by a mountain of spindly chips. Grilled fillet of sea bass was firm and flavoursome, complemented well by its accompaniments of leek mash and dill oil. Finally, to make total pigs of ourselves, we managed to dispatch a petit pot au chocolat, an intense chocolate mousse topped with Cointreau. The wine list is short and to the point, and service is swift and amicable.
Babies and children welcome. Booking advisable dinner Fri, Sat. No-smoking tables. Separate room for parties, seats 40. Tables outdoors (2, pavement). **Map 15/3N**.
For branches see index.

Club Gascon ★
57 West Smithfield, EC1 (020 7796 0600). Barbican tube/Farringdon tube/rail. **Lunch served** noon-2pm Mon-Fri. **Dinner served** 7-11pm Mon-Fri; 7-10.30pm Sat. **Tapas** £3.50-£24. **Set meal** £30 five courses. **Service** 12½%. **Credit** JCB, MC, TC, V.
Refreshing and unique as it is among London's French restaurants, Club Gascon is by no means trading on its novelty value; this is a restaurant of substance. It's an elegant yet relaxed place, with restrained dark wood and fine upholstery offsetting a colourful explosion of flowers at the far end of the room. But the real attraction is the beguiling, highly accomplished regional cooking. The menu, inspired by the flavours and traditions of south-west France, is divided into specific themes: 'Les Pâturages' (literally 'pastures'), for example, includes proper country dishes, such as cassoulet, while 'La Route du Sel' features dishes that have all been cured or cooked in salt. Portions are tapas size, encouraging diners to experiment; we found that seven between two was about right. All seven were magnificent, but top marks went to notably succulent roast pigeon with prune chutney and sticky fennel caramel, and foie gras that had been grilled to dissolving perfection, served with fat grapes. Aromatic red mullet with wild herb sorbet was another intelligent and memorable combination. The wine list is similarly varied and steadfastly regional and the charming staff seem genuinely enthused by the menu. Cellar Gascon next door is the restaurant's faster, noisier wine bar (*see p219* **Wine Bars**).
Babies and children admitted. Booking essential. **Map 15/50**.

Dibbens
2-3 Cowcross Street, EC1 (020 7250 0035). Farringdon tube/rail/55 bus. **Lunch served** noon-2.30pm, **dinner served** 6-11pm, Mon-Fri. **Main courses** £10.50-£16. **Set meal** £14.50 two courses; £10 two courses before 7.15pm. **Service** 12½%. **Credit** AmEx, MC, V.
The arrival of our party of three more than doubled the headcount in Dibbens' slick, muted dining room. Apart from being rather unnerving (there's space for at least another 50), this was hardly encouraging. But great bread – baked around the corner at St John – and decent house wine took us off our guard (and anyway, this is more of a lunchtime venue). A fine signature dish of caramelised shallot and Taleggio tart was to follow, but another starter of seared tuna, potato and green bean terrine quivered apologetically on the plate and was no sooner eaten than forgotten. From the same school of blandness, a stodgy main of salmon ravioli was shipped to the table in an anonymous cream sauce, allowing a far superior slab of perfectly rare steak to hog the limelight. Sticky caramelised pineapple with own-made coconut ice-cream was the sole memorable dessert.
Babies and children welcome. Entertainment: pianist 7pm Fri. Separate room for parties, seats 14. Tables outdoors (2, pavement). **Map 15/50**.

Covent Garden WC2

The Admiralty ★
Somerset House, The Strand, WC2 (020 7845 4646). Embankment or Temple tube. Bar **Open** 11am-11pm daily. *Restaurant* **Lunch served** noon-2.45pm daily. **Dinner served** 6-10.45pm Mon-Sat. **Main courses** £6.50-£18.50. **Service** 12½%. *Both* **Credit** AmEx, DC, JCB, MC, V.
The catering at Somerset House is run by Oliver Peyton, not a man known for taking safe and easy options. Following in the quality footsteps of his other restaurants, the Admiralty is quirky and fun, with high culinary standards. There was evidence of a south-western influence in the terrines of the day, which included duck rillette and a pork terrine, both served in generous bistro portions with superb bread and cornichons. A classic French summer dish is pot au feu of stewed beef served cool in its own clarified jelly with baby vegetables. Veal chop was served rare as requested, with unusual varieties of fresh wild mushrooms and broad beans. All these dishes were more than ship-shape. The only low point was a fillet of red mullet, which had an unpleasant fishy smell that not even a serving of roast fennel could hide. Admiralty's wine list is outstanding, though not cheap. Familiar, easy-to-sell bottles have been avoided in favour of wines from south-west France, echoing the restaurant's theme of 'cuisine du terroir'. However, check the bill: though a service charge of 12½% had been included, the credit card slip had a space for adding on a further 'tip'. If you're as sober as a seaman on shore leave, you can easily end up paying twice for service.
Babies and children admitted; high chairs. Disabled: toilet. No smoking. Tables outdoors (21, riverside terrace). **Map 14/7M**.

S'il vous plaît !

L'Estaminet

14 Garrick Street, WC2 (020 7379 1432). Covent Garden or Embankment tube/Charing Cross tube/rail.

La Tartine wine bar **Open** noon-11pm Mon-Fri. **Main courses** £7-£9.
Restaurant **Lunch served** noon-2.30pm Mon-Fri; noon-2pm Sat. **Dinner served** 5.45-11pm Mon-Sat. **Main courses** £12.40-£16.50. **Pre-theatre menu** (5.45-7.30pm) £10.99 three courses Mon-Fri, £14.50 Sat.
Both **Service** 12½%. **Credit** AmEx, JCB, MC, £TC, V.

Students of restaurant fashion may find the more traditional values of this Covent Garden spot not to their liking, but so much the better for anyone wishing to enjoy good, basic, rich French cuisine with a global spin. The decor has a discreet bourgeois charm and the atmosphere lacks the brashness of many West End eateries. So instead of funky design, L'Estaminet has simple bare brick and sandy colours. Wicker and chrome furnishings surround linen-covered tables attended by studious but cheerful French staff. The menu contains all the trusty classics such as crème vichyssoise, fruits de mer, chateaubriand and coquilles Saint Jacques. For starters, we had a toothsome prawn fricassée in a creamy, tarragon, orange and wine sauce, plus a skewer of fat juicy prawns marinated in Thai spices. Then, from the grill, the entrecote proved a fine, smoky juicy steak with frites and green veg, and Paride de Poissons was a gently cooked parade of fish. A tasty magret de canard was served with a creamy pepper sauce (normally associated with steak), a rubble of chopped, crispy fried potatoes and beautifully fresh spinach. By the end of our post-theatre dinner, it had grown too late to put the luscious French tartes through their paces or cut into the trolley of gloriously high cheeses; we're sure they would have sung with our robust claret from the ample range of regional wines.

Babies and children admitted. Booking essential. Separate room for parties, seats 20. **Map 14/7L.**

Mon Plaisir

21 Monmouth Street, WC2 (020 7836 7243). Covent Garden or Leicester Square tube.

Lunch served noon-2.15pm Mon-Fri. **Dinner served** 5.30-11.15pm Mon-Sat. **Main courses** £13.95-£15. **Set lunch** £14.95 three courses. **Pre-theatre menu** (5.50-7.15pm) £11.95 two courses, £14.95 three courses, incl glass of wine, coffee. **Service** 12½%. **Credit** AmEx, DC, MC, £TC, V.

You'd never guess it from the enormous and rather cheesy tricolore flag outside, but Mon Plaisir is a class act. The menu is typically French, with an emphasis on quality ingredients, while the decor (recently renovated) is that of an upmarket Parisian brasserie: a cosy warren of rooms filled with mirrors, dark wood and rows of sparkling glasses. From a list of daily specials we chose an excellent starter of cured duck with rillettes and haricot salad, which arrived in an earthy nut-oil dressing. A main course of entrecôte grillé, which is something of a house speciality, was cooked to pink perfection and practically buried beneath a tangle of matchstick chips. A second, less impressive main of roast squab pigeon was accompanied by sticky pasta and a stodgy casserole of peas and broad beans. Things got back on track with the desserts, with superb crème brûlée providing a well-judged bitter-sweet finale. The wine list has a good showing of French wines and a rather pointless codicil of five New Worlders. There's also a decent selection of set menus for those on a budget or in a hurry.

Babies and children admitted. Booking essential. Separate room for parties, seats 28. **Map 14/6L.**

Le Palais du Jardin

136 Long Acre, WC2 (020 7379 5353). Covent Garden or Leicester Square tube/Charing Cross tube/rail.

Bar **Open** noon-11.45pm Mon-Sat; noon-11pm Sun.
Restaurant **Lunch served** noon-3pm, **dinner served** 5.30-11.45pm Mon-Sat. **Meals served** noon-11pm Sun. **Main courses** £12.50-£19.50. **Service** 12½%.
Both **Credit** AmEx, DC, MC, £TC, V.

Dinner here raised one unanswerable question: why was this restaurant full? Its stylish interior probably helps, as must its position on the tourist trail, but shoddy food and imperious service left us vowing never to return. From the outset, our waiter seemed determined never to stray more than two steps from the table, self-importantly refilling our wine glasses at every sip (despite numerous requests for him not to). Then there was the food. Roast goat's cheese inexplicably arrived in an armour of breadcrumbs, while a second starter (salad of seared tuna) was gatecrashed by an unannounced boiled egg and a gang of soggy capers, although the fish itself was satisfyingly pink and soft. Following all too rapidly on its heels, steamed lobster and scallops with tagliatelle managed to be simultaneously underwhelming and overpowering, in a cloying, creamy kind of way. The chef did show some mercy with his carré d'agneau, a tender example of well-roasted meat, and the only real bright point in our meal. Desserts (which include the likes of crème brûlée with rhubarb and custard sorbet) passed with a whimper, but decent cappuccino made for an upbeat ending. A glance at the other diners (almost all besuited expense-accounters) seemed to answer our initial question; perhaps a meal this bad feels better when you're spending someone else's money.

Babies and children admitted. Booking advisable. Tables outdoors (4, pavement). **Map 14/6L.**

For branch see index.

Fitzrovia W1

Elena's L'Étoile

30 Charlotte Street, W1 (020 7636 7189). Goodge Street or Tottenham Court Road tube.

Lunch served noon-2.30pm Mon-Fri. **Dinner served** 6-10.45pm Mon-Sat. **Main courses** £11.75-£18.95. **Service** 12½%. **Pre-theatre meal** (6-7pm) 20% discount on total bill. **Credit** AmEx, DC, JCB, MC, £$TC, V.

One of London's great culinary old stagers, this luvvy haunt now pulls in more tourists, business folk and couples than actors. All gaze up at the signed photos of such showbiz luminaries as Bert Kwouk and Tony Slattery, as a phalanx of waiters squeak their way up and down the narrow aisle of what may be the town's creakiest restaurant. The food here is a treat: scallops with bacon and celeriac remoulade was an exercise in gastronomic subtlety, while goat's cheese tartlet with roasted peppers and pesto was a palate-punching yet beautifully harmonious scrum of Mediterranean flavours. A pricey roast sea bass with mash (£18.95) didn't reach such heights, but cod 'Kiev' was an inspired reinvention of the old '70s bistro classic: lightly battered and indulgently oozing with garlicky butter. Desserts are few but fine. A shared cheese plate was generously proportioned, and featured a fragrant Camembert and superb, pistachio-specked bread. The French-biased wine list offers plenty of good bottles at fair prices.

Babies and children admitted. Booking essential. Separate rooms for parties, seating 8-30. **Map 2/5J.**

Holborn EC1, WC1, WC2

High Holborn

95-96 High Holborn, WC1 (020 7404 3338/020 7404 3339) Holborn tube. **Lunch served** noon-2.30pm Mon-Fri. **Dinner served** 6.30-10.30pm Mon-Sat. **Main courses** £14-£26. **Credit** AmEx, DC, JCB, MC, £TC, V.

David Cavalier used to be one of London's most fêted chefs (at L'Escargot and the Michelin-starred Cavlier's in Battersea) before disappearing from public view at Mosimann's private dining club. But now he's back and cooking well, behind the stoves at High Holborn. The drawback? Prices are pitched firmly at expense-account dining. Starters cost £7-£19, main courses £14-£26, desserts £7; this is serious money, so you should expect faultless cooking and service. The service on our visit was forgetful and slow, and the wine list could have been more imaginative for a restaurant of this calibre. The menu favours French classics: a starter of roast foie gras with endives and caramelised orange was delightful, as it should be for £14. A more original dish was smoked wood pigeon with a velouté of jerusalem artichoke. A main of roast veal sweetbreads bourguignon was in a suitably rich red wine reduction, roast rabbit with linguine and mustard jus showed well-judged flavours. For pudding, peach with coconut milk ice-cream was great, but was it really worth £7? For this much money you should be able to expect more than just good cooking: a stylish interior, carefully chosen wine list, sharp service, and a buzz would help, and all were lacking. That's why you'll find us in the downstairs bar instead.

Babies and children admitted. Disabled: toilet. **Map 3/5M.**

Knightsbridge SW3

Brasserie St Quentin

243 Brompton Road, SW3 (020 7589 8005). Knightsbridge or South Kensington tube/14, 74 bus. **Lunch served** noon-3pm Mon-Sat; noon-3.30pm Sun. **Dinner served** 6.30-11pm Mon-Sat; 6.30-10.30pm Sun. **Main courses** £9.25-£19.50. **Set meal** (noon-3pm, 6.30-7.30pm) £12.50 two courses, £15 three courses. **Service** 12½%. **Credit** AmEx, DC, MC, £TC, V.

Brasserie St Quentin is rather reminiscent of innumerable French restaurants that remain remarkably unchanged despite the vagaries of culinary fashion. With its fin-de-siècle-style plain walls, sparkling chandeliers and acres of starched, white table linen, it's a comfortable, friendly place serving a range of traditional French restaurant food rather than the home cooking style that is London's more current translation of un repas français. Hors d'oeuvres included a huge portion of 12 Burgundy snails, cooked in lashings of butter, parsley and garlic. The charcuterie selection was varied and comprehensive, with plenty of cornichons and little pickled onions. Next, fillet of cod wrapped in bacon with braised mange tout and balsamic vinegar butter was flavoursome if a bit solid, while leg of rabbit and green olive casserole, polenta and coriander galette crossed national culinary borders and was wonderfully aromatic and moist, too. Puddings were nothing unexpected, either: tarte tartin, nougat ice cream, crème brûlée, three-chocolate mousse. Food can be accompanied by a range of reasonably priced half-bottles of wine, including an excellent sancerre. Service is brisk and friendly, with none of the slightly sneering superiority too often encountered in London's French restaurants. If you're in the area, Brasserie St Quentin can be relied on for a tasty, somewhat nostalgic meal.

Babies and children admitted. Booking advisable. Separate room for parties, seats 20. **Map 6/10E.**

Marylebone W1

Le Muscadet

25 Paddington Street, W1 (020 7935 2883). Baker Street tube. **Lunch served** 12.30-2.30pm Mon-Fri. **Dinner served** 7.30-10.45pm Mon-Fri; 7.30-10pm Sat. **Closed** three weeks August. **Main courses** £13.20-£14.90. **Set lunch** £15.80 two courses, £18.80 three courses. **Service** 12½%. **Credit** AmEx, DC, JCB, MC, £TC, V.

Don't come here expecting swanky modern decor and front-of-house shtick or, for that matter, brilliant food. This place is traditional to the core, just like the charming, unpretentious staff who run it. Imagine a petit bourgeois medley of faded pastel shades and classic half curtains and you'll be on the right track. Our meal began well with a tasty cream of vegetable and mushroom soup and another interesting starter of oxtail and artichoke caillette, which came liberally doused in a deliciously creamy vinaigrette. Sadly, though, the delicate flavours of our main course, salmon and prawn brochette, were bullied into submission by an aggressively fishy cream sauce and an equally pungent coral mousse. A second main of pig's trotters stuffed with ceps and served with a port jus was another fairly brutal dish that was let down by poor quality, fatty trotters. But dessert restored our faith in the kitchen with a light and citrus lemon tart. An interesting wine list held many temptations (mostly French), including a rare sighting of red Sancerre. Le Muscadet may not be a temple of gastronomy but it is a warm, hospitable venue for a good night out.

Map 2/5G.

Villandry

170 Great Portland Street, W1 (020 7631 3131). Great Portland Street tube. **Breakfast served** 8-11.30am Mon-Sat. **Brunch served** 10am-3pm Sat; 11-4pm Sun. **Lunch served** 12-3.30pm Mon-Fri. **Dinner served** 6-10.30pm Mon-Sat. **Main courses** £10.50-£19.50. **Service** 12½%. **Credit** AmEx, MC, £TC, V.

During the day, the pretty little food market at the front of this restaurant is alive with activity, so lunchtime visitors have the added pleasure of passing among gorgeous piles of vegetables, fruits and cheeses en route to their table. (There's now also a bar, where smoking is allowed.) The dining room itself is a spare space with large windows and bare plaster walls. The menu has a similarly elegant simplicity, offering a handful of fresh, inventive dishes each day and a succinct list of interesting, affordable wines. A starter of cream of cauliflower soup with blue cheese crostini was coarsely textured and beautifully fresh, while the pâté of the day was spirited from the foodstore onto the plate, accompanied by sweet, sharp cornichons and rustic bread. Roast pork loin with apple mash and spinach was crisp and succulent in its cider and mustard sauce. Another main of baked cod with roast fennel and new potatoes came with a generous scattering of crisp prosciutto to complement the tender flakes of fish. We chose a selection of excellent Phillipe Olivier cheeses instead of desserts, which included the likes of ricotta cheesecake with red fruit salad or pear and almond tart.

Babies and children welcome; high chairs. Booking advisable. No-smoking (restaurant). **Map 2/5H.**

Mayfair W1

Mirabelle

56 Curzon Street, W1 (020 7499 4636/www.whitestarline.org.uk). Green Park tube. **Lunch served** noon-2.30pm daily. **Dinner served** 6-11.30pm Mon-Sat; 6-10.30pm Sun. **Main courses** £13.50-£26. **Set lunches** £14.95 two courses, £17.95 three courses. **Service** 12½%. **Credit** AmEx, DC, MC, V.

Four of us dined at this famous basement, a glamorous throw-back to 1930s' elegance complete with pianist and a revolving mirror-studded globe that flung sparkles all over the place. Despite some negative comments from readers, we were excited: Mirabelle has long been one of our favourite restaurants in London, promising expert cooking and service. Reality didn't match expectations. Among starters, ceviche of scallops, chives and ginger was a puddle of sesame oil in which swam a single paper-thin scallop. Quiche of langoustines and sea scallops was curdled and watery with soggy pastry. Mains were better, if not stunning. For example, in magret of duck Marco Polo, the apple wedges were piping-hot but the duck was lukewarm. Of the desserts, lemon tart was impeccable, but tarte tatin was so oily and stale-tasting that we sent it back (it was subtracted from our bill). What really shocked us, however, was the rushed, chaotic service. Starters arrived within minutes of ordering and although our mains were served with a flourish, landing had to be aborted because the starter plates hadn't been cleared. Coffee arrived before dessert and when we ordered two bottles of wine (£22 and £42 per bottle), the sommelier unhelpfully pointed out a couple of completely different Italian reds costing over £60. Marco Pierre White was in the restaurant that evening, but not, it would appear, in charge. We left very disappointed and angry.

Babies and children admitted. Booking advisable. Dress: smart casual. Separate rooms for parties, seating 34 and 48. Tables outdoors (20, terrace). **Map 2/7H.**

Piccadilly W1

Criterion

224 Piccadilly, W1 (020 7930 0488). Piccadilly Circus tube. **Lunch served** noon-2.30pm Mon-Sat. **Dinner served** 5.30-11.30pm Mon-Sat; 5.30-10.30pm Sun. **Main courses** £13.95-£14.50. **Set meals** (noon-2.30pm, 5.30-6.30pm) £14.95 two courses, £17.95 three courses. **Service** 12½%. **Credit** AmEx, DC, MC, £TC, V.

This showcase restaurant, with opulent ceilings of burnished gold and neo-classical paintings set in marble walls, has an equally alluring menu. However, the cooking and the flustered service struggle to keep up with the sense of occasion generated by the palatial setting. Not that this seemed to bother the armies of (mainly suited) lunchers. After all, it's hard to argue with a well-prepared two- or three-course set lunch offering three choices in each section. Dishes included a simple but nicely presented 'frizzy salade' with poached egg, bacon and mustard, juicily spongy calf's liver, with caramelised shallots and lime jus; and a 'Bake-Well' tart mischievously reinvented as fresh raspberrries in a fine pastry basket artfully topped with ice-cream and a sugary grill. While the set menu offers a conservative but balanced choice, it's left to the à la carte menu to provide variety with an ample and imaginative choice of meat and fish. Starters included an appetising risotto with crab, clams and parsley, which was a touch too salty and hard. However, the main course, grilled sea bass à la Moroccaine, sported a crispy skin, well-structured flesh, and was offset by spicily sweet couscous. Often in this kind of restaurant, flamboyance is reserved for the wine list, but even here Criterion maintains solid standards with well chosen wines at all prices.

Babies and children welcome; high chairs. Booking essential; one week in advance for weekends. **Map 13/7K.**

L'Odéon ★

65 Regent Street, W1 (020 7287 1400). Piccadilly Circus tube.

Bar **Open** 11am-1am Mon-Sat.
Restaurant **Lunch served** noon-2.45pm, **dinner served** 5.30-11.30pm Mon-Sat. **Main courses** £14.50-£21. **Cover** £1.50. **Set meals** (lunch, 5.30-7pm) £15.50 two courses, £19.50 three courses.
Both **Credit** AmEx, DC, JCB, MC, £TC, V.

When L'Odéon opened in 1995 it was a critical hit. The restaurant has had its ups and downs since then, and adverse comments about both food and service made us uncertain what to expect on this visit. We were relieved to find the huge, low-ceiling dining area on the first floor as attractive as ever. A perfect vodka Martini from the popular bar lifted

Incognico

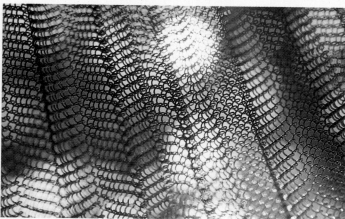

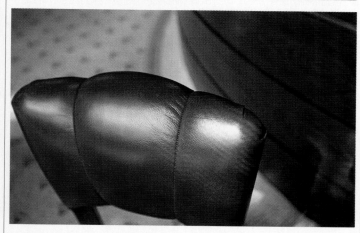

our spirits further. As for the food, we could happily have ordered anything from the menu. Starters were a sensation; lobster and tarragon ravioli was served on a pungent green peppercorn sauce, while langoustine tempura and tiger prawns provided a fine counterpoint to a chilli-touched oriental salad. Rack of lamb was perfectly cooked and came with grilled veg and an individual moussaka (in itself a worthy dish). Roast squab pigeon was just as good, with a heady assemblage of wild mushrooms in a rich reduction. A portion of mixed green veg was, as the friendly waiter promised, more than big enough to share. There's an interesting set of wines by the glass, and good bottles at around £20. L'Odéon is not exactly cheap, but neither is it exorbitant for such accomplished cooking. It might seem less wonderful if you're not sitting at a window table overlooking Regent Street. But the place was packed, and window-less diners weren't complaining. A star reborn.

Babies and children welcome; high chairs. Booking advisable dinner Thur-Sat. Disabled: lift; toilet. Entertainment: jazz 8pm Wed-Fri (bar area). No-smoking tables (lunch). Separate room for parties, seats 20. **Map 13/7J.**

Soho W1

L'Escargot

48 Greek Street, W1 (020 7437 2679). Tottenham Court Road tube.
Ground floor restaurant **Lunch served** 12.15-2.15pm Mon-Fri. **Dinner served** 6-11.30pm Mon-Sat. **Main courses** £12.95. **Set meals** (lunch, 6-7pm) £14.95 two courses, £17.95 three courses. **Service** 12½%.
Picasso Room **Lunch served** noon-2.15pm Tue-Fri. **Dinner served** 7-11pm Tue-Sat. **Set lunch** £27 three courses. **Set dinner** £42 three courses. **Service** 15%.
Both **Credit** AmEx, DC, JCB, MC, £TC, V.
At 7pm, the attractive ground floor room at this Soho veteran was half-filled with Americans, some of them finishing as we sat down. Later, the tables were occupied by a mostly business crowd. We can only hope that they ate better than we did; the menu was full of promise but only achieved a 50% success rate. The prices seem reasonable: starters at £6.75, mains at £12.95 (with some supplements) and desserts at £5.95. We started well enough with a seared tuna salad with marinated tomatoes and niçoise olives, notable for accurate cooking and bold flavours. Escargot tartlet signature de la maison was slightly over-creamy and too salty, but good enough. The meal took a turn for the worse with the arrival of the main courses. Despite its £2 supplement, corn-fed duck breast with crisp noodle and 'confit gallete' was a sad creation; the meat was undercooked and the galette was soggy and unappetising. Roast poussin with wild mushrooms, pancetta and girolle jus was merely OK. Service ranged from friendly to sullen; a query about the condition of one of the wines was handled with a graceless lack of interest. The bill for £85 (with service) for two courses, water and the equivalent of one bottle of wine, left us feeling flat.
Babies and children admitted. Booking advisable. Dress: smart casual. Separate rooms for parties, seating 24 and 60. **Map 13/6K.**

Incognico ★

117 Shaftesbury Avenue, WC2 (020 7836 8866). Leicester Square or Tottenham Court Road tube. **Lunch served** noon-3pm, **dinner served** 5.30pm-midnight Mon-Sat. **Main courses** £9.50-£15. **Set meal** (noon-7pm) £12.50 three courses. **Service** 12½%. **Credit** AmEx, DC, MC, V.
For most of his career, Greek-born Nico Ladenis has devoted himself to classical French cuisine. However, Londoners have stopped wanting overpriced, fussy food, and this latest venture responds to the turning tide. Incognico, while recognisably Ladenis in approach, is neither elitist nor overpriced: the three-course set menu is a bargain at £12.50. Ladenis's longstanding signature dish, pan-fried escalope of foie gras with brioche and caramelised orange is a pricey starter at £11, but it's worth it: thick, fatty slices of liver contrasted with citric sharpness. A main of osso bucco – glazed veal slice (and its marrow-filled bone) perched on a mound of parmesan risotto – also demonstrated well-matched flavours and precise cooking. Decent vegetarian choices included artichoke heart stuffed with finely chopped wild mushrooms, served with a buttery hollandaise sauce. The only disappointment was the fish cake, which contained large lumps of salty white fish. Incognico seems to be emulating the Ivy with its interior and menu design, but the Ivy is the clear winner of the fish cake contest. However, Ladenis has succeeded in making a smart, affordable restaurant with superb French-based cooking. All it currently lacks is buzz.
Babies and children admitted; high chairs. Booking essential. **Map 13/6K.**

Quo Vadis

26-29 Dean Street, W1 (020 7437 9585). Leicester Square or Tottenham Court Road tube. **Lunch served** noon-2.30pm Mon-Fri. **Dinner served** 5.30-11.45pm Mon-Sat. **Main courses** £6.50-£23.50. **Service** 12½%. **Credit** AmEx, MC, £TC, V.
Renewed vigour in the kitchen has sparked a triumphant return to form at Quo Vadis, banishing all memory of the dazed culinary performance that tainted our last visit. The front of house operation remains one of the best in London – we scarcely noticed our coats and bags being spirited away to the cloakroom. The dining room interweaves crisp modernity with original art deco, exploiting every available inch with close-knit rafts of tables (claustrophobes beware). But any unneighbourly niggles vanished with the arrival of a deliciously creamy tart of Gruyère, firm, tender leeks and bosky clusters of morels. Another excellent starter of rich artichoke hearts came with a meaty tangle of wild mushrooms and a cep butter sauce. On to the mains; fat petals of smoked haddock supported a perfectly poached egg, with whipped peaks of colcannon to mop up the juices. Unfortunately, a prettily pink roast rump of lamb didn't get the back up it deserved – its consommé of wild mushrooms was too watery to make an impression. Beautifully presented nougatine was a meltingly good finale, though, and a fine match for the last sips of our Constantia Uitsig chardonnay 1998 from South Africa.
Babies and children admitted (lunch). Booking advisable. Separate room for parties, seats 16. **Map 13/6K.**

West

Chiswick W4

Christian's

1 Station Parade, Burlington Lane, W4 (020 8995 0382). Chiswick Bridge rail/E3 bus. **Lunch served** noon-2.30pm Tue-Fri. **Dinner served** 7-10.30pm Tue-Sat. **Main courses** £10.75-£13.50. **Service** 12½%. **Credit** AmEx, DC, JCB, MC, £TC, V.
There's a refreshing lack of pretension about Christian Gustin's popular local. The pretty tile-floored dining room abuts the open kitchen and a little conservatory at the back, and is soothingly neutral in decor, with an eclectic clutch of prints on the walls. There's also something reassuring about the menu, which offers what is basically comfort food at reasonable prices. We started with a smooth, pale fish soup with rouille and all the trimmings and the house speciality, a celestially light English cheese soufflé. Both mains came cossetted on blankets of mash: fricassée of chicken with peas and pine nuts and a huge hunk of cod with spinach. Both were served in Desperate Dan-sized portions, leaving room for one shared pudding – an agreeably light chocolate mousse with caramel sauce. Wines are few, but include some decent, well-priced bottles such as a wonderfully oily Currabridge chardonnay (£14.75). Overall, nothing stunning, perhaps, but the fact that Christian's knows its limits (and prices accordingly) should be applauded.
Babies and children admitted. Book weekends. Tables outdoors (7, patio).

Holland Park W11

6 Clarendon Road

6 Clarendon Road, W11 (020 7727 3330). Holland Park tube. **Dinner served** 7-10pm Tue-Sat. **Main courses** £12-£15.50. **Credit** MC, V, £TC.
A posh but charming neighbourhood restaurant, 6 Clarendon Road is an ideal spot to take conservative relatives. The short menu manages to be both sober and imaginative, kicking off with such dishes as carrot and ginger soup and sautéed lamb's sweetbreads with brandy sauce and lentils. Fresh, appetising starters – sautéed wild mushrooms with green beans and oak leaf lettuce, and salmon soufflé – were followed by monkfish medallions with king prawns in spicy Creole sauce, and pan-fried chicken breast with preserved lemons. Unfortunately, the chicken was a little dry and was overpowered by the lemons, while the monkfish was a shade eclipsed by the mild Creole sauce. The accompanying garlic potatoes and courgettes were spot on, though. Peppers stuffed with lentils, goat's cheese, pine nuts and dates in herbed tomato sauce, with sautéed spring greens and garlic looked like a good vegetarian option. Desserts are relatively downbeat; we chose poached pear and chocolate cake. One of the little joys here is the clearly laid out wine list: helpful asterisks denote wines offering the best 'rapport' between quality and price.
Babies and children admitted. Booking advisable. **Map 11/7Az.**

Putney Bridge.
See page 67.

Chez Moi

1 Addison Avenue, W11 (020 7603 8267).
Holland Park tube. **Lunch served** 12.30-2pm
Mon-Fri. **Dinner served** 7-11pm Mon-Sat.
Main courses £12.50-£16.75. **Set lunch** £15
three courses. **Credit** AmEx, DC, MC, £TC, V.
Its location – just off the Shepherd's Bush
roundabout – is not exactly a glamour spot, but
Chez Moi otherwise seems geared up to lighten
the wallets of local Holland Parkers and refugees
from the nearby Hilton. The dark luxuriant
colour scheme, gold trimmings and faux-wildlife
upholstery complement a soundly traditional
establishment with smart attentive service. Some
may wonder at the French credentials of a
restaurant serving borscht, Moroccan lamb and
Thai chicken, but there's a marked French
influence in the wine list and on the menu, which
seems to have remained unchanged for the past
year. Decent though the cooking is, with so much
practice, and main courses averaging more than
£15, there is room for improvement. 'Oursins
Chez Moi' (a medley of sea fish served with deep-
fried angel hair noodles, with not a sea urchin in
sight) and a dish of seared scallops were fresh
and finely cooked but at over £9 apiece, they
needed to be. Main course 'medley of seafood'
served with gazpacho sauce was just as good.
However, roasted Gressingham duck was
unexceptional, and came paddling in a thin,
insipid 'orange flavoured Cinzano sauce'. Puds
range from crème brûlée to 'final d'or', a pancake
stuffed with all manner of sweet things and
served with maple syrup. The wine list of French
classics is costly; once ordered, bottles are kept
away from the table, so there was no way of
telling how we'd progressed.
Children welcome. Booking advisable. Tables
outdoors (4, pavement). Vegetarian menu.

South West

Chelsea SW3, SW10

Le Colombier

145 Dovehouse Street, SW3 (020 7351 1155).
Sloane Square or South Kensington tube/14
bus. **Lunch served** noon-3pm Mon-Sat; noon-
3.30pm Sun. **Dinner served** 6.30-11pm Mon-
Sat; 6.30-10.30pm Sun. **Main courses**
£9.80-£19.90. **Set meal** (lunch, 6.30-7.30pm)
£13 two courses. **Credit** AmEx, DC, MC, V.

With its bright blue canvas awning, white paint
and large front terrace, the jaunty Le Colombier
looks like a luxury yacht. It's all light, bright,
cheerful and full of mainly middle-aged, well
conditioned locals enjoying a night out with
friends. The chef clearly caters to their tastes,
with a resolutely untrendy menu. You could start
with that rarely found delight, potted goose pâté,
or choose assiette Le Colombier (a selection of
Breton, native and rock oysters). There's an equal
balance of fish and meat dishes on the menu, plus
a range of grills. We began with king prawns
with parsley in garlic butter that were a bit
sawdust-like; scallops with wild mushrooms
might have been a better choice. Rabbit with cider
sauce and fresh pasta was a tempting main
course, and shepherd's pie was worth
consideration, but we finally plumped for roast
rack of lamb. It was juicy, but not cooked bleu as
ordered. Puds are traditional and cost £4.90 each,
unless you opt for that 1970s throwback, baked
Alaska at £12 for two. The wine list has sufficient
variety to satisfy the menu, including a good
value rosé de Provence. Service was professional
and friendly. Eat outside on a warm summer day
if you can, but don't worry if you can't – the
breezy charm wafts inside too.
Babies and children admitted. Booking
essential. Dress: no shorts. Separate room for
parties, seats 30-45. Tables outdoors (14,
terrace). **Map 5/11D.**

Fulham SW10

ChezMax

168 Ifield Road, SW10 (020 7835 0874).
Earl's Court tube. **Lunch served** noon-3.30pm
Tue-Sat. **Dinner served** 7-11pm Mon-Sat. **Set**
meals £25 two courses; £29.50 three courses;
£35 four courses. **Service** 12½%. **Corkage**
£7.50. **Credit** AmEx, DC, MC, £TC, V.
A throwback to '70s-style French restaurants,
ChezMax has cream-coloured walls covered in
fleurs de lys and pictorial curiosities to give a
cosily old-fashioned, provincial ambience. The
menu is written in French, which allows the
waistcoated, rubicund proprietor to step up and
expatiate on its themes. Unfortunately, this
performance raises too great expectations of the
cooking, which is basically good, rich French
country cuisine with haute pretensions. Risotto au
chorizo et tomate was a tasty, smoky opener but,
in truth, no more exciting than the wholesome

lobster soup. With the main courses, the menu's histrionics reach new heights: grondin rose farçi aux anchois et à l'orange (an imaginatively stuffed red gurnard fish); and suprême de poulet 'label Anglaise' en papillotte (chicken baked in a parcel of paper). A trolley of sumptuous cheeses solicited further orations, but we shared a cracking crème brûlée inlaid with berries instead. The wine list offers a good selection of regional wines by the glass, carafe and bottle. The only problem with the whole experience is the bill: prices are already high, and there are five dishes carrying a supplement of up to £4.50. Presumably this doesn't matter much to the locals.
Babies and children welcome; high chairs. Booking advisable. No pipes or cigars. **Map 5/12B.**

Putney SW15

Putney Bridge ★

The Embankment, SW15 (020 8780 1811). Putney Bridge tube/14, 22 bus.
Bar **Open** noon-midnight Mon-Thur; noon-1am Fri, Sat; noon-10.30pm Sun.
Restaurant **Lunch served** noon-2.30pm Tue-Sat; 12.30-3.30pm Sun. **Dinner served** 7-10.30pm Tue-Thur; 6.30-11pm Fri, Sat. **Set lunch** £18.50 three courses. **Set Sunday lunch** £24.50 three courses. **Set dinner** £32.50 two courses, £39.50 three courses; menu gourmand £50 five courses incl coffee. **Service** 12½%.
Both **Credit** AmEx, DC, JCB, MC, V.
For a classy treat with some of London's best river views, it's hard to beat this architecturally spectacular glass-sided beauty of a restaurant. On the ground floor is a coolly civil bar with a Thames-side terrace, while the sleek, elongated dining room enjoys a fine watery vista from the first floor. Chef de cuisine Anthony Demetre's food is a decidedly contemporary update of classic Gallic cuisine, but there are plenty of old-school touches, from the pre-meal and pre-dessert amuses-bouches (a teeny cup of gazpacho, and a little pot of strawberries with mascarpone and buttermilk, on our visit) to the curious, superfluous explanation of each course by the waiter as it is set upon the table. Presentation of dishes is spectacular, but doesn't overshadow some superb flavour combinations. Red tuna tartare with bean sprouts was a soothingly mild starter, in contrast to a big-punching lasagne of goat's cheese with wild oregano, 'minestrone' of vegetables and basil (perhaps a little too substantial for an appetiser). Main courses were seriously high maintenance, with melting lamb coming in two guises on one plate (rack, and stewed shoulder with pine nuts), accompanied by young vegetables and jus specked with tapenade. Equally tender was guinea fowl with sweetcorn pancake and a cute little 'gateau' of Savoy cabbage. Wild strawberries are not to be resisted on any menu, and these delicate little berries came with a warm jus, basil and mascarpone ice-cream (strangely like the pre-dessert). The cheese board is as comprehensive and impressive as might be expected. Wines are also a strength, so put your faith in the excellent sommelier if the lengthy, unannotated (and not exactly bargain-priced) list is too daunting.
Booking advisable. Disabled: toilet; lift. Dress: smart casual. Entertainment: jazz trio 7.30-10.30pm Sun. Tables outdoors (8, bar terrace).

South

Wandsworth SW17, SW18

Chez Bruce ★

2 Bellevue Road, SW17 (020 8672 0114). Wandsworth Common rail. **Lunch served** noon-2pm Mon-Fri; 12.30-2.30pm Sat; 12.30-3pm Sun. **Dinner served** 7-10.30pm Mon-Sat. **Set lunch** £21.50 three courses. **Set dinner** £27.50 three courses. **Service** 12½%. **Credit** AmEx, DC, JCB, MC, V.
Eating at this restaurant is a real treat. Its location opposite Wandsworth Common is pleasant but not especially memorable and the interior of hulking wooden beams, faux-rustic walls and a pretty crushed silk ceiling is nothing to write home about. However, the combination of Bruce Poole's superlative cooking and the relaxed, informed front-of-house operation makes this restaurant something special. An ordinary-sounding starter of leek and potato soup had the kind of all-pervading richness that comes from a properly made, deeply flavoursome stock. A second starter of brandade and confit of cod with chorizo and rouille was an equally delightful ensemble of meaty textures and pungent purées. Our main course, rabbit leg with stuffed cabbage, creamed polenta and meat juices, was less fussy but bursting with flavour, while a second main of roast monkfish more than merited its elaborate presentation, perched on a dazzling tower of noodles streaked with shellfish, capers and tomatoes. Torn between greed and bloated bellies, we opted for the happy medium of a wickedly rich pannacotta with poached plum compote and a refreshing brace of sorbets (lemon and blackcurrant). At £27.50 for three courses, the set menu must be the best bargain in town.
Babies and children admitted (lunch). Booking essential. Dress: smart casual. No pipe-smoking. Separate room for parties, seats 18 (lunch only).

Waterloo SE1

County Hall Restaurant

County Hall, SE1 (020 7902 8000). Westminster tube/Waterloo tube/rail. **Breakfast served** 6.30-10.30am Mon-Fri; 7-11am Sat, Sun. **Lunch served** noon-2.30pm daily. **Dinner served** 5-11pm Mon-Sat; 5-10.30pm Sun. **Main courses** £12.50-£21. **Set meal** (lunch and pre-theatre) £18.50 two courses, £21.50 three courses. **Credit** AmEx, DC, JCB, V.
It's an oddly melancholic experience eating in this large, riverside restaurant. For over 60 years the building was the seat of London's government; it's now an aquarium, a hotel, a series of restaurants and fast fooderies and an arcade. The County Hall, the poshest restaurant, is reached through the Marriott Hotel entrance lobby (complete with plastic box trees). Should you manage to secure a window table you can view a sculpture by Dali, and, to the right, the London Eye. Inside, a piano plays rather too loudly, and the building's history is commemorated in photographs and cartoons on the walls. Sadly, rock oysters from the oyster bar were unavailable, but compensation was provided by a tasty onion tarte tatin with chorizo and artichoke salad. Ballottine of salmon was less successful, with fromage blanc overwhelming the caviar. To follow, pavé of salmon, pomme sautée and cabbage truffle cream was unchallenging but pleasant; roast sea bass was delicious, but the accompanying 'bubble and squeak' had been turned into an overly sweet arty-farty potato cake stuffed with petit pois. The wine list is catholic and informative. Service was fine, though the 'invitation' to have a pre-dinner drink in the cavernous bar was a little too insistent. When you've sorted out the transport, Ken, see what you can do about making this wonderful river frontage space work for Londoners again.
Babies and children welcome; children's menu; crayons. Disabled: toilet. Entertainment: pianist 7-10.30pm Mon-Sat; 12.30-4pm Sun. No-smoking tables. **Map 7/9M.**

RSJ

13A Coin Street, SE1 (020 7928 4554/020 7401 2455). Waterloo tube/rail. **Lunch served** noon-2pm Mon-Fri. **Dinner served** 5.30-11pm Mon-Sat. **Main courses** £12.95-£16.95. **Set meals** £14.95 two courses, £16.95 three courses incl coffee. **Service** 12½%. **Credit** AmEx, DC, £TC, MC, V.
An anonymous first-floor room just off traffic-choked Stamford Street is an unlikely venue for RSJ's consistently first-rate food and enviable wine list. Perhaps the fact that the place has been under the same management since it opened in 1980 is part of the reason. A fixed price menu is offered alongside the carte. We loved the stunning, celestially fluffy crab quiche with lemon, oil and rocket followed by roast herbed chicken with asparagus from the former. Almost as good was a starter of light wild mushroom frittata, and a main of earthy cod wrapped in prosciutto, served with white beans swimming in fresh tomato sauce. The standard was maintained with desserts: panna cotta with rhubarb, and blood orange mousse. However, it's the lengthy wine list here that offers most thrills for the cognoscenti. RSJ imports wines directly (and sells them on to the public and other restaurants). Organic vintages are prominent, and the Loire is particularly well represented.
Babies and children admitted. Booking advisable. Separate room for parties, seats 22. Tables outdoors (6, pavement and patio). **Map 7/8N.**

South East

East Dulwich SE22

Le Chardon

65 Lordship Lane, SE22 (020 8299 1921). East Dulwich rail/40, 176, 185 bus. **Meals served** noon-11pm daily. **Main courses** £8.95-£10.95. **Set lunch** (noon-6pm) £6.95 two courses, £9.95 three courses. **Set Sunday lunch** (noon-5pm) £12.50 three courses, £6.25 children. **Service** 10%. **Credit** AmEx, DC, MC, £TC, V.
There's a genuine Parisian buzz to the tile-clad interior of this former Victorian grocer's shop; not at all what you'd expect in East Dulwich. Neither is the enclosed patio at the rear, which is a fine spot in which to pass a lazy summer's evening. Given these twin charms, it's no surprise that the area's denizens pack out Le Chardon most evenings, lured also by old-school French cuisine that's not afraid to incorporate a splash of the new. A no-punches-pulled kidney salad was given an appealing tang by the presence of orange rind; while the usual Gallic recipe book went completely out of the window with the Thai fish cakes – a reasonably accurate representation of the south-east Asian original. These were followed by duck breast in a deeply fruity blackberry sauce and a lovely slab of intensely gamey pigeon, well paired with crunchy oriental greens (£9.85). Only the short wine list and the rushed, unengaging service (on an admittedly very busy night) disappointed.
Babies and children welcome; high chairs. Booking advisable. Tables outdoors (28, terrace).

Greenwich SE10

Spread Eagle

1-2 Stockwell Street, SE10 (020 8853 2333). Greenwich rail/DLR. **Lunch served** noon-3pm daily. **Dinner served** 6.30-10.30pm Mon-Sat. **Main courses** £10.75-£14.95. **Set meal** £12.50 two courses, £15.50 three courses. **Service** 10%. **Credit** AmEx, DC, MC, V.
With its faintly saucy postcard allure and new-found millennial status, Greenwich is alive with tourists. None of them, however, seemed to have found this grand old former pub, which we shared with a crowd of locals, splashing out on birthday treats and other occasions that measure up to the rather inflated prices. The cosiest seats are among the booths near the door, while a small back room and creaking first-floor garret offer open-plan alternatives. Pre-prandial saucers of stuffed olives and feta were a nice surprise, as was a wonderfully smoky starter of duck salad with zingy apple and walnut dressing. Equally impressive was a Scandinavian-influenced collage of herring, soft-boiled egg and curry mayonnaise, rounded off with a chilled shot of vodka. Sadly, though, all flavour had been carefully extracted from the main courses; overcooked guinea fowl and crayfish arrived on a bed of adhesive risotto, while sawdusty aubergine boudin trailed miserably behind with a helping of dull couscous. Consistently good, however, was the service – never less than charming throughout.
Babies and children welcome; high chairs. Book weekends. Separate rooms for parties, seating 30 and 50. Tables outdoors (7, courtyard). **Map 19.**

Peckham SE15

Holly

38 Holly Grove, SE15 (020 7277 2928). Peckham Rye rail. **Dinner served** 6-10.30pm Tue-Sat. **Main courses** £9.25-£13.75. **Credit** JCB, MC, £TC, V.
One thing that Norbert and Barbara van Hest's delightful local restaurant doesn't have to fear is competition. Granted, this is the more refined side of Peckham, but the more lavishly heeled citizens of one of London's poorer districts aren't exactly spoiled for dining choice. As this is a one-man kitchen, Norbert sensibly keeps the menu (which changes roughly every two weeks) down to a manageable three choices at each course. No corners are cut, though – starters made no concessions to culinary wimps. Chilled soup (cucumber, watercress and pear) was superbly harmonious and soothing, with just a touch of bite; the sweetbreads, simply served with spring onions and a red wine jus, were equally satisfying. Main dishes weren't overly ambitious, but the execution was first-rate: confit of duck leg served on a pile of ambrosial mash and poached sea trout with a creamy saffron risotto. A shared sloppy-fluffy white chocolate mousse with blueberry sauce was a fine finale. The setting is south London bourgeois living room (with regular changing art exhibitions), but it was good to see a relatively mixed clientele enjoying the food and the admirably friendly service.
Babies and children welcome; high chairs. Booking advisable. Tables outdoors (2, garden).

North East

Dalston N1

Soulard

113 Mortimer Road, N1 (020 7254 1314). Bus 141, 76, 149. **Lunch served** parties by arrangement only. **Dinner served** 7-10.30pm Tue-Sat. **Set dinners** £16.95 two courses, £19.50 three courses; (7-8.30pm Tue-Thur) £16.95 three courses. **Credit** MC, £TC, V.
Soulard could be translated as 'drunkard', which is hardly in keeping with this self-confident, fairly traditional little French restaurant stuck in a residential outpost. The fixed price menu is sensibly short, but there are specials each night advertised on the blackboard. Bland smoked haddock terrine was perked up by watercress sauce. Another starter, fresh anchovy salad (a plat du jour), was generous almost to excess. To follow, fillet of beef served with horn of plenty mushroom sauce was a distinct success, cooked exactly as ordered. The vegetarian option, a country tart made with leeks, onions, St Nectaire cheese and savoy cabbage was less thrilling, involving a wedge of potatoes and heavy pastry. We had mixed feelings, too, about desserts. A nougat glacé 'in its own coulis' was highly satisfactory, though the cheeseboard was uninspiring. A sufficient number of fairly priced half-bottles earned bonus points for the wine list. On our visit, two tables were occupied by single diners, both apparently well known to the patron: a telling sign of a thoroughly integrated local restaurant.
Babies and children admitted. Booking essential Fri, Sat. Separate room for parties, seats 24. Tables outdoors (5, pavement).

North

Crouch End N8

Les Associes

172 Park Road, N8 (020 8348 8944). Finsbury Park tube/rail then W7 bus. **Lunch served** 12-3pm Sun. **Dinner served** 7.30-10pm Tue-Sat. **Main courses** £10.60-£16.30. **Set menu** £15.80. **Set Sunday lunch** £13.50 three courses. **Credit** MC, V.
On the night of our visit, we were the only people in Les Associes who weren't personally known to the patron. This restaurant is very much part of the community, and we can see why the locals love it. The decor is French provincial-suburban auberge (very comforting when the view outside is of Crouch End traffic). But then, this place is French through and through, right down to the welcoming but faintly superior service. Prices are in keeping with the local bistro atmosphere (you can't spend more than around £26 for three courses) and the food, if not amazing, is certainly worth the money. Herb-marinated pork fillet was flavourful, not overcooked (a rarity), and barely needed its basil sauce. Leg of rabbit served with plump cloves of garlic was equally tasty. The salad of duck and tartare of salmon starters were more elaborate and much less successful, while a shared dessert of mousse au chocolat was gooey and a little bland for our taste. The all-French wine list is short, well priced and a pleasure to read: the work of someone with a real interest in the subject. Anyone within striking distance of Les Associes should make its acquaintance sooner rather than later.
Babies and children admitted. Book Fri, Sat. Tables outdoors (4, terrace).

Highgate N6

Village Bistro

38 Highgate High Street, N6 (020 8340 0257/ www.villagebistro.com). Archway or Highgate tube. **Lunch served** noon-3pm, **dinner served** 6-11pm daily. **Main courses** £10.95-£14.95. **Set lunch** £13.50 two courses. **Set Sunday lunch** £14.95 three courses. **Credit** AmEx, MC, £TC, V.
Don't be misled by the mawkish decor, there's more to this restaurant than meets the eye. Admittedly, it does look like a cramped country tearoom; we were half expecting Miss Marple to bob up among the heavy wooden beams, frilly curtains and chintzy clutter. The menu, however, is bright and modern, although prices seem steep for such a distinctly unglamorous venue. A starter of fillet of sea bass on a bed of warm cabbage and smoked salmon salad was bursting with flavour and worth every penny of its £7.25 price tag. Main courses, however, were not good value; each dish arrived with scant accompaniments and once we'd factored in side dishes in excess of the £3 mark, the meal had become a pricey business. Rosettes of lamb with fondant potato and brochette of kidneys were tender and pungent, combining well with a deliciously light herb jus. Grilled Mediterranean vegetables with couscous and feta were also pleasant but too modest to be worth £10.95. Puddings are more traditional and the wine list has been chosen with care (mostly French, mostly well-known bottles). The Village is without doubt a good night out, but it's not exactly a bargain.
Babies and children admitted. Book dinner Fri, Sat. No-smoking tables. Separate rooms for parties, seating 20 and 35.

Hornsey N8

Le Cadre

10 Priory Road, N8 (020 8348 0606). Turnpike Lane tube/Hornsey rail/144A, W7 bus. **Lunch served** noon-2.30pm Mon-Fri. **Dinner served** 7-11pm Mon-Sat. **Main courses** £14-£17. **Set meals** £14 two courses lunch Mon-Fri, dinner Mon-Thur; £16.50 dinner Fri, Sat. **Service** 10%. **Credit** AmEx, DC, JCB, MC, V.

Thirteen years old now, Le Cadre is still at the centre of the local dining scene. It's a place of bare floorboards and candles on tables, with an eclectic taste in pictures that has Matisse odalisques and Humphrey Bogart eyeing each other across the room, while very frankly depicted female nudes hang near the serving area at the back. We like the neighbourhood funk of Le Cadre – local boys playing on the pavement outside the open window; police cars screeching along Priory Road – but we're not quite so keen on the predominance of elaborate, ambitious dishes, which don't always work. The food is billed as French with a modern twist, but the twists are sometimes simply too convoluted. A starter of squid and prawns en brochette was overpowered by a spicy plum and sun-dried tomato sauce. Loin of veal roasted with honey, Parma ham, capers, sage and Noilly Prat sauce was another case of gilding the lily till the lily disappeared. From the good value summer menu (two courses for £14 to £16.50), asparagus in puff pastry with hollandaise was fine, but a flavourful steak didn't need its creamy Cognac and mustard sauce. The wine list is reasonable and wide-ranging, tempering food prices that would feel at home in the West End. If Le Cadre straightened out some of its modern twists, we'd love it a lot more.

Babies and children admitted. Book weekends. Tables outdoors (5, patio).

Palmers Green N13

Café Anjou

394 Green Lanes, N13 (020 8886 7267). Southgate or Wood Green tube. **Lunch served** noon-3pm Tue-Sun. **Dinner served** 6.30-11pm Tue-Sat. **Main courses** £7.25-£9.95. **Set meals** (Tue-Fri, Sat lunch) £10.95 two courses, £11.95 three courses. **Set Sunday lunch** £10.95 three courses (£5.95 children). **Service** 10% for parties of 7 or more. **Credit** AmEx, MC, V.

A wonderful little local. For one thing, the food is simple but good. For another, the owners have managed to foster the ambience of an old-school bistro du coin, treating regulars with assured familiarity. Lautrec posters crowd the wall space and pastis bottles are lined up behind the bar; Café Anjou is French, and proud of it. The menu is far from clichéd, though. Lightly sautéed chicken livers with fresh, juicy raspberries was a sophisticated starter, while chilled curried banana soup was a refreshingly simple dose of strong, clear flavours. A maghrébin main course of spicy lamb meat balls, served with a mint, apple and sour cream sauce, was perfectly cooked and subtly fragrant. Poached Dover sole wrapped around scallops on a leek and sweet pepper mash sounded delicious but was disappointingly bland when it arrived. But a fluffy, nicely scorched crème brûlée ensured that the average standard remained high. Wines of the month are interesting and definitely worth a punt; as for the rest of the list, it's almost all French. No surprises there, then.

Babies and children welcome; high chairs. Booking advisable, essential weekends.

North West

St John's Wood NW8

L'Aventure

3 Blenheim Terrace, NW8 (020 7624 6232). St John's Wood tube/139, 189 bus. **Lunch served** 12.30-2.30pm Mon-Fri; *Easter-Sept* 12.30-2.30pm Sun. **Dinner served** 7.30-11pm Mon-Sat; Easter-Sept 7.30-10pm Sun. **Main courses** £10. **Set lunch** £18.50 three courses incl coffee. **Set dinner** £27.50 three courses. **Service** 12½%. **Credit** AmEx, MC, £TC, V.

We were spoilt on our quiet lunchtime visit to this charming restaurant. Beyond its terraced jungle of potted plants and folding windows is a smart, cosy interior with fewer than a dozen tables and a vaguely Breton decor of tiled floors and bare-brick, whitewashed walls. The menu promised and delivered much: £18.50 buys an excellent three-course lunch with six choices for each course. We went for scallops with basil oil along with smoked salmon crêpes, which were beautifully delicate in a creamy dill sauce. Among the mains, juicy pink duck breast with figs came in a sauce of impeccable consistency, while monkfish was perfectly complemented by a turmeric 'crème de curry'. Both were served with a crisp selection of potatoes and green vegetables. As for desserts, crème brûlée with summer fruits was as light and refined as the apricot compôte was fresh and ample. It's not haute cuisine, but it is very fine cuisine and very good value – with no extra charge for bread or coffee. The broad French wine list is pricey, with little under £20, but house wines (especially the smoothly mellow white) are excellent value. Go.

Babies and children admitted. Booking advisable. Tables outdoors (10, terrace). **Map 1/2C.**

Outer London

Hampton Hill, Surrey

Monsieur Max ★

133 High Street, Hampton Hill, Middx (020 8979 5546). Kew Gardens tube/rail then 68 bus/Fulwell rail. **Lunch served** 12.30-2.30pm Mon-Fri; 12.30-3pm Sun. **Dinner served** 7-11pm Mon-Sat; 7-10.30pm Sun. **Set lunch** £14 two courses, £17 three courses. **Set Sunday lunch** £24.50 three courses. **Set dinner** £24.50 three courses. **Corkage** £10 a bottle. **Service** 12½%. **Cover** £1.50. **Credit** AmEx, DC, JCB, MC, V.

Proudly trumpeting its 'cuisine bourgeoise' from behind an anonymous frontage in Hampton Hill is Max Renzland's consistently superb restaurant. Once past the net curtains, the well-drilled yet chilled staff greet diners in French and waft them to their tables in the curiously eclectic interior (ancient wall tiles, wood panelling, stained glass), harmonised by some lovely art deco details. The set-price menu (with a good number of supplements) is packed with the simple and the complex, the novel and the familiar. We went for a classically simple brown shrimp cocktail with marie rose sauce (£5.50 supplement) and the flavour whirlwind of ultra-light goat's cheese beignet with red pepper mousse, onion cooked two ways (stewed and deep-fried) and spiced tabouleh salad. We then proceeded with severely poshed-up versions of roast beef and Yorkshire, and roast chicken. The former was a melting slab of prime Aberdeen Angus, Yorkshire pud smothered in a (mite too sweet) leeky sauce, with gratin dauphinois and green beans. The latter was a honey-roasted leg of Bresse bird, counterpointed by confit pork belly 'epicé' (and a perfect piece of crackling), creamy risotto of summer truffles and a rich soubise of onions and black muscat grapes. If you can resist the first-rate cheeseboard, then hope that the soufflé of summer fruits 'with its coulis' or the banana tarte tatin with coconut sorbet is on the menu. They're both exquisite. The wine list is a treat for oenophiles with a little cash to splash, with some (relative) steals in the £30-plus class.

Booking advisable.

Richmond, Surrey

Chez Lindsay

11 Hill Rise, Richmond, Surrey (020 8948 7473). Richmond tube/rail. **Meals served** 11am-11pm Mon-Sat; noon-10pm Sun. **Main courses** £8.95-£15.75. **Set lunch** (11am-3pm) £5.99 two courses. **Set meal** (11am-3pm, 6-11pm) £10.99 three courses. **Credit** MC, V.

Looking very picturesque by the banks of the Thames, Chez Lindsay has successfully exported the Breton dining experience to the heart of Richmond. With the possible exception of the London-strength prices, everything here is as exactly as you might find it in deepest darkest Brittany. Even the staff fit the stereotype: knowledgeable and helpful but exuding that all-important Gallic hauteur (service with a smile just wouldn't be the same). Galettes and crêpes are the specialities here, although there are some other regional dishes to be sampled, such as moules à la St Malo or terrine Breton. We started with a dozen palourde clams (really no more than a vehicle for their sticky garlic butter sauce) and an equally simple – but sweet and fresh – dish of langoustines with mayonnaise. Then came the galettes, the first of which was filled with a deliciously light mix of smoked salmon, lemon and chive cream. The second choice wasn't such a success – the filling of assorted seafood and julienne of veg was swamped by an overpowering bisque-like sauce. Crêpes were fantastic, though, as was our bottle of Val de Rance, the undisputed king of ciders.

Babies and children welcome; high chairs. Booking advisable. Separate room for parties, seats 35.

Global

Afghan

North

Islington N1

Afghan Kitchen

35 Islington Green, N1 (020 7359 8019). Angel tube. **Lunch served** noon-3.30pm, **dinner served** 5.30-11pm Tue-Sat. **Main courses** £4.50-£5. **No credit cards.**

This compact split-level restaurant on Islington Green offers communal tables on the ground floor, with a few close-knit upstairs tables for smaller groups. Dusky mint-green walls, a white ceiling and minimalist furnishings create a kind of 'IKEA show-kitchen meets Japanese canteen' effect. Not exactly an authentic experience of the Hindu Kush, then, but Afghan Kitchen does feel like the kind of place in which to chill out and let the conversation flow. The menu is split between meat dishes (chicken and lamb) and vegetarian options. We chose selections of the latter – all arriving within a few microwaveable minutes – which included stuffed sweet peppers, delicious chunks of pumpkin with yoghurt, a mildly spiced dahl, and kidney beans with chickpeas and potatoes. Green tea added a traditional touch of the Central Asian caravan to proceedings, but the music (Simply Red) rather spoiled that illusion. When we asked whether there was any traditional Afghan music, we were told that the chef, who had the restaurant's only tape, had already left.

Babies and children admitted. Book dinner. Takeaway service. **Map 16/2O.**

Alsatian

Central

Soho W1

Schnecke

58-59 Poland Street, W1 (020 7287 6666). Oxford Circus or Tottenham Court Road tube. **Meals served** noon-11.30pm Mon-Sat, noon-10pm Sun. **Main courses** £6-£16. **Service** 12½%. **Credit** AmEx, DC, JCB, V.

The creators of Belgo have now decided to try and put Alsatian cuisine on the culinary map. The illuminated Continental-style menu at the entrance and the log-cabin decor inside may be light-hearted touches but the food is taken seriously. The showpiece of the menu is the tarte flambée, in savoury or sweet varieties. These large, rectangular sheets of pastry are topped with fresh regional ingredients – gratinée is the basic version, beautifully crisp and topped with fromage frais and crème fraîche, smoked bacon, onion and chives. Heartier fare includes the satisfying ménage aux trois saucisses: three types of sausage accompanied by mash (with spring onions and bacon) and red onion cooked in wine sauce. Cherry cheesecake was perfectly creamy, while tarte alsacienne (apple pie) was well made but perhaps not to everyone's liking, with an overly eggy mix and heavy pastry. Surprisingly, given that Alsace is lauded for its beers, there's only one on the menu, but vins d'Alsace get more of a look-in. Service is efficiently laid-back and you can also pay in Euros, which is nice and handy.

Babies and children admitted; high chairs. Disabled: toilet. Separate rooms for parties seating 32 and 100. **Map 13/6J.**

For branch see index.

North

Islington N1

Tartuf

88 Upper Street, N1 (020 7288 0954). Angel tube. **Lunch served** noon-2.30pm, **dinner served** 5.45-11.30pm Mon-Fri. **Meals served** noon-midnight Sat; noon-11pm Sun. **Main courses** £5.50-£9.50. **Set meals** £4.90 (lunch) two courses, £8.90 eat as much as you like. **Service** 12½%. **Credit** MC, V.

This is one of two Alsatian restaurants on this Islington strip (the other is a branch of Schnecke). Both are enjoyable venues, but whereas Schnecke is brightly lit and modern, Tartuf is an altogether cosier joint. It's gently themed, with the odd bit of checked fabric and chunky wooden tables and chairs, plus oddities such as metal cheese-graters used as lampshades. Cheery, French-accented staff whizz around the three-storey premises, bearing Alsatian wines, beers and tartes flambées (around £5-£6.50 each). The tartes appear within minutes of ordering (before the beer in our case) and you're meant to order one, eat it between you, and then order another. Toppings on these very-thin, moreish versions of pizza range from traditionelle (fromage blanc, sliced onion and smoked lardons) to more modern creations such as epinard (fromage blanc, sliced onions, spinach, mushrooms and Emmental) and poulet (fromage blanc, sliced onions, chicken breast and red pepper). There are other dishes available (a couple of salads, a galette and choucroute), but these are bit players rather than star attractions. Not somewhere to spend the whole evening, but a good stop-off.

Babies and children admitted; high chairs. Separate room for parties, seats 30. Tables outdoor (10, pavement). **Map 16/1O.**

Belgian

Central

Covent Garden WC2

Belgo Centraal

50 Earlham Street, WC2 (020 7813 2233). Covent Garden tube. **Meals served** noon-11.30pm Mon-Thur; noon-midnight Fri, Sat; noon-10pm Sun. **Main courses** £8.95-£18.95. **Set lunch** £5. **Set meal** £14.95 two courses incl beer, soft drink or ice-cream. **Service** 15%. **Credit** AmEx, DC, JCB, MC, £TC, V.

Take the funky industrial lift down to this stylish subterranean beer hall, which looks like a cross between the set of *Alien* and a noisy crypt. The friendly waiters are kitted out in pseudo-monk outfits and bring chips and free schnapps to your table straightaway. Standards were much improved from previous visits. Both starters (gravadlax, and spinach and red onion tart) were packed with flavour. For once deciding against Belgo's mussels, we chose instead an excellent beef braised in beer with apples and plums – a light and fruity main course. Seared salmon escalopes on a bed of thinly sliced vegetables were perfectly cooked and strengthened by a gutsy dill flavour. Apricot crème brûlée with caramelised peach made an exquisite end to an enjoyable meal. At weekends (noon-6pm) Belgo Centraal also caters well for children, offering a 'Mini Belgo' menu for under-12s (£5.50).

Babies and children welcome; high chairs. Booking advisable. Disabled: toilet. **Map 14/6L.**

West

Ladbroke Grove W10

Belgo Zuid

124 Ladbroke Grove, W10 (020 8982 8400). Ladbroke Grove tube. **Lunch served** noon-3pm, **dinner served** 6-11pm Mon-Fri. **Meals served** noon-11.30pm Sat; noon-10.30pm Sun. **Main courses** £8.95-£18.95. **Set meal** £14.95 two courses, incl beer, soft drink or ice-cream. **Set lunch** £5 one course, incl beer or soft drink. **Service** 15%. **Credit** AmEx, DC, JCB, LV, MC, £TC, V.

Another link in the Belgo chain, Zuid has a cavernous dining room whose vaulted ceiling gives it the appearance of an upturned arc. Lively flocks of diners are duly shepherded in and an enormous mural of a jowly Belgian presides

Tartuf.
See page 68.

over their meals. Our own got off to a galloping start with mouth-watering tuna carpaccio and pickled cucumber, but crab cakes pan-fried in garlic and chilli with a coriander pink grapefruit sauce lacked any distinctive flavour. Main course roast monkfish tossed with spring vegetables in a tomato vinaigrette sauce was perfectly cooked but its sauce was too acidic. However, delicate red mullet pan-fried with baby leeks and carrots and finished with saffron oil was excellent. Unfortunately, a tasty-sounding pancake filled with vanilla ice-cream, caramelised apples and prunes was a bland letdown. Service was excellent, though, with beer recommendations for every course – but be warned, the raspberry fruit beer loses its appeal once dessert is finished. A more intimate upstairs bar overlooks the restaurant.
Babies and children welcome; crayons; high chairs. Book dinner. Disabled: toilet. **Map 11/5Az.**

North

Camden Town & Chalk Farm NW1

Belgo Noord
72 Chalk Farm Road, NW1 (020 7267 0718). Chalk Farm tube. **Lunch served** noon-3pm Mon-Fri. **Dinner served** 6-10.30pm Mon, Tue; 6-11.30pm Wed-Fri. **Meals served** noon-11.30pm Sat; noon-10.30pm Sun. **Main courses** £8.25-£18.95. **Set lunch** £5. **Set meal** £14.95 two courses incl beer, soft drink or ice-cream. **Service** 15%. **Credit** AmEx, DC, JCB, MC, £TC, V.
All the familiar Belgo trappings are evident in this, the oldest branch of the chain – from the steel and concrete dining area to the habit-clad staff and potent beer selection. The menu is extensive and varied but it takes a long time to read and needs to be laid out more clearly. We kicked off with Cornish brown crab fritters with a pickled cucumber dressing – bland and disappointingly void of any real crab flavour. A better bet was gravadlax marinated in honey-beer, served with a mustard and dill dressing. Next, a kilo pot of mussels congo was tasty but the coconut and lemongrass sauce was a little too glutinous. Puff pastry filled with wild mushrooms in bush beer cream sauce, black truffles and tarragon was satisfyingly rich and filling. The good strong wine beers and the friendly, attentive service help smooth over this outlet's iffy culinary credentials. Note that this and other branches have a time deal (generally around 5.30-7pm Mon-Fri), where the bill (for one course and a beer or soft drink) estimated at the time you arrive; that is, arrive at 6.15pm, pay £6.15.
Babies and children welcome; colouring pens; high chairs. Booking advisable; essential Thur, Fri. **Map 10.**

Islington N1

Bierodrome
173-174 Upper Street, N1 (020 7226 5835). Angel tube/Highbury & Islington tube/rail/4, 19, 30, 43 bus. **Open** noon-11pm daily. **Lunch served** noon-3pm, **dinner served** 5.30-11pm Mon-Fri. **Meals served** noon-11pm Sat; noon-10.30pm Sun. **Main courses** £6.95-£14.50. **Set meal** £12.50 two courses, incl beer, soft drink or ice-cream. **Set lunch** £5 one course, incl beer. **Service** 12½%. **Credit** AmEx, DC, JCB, MC, £TC, V.
It's the bustling bar, rather than the noisy and characterless restaurant section behind it, that dominates this smallest outlet of the mighty Belgo group. Two salad starters – one with asparagus, sweet peas, baby spinach, artichokes and a garlic and lemon dressing, the other a mixed seafood with basil dressing – had tasty ingredients but were drowned in too much dressing. A sharp improvement came with the main courses in the form of decent seared tuna with a fresh herb and sesame crust, served on French beans and new potatoes with a soy dressing. The ever reliable kilo pot of mussels with a Provençal sauce was also good, and the frites were excellent. The small kitchen struggles to prepare the more sophisticated dishes, so stick to the beer and mussels and you won't go wrong. Service was, as in all the Belgo establishments, friendly and helpful.
Babies and children welcome; children's menu; colouring books; high chairs. Booking advisable. Disabled: toilet. Tables outdoors (5, pavement). **Map 16/1O.**
For branches see index.

Burmese

Central

Edgware Road W2

Mandalay
444 Edgware Road, W2 (020 7258 3696). Edgware Road tube. **Lunch served** noon-2.30pm, **dinner served** 6-10.30pm Mon-Sat. **Main courses** £3.90-£6.90. **Set lunches** £3.50 one course, £5.90 three courses. **Credit** AmEx, DC, JCB, MC, £TC, V.
With its location at the scruffy end of Edgware Road and its caff-like exterior, Mandalay looks none too promising at first. Inside, things start to look up. On a midweek visit the restaurant was full: the first good sign. The second was a friendly welcome and some swiftly delivered Tiger beer to keep us busy while we pondered the extensive menu. Burmese food is best described as a cross between Indian, Chinese and Thai. We started with spinach, calabash and beansprout fritters and a crunchy papaya and cucumber salad. A prawn and tomato curry main course consisted of seven enormous, juicy prawns in a piquant sauce, served with mouth-watering coconut rice garnished with caramelised onion. Flavours of fresh mint and ginger in a lamb and mint curry compensated for the slightly tough meat, while carrot pickle combined crunchy vegetables with sweet tomato chilli sauce. This was accompanied by balachuang – a traditional Burmese garnish of dried shrimp, onion and ginger – a very fishy concoction that's not for the faint-hearted. Despite a humdrum dessert of vanilla ice-cream and tinned tropical fruit, we'll certainly be back.
Babies and children welcome; high chairs. Booking essential. No smoking. Takeaway service. **Map 1/D.**

Irish

Central

Mayfair W1

Mulligans of Mayfair
13-14 Cork Street, W1 (020 7409 1370). Piccadilly Circus tube.
Bar **Open** 11am-11pm Mon-Sat.
Restaurant **Lunch served** noon-3pm Mon-Fri. **Dinner served** 6.30-9.30pm Mon-Sat. **Main courses** £9.95-£16.50.
Both **Credit** AmEx, DC, MC, £TC, V.
Most lovers of Irish culture would universally condemn Irish theme bars and restaurants, but Mulligan's is an exception that serves good and simple Irish country cooking. In the downstairs restaurant decor resembles an upmarket lounge bar, with upholstered armchairs and wood and etched glass cubicles affording privacy and comfort. Wines are a mix of well-selected faves and good-quality labels for under £20, and service is relaxed and well informed. Dishes didn't look like much on the menu but they certainly amounted to something on the plate. Black pudding and chicken liver on baby spinach leaves was simple but sophisticated, while potted smoked trout wrapped in cucumber with water cress was every bit as clean, refreshing and smoky as it sounds. Although we were in the mood for the full Gaelic experience, Irish stew seemed a bit too hearty to handle on a warm day, so instead we chose main courses of seared asparagus with Lough Foyle scallops (gorgeous fat cushions of flesh) and a hunky, juicy marinated chump of lamb with olive oil mash and coriander dressing. Sadly, after this little lot, there was no room for dessert, despite the allure of poached rhubarb and vanilla custard.
Babies and children admitted. Booking advisable. **Map 13/7J.**

Marylebone W1

The O'Conor Don
88 Marylebone Lane, W1 (020 7935 9311). Bond Street tube.
Bar **Open** 11am-11pm Mon-Fri.
Restaurant **Lunch served** noon-2.30pm, **dinner served** 6-10pm Mon-Fri. **Main courses** £6.95-£10.95. **Credit** AmEx, MC, V.
Typical of Irish country restaurants, the Ard-Ri (High King) dining room at the O'Conor Don is a royally laid-back mishmash of rickety armchairs, pictures and bare floorboards, with a menu that majors on bivalves, freshwater fish and hearty stews. As so often in the Emerald Isle, the louche ambience beats the ordinary, pub-like cooking, but at these prices, it's no use complaining. Chicken liver salad (£4.25) was hot, fresh and juicy (if unimaginative); Irish stew (£9) was a good hearty dish served with a couple of classic floury spuds. Unfortunately, the enormously rich beef and Guinness casserole (£9) was served with lumpy, slightly old mashed potato. Not a great deal of thought has gone into the basic, catch-all wine list and a Navarra was, frankly, ropey. The highlight instead was a passion fruit and mascarpone syllabub chosen from among six desserts: two huge dollops of the thick cream cheese underpinned by nicely acidic marinated passion fruit.
Babies and children admitted. Booking advisable. **Map 2/5G.**

South West

Fulham SW6

Arkles
Chelsea Village, Stamford Bridge, Fulham Road, SW6 (020 7565 1420). Fulham Broadway tube/11, 14 bus. **Lunch served** noon-2.30pm Sun. **Dinner served** 6.30-10.30pm Tue-Sat. **Main courses** £13-£19. **Set dinner** £19.50 two courses, £22.50 three courses incl glass of champagne and coffee **Set Sunday lunch** £22.50 three courses. **Service** 12½%. **Credit** AmEx, JCB, MC, V.
We picked a non-match night for a visit to Arkles in Chelsea Village, so we had the restaurant completely to ourselves. Surrounded by wood beams, emerald-coloured walls, a mock walkway in the shape of Stamford Bridge and piped music by the Corrs, we settled in for the evening, with service provided by two very efficient but slightly embarrassed members of staff. Starters are fairly grand and include half-a-dozen oysters, Irish smoked salmon with soda bread and a gorgeous-sounding garden salad with West of Ireland sea scallops or Dublin Bay prawns. Main courses were a hit: we went for poached fillet of salmon with lobster cake, which came with asparagus salad and a tasty rosemary dressing. Fillet of Kildare beef was heftily priced at £19.50, but was a faultless option nonetheless, served with mash, roast carrots and claret sauce. We finished with coffees and a shared dessert of chocolate and crème brûlée with pan-fried orange and Grand Marnier noodles; an interesting textured concoction strictly for the sweet-toothed.
Babies and children welcome; high chairs. Booking advisable. Disabled: toilet. Dress: smart casual. Entertainment: Irish theme nights Last Sat of every month. **Map 5/13B.**

Scandinavian

Central

Knightsbridge SW7

Lundum's
119 Old Brompton Road, SW7 (020 7373 7774). Gloucester Road or South Kensington tube. **Open** 10am-midnight Mon-Sat; noon-5pm Sun. **Lunch served** noon-4pm daily. **Dinner served** 6-11pm Mon-Sat. **Main courses** lunch £6.25-£14.75; dinner £10.25-£15.75. **Sunday buffet brunch** £15.50. **Set lunch** £15.50. **Set dinner** £17.25 two courses, £21.50 three courses **Service** 12½%. **Credit** AmEx, JCB, MC, TC, V.
Danish cuisine is an unknown quantity to many, but this prettily located, attractively decorated and charmingly run restaurant proves there's more to it than bacon and pastries. Smartly decked out in ethereal shades of white and cream, with a tastefully appointed terrace, it serves artfully presented, impeccably fresh food with the savoir faire of the French. Light, appetising starters included a sensational citrus marinated cod tartare; we also chose a trio of top-quality tartare, smoked salmon and gravlax, and salted salmon with a gloriously rich horseradish mousse from the Symphony of Salmons menu. Fish mains were cooked without affectation and served with imaginative accompaniments; witness fried fillet of hake with potato and fennel stew in a light, subtle lemongrass and mélisse

sauce. A house speciality of cured duck was a choice, ham-like variation on the old canard, but crispy, tender medallions of pork in a subtly sweet ginger sauce provided the high point of the evening. A side dish of super-fresh summer veg was impressively crisp and steaming. Raspberry and almond terrine, and apple tatin with caramel ice-cream and sauce provided a triumphant conclusion to the meal. Seasoning is arguably too understated for some palates but, with a strong wine list and good humoured, conscientious staff, this is a smart but cool destination that needn't be the solo delight of Scandinavian Sloanes.
Babies and children welcome; high chairs. Booking advisable. Tables outdoors (15, patio). **Map 5/11D.**

Marylebone W1

Garbo's

42 Crawford Street, W1 (020 7262 6582). Baker Street or Edgware Road tube/ Marylebone tube/rail. **Lunch served** noon-3pm Mon-Fri, Sun. **Dinner served** 6-11pm Mon-Sat. **Main courses** £13.25-£15.75. **Set lunch** smörgåsbord £9.95; £7.95 two courses, £8.95 three courses. **Sunday buffet lunch** £11.95. **Cover** £1. **Credit** AmEx, £TC, MC, V.
Named after the Swedish femme fatale of the silver screen, Garbo's is widely considered London's premier Swedish restaurant. This is probably based on its gentle evocation of the old country through a bright interior of painted wood, photos of Greta, posters of Abba and a huge, mournful wall-mounted elk bust. Food is fine but unexceptional and there's a feeling that the chefs cook it, like the staff serve it: in their sleep. However, the changing set menu is value for money. From this, pickled herring salad was good, but the sea bass main course served with spinach had been grilled beyond recognition. Happily, desserts included that famous Swedish dish 'apple crumble and custard', whose crunchy, al dente construction was a far cry from its soggy, lumpy English cousin. The à la carte menu is racily divided into 'international' (actually more like pan-European) and 'traditional' sections. From the former, grilled Dover sole was simple and fresh – more than can be said for the grey, pensionable veg that accompanied it, while traditional offerings ranged from gravadlax to beef rydberg or meatballs.
Babies and children admitted. Booking advisable. Separate room for parties, seats 40. **Map 2/5F.**

North East

Newington Green N1

Anna's Place

90 Mildmay Park, N1 (020 7249 9379/ www.annasplace.co.uk). Canonbury rail/38, 73, 141, 236, 277, 341 bus. **Lunch served** 12.15-2.15pm Sat. **Dinner served** 7.15-10.45pm Mon-Sat. **Main courses** £9.50-£13.80. **Set dinner** £10.95 two courses, £12.95 three courses. **Credit** £$TC.
North Londoners recall this Swedish restaurant nostalgically, but its heyday passed when its titular founder retired. The light, airy establishment is still prettily adorned in pastel colours and the convivial atmosphere remains. The menu is comparatively simple, with only the set menu changing much, but still the cuisine is not great. The set menu featured an ordinary onion soup and a pleasant salmon steak served with leathery, reheated 'new' potatoes. The à la carte menu was scarcely more enterprising, repeating the onion soup and featuring a 'selection of Swedish delicacies' (£7/£9.95 for two) that combined the remaining options of gravadlax, herring and fish roe on one plate. At least grey meatballs with creamy mash were cheered by a lingonberry sauce. The short wine list was uninspired, listing only grape varieties with no notes. It's not that Anna's is bad, just that it needs a rethink.
Babies and children welcome; high chairs. Booking advisable; essential dinner Thur-Sat. Tables outdoors (5, garden).

South African

West

Chiswick W4

Springbok Café

42 Devonshire Road, W4 (020 8742 3149). Turnham Green tube. **Dinner served** 6.30-11pm Mon-Sat. **Main courses** £9.50-£14. **Service** 10% for parties of six or more. **Credit** MC, £TC, V.
'Explore South Africa with a knife and fork' is the motto of this unusual restaurant trapped in the structure of a back-street café. And sure enough, with sunny shades of sky blue and earth orange alongside cartoon maps teeming with wildlife, this really is something of a culinary safari. On top of this, the cooking takes place right under your nose in the open-plan kitchen, giving eaters a real sense of involvement in this cross-cultural edible adventure. In line with the country's Cape-Malay cuisine the dishes tend to combine fruit and spices in interesting, often sweet combinations. A starter of juicy scallops served with morogo (half cabbage, half spinach) and peppadew butter were accompanied by almost caramelised onions; the ostrich fillet served with avocado, sweet peppers, spring onions and olive oil was meaty but sweet-tasting, too; and even the more European rack of Karoo lamb, with its slightly sour meillie-meal (cornmeal) crust, was accompanied by parsley mash and rosemary jus. However, this does not mean desserts are savoury: malva with thick cream was a robust steam-bread pudding with plums. The wine list, too, held further intrigue for those not versed in the big, ripe varieties of South African plonk (£12.50-£40).
Babies and children welcome. Book dinner. Tables outdoors (4, pavement).

Lundum's.
See page 69.

Greek

The downward spiral in the fortunes of London Greek eateries continues, as our coverage struggles to fill two pages. The past year has again seen the closure of several seemingly perennial restaurants, victims either of proprietor retirement or the marketplace. For the harsh reality of the latter is that most Greek-Cypriot restaurants (as the majority of establishments in London are) simply no longer merit attention in the capital's competitive and novelty-craving eating out scene. There's still too much reliance by restaurateurs on tired culinary and decor formulas: predictable mezédes with identikit ready-bought dips; British intrusions such as crabsticks and peppered mackerel; mock-rustic furnishings; and a package-holiday soundtrack.

In both Cyprus and Greece (the latter poorly represented on these pages), a new interest in the cuisine has developed, featuring a revival of undeservedly obscure recipes and ingredients, truly creative mezédes, and wine production that can hold its head (and price) up with the better Italian and Spanish vintages. Except for the valiant attempts of such relative newcomers as **The Real Greek** and **Halepi**, you wouldn't know of its existence in London.

West

Bayswater W2

Aphrodite Taverna

15 Hereford Road, W2 (020 7229 2206). Bayswater or Notting Hill Gate tube. **Meals served** noon-midnight Mon-Sat. **Main courses** £6.95-£16.50. **Mezédes** £16 meat, £13.50 vegetarian. **Credit** AmEx, DC, MC, V.
It being a little chilly to pass the afternoon at one of Aphrodite's handful of sidewalk tables, we retired indoors to witness the kitsch masterpiece that is its interior – which comes complete with a bad oil canvas of the namesake deity mermaid-like in the surf, in the buff. The menu contains the usual intrusions such as avocado vinaigrette and Dover sole, but we stuck to the Hellenic food, and found the quality decidedly uneven compared to previous visits. Complimentary nibbles (piyázi or white bean salad, radishes, tsakistés, black olives and hot chillies) arrived immediately and promised good things to follow. However, grilled halloúmi was not very savoury, while marídes (like whitebait) proved soggy and bland inside despite being just crisp enough outside. Hoúmous and melitzanosaláta were OK, if rather difficult to distinguish between. Mains, too, were a mixed bag: bream, the day's special, was adequate fare, if unimaginatively presented; sheftaliá was dry, tasteless and left unfinished. As is so often the case, the sweets corner of the menu is perfunctory, though 'cream caramel' was more than decent. Wines are abundant and the list is patriotically Greek or Cypriot. To finish, we lingered over two of the weakest Greek coffees in living memory (£1.50 each). The bill of £47.80 for two, excluding alcohol or service, made the entire experience rather indigestible.
Babies and children welcome; high chairs. Booking advisable dinner. Tables outdoors (10, pavement). Takeaway service. **Map 11/6B.**

Xios

47 Moscow Road, W2 (020 7243 0606). Bayswater or Queensway tube. **Meals served** noon-11pm daily. **Main courses** £7.40-£12.50. **Mezédes** £15 per person. **Cover** £1. **Service** 10%. **Credit** DC, JCB, MC, £TC, V.
We're sad to see a continuing decline in standards at Xios, one of the few explicitly peninsular Greek (as opposed to Greek-Cypriot) restaurants in London. The minimalist decor remains much the same: bare walls save for a painting of Mavra Volia beach on Xios island; blond-wood chairs or plush bench seating. But the soundtrack was abrasive Greek pop, and the menu has pulled in its horns and mostly retreated to the timid dips-and-grills norm. Even the wine list, while still Greek rather than Cypriot, has been pared down, though the house white was adequate. Nibbles are now free, but confined to carrot sticks and olives. Gone are the lovely soups of the past; we had to make do with aubergine salad, which had a bitter tang; three smallish but nice grilled sardines doused in oil; and a half-dozen squid rings on iceberg lettuce. Like last year, we had a long wait for the next courses: a bizarre rendition of moussakás, left unfinished, where a Gruyère-style cheese overpowered all else; and a more tempting helping of kleftiko and new potatoes garnished with sun-dried tomatoes. Curiously, both needed additional seasoning. The briefer-than-brief dessert list was augmented by 'unlisted' Greek sweets; galaktobúreko (custard pastry) was an inferior, mealy version. When one reckons the wine, and two bottles of San Pellegrino, were the most memorable part of the evening, how much longer before Xios sinks beneath the Aegean?
Babies and children welcome; high chairs. Booking advisable. Takeaway service. **Map 11/6B.**

East

Shoreditch N1

The Real Greek ★

15 Hoxton Market, N1 (020 7739 8212). Old Street tube/rail/26, 48, 55, 149, 242 bus. **Lunch served** noon-3pm, **dinner served** 5.30-10.30pm Mon-Sat. **Main courses** £14.80-£15. **Credit** AmEx, MC, V.
First impressions of this converted pub are firmly of Islington rather than Real Greece: smoky, packed out and buzzing with the N1 chattering classes. The menu is divided into three sections: mezédes (platters of four or five dishes); fagákia (a single small dish); and main courses. We plumped for mezédes '#2', comprising olives (scrumptious), fava purée (too creamy), 'warm leaf' (hórta) salad, kefalotyri saganáki (perfect fried cheese), and smoked pork loin (carpaccio'd pork slices redolent of fennel), but the combination didn't sit too well together. An all-seafood medley proved more successful: a slice of lakérda (marinated white-flesh bonito), wine-cooked octopus with a strong hint of cumin, a handful of cockles in the shell, roast beetroot with skordaliá. We also ordered a fagáki, epirote courgette phyllo pie, judged a triumph, authenticity aside. But the open-plan kitchen came a cropper on lamb yiouvétsi with hilópittes. This main contained much fat and gristle, and hilópittes was bog-standard tagliatelle. Avoiding the weirder desserts, we enjoyed a three-layer (chocolate, fig, espresso) torte. An impressive wine list sources some of Greece's best wine producers (£15.75-£27.50). Black-clad staff were generally leisurely though not laggard. This is an original restaurant with potential, but our meal cost £90 for two (including the cheapest wine, mineral water and service). We were hoping for the same standards that led to the Real Greek becoming Best New Restaurant in the *Time Out* Eating & Drinking Awards 2000, and were left unsatisfied.
Babies and children admitted. Separate room for parties, seats 8. **Map 17/3Q**

North

Archway N19

Ta Dilina

122 Junction Road, N19 (020 7272 0318). Archway or Tufnell Park tube. **Dinner served** 6-11pm Tue-Sat. **Main courses** £7-£12. **Service** 10%. **No credit cards.**
A much-needed facelift, both inside and out, has left this local taverna with a decor of fetching rural kitsch. Archeological repro art has been

The Real Greek.
See page 71.

hung on the rag-painted orange walls, and gourds and basketry dangle overhead. Little else has changed, including the prices, the workaday quality of the cuisine, and the soundtrack (Greek music – as listened to by Greek Cypriots, not tourists). The cover charge pays for olives, pitta and fiery chillies. Grilled octopus was tender though doused in too much oil; hoúmous had a lovely consistency. Mains comprised a big, succulent slab of swordfish which belied the somewhat elderly appearance it had while in the glass display case. Two quails, out of season, were almost certainly frozen and a bit dry and flavourless. Both main courses were unadorned, save for a solitary lemon wedge. For dessert, the best choice is the seasonal fruit platter, in March featuring melons, grapes, kiwi fruit, pineapple and strawberries. A well-kept bottle of Greek Robola (£12.50) is the only highlight of an otherwise strictly Cypriot wine list. All in all, not bad value for money – perhaps for this reason, Ta Dilina was nearly full by 8.30pm on a Thursday.
Babies and children admitted.

Camden Town & Chalk Farm NW1

Andy's Taverna ★ ★
81-81A Bayham Street, NW1 (020 7485 9718). Camden Town tube. **Lunch served** noon-2.30pm Mon-Fri. **Dinner served** 6pm-midnight Mon-Sat; 5.30-11.30pm Sun. **Main courses** £6.95-£11.50. **Set lunch** £6.95 two courses. **Set meal** £9.95 three courses. **Service** 10% parties of ten or more. **Credit** AmEx, DC, JCB, MC, V.
Of the surviving Greek tavernas that cluster mostly east of Camden High Street, Andy's is clearly the front-runner, judging from week-night crowds. It's easy to see why. There's a lightness of touch, discernible basic ingredients, and an enticingly homemade savour to Cypriot mainstays. Perhaps such standards are attributable to the owner's 15-year stint as a chef in Athens and on the island of Evina. Among several starters, only pastourmá (garlicky, pink wieners rather than the rough-hewn sausages we'd expected), and a bland vinaigrette version

of artichoke hearts with broad beans disappointed. Three huge dolmádes were patently fresh and own-made; and the succulent, green filling of the spanakópitta (fat and oddly tubular), threatened to burst through the most sheer of crusts. Mains were even better: three vegetarian papoutsákia (stuffed aubergines) arrived cooked to perfection, redolent of onion, coriander and other subtle flavours; kalamári, cut in thin slivers, went down a treat. The wine list is mostly Cypriot, though there are a few Greek stars, including a well-priced Cambas Nemea (£10.50). Service is affable, even jocular. During warmer months, the little garden at the back is in demand.
Babies and children welcome; crayons and books; high chairs. Booking advisable Fri-Sun. No-smoking tables. Separate rooms for parties (seating 30 and 40; garden can be booked). Tables outdoors (7, garden). Takeaway service. **Map 9.**

Daphne
83 Bayham Street, NW1 (020 7267 7322). Camden Town tube. **Lunch served** noon-2.30pm, **dinner served** 6-11.30pm Mon-Sat. **Main courses** £6.50-£12.50. **Set lunch** £5.75 two courses. **Mezédes** £10.75 meat and vegetarian, £15.50 fish, per person (minimum two). **Credit** MC, V.
Daphne's doesn't do so badly as second fiddle to its neighbour, Andy's. The furnishings are similarly restrained: 1880s photos of peasant Cyprus, checked tablecloths, stone flooring. The two-course set lunch remains great value, with four choices for each course, but on our visit we opted to go à la carte. Avgolémono soup had a lemony tang, while three medium-sized sardines were appetising and fresh. Afélia proved a decent rendition, redolent of wine and coriander, and with real pork-shoulder cubes and just the right amount of fat. Moussaká in a clay pot failed to satisfy, however, its burnt topping more akin to a supermarket lasagne than real béchamel. Too late, we cast an eye on the daily specials board and made a mental note to sample it next time. For starters it featured trígona pastries, and agávros (fresh anchovy), beans and artichokes; and for mains, a plethora of fish dishes. The well-priced wine list contains a number of decent Greek vintages for either side of a tenner, including a perfectly palatable Cambas Mantinia white. We passed on desserts (the perennial pair of baklavá and kataifi pastries) and instead enjoyed a couple of competent 'Greek' coffees with loukoúmi.
Babies and children welcome. Booking advisable Fri, Sat. Separate rooms for parties, seats 35. Tables outdoors (8, roof terrace; 2, patio). Takeaway service. **Map 9.**

Lemonia
89 Regent's Park Road, NW1 (020 7586 7454). Chalk Farm tube/31, 168 bus. **Lunch served** noon-3pm Mon-Fri, Sun. **Dinner served** 6-11.30pm Mon-Sat. **Main courses** £8-£13.50. **Set lunch** £6.75 two courses incl coffee, £7.95 three courses. **Mezédes** £13.50 per person (minimum two). **Credit** MC, V.
For a long while, Lemonia was London's premier Greek-Cypriot taverna (with prices to match). Now, though, it's showing signs of complacency. The vast, resolutely tasteful interior still fills with Primrose Hill-ites; service remains ready and discreet; and most of the food is several notches above that of the average kebab-and-tarama joint. But we were distressed to find

portions so *minceur*. For starters, a pair of loukánika passed muster, and a few pats of halloúmi were appealingly smoky, but spanakópitta were only just OK, and a day's special – angináres mé koukiá (two artichoke hearts with broad beans) – was a letdown. Next, a joint of kléftiko was tender and non-fatty, and grilled tuna steak (£12.75) was seared to perfection, but it was irksome to have chips (quite good) as the side dish. Two lonely kolokythia (courgettes), another day's special, stuffed with lamb mince and pine nuts and supposedly topped with avgolémono, appeared festooned with spinach shreds instead and had little discernible stuffing. Greek coffee and kataifi were fine, though the fresh fruit salad appeared submerged in syrup. From the excellent Greek red wine list, Skouras Cambello (£12.50) was judged a find. Nevertheless, at a cost of £86 for three including service, everything should have been flawless – and more generous.
Babies and children admitted. Booking essential. Separate room for parties, seats 36. Tables outdoors (8, pavement). **Map 10.**

Limani
154 Regent's Park Road, NW1 (020 7483 4492). Chalk Farm tube/24, 31, 168 bus. **Lunch served** noon-3pm Sat. **Dinner served** 6-11.30pm Tue-Sat; 6-11pm Sun. **Main courses** £6.50-£10.95. **Mezédes** £11.75 (meat), £14.95 (fish), per person (minimum two). **Credit** MC, £TC, V.
Limani remains very much the consolation prize for those failing to get into co-run **Lemonia** (*see above*) across the street, though here too you are wise to book. In summer try to bag a pavement table, or head for the top floor of the rear gallery with its glass roof open a crack for ventilation. The menu is a bit cheaper and slightly less varied than that of Lemonia – and the execution comes a poor second. Many dishes were unavailable on our visit. Service was generally low-key if friendly, though there was nearly an hour's wait between courses, and our waiter's wine advice was 'all Greek whites are pretty much the same, either dry or very dry'. The wine list is mostly Greek, rather MOR, and with only the premium Hatzimihalis label over £10. Among starters, melitzanosaláta was eminently scoopable with the pitta, but louviá with greens had a slightly off taste. A pair of sardines were pilchard-sized and surprisingly bland. Mains were decent if unexciting: two ordigia (quail) were charred to blackness outside but still edible within; moussakás in an oven-ready ramekin was better. Fruit salad was marred by being doused in canned syrup. All the foregoing quibbles notwithstanding, the gallery top deck was full of diners by 8.30pm. Such success almost certainly boils down to the old adage: location, location, location.
Babies and children welcome. Booking advisable. Tables outdoors (4, pavement). **Map 10.**

Retsina
83 Regent's Park Road, NW1 (020 7722 3194). Chalk Farm tube. **Dinner served** 6-11pm daily. **Main courses** £6.40-£10.90. **Mezédes** £10. **Credit** MC, £TC, V.
Little has changed outwardly at Retsina, the least heralded among the trio of Greek-Cypriot tavernas on this upmarket Camden street. There's the same decor of rampant plants scaling the front window; the wine-cork and wine-label ceiling; the eternal free nibbles of carrots, olives and chillies; the same personable

---

Menu

Dishes followed by **(G)** indicate a specifically Greek dish; those with **(GC)** indicate a Cypriot speciality; those without an initial have no particular affiliation.

Afélia (GC): pork, stewed in wine and coriander.
Avgolémono (G): sauce made of lemon and eggs; also a soup made with rice, chicken, lemon and egg.
Dolmádes, dolma: vine leaves stuffed with rice, minced meat and spices.
Fasólia p(i)laki: a vegetarian bean casserole with garlic, tomatoes and oregano.
Garídes: king prawns.
Gígantes: blond haricot beans in

tomato sauce; pronounced 'yígandes'.
Halloúmi (GC): a cheese, usually served grilled. Also spelled hallúmi.
Horiátiki: Greek salad (tomato, cucumber, onion, feta and sometimes green pepper, with olive oil).
Hoúmous (GC): a dip of puréed chickpeas, sesame seed paste, lemon juice and garlic. It's an Arabic, rather than a Greek, dish.
Kalamári, calamares etc: squid, briefly fried.
Kataifi: syrup-soaked 'shredded wheat' rolls.
Keftédes: herby meatballs.
Kléftiko: slow-roasted lamb-on-bone (often shoulder), flavoured with oregano and other herbs.

Loukánika: a spicy sausage, marinated in wine and flavoured with coriander.
Loúntza (GC): smoked pork loin.
Lukúmi: 'Turkish' delight.
Marídes: fish, like whitebait.
Melitzanosaláta: a salad of mashed aubergines with garlic, oil and vinegar.
Mezé (plural **Mezédes**): a selection of appetisers and main dishes that can be either hot or cold.
Moussakás (G): a baked dish of minced meat, aubergines, vegetables and herbs, usually topped with a béchamel sauce.
Pourgoúri also spelt gourgari: cracked wheat.
Saganáki: grilled cheese, either halloúmi, qv (GC) or kefalotyri (G);

in mainland cuisine, can apply to anything (mussels, spinach) made in a cheese sauce.
Sheftaliá: minced and seasoned lamb, char-grilled on a skewer.
Skordaliá (G): garlic-based dip.
Soutzoukákia (G): baked meat rissoles, often topped with tomato-based sauce.
Soúvla: lamb, often marinated in wine and spices, cooked on a skewer over charcoal.
Souvláki: meat, usually lamb, grilled on a skewer (outside Greece this dish is known as a shish kebab).
Spanakópitta (G): small spinach and feta pies. In the UK, filo pastry is used.
Stifádo: a rich, wine-based beef or vegetable stew.

Taboúlleh: a starter made with crushed wheat, chopped parsley, cucumber and lemon juice.
Taramá: fish roe pâté, originally made of mullet roe, now more usually cod roe mixed with olive oil and breadcrumbs.
Tavás (GC): meat, onion and herbs, cooked in earthenware bowls.
Tzatzíki: a dip of shredded cucumber, yoghurt, lemon juice, mint and garlic.
Tsakistés (GC): split green olives marinated with lemon, garlic, coriander seeds and other flavourings.
Tyrópitta: like **spanakópitta** (qv), but without the spinach and with more feta.

host family on first-name terms with their guests – and the same need to book just about any night of the year. But we felt the food wasn't quite up to the standard of previous visits. Among starters, aubergine salad was super-puréed but tasty, while three albeit succulent sardines came without the promised garlic sauce. Halloúmi slices were unmemorable, as were skinny loukánika. Soutzoukákia (baked meat rissoles) arrived doused in an out-of-the-bottle sauce; lamb kebabs were better, though there wasn't anything special about the 'special' rice side-dish, plus salad garnish. The wine list is lo-tech, mostly Cypriot plonk plus a few MOR French, Italian and German options. We finished with a creditable kataifi and rather flat Greek coffees. The usual complimentary fruit plate and liqueur, plus the possibility of eating alfresco, partly compensated for what we hope was an off night at Retsina.
Babies and children welcome. Booking advisable. **Map 10**.

Swiss Cottage NW3

Halepi ★

48-50 Belsize Lane, NW3 (020 7431 5855). Belsize Park or Swiss Cottage tube. **Dinner served** 6-11pm Mon-Fri. **Meals served** noon-midnight Sat, Sun. **Main courses** £7-£9. **Mézedes** £15-£20. **Set lunch** £10. **Cover** £1. **Credit** AmEx, DC, JCB, MC, TC, V.
Halepi doesn't do retro or cosy – its minimalist modern decor extends from trendily uncomfy chairs to upended tables muting the overhead lighting. The long and ambitious menu, too, aspires to be cutting edge and generally succeeds. Pulses are well-represented among the generous hot starters; goutsiá (broad beans) were off that day, but we enjoyed a large plate of fluffy lentils flecked with carrot. Koúpes (a rarely seen dish of lamb in rissole-shaped crust) was more than decent though tended to disintegrate; grated halloúmi on a massive pile of cheese-filled ravioli seemed to disappear without trace into the sauce. We hadn't booked such made-to-order specialities as goat, suckling pig or milk-fed lamb, but we were sorely tempted by the wild, not farmed, fish and seafood, sourced three times a week – and priced accordingly at £15-£18. Three squid stuffed with pine nuts and other goodies seemed mean compared to the starters, yet proved deceptively rich, the ingredients palpably fresh; but a side of spinach required olive oil and squeezed lemon to rescue it from blandness. No puds save ice-creams were available on our visit. Waiters are civil and easy to flag down. Halepi is several cuts above the London Hellenic norm, but after two years in business there are signs of stress at this Swiss Cottage restaurant – epitomised by scuff marks around the walls.
Babies and children admitted. Booking advisable dinner. Separate room for parties, seats 120. Takeaway service.
For branch see index.

Wood Green N22

Vrisaki

73 Myddleton Road, N22 (020 8889 8760/ 020 8881 2920). Bounds Green tube. **Lunch served** noon-3pm, **dinner served** 6-11.30pm Mon-Sat. **Main courses** £8.50-£14. **Mezédes** £15 per person (minimum two). **Service** 10%. **Credit** MC, £TC, V.
'Kebab House' in big letters outside, and a takeaway counter inside, appear to confirm the mundanity of this spot, marooned on a slightly shabby, rubbish-strewn parade. Once beyond the grill, it's far more salubrious: fans twirling over the mock-rustic seating area, patrolled by jolly, efficient waiters (over-eager to make sure our wine was just so). The menu promises a compact range of char-grilled dishes and fish, but to come to Vrisaki and not order the famous, huge meze is to miss the point. The first relay comprised 20 platelets ranging from the ridiculous (shredded fake crab sticks, noodle salad) to the sublime (subtle taramá, and an avocado and coriander dip). Next came small chilled prawns, a dressed crab (ace), smoked mackerel with salmon, and dolmades let down slightly by a desiccated exterior. After a token hot vegetarian interlude (grilled halloúmi and portobello mushrooms), the mains arrived: a grilled bream (smaller than in the past), butterflied prawns and fried squid rings, followed by the meat course: sheftaliá (average), succulent lamb ribs and tender pork kebab – accompanied by a lovely salad. The sweet trolley is better than most of its genre, but we went for the fruit platter instead: a stunningly presented pineapple boat garnished with melon, strawberries, nectarines, dates, black grapes and other delights). The final bill of £57, including service and mineral water, has crept up considerably in the past few years, but Vrisaki is still great value.
Babies and children welcome. Booking essential weekends. Separate room for parties, seats 16. Takeaway service (noon-3.30pm, 5pm-midnight Mon-Sat).

North West

St John's Wood NW8

Greek Valley

130 Boundary Road, NW8 (020 7624 3217/ 020 7624 4717/www.greekvalley.co.uk). Maida Vale or Swiss Cottage tube/16, 98, 139, 189 bus. **Lunch served** *Dec only* noon-2.30pm Mon-Sat. **Dinner served** 6pm-midnight Mon-Sat. **Main courses** £6.50-£10.95. **Set meals** (Mon-Fri) £9.95 three courses. **Service** 10%. **Credit** MC, V.
Tucked away at the end of a shopping parade, Greek Valley seems more suburban English in decor than Hellenic: framed pastel prints on the walls, planter boxes outside. The wine list contains many South African, French and Italian labels (most under £12) to vary the usual Cypriot plonk. We enjoyed a bottle of the newish Greek lager Mythos. Service was often obtrusive and overbearing (far too much shuffling of plates or having them whisked away, unbidden), and duo diners tend to get the worst tables. However, starters arrived almost instantly, and mostly passed muster. Dolmádes were competently done, with visible flecks of lamb mince; loukánika came grilled to perfection; the kalamári rings were delectable. Only spanakópitta provoked dissent; there was no cheese amid the leafy filling, and the exterior was bland, soggy and not proper filo. As for the mains, 'Salonica' chicken wasn't a recipe we had encountered in that city – the cut was clearly processed, frozen breast, though grilled correctly. It came with a nice tangy red sauce which did well mixed with the side dish of fluffy rice. Louviá me láhana (black-eyed peas with greens) was an excellent rendition. To finish, we ate a marvellous fruit salad: palpably fresh with such exotica as mango. Watery cappuccinos let the show down a little, but such blips aside, this is a decent local.
Babies and children welcome. Booking advisable; essential Fri, Sat. Separate room for parties, seats 25. Tables outdoors (3, pavement). Takeaway service (6-7.30pm). Vegetarian menu.

West Hampstead NW6

Mario's

153 Broadhurst Gardens, NW6 (020 7625 5827). West Hampstead tube/rail/28, 139, C11 bus. **Dinner served** 6-11.30pm Mon-Thur, Sun; 6pm-midnight Fri, Sat. **Main courses** £6.50-£20.50. **Mezédes** £12.50 per person (minimum two). **House wine** £8.75 bottle, £1.85 glass. **Mineral water** £2.60 large bottle, £1.25 small bottle. **Credit** AmEx, DC, MC, £TC, V.
Mario's has brightened itself up since our last visit: bar centre-stage, photos of Cypriot scenes on the walls, proper napery (no paper) on the tables. It was half full on a Thursday night. 'Free' nibbles comprise tsakistés, cooked carrot slivers and peperoncini; pitta costs 35p extra. The meze set meal has a decent reputation; it is all vegetarian (or with seafood on request). Instead, we chose a few à la carte mezédes. Fasólia was the genuine article: Greek bean soup (ask for it hot or you'll get it cold). F'ul medames was an odd but palatable version consisting of cold kidney beans with minced onions. A plate of marides was up to scratch; latheró (like mainland Greek briám, stewed vegetables) passed muster, too; and loukánika were exceptionally nice. Only the spanakópitta let the side down, with a rubbery crust. We had an exceptionally long wait for main courses – a single waitress was evidently overstretched. When it arrived, the afélia was flavourful, and came with a dollop of yoghurt, roast potatoes and pourgoúri, but an entire pork steak was presented, instead of the regulation cubes. We passed on the long wine list (with Greek, French, Italian and sickly-sweet German offerings) in favour of a large, sharp Keo beer, but ended the evening on a low note: two 'American strength' filter coffees. Still, Mario's offers better cooking than the London Greek norm, and it's not overpriced for its neighbourhood.
Babies and children welcome; high chairs; reduced-price children's portions. Booking advisable weekends. No-smoking tables. Tables outdoors (7, patio). Takeaway service (6-11.30pm).

Hotels & Haute Cuisine

Those who are willing to spend £100 per head on a meal out fall into various categories, but regardless of our circumstances, it is universally true that our expectations of a meal increase in proportion with the prices on the menu. So how did we get on this year with London's finest?

Set lunches are still excellent value. There's less difference in the quality and range of ingredients used for set meal deals than you might expect, although inevitably you'll have fewer choices. However, non à-la-carters are always second-class citizens in the posh restaurant. Ordering a set meal can often mean the restaurant, rather than you, decides at which time you can eat. Often, too, set-menu diners are ousted from the table as soon as the dessert spoon is down from the final mouthful. Of course, none of these things should happen, but in reality, it's often the case at the gastronomic end of the restaurant food chain.

Choosing the wine is fraught with similar tensions – those who order the house wine can receive a dose of chilly disdain from the sommelier. Indeed, most of these establishments have scrapped lower priced in-house recommendations and just hand over a daunting volume about which few of us are truly knowledgeable – but that's what the sommelier is there for. Wine snobbery went out of the window several years ago, but it seems some upper-end restaurants still need reminding.

The good news, however, is that London is still one of the best places in the world for fine dining. At these prices one expects the full bells-on experience. Often the risk lies with ourselves for choosing a restaurant not best suited to the occasion and our requirements. Phone beforehand and ask for the menu to be faxed to you, and speak with the staff: why not go and look at the place or even try it for lunch first if you're about to propose to your loved one there? Then sit back, open your mind and mouth, and relish London.

Central

Belgravia SW1

Stefano Cavallini Restaurant at the Halkin ★

5-6 Halkin Street, SW1 (020 7333 1234/ 1000). Hyde Park Corner tube.
Bar **Open** 11am-11pm daily. **Main courses** £8-£18.
Restaurant **Lunch served** 12.30-2.30pm Mon-Fri. **Dinner served** 7.30-10.30pm Mon-Sat; 7-10pm Sun. **Main courses** £24-£29. **Set lunch** £23 three courses incl coffee. **Set dinner** £55 six courses incl coffee. **Corkage** £10. **Credit** AmEx, DC, JCB, MC, £TC, V.
Two slabs of frosted glass glide back to reveal Stefano Cavallini's no-frills dining room. Cool colours, a few arches, quiet staff; nothing embeds itself in the memory, apart from the food. An evening à la carte menu is divided into antipasti, pasta and rice ('primi piatta'), main courses of fish and meat, followed by desserts. One of each would financially displace the £55 set six-course menu with ease, but portions are generous. From the pasta section, cappelletti di ribiola was sublime – meat broth, sliced quail breast and cheese cappelletti resting on wilted radicchio. A simpler primi piatta of cep risotto was on the crunchy side of al dente but teeming with savoury flavour and topped by a luscious halo of scallops. Main-course fillet of sea bass was roasted to crisp supremacy, alongside deceptively simple wedges of savoy cabbage, silky-smooth pumpkin purée and a sweetly tart reduction of balsamic vinegar. However, steamed sliced beef with herbs and baby vegetables was melting to the point of insubstantiality and struggled with its distinctive hazelnut dressing. Signs of real flair soon returned, though, as relaxed chunks of Parmesan arrived with a crisp, spicy poached pear and dewy apricot toast. The sommelier refused to be cornered into a specific recommendation from the mostly Italian, desirable and expensive wine list (for all its 29 pages, there are few bottles under £30), so we defaulted to an irresistible 1997 Sicilian chardonnay from Tasca d'Alemetria, at the considerable cost of £59. Price quibbles aside, though, Stefano Cavallini is still an event for the discerning diner.
Book dinner. Children over seven years admitted. Disabled: toilet. Dress: smart casual; no shorts. Entertainment: harpist 7-11pm nightly; guitarist dinner Tue, Thur. No pipe or cigar smoking. Separate room for parties, seats 30. **Map 6/9G**.

Fitzrovia W1

Pied à Terre ★

34 Charlotte Street, W1 (020 7636 1178). Goodge Street or Tottenham Court Road tube.
Lunch served 12.15-2.15pm Mon-Fri. **Dinner served** 7-10.45pm Mon-Sat. **Minimum** £19.50 lunch. **Set lunches** £19.50 two courses, £23 three courses. **Set dinners** £39.50 two courses, £50 three courses, £65 eight course tasting. **Service** 12½%. **Credit** AmEx, DC, JCB, MC, £TC, V (2½% handling charge for AmEx and DC).
In the squash of Charlotte Street's restaurant row, the frosted glass frontage of Pied à Terre gives nothing away. Inside, ingenuous staff and unpretentious decor might wrong-foot those used to spending three figures on two dinners, but a little patience is amply rewarded. Amuse-bouches lived up to their name with truly exciting mouthfuls – soft quail's egg enclosed in peppery caramel was one. Starters kept the flag flying, with a dish of langoustine tails, crunchy fried thyme, refreshing tomato and herb tian and a velvet border of garlicky purée. Meanwhile, barely poached foie gras in Sauternes consommé with peas, herbs and the thinnest veil of pasta was another intensely satisfying dish. Such dizzy heights were not reached by a gamy main-course fillet of venison (slightly too chewy), although its partnering savoy-wrapped juniper boudin and deep-fried celeriac were excellent. Similarly, a plate of pork cooked four ways (cheek, belly, trotter and fillet) was technically spot-on, but the indifferent savour of the meat disappointed. Pre-dessert crème cassonade soon revived the tastebuds, though, and fig tarte tatin with cinnamon ice-cream and a port and rosewater syrup followed through well. With a final flourish, daisy-fresh petits fours and a huge cup of cappuccino took us close to delicious surfeit. The menu suggests wines by the glass for each course, which generally worked well, while quiet, useful and polite service further enhanced the sense of occasion. Pied à Terre is an accomplished restaurant whose feet remain firmly on the ground.
Babies and children welcome. Booking advisable. Dress: smart casual. No-smoking tables. Separate room for parties, seats 16. **Map 2/5J**.

Knightsbridge SW1, SW3

The Capital

22-24 Basil Street, SW3 (020 7589 5171). Knightsbridge tube.
Bar **Open** noon-midnight daily.
Restaurant **Breakfast served** 7-10.30am Mon-Sat; 7.30-10.30am Sun. **Lunch served** noon-2.30pm daily. **Dinner served** 7-11.15pm Mon-Sat; 7-10.15pm Sun.

Foliage

Main courses £22-£60 dinner. **Set breakfast** £12 continental, £16.50 English. **Set lunch** £24.50 three courses incl coffee and petit fours. **Credit** AmEx, DC, JCB, MC, TC, V.
What the Capital lacks in grandeur it makes up for with civility and unpretentiousness. The beige dining room, with its enigmatic wooden sculptures and topiary-themed windows, may be showing its age but it still runs to the soothing hum of French accents and the contented murmurings of customers. Our lunchtime sortie got underway with a starter of intensely flavoured, luscious celeriac velouté, served at optimum temperature and incorporating fine shreds of crispy duck meat for texture. A twirled cylindrical salad of baby leeks was fresh but less impressive, despite its pseudo-illustrious pairing with a truffle vinaigrette. Main courses were a similarly mixed bag. Intriguing sea bream, pan-fried in a dusting of brioche crumbs, combined ethnic spring onion and salty soy sauce flavours with a discreet horseradish nip. Unfortunately, less than fresh fish let the accompaniments down. Roasted rabbit, however, was successful without reserve. Precisely arranged, perfectly cooked elements of rolled and stuffed saddle, kidney, leg meat and liver provided dainty snapshots of a complete picture, set against an inspired backdrop of creamy pearl barley and goat's cheese risotto. In the end, simple, generous desserts – sticky date pudding with prune and Armagnac ice-cream, for example – couldn't tempt us away from a tray of beautiful cheeses. Interesting wines of the month supplement an extensive and not outrageously priced list. Start and finish with a spell in the intimate bar, where the scent of lilies and an impressive line-up of whiskies encourage lingering.
Children over eight years admitted (lunch and early dinner only). Booking advisable. Dress: smart casual. Separate rooms for parties, seating 6 and 24. **Map 12/9F.**

Foliage

Mandarin Oriental Hyde Park Hotel, 66 Knightsbridge, SW1 (020 7235 2000). Knightsbridge tube. **Lunch served** 12.30-2.30pm, **dinner served** 7-10.30pm daily. **Set menu** £32.80 three courses. **Set lunches** £19 two courses, £23.50 three courses. **Credit** AmEx, DC, JCB, MC, £TC, V.
Things have changed for the better at the Mandarin Oriental, which, in the course of a £43m refit, has completely revamped and rebranded its restaurant (formerly the Park). No longer one huge room, Foliage is now a collection of calm, contemporary and intimate spaces. David Nicholls is still the chef. His cooking, together with the newly elegant surroundings, make this one of the best-value haute cuisine destinations in town. Roast scallops came with turnip purée, creamed parsley, verjus glaze and a fricassée of ceps and snails, while butternut and red onion risotto partnered sweetbread beignets and sherry vinegar caramel. To follow, main course sea bass was served with lobster tortellini, braised celery hearts and a raisin and caper vinaigrette, and spiced venison came with crushed potatoes, roast endive, bone marrow fondants and sloe gin. Everything was presented in a refreshingly uncluttered style, but what struck us most forcibly was the understanding and subtlety behind each dish. Desserts were light but similarly tasty; hot apple and Calvados soufflé with spiced bread ice-cream, and goat's-milk panna cotta with cinnamon roast figs and almond biscotti were equally delicious. Both the wine list and the bar selection (drinks and cigars) are excellent.
Babies and children admitted. Booking advisable. Dress: smart casual. **Map 12/9F.**

Restaurant One-O-one

101 William Street, SW1 (020 7290 7101). Hyde Park Corner or Knightsbridge tube. **Lunch served** noon-2.30pm, **dinner served** 7-10.30pm daily. **Minimum** £21 lunch, £32 dinner. **Set lunch** £21 two courses, £25 three courses. **Credit** AmEx, DC, JCB, MC, £$TC, V.
Wearing its piscine credentials on its sleeve (there's an abundance of shiny tiles, flashes of turquoise, even a leaping fish structure), this restaurant beneath the Sheraton Tower is a treat for anyone who loves seafood. As you read through Pascal Proyart's menu, ingredients and influences from every continent abound. Brill roasted with Asian herbs and curried coconut emulsion appears alongside whole sea bass cooked in a crust of sea salt and served with olive oil and parsley, for example. From the modest set lunch menu, a tian of salmon confit, cauliflower mousse and truffle-scented basil sauce was love at first bite. Likewise, langoustine bisque was smooth and creamy without being overly rich; it came with a lively mushroom, tomato and onion gourade. Main course roast cod wasn't so strongly flavoured, but Parma ham, mozzarella and basil-crushed potatoes gathered it into a pleasing whole. Vegetable accompaniments, on the other hand, were buzzing with flavour, especially 'just picked' tomatoes. Seafood pot-au-feu incorporated luxury fish (tuna, sea bass, salmon and their ilk) in a light sauce with fresh linguini and copious vegetables. Desserts are classic but nonetheless excellent, as are the bottomless cups of coffee, speciality teas and petits fours that follow. Recommended for fish-lovers and meat-eaters alike.
Babies and children welcome; high chairs. Booking advisable. Dress: smart casual. No-smoking tables. **Map 12/9F.**

La Tante Claire ★

The Berkeley, Wilton Place, SW1 (020 7823 2003). Hyde Park Corner or Knightsbridge tube. **Lunch served** 12.30-2pm Mon-Fri. **Dinner served** 7-11pm Mon-Sat. **Main courses** £23-£35. **Set lunch** £28 three courses incl coffee. **Minimum** £50 dinner. **Service** 12½%. **Credit** AmEx, DC, MC, £TC, V.
Amid soft shades of bruised mauve and grass-green, striped carpeting and squat mint couches, the tables at Pierre Koffmann's food mecca are adorned with a piece of fruit in place of flowers – a sort of dignified still life entirely appropriate to the quiet carnival that unfolds. There's a wide range of options on the well-priced wine list. As for the food, culinary comfort doesn't get much better than this, and sophisticated restaurants don't get any more relaxed. No plate is dressed up purely for artistry's sake, but the business of eating is taken very seriously. A starter of scallops in buttery, viscous squid ink, and another of crab meat boldly strewn across asparagus, poached egg and caviar were generous and effortlessly attention-grabbing. Main course rabbit, arriving in perfect time, was cooked four ways and came with an intense pastry-wrapped liver, caramelised carrots and girolles. Roasted pigeon was subtly matched with batons of celery and celeriac and a large raviolo of foie gras and confit onions. Finally, rice condé with peaches delivered succulent peachiness, brûlée topping and miraculously light but creamily set rice. Coffee, from a choice of two types of bean, is served with petits fours, while a chocolate send-off is offered in the form of a few truffles. Prepare to be amazed.
Babies and children admitted. Booking essential. Disabled: toilet. Dress: jackets for men. Separate room for parties, seats 14. **Map 12/9G.**

Marble Arch W1

The Crescent

Montcalm Hotel, Great Cumberland Place, W1 (020 7723 4440). Marble Arch tube. **Lunch served** 12.30-2.30pm Mon-Fri. **Dinner served** 6.30-10.30pm daily. **Set lunch** £20 two courses, £25 three courses incl ½ bottle wine. **Set dinner** £25 three courses incl ½ bottle wine. **Set Sunday supper** £15 two courses, £20 three courses. **Credit** AmEx, JCB, MC, £TC, V.
Taking the food scene by stealth is not usually the way of the hotel restaurant, but the Crescent seems to be the exception. Buff and bright with a dignified and genuinely comfortable lounge bolted on, the setting is just right for this brand of well-priced good cooking. From a choice of seven starters plus salads, an assiette of foie gras (£3 supplement) included a buttery pan-fried sampler on a raft of toast, orange and chives and a cold terrine surprisingly dotted with dried fruit and superbly partnered with toasted gingerbread. Chilled pear soup came with Gorgonzola mousse, pine nuts, poached pear and lashings of cream. Beautifully cooked John Dory followed, along with an abundance of spring vegetables and, again, lots of cream in the sauce. A vegetarian option of slightly gloopy Camembert crêpes was given definition via herbs, a bitter leaf salad and Calvados-drenched apples that dissolved provocatively on the tongue. Desserts were oversized and overdressed to the point of overkill – assiette of chocolate was notably messy. Our only request would be that a little more time is spent on fewer ingredients. Stick to two courses if your day involves post-lunch mobility, but be sure to restore Marble Arch to your eating circuit.
Babies and children welcome; high chairs. Disabled: toilet. Dress: smart casual. No-smoking tables. Separate room for parties, seating 20, 70. Vegetarian menu. **Map 2/6F.**

Marylebone NW1

The Landmark

222 Marylebone Road, NW1 (020 7631 8000). Baker Street tube/Marylebone tube/rail. **Breakfast served** 7-11.30am daily. **Lunch served** noon-2.30pm Mon-Fri, Sun. **Dinner served** 6.30-10.30pm Mon-Sat. **Main courses** £20-£39. **Set meals** £20 three courses (lunch), £45 three courses (dinner), £80 seven course menu (lunch/dinner). **Credit** AmEx, DC, JCB, MC, TC, V.
A spectacularly elegant building, inside and out, the Landmark is now home to the cooking of John Burton-Race, who has arrived from his L'Ortolan restaurant in Berkshire. Burton-Race has brought the key elements of his operation with him – most of his staff, plus a lot of crockery and wine glasses – and the menu design remains the same (although his two Michelin stars were lost in the move). Prices are still stellar, though: a starter of foie gras terrine with Jurançon jelly and pepper dressing was £27 (managed by others for half the price), and roasted scallops on light garlic cream with crunchy potatoes £22. We bypassed these in favour of main courses. Fillet of beef was simple but spot-on, with a soft tomato and shallot paste covering the meat, served with crunchy potato galette and port sauce. Excellent roasted baby chicken (the leg portions infused with marc de Bourgogne) was served with a cushion of foie gras and a pile of asparagus, cream and morels in the middle. Next came beguilingly ripe cheese (expertly served and explained), followed by a delicious assiette of chocolate costing a staggering £18. A carefully chosen globe-trotting wine list completes the picture. Standards have certainly improved at the Landmark, but at a high price.
Babies and children welcome; high chairs. Booking advisable; bookings not accepted for breakfast. Disabled: toilets. Dress: smart casual; no trainers or shorts. Entertainment: jazz trio Sun lunch. No-smoking tables. Separate rooms for parties, seating up to 500. **Map 2/4F.**

Mayfair W1

1837 ★

Brown's Hotel, 33 Albemarle Street, W1 (020 7408 1837). Green Park tube. **Breakfast served** 7-10.30am Mon-Fri; 7.30-11am Sat, Sun. **Lunch served** 12.30-2pm Mon-Fri. **Dinner served** 7-10.30pm Mon-Sat. **Set lunch** £19 two courses, £24 three courses. **Set meal** £36 seven course grazing menu. **Credit** AmEx, DC, JCB, MC, £TC, V.
Lunch at this oak-panelled, linen-crisp bastion of British dining started with a profuse apology – a menu had not been faxed to us as requested – but this was soon forgotten when the real McCoy was politely pressed into our hands. From a choice of ten starters (half seasonal, half from the evening à la carte), we liked the sound of gazpacho with courgette mousse. The courgette came as three super-smooth, vibrant green quenelles linked by a generous dollop of caviar, while a second phase of perfectly judged tomato infusion arrived in a cocktail shaker (which wouldn't unscrew at first and had to go back to the kitchen) before being decanted around the courgette. Main courses follow a similar pattern to starters (some seasonal, some traditional) plus a gleaming trolley of English favourites doing the rounds. Outstanding saddle of rabbit (crisp outside, pink and juicy inside, with livers wrapped in spinach used as a tasty forcemeat) was counterpoised by vanilla fumet, airy herb and potato blinis, a hint of truffle and squares of smoky aubergine. The wine list offers a wide choice by the glass and, if you can't make up your mind, the sommelier will select three wines to go with your food (a third of a measure each) for the price of a single glass. Desserts are either classic or quirky, as in summer pudding soufflé or an 'emphasis on orange' apple and fennel tart with liquorice ice-cream. Hard as it may be, food as effortlessly enjoyable as this should not be hastily consumed. It should be relished.
Babies and children welcome; high chairs. Booking advisable. Dress: smart casual. No-smoking tables. Separate room for parties, seats 12. **Map 13/7J.**

cheznico at Ninety Park Lane

90 Park Lane, W1 (020 7409 1290). Hyde Park Corner or Marble Arch tube. **Lunch served** noon-2pm Mon-Fri. **Dinner served** 7-11pm Mon-Sat. **Main courses** £8-£20. **Set lunch** £25 two courses, £30, £40, three courses. **Set dinner** £52 three courses, £62 eight courses, £75 ten courses. **Service** 12½%. **Credit** AmEx, MC, TC, V.

Nico Ladenis may have 'relinquished' three Michelin stars, but his grip on the diner's palate holds firm. The chef's intention to cut down on ingredients such as lobster, truffles and foie gras was not entirely borne out by a typical menu, which featured the latter in delicious multiplicity. We chose a starter of baby Dover sole, which fell effortlessly from the bone, combining milky flesh with a piquant tartare sauce. Bursting with robust flavours, by comparison, was a large artichoke stuffed with duxelles, and discreetly partnered with hollandaise. Both were delicious and generous. There were bargains to be had among the main courses (corn-fed chicken came with morels, foie gras ravioli and a remarkable £10.50 price tag, for example), but we pushed the boat out for a melt-in-the-mouth osso bucco – shiny, stickily rich and the ultimate comfort food. The dish was served with delicate, creamy Parmesan risotto and a garnish of orange juliennes and raisins, perhaps a little too sweet and orangey for a savoury accompaniment. Beautifully ripe French cheeses come with grapes and further portions of the excellent bread, while a deceptively ordinary-sounding list of puddings belies some carefully layered and surprising flavours, as in a chocolate mousse that was stunningly rich, impossibly light, and suffused with tantalising whiffs of mint, almond and vanilla. Apart from the disappointing coffee and petits fours, any changes at cheznico have merely compounded the pleasure.
Booking essential. Children admitted. Dress: smart casual. Separate room for parties, seats 18. **Map 2/7G.**

The Connaught ★

Carlos Place, W1 (020 7499 7070). Green Park tube. **Lunch served** 12.30-2.30pm, dinner served 6.30-10.45pm daily. **Main courses** £13.50-£45. **Minimum** £25. **Set lunch** £28.50 three courses. **Set dinner** £48 four courses. **Service** 15%. **Credit** AmEx, DC, JCB, MC, £TC, V.

Too much information is never a good thing. A menu faxed the day before lunch at Michel Bourdin's shrine to gastronomy had us baulking at the prices and running for a dictionary of French culinary terms. But once here, courteous waiting staff and the quietly sumptuous dining room dispelled any doubts (despite the columns of zeros supporting the wine list). Oysters, truffles, game, lobster and foie gras jostle for menu space, but we settled on that great leveller of chefs, the omelette – which would have been much improved by a few molten pockets beneath its firm exterior. A second starter of croustade d'oeufs de caille Maintenon, however, was nothing short of brilliant: two pastry boats baked to crisp collapsibility, filled with velvety chopped morels, quiveringly tender quails' eggs and a coating of warm hollandaise. Seven people got involved in the serving of our main courses, and the first to arrive, quail breasts 'Belle Epoch', swam in a deeply delicious truffle sauce, but the meat was less than tender. However, despite a superbly yielding dish of guinea fowl, champagne, cream and mushrooms, it was a heavenly side order of potato croquettes that eventually stole the show. Desserts also scored highly: both raspberry crème brûlée and English trifle, pliant with blackberries and alcohol, were faultless. The Connaught is not the place for the loud, the unappreciative or the health-conscious (or the poor). On the other hand, if you can say, with the aplomb of an elderly lady, to one of the waiters, 'We eat caviar every day anyway, it's just so delicious,' you'd be a natural.
Babies and children welcome; high chairs. Booking advisable. Dress: jacket and tie (lunch and dinner). No cigar or pipe smoking. Separate rooms for parties, seating 12 and 22. **Map 2/7H.**

Le Gavroche

43 Upper Brook Street, W1 (020 7408 0881). Marble Arch tube. **Lunch served** noon-2pm, **dinner served** 7-11pm Mon-Fri. **Main courses** £27.80-£34.60. **Minimum** £60 dinner. **Set lunch** £38.50 three courses incl coffee, ½ bottle of wine, mineral water. **Credit** AmEx, DC, JCB, MC, £TC, V.

Ensconced in the small lounge at Le Gavroche, menu in hand (women don't get prices on theirs), we tingled with anticipation. Perhaps it was just nerves as we mentally notched up the £25-£30 starters, £35 main courses and so on. Similarly, the wine list, among the most extensive in London, must also be the most expensive. So, first dish out

of the kitchen and into the plush green and claret basement den was a circle of buttery bread surrounded by smoked salmon and crab meat and a beguiling pool of nearly-cooked egg and caviar. Next, a perfect scallop, hemmed into its shell by a rim of puff pastry, was simply supported by micro-shredded leek and carrot and a few grains of sea salt. Dish three was an artichoke heart under a dome of hot mousse-like chicken and a generous layer of sliced truffle, with a slice of foie gras nestling inside, but this was more of a lesson in luxury than a dish with direction. A small, perfectly flavoured lamb rack was served as the main course with soft caramelised ratatouille and Madeira jus. Finally, a fragrant millefeuille of summer berries with mango coulis was followed by coffee, petits fours and chocolates. The skill, precision and quality of Michel Roux's cooking is beyond dispute, and the staff are immaculate, but the bill, when it arrives, can be really quite brutal.
Babies and children admitted. Booking essential. Dress: smart casual. No pipe or cigar smoking. Separate room for parties, seats 20. **Map 2/7G.**

Le Soufflé

Hotel Intercontinental, 1 Hamilton Place, W1 (020 7409 3131). Hyde Park Corner tube. **Lunch served** 12.30-3pm Tue-Fri, Sun. **Dinner served** 7-10.30pm Tue-Sat. **Main courses** £12.50-£28.50. **Set lunches** £21.50 two courses, £39 chef's five course organic selection. **Set dinners** £39 three courses, £46 four courses. **Credit** AmEx, DC, JCB, MC, TC, V.

Unchanged from last year – or the year before – Le Soufflé certainly couldn't be described as visually stimulating (think Odeon cinema meets beige cardigan), but try not to let that put you off. There's a good choice of wine and cocktails, staff are competent and polite, and chef Peter Kromberg's accomplished cooking and penchant for organic ingredients make for an unusually health-conscious fine dining experience. From the five-course, wholly organic menu, we began with pencil cannelloni filled with lightly cooked lobster and langoustine on courgette spaghetti, and a neatly compressed disc of roasted vegetables served with spinach and ricotta tart. Next, traditional fillet of beef was nicely grilled and backed by garlicky wild mushrooms, Macaire potatoes and quaintly named 'spin-top' carrots. Lemon soufflé with a slice of lemon tart and chocolate ganache completed a filling, well-presented meal. It was difficult to detect any difference between the organic menu and dishes we sampled from another menu, at least in terms of flavour and presentation (internal benefits being harder to identify). An excellent starter of fresh tuna on potato salad with lemony dressing, and main-course crisped fillet of sea bass on dauphin potatoes with tomato and caper jus, were particularly memorable. The food here is reliable, straight-talking and judiciously uncluttered by alcohol or cream; surely now it's time to address the decor.
Babies and children admitted. Booking advisable. Disabled: toilet. Dress: smart casual. Entertainment: pianist and singer nightly; string trio Sun lunch. No-smoking tables. **Map 6/8G.**

The Landmark

The Square

6-10 Bruton Street, W1 (020 7495 7100). Bond Street or Green Park tube. **Lunch served** noon-2.45pm Mon-Fri. **Dinner served** 6.30-11pm Mon-Sat; 6.30-10pm Sun. **Set lunches** £20 two courses, £25 three courses. **Set dinner** £50 three courses, £70 eight courses. **Service** 12½%. **Credit** AmEx, DC, MC, £TC, V.

Our fellow lunchtime diners all seemed relaxed and unhurried by the efficient staff at The Square. The £25 set lunch menu has been pared down from the evening à la carte – two choices for each of the three courses and a cheese option for £5 extra – but the quality of the cooking makes it excellent value for money. Starters may be warm watercress soup with a cannelloni of trout and crayfish tails, or duck ravioli with persillade of snails and red wine sauce, for example. We chose wild Cornish prawn cocktail, which was somewhat lacking the advertised wildness and vitality. Of the two main courses, rump of lamb with shallot purée and rosemary was barely cooked, but the waiter wasn't averse to returning it to the kitchen for another skip through the oven. There were no such problems with the fresh and well-timed fillet of sole with parsley mash, however, nor with the equally laudable accompaniment of buttered vegetables. Of the desserts, tarte tatin, which came with an unusual, super-smooth malt ice-cream, was particularly delicious and well worth waiting for. Staff, location and food are all good reasons for visiting the Square at midday, but there's no real atmosphere in the bland, modern surroundings. Something more is needed to entice the evening crowds.

Booking essential. Children admitted. Disabled: toilet. Dress: smart. No cigars. Separate room for parties, seats 18. **Map 2/7H.**

Windows

Hilton Hotel, 22 Park Lane, W1 (020 7208 4021). Green Park or Hyde Park Corner tube.
Bar **Open** noon-3pm, 5.30pm-2am Mon-Fri; **Cover** £6 after 11pm for non-residents.
Restaurant **Breakfast served** 7-10.30am daily. **Lunch served** 12.30-2.30pm Mon-Fri. **Brunch served** 12.30-2.30pm Sun. **Dinner served** 7-10.30pm Mon-Thur; 7-11.30pm Fri, Sat. **Main courses** £23.50-£27.50. **Cover** £5 Fri, Sat. **Set dinner** £55 five courses incl coffee. **Credit** AmEx, DC, JCB, MC, £TC, V.

The sight of London's cityscape disappearing towards the horizon far exceeds the rather tacky decor of this 28th-floor dining room. On the evening of our visit, waiters seemed to be in short supply and we waited 50 minutes without so much as a bread roll, leaving us plenty of time to scrutinise the menus. The 'Tour de France' menu offers regional French specialities, while the à la carte holds more interest but less volume. From the latter, a starter of pea soup was pleasant and simply garnished with artichoke and celeriac dice. Asparagus salad with french beans had a poor showing of asparagus, but plenty of pungent white truffle oil and a perfectly poached egg. Main course chicken and lobster fricassée was a discreet combination of divine caramelised chicken pieces, chunks of moist, shell-on lobster, a few peeled broad beans and a casual dribble of perfect stock. Fillet of veal was similarly understated on a fine potato galette with a hint of anchovy jus and three mounds of palate-grabbing parsley mash. Dessert of white chocolate parfait was neat, intense and texturally inventive. You may need assistance with the occasionally obscure wine list, where a request for 'nothing too expensive' is likely to yield something for £35. In all, Windows is a good bet for an 'occasion' meal.

Babies and children welcome; high chairs. Booking advisable. Disabled: toilets in hotel. Dress: smart casual (lunch), jacket and tie (dinner). Entertainment: 5.30pm-2am Mon-Fri pianist in bar; dinner dance 9.45pm Fri, Sat. **Map 6/8H.**

Piccadilly W1

Oak Room

Le Meridien Hotel, 21 Piccadilly, W1 (020 7437 0202). Piccadilly Circus tube. **Lunch served** noon-2.30pm Mon-Fri. **Dinner served** 7-11.15pm Mon-Sat. **Set lunch** £20 two courses, £25 three courses, £28.50 three courses incl coffee. **Set dinner** £38 three courses, £48 seven courses. **Service** 12½%. **Credit** AmEx, JCB, MC, £TC, V.

Occupying two rooms of Le Meridien Hotel, the Oak Room squanders its space massively and decadently on a handful of tables. Pale pink oak stretches upwards and outwards for miles; chandeliers hang like stalactites over great tracts of carpet. Gastronomical prices counterbalance the lack of covers, though – a three-course à la carte menu is a painful £80, plus coffee at £7.50 and a few double-figure supplements. And Marco Pierre White isn't even in the kitchen anymore. One of the set menus is much better value. Royale d'atrilles, lobster gelée and salade de crevettes roses was a cool, soupy dish of intense lobster mousse swirled with sultry dark jelly and rosebud-fresh prawns. Deceptively simple grilled scallops charged with vibrant bolts of chive and ginger, closely followed by a slice of the trademark foie gras parfait, was sensual and delicious. Following this, duck breast was rare and tasty with roasted white peaches and creamed cabbage, although fondant potatoes added more fattiness than necessary. Desserts might be hot raspberry soufflé or tiramisù with coffee ice-cream. Yet for all the hype, we were disappointed with our meal. Foodwise, a propensity to over-season with salt flawed some otherwise excellent cooking. Service, however, was bad: waiters understandably have to train somewhere, but the Oak Room is hardly the place for the beginners who fumbled their way around our table for a few hours.

Babies and children welcome; high chairs. Booking advisable, two weeks in advance. Vegetarian dishes. **Map 13/7J.**

The Ritz

Piccadilly, W1 (020 7493 8181 ext 3351). Green Park tube.
Bar **Open** 11am-11pm Mon-Sat; noon-10.30pm Sun.
Restaurant **Lunch served** 12.30-2.30pm Mon-Sat; 12.30-3pm Sun. **Dinner served** 6-11.15pm Mon-Sat; 6.30-10.30pm Sun. **Main courses** £35-£46. **Minimum** £34. **Set lunch** £35 three courses. **Set dinner** £43 three courses, £51 four courses, £59 four courses (Fri, Sat). **Credit** AmEx, DC, JCB, MC, TC, V.

One of the prettiest dining rooms in the world – depending on your opinion of all things pink, gilt and rococo. Deep beyond the golden arches of the hotel's lobby, this splendid restaurant unveils the vista of Green Park through its sky-high, pink-draped windows. But can the kitchen provide the necessary theatre for such a stage? The first dish would suggest it could: baby vegetables and braised radicchio in puff pastry with Fontina fondue had fine counterpoints of flavour, texture and colour. Yet another starter of culatello ham scattered with pomegranate seeds, although soft, delicate and delicious, was shamed by its accompaniment of pedestrian deep-fried ravioli. On the same note, pot-roast brill was tepid and chewy beneath its 'crust' of spindly potato slices, and was further marred by braised salsify, trompettes des morts and celery sauce (like wallpaper paste) that were all stone cold. This was probably intentional, but some indication on the menu would have been nice. Infinitely more pleasurable were tender tournedos of beef topped with a few slices of superb venison and served with glazed chestnuts, sprouts and poivrade. Pudding of hot raspberry soufflé was exquisite, but iced prune and Armagnac parfait was a bland disappointment. Plentiful coffee and accomplished petits fours rounded off an excellent-value £35 lunch, but be warned: prices climb much higher on the evening à la carte menu. Service, too, seemed strangely out of sync and occasionally gruff. Perhaps it's the strain of non-stop functions, but we were left with the impression that the calmly controlled grandeur is slipping a bit.

Babies and children welcome; children's menu; high chairs. Book lunch, and dinner dance, two weeks in advance. Disabled: toilet in hotel. Dress: jacket and tie, no jeans or trainers. Entertainment: dinner dance 7.30-11pm Fri, Sat; pianist 7-11pm nightly. Separate rooms for parties, seating 20, 30 and 50. Tables outdoors (5, terrace). **Map 13/7J.**

St James's SW1

L'Oranger

5 St James's Street, SW1 (020 7839 3774). Green Park or Piccadilly Circus tube. **Lunch served** noon-3pm Mon-Fri. **Dinner served** 6-10.30pm Mon-Sat. **Set lunches** £19.50 two courses, £24.50 three courses. **Set dinners** £35.50 two courses, £39.50 three courses. **Credit** AmEx, DC, JCB, MC, V.

Evening bookings here come with a warning: you will lose your table if you don't confirm by 5pm. Those who do manage to make it as far as the elegant dining room will find that the three-course menu has changed little in content from last year, although prices have acquired a few pounds and supplements. Suitably tantalised by amuse bouches of spicy fish goujons and some great bread, we were ready for a first starter of tender and tasty sliced potato salad, accompanied by a languid poached egg, shallot vinaigrette, two teaspoons of caviar and a £4.50 surcharge. Alongside that, a special of artichoke hearts and veal batons was served cold with a barely perceptible but very pursuable garlic butter dressing and an attractive assembly of halved quails' eggs. Another special, this time a main course, was beef transformed to melting perfection through extended braising. It was crowned by a dissolve-on-contact slice of foie gras (and on top of that, another supplement). Across the table, poached red mullet on a bed of warm white crab meat and cross-cut asparagus stalks was pleasant in a light gingery way, without succumbing to oriental pretensions. Dessert came after a long wait. Pineapple sablé couldn't be faulted, but a tart bourdaloue filled with vanilla-scented dried fruit and nuts was too sickly on its thick chocolate sauce. A total of 20 varieties of petits fours for two people, served with dessert but a long while before coffee, was also off-putting. Nevertheless, notable food, fair prices and unstuffy service mean that L'Oranger is still a fun option for serious eaters.

Babies and children admitted. Booking essential. Dress: smart casual; no jeans or trainers. Separate room for parties, seats 22. Tables outdoors, 6 terrace. **Map 13/8J.**

Pétrus

33 St James's Street, W1 (020 7930 4272). Green Park tube. **Lunch served** noon-2.45pm Mon-Fri. **Dinner served** 6.45-11pm Mon-Sat. **Set lunch** £24 three courses. **Set dinner** £40 three courses. **Credit** AmEx, DC, MC, £TC, V.

Prices here have been creeping steadily upwards over the last year, so Pétrus is no longer the good-value meal out that it once was. The suavely understated surroundings haven't changed, though, and on our weekday lunch visit the handful of tables in this small room were all occupied by suits and well-to-do shoppers. Polite waiters are available to answer any questions (particularly handy when it comes to the aristocratic and costly wine list). We began our meal with a silky pumpkin soup graced with wild mushrooms, sautéed artichokes and a distinctive nudge of marjoram. Another starter, langoustine tortellini and consommé, served with more wild mushrooms and crunchy mangetout, was awash with clear, crisp flavours. Main courses continued in the same vein, with perfectly roasted sea bass accompanied by spinach, baby leeks, more mushrooms and a restrained vermouth velouté. The only meat option, tender saddle of venison, arrived with ceps and a superb truffley Madeira jus. Desserts, almost too pretty to eat, came in the form of a competent vanilla crème brûlée, and a tangy grapefruit and blood-orange terrine, intelligently paired with peach sorbet. So a good meal, but (and this might just be a seasonal hazard) mushrooms did seem to recur in every dish with alarming regularity. Minor gripes aside, though, Pétrus is a safe bet for accomplished, interesting cooking.

Babies and children admitted. Booking essential. Dress: smart casual. Vegetarian dishes. **Map 6/8J.**

West

Holland Park W11

The Room at the Halcyon

129 Holland Park Avenue, W11 (020 7221 5411/020 7727 7288). Holland Park tube/12, 94 bus.
Bar **Open** 11am-11pm daily.
Restaurant **Brunch served** noon-10pm Sun. **Lunch served** noon-2.30pm Mon-Fri. **Dinner served** 7-10.30pm Mon-Thur; 7-11pm Fri. **Set lunches** £14.95 two courses. **Set dinner** £35 three courses. **Credit** AmEx, DC, MC, V.

The Halcyon is a hotel of creamy composure and pom-pom topiary; the Room has absorbed much of its Holland Park sang-froid. When we ate there, the food was French and bore all the hallmarks of Toby Hill's unfussy, Mediterranean-inflected cooking. During late summer 2000, Nigel Davies (ex Greenhouse and the Ivy) stepped into the head chef role here. Some changes will have occured, therefore, but the essence of this relaxed venue will surely remain. We enjoyed a sophisticated first course of red mullet and saffron soup supported an island of crisp mullet and domed satellites of rouille piped on to tiny deep-fried croûtons (which seemed too oily to fit the clarity of the rest of the dish). A second starter of cold vegetable terrine was a pretty tile of cross-sectioned leek, carrot and turnip, with a truffle-infused vinaigrette adding interest but, again, a slick of oiliness. From a choice of seven main courses came a dish of poached and grilled Bresse pigeon. The twin trials of fire and water had reduced it to a state of tender collapse, deserving of its fine accompaniments (miniature liver-stuffed cabbage leaves, wild ceps and trompettes des morts, all bathed in a dark, truffley gravy). Main course number two, sliced lamb with faultless fondant potato, was let down by meat sadly deficient in flavour. As for dessert, orange tart with mandarin sorbet was an interesting mirror of the rest of the meal: neatly presented, precisely cooked and not technically lacking in anything other than wow factor. There's a good selection of champagnes and digestifs bolstering the wine list. Service was refreshingly down-to-earth (for a hotel); fair prices and peaceful surroundings also recommend the place.

Babies and children admitted; high chairs. Booking advisable. Dress: smart casual. Separate room for parties, seats 12. Tables outdoors (8, terrace). Vegetarian dishes. **Map 11/8Az.**

South West

Chelsea SW3, SW10

Aubergine

11 Park Walk, SW10 (020 7352 3449). South Kensington tube/14 bus. **Lunch served** noon-2.30pm Mon-Fri. **Dinner served** 7-10.45pm Mon-Sat. **Set lunch** £16 two courses, £19.50 three courses. **Set dinner** £59.50 menu gourmand. **Service** 12½%. **Credit** AmEx, DC, JCB, MC, TC, V.

Since our enthusiastic remarks last year about this restaurant's lunchtime bargains, both the set lunch and the house wine have fallen prey to price hikes. But the *chiaroscuro* of the restaurant's two rooms is still impressive: an initial, dim cloister leads to the dining room proper, where light spills over harlequin-coloured chairs and bold pictures of the French rural idyll. The process of menu perusal was given a welcome shot in the arm by jaunty little saucers of richly coated crab meat, which, along with the extraordinarily airy bread rolls, provided ample assurance of fine things to come. Starters made good this promise with a warm salad of quail breast with french beans, red pepper mousseline and deep-fried courgettes; and nage of linen-white sole with soft herbs (delicious but perhaps a touch heavy). A particularly striking main course was braised loin of lamb with confit tomatoes: a succulent, vivid dish of intensely green and silkily smooth basil pommes purées, balanced by excellent tomatoes, partly dried and wholly nurtured to a state of sublime concentration. The lamb itself was faultless, but the fact it was served whole gave it an unsightly tendency to collapse into long, unappetising strings. The final chapter of dessert also has a comfortingly familiar ring to it (cherry clafoutis, peach sablé, prune and Armagnac ice-cream), rounded off by accomplished coffee and petits fours. Aubergine does not claim to be a hotbed of culinary innovation, but contents itself instead with the simple pleasures of hand-picked ingredients, finely cooked in classic style. And lunch is still a bargain.

Booking essential. Dress: smart casual. No pipe or cigar smoking. **Map 5/12D.**

Gordon Ramsay

68-69 Royal Hospital Road, SW3 (020 7352 4441/3334). Sloane Square tube. **Lunch served** noon-2pm, **dinner served** 6.45-11pm Mon-Fri. **Set lunch** £28 three courses. **Set meal** £60 three courses, £75 seven courses. **Credit** AmEx, DC, JCB, MC, £TC, V.

A strict booking procedure here means that dinner has to be at either 6.45pm or 9pm; you can either refuse or else dine at Mr Ramsay's convenience. Service was brusque. Our wine – a deliciously fruity Côtes du Roussillon – had been decanted into huge glasses within 15 minutes of our arrival, and the bottle promptly whisked away. An exquisite starter helped us feel less resentful: terrine of Bresse chicken and foie gras layered with girolles and baby leeks, garnished with figs, green beans, trompettes des morts and a gossamer layer of port jelly. Just as good were scallops fringed with golden crispness and served with silky buttons of cauliflower purée stained red with Barolo dressing, and tart salad leaves. Main-course monkfish was neat, tender and cooked with a rich five-spice dressing, served with ceps and a delightful scallop beignet. However, Chalonnaise duck breast was tough and undercooked, although its accompanying endive tarte and Saint-Emilion sauce were spot-on. Finally, tarte tatin, despite being served with clumsy haste at the table, was beautifully offset by melting caramel, a cone of lemon mousse and a minuscule dish of divine vanilla ice-cream. Nevertheless, we winced at paying £170 for two, not because the food was anything less than perfect but because (great cook or not) Gordon Ramsay's hospitality leaves a lot to be desired.

Children admitted. Booking essential, one month in advance only. Dress: smart casual. Vegetarian dishes (on request). **Map 6/12F.**

Indian

Our job used to be easy. Each year we have the task of whittling down London's more than 1,500 'Indian' restaurants (by which we mean Bangladeshi, Nepalese, Pakistani and Sri Lankan, as well as from the modern state of India) to the 80 or so that best represent all facets of the cuisine. Large swathes of curry houses could be swiftly discounted, simply by glancing through their menus. Prawn vindaloo, chicken dopiaza and lamb Madras – amid a myriad bhunas, kormas and baltis – were tell-tale signs of the curry conveyor-belt approach that involves pre-cooked ingredients being drenched in a preordained sauce (derived from catering-pack pastes), heated and served.

Proper Indian cookery is a labour-intensive process where spices are roasted, ground and mixed by the chef. 'Curries' or stews should be simmered slowly to allow flavours to combine and the ingredients to become tender; tandoori food should be marinated in distinct spices (rather than smeared with out-of-a-jar paste) before char-grilling.

We include the establishments that follow these time-honoured methods of cooking. Sadly, they are only a small proportion of the total, and tend to be concentrated in areas where British Asians live (such as Wembley, Tooting, Southall, and parts of the East End). The good news has always been that these restaurants charged no more (and often considerably less) than high-street tandooris for food that is incomparably better.

However, distinctions are becoming obscured. More local curry houses are attempting to pitch themselves upmarket, seeing that competition from supermarket ready-meal counters is decreasing takeaway trade. Some are producing genuine high-quality food, dispensing with the tandoori paste and going the distance along previously cut corners. Most others, though, are simply jazzing up their decor and the descriptions used on their menus. Chicken korma in such venues might now be described as 'malai wali murghi: tender escalopes, steeped in yoghurt and finished in a cream and cashew sauce', yet in preparation and taste, the dish hasn't changed one iota from the curry house standard.

At the same time, top-class restaurants and proponents of 'New Indian' cuisine (inventive cross-cultural cooking modelled on Modern European eclecticism) are rediscovering their roots and producing sublime versions of traditional dishes such as biriani and roghan gosht. Sample, for instance, the supreme take on biriani at **Zaika**, where a crisp pastry lid seals in the flavours.

So how do we divide the wheat from the chaff, the sublime from the sloppy? One sure-fire method we've found of ascertaining a restaurant's worthiness comes with the popadom. If the pickles and chutneys arrive in a congealed blob, looking as if they once came out of a long-distant jar, then the chances of the kitchen being up to scratch are slim. But if they look as if someone has spent time selecting the freshest ingredients and most apt spices; then combining them to create something exciting and adventurous, your luck's in. And on the rarest of occasions, you might even find that the popadoms, as well as the chutneys, have been made in-house – see, for instance, the **Rasa** restaurants. Then you know you're in for a treat.

Starters

Spellings of Indian dishes vary widely; dishes such as do pyaza or gosht may appear in several versions on different menus as the word is transliterated from (in this case) Hindi. There are umpteen languages and several scripts in the Indian subcontinent, the most commonly seen on London menus being Punjabi, Hindi and Bengali. For the sake of consistency, however, we have used the same spellings throughout.

Bhajia or bhaji: snack made with chickpea flour and vegetables, deep-fried; in India, 'bhajia' refers to vegetables, often stir-fried. **Pau bhajia** is an unrelated dish of a white bread roll filled with heavily spiced, slightly mashed vegetables.
Ganthias: Gujarati name for crisply fried savoury confections made from gram-flour; they come in many shapes.
Kachori: pastry balls with a spicy mung-bean filling.
Lassi: a yoghurt drink, ordered with salt or sugar (the usual choice of non-Asians), sometimes with fruit. Ideal to quench a fiery palate.

Mogo: deep-fried cassava, often served as chips with a sweet and sour tamarind chutney; an East African Asian dish.
Pakora or pakoda: savoury fritters, North Indian version of bhajias (qv).
Popadom, poppadom, papadum, etc: large thin wafers, similar to potato crisps, eaten here with relishes (such as mango chutney, lime pickle or a cool minty sauce) as a starter while waiting for the meal to arrive.
Samosa: triangular pastry packets of vegetables or meat.

North Indian

Central

Belgravia SW1

Salloos
62-64 Kinnerton Street, SW1 (020 7235 4444). Hyde Park Corner or Knightsbridge tube. **Lunch served** noon-2.30pm, **dinner served** 7-11.15pm Mon-Sat. **Main courses** £10.90-£14.90. **Set lunch** £16 three courses incl coffee. **Service** 12½%. **Credit** AmEx, DC, MC, £TC, V.
Glamorous Fareezeh Salahuddin oversees the front-of-house of the restaurant her father founded in Lahore and moved to Knightsbridge in the 1970s. It's downright posh here, set on a select villagey backstreet in first-floor premises decked out with gold chandeliers and white walls adorned with pictures of rural Pakistan. The elite of Pakistan and west London come to munch on Salloos' exquisite tandoori food: the famous, delicate, tandoori lamb chops ('marinated for at least 24 hours'); the delectably light breads. This year we strayed from the fruits of the clay oven, with varying results. Yakhni soup consisted of notable lamb stock, but very little else; jheenga masala was a nondescript prawn curry; and the dahl was resoundingly ordinary. However the rice, pulau jehangiri, was a classy delicacy: the grains faintly flavoured with cloves and the lamb stock in which they had been simmered, and topped with raisins and crisp nuts. Portions were big. Service was also a mixed bag, veering between the over-abundance meted out by the bear-like maître d' (a character much loved by regulars), and near-negligence at the end, when we had a lengthy wait before popadoms, rather than the expected kulfi, arrived. True, Salloos' tandoori food has few equals – but equals there are (see p87 **Southall**), and for a fraction of the cost.
Children over eight years admitted before 9pm. Booking essential. Dress: smart casual. Takeaway service. **Map 12/9G.**

Bloomsbury WC1

Char Bar
68 Brunswick Centre, WC1 (020 7837 8357/ www.charbar.com). Russell Square tube/Euston or King's Cross tube/rail. **Meals served** 8am-6pm Mon-Fri; 10am-5pm Sat, Sun. **Main courses** £3.95-£4.95. **Set meal** £3.95. **No credit cards.**
As refreshing as a freshly brewed cuppa, this fast food joint was set up with a grant from the Prince's Trust. We dropped by to find an enthusiastic young woman bellowing instructions to her team of green, keen, work-experience waiters. Place your order at the tiny counter and take a look at the cooks jostling in the minute kitchen, then bag a seat in the mustard-coloured sliver of a dining area, or outside at tables on the Brunswick Centre's concrete paving slabs. Like the staff, food is a multicultural mix. 'Naanwiches' are a popular choice, with fillings such as tuna, sweetcorn and lime pickle, or couscous with tomato and mango chutney. Breakfast might be dum biran, a savoury Indian omelette roll. Soup noodles – a bowlful of freshly prepared tomato and coriander with a little mound of soft noodles – gladdened the heart. The tibbin lunch was more of a traditional Indian affair, served on a thali plate and including a well-packed, crisp vegetable samosa, decent vegetable bhajia (mostly strips of cabbage) and a dull centrepiece of pub-standard lamb roghan gosht on overcooked rice – for £4.50. Still, the Energiser tea (with honey and orange juice) bucked us up a treat; next time we might venture a 'Char-puccino' from the fair choice of leaf, herbal and flavoured teas.
Babies and children welcome. Tables outdoors, 8 patio. Takeaway service. Vegetarian menu. **Map 3/4L.**

City EC2

Shimla Pinks
7 Bishopsgate Churchyard, EC2 (020 7628 7888). Liverpool Street tube/rail. **Lunch served** 11.30am-3.30pm Mon-Fri. **Dinner served** 5.30-10pm, Mon, Tue, Fri; 5.30-10pm Wed, Thur. **Set meals** £18.95, £23.95 three courses. **Service** 12½%. **Credit** AmEx, DC, JCB, MC, TC, V.
The menu blurb isn't promising: '… if you're… fanatical about your vindaloo… Shimla Pinks will see you right.' The setting is impressive, though: the City branch of this Birmingham-based chain of posh Indian restaurants occupies what were once Turkish baths. The basement dining room and bar are decorated with original 1890s tiling, sensitively incorporated into modern restaurant design. Marble on the floor and Tom Jones on the sound system complete the picture. The menu is divided into 'traditional' and 'dum pukht and mughli' sections, the former containing onion bhajias, vindaloos and the like, the latter more interesting concoctions. Beginning with the dum pukht mixed starters for two, we were presented

Char Bar

with a big white bowl of somewhat ill-matching snacks that were individually very enjoyable. Best was dhungar machli tikka, salmon marinated in dill, fennel, ginger, honey and mustard oil then roasted in the tandoor. To follow, murg Wajid Ali had chicken breast stuffed with pomegranates and served with orange and saffron gravy to pleasing effect, the citric tang of the pomegranate balanced by the sweet sauce. The vegetarian dish of khazanna-E-lazzat (three rissoles of squash, condensed milk and cream cheese in a tomato-based sauce) failed to excite, though. Presentation throughout was to a high order, but prices are steep and service was irritating. Waiters were officious and chivvying while we ordered, then lost interest and were difficult to attract at bill time. *Babies and children admitted. Booking essential. Dress: smart casual. No-smoking tables. Takeaway service.* **Map 4/6Q.**

Covent Garden WC2

Mela
152-156 Shaftesbury Avenue, WC2 (020 7836 8635). Leicester Square tube. **Meals served** noon-11.45pm Mon-Sat; noon-10.30pm Sun. **Set lunch** £4.95. **Set dinner** £9.95 three courses (pre-theatre). **Set meals** £29.95 (for two), £54.95 (for four), £79.95 (for six). **Main courses** £5.95-£11.95. **Service** 12½%. **Credit** AmEx, MC, V.
Mela opened to a flurry of press releases in December 1999. It's a snazzy gaff promoting 'Indian country style' dishes. The lunch menu is a complicated affair, offering a choice of stuffings (including spinach, horseradish, masala shrimps, and spicy goats' brains) wrapped in a bread – nan, paratha, dosai, roti and so on. On a midday visit, the place was nearly deserted, but in the evening the split-level dining room – with shiny blue bar, turquoise and orange walls, and a glassed-in kitchen – was full of a young, animated crowd. Service, from chaps in smart kurtas, isn't always attentive, and we were disconcerted by one waiter urging us to add extra to the bill as 'the service charge doesn't go to the staff'. Food, from chef Kuldeep Singh, is exciting, but not fail-safe. Fried pea-based spiced potato cakes were expertly spiced and flavoursome. Good, too, were the spiced guinea fowl samosas. A main course of Alleppey seafood curry was even better (scallops, prawns squid and salmon in an enticing coconut and mango sauce) and baby aubergines in a peanut-flavoured yoghurt sauce proved very moreish. However, mixed veg pilau rice seemed to hail from a freezer pack, and a special of spinach with buttermilk was too salty. A fine, fudgy shahi tukra (like bread and butter pudding) put things back on track. All in all, Mela deserves to succeed.
Babies and children admitted; high chairs. No-smoking tables. Separate room for parties (seats 38). Tables outdoors (3, pavement). **Map 14/6K.**

Mela

Euston NW1

Great Nepalese
48 Eversholt Street, NW1 (020 7388 6737). Euston tube/rail/68, 168, 253 bus. **Lunch served** noon-2.45pm Mon-Sat; noon-2.30pm Sun. **Dinner served** 6-11.30pm Mon-Sat; 6-11.15pm Sun. **Main courses** £5-£15. **Minimum** £5.50. **Set meal** £8, £17.25 three courses incl coffee. **Service** 10%. **Credit** AmEx, DC, LV, MC, V.
Still we search for serious competition to this long-standing favourite, but nowhere offers such a breadth of Nepalese cuisine. The premises are scarcely imposing; the small interior resembles that of a curry house, though the light-green walls are decorated with pictures of Everest and Gurkha memorabilia. The smart, pleasant waiter wears a waistcoat and tie bearing Gurkha insignia, too. True, the menu can provide everything to make 1970s curry fiends moist with nostalgia – from mulligatawny soup to chicken phal – but there's also a score or more dishes from the mountain kingdom.

Of these, starters of mamocha (momo: steamed spicy meat dumplings) firmly place the cuisine between that of India and China. Masco bara (two deep-fried meat and lentil rissoles) can also be recommended. Main course pork bhutuwa (£5.25) was a prosaic curry, though tori ko sag (spinach) was abundant and fresh. Intense dhaniya achar (coriander pickle) will enliven any dinner, though to order it alongside the Nepalese set meal (a good-value two-courser that includes the Russian salad-like aloo bodi) might mean too many sharp flavours. Still, this is a popular spot to enjoy a low-key culinary trip to the Himalayas without the altitude.
Babies and children welcome. Booking advisable. Separate room for parties, seats 35. Takeaway service (10% discount). **Map 3/3K.**

Fitzrovia W1

Indian YMCA ★
41 Fitzroy Square, W1 (020 7387 0411). Great Portland Street or Warren Street tube. **Lunch served** noon-2pm Mon-Fri; 12.30-1.30pm Sat, Sun. **Dinner served** 7-8pm daily. **Main courses** £2.10-£4.50. **Set lunch** (Sat, Sun) £4.50 two courses. **Unlicensed** no alcohol allowed. **No credit cards**.
Usually we pop into the canteen of this student hostel for lunch, when a varied mix of office workers and Indian students sit at the Formica tables, and there's more choice of food. This time we sampled the evening meal. First we had to immerse ourselves in Indian culture by paying for the meal (£4.50) in advance at the reception, gaining a receipt and handing said receipt to the restaurant manager, before queuing up with our tray. The menu is on a seven-day rota, so this being a Thursday, we were treated to two small vegetable kofta in a tangy vindaloo (vinegar and garlic-based) sauce; potato and pea curry, with spices permeating the dish; a rather limp roti; and two small meat kofta in a copious onion-based sauce. Rice and dahl are provided in big white bowls at each table (you may have to take them to the kitchen for a refill). We forewent pudding

---

North Indian menu

Aloo: potato.
Ayre: a Bengali white fish.
Baigan or bainghan: aubergine.
Balti: West Midlands cooking term for karahi cooking (qv), which became all the rage a few years ago. Unfortunately, many inferior curry houses now apply the name to dishes that bear little resemblance to real karahi-cooked dishes.
Bateira, batera or bater: quail (Bangladeshi).
Bengali: Before Partition in 1947, Bengal was a large province covering Calcutta (now in India's West Bengal) and Bangladesh. In London restaurants, 'Bengali' cooking is commonly used to refer to fish curries, very popular in Bangladesh and increasingly common here.
Bhindi: okra, ladies' fingers.
Bhuna gosht: a dry, spicy dish of lamb.
Biriani, biryani, etc: a rich risotto, with spiced meat or vegetables all cooked together with the rice. Too often they aren't.
Brinjal: aubergine (eggplant).
Channa: chickpeas.
Chapati: a flat wholewheat pancake.

Dahi: yoghurt.
Dahl or dal: a lentil curry similar to thick lentil soup; served thinner in the south.
Dhansak: a Parsee (qv) casserole of meat and lentils.
Dhaniya: coriander.
Dopiaza, do pyaza, etc: cooked with onions.
Dum: a cooking technique where food is simmered slowly in a casserole (typically a clay pot sealed with dough), allowing spices to permeate.
Garam masala: a blend of ground, mixed spices. Literally, 'hot spices'.
Ghee: clarified butter used for frying.
Gobi: cauliflower.
Gosht: (also spelt josh or ghosh) meat, usually lamb.
Gram flour: chickpea flour.
Gurda: kidneys.
Haandi: an earthenware cooking pot.
Jalfrezi: marinated in yoghurt and cooked in fresh green chillies – a recipe applied to chicken.
Jhingri, chingri: prawns.
Kaleji or kalezi: liver.
Karahi or karai: a small iron, wok-like cooking dish. Similar to the 'balti' dish of Birmingham.

Kheema, keema: minced lamb, as in kheema nan (stuffed nan).
Kofta: meatballs or vegetable dumplings.
Korma: braised in yoghurt and/ or cream. Often mild, but rich.
Machli: fish.
Magaz: brain.
Makhani: cooked with butter ('makhan') and sometimes tomatoes, as in murgh makhani.
Masala/masaladar: with spices.
Massalam: a marinated then casseroled chicken dish, popular in Muslim areas.
Methi: fenugreek.
Moghul or Mogul: from the Moghul period of Indian history, used in the culinary sense to describe typical North Indian Muslim dishes.
Murgh or murg: chicken.
Mutter, muter or mattar: peas.
Nan: teardrop-shaped, flat bread cooked in a tandoor (qv).
Nihari: long-simmered lamb shank.
Palak: spinach.
Paneer, panir: Indian curd cheese, a bit like tofu in taste and consistency.
Paratha: a large griddle-fried bread that's sometimes stuffed with spicy mashed potato or minced lamb.

Parsee: a religious minority based in Bombay but originally from Persia, renowned for their cooking.
Pasanda: korma-like preparation with thin fillets of lamb.
Paya: lamb's feet, usually served on the bone as paya curry (long-cooked and with copious gravy); seldom found outside Southall.
Phal: refers to very hot dishes.
Pilau, pillau, pulao, etc: rice cooked in ghee, then in water or stock. It is supposed to be coloured with saffron, but more usually turmeric is used.
Poori or puri: a disc of deep-fried wholewheat bread; the frying makes it puff up like an air-filled cushion.
Punjabi: Since Partition, the Punjab has been two adjoining states, one in India, one in Pakistan. Lahore is the main town on the Pakistani side, which is predominantly Muslim; Amritsar on the Indian side is the Sikh capital. Punjabi dishes tend to be thick stews or cooked in a tandoor (qv).
Raita: cucumber and yoghurt.
Roghan gosht, rogan josh: lamb cooked in a spice-rich sauce.

Saag: spinach.
Seekh kebab: skewered and grilled meat.
Tak-a-tak: a cooking method – ingredients (usually meat) are chopped as they cook on a griddle.
Talapia: a freshwater fish, farmed in the lakes of East Africa.
Tamarind: the pods of this East African tree, grown in India, are made into a paste that imparts a sour taste.
Tandoor: clay oven originating in north-west India in which food is cooked without oil.
Tandoori: cooked in a tandoor oven, sometimes marinated in spicy yoghurt first.
Tarka: a Bengali technique where spices and flavourings are cooked separately, then added to the main dish at a final stage.
Tikka: meat cut into cubes, then marinated in spicy yoghurt and baked in a tandoor; for example, chicken tikka masala.
Vindaloo: hot curry originally from Goa. Authentic vindaloos should be sour (made so with vinegar) and cooked with garlic.
Xacuti: a complex Hindu and Christian dish from Goa, made with lamb or chicken pieces.

(a single scoop of pink ice-cream) and coffee (which came out of a tea urn). What might be a rather dire atmosphere (the large dining hall occupies the ground floor of a utilitarian postwar block) was transformed by the clientele: a gregarious bunch of mostly Indian students happily complaining about the food. Whatever the shortcomings, it's a privilege to be allowed to sample such unadulterated Indian cooking and ambience for such low prices.
Babies and children admitted. No smoking. Separate rooms for parties, seating 30 and 200. Takeaway service. Map 2/4J.

Marble Arch W2

Porte des Indes
32 Bryanston Street, W1 (020 7224 0055/ www.la-porte-des-indes.com). Marble Arch tube. **Lunch served** noon-2.30pm Mon-Fri; noon-3pm Sun. **Dinner served** 7-11.30pm Mon-Sat; 6-10.30pm Sun. **Main courses** £8.50-£19.20. **Set buffet lunch** £15. **Set meals** £29 (vegetarian), £31 three courses. **Credit** AmEx, DC, JCB, MC, £TC, V.
The setting is fabulous, the food bears inspection, but the service at Porte des Indes was off-key on our trip. Grim greeters disdainfully pointed us down the stairs to the bar, which is decked out in tropical-colonial style. Once at a table, we had to endure long waits between courses, a couple of mistakes in our order, and staff (in beautiful flowing garments) eager to hurry us. Never mind: from our small table on the ground-floor gallery we could gaze at the splendour of this former Edwardian ballroom with its large domed skylight, impressive marble staircase, red-wood flooring and spectacular flower displays. Pondicherry, a former French colony on the south-east coast of India, is the supposed influence behind the menu, though the fact the place is run by the owners of **Blue Elephant** (*see p165* **Thai**) is of equal import. Several dishes turn out to be standard recipes with fancy names. The 'menu maison' offers the most enticing and least expensive choices. Highlights include starters of Parsee fish (sole steamed with mint and coriander chutney) and rasoul (flaky lamb samosa) and mains of adrak ke panje (well-marinated, tender lamb chop). Poulet rouge turned out to be a bland butter chicken; crevettes assadh were juicy prawns in little more than coconut milk. Ingredients were first-rate, though spicing seemed timid. Still, this large venue was full on a Tuesday night, with opulent Indian families as well as office parties and businessmen.
Babies and children welcome; high chairs; toys. Book dinner Thur-Sat. Dress: smart casual. Separate rooms for parties, seating 10 and 12. Takeaway service. Vegetarian menu. Map 2/6F.

Mayfair W1

Chor Bizarre
16 Albemarle Street, W1 (020 7629 9802/ www.chorbizarrerestaurant.com). Green Park tube. **Lunch served** noon-3pm daily. **Dinner served** 6-11.30pm Mon-Sat; 6-10.30pm Sun. **Main courses** £6.80-£14. **Set meal** pre-theatre £11 two courses, £18 four courses incl taxi to Theatreland. **Credit** AmEx, DC, JCB, MC, £TC, V.
Domineering service and a greedy bill spoilt our meal here – a pity, as Chor Bizarre has much going for it. The room is a riotous assembly of mismatched furniture, most of it intricately carved dark wood. It's like dining in an antiques shop. The fascinating menu includes a batch of 'tak-a-tak' dishes (finely chopped and cooked on a griddle). Kekada (crab) tak-a-tak looked appalling but was well-spiced with chilli and mustard seeds; bitter gourd tak-a-tak was more challenging (the bitterness counteracted by raw onion and lemon juice), but enjoyable. South Indian tiffin (a set meal including chicken Chettinad and avial) being off, we ordered Goan lemon sole curry. This, too, was off, so we finally gave in to the waiter's bossiness and chose Keralan prawn curry: chewy prawns in a sweet, dark-grey coconut sauce. Better was the side dish of lotus root in mousse-like spinach (nadroo palak), and the venison with figs (shahi shikar) where the meat's flavour was manifest in the gravy. Dessert was laughably bad: tandooried pineapple was in fact tepid, raw fruit on to which half a pot of cinnamon powder had been poured. True, the Indian Anarkali 1994 (£14.75) was a mellow wine, but we doubted it matched the food. Even with a shared pudding and the second-cheapest wine (from an extensive list), the bill for two came to over £100 with service. And the credit card slip was left open. News is that changes to the service and the menu are afoot – we await developments.

Babies and children welcome; high chairs. Booking advisable. Dress: smart casual. Separate room for parties, seats 30. Takeaway service. Map 13/7J.

Tamarind
20 Queen Street, W1 (020 7629 3561/ www.tamarindrestaurant.com). Green Park tube. **Lunch served** noon-3pm Mon-Fri; noon-2.30pm Sun. **Dinner served** 6-11.30pm Mon-Sat; 6-10.30pm Sun. **Main courses** £25-£100. **Set lunches** £10 two courses, £14.95 three courses. **Set dinners** (6-7pm, 10.30-11.30pm Mon-Sat) £16.50. **Pre-theatre dinner** £22.50 incl taxi to Theatreland. **Service** 12½%. **Credit** AmEx, DC, JCB, MC, £TC, V.
Dressed to impress, Tamarind's large basement features golden pillars, wooden flooring, a bar displaying sparkling glasses, and a window through to the kitchen. Order a roomali roti, then witness the skill of the tandoori chef in creating this flannel-thin bread. Business parties and prosperous locals flock here, to be waited on by plentiful, unnervingly attentive staff. The menu holds few surprises these days, with tandooris and curries accounting for most dishes, but presentation is exquisite and spicing enticing. The starter of murg bemisal (chicken cakes with mace, ginger and basil), one of many 'lighter dishes' marked with an asterisk, included three discs of breadcrumbed meat with a delicious yoghurt-based dressing. Hari machli (John Dory with crispy spinach) is a house special and consisted of a sizeable chunk of filleted fish fried in a spicy batter, with feather-light leaves of deep-fried spinach strewn over the top – an interesting dish, but one that needs a sauce. The creamy, rich dahl bukhari is too strong an accompaniment for the fish, but would give a fine protein-kick to a vegetarian repast. Breads and rice, too, are beyond reproach. Pricing is the problem here. A meal for two with wine can easily soar over £100, and after we had paid nearly a tenner for the service charge, we were disgruntled to receive an open credit card slip.
Babies and children welcome; high chairs. Book dinner Wed-Sat. Dress: smart casual. Takeaway service. Map 2/7H.

Veeraswamy ★
Mezzanine floor, Victory House, 99-101 Regent Street, W1 (020 7734 1401/ www.realindianfood.com). Piccadilly Circus tube. **Lunch served** noon-2.30pm Mon-Fri; 12.30-3pm Sat, Sun. **Dinner served** 5.30-11.30pm Mon-Sat; 5.30-10.30pm Sun. **Main**

courses £9.75-£17.50. **Set lunches** (Mon-Sat) £11 two courses, £14 three courses; Sun (eat as much as you like) £15 three courses. **Set dinners** (5.30-6.30pm, 10-11.30pm) £11 two courses, £14 three courses. **Sunday brunch** £15 three courses. **Service** 12½%. **Credit** AmEx, DC, JCB, MC, £TC, V.
During 74 years of trading, London's oldest Indian restaurant has been through many guises. Its current manifestation (a result of a takeover by the owners of **Chutney Mary** three years ago) is as a vibrant modern establishment at the forefront of New Indian cookery. The first-floor restaurant is reached via a dull, office-like entrance and staircase, making its large interior – at turns purple, mustard and orange, with chairs and waiters' shirts matching the walls – all the more welcome. We sat at a small table by the window, listening to bossa nova and looking down on the madness of Regent Street. Many of the main courses are commonplace Indian regional dishes, yet the menu also provides innovative concoctions among the starters and puds. One such newcomer, oysters stir-fried with coconut and Keralan spices, was an utter delight: creamy oysters spilling out of a shell, spiced with curry leaves and mustard seeds, and presented with the fluffiest of idlis. White lamb curry being unavailable, we chose instead lamb biriani to follow. It was on the dry side of perfect, the discoloured rice and tender meat signalling they had been cooked together (as is proper) and the scented wafts of lamb stock and herbs giving added pleasure. Lubrication, in the form of a decent dahl and raita, comes as part of the package. White chocolate kulfi, another modern take on a classic, brought the meal to a fitting finale. Prices here are high, but the setting impresses, as does the service, and the food – whether traditional or ground-breaking – rarely fails to excite.
Babies and children welcome; children's menu (Sun). Dress: smart casual. Separate room for parties, seats 36. Takeaway service. Map 13/7J.

Yatra ★
34 Dover Street, W1 (020 7493 0200). Green Park tube. **Lunch served** noon-3pm daily. **Dinner served** 5.30-11pm Mon-Sat. **Main courses** £12.50-£24. **Set meals** £12.50 two courses, £14.50 three courses. **Credit** AmEx, JCB, MC, £TC, V.
The much-abused trend of 'Asian fusion' has produced some appalling mismarriages. Yatra, however, draws on the breadth of Indian and South-east Asian cuisine to triumphant effect. The decor sets the mood nicely. Behind a brazen expanse of glass is a twin-roomed restaurant with primrose-ragged walls, terracotta mosaic-effect tiling and alcoves housing displays of oriental foliage. Tables are split into two sections: the standard dining set-up and 'traditional' low floor seating. Waitresses dress in saris. The menu's seven starters range from seafood and coconut soup to stuffed idli. Popadoms arrived accompanied by three of the best own-made chutneys we've tasted. Next, Yatra's salad was a deliciously savoury grilled Parmesan tower nestling against caramelised roast paneer tikka and salad leaves. Main courses include railway lamb (an Anglo-Indian speciality, cooked with baby potatoes and served with spinach). We opted for warm grilled beef salad, the meat marinated in soy sauce and peppercorns, cut into thin steaks, char-grilled and served with boiled quails' eggs, rocket and crispy garlic flakes – difficult to fault. Our other choice, stir-fried morels, came fried with green peas, Indian spices and sweet basil, and served with coriander khichdi, a rice-pulse mixture; the taste justified the £23 price tag. For dessert, both a creamy mango-rich concoction and a chocolate mousse inside a crisp white-and-dark chocolate shell were superb. Yatra isn't cheap, but for food of this calibre in this location, it's almost a bargain.
Booking advisable (weekends). Disabled: toilet. Separate room for parties, seats 180. Map 2/7H.

St James's SW1

Quilon ★
St James's Court Hotel, 41 Buckingham Gate, SW1 (020 7821 1899). St James' Park tube. **Lunch served** noon-2.30pm Mon-Fri. **Dinner served** 6-11pm Mon-Sat. **Main courses** £5.95-£18.95. **Set lunch** £12.50 two courses, £15.95 three courses. **Credit** AmEx, DC, MC, V.
We visited Quilon shortly after it opened in October 1999 and were less than impressed with its cautious spicing and high prices. So this year's visit was a revelation. The three-course lunchtime deal allows you the run of the full menu, with few supplements. Many dishes hail from Kerala (Quilon is a backwater town in that state), so seafood is prominent. The fact the restaurant is owned by Taj Hotels – and so kindred to the **Bombay Brasserie** (*see p83*) – also colours the menu. Main courses come with 'a vegetable preparation' included. Alleppey fish curry arrived with a side-kick of okra in yoghurt. Both dishes were sublime: the chunks of fresh white

Quilon

The Delhi Brasserie

44 Frith Street, Soho W1

WE ARE RENOWNED FOR OUR HIGH STANDARDS OF FOOD AND SERVICE

SOME OF THE FOOD CRITICS' RECOMMENDATIONS:

EGON RONAY'S
CRISP SERVICE AND TALENTED COOKING

LLOYDS LIST INTERNATIONAL GUIDE
THE DELHI BRASSERIE IS A "MUST" FOR THEATRELAND

TIME OUT
THE VISITORS BOOK BOASTS LUMINARIES LIKE TWIGGY, HOWARD SCHUMAN AND FAY MASCHLER. ATTENTION TO CULINARY DETAIL IS A STRONG POINT OF THE DELHI BRASSERIE

ASIAN TIMES
DELICIOUS FOOD, EXCELLENT SERVICE AND PLEASANT SURROUNDS ALL IN THE TRADITIONAL INDIAN STYLE

LONDON RESTAURANT GUIDE
CONSIDERED ONE OF LONDON'S BETTER INDIAN RESTAURANTS

ENJOY OUR RELAXED RESTAURANT ATMOSPHERE FOR YOUR BUSINESS LUNCH OR PRE AND AFTER THEATRE DINNER

OUR GROUND FLOOR PRIVATE ROOM IS AVAILABLE FOR A MINIMUM 6 OR MAXIMUM 10 COVERS

WE HAVE 2 PRIVATE ROOMS WHICH ARE AVAILABLE FOR LUNCH AND DINNER

PARTY MENUS ARE AVAILABLE HOWEVER WE WILL BE PLEASED TO SUGGEST A MENU SUITED TO YOUR OCCASION

FAMOUS FOR DISHES FROM ALL OVER INDIA

**44 FRITH STREET
SOHO
LONDON W1V 5TE
TEL:020 7437 8261
FAX:020 7437 3789**
(*NEAR RONNIE SCOTTS*)
EMAIL:
delhibrasseriesoho@talk21.com
www.delhibrasserie.com

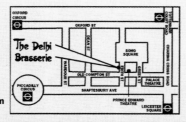

**134 CROMWELL ROAD
KENSINGTON
LONDON SW7 4HA
TEL: 020 7370 7617
FAX: 020 7244 8639**
EMAIL:
delhibrasseriekensington@talk21.com

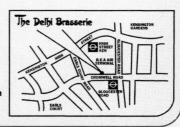

fish in a copious sauce of coconut milk and curry leaves; the okra lightly stewed with turmeric flavouring the yoghurt. Flaky Malabar paratha, fluffy short-grained red rice (rare to London) and a freshly cooked milk hopper (a Sri Lankan rice pancake) were also included. After a bowlful of interesting mixed popadoms (served with two tame relishes; best try the on-table pickles for fiery satisfaction), an appetite-honing glass of exquisite rasam soup, and a sizeable starter of partridge masala (two bony pieces in a green sludge of herbs and spices – far better than it sounds), this filled us almost to capacity. The almost mousse-like jackfruit pudding was worth stretching a point (and a stomach) for, though. Make a visit, but make it for lunch.
Babies and children admitted; high chairs. No-smoking tables. **Map 6/9J**.

Soho W1

Cafe Lazeez

21 Dean Street, W1 (020 7434 9393). Leicester Square or Tottenham Court Road tube. **Open** 11am-1am Mon-Sat; 11am-10.30pm Sun. **Set meals** *brasserie* £7.50 two courses (lunch and pre-theatre); *restaurant* £12 two courses (post-theatre). **Main courses** *brasserie* £5-£9; *restaurant* £8-£15. **Service** 12½%. **Credit** AmEx, DC, JCB, MC, V.
This third branch of Lazeez outstrips its stable mates by dint of a talented chef (fresh from the Oberoi Hotel in Delhi) and impressive design work. It is tucked under the new Soho Theatre Company building and incorporates a noisy ground-floor bar and brasserie (serving burgers, snacks and a few Indian dishes), and a quieter, costlier basement restaurant. We were asked to wait at the bar and have a drink, although the restaurant was empty – why? Once at our table we had to endure the drinks and popadoms hard sell, followed by the menu. The restaurant dishes are mostly popular, modish classics. However, lamb shami kebabs were dull and lifeless; saffron prawns were more pleasing, though £10.75 is a bit steep for a starter portion. Main courses were much better. Tilapia fish was cooked with yoghurt, mustard seeds and curry leaves; while chicken dum pukht was creamy yet had slightly too much cardamom. A side dish of aubergines with a tomato-ish sauce had a mild chilli kick, but was otherwise almost Italian. Nans were perfect. For dessert, pistachio kulfi tasted just like green tea. Table service was attentive without being intrusive. Café Lazeez doesn't break any new ground, but is a good Indian restaurant with proper cooking (no brought-in curry sauces here). Another bonus was that none of our dishes was oily.
Babies and children welcome; high chairs; crayons. Disabled: toilet. Dress: smart casual. Separate room for parties (seats 10). Tables outdoors (4, pavement). **Map 13/6K.**
For branches see index.

Soho Spice

124-126 Wardour Street, W1 (020 7434 0808/www.sohospice.co.uk). Tottenham Court Road tube. **Meals served** 11.30am-midnight Mon-Wed, Sun; 11.30am-3am Fri-Sat. **Main courses** £8.50-£15.95. **Set lunch** £7.50. **Set dinner** £15. **Credit** AmEx, DC, JCB, MC, £TC, V.
We've often found Amin Ali's restaurants to value style over content, and last year reckoned Soho Spice to be a prime culprit. The style is still present – a Fitch-designed colour scheme of orange, purple and turquoise is matched by kurtas of the highly efficient staff (who change ashtrays after every puff) – but this time we found the food, too, to have verve. Whitebait Amritsar was a mouthwatering starter, the fish crisp, abundant, lightly spiced and served with a zesty tomato-based dip. Another cross-cultural concoction, nargisi kebab (lamb rissoles stuffed with stringy Cheddar and served with good mixed salad and a minty dip) also showed admirable lightness of touch. Main courses all come thali-style with 'rice, nan, dahl and seasonal vegetables' – annoying for those simply wanting a pre-session snack. Still, the chickpea 'dahl' came in an appetising sauce, the rice was enticingly aromatic, and the centrepieces of our meals, tandoori fish and Bengal fish curry, were executed with some flair. The oft-changing set menus based on regional Indian cooking are also worth investigation. Skip the standard desserts (kulfi, fruit salad) and head downstairs to the groovy bar for spiced cocktails: as do droves of London's young office-workers.
Babies and children admitted. Booking essential. Entertainment: DJ 10.30pm-3am Fri, Sat (bar). No-smoking tables. Separate room for parties, seats 40. Takeaway service. **Map 13/6K.**
For branch (Red Fort) see index.

Strand WC2

India Club ★

Second floor, Strand Continental Hotel, 143 Strand, WC2 (020 7836 0650). Temple tube. **Lunch served** noon-2.30pm, **dinner served** 6-11pm Mon-Sat. **Main courses** £4-£10. **Set meal** £11 two courses. **Unlicensed. Corkage** no charge. **Credit** £TC.
After 50 years, the India Club has become an institution, offering inexpensive curries to generations of curry freaks and ex-pats. Reached via two flights of steep, gloomy stairs, it's hardly a picture when you arrive: Formica tables, linoleum floor and bare white walls dotted with framed portraits of Indian notables. The white-coated waiters are efficient but expect you to know the place's many idiosyncrasies, one of which is that you can buy beer from the hotel bar downstairs, so long as you're a member of the drink club. We've never got to the bottom of this ourselves and tend to stick with Seven-Up. As in all good Indian hotel restaurants (that is, hotel restaurants in India), the menu is split between vegetarian and non-vegetarian, and the food is pretty much what you'd get in India. The head chef is from the south, so dosais (masala dosai, £3.20) and sambar remain the India Club's forte. North Indian dishes are not as striking and the tandoori food lacks sparkle. Other highlights include bhuna chicken, keema peas and that Indian hotel standby, egg curry.
Babies and children welcome; high chairs. No-smoking tables. Takeaway service. **Map 14/7M.**

West

Hammersmith W6

Rafique's

291 King Street, W6 (020 8748 7345). Ravenscourt Park tube. **Lunch served** noon-2.30pm Mon-Fri, noon-3.30pm Sat-Sun. **Dinner served** 6-11.30pm Mon-Sat, 6.30-10.30pm Sun. **Main courses** £6.95-£8.95. **Service** 10%. **Credit** AmEx, DC, JCB, MC, £TC, V.
Though the ownership here has remained constant since a swanky refurb decorated both ground floor and basement with wooden flooring, white cane chairs and orange walls of varying vividness, its chefs and its name have changed twice in two years. Indian Summer became Vineet Bhatia, and when the esteemed Bhatia left to open **Zaika** (*see below*), Rafique's was born. Service is efficient, if grasping (eager for us to have popadoms, a second bottle of house wine – good Chilean sauvignon blanc – and to pay the service charge twice). Three courses of high-class, New Indian food with wine and service came to £65: not cheap, but significantly lower than West End prices. The menu is exciting, with many new (if occasionally ill-conceived) dishes. Lobster samosas (four delicate parcels, well presented but with the lobster bulked out by lentils, and mismatched with chunks of sweet apple) were outclassed by a huge starter portion of prawn thoran: a nutty stir-fry of shellfish, lentils and curry leaves. Next, Hyderabadi chicken korma had an appetising tangy sauce, much needed as the crab masala (a decent stir-fry with coconut), stuffed baby aubergines (slightly undercooked, but with a crunchy peanut filling), and dum aloo Kashmiri (potatoes in a scant yoghurt and onion sauce) were a mite dry. Wild strawberry kulfi was enjoyable, yet with only faint fruit flavour. So, even if execution doesn't quite match up to the creativity, Rafique's deserves its popularity among Hammersmith's bourgeoisie.
Babies and children welcome. Separate room for parties, seats 40. Takeaway service. Vegetarian menu.

Paddington W2

Indian Connoisseurs

8 Norfolk Place, W2 (020 7402 3299). Edgware Road tube/Paddington tube/rail. **Lunch served** noon-2.30pm, **dinner served** 6pm-midnight daily. **Main courses** £4.75. **Set lunch** £6.95 three courses. **Set meals** £9.95. **Credit** AmEx, DC, MC, £TC, V.
Marked out from the curry house norm by a batch of Bangladeshi dishes, Indian Connoisseurs continues its unassuming existence near to St Mary's Hospital. Regular customers include NHS workers as well as the odd passenger seeking refuge from Paddington. The small dining room might seemed cramped if full, but this is rarely the case. A light colour scheme is made more diverting by bright Bangladeshi paintings hanging on the walls. All the usual formulaic curry dishes can be had for around a fiver, but look to the game dishes (tandoori pheasant, anyone?) or 'regional cuisine' specials for more distinctive flavours. Ayre cutlet is a good way of starting a repast, the meaty white fish coming with plenty of fried onions. Haas baas, duck with bamboo shoots, has a moderately spiced tomato sauce as its companion; other regional specials include khashi gazar (goat meat with baby carrots), and channa kaleji (chicken liver with chickpeas). Over the years standards have been reliable: never thrilling, but never disappointing.
Babies and children admitted. Booking advisable. No-smoking tables. Separate room for parties, seats 28. Takeaway service (free delivery within five-mile radius). **Map 1/5E.**
For branch see index.

South West

Chelsea SW10

Chutney Mary

535 King's Road, SW10 (020 7351 3113). Bus 11, 22. **Lunch served** 12.30-2.30pm Mon-Sat; 12.30-3pm Sun. **Dinner served** 7-11.30pm Mon-Sat; 7-10.30pm Sun. **Main courses** £9.50-£16. **Set lunch** £11.50 two courses. **Service** 12½%. **Cover** £1.50. **Credit** AmEx, DC, JCB, MC, £TC, V.
Last year we relished Chutney Mary's classy take on Indian regional cuisine, and this year, too, found the cooking of a high standard. Yet our late-evening meal was marred by sloppy service. True, the waiters couldn't be blamed for our neighbouring diners, the Couple from Hell (near Eltham) out for a 'posh curry' and sluicing brandy with abandon. But our drinks order was twice wrong; saffron rice arrived sans saffron; and the waiters' disdain for our neighbours seemed to overflow on to us. The food was a refuge. Mixed starters of lobster samosa, crab cake and papri chat (a lentil and potato rissole) were crisp and juicy in all the right places. Next, chicken biriani had rice suffused with chicken flavour, and cardamom dominant among the spices (too much so for some, perhaps); lamb shank xacuti was a tender joint with gravy to savour. A side dish of stuffed aubergines seemed comparatively drab: babies stuffed with fried onions, minimal spicing and no sauce. To finish, hill station bread and butter pudding, one of the few Anglo-Indian dishes on a menu that once specialised in this cooking, had a suitably crisp topping and eggy interior. Mary's wine list remains one of Indian London's best, and the premises – a ground floor bar and small dining area decorated with bright depictions of Anglo-Indian life; and the large split-level basement room with a mock-conservatory, palms, and banquette or cane chair seating – are well-liked by Chelsea locals.
Babies and children welcome; high chairs. Book dinner. Dress: smart casual. Entertainment: jazz band lunch Sun. No-smoking tables. **Map 5/13C.**

Vama ★

438 King's Road, SW10 (020 7351 4118/ www.vama.co.uk). Bus 11, 22. **Lunch served** 12.30-3pm, **dinner served** 6.30-11.30pm daily. **Main courses** £5.75-£18. **Set lunch** £9.99. **Set dinner** 6.30-8pm Mon-Thur £15. **Service** 12½%. **Cover** £1. **Credit** AmEx, JCB, MC, £TC, V.
We rate Vama as one of the most reliable of the new-wave high-class Indian restaurants: we've yet to receive a complaint about it, and we've yet to be served a duff dish. This year's lunch was a sparsely attended affair, though evenings are usually a-hum with Chelsea diners. There's a pleasing balance between gravitas and informality in the two small rooms. Large canvases with carved wooden frames, heavy wooden chairs and a flag-stoned floor provide some ballast; walls and table-cloths the colour of Dijon mustard, and breezy, informed staff leaven matters. Food here is inventive, but entirely in keeping with Indian traditions. Chef Birender Narula has full command of all relevant techniques (indeed, he offers cookery classes). The varied menu is supplemented by daily specials such as khandari murg (chicken breast stuffed with minced chicken, potatoes and herbs). We started with rustami khumb bahar, five mushrooms filled with slivers of potato and topped with toasted cheese; pomegranate juice giving the whole a tangy zest. To follow, nariyal wali machli was chunks of seared salmon in a thick creamy sauce that, though only hinting at the promised coconut flavour, had spicing that perfectly matched the fish. Rice and bread (an expertly rendered, wafer-thin and green, palak roomali) were both top-notch, and pudding of mango kulfi and sliced fruit also demonstrated expert presentation and attention to detail. Zaika may offer stern local competition, but Vama won't disappoint.
Babies and children welcome; high chairs. Book weekends. Entertainment: cabaret and belly dancer (phone for details). No-smoking tables. Separate room for parties, seats 35. Tables outdoors (4, patio). Takeaway service. **Map 5/12D.**

Zaika ★

257-259 Fulham Road, SW3 (020 7351 7823). South Kensington tube/14 bus. **Lunch served** noon-2.30pm Mon-Fri. **Dinner served** 6.30-10.30pm Mon-Sat. **Main courses** £9.80-£13.95. **Set lunch** £9.95 two courses, £11.95 three courses. **Set meals** £25 five courses, £33 five courses incl wine. **Service** 12½%. **Credit** AmEx, MC, JCB, V, £TC.
Purists of Indian food might find some of Vineet Bhatia's dishes hard to swallow – but there's no doubting his talent. Since 1999, Bhatia, one of Indian London's most high-profile chefs, has been operating from these utterly restrained, utterly classy premises. Subtle lighting illuminates a muted colour scheme of beiges, expensive Indian artefacts, and the faces of the equally restrained, equally opulent customers. The menu lists many of the dishes Bhatia has made famous. After a complimentary espresso cup of mango lassi, we tucked into the Zaika platter of three starters: the renowned dhungar machli tikka (hot-smoked salmon well-matched with a dill and yoghurt relish); a seekh kebab of almost pâté-like lightness; and black chicken (resembling black pud, but a refined version of chicken tikka). Kerara kekda (deep-fried soft-shell crab), an Indian take on a Chinese idea, was also faultless. Main courses include dishes that owe most to Modern European cooking (a juicy halibut steak with too-salty masala mashed potato scattered with wild mushrooms), but better are the innovative twists given to Indian classics (a perfect lamb biriani comes with a delicious pastry crust). Tandoori phal mixed fruits (a kebab of spiced dates and pineapple) was gorgeous, too. We have two caveats. First, Bhatia's keenness to get away from curry-house slop means that sauces are a rarity and a meal can seem dry. Second, service, though polite, is haphazard. We had long waits between courses, and our bill was monumentally wrong; to be charged £33 for popadoms is – when it comes to the crunch – unforgivable.
Babies and children admitted. Booking essential. Dress: smart casual. **Map 5/11D.**

Earl's Court SW5

Loofs

234 Old Brompton Road, SW5 (020 7370 1188/1199). Earl's Court tube. **Lunch served** 12.30-2.30pm Sat, Sun. **Dinner served** 5pm-midnight daily. **Main courses** £5.50-£9.95. **Credit** AmEx, DC, MC, V.
Despite around 85% of British 'Indian' restaurants being Bangladeshi-owned, food from this country rarely appears on menus. Loof seems eager to right this wrong. It's a bright, fashion-conscious place with bare floorboards, vibrant blue walls, a modern bar, French windows revealing noisy Old Brompton Road, and a soundtrack of 1970s soul. Avoid the ingenuously named 'traditional menu' of bhunas, vindaloos and the like, and look to the varied Bangladeshi list for interest. Mustard seeds, pumpkin, citrus fruit and various fish are key ingredients. We began with biran mass: a thin meaty steak of the boal fish, lightly spiced, fried with an excess of onions and well presented with a mixed salad. To follow, leboor gosht paired lamb with delicate slivers of Bangladeshi lime, rind and all, providing an enjoyably bitter foil to the ghee-rich dish. Certain side dishes from the region also look worth exploring; a reader vouches for the sissingra bhajia, spiced-up Bengali courgette. Kulfi was the sole dessert on our trip, so we must wait to sample the komrar morobba ('an historic dessert made especially for Bengali weddings').
Babies and children admitted. No-smoking tables. Takeaway service (local delivery). **Map 5/11B.**

Putney SW15

Ma Goa

242-244 Upper Richmond Road, SW15 (020 8780 1767). East Putney tube/Putney rail/74, 337 bus. **Dinner served** 6.30-11pm Tue-Sat; 6-10pm Sun. **Main courses** £5.75-£9.95. **Set dinner** (7-8pm Mon-Thur) £8.95 two courses. **Credit** DC, MC, £TC, V.
The Kapoor family, London restaurateurs for more than 30 years, opened the capital's first Goan restaurant in 1993. Since then Ma Goa has expanded into a back room, but its interior still reflects Goa's Portuguese influence, with white textured walls, terracotta coloured ceiling, solid wooden furniture, wooden flooring and earthenware pottery. The menu has seafood to the

fore, with pork a star attraction (explained by Goa's Christian heritage). We had several minor niggles about the meal, but left happy. First the grumbles: the starter of Ma Goa's sausage was more a spiced-up pork banger than the chouriço for which we'd hoped; a side dish of green herb chutney was a tiny dollop for 75p; the 'vegetable special' was a so-what dish of scarcely spiced green beans, sesame seeds, garlic and baby corn; and service, from an unsmiling waitress, was slightly flat. Now to the treats: sorpotel, a starter-sized portion of rich meaty stew involving lamb's liver, kidney, pork, nutmeg, coriander and lime; coco borrego, lamb shank with coconut slow-cooked to perfection; alazama, a comforting dessert of figs and dried apricots in cardamom custard, nicely presented on a big white plate. Next time, we'll join Ma Goa's well-heeled Putney regulars and try the 'catch of the day' (perhaps hot and spicy green curry with scallops, calamares and prawns). The Kapoors plan to open a spice and deli shop next door soon.
Babies and children welcome; high chairs. Booking advisable. Separate room for parties, seats 55. Tables outdoors (4, garden). Takeaway service.

South Kensington SW5, SW7

Bombay Brasserie

Courtfield Road, SW7 (020 7370 4040/ www.bombaybrasserielondon.com). Gloucester Road tube. **Lunch served** 12.30-3pm, **dinner served** 7.30pm-midnight daily. **Main courses** £14.95-£25.95 (dinner). **Minimum** £30 (dinner). **Set buffet lunch** £16.95 incl tea or coffee. **Credit** DC, MC, £TC, V.
In the 1980s, the Brasserie set the standard for upmarket Indian dining in Britain. It spawned many imitations (particularly in opulent south-west London) of its Raj-style cocktail lounge, its grand, spacious dining room, and its lighter, more informal conservatory. It became a fixture in foreign guidebooks and has rested on its laurels. What you get now is slick but slightly cynical service, roomfuls of business and tourist diners, and food that, though enticing on the page, often fails to live up to the promise. Bombay street snacks (at prices that would make Bombay street sellers weep) account for many of the starters. Sev batata poori (pooris with cubed boiled potatoes, sev, coriander leaves and chutneys) is certainly authentic – save for the £6.50 price tag. Our advice would be to pay a few pounds extra and go for luxury ingredients or dishes requiring lengthy preparation, perhaps starting with scallops peri peri, or dum ka bater (quail cooked in a sealed pot with a yoghurt-based sauce), then continuing with masala fried lobster (from the 'specialities of Goa' list) or the long-cooked lamb nihari. All main courses come with a (sometimes inappropriate) 'potato preparation', a vegetable of the day, and a lentil dish. The lunchtime buffet consists of the relatively more mundane curries and is of even more questionable value.
Babies and children welcome (lunch; over-7s admitted dinner); high chairs; half-price buffet for under-12s. Book dinner; lunch Sun. Dress: smart casual. Entertainment: pianist 9.30pm-1am Mon-Fri; 12.30-3pm, 9.30pm-1am, Sat, Sun. No-smoking tables. Separate conservatory for lunch parties, seats 160. **Map 5/10C**.

Star of India

154 Old Brompton Road, SW5 (020 7373 2901/www.starofindia.co.uk). Gloucester Road or South Kensington tube. **Lunch served** noon-2.45pm daily. **Dinner served** 6-11.45pm Mon-Sat; 7-11.15pm Sun. **Main courses** £9.50-£15.50. **Cover** £1. **Credit** AmEx, DC, MC, £TC, V.
Reza Mohammed's Star seemed on the decline following the departure of his top chef Vineet Bhatia (now at **Zaika**, *see p81*) a couple of years ago. There's no doubting this is an impressive venue, though. Murals depict classical sculptures and pillars, while a trompe l'oeil ceiling has an angel soaring skywards. Staff are slinky, smart and on the ball. The would-be bohemian wing of Chelsea's rich can be spotted here, clad in black and perhaps listening to a jazz soundtrack. A few Bhatia trademark dishes remain on the menu, including the pudding of chocomosas (samosas filled with gooey white and plain chocolate). Many of the novel dishes appear on the starters list, including samundri ratan (saffron-infused char-grilled scallops in a creamy sauce) and chenna samosas (stuffed with a trio of goat, buffalo and cow's cheeses). Main courses are more familiar, but specials continue the innovative theme. Achari hiran champen involves venison being simmered in spices with roast garlic and button onions; Malabar meen curry pairs halibut with a sauce of onions, tamarind and coconut. Vegetarians can experiment, too, with the likes of subz kaju thoran, a spicy stir-fry of asparagus, cashew nuts and coconut. We've witnessed slips in the execution of dishes, but the constantly evolving menu is a good sign – and the decor's a hoot.
Babies and children admitted (lunch, early evening). Book Tue-Sat. Dress: smart casual. Entertainment: jazz evenings Wed-Fri. Separate rooms for parties, seating 12 and 14. Takeaway service.
Map 5/11C.

South

Norbury SW16

Mirch Masala ★

1416 London Road, SW16 (020 8679 1828/ 020 8765 1070). Norbury rail. **Meals served** noon-1am daily. **Main courses** £3-£10. **Set buffet lunch** (noon-4pm Mon-Sat) £5.99. **Unlicensed. Corkage** no charge. **Credit** AmEx, DC, MC, £TC, V.
The Ali family pioneered Karahi King in Wembley and now they've established a reputation in south London. The food is robust Punjabi-style cooking, served to a predominantly Asian crowd that gets more western as the day progresses. The tables are Formica-topped, the walls plain white and the service pleasant but erratic. After we'd asked for a bottle of sparkling water three times without success, we worked out that 'no problem' roughly translates as 'Big problem – we don't sell it.' And does the rice always have to appear after the main course? The menu is divided up into warmers (starters), steamers (main courses) and coolers (rice, breads, etc) and further between vegetarian and non-veg. Masala lamb chops is a speciality and is a bone and meat pile bursting with fleshy flavours. Most of the families around us were tucking into generous plates of tandoori chicken wings (£2.50) that outshone anything of the Colonel's. A warmer of patra was hard and over-cooked but the chutneys that accompanied the salad came to the rescue. Karahi methi egg came with plenty of egg and was thick with methi leaves, a good combination, while the karahi king prawns was packed with prawns, perfectly-spiced and totally authentic. The nan arrived last of all, was flatter than a Dutch pancake and Kray-hard. Those who expect a perfect dining experience should probably avoid Mirch Masala; those of us prepared to take the rough with the smooth in return for some fantastic Punjabi food will keep persevering.
Babies and children welcome; high chairs. Book dinner. Disabled: toilet. Takeaway service.

Shamyana ★

437-439 Streatham High Road, SW16 (020 8679 6162/www.shamyana-restaurant.co.uk). Norbury rail. **Meals served** noon-midnight daily. **Main courses** £4.50-£7. **Set buffet lunch** £5.50. **Service** 10%. **Credit** AmEx, LV, MC, V.
Any restaurant that combines organic ingredients with pungent Punjabi cooking has got to be on to a winner, and so Shamyana is becoming as popular as its longer established neighbour. Service is friendly and helpful, and the food is good, going on excellent. A starter of paneer tikka, thick cheese fingers barbecued in the tandoori and fried with onions and spices was delicious, and masala fish was crisp on the outside with a crust of masala spices to-die-for, and well-flaked within. But best of all were potato cutlets, delicious torpedoes of mashed vegetable, peppered with fresh coriander and spices, fried in hot oil until crunchy on the outside and softly steaming within. Fans of the Shamyana urged us to try ginger chicken and karahi gosht, which are signature dishes, but we went instead for karahi king prawn, which was bursting with juicy prawns in a pungent sauce, while masala prawn, although slightly over-salty, benefited from a strong stock and excellent use of herbs and freshly ground spices. Chunky, well-cooked mixed vegetables were hard to fault. We didn't have room for pudding (portions are generous) but the kheer is said to be out of this world.
Babies and children welcome; high chairs. Book weekends. Disabled: toilet. Entertainment: Indian musicians Sun (phone to check). No-smoking tables. Separate room for parties, seats 200. Takeaway service.

Southfields SW18

Sarkhel's ★

199 Replingham Road, SW18 (020 8870 1483/takeaway 020 8871 0808). Southfields tube. **Lunch served** noon-2.30pm Fri-Sun. **Dinner served** 6-10.30pm Tue-Thur, Sun; 6-11pm Fri, Sat. **Main courses** £3.50-£9.95. **Set lunch** £9.95 four courses. **Credit** AmEx, MC, £TC, V.
Sarkhel's had a major expansion and refurb in late 1999. Prices are high for a suburban Indian restaurant and portion sizes are not balti-generous, but then Udit Sarkhel's cooking is subcontinental, not suburban. It's the sort of cooking you find in very good restaurants and homes: not showy, understated even, with precise cooking and careful, balanced spicing. High points of our meal were the meltingly tender slow-cooked lamb shank (£9.95), and a prawn masala (kolmi nu patia, £8.50) which combined juicy pieces of aubergine and red pumpkin with black tiger prawns; the mix of sweet (jaggery), sour (vinegar) and hot (chilli) are a distinctively Parsi cooking style. Kormas in the UK are usually mild, but the mirchi korma (lamb and chilli) contained fiery heat, in part due to a spice called chirpal, which is described as a kind of Sichuan pepper from Kashmir; we needed yoghurt as a palliative to the spice. Not every dish was a success: a small dry portion of okra in mango powder was dreary, and it cost £5.50. Likewise, £4.50 is expensive for a single mango, no matter how good (it was ambrosial). All in all, Sarkhel's is an outstanding Indian restaurant with an outstanding chef.
Babies and children welcome; high chairs. Book Sat, Sun. Disabled: toilet. No-smoking tables. Takeaway service. Vegetarian menu.

Tooting SW17

SW17 seems to have become London's centre for diverse Indian cuisine. On the mile-long road that changes name from High Street to Upper Tooting Road, there's a plethora of restaurants offering good food at practically suicidal prices. Relish the choice of three south Indian, two Pakistani, a couple of East African diners, and a Gujarati vegetarian café, all of which are among the best in town. And that's not counting the area's many sweet sellers, formula curry houses and Punjabi kebab shops, none of which could be classed as bad. In the last couple of years, Keralan veteran Shree Krishna has spawned a couple of upstart kids – Vijaya Krishna and Radha Krishna Bhavan – and all of them dish up avial, uthappam and dosais to die for. A little further north, Ugandan exiles the Thanki family continue to serve first rate vegetarian food at the Kastoori, where unusual dishes like chilli bananas and mogo (cassava) set it aside from the herd. Tooting's vibrant Sri Lankan community have their own restaurant/café in Jaffna House, where hot chillies are pretty ubiquitous; and worshippers of pungent Pakistani-style meat dishes can thank the Lord for Lahore Karahi and the East African-oriented Masaledar. Milan offers fantastic Gujarati vegetarian food and sweets, in an atmosphere of absolute serenity – even on Sundays. Tiffin of tea and their shrikhand is simply the best.

Lahore Karahi ★

1 Tooting High Street, SW17 (020 8767 2477). Tooting Broadway tube/133 bus. **Meals served** noon-midnight daily. **Main courses** £3.75-£4.95. **Unlicensed. Corkage** no charge. **No credit cards**.
The walls of this large cafeteria-style diner are plastered with slogans like 'the restaurant where customers recommend their friends' (sic) and 'genuine spicy taste'. Despite the counter running down almost one side, it's not self-service. If you sit patiently, a waiter will eventually come and take your order, and as long as you're not fussy about which dishes come when, you'll get on fine. Expect above average Pakistani-style fast food; the success of the operation can be judged by the number of locals who perpetually pack the place. Vegetarians are well looked after ('prepared under strict precaution') but the métier here is meat and plenty of it. The seekh and shami kebabs (£1.20, £1.40 respectively for two) are good examples of their type, being spicy and intensely savoury, while the fried masala fish is chunky, crispy on the outside and crusted with delicious masala. Karela (bitter melon) gosht was, said a Pakistani neighbour, the best thing on the menu, and it arrived bubbling in its own karahi; chunky meat chunks in a gourd-rich gravy that was slightly tart but well-balanced. Tarka dahl was thick and well-spiced, but the mixed vegetables, good though they were, had obviously been sitting around for a while and would have been better for a drop or two less oil. Strawberry kulfi was a surprise that went down well and the mango lassis could not be faulted.
Babies and children welcome; high chairs. Book Fri-Sun. No-smoking tables. Separate room for parties, seats 50. Takeaway service.

Masaledar ★

121 Upper Tooting Road, SW17 (020 8767 7676). Tooting Bec or Tooting Broadway tube/155, 219, 355 bus. **Meals served** noon-midnight daily. **Main courses** £3.95-£7.95. **Set lunch** £2.25 for six items. **Unlicensed** no alcohol allowed. **Credit** MC, V.
Occupying an impressive corner spot, with a split level interior that reminded a colleague of a BBC radio canteen – all palms, terracotta tiles and dark wood – the Masaledar has carved out a name for itself in Tooting. The name of the game here is Pakistani-style karahi cooking by way of East Africa, and although the menu features such delights as fries (chilli or salted, £1.25) and a strong vegetarian section, it's the likes of ginger chicken and achar gosht that get the locals going. We tried a deliciously savoury karahi king prawn that was full of plump shellfish surrounded by a much-reduced sauce; and a mixed vegetable karahi, a dish in the same rich, savoury tradition, although maybe just a tad too sweet. Tarka dahl was thick, gingery and rich in fresh coriander and a starter of aloo tikki was aggressively spiced and well sorted in the potato department. Service was friendly, if a little frenzied, and although the single chef on view was coping well, the three waiters were struggling to serve a full house and a mountain of takeaways on a Sunday afternoon.
Babies and children welcome; high chairs; toys. Booking advisable. No-smoking tables. Takeaway service.

South East

Forest Hill SE23

Babur Brasserie

119 Brockley Rise, SE23 (020 8291 2400/ 4881). Honor Oak Park rail/122, 171, 271 bus. **Lunch served** noon-2.30pm Mon-Thur, Sat, Sun. **Dinner served** 6-11.30pm daily. **Main courses** £6.95-£11.75. **Set meals** £11.75 (vegetarian), £13.95. **Set buffet lunch** (Sun) £8.95. **Credit** AmEx, DC, JCB, LV, MC, V.
Brockley and Forest Hill-ites are lucky to have a restaurant like this in their neighbourhood, offering an adventurous menu and above-average cooking. The place is smartly decorated in a bright Last Days of the Raj-meets-modern style, further reflected in the large, colourful menus. A starter of prawn bulchao came with a small nan and was pleasantly piquant, with a fiery chilli flavour, tempered by tamarind tartness. Similarly, ros-tos crab served in its shell was a winner, being delicately spiced, cooked with wine and mango juice and served with cheese. However, Mala mach (battered slivers of fish) was bland and over-oily. A main course of Bangalore duck was another Raj-style dish, with thick slices of just-pink Barbary duck accompanied by a sauce that accentuated the flavours, rather than wrestling them to the ground. Stand-out vegetable dishes included avial – not much like the versions we've enjoyed in Kerala, but tasty with crisp vegetable sticks in a tangy yoghurt sauce – and spicy dum aloo which married new potatoes with an onion-rich sauce. Vegetarians have the option of desi bhojan (£11.75), a thali offering a choice of four vegetables.
Babies and children welcome; high chairs; Sunday buffet lunch free for under-7s, half-price for 7-10s. Book weekends. No-smoking tables. Tables outdoors (4, pavement). Takeaway service (dinner).

Herne Hill SE24

3 Monkeys ★

136-140 Herne Hill, SE24 (020 7738 5500). Herne Hill rail/3, 37, 68 bus. **Lunch served** noon-3pm Sun. **Dinner served** 6-11pm daily. **Main courses** £5.25-£14.75. **Set dinner** £14.95 three courses. **Set buffet lunch** (Sun) £12.95 (£7.95 children). **Service** 12½%. **Credit** AmEx, DC, JCB, MC, TC, V.
It took a while, but 3 Monkeys has found favour with the locals – so much so that it's practically impossible to walk in and get a table these days. Owner Jan Peacock has added a cooking school, deli and wine shop to the site, but it's chef Prem Singh's pan-Indian cooking that keeps us coming back. Dishes are culled from all over the Indian

3 Monkeys. *See page 83.*

subcontinent, so a starter of murgh beab – spicy battered chicken served with fried green chillies – shows south Indian roots and shammi kebab is spiced in the Bengali manner. Goan fish curry (£11.95) consists of large chunks of white fish served in a pungent sauce rich in chilli and piquant spices, almost (but never quite) tamed by smooth coconut. We particularly enjoyed yetti ajowani, which combines succulent prawns with curry leaves, carum seed and asafoetida in a thick, reduced sauce, and the dahl bukhara dugari, a side dish of creamy black lentils combined with butter and hot northern spices. Prices – especially for vegetable dishes, which start at £4.50 – are high, especially for Herne Hill, and although the cooking is of a high standard, £2.75 for boiled rice and £1.95 for a nan does seem a little over the top. Service was friendly and efficient at all times, and the worst, most watery mango lassi we've ever tasted was replaced without a word.
Babies and children welcome; children with adult eat free 6-7pm; high chairs. Booking advisable. Disabled: toilet. No-smoking tables. Separate rooms for parties, seating 16 and 40. Takeaway service.

East

Up to a decade or so ago, the restaurants in Brick Lane were primarily there for the benefit of the local population, and it was possible to get good quality, authentic Indian, Pakistani and Bangladeshi dishes for a song. On a Sunday afternoon the original Clifton restaurant was packed with families enjoying well-cooked food that came with crisp salads, fluffy nan and warm cans of coke. No one was licensed to sell booze and (because of strict Muslim rules) bringing your own bottle was a risky business.

However, the boom in the City combined with word of mouth to bring in a new breed of curry eater; slowly, the local restaurateurs saw the way the wind was blowing (no pun intended) and menus started to change. The word 'balti' is now as ubiquitous as popadom. Restaurants sprang up everywhere in the Lane and now it's possible to get a chicken korma in 25 different places.

We've sampled some sorry meals lately and a decent dish now appears to be the exception rather than the rule. But the Bangla Town restaurateurs will tell you that they're only providing what people want, and, judging by the full tables, this seems to be true. Most of the kitchens seem to source their sauces out of jars (at least it ensures a consistency) and with a range of dishes on the menu that extends in some cases to over 250, it's hardly surprising that the standards are more than a little low. The return of Bangladeshi dishes to menus we commended last year also has its down side. We made a point of ordering specialist dishes on most of our visits and with a couple of exceptions (detailed below) the results were either variations on a Madras or, in some cases, poorly cooked and totally inedible.

Increasingly, it seems to be the case that the further you move away from Brick Lane, the better the food. The area south of Whitechapel Road is where the Pakistani community tends to hang out these days, while Green Street is showing something of the vibrancy that Brick Lane used to have.

Brick Lane E1

Café Naz ★
46-48 Brick Lane, E1 (020 7247 0234). Aldgate East or Whitechapel tube. **Meals served** noon-midnight Mon-Fri; 6pm-midnight Sat. **Lunch served** noon-3pm, **dinner served** 6pm-midnight Sun. **Main courses** £5. **Minimum charge** £6.50. **Service** 12½% upstairs only. **Credit** AmEx, DC, JCB, MC, V.
There are those who rave about this modern-style brasserie, but we've never had better than an OK meal here. All right, so the glass, chrome and black interior looks good and there's no shortage of waiting staff, eager (well, maybe not eager) to attend to your every wish, but the food is strictly formula stuff, even with 'Bangladeshi specials'. Prices are slightly above the Brick Lane average, with starters around £2-£2.50 and main courses around a fiver.
Babies and children admitted. Booking advisable. Separate room for parties (seats 100). Takeaway service. **Map 4/5S.**
For branch see index.

City Spice ★
138 Brick Lane, E1 (020 7247 1012/ www.cityspice.co.uk). Aldgate East or Shoreditch tube. **Lunch served** noon-3pm, **dinner served** 6pm-12.30am daily. **Main courses** £2.95-£9.95. **Set lunch** £5.95 three courses. **Credit** MC, V.
One of the more friendly Brick Lane curry houses and, although the food isn't terrific, it is among the best in the Lane these days. Leave the baltis, Madras and korma dishes to the tourists and choose from the short list of Bangladeshi specials. The likes of biran mass (marinated fried fish with spices and onions) and ureebisi biran (Bangladeshi bean seeds cooked in the same style) might not make you want to emigrate, but they beat prawn cocktail hands down. Similarly, tandoori roopchanda (a flat skate-like fish) is a tastier option than the usual chicken or prawn, and shatkora gosht (lamb cooked with the lemon-like fruit) works well. When we asked for a takeaway menu we were given one for the Shampan across the road – which we always find too crowded, too cramped, too noisy and too hurried – and on closer inspection we found that they serve exactly the same dishes at exactly the same prices. Funny, that.
Babies and children admitted. Separate room for parties, seats 70. Takeaway service. **Map 4/5S.**

Preem
120 Brick Lane, E1 (020 7247 0397) Shoreditch or Aldgate East tube. **Lunch served** noon-3pm, **dinner served** 6pm-midnight daily. **Main courses** £3.90-£9.15. **Credit** AmEx, DC, JCB, MC, £TC, V.
Preem is a relative newcomer to Brick Lane and, provided you order sensibly, we found it one of the better curry houses in the area. The owner

---

Sweets

Barfi: a dry sweetmeat.
Falooda: a rose-syrup flavoured milk drink, which is often served with china grass (vermicelli), ice-cream and other sweet ingredients.
Gajjar halwa, halwa gajar, etc: a grated carrot-based sweetmeat, flavoured with cardamom. It varies in style, but the best ones are like warm, moist carrot cake.
Gulab jamun: small brown sweetmeats served in sugar syrup. They taste best hot.

Halwa: a fudge-like sweet.
Jalebis: spirals of sugary batter, deep-fried.
Kheer: essentially, milk rice pudding, North Indian-style.
Kulfi: a form of ice-cream made from milk reduced by boiling, pistachio nuts, sugar and a trace of saffron. There are fruit versions (mango, lychee), too.
Pan: betel leaf folded into a triangle and stuffed with a cocktail of fennel seeds, betel nuts and coconut. Available sweet or salty, and eaten at the

end of a meal as a digestif.
Ras malai: sour milk and flour patties in sweet and thickened milk, served cold.
Rasgullas: sour milk and flour balls in syrup, served cold.
Saunf: the little bowl of aniseed-like spices often brought with your bill.
Shrikhand: an ultra-sweet paste made from concentrated yoghurt and saffron, eaten here as a dessert, although in India it often appears as part of a thali to be scooped up with pooris.

can usually be found sitting on a stool outside the door (in a thick overcoat in winter) enticing in the customers and it's almost worth the price of a meal just to watch a skilled marketeer at work. His sidelines include organising curry classes and he's expert at getting his picture into the papers. The 'house speciality' of masala dosai (£5.50) was surprisingly good and although it owes about as much to Kerala as a hamburger does to Hamburg, it was tasty, fluffy and came not only filled with a pleasing mix of potato, cashew and onions, but with a side dish of (standard) vegetable curry. Chicken jalfrezi consisted of tender meat chunks cooked with crisp, fresh vegetables and was surprisingly uncompromisingly spiced. Prawn musallum passed muster, largely for its 'Kashmir' spicing, which was practically pungent and very un-madras like. Nevertheless, a chicken korma on a neighbouring table looked pretty gooey, and although it found favour with the eater, we would have run a mile.
Babies and children welcome; high chairs. Disabled: toilet. Separate room for parties, seats 20. Tables outdoors (5, pavement). Takeaway service. **Map 4/5S.**

Sweet & Spicy ★
40 Brick Lane, E1 (020 7247 1081). Aldgate East or Whitechapel tube. **Meals served** 8am-10pm Mon-Sat. **Main courses** £2.80-£7.95. **Unlicensed** no alcohol allowed. **No credit cards.**
Around 30 years ago, Brick Lane was full of cafés like this, offering good food at decent prices, primarily for the local community. Now, Sweet and Spicy is the only Pakistani establishment left (go south of Whitechapel Road for more) and somehow the Formica-topped tables and pictures of wrestlers and inter-college weightlifters from the 1950s still manages to repel most of the usual drunken curry freaks. That and the no smoking, no alcohol policy. Food is served from a cramped, glass-fronted serving area by the door. There's no messing about, and you can expect to have your tray full of bowls of freshly-cooked curry ladled from constantly-replenished containers within minutes. Various permutations of meat and chicken dishes are all in the £2.95-£3.60 range, including a highly recommended bhuna gosht, while assorted vegetables and dahls can be had for under £2.50. Starters, being based around samosas (50p), are less successful, the pastry turning hard in the microwave, and those worried by food colouring will avoid the red sauce that accompanies the salad. Let's just keep this our little secret, shall we?
Babies and children welcome. No smoking. Takeaway service. **Map 4/5S.**

Docklands E14

Tabla
West India Dock Gate, Hertsmere Road, E14 (020 7345 0345/ www.tablarestaurant.com). West Ferry or West India Quay DLR. **Lunch served** noon-3pm, **dinner served** 6-10.30pm Mon-Sat. **Main courses** £7.95-£15.95. **Credit** AmEx, JCB, MC, V.
Since we last ventured to this 1807-built former dockmaster's mansion, we've seen its name change from Dockmaster's House to Cassia and now to Tabla. The new owners include Iqbal Wahhab, the founding editor of *Tandoori* magazine. To our untrained eye, the makeover was restricted to a coating of off-cream paint and strategically placed wall and ceiling lamps. On a fairly quiet midweek evening we were shown to a table out of sight of the serving staff, but near the toilets and the cutlery tray. As an added bonus, when the spotlights came on outside at dusk, two of them shone brightly in our eyes. The service was pleasant but hardly attentive. Luckily, the food was the high point of the evening. Pea and coriander soup worked well, with just the right amount of spiciness to offset the savoury flavour of the legumes; and flaked crab cakes, although coming with little slivers of inedible cartilage, were tasty. The menu balances interesting innovations, such as fried paneer stuffed with pineapple chutney, with rather more traditional dishes, such as Rajasthani-style lamb in a red chilli paste. Pickled king prawns with chillies was robustly-spiced and a triumph, although the ratio of prawns to pounds (five to £12.95) was a little disappointing. Also notable was a side dish of potatoes in a green chutney sauce, although it might be a little too minty and flavoursome to accompany most dishes.
Babies and children welcome; high chairs. No-smoking tables. Separate rooms for parties, seating 25 and 50. Tables outdoors (10, garden). Takeaway service.

Mem Saheb on Thames
65 Amsterdam Road, E14 (020 7538 3008/ www.memsaheb.demon.co.uk). Mile End tube then D7 bus/Crossharbour DLR. **Lunch served** noon-2.30pm Mon-Fri. **Dinner served** 6-11.30pm daily. **Main courses** £5.95-£9.95. **Credit** AmEx, DC, JCB, MC, V.
The welcome appears genuine and the service is hard to fault at this upmarket Docklands eaterie, nattily decorated with beige-painted wood panelling taken from a refurbished pub. An airy no-smoking room is the quiet room; elsewhere a lively crowd transcends the truly appalling background music (orchestral versions of cheesy rock classics). The chef here is obviously a gambler. Aside from the usual kormas, vindaloos and what-have-you ('for the takeaway trade', confided the waiter with an upward-shooting eyebrow), look out for the innovative likes of aloo tikki, four flattened and quite acceptable potato cakes served in a rich tamarind sauce, and king prawn piary, a single but perfectly juicy prawn plonked in a cheese sauce that shouldn't have worked but did. Main courses of konju papas (a south Indian style prawn curry) and boal dopiaza were much better, with the prawns possibly suffering from that rare ailment of too many prawns and too little sauce, and the Bangladeshi-style fish was hard to fault. Both the prawns and a pungent side dish of tarka dahl came with delicious caramelised whole red chillies, which may surprise unsuspecting docklanders.
Babies and children admitted. Book weekends. Dress: smart casual. No-smoking tables. Separate room for parties, seats 75. Tables outdoors (8, pavement).

Forest Gate E7

Mobeen ★
222-224 Green Street, E7 (020 8470 2419). Upton Park tube/58 bus. **Meals served** 11am-10pm daily. **Main courses** £2.90-£3.50. **Unlicensed** no alcohol allowed. **No credit cards.**
This simple self-service style cafeteria, with its plain Formica-topped tables and utilitarian furniture never seems to change. It's the meeting place for a good proportion of Green Street's largely Pakistani-originated population, especially at the weekends, so unless you want a long wait for a table and/or a scrum at the counter, avoid at busy times. The owners are strict Muslims and so no alcohol is sold or allowed on the premises. You'll not find a fluffier nan anywhere in London, especially not for 50p, and the kebabs (55p a stick) are rich, meaty and savoury. Most of the curries sit in large tubs waiting to be bought, but as the turnover is rapid, this tends to help enforce the already intense flavours. Mixed vegetables came with the cauliflower and potato intact and firm in a pleasant gravy, and the dahl was thick and savoury with a satisfyingly spicy back-bite. The wide range of meat dishes includes kidney and liver, a particularly meaty bhuna meat and bateira (quail, £3.50 each). Masala fish is a bargain £3.30 a pound and sweets like laddu, barfi and basan are just over £2 for a half kilo.
Babies and children welcome. No smoking. Separate room for parties, seats 58. Takeaway service.
For branches see index.

Whitechapel E1

Café Spice Namaste ★
16 Prescot Street, E1 (020 7488 9242). Tower Hill tube/Tower Gateway DLR. **Lunch served** noon-3pm Mon-Fri. **Dinner served** 6.15-10.30pm Mon-Fri; 6.30-10.30pm Sat. **Main courses** £6.25-£18.95. **Credit** AmEx, DC, JCB, MC, £TC, V.
It's coming up to five years since Cyrus Todiwala's flagship restaurant opened here. A Parsee who had made his name at a Taj Hotel in Goa, Todiwala has never been afraid to use unusual ingredients or to combine the traditional with the distinctly untraditional. Although practically every high-street curry house now features tandoori venison ('heron'), and exotic fish have been scooped out of the ornamental tank and plopped into the tandoori, things were different when he was making his name. There are two large dining rooms, decorated in striking peach, cyan and magenta colours. Regimental rows of tables are crowned with stiff white linen, and service from the uniformed waiters is inevitably friendly but attentive, which is not always easy to retain with a customer base that largely consists of bankers and corporate beanos. The menu constantly evolves and on our last visit included a breast of Barbary duck tikka and the classic Goan dish of vindalho de porco. As ever, food is fiercely pan-Indian – and beyond. We went for a starter of channa chutt putti, a variation on bhel poori that combines cold chick peas with yoghurt, tamarind, chilli and shallots. Delicious. The prawns in Goan xit ani suncta chi kodi were rock hard – a result of over-cooking – not good for £10.25 (usually they're perfectly plump). The Keralan vegetable side dish was well cooked, with crisp vegetables and a delightfully piquant sauce. Heaven.
Babies and children welcome; high chairs. Booking essential. Takeaway service.
Map 4/7S.
For branch see index.

Lahore Kebab House
2 Umberston Street, E1 (020 7488 2551). Aldgate East or Whitechapel tube/Shadwell DLR. **Meals served** noon-midnight daily. **Main courses** £4.50-£6. **Minimum** £10. **Unlicensed. Corkage** no charge. **No credit cards.**
At its peak, the Lahore was an institution. A colleague surrendered his vegetarianism to their robustly spiced kebabs and hasn't been able to look a nut cutlet in the eye since. But though standards may have slipped slightly over the years as the besuited City worker came to be treated more as a valued source of revenue than as an encroachment, they do still serve up a wicked chunk of charred flesh. Meaty and savoury seekh kebabs are 50p each, karahi gosht (£4.50) is lean lamb in a fabulously-reduced sauce. and the masala fish (£4.50) is a little less robust than we've had elsewhere, but still excellent, with chunks of white fish crusted with spicy masala. Although not really their kind of place, vegetarians needn't feel left out, with thick Punjabi-style dahl virtually vibrating with flavour and a mixed vegetable karahi that was as flavoursome and well-spiced as the meat dishes. Although we've had reports of surly waiters, we've found that a little respect goes a long way.
Babies and children welcome; high chairs. Booking advisable. Takeaway service.

New Tayyab ★
83 Fieldgate Street, E1 (020 7247 9543/ www.tayybs.co.uk). Whitechapel tube. **Dinner served** 5pm-midnight daily. **Main courses** £3.80-£9. **Unlicensed. Corkage** no charge. **No credit cards.**
Taking up a significant chunk of Fieldgate Street, the three Tayyab outlets continue to offer exemplary Pakistani cuisine at knockdown prices. During the day, the Tayyab café and sweet outlet at numbers 85 and 89 cater to the large number of Punjabi-origin workers in the area; then, when the café closes at 5pm, the chefs trundle off to these smarter premises. A former pub, this is (ironically, perhaps) where groups of Muslim businessmen and families stop off after visiting the nearby mosque and where staff from the nearby London Hospital come for splendidly juicy shami kebabs (60p a stick) and near-legendary seekh kebabs (70p). The emphasis is on fresh ingredients with meat dishes uppermost on the menu and the list of daily specials – including paya, nehari and authentically bony meat biriani – offers no compromise to western tastes. Karahi bateira (quail) was pungent and gamey, finely spiced with a fresh after-taste, while saag gosht was bursting with more flavours than we could count. The obese vegetable samosa starter had a tad too much pastry around an adequate filling and despite the potato in the mixed vegetable karahi being cool in the centre, we had a good meal for less than £8 a head, including fruity mango lassis (£2). Catering predominantly for Muslims, alcohol is tolerated rather than encouraged and bottles should be kept out of sight.
Babies and children welcome; high chairs. Tables outdoors (2, pavement). Takeaway service.
For branches see index.

Tiffin
165 Cannon Street Road, E1 (020 7702 3832). Whitechapel tube/Shadwell DLR. **Lunch served** noon-3pm daily. **Dinner served** 6pm-midnight Mon-Thur, Sun; 6pm-12.30am Fri, Sat. **Main courses** £4.95-£14.95. **Set lunch** £4.95 (two dishes and rice). **Credit** AmEx, DC, MC, £TC, V.
Although the menu at Tiffin contains some welcome innovations and the cooking is often better than average, we've never encountered any other diners in all the times we've visited. The slight off-handedness of the waiters suggests that they expect a hard time, maybe a by-product of being an up-market restaurant in a street of sweat-shops and halal chicken takeaways. The Tiffin special (£3.95) is a selection of competently-cooked tandoori starters, including murghi tikka, kheema chops and seekh kebab. The vegetarian version is 75p cheaper but limited to pakoras: good but no prizes. Raj chingru projapti, a small plate of battered spicy king prawns, was good, but would have benefited from hotter oil and more spicing. Goan fish curry was surprisingly authentic, although again, the spicing appeared toned down for western tastes. The secret of the brace of 'low cholesterol' dishes appears to be that they're cooked in olive oil and less of it. Lebu murghi (£9.95 with rice) worked well, being suitably lemony and nicely flavoured with coriander, ginger and lemongrass. Saag-shobze bhajia was not as successful, being a bland selection of barely-spiced vegetables in an oily sauce. Bateira is a well-cooked dish of quail in a thick spicy sauce that made up for other short-comings. But beware the raj chingri mughlai, an over-sweet bog standard king prawn masala without the tandoori flavours.
Babies and children welcome; high chairs. Book dinner Fri, Sat. No-smoking tables. Takeaway service (free local delivery).

North West

Neasden NW9

New Kabana
43 Blackbird Hill, NW9 (020 8200 7094). Wembley Park tube. **Meals served** 2pm-midnight Tue-Thur, Sun; 2pm-1am Fri, Sat. **Main courses** £4.95-£9.95. **Set meal** £12. **Credit** MC, V.
If you love **Karahi King** (*see p89* **Wembley**), you'll like New Kabana. Though it has little of the buzz of its more illustrious neighbour, this unassuming place – set on a parade by a busy road – incorporates a similar style of African-Asian karahi cooking. See the woks being wielded in the open-view kitchen at the end. Spotlights and green carpets add a measure of decorum to the place. We've never had a duff meal here, and enjoy the unusual dishes such as karahi sweetcorn with coconut (the nutty flavours combining impressively) as well as the expertly rendered staples such as nans and rotis. Starters of paneer bhajia (crisp batter encasing the cheese) and mogo chips can also be recommended. Urad dahl is a rich concoction of pulses and will make a feast for two alongside a large helping of karahi methi chicken (nicely spiced, though with few fenugreek leaves). If you're lucky, a large party of local African Asians will coincide with your visit, lifting the otherwise low-key proceedings considerably.
Babies and children welcome; high chairs. Takeaway service.

Outer London

Addington, Surrey

Planet Spice
88 Selsdon Park Road, Addington, Surrey (020 8651 3300/www.planet-spice.com). East Croydon, South Croydon rail. **Lunch served** 12.30-2.30pm daily. **Dinner served** 6.30-11.15pm daily. **Main courses** £5.95-£12.45. **Set meal** £9.95 three courses (Sun brunch). **Credit** AmEx, DC, JCB, MC, £TC, V.
The credentials of this Surrey golf-belt restaurant are impeccable. Opened by Emdad Rahman from Brockley's Babur Brasserie and Hardev Bhatty, former head chef at Chutney Mary, with a former cook for the Indian President and a south Indian specialist running the kitchen. The walls are painted in striking primrose, green and brown, with clean lines, a bare wood floor, and ultra-modern furniture. The menu contains some interesting innovations. Samosas are filled with goat cheese and mozzarella and traditional Keralan fish moilee becomes untraditional seafood moilee (£10.95) with crab, king prawns, mussels and squid. After popadoms with three superior own-made chutneys – including a lime pickle you could have sex with – we kicked off with ragda pattice (well-spiced potato cakes topped with dahl) which were pretty good, and a prawn chilli-fry, which turned out to be a prawn-rich jalfrezi-like stir fry, popping with slices of fresh green chilli. Caldine is a fancy name for chunks of monkfish cooked in a creamy, minty sauce, which was fine, if a tad sickly towards the end. The vegetarian thali (£11.95) allows for a choice of three vegetable dishes, served with a stand out creamy dahl makhani, tomartar (sic) rice, raita and nan. We plumped for baigan bartha (aubergine and baby corn), dum tori (courgettes cooked with mango), and tarka saag dahl (spinach and lentils) of which the aubergine and courgettes shone particularly brightly. Service was attentive and friendly, with five waiters attending to our various needs.
Babies and children welcome; high chairs. Booking advisable Fri, Sat. Entertainment: pianist Tue, Wed. No-smoking tables. Takeaway service. Vegetarian menu.

Ilford, Essex

Curry Special

2 Greengate Parade, Horns Road, Newbury Park, Ilford, Essex (020 8518 3005/ www.curryspecial.com). Gants Hill or Newbury Park tube. **Lunch served** 12.30-2.30pm Tue-Fri. **Dinner served** 6-11.30pm Tue-Thur, Sun; 6pm-midnight Fri, Sat. **Main courses** £3.75-£9. **Credit** AmEx, DC, MC, V.
Looking not unlike a cross between a 1960s dining room and a Punjabi disco, Curry Special screens the best Indian dance videos while purple-uniformed waiters get on with offering a formal but friendly service to a predominantly Asian family clientele. It is owned by cousins of the owners of **Madhu's Brilliant** in Southall (*see p89*), and the food here has the same Punjabi-by-way-of-East Africa robustness. Starters include chicken cooked in a variety of ways: butter fried, jeera, chilli and garlic – as well as the likes of samosas, various pakora and masala fried fish (£4). The fish was a generous portion of two large pieces of flaky fresh cod crusted in a powerful spice mixture. Aloo tikka was a fresh-tasting potato patty served in yoghurt with tamarind sauce and a scattering of chick peas. It was pretty wonderful in a bhel puri kind of way and, oddly enough, served on a metal tray over a flame. The birianis (from £6 for mushroom/vegetable to £9 for king prawn) come with a dollop of pungent masala in the centre and a small bowl of highly reduced curry sauce. Pungency is something they do well here and gravies are reduced to offer thick, tasty eating experiences. Our first solo taste made us think that karahi king prawn was a little salty, but when eaten with rice it was perfect. Jeera aloo was alive with cumin and an unusual karahi Mexican mixed vegetables was peppers, corn and suchlike given a similar saucing. A good reason for living in Ilford.
Babies and children admitted. Booking advisable dinner Fri, Sat. Separate room for parties, seats 36. Takeaway service.

Rayners Lane, Middlesex

Balti Hut ★

435 Alexandra Avenue, Rayners Lane, Middx (020 8868 0007). Rayners Lane tube/H10, H12 bus. **Dinner served** 5-11.30pm Tue-Thur, Sun; 5pm-midnight Fri, Sat. **Main courses** £4.70-£8.50. **Unlicensed. Corkage** no charge. **Credit** MC, V.
Would that all self-proclaimed 'balti houses' produced such zesty cooking as the Hut. Its simple, caff-like premises – tiled floor, plate-glass windows, grey plastic-topped tables – have been jazzed up with bright yellow walls, crimson highlights, paintings and uplights. A couple of chefs get down to work in the open-view kitchen. Nans are slapped into the tandoor, seekh kebabs are seared over the charcoal, and karahis (aka baltis) are shaken over fierce gas burners. Watch as first a measure of ghee is heated in the utensil, followed by a ladle of spice mixture and then the pre-cooked meat, fish or vegetables. The process is speedy, aromatic and full of sizzle. Tangy relishes (tamarind and chilli, and yoghurt and mint) are provided gratis, just as in Birmingham's balti houses. We like the karahi methi chicken (even if, as last time, there was a paucity of fenugreek leaves in the dish), and though the tarka dahl is more liquid than the norm, the garlicky flavours are mouthwatering. Specials – 'Hut hits' – might include balti fish masala or balti chicken paneer. Locals bring cans of lager and tuck in with relish. Staff are happiest (and the atmosphere most congenial) when things are busy.
Babies and children welcome; high chairs. Book weekends. No-smoking tables. Separate room for parties, seats 35. Takeaway service.

Southall, Middlesex

Southall is rightly famed for having some of the best Punjabi restaurants in Britain. There are two major strands to the cuisine of the subcontinent's north-western region (of which the Punjab, straddling India and Pakistan, is part): tandoori food (from the clay oven) and karahi (or balti) dishes (flash-fried in a wok-like saucepan). Any fans of this cooking should pay the area a visit, calling in at **Gifto's**, **Balti & Tandoori World** or the **Tandoori Kebab Centre** to sample the best. Bread, rather than rice, is the staple food of this cuisine, and ghee (clarified butter) is an integral part of many dishes.

However, at least two other styles of south Asian cookery can be found in Southall: Sri Lankan food (*see page 91*) and Kenyan-Asian restaurants. **Brilliant** and **Madhu's Brilliant** are the best examples of the latter, run by different branches of the Kenyan Asian Anand family. Sweetcorn, tilapia fish and mogo (fried cassava root) are among the distinctive ingredients used by these restaurants, though cooking is otherwise similar to that of Punjabi cuisine.

To get immersed in Southall life, walk down The Broadway or South Road, taking in the sari shops, the cash and carries (great for stocking up on spices and pulses) and the exotic fruit and vegetable stores. For an unusual aperitif, drop into the Glassy Junction pub (at the corner of South Road and Park Avenue), run by and for the local Asian community. Here the beer is Cobra and bar snacks include sizzling lamb tikka.

Balti & Tandoori World ★

185-187 The Broadway, Southall, Middx (020 8867 9991/9993). Southall rail/ 207 bus. **Meals served** 11.30am-11.30pm daily. **Main courses** £3-£8. **Set meal** £3.99 vegetarian, £4.99 non-vegetarian. **Unlicensed. Corkage** no charge. **Credit** AmEx, DC, MC, £TC, V.
Variety adds spice to this lively two-year-old, where flavours from across the subcontinent and Asian Africa are up for savouring. Sit at easy-wipe tables in the spacious dining area (with its mock-marble tiled floor and baskets of artificial flowers) and scrutinise the every move and habit of the kitchen staff, as they flip rotis into the tandoor, sear meat over the charcoal, and manipulate baltis over the gas. Or you could listen to the loud Pakistani music. Or watch satellite TV. You might not have time, though, if the huge menu is given the attention it deserves. There's a multitude of choices for vegetarians, ranging from undhia (a tangy meal-in-one Gujarati dish of mixed vegetables and pulses), to masala dosais, bhel pooris and sizzling chilli mogo. The non-veg section is equally expansive, including the well-timed tandooried kaleji and gurda (juicy liver and kidney), a batch of enticing seafood (crab curry, for instance), handi methi chicken (tender chunks of breast with verdant fenugreek) and, the highlight of this year's meal, nihari (described, picturesquely, as 'piece of leg with gravy' – but a tender-as-mercy joint of long-simmered lamb). Even the breads veer from the prosaic; gobi paratha, stuffed with herbs and morsels of cauliflower, beat a heavy-going maki-ki-roti (made with cornmeal). Come prepared for an adventure.
Babies and children admitted. Separate room for parties, seats 100. Takeaway service. Vegetarian menu.

Brilliant

72-76 Western Road, Southall, Middx (020 8574 1928). Southall rail/105, 195, 232 bus. **Lunch served** noon-2.30pm Tue-Fri. **Dinner served** 6-11.30pm Tue-Sun. **Closed** August. **Main courses** £8-£11. **Credit** AmEx, DC, JCB, MC.
We've had very good meals at this renowned African-Asian stalwart – and mediocre offerings, too. Food this year occupied the middle ground. We kicked off with a Kenyan-Asian speciality: fish pakora. Four big meaty chunks of the tilapia fish arrived, freshly fried in a pleasurably spicy batter. Undaunted by the huge portion, we then launched into lamb biriani, which seemed pricey at £13 until our eyes fell upon its vast dimensions. The dish seemed to consist of roghan gosht and pilau rice mixed together at a late stage in the cooking process. True, both the rice and the long-simmered stew were fine versions, but the rice had none of the flavour of the meat. Buttery dahl makhani also came in a huge helping, which, together with the six zesty own-made chutneys and relishes (try the dahl with the lemon pickle) put paid to any thought of pudding. Brilliant's setting is less than lustrous, down a hard-to-find backstreet about a mile south of the Broadway. Inside, though, it is large and eye-catching, with one section flaunting chandeliers, the other a maroon colour scheme and artificial foliage aplenty. Asian families and a few non-Asians eat here (Brilliant is best suited to group dining), listening to Bollywood film music and generally having a good time.
Babies and children welcome; high chairs. Car park. Entertainment: karaoke (Hindi and English). No-smoking tables. Separate room for parties, seats 120. Takeaway service.

Planet Spice. *See page 85.*

The Genuine Lahore Karahi

37 Featherstone Road, Southall, Middx (020 8893 5270). Southall rail/E5 bus. **Meals served** noon-midnight daily. **Main courses** £4-£7. **Unlicensed. No credit cards.**

As echt as its name suggests, this place is one for Southall devotees. On a parade of shops down an old backstreet, it's a small caff of rudimentary design. A counter dominates the neon-lit front room, which has plastic-top tables, lino floor, scruffy walls and a halo of plastic flowers by the ceiling. Men smoking cigarettes inhabited a neighbouring table. The back room is almost as basic, popular with local families, and the toilets are up a creaky staircase. The menu (adorned by a photo of the dapper owner) seems ambitious for such a lowly operation, and true to form, our first order of tandooried liver followed by lamb nihari drew a blank. Never mind: chapli kebabs were three big discs of still-sizzling meat and coriander served with copious onions; butter chicken had slices of breast in an almond-topped sauce of Bill Gatesian richness; dahl was equally oleaginous, and crunchy with spices. Sure, the chef was too free with the ghee, but this food comes from the karahi or tandoor to the table in a trice, making the breads irresistible and tandooried meats full of zing. Worth a trip if food rather than furnishings matter to you.

Babies and children welcome; high chairs.

Gifto's Lahore Karahi ★

162-164 The Broadway, Southall, Middx (020 8813 8669/www.gifto.com). Southall rail/207 bus. **Meals served** noon-11.30pm Mon-Thur; noon-midnight Fri-Sun. **Main courses** £3.50-£9.90. **Unlicensed. Corkage** no charge. **Credit** AmEx, DC, JCB, LV, MC, V.

Our choice for witnessing the Southall buzz in full flow would be Gifto's. It's a lively, exuberant place where the team of chefs – karahis or tandoori skewers in hand – produce a command performance from their open-view kitchen, often to a bhangra soundtrack. Diners don't need to rough it, either; there's plenty of space in the large, bright room, and decorations of artificial foliage, flamboyant chandeliers and colourful murals add a certain flair. Many local Asian families eat here. Food is wide-ranging (the firm also owns a large cash and carry store across the road), taking in bhel poori snacks, tawa (hot stone) specials such as tak-a-tak chopped liver and kidney, and Kenyan-Asian ingredients (tilapia fish tandooried whole, for instance). Long-simmered dishes such as paya (lamb's trotters) and nihari (leg of lamb) are also on the list, but it is the tandoori and karahi dishes that are supreme. We know of no better place for breads (nans and rotis are both only 80p); the seekh kebabs arrive perfectly singed; and the methi chicken and tarka dahl are utterly mouthwatering. Punjabi cuisine at its best.

Babies and children welcome; high chairs. Disabled: toilet. No-smoking tables. Separate rooms for parties, seating 100 and 350. Takeaway service.

Madhu's Brilliant

39 South Road, Southall, Middx (020 8574 1897/6380). Southall rail/105, 207 bus. **Lunch served** 12.30-3pm Mon, Wed-Fri. **Dinner served** 6-11.30pm Mon, Wed, Thur, Sat, Sun; 6pm-midnight Fri. **Set lunch** £12.50 three courses. **Set dinner** £15 three courses. **Credit** AmEx, DC, JCB, MC, £TC, V.

Always the most westernised Southall restaurant, Madhu's has taken a leap upmarket in the past year. An expensive refit on both ground and first floors has given it walls that are variously golden, dark red, and cream and brown; thick cream linen on the tables; and waiters togged up like ship's stewards. However, the laminated menu seems not to have changed a jot – mercifully. Group dining is the best way to experience the place, and on our visit a party of 14 were tucking into boozi bafu (lamb on the bone) kept in vast copper vessels over burners on the table. For starters, they might have enjoyed an entire butter chicken or two. Dining duos needn't feel neglected, though. We relished a starter of masala fish – chunks of freshly fried, meaty tilapia in startlingly spicy batter – despite the small portion. In contrast, methi chicken contained a plentiful supply of breast chunks with flecks of fenugreek in an intensely savoury sauce. Mutter paneer had cheese of almost squeaky consistency, and bhindi (okra) was slightly overwhelmed by the onions with which it was paired. These gripes were put aside, however, when we tasted the perfectly stewed meat in the karahi gosht, and the featherweight bhatura bread. Apart from forgetting our desserts (ras malai and gulab jamun), waiters were solicitous throughout, making Madhu's a prime spot for business diners wanting to experience Southall, not on the cheap, but on expenses.

Babies and children welcome; high chairs. Book dinner Fri-Sun. Separate room for parties, seats 50. Takeaway service.

New Asian Tandoori Centre ★

114-116 The Green, Southall, Middx (020 8574 2597). Southall rail. **Meals served** 9am-11pm Mon-Thur; 10am-11pm Fri-Sun. **Main courses** £2-£6. **No credit cards.**

Waiter service is now the norm at this well-loved stalwart of the Southall Green Punjabi enclave. Gone is the appetising aperitif of queueing at the brightly lit counter with your tray (only takeaway customers now have that pleasure). Instead, you are seated next door on comfy wooden chairs, beneath vibrant pictures of subcontinental folklore, near speakers quivering to the sound of Sunrise Radio. Mugs of water are provided, or there's beer or non-specific 'wine (£6)'. Food has improved markedly, the microwave being used less frequently, and the menu expanded to include more vegetarian dishes (karela, for instance). Gol guppa is a DIY Bombay beach snack (pack the water-tight puris with cold chickpeas and potato cubes, then fill them with a spicy tamarind liquid) – good fun, despite the tooth-breaking stone we overlooked nestling amid the chickpeas. Next, sag paneer was mousse-like and pleasing, while prawn curry (the priciest dish at £7) accentuated the sweetness of the shellfish – both dishes came in huge portions and with an abundance of ghee. A small roti arrived straight from the tandoor. Pudding of gajrela (gajjar halwa, served hot) was sweet and also dripping in ghee. In all, there are few better ways of running up a dentist's bill.

Babies and children welcome; high chairs. Takeaway service.

Tandoori Kebab Centre

161-163 The Broadway, Southall, Middx (020 8571 5738). Southall rail/83, 105, 207 bus. **Meals served** 10am-midnight daily. **Set buffet** £6, £6.99 with starter. **Main courses** £3-£7. **Unlicensed. Credit** AmEx, DC, JCB, LV, MC, TC, V.

In 1965, when the TKC was born, tandoori cooking was a rarity in Britain. Now the name is (ab)used by a myriad high-street curry houses. This large, brash landmark of Pakistani Southall provides the genuine article – as long as you come at busy times (beware of microwaving when business is slack). Just sample, as we did, the mixed grill roll special: three pieces of succulent lamb tikka, another three of chicken tikka, a seikh kebab, a profusion of fried onion, tomato and green pepper, plus a perfectly baked nan in which to wrap the lot. It was sublime, but was way too much food for a starter. To follow, tarka dahl arrived super-heated in a balti dish, so sizzling it stuck to the base, but the taste of toasted cumin mixed with the lentils was irresistible. Saag chicken, with luxuriant spinach and thin strips of succulent meat, was equally appetising. Next time, we'll come in a group and phone ahead, making sure there'll be a ready supply of house specialities such as 'full chargha' (roasted, spiced free-range chicken: 'a recipe from the inner suburbs of Punjab'). An open-view kitchen, caff-style seating, or, in the adjoining space, a carpeted dining room provide the backdrop. Service was divided between a solicitous waiter and a frosty waitress.

Babies and children welcome; high chairs; playroom area; toys. Disabled: toilet. No-smoking tables. Separate room for parties, seats 150. Tables outdoors (4, pavement). Takeaway service (free local delivery).

For branches see index.

Wembley, Middlesex

See also pages 91 and 93.

Karahi King ★

213 East Lane, North Wembley, Middx (020 8904 2760/4994). North Wembley tube/245 bus. **Meals served** noon-midnight daily. **Main courses** £3.50-£12. **Unlicensed. Corkage** no charge. **No credit cards.**

Karahi King has seen the balti craze come and go, yet to our minds remains one of London's best exponents of flash-in-a-pan cuisine. Busy East Lane is soon forgotten as you enter the modest premises. Slatted blinds cover the plate-glass windows while the noise of traffic is drowned out by the sizzle, clatter, scrape and chatter from the open-view kitchen and small dining area. Sunrise Radio gives added accompaniment. Last year's refurbishment still looks good, the parquet floor, wooden tables and extended back room holding up well despite the crowds. Staff weave in and out of the kitchen and between the tables with practised skill. This time they brought us mogo bhajia, moreish and well-spiced sweet potato chunks in batter; seared, succulent lamb tikka; a big portion of karahi methi chicken, the fenugreek leaves adding greenery and pungency; and expertly executed karahi mutter paneer. Nans and rotis came straight from the tandoor and were as good as can be. Locals – young African-Asians and others – continue to flock here, many bringing their own alcohol.

Babies and children welcome. Booking advisable. Takeaway service.

Vegetarian & South Indian

As around half the population of India is vegetarian, you'd expect Indian restaurants in this country to be able to provide good quality veggie food. But most of them are run by meat-eating Muslim Bangladeshis and Pakistanis, and so you'd be wrong. Efforts are being made, but rather than stick to fresh vegetables cooked to order and in own-made sauces, most high street restaurants are offering 'formula' curry dishes made with pre-cooked vegetables, and emulating snack dishes such as dosais and bhel poori. And a poorly prepared dosai that's made from the wrong ingredients with a batter that's not been fermented is invariably dreadful. The best Indian vegetarian food is still to be found in specialist restaurants run by vegetarians or where the meat-free cooking is done by a separate chef, as at **Malabar Junction**.

The traditions of Keralan, Gujarati and of East African Indian cuisine produce vegetarian food that is divine. Concentrated in areas like Wembley, Kilburn, Tooting and at various outposts of north and east London, such as **Vijay's Chawalla** in Green Street, **Rasa** in Stoke Newington and the West End and **Rani**, London has a number of superb Indian vegetarian restaurants. Drummond Street, long the home of the bhel poori house, is in danger of going the way of Brick Lane. We have seen a rise in the number of meaty tandoori restaurants and in the vegetarian diners standards vary enormously from day to day, even from hour to hour. We've visited every restaurant at least twice during a six month period and encountered food and service that's been good and poor: on one occasion, it was good at lunchtime and below par in the evening.

Central

Bloomsbury WC1

Malabar Junction

107 Great Russell Street, WC1 (020 7580 5230). Tottenham Court Road tube.

Bar **Open** 11am-11pm Mon-Sat; noon-10.30pm Sun.

Restaurant **Lunch served** noon-3pm, **dinner served** 6-11.30pm daily. **Main courses** £3.50-£9. **Minimum** £10 after 7pm.

Both **Credit** AmEx, MC, £TC, V.

For sumptuous central location and vibrancy of cooking, this upmarket Keralan restaurant takes some beating. The room is large and decorated in cool whites and greens with a large skylight that provides a bright central light during the day and a gentle urban glow at night. Service is helpful and attentive and the food is invariably good. Expect the usual Keralan fare of dosais – including a light and crispy rava dosai – idli and vadais, as well as fish and meat dishes (including an authentic kozhi varutha curry: curried chicken breast, Keralan style) as well as the odd sop to western tastes such as lamb korma (complete with cashew nuts, sultanas and a creamy sauce). Malabar fish fry (£7.50) is a marinated flat fish, deep fried and served on an ample green/onion salad, and pretty much as you'd get in Kovalam, albeit with something of a price difference. Cochin prawn curry was similarly impressive, with a large number of juicy tiger prawns, nestling in a savoury sauce in which lurked large, sweet red chillies. Sambar is among the best we've ever had, avial was suitably tangy and the tomato curry a savoury delight of fried tomatoes in a creamy but sharp yoghurt sauce. Not cheap, but good.

Babies and children admitted. No-smoking tables. Takeaway service. Vegan dishes. **Map 3 or 145K.**

For branch (Ragam) see index.

South Indian menu

Avial: a colourful mixed vegetable curry from Kerala cooked with coconut and yoghurt (or curds) sauce, often containing drumsticks (like long, tough okra). Literally, 'mixture' in Malayalam (the language of Kerala).

Bhel poori: small snacks sold from street stalls in Bombay, now common in British Indian restaurants as starters. They generally contain tiny, crisp, deep-fried pooris (like crisps) with puffed rice, sev (deep-fried gram-flour vermicelli), finely chopped onion and potato, mixed with chutneys (chilli, mint and tamarind).

Channa: chickpeas.

Chaat or chat: snack.

Dahl: lentil curry, often of gravy-like consistency and commonly poured over rice.

Dosai or dosa: very thin, lightly fried pancake, often sculpted into interesting shapes. Dosais are usually made of rice flour and lentil flour, but variants include **rawa dosai**, made with 'cream of wheat' semolina. Dosais usually come with a spicy potato and vegetable filling, a hot lentil sauce (sambar) and bright green coconut chutney. Then they are called **masala dosais** ('masala' means spices). Dosais are very popular in Madras and Bombay. Eaten here as a main course.

Idli: steamed sponges of rice and lentil flour. Eaten with sambar (qv), and/or coconut and yoghurt chutney.

Kachori: spiced mung dahl with coriander and peas wrapped in a crispy pastry.

Kalan: a thin curry from the southern states made from butter milk, coconut and mangoes; variants include **moru kachiatu**.

Khadi: a buttermilk gravy with coconut and cloves.

Patra: a 'Swiss roll'-style savoury dish made of a leaf vegetable (arvi) and gram-flour.

Payasam: a pudding made of reduced milk with saffron and cardamoms, available in various flavours, such as pistachio or orange.

Rasam: a consommé made with lentils that tastes both peppery-hot and tamarind-sour.

Sambar or sambhar: similar to dahl (qv) but usually hotter, with chillies, tamarind and diced vegetables.

Thali: literally, 'plate'. A large plate with rice, bread, dahl and a few types of vegetable curries and yoghurt, all served in small bowls. A cheap way to eat both here (where meat curries are sometimes included) and in India – there it's 'all you can eat' for no extra charge, while in London restaurants the portions are so generous you'd be mad to order anything else.

Uthappam: a spicy, crisp pancake/pizza made with lentil and rice flour topped with tomato and chillies.

Vadai, wada, and so on: a fritter of ground lentils – which is often served at room temperature as dahi vadai, in yoghurt with a tamarind and date sauce.

Euston NW1

Chutneys ★

124 Drummond Street, NW1 (020 7388 0604). Euston Square or Warren Street tube/ Euston tube/rail. **Lunch served** noon-2.45pm, **dinner served** 6-11.30pm Mon-Sat. **Meals served** noon-10.30pm Sun. **Main courses** £3.95-£9.95. **Set buffet meal** (lunch Mon-Sat, all day Sun) £4.95. **Set meal** £7.95 three courses. **Service** 10% (dinner). **Credit** MC, V.

All Drummond Street menus tend to be very similar, but if you've wondered why the menu at nearby Ravi Shankar is identical but cheaper, it's because they're part of the same chain. The under-a-fiver lunchtime buffet is a good introduction to the menu and although the specials vary from day to day, favourites like dahl and mixed vegetables (often with an oil slick) are perennial. Some food takes to simmering for hours on end, some – including most vegetables – doesn't. So expect slightly under-cooked potato at noon and fragments at 2.45pm. From the à la carte menu, we've always enjoyed special rava dosai (£4.30) which can be heavenly, and saag bhajia (£2.80), which, in the right hands, is freshly spiced spinach, cooked with plenty of butter. Finish off with a sweet and creamy shrikhand (£1.50) and wonder where they could possibly squeeze in another table.

Babies and children admitted. Booking advisable. No smoking (lunch); no-smoking tables (dinner). Separate rooms for parties, seating 40 and 60. Takeaway service (6-11.30pm Mon-Sat). **Map 2/3J.**

For branches (Ravi Shankar) see index.

Diwana Bhel Poori House ★

121 Drummond Street, NW1 (020 7387 5556). Euston Square or Warren Street tube/Euston tube/rail. **Meals served** noon-11.30pm daily. **Main courses** £3-£6.20. **Set buffet lunch** noon-2.30pm £4.50 (under-5s half-price). **Set meal** £6. **Unlicensed. Corkage** no charge. **Credit** AmEx, DC, MC, V.

If bhel poori is your thing, then look no further for the best in Drummond Street. Variations include sev poori, aloo poori and dahi bhalle chat, all at the same price. The tamarind and chilli flavours are pungent, the yoghurt suitably soothing and the various crunchy bits are fresh and, er, crunchy. Leaving aside their cheap eat-all-you-can buffet (£4.50), which is pretty much the same as the street's others, we particularly go for kofta malai and paratha, with the savoury vegetable balls in a thick tomato sauce, and the paneer dosai, in which cheese joins the equation and adds a piquancy to the classic dish. Annapurna thali (£6.20), the priciest dish on the menu, is more than most people can eat, and includes dahl, rice, two vegetables, a savoury starter, with chapatis or pooris, pickles and a portion of rich, particularly cheesy shrikhand. Try and avoid the uncomfortable wooden bench seating if possible, although the waiting staff have firm and definite ideas about where they'd like you to sit.

Babies and children admitted. Bookings not accepted Fri-Sun. No-smoking tables. Separate room for parties, seats 40. Takeaway service. Vegan dishes. **Map 2/3J.**

Fitzrovia W1

Rasa Samudra ★

5 Charlotte Street, W1 (020 7637 0222/ www.rasarestaurants.com). Goodge Street tube. **Lunch served** noon-2.45pm Mon-Sat. **Dinner served** 6-10.45pm daily. **Main courses** £8.95-£12.50. **Set meals** £22.50 vegetarian, £30 seafood, four courses. **Service** 12½%. **Credit** AmEx, MC, TC, V.

From humble beginnings in Stoke Newington Church Street to the £30-a-head Kerala seafood feast, Siva Das Sreedharan's Rasa empire has come a long way in a little time. We allowed ourselves to be talked into enjoying a vegetarian feast (£22.50), as well as the seafood extravaganza. The first course isn't really classed as a course at all, being pre-meal snacks: spicy popadoms, and rock hard achappam and pappadavadai (they must have good teeth in Kerala) served with a tray of divine pickles and chutneys. Starters highlights included Samudra rasam, a chowder-like bowl of seafood and vegetables that was thick and tasty, but very un-rasam like; and masala vadai, which was well up to Rasa standard. The main courses arrived with a flourish, with a meaty fish molly (sic), and a bowl of chemeen theeyal (king prawns cooked with shallots and coconut) standing out. As ever, avial was good going on terrific, but at £6.25 a portion it had better be. The sweet – pal payasam: spicy rice pudding with cashews and raisins – was OK, but came as something of an anti-climax. Maybe we should have asked for a banana dosai instead. The decor is a cross between an Indian palace and a swanky solicitor's waiting room and the service is helpful, attentive, but sometime stretched. A separate takeaway outlet has opened at the back of the restaurant.

Babies and children admitted. Booking advisable. No-smoking tables. Separate room for parties, seats 40. Vegetarian menu. **Map 3/5K.**

For branch (Rasa W1) see index.

Leicester Square SW1

Woodlands

37 Panton Street, SW1 (020 7839 7258). Leicester Square or Piccadilly Circus tube. **Lunch served** noon-2.45pm, **dinner served** 5.30-10.45pm daily. **Minimum** £5. **Set lunch buffet** (Mon-Fri) £5.99. **Thali** (dinner) £6.95. **Service** 12½%. **Credit** AmEx, DC, MC, £TC, V.

There's been a makeover at this central London branch of this international restaurant chain (London, Singapore and India), giving it something of the air of a light, modern art gallery. As ever, when we last called in, the place was full of middle class Indian exiles and mystified tourists. The menu is based around south Indian specialities, with explanations that are aimed at the complete novice. The dosais are hard to beat. After a starter of tasty potato bonda, we tackled an onion rava masala dosai, which was rich in caramelised onions and pungent chopped green chillies, with a potato filling that balanced the flavours nicely. Thalis (from £10.95 to £11.95) are ever popular, the best of which is the Delhi Royal, which features a wicked vegetable korma enriched by roasted cashews. Woodlands can hardly be beaten for good, solid Indian vegetarian food that is consistently good if not always outstanding. Don't go without trying a dessert of jaggery dosai, filled with gooey cane sugar and flavoured with cardamom. Mmmm.

Babies and children admitted. Book weekends. Takeaway service. Vegan dishes. **Map 13/7K.**

For branches see index.

South

Tooting SW17

For north Indian restaurants in Tooting, *see page 83.*

Kastoori ★

188 Upper Tooting Road, SW17 (020 8767 7027). Tooting Bec or Tooting Broadway tube. **Lunch served** 12.30-2.30pm Wed-Sun. **Dinner served** 6-10.30pm daily. **Minimum** £5. **Thalis** £7.95-£15.50. **Credit** MC, V.

The Thanki family's Indian-vegetarian-by-way-of-East-Africa restaurant has long been a favourite, despite the fussy pink decor. The welcome is invariably friendly, the service helpful and the food innovative and a cut above the competition. Among the must-haves are the spicy special tomato curry, spring onion curry (sounds weird, but try it) and green leaf curry, a delicious blend of spinach, coriander and suchlike in a yoghurt and onion sauce spiced up with red chillies. Best among the limited range of starters are corn bhel, a novel variation on a familiar theme. The Kastoori special thali which offers lassi, corn bhel, dahl, a choice of three curries, a sweet and enough chapatis or pooris to stock a Bombay bakery. It's not cheap at £15.50, but you won't have to eat for a day or two. The Sunday special of rotlo (millet loaf), aubergine curry, moong rice and khadi (£7.75) is raved over, but it's an acquired taste we've never acquired.

Babies and children welcome. Booking essential. Takeaway service. Vegan dishes.

Milan ★

158 Upper Tooting Road, SW17 (020 8767 4347). Tooting Bec or Tooting Broadway tube. **Meals served** 11am-9.30pm Mon, Wed, Thur; 11am-6pm Tue; 10am-10pm Fri-Sun. **Main courses** £3-£7.95. **Minimum** £2. **Credit** AmEx, LV, MC, V.

Milan is a small air-conditioned, no-smoking vegetarian café with a peaceful atmosphere that attracts a diverse mix of fanatical devotees. A good place to pop in for tea and sweets (the display at the glass-fronted serving area at the rear of the shop is one of London's most colourful sights) or for a full meal of Gujarati-style cooking. Special thali (at £5.25) comes with super-light basmati rice, a bowl of thin dahl practically glowing with flavour, a fresh-tasting vegetable curry, chickpeas in a tamarind and onion sauce, a couple of crisp fried potato cakes, chutney, chapatis and a sweet. Bhel, sev and dahi pooris are fresh, crisp and clean-tasting, while vegetables kofta (a lentil-based curry featuring a cluster of light and intensely flavoured ground vegetable balls, £2.50) is a must. The Milan version of shrikhand (£1.75) is a smooth, creamy delight that sends us off happy every time.

Babies and children admitted. Book weekends. No smoking. Takeaway service. Vegetarian menu.

Radha Krishna Bhavan ★

86 Tooting High Street, SW17 (020 8682 0969). Tooting Broadway tube. **Lunch served** noon-3pm daily. **Dinner served** 6-11pm Mon-Thur, Sun; 6pm-midnight Fri, Sat. **Set thali lunch** (Sun) £4.95 vegetarian, £6.95 meat. **Main courses** £3.55-£6.95. **Minimum** £5. **Service** 10%. **Credit** AmEx, DC, MC, V.

A finalist in the 2000 Time Out Eating and Drinking Awards, Radha Krishna Bhavan is a splinter operation from the nearby **Shree Krishna** (*see below*), with the chef and another key member setting up here. The decor is based around tourist posters of Kerala and effigies of Hindu Gods, and the menu is roughly divided between south Indian specialities and bill-paying meat dishes like lamb vindaloo and chicken korma. Leaving these aside, we particularly enjoyed ghee roast masala dosai – rich and savoury and served with a suitably fiery sambar and green chilli-coconut chutney to die for. Rasam is deliciously peppery and savoury, tomato curry was rich and creamy and cabbage thoran could win prizes. The avial is perfectly balanced between the creamy curds/yoghurt and the tangy tamarind and spices. Although the food is top class, the service is pretty casual and totally authentically Keralan. Don't expect much of a rush about anything.

Babies and children admitted.

Shree Krishna ★

192-194 Tooting High Street, SW17 (020 8672 4250). Tooting Broadway tube/57, 219 bus. **Lunch served** noon-3pm daily. **Dinner served** 6-11pm Mon-Thur, Sun; 6pm-midnight Fri, Sat. **Main courses** £1.95-£6.45. **Minimum** £5. **Credit** AmEx, DC, LV, MC, £TC, V.

It seems the departure of the chef and another key member of staff to Radha Krishna Bhavan (*see above*) hasn't had much effect. We arrived on a hot Sunday lunchtime to find the place comfortably full, the welcome as warm as ever and the food as good as we've had here. As always, we disregarded the vindaloos, kormas and madras dishes in favour of the south Indian specialities. Masala dosai was light and fluffy with a nice tang to it, and a filling that was rich in mustard seeds and curry leaves. Avial was piquant and full of succulent drumstick pieces, while sambar was chilli hot and flavoursome. We could find nothing wrong with the beetroot or cabbage thoran and the mango lassis had that vague hint of cheesiness that points to them being the real thing. A Sunday special vegetarian thali was impressive, especially for £4.95, coming with avial, sambar, carrot, a tasty fried potato mix, rice, a paratha and a sweet. One of the popadoms was ever so slightly soggy, but the pickles and chutneys that came with them (especially the mango) were so superb, we barely noticed.

Babies and children admitted. Book dinner Thur-Sat. Separate room for parties, seats 70. Takeaway service. Vegan dishes.

Vijaya Krishna ★

114 Mitcham Road, SW17 (020 8767 7688). Tooting Broadway tube/44, 77, 219, 254, 270, 355 bus. **Lunch served** noon-3pm daily. **Dinner served** 6-11pm Mon-Thur, Sun; 6-11.30pm Fri, Sat. **Minimum** £5. **Service** 10%. **Credit** MC, £TC, V.

One of the two splinter operations from nearby **Shree Krishna** (*see above*), Vijaya Krishna suffers from being off the main drag and seems to have become a haunt of local formula curry freaks. Nevertheless, the south Indian menu offers the best of the cooking. The service is much more traditional than at the area's other south Indian restaurants and our waiter seemed surprised when we headed in the direction of masala dosai and fish fry. The dosai was good (although the filling was a tad too mild for our taste) and the fish fry was exactly as we'd hoped, being flavoursome and not overcooked, as is often the case. Oddly enough, the coconut rice was by far the best dish we tasted (and among the best we've ever had) and the avial was well up to scratch. A token prawn Madras was pretty ordinary. Serves us right.

Babies and children admitted. Book dinner Fri, Sat. Disabled: toilet. Takeaway service. Vegan dishes.

East

Forest Gate E7

Vijay's Chawalla ★

268 Green Street, E7 (020 8470 3535). Upton Park tube. **Meals served** 11am-9pm daily. **Thali** £5, £6 incl dessert. **Unlicensed. No credit cards.**

Looking something like an upmarket Disney version of a Wimpy bar, Chawalla is a clean and modern vegetarian diner with peach-coloured walls and film music videos playing on small screens around the large L-shaped room. It's difficult to get a table, especially at weekends, and although service is more enthusiastic than on-the-ball, the quality of both cooking and ingredients is remarkably good, especially for a 'fast food bar'. The best bhel poori ever was £2: a sizeable mound that contrasted crisp and soft, sweet and sour, hot and cool perfectly. A large, crispy masala dosai was served on a stainless steel tray with a tamarind-rich sambar and an exemplary coconut chutney. Chilli paneer was precisely spiced and fried with onions and peppers, and the Gujarati thali (£5) came with nutty dahl and a spirited potato curry that went almost as fast as it arrived. We didn't try the vegetable burger and chips, but the chubby young boy on the next table who did, reported it 'awesome'. Falooda at £2.75 sounds expensive, but the over-the-top glass of cream, rose-flavoured milkshake with fruit and vermicelli that arrived was worth every penny.

Babies and children admitted. Disabled: toilet. No smoking. Takeaway service. Vegan dishes.

North East

Stoke Newington N16

Rasa★

55 Stoke Newington Church Street, N16 (020 7249 0344). Stoke Newington rail/73 bus. **Lunch served** noon-3pm Sat, Sun. **Dinner served** 6-11pm Mon-Thur, Sun; 6pm-midnight Fri, Sat. **Main courses** £3.50-£5.50. **Set meal** £15 three courses. **Credit** AmEx, JCB, MC, V.

Rasa and its central London branch – same menu, plusher surroundings, West End prices – are pioneers of the vegetarian cuisine of the small Keralan Nair community. This is a small, 14-table restaurant that's invariably packed. We last went on a Friday lunchtime and felt the need to book; we were glad we did. Many dishes (like beet cheera pachadi, beetroot and spinach in a yoghurt and coconut sauce) are unique and ought not be missed. So long as you've not eaten for a day or two and plan to fast for another few, the best plan is to try the Kerala feast (£15) set meal. First of all come a selection of popadoms and sev-like snacks, served with knock-out own made chutneys and pickles. Then come the starters. Expect something like kathrikka (fried spiced and battered aubergine), Mysore bonda and masala vadai. After this comes a table-groaning selection of main and side dishes with coconut rice. Ask for thakkali curry if you fancy tomatoes cooked in a yoghurt sauce infused with ginger and garlic, and moru kachiathu if sweet mangoes and green bananas in a khadi-like sauce is up your avenue. Avial is as good as you'd expect and mottakrose thoran (cabbage and carrots, £3.35) probably better. The sweet can come as something of a shock, but if it's pal payasam (nutty and raisiny rice pudding £2.50), try and force it down.

Babies and children admitted. Booking essential. No smoking. Takeaway service. Vegan dishes.

For branch (Rasa W1) see index.

North

Finchley N3

Rani

7 Long Lane, N3 (020 8349 4386). Finchley Central tube. **Lunch served** 12.15-2.30pm Sun. **Dinner served** 6-10.30pm daily. **Main courses** £5-£15. **Set meal** £12.45 per person (minimum two) two courses. **Thali** £9.80. **Service** 10%. **Credit** AmEx, MC, V.

We're pleased that the Patni family have knocked pizzas on the head (good though they reputedly were), because it means that the kitchen can concentrate on the East African brand of Indian vegetarian cooking that made its name. No eggs, meat, fish or animal fats (except dairy) are allowed on the premises, and the menu is usefully marked with what contains sugar, wheat, dairy products, nuts and so on. Hot starters are £3 or

less and include a toothsome aloo tiki, delicious deep fried stuffed chillies (akhaa murcha) and good kachori. Bhel poori was good if not spectacular, whereas a main course kofta paneer was spectacular and delicious. The Rani thali (£9.80) is good value and includes a sak of your choice, together with rashia vall (beans in a sauce flavoured with cinnamon and cloves), dahl, bread, raita and various pickles and chutneys. The own-made kulfi is creamy, fruity and moreish, while the shrikhand defies description. Service is usually attentive and friendly. Although prices at Rani couldn't be described as bargain basement, and portions aren't huge, the cooking and smart modern decor makes it good value.
Babies and children welcome; children's menu; high chairs. Book Fri-Sun. Dress: smart casual. No-smoking tables. Separate room for parties, seats 12. Takeaway service. Vegan dishes.

Southgate N14

Jhopri ★

725 The Broadway, N14 (020 8245 0090). Southgate tube. **Lunch served** noon-2.30pm Mon-Fri. **Dinner served** 6-11.30pm Mon-Sat. **Meals served** 12.30-10.30pm Sun. **Main courses** £4.50-£7.95. **Set buffet** (lunch, all-day Sun) £4.95. **Credit** MC, TC, V.

They really push the south Indian vegetarian dishes to the fore at this modern, airy restaurant just off Southgate's main drag. And quite rightly so. The masala dosai is light and properly the texture of extremely aged parchment, filled with a perfectly-spiced potato mix, accompanied by pleasantly fiery sambar; while kofta malai is a heavenly mix of spicy own-made vegetable balls in a thick savoury sauce, served with a buttery, crumbly paratha. Methi aloo is a dish in itself, bursting with green leaf, and the bhel poori is a winner. But even if they cook meat because they have to, the omnivorous part of the menu reveals some damn fine cooking skills, too. A starter of Mangalorean crab was a flavoursome package served on a large lettuce leaf, and bursting with crab and fresh herb flavours. The bada jhinga makani that followed looked horribly like a tandoori king prawn masala, but in fact the deep red sauce was based on reduced tomato, well-spiced and well suited to its cargo of large, juicy prawns. Although chicken in a sealed pot, dum ka murgh, is not a dish anyone can throw together, the version here came in a sauce any devotee would recognise. Even the nariyal pilau (coconut rice) was above average.
Babies and children welcome; half-price buffet. No smoking (Sun). Takeaway service (6-11pm daily).

Stroud Green N4

Jai Krishna ★

161 Stroud Green Road, N4 (020 7272 1680). Finsbury Park tube/rail then W3, W7 bus/ Crouch End rail. **Lunch served** noon-2pm, **dinner served** 5.30-10.30pm Mon-Sat. **Main courses** £4.50-£6. **Unlicensed. Corkage** 75p wine, 20p beer. **Credit** LV.

Standards vary enormously at this family-run vegetarian diner: although we've had some good meals, we've also had the occasional stinker. The last jeera aloo we ordered was barely edible, with bullet-hard potato pieces sitting on a 'caramelised' pool of oil, onion and cumin seed, and a recent starter of patra was similarly over-cooked and couldn't have been harder if it had served in the paras. But generally speaking, we enjoy the food at Jai Krishna. We tend to go for the special thali (£16.95 for two), with spinach paneer, a well-balanced dish we'd certainly take to our desert island, and aubergine curry, one of the tastiest in town. Add in a mountain of chapatis or puri, dahl, various bhajia and all the usual odds and ends, and you're set up. Sabzi bahar (potato, spinach and methi) is never anything other than delicious, and mango ice-cream is sensational. The cooking here is home-style and robust and subtle isn't an adjective we'd use to describe anything we've ever eaten. But making the customer write down their orders is just plain daft.
Babies and children admitted. Book dinner Fri, Sat. No-smoking tables. Takeaway service. Vegan dishes.

North West

Kilburn NW6

Geeta ★

57-59 Willesden Lane, NW6 (020 7624 1713). Kilburn tube/Brondesbury Park rail/98 bus. **Lunch served** noon-2.30pm daily. **Dinner served** 6-10.30pm Mon-Thur, Sun; 6-11.30pm Fri, Sat. **Main courses** £3-£6.90. **Credit** AmEx, DC, LV, MC, TC, V.

Geeta has been serving up sensational samosas and succulent sambars to the good folk of Kilburn for over two decades now, and although the place may appear to be a brown, dingy diner, it's got that authentic Indian atmosphere. As ever, ignore the chicken and meat dishes (with the possible exception of fried meat, Kerala style) and go with the south Indian vegetarian specialities. Masala dosais are well up to standard, with a hint of asafoetida, and fresh curry leaves much to the fore in the potato filling. Sambar is rich and dark, avial is everything you want it to be, and even the drumsticks here seem juicier and less fibrous than we're used to. During our taste trip around Kerala, we watched a couple of twentysomething blokes get plastered on three quick pints of Indian lager (maybe too cheap at £2 a throw) and then proceed to demolish a meal of chicken soup (£1.20), beef Madras (£3.20) and chicken chips and peas (£3.50). 'We're going to India, tomorrow,' one of them told a passing woman. 'We're getting our bellies in training.' Good luck, lads.
Babies and children welcome. Booking advisable, weekends. Separate room for parties, seats 35. Takeaway service.

Vijay ★

49 Willesden Lane, NW6 (020 7328 1087). Kilburn tube. **Lunch served** noon-2.45pm daily. **Dinner served** 6-10.45pm Mon-Thur, Sun; 6-11.45pm Fri, Sat. **Main courses** £2.30-£8. **Minimum** £6. **Service** 10%. **Credit** DC, MC, JCB, V, £TC.

Discerning diners will ignore everything else and dive straight into the small selection of south Indian specialities on offer at this long-established family restaurant. Founded in 1966 and a comfortable haven for Kilburn's Keralan curry lovers, it is invariably busy, and for a reason. We sat next to a pair of estate agents on their way to the Tricycle Theatre, and despite the dreary details of property hazards in Holland Park, the food was good enough to transcend the crassness of their conversation. Masala dosai with sambar is a good place to kick in – the familiar giant flap of crisp pancake is filled with a toothsome mix of spicy potatoes and fried onions, and served with a wonderful sambar. Rasam was a fiery mixture that pushed ginger and pepper flavours to the fore, while avial was suitably creamy, with just the right amount of sharpness around its edges. Salted lassi was good and the uthappam was fresh and alive with tomato, chilli and onion flavours. The estate agents seemed to enjoy their chicken curry and prawn whatever, too.
Babies and children welcome; high chairs. Booking advisable. No-smoking tables. Takeaway service.

Willesden NW10

Sabras

263 High Road, NW10 (020 8459 0340). Dollis Hill tube/6, 52, 98, 260, 266, 297, 302 bus. **Dinner served** 6.30-10.30pm Tue-Sun. **Main courses** £5.95-£15.95. **Set meals** (6-8pm) £6.50, £10.95, £14.95. **Service** 12½%. **Credit** AmEx, DC, JCB, MC, V.

Sabras opened in 1973; though a recent makeover has replaced the cosmic burger bar look with a gentler, pastel-shaded bistro-style layout, the place hasn't altered that much over the years. Service is friendly and helpful: it's still the sort of place where a smile comes naturally. Starters (all £2.95) include many of the usual suspects, including patra, kachori and samosas, although the bhajias are made with red onion and there's the option of samosa deluxe, served chat-style with yoghurt sauce, chutneys, masala and various pickles for £3.95. Dosais are invariably good, with the unusual Madras masala dosai (spread with chilli garlic and pepper sauce) topping the list. Other notables include ravaiya (baby aubergines and bananas stuffed and slow cooked), makkai-kaju (sweetcorn and cashews in a reduced, sweetish tomato sauce) and panch-kuti-dal which is made from five kinds of lentil and bean and hard to beat for intensity of flavour. It's a pity that desserts come at the end of the meal, because portions are generous and the sweets are so tempting. You've got to try the honey and ginger kulfi, although the shrikhand with khajau (a crumbly sweet pastry biscuit) is pretty damn good, too.
Babies and children admitted. Booking advisable. No-smoking tables. Takeaway service. Vegan dishes.

Outer London

Twickenham, Middlesex

Pallavi

Unit 3, Cross Deep Court, Heath Road, Twickenham, Middx (020 8892 2345/4466). Twickenham rail. **Lunch served** noon-3pm, **dinner served** 6-11pm Mon-Thur, Sun; 6pm-midnight Fri, Sat. **Main courses** £3.95-£6.95. **Service** 10%. **Credit** AmEx, MC, V.

Twickenham has kept this Keralan gem to itself for too long. There's little to give the game away in the small entrance lobby, but climb the stairs and you'll find a rickshaw suspended from the ceiling, various mementoes of Kerala (from tourist photos to kathakali drums), a small bar and a large first-floor restaurant fronted by a sparkling open-view kitchen. Suburban curry-house touches – ruched curtains and well-worn carpets – are soon forgotten as you ogle the menu. south Indian favourites such as idli, dosais and uthappam are all present, and so too are north Indian dishes like lamb methi or chicken korma, but it was the many and varied Keralan specials that so impressed us. Kappa and meen masala was a hefty starter of zesty fish curry paired with chunks of potato-like tapioca, crunchy with coconut and spices: superb. To follow, the yoghurty tang of curd rice would have made a simple and perfect meal combined with the authentically spiced parippu lentil curry. Unable to contain ourselves, though, we ordered chicken fry curry (its tamarind flavouring reminiscent of HP sauce), Cochin prawn curry (with abundant plump shellfish in a tomato-based sauce), and kalan (sweet with slippery mango). Next time we'll try a thoran, or the avial, or perhaps the payasam for afters.
Babies and children welcome; high chairs.

Wembley, Middlesex

The Ealing Road – especially the stretch between the tube stations of Alperton and Wembley Central – has become a shopping centre for the area's large population of East African Asians. Some of London's best shops for fresh, exotic fruit and veg can be found here, as well as sari-sellers, traders in bhangra tapes or Bollywood videos, and a growing number of cafés and restaurants.

The food is extremely varied, ranging from the sambols and hoppers served at **Sri Lankan** restaurants (*see below*) to the Gujarati vegetarian snacks popular at **Chetna's** and **Sakoni**. Ingredients such as sweetcorn and cassava chips (mogo) – first incorporated into the cuisine by Asian families who lived in East Africa until the 1970s – can also be sampled at snack joints such as **Maru's**.

Chetna's ★

420 High Road, Wembley, Middx (020 8900 1466/020 8903 5989). Wembley Park tube/ Wembley Central tube/rail. **Lunch served** noon-3pm, **dinner served** 6-10.30pm Tue-Fri. **Meals served** 1-10.30pm Sat, Sun. **Minimum** £3.50. **Credit** MC, £TC, V.

Many locals of African-Asian descent come for an early evening chat at Chetna's. As well as a chin-wag – sitting on the well-sprung banquettes under flamboyant chandeliers, and gazing out at the busy High Road through plate-glass windows – this involves tucking into a 'seaside savoury' such as aloo papadi chat (crisp pooris filled with chickpeas, potatoes and sweet-and-sour chutney: popular on Bombay's beaches). Or perhaps a more substantial snack will be devoured; we recommend the masala golapa, a filling mix of moong beans, chutneys, sev and potatoes. A full meal might include a vegetable biriani, paper dosa (with a thin filling of vegetable sambar and coconut chutney), a thali of Gujarati and north Indian dishes, or even a vegetarian pizza. Staff can get flustered during the early evening rush, but there's a companionable, engaging feel to the place, helped along by the low prices.
Babies and children welcome; high chairs. Bookings not accepted. No smoking area. Takeaway service. Vegan dishes.

Jashan

1-2 Coronet Parade, Ealing Road, Wembley, Middx (020 8900 9800). Alperton tube. **Meals served** noon-11pm daily. **Main courses** £2.95-£5. **Unlicensed** no corkage.**Credit** AmEx, MC, £TC, V.

With two branches in Dubai and a curry house in Turnpike Lane, plus place mats displaying quotes from Aristotle, Alexander Pope and Henry Kissinger, Jashan does a good line in bathos. Yet the firm's new vegetarian restaurant on the Ealing Road shows it also knows how to please the local market. Wembley's African-Asian families flock to the place, drawn by the bright, modern, utilitarian furnishings (easy-wipe tables, stone-tiled floor, vibrant geometric patterns on the white walls and ceiling), by the well-practised, pleasant staff, and by the raft of pan-Indian and Chinese dishes on the menu. The choice is almost stupefying, encompassing snacks (try the excellent makai paneer ke pakore: freshly fried croquettes of fluffy cheese and sweetcorn), south Indian staples (idli with sambar was utterly authentic), various pooris, breads (both potato-stuffed lachedar paratha and garlic-studded lasoori nan can incite craving), stir-fries (Sichuan vegetables with cashew nuts), main-course specialities, and beverages (a refreshing carrot juice among them). We loved nilgiri pilau rice, green with puréed coriander, and the creamy methi mutter malai (though it could have had more fenugreek), but the kofta malmali (with curd-based veg-balls) came in a lurid orange, creamy sauce reminiscent of curry house masala. Off-notes are minimal, though, and Jashan has an alluring buzz to it. Queues were forming on Thursday night.
Babies and children welcome; high chairs. Takeaway service. Vegetarian menu.

Maru's Bhajia House ★

230 Ealing Road, Wembley, Middx (020 8903 6771). Alperton tube/Wembley Central tube/rail. **Meals served** 12.30-8.30pm Mon-Fri; 12.30-9.30pm Sat, Sun. **Main courses** £1.40-£5. **Unlicensed** no alcohol allowed. **Credit** LV, £TC.

A snack joint that has built its fame on frying root vegetables. The Maru brothers' bhajias are simply sliced potatoes clothed in a crisp, coriander-speckled batter and served with a salsa-style chilli relish, tamarind sauce (from an old squash bottle) and Heinz tomato sauce – smashing. Variations include mogo (chips made from cassava root), and other snacks such as kachoori (deep-fried dahl pastries) and pani poori (a portion of six pooris to be filled with potato cubes, chickpeas, chutney and mint-flavoured 'herbal water'). Decorations are rudimentary: partially tiled walls, a counter at the rear, and easy-wipe banquette seating. A perfect stop-off point during a spicy shopping trip along the Ealing Road.
Babies and children welcome; high chairs. Book weekends. No smoking. Takeaway service. Vegan dishes.

Sakoni ★

127-129 Ealing Road, Wembley, Middx (020 8903 9601). Alperton tube/183 bus. **Meals served** 11am-11pm Mon-Thur; 11am-11.30pm Fri-Sun. **Main courses** £3.50-£5.25. **Unlicensed** no alcohol allowed. **Credit** MC, £TC, V.

The odd ante room that separates Sakoni from the outside world gets you into the South Asian swing of things with a stall that sells Bollywood music tapes, incense, and much else. The snackery proper is a brightly lit, long space with a counter full of crispy snacks and Indian sweets near the front, tables packed with local families in the middle, and a large spick and span kitchen at the rear. In common with many restaurants in India, Sakoni offers a batch of Chinese dishes 'prepared Indian style', so you could have stir-fried paneer and chilli along with hakka noodles. We kept south of the Himalayas and contemplated the menus of 'eats' and 'bites'. Chutney dosai was slightly spicier than the masala version; potato-packed and satisfactorily crisp it came with coconut chutney and an appetising sambar sauce. Mix chat was based on cold cubes of potato and raw onion, but also had fried puris and idlis, all served with a sweet and spicy yoghurt. Uthappam are another popular line, and there are various fresh juices (including refreshing green coconut) and ices. The snack range is somewhat limited (focusing on the potato and the crisp, with precious few green vegetables), but for a concentrated draught of subcontinental life, Sakoni is unmissable.
Babies and children welcome; high chairs; nappy-changing facilities. Book Fri-Sun. Disabled: toilet. No smoking. Takeaway service. Vegan dishes.
For branches see index.

Sri Lankan

'Going for a Sri Lankan' has yet to trip off Londoners' lips. This enticing and varied cooking has had a remarkably low profile in London, with restaurants scattered around the outer suburbs. But although the relative obscurity of their cuisine is a problem for Sri Lankan restaurateurs, it is a boon to diners lucky enough to live close to one of these establishments. Prices tend to be low, while dishes are palpably different from the north Indian norm.

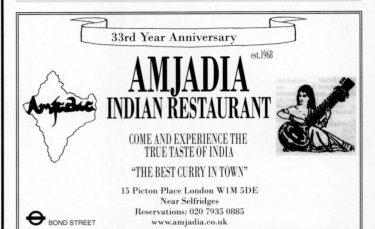

Fish and seafood – especially crab and squid – are prominent on the menus. Dishes tend to be chilli-hot, particularly so in the case of sambols (relishes often served warm). There are similarities to south Indian food; dosais and vadais are usually served, and bananas and coconut are common ingredients. Instead of rice, try string hoppers (steamed rice-flour noodles) or pittu (a log-like roll of rice flour steamed with grated coconut). Kiri hodi or sothi (coconut-based gravy) should be part of every meal, as a moistener for the string hoppers.

West

Ealing W13

Sigiri
161 Northfield Avenue, W13 (020 8579 8000). Northfields tube/E2, E3 bus. **Dinner served** 6.30-11pm Tue-Sun. **Main courses** £10-£14. **Credit** MC, V.
We've got to know Sigiri's strengths and weaknesses over the years, and now don't bother with starters (satay, or various rolls and rissoles that seem to hail from a freezer pack). Instead, we plunge into the main courses, a long and varied choice of south Indian and Sri Lankan food. Top this year was dhoonthel rice, Maldives fish imparting a subtle fishy tang to the grains. We can also vouch for 'green banana dry' with its pleasurable pulse-like texture, and the fish seer (meaty white fish in a superb coconut-based sauce). A heavy pol roti (unleavened bread with coconut) was the only thing we'd not order again – stick to the string hoppers. There was a bit of a wait for the food, but the traditionally attired waitresses were friendly and clued-up. Sigiri has a relaxed feel to it, helped by well-spaced tables, pine ceiling and bar, traditional cotton prints on the walls, and Chopin seeping out of the speakers.
Babies and children welcome. Book weekends. No-smoking tables. Takeaway service.

South

Colliers Wood SW19

Suvai Aruvi ★
96 High Street, SW19 (020 8543 6266/020 8286 6677). Colliers Wood tube. **Meals served** 11am-midnight daily. **Main courses** 50p-90p. **Unlicensed. Corkage** no charge. **No credit cards.**
Low prices, fiery flavours and uncommon dishes sum up Suvai Aruvi's contribution to Colliers Wood life. This lowly caff – with only half a dozen shiny wooden tables, a splash of greenery, a TV and a glass counter for decoration – does much of its business in takeaways. However, the menu of rare-to-London dishes is worth sampling. Some starters and puds are displayed behind the counter, perhaps including soosyam: a doughnut with a sweet coconut and lentil filling eaten as an appetiser. Tomato kulambu (halves of tomato in a savoury milky sauce) makes an enjoyable companion to more substantial dishes such as seafood pittu kolambu (meaty fish, prawns and vegetables, small lumps of steamed rice and wheat flour). Fried mutton also packs a flavourful punch. Unless you're best chums with chilli, stipulate 'mild' when ordering – eye-watering might then be kept to manageable proportions. Laddu, a rock-like fusion of rice crispies and lentils, makes a filling, yet pleasing, end to a meal. Staff are keen to help, but language problems can lead to confusion. Pointing at dishes helps.
Babies and children admitted.

Tooting SW17

Jaffna House ★
90 High Street, SW17 (020 8672 7786/www.curry2go.cc). Tooting Broadway tube. **Meals served** noon-midnight daily. **Main courses** £2-£3.75. **Set lunch** (noon-3pm Mon-Fri) £4 (vegetarian), £5, two courses. **Credit** AmEx, MC, V.
Whether you chose the cafeteria-style front dining room with its rows of wooden furniture or the more chintzy tandoori restaurant at the side – more of a front room with a bar and tables, really – you're in for a treat at this family-run Tooting enterprise. Prices have hardly changed over the years and starters of vadai, bonda and bhajia can still be had for 50p and under. Forget the tandoori menu and go for the Sri Lankan specialities, but be aware that spicing is geared towards Sri Lankan tastes and chopped green chillies are ubiquitous. The Sunday afternoon we last visited the place was packed (mostly with families of Sri Lankan origin) and we were lucky to get a table at 2pm. Fried string hoppers were packed with flavour and just about perfect, while the masala dosai (ludicrously cheap at £1.50), and ultra savoury devilled liver were well up to scratch. Even side dishes of potato pirattal, fried cabbage and tomato kulambu (all £1.25) were fresh, pungently flavoured and just about faultless. Thick and fruity mango lassis were the only sweet we could force down. Service was friendly and surprisingly prompt considering the business they were doing – all in all, a very pleasant afternoon in genial surroundings.
Babies and children admitted. Takeaway service (noon-midnight daily).

South East

Lewisham SE13

Everest Curry King ★
24 Loampit Hill, SE13 (020 8691 2233). Lewisham DLR/rail. **Meals served** 11am-11pm daily. **Main courses** £3-£5. **Set meal** £3.95. **Unlicensed** no alcohol allowed. **No credit cards.**
Sometimes a restaurant wows you with the sheer quality of food on offer, at other times it's something else that grabs you. We particularly enjoy the happy-go-lucky atmosphere at this small, burger bar-style café, which serves good, cheap Sri Lankan food to a predominantly ex-pat population. The menu includes unusual dishes like Ceylon beef liver (small £2, medium £3, large £4.95), together with usual suspects such as pittu and string hoppers, kuttu roti and vadai (from 50p). A welcome innovation are the children's dishes – medium portions of lightly-spiced string hoppers, kuttu roti and a special of mango chicken and rice – from around £3.50. Set meals include a one plate vegetarian option of three dishes and rice for £3.95, with a non-veggie version for a pound extra. We were particularly impressed by curries of beetroot, carrot and pumpkin, while dosais from £1.25 (plain, including sambol/sambar) were ridiculously cheap and well up to standard. Prawn kuttu roti was bursting with shellfish and coconut milk hoppers were just brilliant. For Sri Lankan food on a budget, Everest is hard to beat.
Babies and children admitted. No smoking. Takeaway service.

Green Cabin ★
244 Lewisham High Street, SE13 (020 8852 6666). Lewisham DLR/rail/Ladywell rail/36, 47, 199 bus. **Lunch served** noon-3pm, **dinner served** 6-11pm Tue-Sun. **Set meals** £7.50 per person (minimum two) two courses incl beer. **Set lunch** £3.95 noon-3pm Tue-Sat. **Credit** AmEx, MC, V.
Lewisham's Sri Lankan community is well-served by its pair of local restaurants, with Green Cabin the more upmarket of the two. The green and white paintwork makes for a cool, relaxing atmosphere, which is carried over into the service. Although attentive and efficient, you get the idea that the staff wouldn't panic if a bull elephant decided to turn up and order venthayakulambu (onions and garlic in a thick, brown, spicy sauce, £1.75). Although the menu is based around traditional Sri Lankan dishes, this being Lewisham, there's more than a nod to tandoori tastes. But anyone who expects a chicken Madras to taste as if it's come straight out of a jar will be disappointed – even these restaurant staples have a fresh spiciness and a tad more aromatic herbs (such as cassia and curry leaves) than northern cousins would sanction. Starters include delicious freshly-made ulunthu vadai, crispy fish cutlet that came with a near-commercial tomato sauce that went down very well with a Sri Lankan neighbour, as well as the usual bhajias and tikkas. Squid curry (cooked in thick masala gravy) and devilled mutton were stand-outs, as were vegetable dishes of potato kulambu (with coconut milk and chilli, £1.75) and cabbage mallung (£2).
Babies and children admitted. Book weekends. No-smoking tables. Takeaway service.

North West

Hendon NW4

Prince of Ceylon
39 Watford Way, NW4 (020 8202 5967). Hendon Central tube. **Meals served** noon-midnight daily. **Minimum** £7. **Set buffet** (noon-5pm Sun) £8.50. **Credit** AmEx, DC, MC, V.
The self-proclaimed 'oldest Sri Lankan restaurant in Europe' now stays open through the day, perhaps to provide a refuge for locals fleeing the dual-carriageway roar of the A41 outside. Blinds keep the traffic at bay, and tropical-style furnishings (much bamboo, matting and pine, with low red and yellow lighting) engender a measure of serenity. All the curry house staples are on the long menu, but vastly more enticing Sri Lankan food takes centre stage. We can recommend the fish cutlets (which come freshly fried, and served with tomato ketchup) for starters. Cashew nut curry, the nuts simmered to softness, makes an unusual follow-up (though the accompanying curry sauce is prosaic). Ambul thiyal (blackened chunks of a meaty fish served on lettuce and raw onion) gives a meal some bite, while perfectly steamed string hoppers and kiri hodi provide a counterbalance. Good-natured, informative service and reliable cooking make for an enjoyable meal.
Babies and children welcome. Book Fri-Sun. Separate rooms for parties, seats 50, 120. Takeaway service.

Outer London

Southall, Middlesex

Palm Palace ★ ★
80 South Road, Southall, Middx (020 8574 9209). Southall rail/105, 120, 195, 207 bus. **Meals served** 11.30am-11.30pm Mon-Sat. **Lunch served** 11.30am-2.30pm Sun. **Dinner served** 6-11.30pm Sun. **Thalis** £4 (vegetarian), £5. **Credit** AmEx, MC, V.
Word has spread about Palm Palace's low-priced, high-quality cooking in the past year, and Sri Lankan families, as well as a multicultural mix of others, nearly filled the place on a Thursday night. Behind the plate-glass frontage, the small dining area is modest yet spruce, with spot lighting, traditional linen prints on the walls, and a tropical fish tank built into the bar at the rear. Staff are quietly engaging and on the ball. North and south Indian dishes play only bit-parts in the long and varied menu of Sinhalese favourites. Our meal was not without faults, yet we still reckon the Sri Lankan food here to be among the best in London. The grumbles: string hoppers were too dry, and 'baby bigon masala' (the small aubergines we so relished last year) this time came in a cream-laden tomato sauce inappropriate to the cuisine. There were no other let-downs in a feast that began with freshly made, well-packed mutton rolls and fish cutlets (tuna rissoles), and continued with squid curry (tender hoops in a rich tomato sauce). Spinach arrived lightly cooked and enticingly seasoned with fried onions and raw ginger: superb. Good, too, was the fried mutton with more fried onions, and the bowl-shaped milk hopper pancake with its sweet centre. The Sri Lankan Lion stout being off, we accompanied our splendid repast with a Goan Ambari lager.
Babies and children admitted. Takeaway service.

Northolt, Middlesex

Amirthaam
200B Alexandra Avenue, Northolt, Middx (020 8423 9666/020 8864 6636). Northolt Park rail. **Lunch served** noon-3pm, **dinner served** 6-11pm Mon-Thur. **Meals served** noon-midnight Fri, Sat; noon-11pm Sun. **Main courses** £3-£6.50. **No credit cards.**
They don't come much smaller than this simple Tamil caff, hemmed in on a parade alongside the A4090. Much business is in takeaways; punters wait for their carry-outs at a table by the plate-glass window. A tiny counter is surrounded by Tamil CDs and videos for hire. Then there's three further tables in the dining area, with its clean, pine-clad walls, parquet floor, spot lights and Sri Lankan satellite TV. Along with six Tamil regulars (all young men), we looked incredulously as an Imelda Marcos lookalike staggered through a Sri Lankan version of Cab Calloway's *Mini the Moocher*. The genial young son of the chef brought a laminated menu full of Sri Lankan classics. Few break the £4 barrier. Fish rolls were freshly fried, but seemed bought-in. Best go straight for mains. Squid curry had an excellent flavour born of long simmering; brinjal Jaffna-style likewise, the aubergine smoky and delicious. Chilli-heat was such that our lips throbbed (even the sothi had a green one lurking – and, oddly, a segment of orange). Our neighbours' special kothu looked good, too. Stainless-steel plates and cutlery of a single spoon added still more authenticity.
Takeaway service. Vegetarian dishes.

Wembley, Middlesex

Palm Beach
17 Ealing Road, Wembley, Middx (020 8900 8664). Wembley Central tube/rail/79, 83, 297 bus. **Lunch served** noon-3pm (not Tue), **dinner served** 6-11.30pm daily. **Main courses** £1.95-£6.95. **Credit** AmEx, DC, MC, V.
Young Sri Lankan men and the occasional woman seem to have taken to Palm Beach in the past year, making for a good-natured, relaxed atmosphere. Polite, well-dressed young waiters help things along, but tend to allow food to stand a while at the bar before it is served. Large tinted windows give a good view of glitzy Ealing Road, while within the comfy dining room (akin to that of a local tandoori), linen prints in elaborate wooden frames join the odd tourist poster to divert the eye. North Indian, south Indian and a goodly number of Sri Lankan dishes cluster on the menu. Chicken 65 (supposedly from a 65-day-old bird) was our first dish. At £4.50 it is the most expensive starter, and the reason soon became apparent. Piled upon a woefully inadequate side plate were eight boulders of succulent, deep-fried fowl resplendent in spicy red batter and served with a profusion of dull salad. Already full, we then had to tackle squid ceylon, a tender cephalopod in spicy tomato and coconut gravy; abusively hot seeni sambol, crunchy with chilli seeds; Ceylon potato, in an identical sauce to that of the squid; and comforting sothi and string hoppers. Thin on finesse, maybe, but Palm Beach provides unquestionably good value.
Babies and children welcome; high chairs. Book weekends. Takeaway service (10% discount). Vegetarian menu.

Sri Lankan menu

Ambul thiyal: a sour fish curry cooked dry with spices.
Appam: *see* hoppers.
Badun: black. 'Black' curries are fried, dry and usually very hot.
Godamba roti: flaky, thin Sri Lankan bread, sometimes wrapped around egg or potato.
Hoppers: confusingly, hoppers come in two forms, either as saucer-shaped, rice-flour pancakes (try milk hopper, sweet and moreish), or as string hoppers (qv). Also called appa or appam.
Iddi appam: *see* string hoppers.
Katta sambol: onion, lemon and chilli relish – fearsomely hot.
Kiri: white. 'White' curries are based on coconut milk and are mild.
Kiri hodi: coconut milk curry with onions and turmeric; a soothing gravy. Also called pol kiri or sothy.
Kuttu roti, kothu roti, etc: chopped bread, often mixed with mutton, chicken or prawn to form a 'bread biriani'; very filling.
Lamprais or lumprice: a biriani-style dish where meat and rice are cooked together, often by baking in banana leaves.
Lunnu miris: a relish of ground onion, chilli and Maldives fish.
Maldives fish: an ingredient used in sambols (qv). These creatures are small, dried fish with a very intense flavour.
Pittu: rice flour and coconut steamed in bamboo to make a 'log'; an alternative to rice.
Pol: coconut.
Pol kiri: *see* kiri hodi.
Pol sambol: mixture of coconut, chilli, onions, Maldives fish and lemon juice.
Sambols: strongly flavoured relishes, often served hot; they are often chilli hot, too.
Seeni sambol: a caramelised onion relish; sweet.
Sothy or sothi: *see* kiri hodi.
String hoppers: fine rice-flour noodles formed into flat discs. Served either steamed (in which case they're dry; an ideal partner for kiri hodi) or fried. Also called iddi appam. *See also* hoppers.
Wattalappan or vattilapan: a version of crème caramel made with kithul palm syrup.

International

Central

Bloomsbury WC1

Townhouse Brasserie
24 Coptic Street, WC1 (020 7636 2731). Holborn or Tottenham Court Road tube.
Meals served noon-11pm Mon-Fri; 3-11pm Sat; 10am-6pm Sun. **Main courses** £9.45-£13.50. **Set meals** £9.95 two courses, £13.45 three courses. **Set dinner** £5 two courses (5.30-8pm). **Service** 12½% for parties of four or more. **Credit** AmEx, DC, JCB, MC, £TC, V.
On entering the Townhouse Brasserie no one could be blamed for thinking it was a classic London-French brasserie. A long, corridor-like space leads to the main dining room where there's very comfortable seating and very Gallic service. The staff's English is sometimes a bit thin but the charm remains. The departures from French tradition come on the menu, with dishes such as spinach and ricotta ravioli with bok choi stir-fry, prawns in filo pastry with Chinese spices, and a squid salad with herbs (one of several 'light meals' offered as an alternative to full main courses). For the most part these fusions work well; roast guinea fowl with tarragon, garlic and coconut crème fraîche was a slightly over-the-top mix of French creaminess and tropical flavour, but still enjoyable. For desserts go back to basics with tarte tatin and avoid the disappointing own-made pistachio ice-cream. The wine list, like the menu, combines a French base with a range of international alternatives. Calm and relaxing, the Townhouse makes a likeable standby in a busy area.
Babies and children welcome; children's menu; high chairs. Book lunch Mon-Fri. No-smoking tables. Separate room for parties, seats 40. Tables outdoors (3, pavement). **Map 14/5K.**

City

Bar Bourse
67 Queens Street, EC4 (020 7248 2200/2211). Mansion House tube. **Open** 11am-11pm, **lunch served** 11.30am-3pm Mon-Fri. **Main courses** £11-£19. **Credit** AmEx, JCB, MC, V.
The cooking may not be the greatest in London, but the flavours are strong and the atmosphere is lively in this modern, theatrically realised basement bar-restaurant. The best feature of the L-shaped room is the stripy inlaid wood floor and the neo-Egyptian gold, red and blue decor. The catch-all style of the menu with its Eastern tendencies is aimed at a mixed, young crowd. Starters featured an average assortment of carpaccios and salads; oriental fritto misto (deep-fried scallops, squid and prawns) bizarrely seemed to contain a piece of lamb. Buoyed up by the atmosphere we pressed on to a warm crispy (viz, overcooked) duck salad with water-cress and salmon, and a lightly cooked vegetable lasagne, with fresh, creamy flavours. However, disconcertingly pink herb roasted chicken could have spent longer in the oven and was served with a hefty slab of black pudding, which, like the lamb in the fritto misto, was not forecast by the menu. Prices make it easy to reach the minimum spend of £20 a head, but don't represent particularly good value.
Babies and children admitted. Disabled: toilet. Vegetarian menu. **Map 4/7P.**

Fitzrovia W1

Spoon+ at Sanderson
50 Berners Street, W1 (020 7300 1400/1444). Oxford Circus tube. **Lunch served** noon-3pm daily. **Dinner served** 6-11pm Mon-Sat; 6-10.30pm Sun. **Main courses** £14-£28. **Service** 15%. **Credit** AmEx, DC, MC, V.
If you think that anyone goes to Spoon for a good meal, you're missing the point. Spoon+ at Sanderson is an artifice of clever presentation, for which you pay absurdly high prices (starters cost double figures, main courses are around £20, and even a double espresso costs an astounding £4.50); conspicuous consumption is the goal here, and the food is secondary. The menu (written in French, then nonsensical English), may be badly structured and barely comprehensible, and the service from the French-speaking staff may be slow and vacuous, but the (surprising) good news is the cooking. Frog soup was a brilliantly conceived dish; pieces of the boneless white meat were suspended in a creamy sauce and served with a jug of watercress soup to complement the flavours. Desserts were a strong point, too: a simple but sublime cheesecake, and a 'chocolate pizza' topped with excellent, high cocoa content couverture. Other dishes were less impressive and completely overpriced; a starter of shredded iceberg and chilly chicken breast was served in a plastic fridge storage bowl (très amusant, n'est-ce pas?) for £12, while pork and veal main courses were competent but not terribly exciting. The wine list has many trendy, quality bottles at predictably high prices. Spoon is a wonderful place if someone else is getting the bill. But if you are paying, eat at the Sanderson's Long Bar instead.
Babies and children admitted; high chairs. Disabled: toilet. Tables outdoors (15, courtyard). **Map 13/5J.**

Stargazer
11 Rathbone Street, W1 (020 7636 1057). Tottenham Court Road tube.
Bar **Open** noon-3pm, 5.30-11pm Mon-Fri. **Bar snacks** £2.75-£7.95.
Restaurant **Lunch served** noon-3pm, **dinner served** 6-11pm Mon-Fri. **Main courses** £9.95-£12.95. **Service** 12½%.
Both **Credit** AmEx, JCB, MC, V.
Strange that the restaurant at the back of Stargazer was practically deserted on our visit (besides us, there were two other diners), while the front tapas bar was brimming with a lively evening crowd. It didn't seem to faze our affable and efficient waiter, though, who stopped to chat to us a few times between serving in the busier section, making us feel a little less out on a limb. Starters include simple but delectable battered pieces of cod with tartare sauce; and lovely goat's cheese in pastry with artichoke, sun-blush tomatoes and olives with salad leaves. A main course of pan-fried slices of fillet steak with wild mushroom sauce was beautifully cooked and delicately flavoured, while escalope of salmon with tomato and cucumber salsa seemed a bit small in comparison. Lemon posset with own-made shortbread was a nice idea, although it proved far too sweet; never mind – sticky pudding with hot toffee sauce and cream was soft and delicious.
Babies and children welcome. Booking advisable. Separate rooms for parties, seating 20 and 30. **Map 2/5J.**

Holborn WC2

115 at Hodgson's
115 Chancery Lane, WC2 (restaurant 020 7242 2836/wine bar 020 7404 5027). Chancery Lane tube.
Bar **Open** 5-11pm Mon-Fri.
Restaurant **Lunch served** noon-3pm, **dinner served** 6-10pm Mon-Fri. **Main courses** £12.50-£16. **Set meal** £18.95 three courses. **Service** 12½%. **Credit** AmEx, DC, JCB, MC, V.
Sporting a new name and new management, 115 at Hodgson's surprises with one of the most elegantly contemporary dining rooms in London; black and burgundy-red chairs contrast with the white linen, dark wood flooring, while Rothko-esque artwork and dramatic flower arrangements decorate the scene. With the Law Society, Lincoln's Inn and similarly august judicial institutions all nearby, suited legal bodies naturally make up a large part of the lunchtime clientele. The menu, however, is far from stuffy, with a modish but not excessively faddish mix of global combinations on an English base. From the set lunch menu, Dorset parma ham with a baby fig salad was enjoyable and had a fine, subtle tomato dressing, although the ham itself was excessively salty. A filo parcel of roast spinach, tomato and goat's cheese on a bed of creamed black cabbage and dandelion leaves was an excellent vegetarian main course – a delicious combination of satisfying flavours. Best of all was dessert: griddled blueberry pancakes with mascarpone ice-cream, made with explosively flavoursome fruit. Very smooth but unpompous service, good coffee and scrumptious complimentary petits fours all added to the atmosphere of tranquillity and superior comfort. 115 at Hodgson's offers an impressive, wide range of wines and morphs into a stylish cocktail bar in the evening. The wine selection is also available in Hodgson's Wine Bar & Brasserie in the basement.
Separate room for parties, seats 16. **Map 3/6N.**

Leicester Square WC2

Asia de Cuba
45 St Martin's Lane, WC2 (020 7300 5588). Leicester Square tube. **Lunch served** noon-2.30pm Mon-Fri. **Dinner served** 5.30pm-midnight Mon-Sat; 5.30-10.30pm Sun. **Main courses** £15.50-£19.50 (two people). **Service** 12½%. **Credit** AmEx, DC, MC, V.
Though it may have been overshadowed by the more recent opening of his Sanderson hotel, Ian Schrager's St Martin's Lane restaurant is still pulling in the trendy punters. Tempted by the interesting fusion of Asian and Cuban ingredients on the menu, we were disappointed when the kitchen failed to deliver. A starter of Margarita-marinated salmon with spring onion pancakes was limp and tasteless, and served with alarmingly green fritters that tasted of virtually nothing. A main course of thinly sliced Wagyu sirloin (from the special promotion beef menu) was pricey at £30 but in its simplicity was the most successful dish we tried. Chocolate and pecan nut tart with rum cream was a moreish calorie-fest, while 'coconut invasion' was actually a light and moist coconut cake accompanied by watery coconut ice-cream. Hotel food like this was acceptable in the 1980s, but nowadays it's not worth the hefty price tag. Neither did we appreciate being treated like conveyor-belt diners, with our cutlery barely touching the plate before the next course arrived. On the plus side, service is friendly, the drinks list is impressively long (international rums are especially prominent) and the atmosphere is buzzing.
Babies and children admitted. Disabled: toilet. **Map 14/7L.**

Pimlico SW1

Tate Gallery Restaurant
Tate Britain, Millbank, SW1 (020 7887 8877/www.tate.org.uk). Pimlico tube/77A, 88, C10 bus. **Lunch served** noon-3pm Mon-Sat; noon-4pm Sun. **Main courses** £9.50-£15.75. **Set lunch** £16.75 two courses, £19.50 three courses. **Credit** AmEx, DC, MC, £TC, V.
Rex Whistler's colourful and dynamic mural, which covers the whole stretch of wall at the Tate's basement restaurant, softens the stark black and white appearance of the rest of the room. Black leather benches stretch across one wall, tablecloths are white and napkins black, giving an effective, if a little retro feel. What was once a British menu now globetrots with abandon. A succulent piece of squid had a classic Thai-style sweet chilli sauce; and a wheel of goat's cheese was peppered with rocket and sweetened with slices of fig. Mains met a mixed reception. Roast peppers and aubergine made a tasty addition to a mammoth burger (cooked perfectly medium rare) that came with a roast tomato on top and wedged between two slabs of bread, one imbedded with crusty cheese. Rack of lamb was tender, and the accompanying dauphinoise potatoes were excellent, but the dish was ruined by a sauce so reduced it resembled Marmite. Quantities were ample, but we reckoned £70 for lunch for two was a bit steep (the set menu is better value). The superb wine list offers a good selection of house wines by the glass, and others by the half-bottle. Service was efficient, if a little brusque.
Babies and children welcome; high chairs. Booking advisable. Disabled: toilets. No-smoking tables. **Map 7/11L.**

St James's SW1

Che
23 St James's Street, SW1 (020 7747 9380). Green Park or Piccadilly Circus tube.
Bar **Open** 11am-11pm Mon-Fri; 5-11pm Sat. **Average** £10.
Restaurant **Lunch served** noon-3pm Mon-Fri. **Dinner served** 6-11.30pm Mon-Sat. **Main courses** £10.25-£22.50. **Cover** £1.50. **Set lunch** £15.50 two courses, £17.95 three courses. **Service** 12½%. **Credit** AmEx, DC, MC, V.
Reading the globetrotting menu at Che is like playing 'spot the missing cuisine', with Thai, Middle Eastern, Spanish, American, Italian, French and more all covered. There have been reports of inconsistent cooking here (one of the dangers, perhaps, of such an eclectic approach), but when we popped in for lunch, we had no complaints about the food. Gazpacho was a refined but flavourful rendition of this classic summer soup, and Middle Eastern mezze was a terrific light main course (or starter to share between two), with every component skilfully executed. The espresso was first-rate, service (on a quiet day) was prompt and friendly, and the light pouring in through huge windows made our stay in the ultra-modern dining room a pleasant one. Based on that meal, we'd happily go back. However, before you all rush over there, note that Che is located in one of London's richest

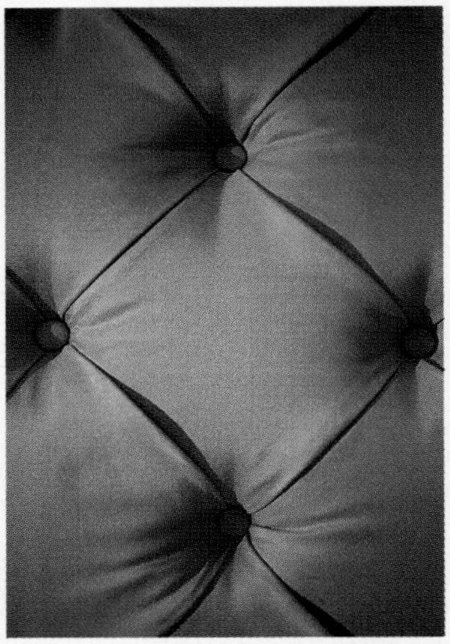

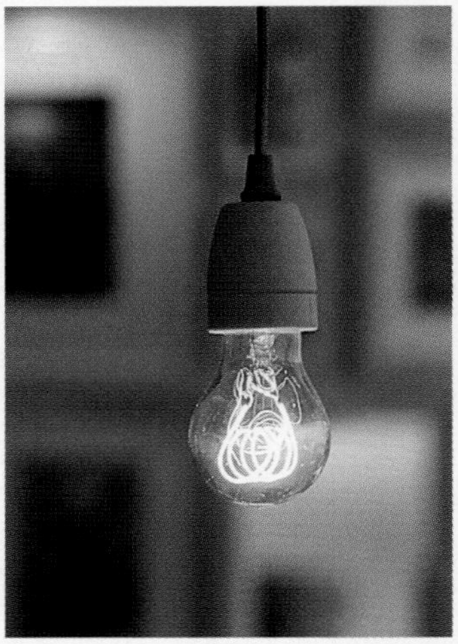

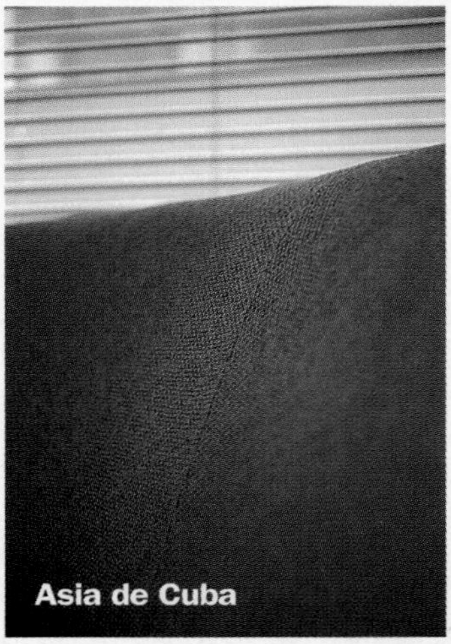

Asia de Cuba

areas, which means a lot of guys in suits. It also means a bill that can easily reach £40 a head for three courses and a wine list that can break the bank. Order from the Sommelier's Selection (£20-£25), and stick with a set lunch menu at £17.95 for three courses (plus annoying £1.50 cover charge) to keep costs down, and treat yourself to an impeccable cocktail at the bar downstairs.
Babies and children admitted. Booking essential. Disabled: toilet. Separate room for parties, seats 14. **Map 13/8J.**

Soho W1

Balans

60 Old Compton Street, W1 (020 7437 5212). Piccadilly Circus or Leicester Square tube.
Meals served 8am-5am Mon-Thur; 8am-6am Fri, Sat; 8am-2am Sun. **Main courses** £7.95-£14. **Service** 12½% for bills over £50. **Credit** AmEx, MC, V.
Tightly packed tables presided over by friendly, well-groomed waiters give gay-friendly Balans a laidback, cheerful vibe, particularly in the summer when the doors open out on to Old Compton Street. The music is loud, which can annoy those in search of a quiet chat, but the menu is extensive and well thought out. We were more taken by starters than main courses on this visit: chilled chilli mango and coconut soup was a refreshing lift; crab cakes (pricey at £6.25) with green papaya salad and Thai dressing were firm, fresh and tangy. Main-course spaghetti with roast vegetables and shaved Parmesan was no more than adequate, while a large helping of smoked chicken with pepperjack potato cake and avocado lime salsa was disappointingly bland. The flamboyant desserts certainly were not lacking in flavour, though. Pineapple surprise turned out to be a sweet and busy concoction of meringue, cream, rum and pineapple sorbet, while a house special of Jamaican ginger cake with toffee sauce, strawberries and vanilla ice-cream was a decadent treat.
Babies and children admitted. Bookings not accepted dinner. **Map 13/6K.**
For branches see index.

Boardwalk

18 Greek Street, W1 (020 7287 2051). Leicester Square or Tottenham Court Road tube. **Dinner served** 4pm-1am Mon-Sat. **Main courses** £8.50-£13.95. **Set dinner** £12 two courses. **Cover** (after 10pm for non-diners) £5 Thur-Sat. **Service** 10%. **Credit** AmEx, MC, JCB, V.
Despite the rising sun and Statue of Liberty motif on the front of the building, Boardwalk no longer quite fits its Stateside trappings – at least as far as the cuisine is concerned. Most customers (the majority under 30) come here to drink; food has always been an afterthought. Now, despite a small dining area overwhelmed by thudding rock music and disadvantaged by staff who divide their time between bar work and waiting at table, the menu has been brought up a notch. Roast tomato soup had a lovely, tangy flavour and came with a blob of crème fraîche and shreds of basil. Seared peppered lamb fillet was declared 'very good' though ill at ease with its bedfellows of feta, salty olives, sun-dried tomatoes and salad leaves. Main courses include retro classics like chicken Kiev and a mixed grill. Pan-fried cod with Parma ham was competently cooked and sat on masses of mash with spring onions; but at £13.95, char-grilled fillet steak sitting on a poor sauce almost bereft of the advertised peppercorns was not good value. Much about Boardwalk is slapdash. Side orders were forgotten then delivered almost by chance; and ne'er a crumb of bread was offered. Much has improved, but more work is needed to make Boardwalk an acceptable venue for diners as well as drinkers.
Booking advisable. Entertainment: DJ 11pm-3am Mon, Fri, Sat; comedy midnight Tue. Separate room for parties, seats 60.
Map 13/6K.
For branch see index.

Westminster SW1

The Atrium

4 Millbank, SW1 (020 7233 0032). Westminster tube/3, 77A bus.
Bar **Open** 8am-11pm Mon-Fri.
Restaurant **Breakfast served** 8-10am, **lunch served** noon-3pm, **dinner served** 6-10pm Mon-Fri. **Main courses** £7.95-£14.95. **Service** 12½%.
Both **Credit** AmEx, DC, MC, £TC, V.
True to its name, this restaurant sits at the bottom of the towering glass-roofed atrium at the centre of the Four Millbank building, also home to the Westminster studios of the main TV networks and other important bodies. Being so close to the corridors of power it's naturally popular with political types, who indulge in conversation at the linen-clad tables scattered between potted palms. Atrium's menu combines mainly British and Med influences, with a few Oriental touches (such as thyme risotto with baby poussin in a shiitake mushroom sauce), without going in for anything too daring. The house Caesar salad was pleasantly refreshing, if a tad minimalist (no anchovies), while a honey-glazed hock of ham with roast root vegetables featured very tender meat, but the glaze and sauce were a little overpowering. Some of the desserts were also on the rich and heavy side. Service is efficient but sometimes oddly casual, although maybe this acts as a counterweight to the self-importance of the clientele. The mainly French, Italian and Australian wine list is amenably priced, although, given the Atrium's popularity as a lunch venue, the odd half-bottle wouldn't go amiss.
Babies and children admitted. Book lunch. No-smoking tables. Separate room for parties, seats 26. **Map 7/10L.**

West

Goldhawk Road W12

Gallery One Twenty

120 Goldhawk Road, W12 (020 8749 5505). Goldhawk Road tube. **Brunch served** 11.30am-5pm Sun. **Dinner served** 6pm-midnight Tue-Sat. **Main courses** £8.50. **Set meals** (before 8pm) £10 two courses, £12.50 three courses. **Credit** AmEx, DC, JCB, MC, £TC, V.
The ice-blue walls, metal chairs and aluminium place settings probably seemed modern and funky when this place first opened, but three years on, things have become rather shabby. The dining area divides into two levels: a long narrow ground floor and a cosy balcony with enough room for three tables. We arrived early and took a table on the balcony as droves of thirty-something regulars began to arrive. We opted for the set menu. Halloumi with tomatoes, new potatoes and fennel was a pleasant if unexciting starter, while baked asparagus, served with a soy and honey dressing, was overly charred on the outside and raw in the middle. Next, bouillabaisse came with a generous amount of fish, but it seemed stale and unpleasantly pungent. Red mullet fillets with tomato vinaigrette and new potatoes was acceptable but not remarkable. To finish we had a plate of cheese and a sorbet, which took so long to arrive that it had turned to liquid. Gallery One Twenty has good intentions but fails to live up to them in practice.
Babies and children welcome. Book weekends.

Hammersmith W6

Moon

206 King Street, W6 (020 8742 6661). Ravenscourt Park tube. **Lunch served** 12.15-3pm Mon-Fri. **Dinner served** 6.30-11pm Mon-Sat. **Average** £20. **Set lunch** £9.50 two courses, £12 three courses. **Credit** AmEx, DC, JCB, MC, £TC, V.
With its softly lit cream interior, Moon has a dreamy and romantic atmosphere. Closer inspection suggests the walls could do with a lick of paint but tablecloths are crisp, white and linen, glasses sparkle and the tables are well spaced. When we arrived a woeful selection of Muzak was playing, but by the time wine and freshly baked rolls appeared, somebody had done the decent thing and turned it off. The eclectic wine list has a good choice of reasonably priced, unusual bottles from Europe and the New World. Similarly, the evening menu spans the globe, with more traditional English choices at lunchtime (steak and kidney pie, for example). Starter number one was a beautifully presented lemon sole salad with a creamy Caesar dressing; a deceptively simple butter bean and cauliflower salad was also pleasing. A huge Thai fish cake served on a bed of wilted spinach with a coriander tartare sauce was succulent, flaky and faultless, if not authentic. The only disappointing dish was a slightly dry bowl of rigatoni with chorizo. Portions are generous (although we still managed a bowl of creamy mustard mash) and service is friendly and efficient. We were impressed.
Babies and children welcome; high chairs. Booking advisable.

Holland Park W11

Wiz

123A Clarendon Road, W11 (020 7229 1500). Ladbroke Grove tube.
Bar **Open** noon-11pm Mon-Sat.
Restaurant **Lunch served** noon-3pm Mon-Fri; noon-4pm Sat, Sun. **Dinner served** 6.30-11pm Mon-Thur; 6.30pm-midnight Fri, Sat. **Main courses** £3.50-£6.50. **Set meals** £29.50 four courses incl. coffee (upstairs in Woz only). **Service** 12½%.
Both **Credit** AmEx, MC, JCB, £TC, V.
Our visit to Antony Worrall Thompson's trendy west London creation didn't get off to a good start: the waiter unapologetically knocked over a bottle of beer, leaving us to wipe it up with our napkins. But the soothing mix of candle light, exposed brick walls, cushioned banquettes and big wooden tables soon lulled us into a forgiving mood. The menu is divided into geographical sections and the idea is to order tapas-style from the six to eight choices in each section. Mindful of the steep prices, we chose just five dishes and a side of rice. Prawn samosas with pomegranate raita tasted nice enough, as did a roast red pepper and aubergine salad. Unfortunately, we had to send the other dishes back – they were either raw (tea-smoked quail) or over-salted (crispy vegetables and green salad). Despite these items being removed from the bill, and despite the wine list having some reasonably priced, varied bottles, the overall dining experience is much more swizz than Wiz.
Babies and children admitted. Separate room for parties, seats 50. Tables outdoors (10, roof terrace). **Map 11/6Az.**

Kensington W8

The Abingdon

54 Abingdon Road, W8 (020 7937 3339). High Street Kensington tube.
Bar **Open** 12.30-11pm Mon-Sat; 12.30-10.30pm Sun.
Restaurant **Lunch served** noon-2.30pm Mon-Sat; noon-3pm Sun. **Dinner served** 6.30-11pm Mon-Sat; 6.30-10.30pm Sun. **Main courses** £9.75-£15.50. **Set lunch** £10.95 two courses. **Service** 12½%.
Both **Credit** AmEx, MC, £$TC, V.
Large and pastel-pink, the Abingdon is pretty hard to miss in one of Kensington's best-preserved side streets. Inside, shades of magnolia and mint dominate this one-time pub, which benefits from plenty of natural light during the summer months. Restaurant seating is arranged corridor-style, with a less formal area at the back, but if you prefer, you can choose (as we did) to perch at the central bar. King prawns in puff pastry with Provençal sauce was a lively, balanced dish, but Taleggio and savoy cabbage filo parcels were somewhat flavourless and slightly oily. From the selection of main courses we went for pan-fried lemon sole fillets in a herb dressing, with a very generous side order of mash that was creamed and buttered to utter perfection. Tagliatelle with Jerusalem artichokes and oyster mushrooms was a good vegetarian option and surprisingly filling. However, despite some good food, the Abingdon's high prices are more a reflection of its location than an indication of the quality of its cooking.
Babies and children admitted. Booking essential. Tables outdoors (4, pavement).
Map 5/9A.

Goolies

21 Abingdon Road, W8 (020 7938 1122). High Street Kensington tube. **Open** noon-11pm Mon-Sat; noon-10.30pm Sun.
Lunch served 12.30-3pm daily.
Dinner served 6.30-10.30pm Mon-Sat; 6.30-10pm Sun. **Main courses** £10-£17. **Set lunch** £10.95 two courses, £13.95 three courses, incl coffee. **Service** 12½%. **Credit** AmEx, DC, MC, V.
Goolies, despite the daft name, is a sleek, stylish Kensington bar-restaurant containing a fair few ex-public schoolboys tucking into adventurous modern British-Pacific Rim cuisine. Ingredients are of an impressively high quality, but are not always shown to best advantage by some of the busier recipe combinations. Witness parcels of parma ham with cream cheese, and tomato and goat's cheese terrine. The cheese tended to overpower the subtleties of the ham in the former dish, while the first deliciously fresh taste of tomato in the latter didn't prepare us for a dose of coarse, hot chilli that came along behind (unmentioned on the menu). Of the mains, rack of lamb with mint dressing and couscous was an innovative and tasty variation of an old English standard; best of all was a superb, perfectly flavoured seared tuna steak. A touch of the school room returned with the speciality dessert, a very chunky bread and butter pudding ice-cream (possibly an acquired taste). The wine list is entirely New World (except for champagnes), with plenty of choice for under £20; service is friendly, relaxed and efficient.
Babies and children admitted. Booking advisable. **Map 5/9A.**

Notting Hill W11

Rotisserie Jules

133A Notting Hill Gate, W11 (020 7221 3331). Notting Hill Gate tube. **Meals served** noon-11.30pm daily. **Main courses** £4.95-£7.25. **Service** 10% for bills over £15. **Credit** AmEx, MC, £TC, V.
This fast-food joint is geared towards take-aways, but it's no hardship to eat in. It's a simply furnished, whitewashed place: no frills but presentable. The speciality roast chickens are all free-range, and come in leg and thigh or breast and wing portions. Prices rise when the chicken is accompanied by a side dish such as gratin dauphinois, french fries, ratatouille or sweet corn. Lamb steak (the mainstay chicken alternative) arrived char-grilled and juicy, and its accompanying dauphinois was chunky and cheesy, while the ratatouille tasted a cut above the tinned version. Vegetable soup and Caesar salad were of acceptable canteen standard, but the chocolate mousse seemed a little artificial in flavour. All the above can be ordered as a takeaway, with cheap delivery to W and SW London postcodes, and there's also a limited drinks list.
Babies and children welcome; high chairs. Book dinner. Disabled: toilet. No-smoking tables. Takeaway service; delivery service.
Map 11/7A.
For branches see index.

Shepherd's Bush W12, W14

Maloney's

25 Richmond Way, W14 (020 7602 6778). Shepherd's Bush tube. **Lunch served** noon-3pm Sun. **Dinner served** 7-11pm daily. **Set dinners** £10.75 one course, £14.25 two courses, £17.75 three courses. **Service** 12½%. **Credit** MC, £TC, V.
The name of this small friendly local behind Shepherd's Bush strongly suggests it's Irish; in fact it's an American-run outfit with a wandering menu. The decor is a collision of pastel colours, lurid photos, faux drapery and oil-powered candles on crowded tables. Like the furnishings, the menu is very busy and mistakenly seeks to please all of the people all of the time with 11 starters and 11 mains for less than ten tables. Nor is it especially cheap, particularly if you consider that a third of the dishes carry a supplement of £1.50 to £3 and the 'accompanying' side dishes add a further £2. At these rates the ordinary cooking should have been better. Certainly stir-fried tiger prawns with oriental vegetables needn't have been drowned in oyster and black bean sauce, while a field mushroom stuffed with crabmeat, topped with Gruyère cheese was more about stuffing than refinement. Roast rack of lamb was nicely pink and imaginatively accompanied by garlic and courgette mash, but let down by a glutinous peppercorn gravy. And grilled lemon sole with a smoked salmon julienne lacked the sophistication of its title. Moreover, the heaviness of the food meant we were unable to consider the groaning dessert trolley. Despite its pleasant atmosphere, its wine list (short, but with some good entries) and its warm, up-beat service, Maloney's is not a destination for picky epicureans.
Babies and children welcome. Booking advisable.

The Rotisserie

56 Uxbridge Road, W12 (020 8743 3028). Shepherd's Bush tube. **Lunch served** noon-2.45pm Mon-Fri. **Dinner served** 6.30-10.30pm Mon; 6.30-11pm Tue-Thur; 6.30-11.30pm Fri, Sat. **Main courses** £8.95-£15.95. **Set meal** (Mon-Fri until 7.15pm) £11.95 two courses. **Credit** AmEx, DC, JCB, MC, £TC, V.
Somewhere between a Stockpot and a Café Med, the Shepherd's Bush Rotisserie is a good destination for parents plea bargaining with McDonald's-fixated children or young adults with undemanding palates. Aesthetics are organised accordingly in an anodyne corridor of whitewash and tiles with pinky-purple trimmings and glossy pictures. The menu breaks down into a two-course special and a selection of starters, steaks and main courses, ranging from various forms of chicken, to fashionable fish (tuna, halibut), steaks and a changing vegetarian option. Don't raise your hopes and you won't be disappointed. Starters include merguez sausages, spare ribs, gravadlax and standardised salads; we chose goat's cheese on toasted bread with a thicket of foliage, which was designed not to offend and didn't. 'Famous' steaks are organised on a pick-and-mix basis: rib-eye, sirloin, fillet, t-bone and chateaubriands with pepper, bearnaise or garlic butter sauce. But spicily barbecued peri-peri chicken and distinctively herby corn fed chicken in rosemary butter

are just as good. The small selection of popular wines stay sensibly south of £20 and service was distracted but friendly.
Babies and children admitted. Booking advisable. No-smoking tables.
For branches see index.

Westbourne Grove W11

Bali Sugar ★
33A All Saints Road, W11 (020 7221 4477). Westbourne Park tube. **Lunch served** 12.30-2.30pm Tue-Sun. **Dinner served** 6.30-11pm daily. **Main courses** £12.80-£15.90. **Credit** AmEx, DC, MC, V.
Occupying the former Notting Hill base of its parent the Sugar Club, Bali Sugar offers pretty definitive Pacific Rim-European-and-elsewhere fusion food to celebrity diners and a fair cross-section of the executive classes of W11. Smokers occupy the yellow-toned ground floor, while non-smokers enjoy the airy basement, where there's a small conservatory and a sunken garden. The restaurant's primary attraction, though, is the very skilful cooking of New York-trained Uruguayan chef Claudio Aprile, in which very inventive combinations are never allowed to overwhelm the flavours of the essential ingredients. Warm nori roll with wild mushrooms and a yuzu dressing was a wonderful, trademark starter, in which all the multi-continental elements were perfectly blended; equally impressive was a beautifully simple but imaginative starter of watermelon, feta and pine nuts. Main courses made less of an impact, though roast chicken breast with Thai curry broth had an enjoyably delicate jus, while the dressing on a confit of duck leg with fruit glaze satisfyingly offset some slightly dry meat. For dessert a combination of red wine and cardamom ice-creams was a subtle experience rather than the all-out blast it could have been. The wine list offers a distinctly superior selection of European and New World labels, and service is hip but charming. A place that could show other experimenters how it's done.
Babies and children admitted. Booking advisable. Tables outdoors (6, courtyard). No-smoking tables. **Map 11/5Az.**

South West

Fulham SW10

Deco
294 Fulham Road, SW10 (020 7351 0044). Fulham Broadway tube/14, 211 bus.
Bar **Open** 5.30pm-midnight Mon-Wed; 5.30pm-1am Thur-Sat.
Restaurant **Lunch served** noon-4pm Sat. **Dinner served** 6-11pm Mon-Sat. **Main courses** £7.95-£12.95. **Set lunch** £7.95 two courses. **Credit** AmEx, JCB, MC, V.
Opened in 1998 by an enthusiastic husband-and-wife team, this chrome, marble and faux-deco restaurant-cum-bar feels very '80s. Decorative timewarp aside, however, Deco has built up a loyal following among well-heeled, Sloaney locals who return for the friendly atmosphere, reliable food and good deals: arrive before 8pm and have a three-course set dinner for £12.95. A cocktail menu provided a couple of potent Caipirinhas. Foodwise, predictable starters include Parma ham and fig salad, tempura prawns with sweet chilli sauce and Caesar salad. More tempting were wild mushroom ravioli, which was bursting with flavour, and a perfectly cooked dish of duck with pear and passion fruit. The only disappointment was an overpoweringly sweet mango chutney sauce that spoiled an otherwise very fresh and generous portion of roast sea bass. A mouth-wateringly intense hot and cold chocolate pudding accompanied by perfectly plump raspberries made a good finale. Service was efficient and friendly. Overall, Deco deserves to do well.
Babies and children admitted (restaurant only). Tables outdoors (4, pavement). **Map 5/12C.**

Parsons Green SW6

Upstairs at the Pen
51 Parsons Green Lane, SW6 (020 7371 8517). Parsons Green tube.
Bar **Open** 11am-11pm Mon-Fri; 5-11pm Sat; 5-10.30pm Sun.
Restaurant **Dinner served** 7.30-11pm Mon-Sat. **Main courses** £9.50-£14.50. **Service** 12½%.
Both **Credit** DC, JCB, MC, £TC, V.
A classical marble statue, white half-panelled walls and linen tablecloths set against a dark-wood floor give Upstairs at the Pen the atmosphere of a Victorian luncheon room to contrast with its modern ground-floor bar. The softening effect of uplighting and oil lamps on the tables provides a relaxing ambience. From the starters,

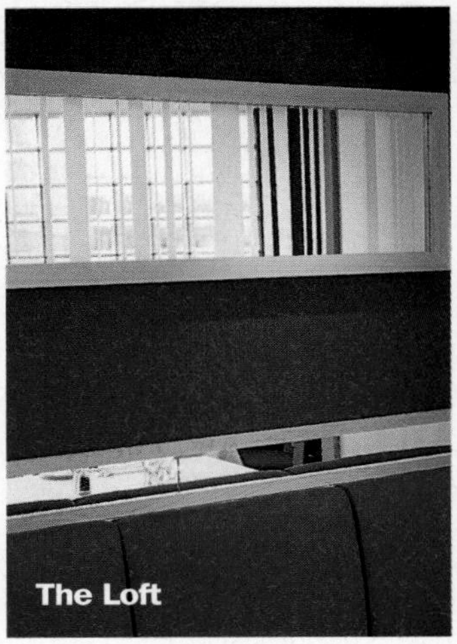
The Loft

including Mediterranean prawns, deep-fried goat's cheese and Caesar salad, filo-wrapped Camembert with red onion jam and frisse leaves was disappointingly bland. More successful was grilled garlic mushroom and spinach tartlet, Emmental and Worcestershire sauce. Roast marinated rump of lamb was first class, with roast parsnips, potato gratin and rioja jus providing an excellent accompaniment, while the passable baked spiced salmon fillet was enhanced by sweet potato purée with a light herb, tomato and white wine relish. To finish came delectable light and tangy lemon tart with crème fraîche and strawberries and an enjoyably creamy white chocolate and candied ginger brulée. An interesting and varied wine list provided a satisfyingly rich and aromatic Argentinian Libertad sangiovase/malbec and a dry pinot grigio 1997 Mosole. Agreeable food plus affable and obliging service made it deceptively easy to linger.
Babies and children admitted. Booking advisable. Entertainment: jazz 5-11pm Sun (bar). Tables outdoors (8, garden).

Putney SW15

Blue Pumpkin
147 Upper Richmond Road, SW15 (020 8780 3553). East Putney tube/Putney rail. **Meals served** noon-10.30pm Mon-Thur, Sun; 11.30am-11pm Fri, Sat. **Main courses** £7.95-£10.95. **Set lunch** £8.95 two courses, £10.95 three courses. **Credit** AmEx, DC, MC, V.
Bleached pine furnishings, loud splashes of orange, electric blue and deep yellow – all bathed in bright artificial lighting – give the Blue Pumpkin the gaudy demeanour of a West End pasta chain. Bland background music (George Michael, followed by some insipid boy band) didn't do much to correct this impression on a recent visit, but a decent monthly menu and warm, personable staff soon set us straight. From the list of starters we chose warm bacon and avocado salad in a Caesar dressing with garlic croûtons (delicious), and marinated mushrooms and vegetables with baby spinach (nice enough). Mains included Moroccan spiced lamb burgers with chunky chips, and a good but slightly salty poached salmon salad with new potatoes and French beans. The dish of the day was grilled sea bass on mash with salad, lemon and olive oil. We skipped dessert (the likes of apple pie and baked lime cheesecake), instead settling for Irish coffee, at which point the management mercifully decided to dim the lighting.
Babies and children welcome.

Moomba
5 Lacy Road, SW15 (020 8785 9151). Putney Bridge tube/Putney rail/14, 37, 39, 85, 93 bus. **Meals served** 10am-10.30pm daily. **Main courses** £6.80-£11.90. **Set meal** £9.50 two courses. **Service** 12½%. **Credit** AmEx, DC, MC, £TC, V.
Green and white walls, displaying ethnic prints, bring harmony to the mixed rustic and bistro-chic furnishings in this popular, casually trendy world café bar. Starters include 'Indonesian' pork and spiced prawn salad and Cornish crabcakes with caper salad. We chose a scrumptious Welsh goat's cheese rarebit on an English muffin, and French brie, smoked bacon and avocado salad, which afforded a pleasant combination of textures and flavours. From an assortment of basic international dishes, we went for an unpretentious but appetising Cumberland sausage with onion gravy and vegetarian Mexican meze (enchiladas, nachos,

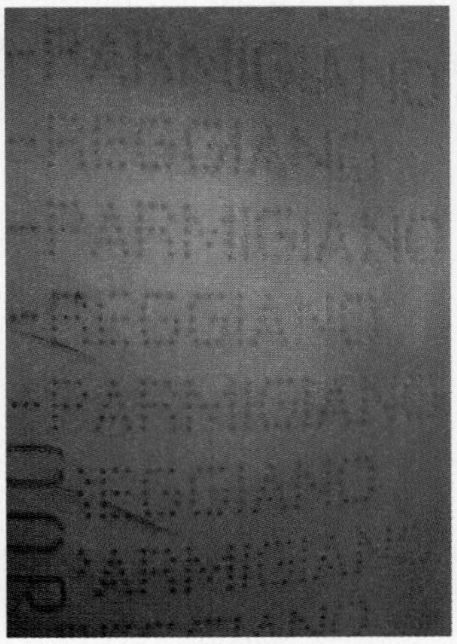

taco and refried beans). The latter, though substantial, was marred by an unnecessary blanket of relishes. For dessert, lime parfait on a biscuit base was deliciously complemented by blueberry sauce; hot chocolate fudge cake was a little dry. Friendly, animated service and a hint of taped background pop music maintain a lively atmosphere in which to enjoy a value-for-money meal.
Babies and children welcome; high chairs. Book weekends. Separate room for parties, seats 40. Tables outdoors (5, pavement).

South Kensington SW3

The Collection
264 Brompton Road, SW3 (020 7225 1212). South Kensington tube.
Bar **Open** 5-11pm Mon-Fri; noon-11pm Sat; 6-10.30pm Sun.
Restaurant **Meals served** 5-11pm Mon-Fri; noon-11pm Sat; 6-10.30pm Sun. **Main courses** £11.50-£16.95. **Service** 15%.
Both **Credit** AmEx, DC, JCB, MC, V.
Before you reach the intimidating catwalk that leads to the restaurant you have to shuffle past a large doorman and deal with the hassle of a guest list. Once inside you'll probably need a drink, so head for the long bar and try an excellent Bloody Mary or Hong Kong Fizz. Decorated in a style that can only be described as 'tiki bar meets urban warehouse' – bamboo walls, big leather sofas and exposed brick – the Collection exudes a predatory atmosphere. This is exaggerated by the black-clad waiters who lean over the restaurant balcony, silently observing customers in the bar below. Nevertheless, the food is remarkably good. A starter of seared tuna with shiitake, mooli and cucumber salad was fantastically fresh, while smoked chicken 'escabeche' with coriander, chillies and lime had bags of flavour and texture. To follow, a haddock and potted shrimp parcel with ruby chard was mouth-wateringly succulent, and crispy duck with soba noodles came with a perfectly balanced plum sauce. The only disappointment was a slightly sickly crème brûlée that was more mousse than brûlée. Portions are generous, presentation is elegant without being overly formal, and service is efficient.
Babies and children admitted. Book weekends. Disabled: toilet. Dress: smart casual. **Map 12/10E.**

Wandsworth SW18

The Garratt
205 Garratt Lane, SW18 (020 8871 2223). Earlsfield or Wandsworth Town rail. **Lunch served** noon-2.30pm Tue-Fri; noon-3pm Sat, Sun. **Dinner served** 7-10.30pm Tue-Thur; 7-11pm Fri, Sat. **Main courses** £10. **Set meal** £17.50 three courses. **Credit** MC, £TC, V.
A Saturday night at the Garratt was a welcome respite from the outside world. Bright but homely colours, easy-going staff and the soothing buzz of conversation made us feel as if we'd joined a late-night gathering in an unfamiliar but welcoming house. A daily menu is chalked on a large board beside the bar and efficient, charming waiters are on hand to answer any questions. We asked for a main course portion of what sounded like a particularly appetising starter (spinach and ricotta pie with black bean salad and salsa). A generous helping duly arrived, combining all its full flavours with a light filo pastry. Crispy roast cod with mash, cannellini beans and spinach was even better. A shared

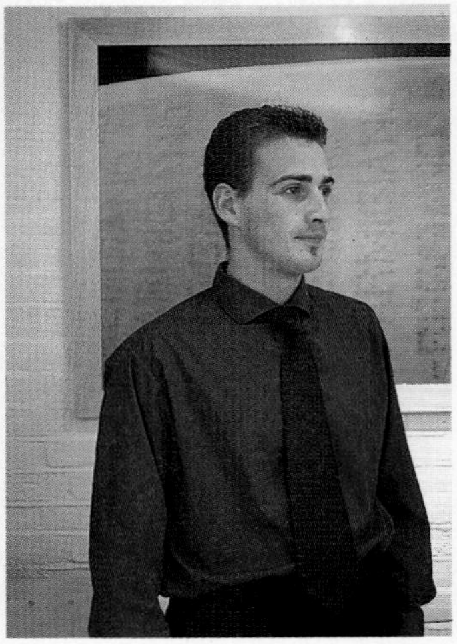

dessert of hot toffee cake with cream rounded off the meal nicely, and the whole experience left us promising to return.
Babies and children welcome; toys and crayons. Booking advisable. Tables outdoors (8, garden).

Wimbledon SW19

Light House
75-77 Ridgeway, SW19 (020 8944 6338/020 8946 4440). Wimbledon tube/rail then 200 bus. **Lunch served** noon-2.30pm, **dinner served** 6.30-11pm daily. **Main courses** £9.70-£15.70. **Set meals** £15.50 two courses. **Service** 12½%. **Credit** AmEx, MC, V.
We were very pleasantly surprised by the Light House when we visited shortly after it opened, and subsequent visits have done nothing to make us revise our opinion. A stark, stylish bare interior makes for a pretty noisy setting, but we were hooked by the modern, globetrotting menu. Dishes on the menu are divided into antipasti, primi, dolci and so on, despite the fact that very few have any links with Italy – even the ravioli is filled with beetroot, Manchego and oregano. More typical are starters such as feta and sweetcorn fritter with chicken livers, roast pepper and avocado salad, or parsley and garlic marinated artichoke with aubergine salad, spiced carrots and butter bean dip. Mains are in a similiar vein – grilled veal cutlet on miso Puy lentils and hijiki seaweed with tamarillo and ginger chutney, for example. Pudding-wise, a haven of familiarity is offered by Neal's Yard cheeses, but those with some spirit of adventure left could try coconut, lemongrass and mint parfait with roast plums and toasted coconut. The wine list is as modish as the cooking. Wimbledon's looking up.
Babies and children welcome; high chairs. Disabled: toilet. No-smoking tables. Tables outdoors (5, courtyard).

South

Bankside SE1

The Loft ★
17 Lavington Street, SE1 (020 7902 0800). Southwark tube.
Bar **Open** noon-11pm Mon-Sat; noon-10.30pm Sun.
Restaurant **Lunch served** noon-2.30pm, **dinner served** 6.30-10.30pm daily. **Main courses** £12.50-£14.50
Both **Credit** AmEx, DC, MC, V.
The Loft is housed in what looks like a large grey nuclear bunker, so it's a pleasant surprise to climb the tier of steps and find yourself in an open-plan room, tastefully decorated with aubergine-tinted walls and modern art. Another flight of stairs leads to the dining area, where a brief à la carte menu offers some startling modern global combinations. We practically scraped the pattern off the bowl to get at the last drop of a deliciously piquant black bean soup with Mexican salsa, while a salad of chorizo, fig, sweet potato and poached egg, with goat's cheese dressing was positively purred over. Although sorely tempted by the fennel-cured salt cod, we plumped for roast salmon with paella-style risotto and squid salsa. The salmon was seared on the outside, yet flaked away to perfection; the risotto was lively with mussels, prawns and squid; and the squid, onions and tomatoes came together like a dream. But in one dish there were just too many flavours fighting for attention. We were glad we went for a simple

We've rounded up a bunch of wild new flavours.

And every night our Chef lets them loose.

At Soviet Canteen, we've tracked down recipes from the Baltic to the Barents and we've pursued ingredients from Minsk to Vladivostok.

Now we've brought them all together in a healthy, modern style that everyone can enjoy.

You'll find our £9.95 Prix Fixe menu makes a mellow introduction to our cooking. Or let yourself run free among our à la carte dishes.

But don't take on too many of our 100 authentic vodkas at once. They tend to gang up on the unwary.

SOVIET CANTEEN

Tasty modern cooking with a Russian twist.

430 Kings Road, Chelsea 020 7795 1556 www.sovietcanteen.com

but effective side order of Asian-style vegetables to offset the excesses of the main dish. The Loft's wine list consists of a reasonably priced main list, and a special selection of Grand Vins Mercure that carry a flat-rate mark-up of £5. Service was friendly and efficient throughout – an impressive achievement, given the number of stairs.
Babies and children admitted; high chairs; children's menu. Disabled: toilet. No-smoking tables. **Map 8/8O.**

Battersea SW11

Cinnamon Cay
87 Lavender Hill, SW11 (020 7801 0932). Clapham Junction rail then 27, 77A bus. **Lunch served** 11.30am-3.30pm Tue-Fri; 11am-4pm Sat, Sun. **Dinner served** 5-11pm Mon-Fri; 5-11.30pm Sat. **Main courses** £8.50-£12.50. **Service** 12½%. **Credit** MC, V.
One of Battersea's newer additions, Cinnamon Cay has built up a positive word-of-mouth reputation. A modestly sized restaurant, it has interesting interior features, including a curved and spotlighted pinewood ceiling, and lush red varnished walls that give a smart leatherlike effect. A mixed menu includes brunch (Greek yoghurt, fresh mango and strawberries, buttermilk pancake stack with organic maple syrup, blueberries and crème fraîche); or the likes of honey roasted octopus, squid and chorizo salad with red onions, wild rocket and shaved Manchego. From the evening menu we went for a refreshing starter of warm glazed beetroot, sugar snap and fresh orange salad with mustard seed vinaigrette. Goat's cheese mousse would have been a bland option save for an accompanying smoked aubergine purée and vine tomatoes in Parmesan oil. To follow, char-grilled beef fillet with roast baby vegetables was a good sturdy option; Australian reef fish with sugar grilled figs, endive salad and olive oil was exotic and tasty, although the figs were superfluous. Service is warm and laid-back and the venue is well worth a visit.
Babies and children admitted; high chairs. Disabled: toilet. Tables outdoors (5, patio).

The Drawing Room
103 Lavender Hill, SW11 (020 7350 2564). Clapham Junction rail. **Open** 6pm-midnight Tue-Fri; 11am-midnight Sat; 11am-10.30pm Sun. **Brunch served** 11am-3pm, **tea served** 3-7pm Sat, Sun. **Dinner served** 6-11pm Tue-Sun. **Main courses** £8.95-£12.95. **Credit** MC, V.
Slightly tatty furnishings in deep orange and red combine with mix-and-match tablecloths to give the Drawing Room a classic air of faded glory. On the evening of our visit, the lone waitress coped well with a steady stream of diners (mainly couples). Lentil and bacon soup was an undeniably smooth, delicious and comforting starter, but quite pricey at £4.95 – especially when you've factored in the extra 95p for a selection of own-made breads. We had no complaints regarding the mains, though, all of which come with a selection of vegetables. A filling option of tomato and mixed herb crêpes stuffed generously with wild mushrooms, onions and feta was spot on, its subtle port and cream sauce tempering the busy line-up of ingredients. Char-grilled chicken breast with tagliatelle and Gorgonzola sauce was another winner. We decided to skip desserts (the likes of dark and white nougatine with mint sauce) content just to sit back and enjoy the sound of Louis Armstrong and Ella Fitzgerald in the background.
Babies and children admitted. Tables outdoors (4, pavement).

Brixton SW9

Helter Skelter ★
50 Atlantic Road, SW9 (020 7274 8600). Brixton tube/rail. **Dinner served** 7-11pm Mon-Thur; 7-11.30pm Fri, Sat; 6-10.30pm Sun. **Main courses** £9.50-£12.50. **Credit** AmEx, MC, £TC, V.
This modern steel-fronted restaurant seems out of place opposite the tatty railway arches of Atlantic Road, but it remains a Brixton favourite despite its upwardly mobile prices. The long dining room is informal and inviting and the menu is a creative global mix. We got off to a great start with a delicious spicy ceviche of whiting with a chilli crouton and mizuma (a little overpowered by the chilli). Whitebait and shrimp fritters with anchovy mayonnaise and mixed leaves was also good despite a slightly oily, heavy batter. Griddled salmon on saffron mash with grilled asparagus and artichokes was a perfectly balanced main course, while a miso broth with udon noodles, choi sum, red peppers and shredded nori was an intriguing Japanese-inspired vegetarian option. We finished with a moreish blood orange and mango tart with rock melon yoghurt ice-cream and a lavender crème brûlée with biscotti. The combination of friendly service and high standard of cooking continue to make Helter Skelter an asset to the area.
Booking essential. **Map 18.**

Clapham SW4

The Rapscallion
75 Venn Street, SW4 (020 7787 6555). Clapham Common tube. **Breakfast served** 8am-noon Mon-Fri. **Brunch served** 10am-4pm Sun. **Lunch served** noon-3pm Mon-Fri. **Dinner served** 6-11.30pm Mon-Sat; 6-10.30pm Sun. **Main courses** £5.50-£12.50. **Service** 12½%. **Credit** AmEx, DC, JCB, MC, £TC, V.
In a street with three other popular restaurants, the two-year-old Rapscallion is definitely staking out its own territory, with what seems to be a full house on most nights of the week. The menu wanders off in all directions: starters include char-grilled beef rump skewers with pineapple jam and satay sauce, and grilled vegetables with honey mustard mayonnaise, but we went straight for mains. Lemon and oregano marinated chicken breast with warm feta and chickpea salad was a generously sized portion sporting pretty bland chicken. Ghanaian plantain cake, a well-sculpted creation of sweet potato, pickled cucumber and coconut salsa, was a far tastier and extremely filling choice. We risked chocolate sushi for pudding – a sweet concoction of coconut, chocolate banana cream and ice-cream. Service was laid back and pleasantly unrehearsed, and given by staff who looked good in a trash-chic kind of way. For details of Rapscallion's smarter sister restaurant, the **Sequel**, *see p131* **Modern European**.
Babies and children welcome; high chairs. Booking advisable. Tables outdoors (8, pavement).

Waterloo SE1

Honest Goose
61 The Cut, SE1 (020 7261 1221). Southwark tube/Waterloo tube/rail. **Lunch served** noon-2.30pm Mon-Sat, noon-3pm Sun. **Dinner served** 6-10.30pm Mon-Sat. **Main course** £7-£12. **Set lunch** £6 main course, drink. **Credit** DC, MC, V.
The Honest Goose takes its name from the 17th-century slang for prostitute, a career that sustained thousands of women in latter-day Southwark. It is not, however, a knocking shop, but rather a branch of the **Honest Cabbage** (*see below*). But it does have an olde worlde feel to it, with bistro chairs and seats from an earlier, earthier era. The menu is also strangely, but not unpleasantly dated. Starters from the daily changing menu might include meat pies, Waldorf salad, or pan-fried veal Holstein: all well executed but bizarrely retro choices. If your tastes are altogether more modern, you can order linguine with scallops and rocket, grilled cod with butter bean and roast pepper, and even tiger prawn brochette with coriander salsa. Most main courses are served with mash or posh chips and two veg. Puds and drinks lists are basic and satisfying. The Honest Goose is a slightly quirky, unassuming place that neatly bridges the gap between the alehouses and taverns that still dominate dining culture south of the Thames, and the smarter, more expensive South Bank establishments.
Babies and children admitted; high chairs. **Map 7/8N.**

Laughing Gravy
154 Blackfriars Road, SE1 (020 7721 7055). Southwark tube/Waterloo tube/rail.
Bar **Open** 11am-midnight Mon-Fri; 6.30pm-midnight Sat.
Restaurant **Meals served** 11.30am-11pm Mon-Fri; 6.30-11pm Sat. **Main courses** £8.25-£12.45.
Both **Credit** AmEx, DC, MC, V.
While some people might find this very friendly and well thought-out bar-restaurant a little off the beaten track, it's still only a short walk from the South Bank and definitely worth a visit. Snacks are available in the front bar but those in search of something more substantial should carry on through to the glass-roofed dining room at the back. Balsamic-glazed sardines stuffed with baby plum tomatoes, oregano and orange was a nifty starter but a delicately flavoured Cornish crab linguine lost out to the accompanying charred chorizo. A main course of roast breast of duck marinated in crushed redcurrants and gin served with sugar snaps was tender, moist and full of flavour, as was a spring chicken with tarragon and brioche breadcrumbs on a bed of creamed mushrooms. For pudding, Eton mess was a fine mix of meringue, yoghurt, strawberry and cream, while a simpler dish of gooseberry fool was just as tasty. There is a concise, intelligent wine list and the attentive staff are happy to answer any questions.
Babies and children welcome; high chairs. Book lunch. Tables outdoors (3, pavement). **Map 7/9O.**

South East

London Bridge SE1

Honest Cabbage
99 Bermondsey Street, SE1 (020 7234 0080). London Bridge tube/rail. **Brunch served** noon-4pm Sat, Sun. **Lunch served** noon-3pm Mon-Fri. **Dinner served** 6.30-10pm Mon-Wed; 6.30-11pm Thur, Fri; 7-11pm Sat. **Main courses** £9-£12. **Credit** MC, £TC, V.
The Cabbage is the kind of classy local that makes you want to up sticks and move to SE1. Quirky knick-knacks and Victorian frosted glass give the light dining room an unpretentious appeal and the menu (although pricier than last year) offers a reliable template of ten dishes. These include a soup, a sandwich, a salad, a pasta dish, a pot, a pie and a vegetarian choice, all cooked to a high standard. Smoked chicken and oyster mushroom broth was delicious, while the crab cakes were some of the best we've tasted. Lamb and spring vegetable pie was hearty and warming, while a special of oven-roasted sea bass, pak choi and lemon and chive oil was impressive, if a little oily. A sturdy portion of garden-fresh sugar snap peas and two great hunks of corn on the cob, with moreish chunky chips, completed the picture. Puds were less appealing, though a generous blackcurrant sorbet was refreshingly tart. Add to all this unlimited bread and olives for 50p and decent house wine and you have a winning formula. You'll find its sister restaurant, the **Honest Goose**, in Waterloo (*see above*).
Babies and children welcome; high chairs. Book dinner. Disabled: toilet. **Map 8/9Q.**

East

Bethnal Green E2

Perennial
110-112 Columbia Road, E2 (020 7739 4556). Bus 26, 48, 55. **Lunch served** noon-3pm Fri, Sat; 8am-4pm Sun. **Dinner served** 7-10pm Tue-Sat. **Main courses** £9-£13. **Service** 10%. **Credit** MC, V.
Columbia Road bursts into life on Sunday mornings for the flower market, but this latest blossom is a likeable local that has settled into its name with aplomb and could have been here for years. We warmed to its friendly staff and its unassuming mustard and scarlet interior dotted with photos. Some quirky food combos – salmon with coriander and ginger accompanied by herb tagliatelle – raised our eyebrows, but a starter of rocket salad with toasted hazelnuts and grano padano combined well and the slightly charred nuts really worked. Asparagus-filled pancake with baked shaved Parmesan and toasted pinenuts was fine, too. Best end of lamb was pink inside with a whiff of rosemary and so crisp outside that even the fat was irresistible, and nicely cooked 'Irish cabbage' compensated for over-hard new potatoes. Char-grilled tuna with horseradish cream, lime and fried egg noodles (£11.50) was slightly over-imaginative: the tuna was medium rare perfection and the noodles held their own but lime with horseradish tasted soapy. Puddings (rhubarb and ginger fool and summer pudding) were happily conventional and worth ordering. House wines are very easy drinking particularly at this price (£9.50 a bottle). A good local in an underserved area.
Babies and children admitted. No-smoking tables. Tables outdoors (6, garden).

Victoria Park E9

Frocks
95 Lauriston Road, E9 (020 8986 3161). Mile End tube then 277 bus. **Brunch served** 11am-4pm Sat, Sun. **Lunch served** 11am-2.30pm Tue-Fri. **Dinner served** 6.30-11pm Tue-Sat. **Main courses** £10.50-£12.50. **Set lunch** £9.50 two courses. **Closed** Aug. **Credit** AmEx, DC, MC, £TC, V.
A welcoming little local, with a particularly good line in weekend brunches: toasted muffin with smoked halibut and poached egg with hollandaise sauce, kedgeree, pancakes with maple syrup and cream, for example. The brunch menu is unchanging, lunch and dinner menus change every fortnight. Prices are a little high for the quality, which is good but not stunning, with starters around £6 and mains all over £10. Spicy fish cakes with peanut and coriander relish might be followed by pan-fried veal cutlet on chorizo mash with sage gravy; goat's cheese and black olive croustade with salad could be paired with grilled sea bream fillets with coconut and lime basmati rice. Puddings are less adventurous, although a little novelty can't be resisted – bread and butter pudding comes with marmalade custard. The decor, which has a certain charm, is 1970s Victoriana. A short wine list and very pleasant staff complete what is invariably a decent evening out in an area short on restaurants.
Babies and children welcome; high chair. Booking advisable weekends. Gluten-free dishes. Separate room for parties, seats 30. Tables outdoors (5, walled-garden; 2, pavement).

Wanstead E11

Hadley House
27 High Street, E11 (020 8989 8855). Snaresbrook or Wanstead tube. **Lunch served** 11.30am-2.30pm Mon-Sat; noon-9pm Sun. **Dinner served** 7-10.30pm Mon-Sat. **Main courses** £10.50-£16. **Credit** MC, V.
With tables outside in summer facing a small, leafy stretch of common, and an interior of pine tables and tastefully muted yellows and blues, Hadley House comes as a surprise in an area not associated with tranquil, intimate restaurants. There's a frequently changing menu, offering a fashionable variety of ingredients and com binations, and an equally enterprising wine list, with plenty of good options for under £20. To start, filo parcels of Brie with gooseberry chutney were pleasantly crisp and refreshing. A main dish of mixed seafood (squid, prawns and scallops) with salad was less impressive than it looked and a bit bland, but rack of lamb with Parmesan potato cake and avocado and mint salsa had plenty of flavour. Tarte tatin was lacklustre, but came with excellent cinnamon ice-cream. Service was a little flustered at times, even though the restaurant was not especially busy, but staff were otherwise helpful and charming. Very well suited for a quiet, relaxing meal, Hadley House makes a very attractive local in an under-supplied part of town.
Babies and children welcome; high chairs. Book weekends. Tables outdoors (4, pavement).

North

Archway N19

St John's
91 Junction Road, N19 (020 7272 1587). Archway tube. **Meals served** noon-11pm Mon-Sat; noon-10.30pm Sun. **Main courses** £7.50-£14.50. **Credit** MC, V.
St John's occupies what was formerly one of Archway's most prominent Irish boozers (a few of the old clientele still sit around the bar, apparently unfussed by all the changes). The bar is now all stripped wood, while in the dining room at the back velour banquettes, heavy wooden tables, candelabras and a range of artwork around the walls create a boho-Gothic-meets-Parisian-bistro look. The cooking has a similar upfront, go-for-it quality, with busy combinations that are great when they work. To start, a terrine of pork, rabbit and black pudding with toast and chutney was powerfully meaty, while char-grilled calamares with roast peppers featured excellent ingredients. To follow, lamb shank in a red wine and rosemary sauce with lentils, spinach and celeriac mash was a tad heavy, but char-grilled monkfish with a saffron, pea and mussel risotto, roast red onion and a herb jus was wonderfully subtle for all its many parts. Portions are very generous. The constantly changing wine list is also well above the norm, and put together with real enthusiasm. Service is often scatty rather than professional, but generally gets there in the end. Deservedly popular.
Babies and children welcome. Tables outdoors (7, patio).

Camden Town & Chalk Farm NW1

Blakes
31 Jamestown Road, NW1 (020 7482 2959). Camden Town tube.
Bar **Open** 11am-11pm Mon-Fri; noon-10.30pm Sat, Sun. **Food served** noon-10.30pm daily. **Bar snacks** £2.50-£7.
Restaurant **Lunch served** noon-3pm Mon-Fri; noon-4.30pm Sat, Sun. **Dinner served** 7-10.30pm Mon-Thur, Sun; 7-11pm Fri, Sat. **Main courses** £7.50-£13.50. **Credit** AmEx, DC, MC, V.
The downstairs section of this old converted pub was bustling and frenetic during our mid-week visit, unlike the deserted upstairs dining room,

whose candlelit purple interior creates a subdued and relaxing atmosphere. The wide-ranging menu lives up to its ambitions, in the main. Excellent tempura prawns with a spicy mayonnaise sauce arrived coated in a fresh light batter. Baked ricotta filo parcel with red pepper coulis was similarly well-turned out and flavoursome. To follow, tranche of honey cod with sun-dried tomato was a delicate combo but the accompanying rösti was a bit soft. Again, a tasty ravioli of duck with a green Thai sauce was marred by insufficient attention to detail – the pasta was a touch too al dente and there was too much cumin in the sauce. The meal ended on a high note, though, with excellent lemon tart surrounded by a delicious fruit coulis. Staff were friendly and attentive, although, with a total of four diners in the upstairs room, they weren't exactly rushed off their feet. Altogether, then, a pleasing local.
Babies and children welcome; high chair. Entertainment: cabaret (Thur). Separate room for parties, seats 20. Tables outdoors (12, pavement). **Map 10.**
For branch see index.

Islington N1

Frederick's

Camden Passage, N1 (020 7359 2888). Angel tube.
Bar **Open** 11am-11pm Mon-Sat.
Restaurant **Lunch served** noon-2.30pm, **dinner served** 6-11.30pm, Mon-Sat. **Main courses** £9.50-£17. **Set lunches** and pre-theatre (6-7pm) £12.50 two courses incl coffee; £15.50 three courses incl coffee.
Both **Credit** AmEx, DC, JCB, MC, £TC, V.
Behind the old frontage of this well-established joint is a formal modern bar frequented by opulent middle-aged locals sipping cocktails and eating olives. The bar leads into a buzzy restaurant situated in an airy and spacious conservatory. The menu has an interesting and tempting choice of dishes, using a wide variety of ingredients, but the results are variable. A starter of spicy salt cod and crayfish crêpe with spring onions and crème fraîche was heavy and lacked distinction. Cos lettuce, watercress and mint salad with apple was a better blend but the best dish was a tender and flavoursome griddled guinea fowl glazed with Parmesan and served with a field mushroom risotto. Standards dipped again with smoked haddock fish cakes that had far too much potato and not enough fish. Our pudding choice was made easy by the offer of a trio of three desserts – crème caramel, chocolate mousse and lime parfait – all excellent despite the presence of nuts, after the waiter had assured us otherwise (a nut allergy sufferer was part of our party). The wine list is extensive and is geared to the affluent clientele.
Babies and children welcome; children's menu (£5.95 lunch Sat); high chairs. Booking advisable. No-smoking tables. Separate rooms for parties, seating 18 and 32. Tables outdoors (16, garden). **Map 16/2O.**

Swiss Cottage NW3

Globe

100 Avenue Road, NW3 (020 7722 7200). Swiss Cottage tube/13, 31 bus. **Lunch served** noon-3pm Tue-Fri; Sun. **Dinner served** 7-11pm Mon-Sat; 6-10pm Sun. **Main courses** £9.50-£13.50. **Set lunch** £14 two courses, £16 three courses, incl glass of wine, mineral water and coffee. **Credit** AmEx, MC, £TC, V.
Tucked behind an office building on the busy Swiss Cottage roundabout, this modern and airy conservatory restaurant remains a comfortable and welcome retreat from the traffic. That said, the interior is starting to show its age (particularly around the windows). Presumably it's not a shortage of funds that has prevented the refurb, since a retro starter of prawn cocktail cost £6 for just three (albeit succulent) tiger prawns. Salmon fish cakes with oak-smoked salmon and dill crème fraîche was more substantial. Mains were a mixed bag: char-grilled seabass with pak choi and oriental stir-fry was perfectly cooked; duck breast with sautéed potatoes, red cabbage and caramelised apple was full of flavour but the meat was rather tough. Kiwi and guava sorbet was a delicious dessert, whereas a dry chocolate brownie served warm with vanilla ice-cream and chocolate sauce was amateurish. Wine was excellent (Chilean Caliterra sauvignon blanc) but the service was erratic and the staff seemed bored. In an area where good restaurants are hard to find, this might be worth a visit but standards could be improved, especially for the price.
Babies and children welcome; children's menu (£5 a head). Booking advisable. Entertainment: cabaret Thur (see p222 Eating & Entertainment). Separate room for parties, seats 20.

North West

Queen's Park NW6

Organic Café

21-25 Lonsdale Road, NW6 (020 7372 1232). Queen's Park tube/rail. **Meals served** 9.30am-4pm, **dinner served** 7-11.30pm daily. **Main courses** £8.50-£19.50. **Minimum** £5 dinner. **No credit cards.**
This spacious brasserie has a welcoming interior of fairy lights, curly twigs and stripped-pine floor. Service was prompt, a basket of moist bread speedily delivered, along with our wine and a dish of ripe olive oil. The eclectic menu explains that, unless specified, everything is organic and that, for those in a rush, there's a selection of 'one course' dishes. A crostini platter came with a rich sun-dried tomato dip, coarse tapenade and gutsy guacamole. Tarragon-cured salmon served with fat capers and lemon oil looked too pink to be organic, but we were assured it was. A second course of roast monkfish with wild rice galette, vegetable tempura and coconut lime leaf sauce came with a generous amount of fresh, faultlessly cooked fish. Grilled dorado with beetroot risotto and salsa verde had lingered a few seconds too long under the grill, but a creamy risotto balanced things out. Glazed lemon tart was, as it should be, tart; ginger and honey ice-cream with cardamom pear was merely pleasant. Although pricey, the Organic Café deserves to do well.
Babies and children welcome; high chairs. Book dinner. Entertainment: opera nights (phone for details). No-smoking tables. Tables outdoors (7, pavement). Takeaway service.

Penk's

79 Salusbury Road, NW6 (020 7604 4484). Queen's Park tube. **Open** 9am-3.15pm, 7-10.45pm Tue-Thur; 9am-3.15pm, 7-11.30pm Fri, Sat; 10.30-5pm, 6-10pm Sun. **Lunch served** 11.30am-3.15pm Tue-Sat; 10.30am-5pm Sun. **Dinner served** 7-10.45pm Tue-Thur; 7-11.30pm Fri, Sat; 6-10pm Sun. **Main courses** £8.95-£13.95. **Credit** MC, V.
Penk's has a loyal following among well-heeled locals. The blackboards and wooden shelves holding cookery books create a comfortable, '70s-bistro vibe. There's a good selection of wines and sherries by the glass, and the small, moderately priced menu reads well, even if the delivery sometimes disappoints. A starter of duck and chicken terrine was under-seasoned; marinated prawns, with a delicious avocado salsa, was let down by a cloying marinade. Things improved. An exceptionally tender boned and stuffed quail on green lentils was accompanied by a generous side order of courgette fritters served piping hot in a light, crisp batter. Greek-style pork stuffed with feta, green pepper and oregano was not as flavoursome as it could have been, but was saved by crisp lemon roast potatoes. Desserts are British staples such as steamed syrup pudding and bread and butter pudding. Service is efficient, but more attention to detail is needed.
Babies and children welcome. No-smoking tables. Tables outdoors (4, patio).

St John's Wood NW8

Gascogne

12 Blenheim Terrace, NW8 (020 7625 7034). St John's Wood tube.
Bar **Open** 11am-11pm Mon-Sat; 11am-10.30pm Sun.
Restaurant **Lunch served** 12.30-3.30pm Mon-Sat; 12.30-4.30pm Sun. **Dinner served** 6.30-10.30pm daily. **Main courses** £7-£14.50. **Service** 12½%.
Both **Credit** AmEx, JCB, MC, £TC, V.
An inviting Parisian-style local, Gascogne is most attractive when the weather is warmer and its pretty patio comes into its own. Inside, a clutch of comfortable candlelit dining areas extends below street level. From the short, varied menu we chose scallops cooked in garlic, ginger and chilli served on rocket with lemon oil. Unfortunately, the balance of flavours tipped too far towards the chilli and the puny size of the scallops didn't help. Also disappointing was a thin watercress soup, lacking any distinctive taste. This was followed by duck and apricot sausages with sweet potato mash and onion gravy: glorified bangers and mash, but still good. Fish of the day – small filleted Dover sole with pesto mash – was bland and overpriced. We finished with a perfectly acceptable rice pudding, but the chocolate brûlée would have been more accurately described as chocolate mousse. In short, the atmosphere and service here is better than the food.
Babies and children welcome; high chairs. Booking advisable. Separate room for parties, seats 26. Tables outdoors (15, patio).
Map 1/2C.

Italian

Central

Belgravia SW1

Il Convivio

143 Ebury Street, SW1 (020 7730 4099). Sloane Square tube/Victoria tube/rail. **Lunch served** noon-3pm, **dinner served** 7-11pm Mon-Sat. **Set lunch** £16.50 two courses; £20 three courses. **Set dinner** £20 two courses; £25 three courses. **Service** 12½%. **Credit** AmEx, DC, MC, V.
From the same stable that produced Caravaggio, among others, Il Convivio has a lot going for it. Attractive, definitely: it's a long, low room with a skylight, and a deck at the back when weather permits. Service is mostly competent and eager, and prices are reasonable, but what perplexed us was the quality of the food, which ranged from sublime to downright dismal. Starters were wildly mixed. An artichoke and mushroom soup was heavenly. A crab salad with avocado and fennel featured bland crab, unripe, completely tasteless avocado and a method of construction that made eating a chore. Of the mains, veal chop with courgettes and lemon and thyme sauce was pretty good, if not stunning. Stuffed leg of rabbit wrapped in prosciutto was delicious. So there's definitely talent in the kitchen, even if the simpler, more traditional dishes seem to fare better than clever-modern combinations. Our most serious complaint, though, was the way in which our bottle of wine was removed to a table where we couldn't reach it and every passing waiter felt obliged to top up our glasses. That (and the crab salad) aside, though, this is a good, serious place in an area that's not over-endowed with fine eating.
Babies and children admitted. Separate room for parties (seats 12). **Map 6/10G.**

Olivo

21 Eccleston Street, SW1 (020 7730 2505). Sloane Square tube/Victoria tube/rail.
Lunch served noon-2.30pm Mon-Fri. **Dinner served** 7-11pm daily. **Main courses** £8.50-£18. **Set lunches** £15 two courses, £17 three courses. **Cover** £1.50. **Credit** AmEx, MC, £TC, V.
Impressively crowded on our Monday night visit, Olivo is clearly beloved of the monied locals who appreciate its bustling, informal style. The interior is modern but not slickly streamlined – a clever mix of dark wood and brightly painted rough plastering. Char-grilled meat and seafood feature strongly on the menu, which also typically offers a choice of several starters, five or so pasta dishes available as starters or mains, and a risotto (seafood on our visit). But the cooking veers from divine to deeply disappointing. Fresh tortelli with prawns, spinach and tomato sauce sounded great, looked good but had an astonishingly bitter sauce that ruined the whole dish. Spaghetti all bottarga, however, was genuinely superb. We also enjoyed prettily arranged buffalo mozzarella with marinated aubergines, and stuffed baby squid with plum tomatoes and basil, but things slipped again at dessert. Blueberry frozen yogurt was the only refreshing choice on a hot day but the supplier had failed to deliver. Lemon and mascarpone tart was a heavy, uninspiring wedge difficult to finish, but tiramisu was good. Excellent coffee, pleasant service and a policy of not pushing customers out the door to make room for more outweigh the negative stuff though.
Babies and children admitted. Booking essential. **Map 6/10H.**
For branch see index.

City EC3

Caravaggio

107 Leadenhall Street, EC3 (020 7626 6206). Aldgate tube/Bank tube/DLR/25 bus.
Lunch served 11.45am-3pm, **dinner served** 6.30-10pm Mon-Fri. **Set dinner** £23.50 three courses, £28 four courses, incl coffee. **Main courses** £13.50-£17.50. **Cover** £1.50. **Service** 12½%. **Credit** AmEx, DC, JCB, MC, £TC, V.
By the simple introduction of a mezzanine floor, the designers of Caravaggio have managed to create an intimate dining space from the lofty expanse of this former banking hall without devaluing its original decorative assets. Similarly, this restaurant's innovative take on Italian food still tends to be rooted in the traditional flavours and techniques of that country's regional cooking. That said, one of our starters actually showed very little evidence of any Italian influence – a surprisingly strong-tasting salad of chinese leaves and beetroot crisps paired with the subtle flavours of four, perfectly seared sea scallops. More typical, but no less tasty, were the wheels of goat's cheese and smoky aubergine that accompanied another starter of fresh sardine fillets. A main course of milk-fed wild boar was a thickly sliced, expertly roasted piece of creamy white meat. Another main, this time a large portion of spaghetti with mangetout and fresh crabmeat, was also a delight, although the strong seafood flavour did eventually become a little overpowering. Finally, pear sorbet was superbly rendered both in terms of taste and texture. Fans of sophisticated Italian cooking could certainly do a lot worse than Caravaggio.
Babies and children welcome. Book lunch. Disabled: toilet. Separate room for parties, seats 30. **Map 4/6R.**

Covent Garden WC2

Duemila

27-29 Endell Street, WC2 (020 7379 8500). Covent Garden tube.
Bar **Open** noon-11pm Mon-Sat.
Restaurant **Lunch served** noon-3pm, **dinner served** 6.30-11.30pm Mon-Sat. **Service** 12½%. **Main courses** £6.95-£8.95 lunch, £10.95-£12.95 dinner. **Set meal** (lunch, 10.30-11.15pm) £9.95 two courses. **Credit** AmEx, JCB, MC, V.
Duemila has a gut-wrenchingly tacky cherry-wood-and-stone interior (think Heal's circa 1988) far better suited to a bar or club than a restaurant. It's certainly the wrong choice for lunch – on our visit they were so intent on carrying through the ill-conceived grotto concept that they had lit the fire on a scorchingly hot day. Service was sweet and very friendly though the silver service pretensions (ceremoniously serving the side veg, for example) did seem incongruous with the setting. The menu clearly also has gourmet aspirations but the quality and presentation of the food is still more Versace Jeans than Armani. Our bread basket contained flavourless carta da musica, common-or-garden grissini and some wholemeal loaf that looked as though it had just come out of its supermarket wrapping. However, a starter of char-grilled squid, despite its unnecessarily elaborate construction involving a framework of skewers, was perfectly cooked, and we also enjoyed spinach and prosciutto salad presented in a thick and curly Parmesan basket. Grilled tuna and linguine with prawns were reasonable mains and the meal ended on a high note with nice panna cotta and a delightful nougat semifreddo.
Babies and children admitted. No-smoking tables. Separate room for parties, seats 60.
Map 14/6L.

Luna Nuova

Thomas Neal's Centre, 22 Short's Gardens, WC2 (020 7836 4110). Covent Garden tube. **Meals served** noon-11.30pm Mon-Sat; noon-10.30pm Sun. **Main courses** £5.95-£11.50. **Set meal** (5-8pm, 10-11.30pm Mon-Sat) £9.95 two courses, £12.95 three courses. **Service** 12½%. **Credit** AmEx, DC, JCB, MC, £TC, V.
Popular with harried shoppers retreating from the scrum of the surrounding shopping mall, Luna Nuova's fake marble pillars and murals of Roman arches are more reminiscent of the palaces of Vegas than Verona. But amiable staff soon took our mind off the decor. The menu is typically Italian and on the non-pizza dishes we found that tomato featured particularly heavily: a rich layer of pasatta, for example, provided a tasty mortar between layers of melted cheese and

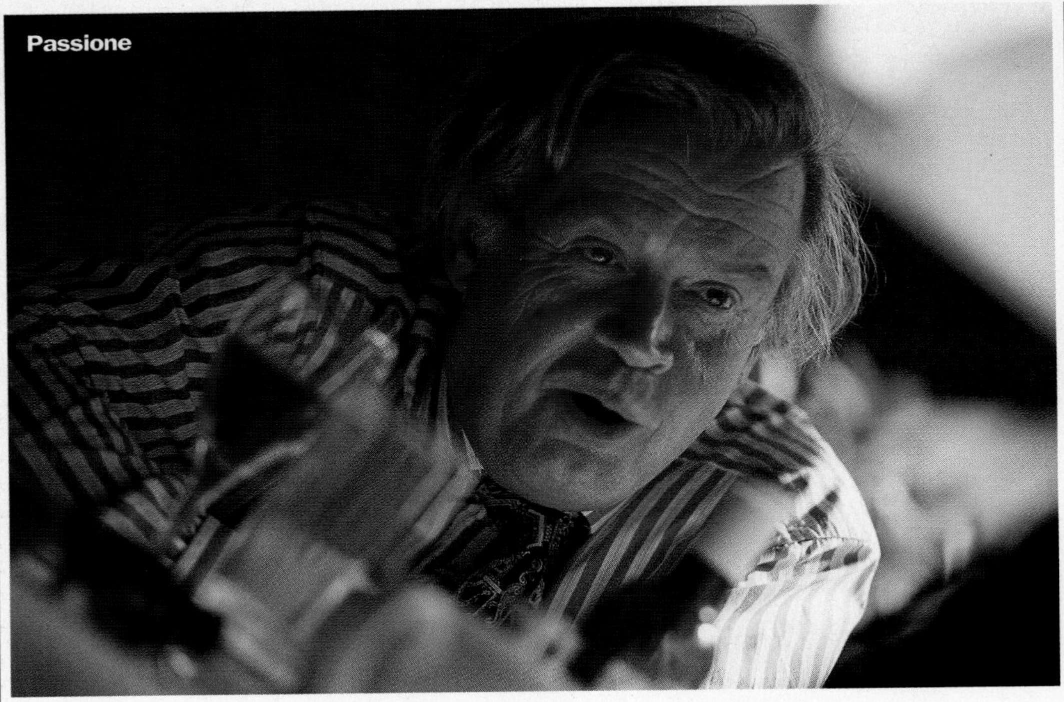

Passione

olive oil-soaked aubergine. A thick, spicy tomato sauce also accompanied another main course of fennel-flecked meatballs, and both dishes came with a helping of delicious bread to mop up the juices. When our pudding choice was unavailable the helpful and friendly staff brought out a slice of silky smooth mascarpone, cheesecake and then charged it to the house. Be warned: an open pizza oven means that the heat can become almost unbearable in summer.
Babies and children welcome; children's menu; crayons; high chairs. Booking advisable. No-smoking tables. Takeaway service. **Map 14/6L.**

Neal Street

26 Neal Street, WC2 (020 7836 8368). Covent Garden tube. **Lunch served** 12.30-2.30pm, **dinner served** 6-11pm Mon-Sat. **Main courses** £7-£19.50. **Service** 15%. **Credit** AmEx, JCB, MC, £TC, V.
There are two things you need to enjoy Antonio Carluccio's restaurant – a healthy bank balance and a penchant for mushrooms. Yep, the man loves his shrooms but this obsession also extends deeper underground to the truffle, another regular on the menu. The restaurant itself is much lighter and brighter than it looks from the outside, with a pleasantly airy, rather masculine feel; all beige seating and (during our weekday lunch visit) plenty of smart business types. The food is excellent, making imaginative use of quality ingredients, but it comes at a price. Starters range as high as £15, while main course meat and fish dishes hover around the £20 mark. We began with a delicate warm mushroom and pancetta salad, and an equally tasty, very generous serving of prosciutto. Next, a beautifully presented prawn raviolini (flat pasta parcels of delicate prawns in a dazzling saffron sauce) was effortlessly light. Pasta of the day with scallops and mushrooms was also a winning dish. Note that side orders of vegetables or salad add an extra £3-£4 to the total. Pastiera di grano – a light pastry tart with ricotta, served with marmalade – was a particularly interesting dessert. The service charge of 15% is as high as anyone dare charge in London – though admittedly, the service is some of the best in town.
Babies and children admitted. Booking advisable. Dress: smart casual; no shorts. Separate room for parties, seats 24.
Map 14/6L.

Orso

27 Wellington Street, WC2 (020 7240 5269). Covent Garden tube. **Meals served** noon-midnight daily. **Main courses** £12.50-£14.50. **Set lunches** (noon-5pm Sat, Sun) £15 two courses, £17 three courses, incl a glass of champagne or Bloody Mary. **Pre-theatre menu** (5-6.45pm Mon-Sat) £13 two courses, £15 three courses, incl coffee. **Credit** AmEx, MC, £TC, V.
The discreet entrance set back from the street gives an aura of exclusivity to Orso, even though it's widely patronised by out-of-town theatre- and opera-goers. The food may not be brilliant, the theatrically themed decor slightly tatty and the subterranean dining room a bit gloomy, but it remains a lively, buzzy place that offers satisfying food at reasonable prices. A wide range of antipasti, pizzas and pastas are all served in generous portions. Watercress, cherry tomato, walnut and Gorgonzola salad contained enough greenery to feed a whole warren of rabbits and there were lashings of garlic in the squid ink pasta with prawns. Occasionally dishes do misfire, however. A warm baby artichoke, slow-roasted tomato, new potato and mint stew suffered from excess olive oil, and we suspected the spuds had been left over from lunch. But these are quibbles. This is solid nosh and solid value by London standards. A tip: unless you're on a strict budget avoid the house white; the full (Italian) wine list has much more to offer.
Babies and children admitted. Booking advisable. No-smoking tables. **Map 14/7L.**

Fitzrovia W1

Bertorelli's

19-23 Charlotte Street, W1 (020 7636 4174). Goodge Street tube.
Bar **Open** noon-11pm Mon-Sat.
Café **Lunch served** noon-3pm Mon-Fri. **Dinner served** 6-11pm Mon-Sat. **Main courses** £6.50-£12.95.
Restaurant **Lunch served** noon-3pm Mon-Fri. **Dinner served** 6-11pm Mon-Sat. **Main courses** £7.25-£14.95.
All **Service** 12½%. **Credit** AmEx, DC, MC, V.
Bertorelli's is decked out with plenty of blond wood, etched glass and bright colours. The upstairs restaurant is a little more refined than the day-glo downstairs café and offers spacious seating among tables graced with linens and bottles of good, fruity olive oil. Our meal began with iced cucumber and rosemary soup – a creamy, frothy concoction that, despite its pleasant herby flavour, was poorly seasoned – and a disappointing spinach salad consisting of bruised leaves and only two small cubes of avocado (for £5.95 we expected more). Main courses were equally patchy. The day's special, ravioli contained robust goat's cheese and tender roast vegetables but was marred by too much oil, while fusilli came with stingy amounts of green beans and chorizo. But portions were generous and both dishes were accompanied by a rich tomato, onion and balsamic salad. For dessert, peaches roasted with amaretto, served with a pistachio galette and lemon sorbet, was very tasty. On the whole, Bertorelli's would benefit from more consistency in its cooking and pricing.
Babies and children welcome. Booking advisable lunch. No-smoking tables. Tables outdoors (3, terrace). **Map 2/5J.**
For branch see index.

Passione

10 Charlotte Street, W1 (020 7636 2833). Goodge Street tube. **Lunch served** 12.30-2.30pm Mon-Fri. **Dinner served** 7-10.30pm Mon-Sat. **Main courses** £6.50-£16. **Service** 10%. **Credit** AmEx, DC, JCB, MC, TC, V.
Passione has the potential to be relaxing – eau-de-Nil walls hung with elegant food photographs, French windows revealing a cosmopolitan view, the cheery welcome – but the dinky wood and metal chairs make a meal here a rather uncomfortable experience. Small nibbles of crostini with tasty tapenade and cherry tomatoes were swiftly brought to the table, but our stingy allocation of bread only arrived with the starters. Things picked up at this point, however, in the form of delicious stuffed cold chicken dressed in balsamic vinegar, and a courgette parcel with cheese, also a sheer delight. We skipped the meat and fish options in favour of main course pasta (one truffley, one shellfish and mushrooms), and a generous rocket and Parmesan salad, all of which were fine. Finally, tiramisu and strawberries with balsamic ice-cream tasted all right but the plates were so over decorated with cocoa and icing sugar that our sleeves even got dirty. House wines are good and fairly priced – we chose Castel del Monte Rosso 1998 for £10.50 – and the coffee here is excellent. Despite the further prospect of bum-numbing chairs, we would definitely come back to Passione.
Babies and children welcome. Booking essential. Separate room for parties, seats 12.
Map 3/5K.

Sardo

45 Grafton Way, W1 (020 7387 2521). Warren Street tube. **Lunch served** noon-3pm Mon-Fri. **Dinner served** 6-11pm Mon-Sat. **Main courses** £4.75-£12.75. **Service charge** 12½%. **Credit** AmEx, DC, MC, V.
There aren't many Italian restaurants in London that offer good Sardinian dishes, so we were eager to see what this new restaurant had to offer. There are a few outdoor tables, the interior is appealingly simple and the atmosphere is friendly and very Italian. Skipping the usual pizzas, salads and pastas, we tried a couple of the interesting and well-made Sardinian specials. The first was bottarga, a grey mullet roe that has been salted, pressed and dried in the sun. It has become a trendy ingredient in some of London's Italian restaurants, but at Sardo it was served traditionally – freshly grated over good-quality, perfectly al dente spaghetti. The result was sensational. We also tried suchittu, a kind of fricassee usually made with hare or rabbit, but this version successfully switched to chicken and was accompanied by potato and artichoke purée. A basket of pane carasau – the parchment-like Sardinian crispbread, served with good olive oil – was quickly demolished, too. Desserts are less impressive (there's a photo-menu of bought-in ices) and the wine list is ordinary and dull. But stick to the Sardinian dishes and you should have an interesting meal at a very reasonable price.
Babies and children welcome. Booking essential lunch. Entertainment: jazz musicians (phone for details). No-smoking tables. Tables outdoors (3, pavement). **Map 2/4J.**

Table Café ★

Habitat, Tottenham Court Road, W1 (020 7636 8330/020 7255 6043). Goodge Street tube. **Meals served** 10am-5.30pm Mon-Wed, Fri, Sat; 10am-7.30pm Thur; noon-5.30pm Sun. **Breakfast served** 10-11.50am Mon-Sat. **Lunch served** noon-4pm daily. **Tea served** 4-5.30pm daily. **Main courses** £6.60-£7.50. **Set lunch** £7.50 two courses. **Service** 10% for parties of five or more. **Credit** MC, £TC, V.
The vibrant red and blue plastic chairs are not nearly as funky as the furniture sold in the rest of the store, but at least they're child friendly, which is good because Table Café seems to attract a lot of mums. The menu inevitably has a daily risotto, perhaps smoked salmon, spring onion and rocket, along with some pasta dishes – on our last visit, penne with tomato, courgettes and ricotta tasted like something out of *Grub on a Grant*. Hearty main courses such as mushroom-and-lemon-stuffed chicken with sautéed garlic and rosemary potatoes, and a fresh tuna fillet served with rocket and spinach salad were also on offer. The excellent house salad will typically be offered as a starter to your choice of pasta or risotto in the set menu of the day (reasonably priced at £7.50). Ciabatta sandwiches are not such good value – £3.70 for BLT and £3.50 for tomato, mozzarella and basil. Milkshakes and cakes are also a key attraction. Sandwiches, snacks and coffees are only served at the bar or long table at the back of the room. Service is prompt and friendly.
Babies and children welcome; high chairs. Disabled: toilet in shop. No smoking.
Map 3/5K.
For branches see index.

Knightsbridge SW1, SW3

Emporio Armani Caffè

191 Brompton Road, SW3 (020 7823 8818). Knightsbridge or South Kensington tube. **Open** 10am-6pm Mon-Sat. **Breakfast served** 10am-noon Mon-Sat. **Lunch served** noon-3.30pm Mon-Fri; noon-4pm Sat. **Main courses** £9-£14.50. **Credit** AmEx, DC, JCB, MC, £TC, V.
The place mats in Emporio Armani Caffè are to die for. They're pure linen (of course) and the colour of cappuccino. Hundreds must get stolen every year, which may account for the inflated prices on this restaurant's small but perfectly formed modern Italian menu. The cooking is good but lacks pzazz, and the portions are incongruously large given the fashionably trim proportions of the clientele. You'd certainly be pushed to wade through three full courses. An artichoke and sage frittata sounded mouth-wateringly good but was a disappointingly bland accompaniment to a couple of slices of slightly wimpy prosciutto. Beef carpaccio suffered from inadequate seasoning, but a faultlessly creamy crab risotto (although a painful £14.50) was as good as you'd find anywhere in London. And brownie points, too, for some interesting, well-priced wines by the glass, including a gavi and a prosecco. On the whole, though, it's hard to see why you would eat here, unless you were on a mega-clothes-buying spree and needed to recover.
Babies and children admitted. Booking advisable. Disabled: toilets in shop.
Map 12/9E.

Floriana

15 Beauchamp Place, SW3 (020 7838 1500). Knightsbridge tube.
Bar **Open** noon-11pm Mon-Sat.
Restaurant **Lunch served** 12.30-3pm Tue-Sat. **Dinner served** 7-11pm Mon-Sat. **Main courses** £17-£25.50. **Set lunch** £10 one course, £15 two courses, £19.50 three courses. **Set meal** £50 five courses incl coffee. **Service** 12½%. **Credit** AmEx, DC, JCB, MC, TC, V.
A meal at Floriana can be a blissful treat. The spacious main dining room has an unmistakable Knightsbridge buzz to it and, although some tables are too close together, the atmosphere is convivial. The menu seems to favour risotto over pasta, while the diverse range of meat and fish dishes is supplemented by several interesting daily specials. We chose two of these – a mixed cheese risotto starter and a main dish of roast veal with mushrooms and sweetish gravy. From the menu proper, we opted for an extremely expensive (£23) but delicious starter of home-made crab ravioli with grilled scallops,

Floriana

Duemila

ITALIAN RESTAURANT • BAR • CAFÉ

Something unusual in the West End

At Duemila once you have a table for lunch or dinner, you may stay as long as you wish.

This, together with the quality of our food and service plus our very friendly staff in beautiful surroundings, creates a unique blend in the London restaurant scene.

We think you will like this.

Why?
According to the Time Out Survey, top of your wish list is being able to spend all evening in a restaurant if you want to

AN END TO TWO-HOUR SITTINGS!

"Great value for cooking of this high standard in WC2"
Time Out

"...A real bargain. The frequently changing menu is steeped in both innovation & tradition."
Newswatch UK

"...a stylish place offering sophisticated Italian cooking. Superb."
Time Out

"Toast the end of the century at Duemila"
Sunday Times

"The surroundings are top quality, the service is top quality, and the food and drink? Just go there and you won't be disappointed"
Right Angle

**27-29 Endell Street,
Covent Garden, London WC2
Tel: 020 7379 8500**

artichokes and tomatoes. Our cheaper main course – steamed sea bass fillet on a pyramid of baby vegetables – was also excellent. Among the desserts, the trio of flavoured crème brûlées – almond, pistachio and vanilla – was a delight, and the extravagantly presented chocolate tart with chocolate sorbet and tuile was faultless. But the bill was a shock: added to the hefty prices was a cover charge of £2 per head, £4 for a bottle of water, £5 per side dish, £3 for a cup of coffee and 12.5% service. Even when the food's this good, are such astronomical prices justifiable?
Babies and children admitted. Booking advisable. Separate room for parties, seats 32. No-smoking tables. Tables outdoors (4, pavement). **Map 12/9F.**

Grissini

Hyatt Carlton Tower Hotel, Cadogan Place, SW1 (020 7858 7171/www.london.hyatt.com). Knightsbridge or Sloane Square tube.
Breakfast served 7-11am Mon-Sat; 8-11am Sun. **Lunch served** 12.30-2.45pm Mon-Fri. **Dinner served** 6.30-10.45pm Mon-Sat. **Main courses** £15-£21. **Set lunches** £16 two courses, £21 three courses. **Credit** AmEx, DC, MC, V.
Despite some charming design touches and a separate entrance, there's still no escaping the fact that Grissini is a hotel restaurant. Luckily, high-quality cooking, excellent service and a view of leafy Cadogan Place help you to forget this. An additional bonus is the offer of substantial discounts on the supplementary wine list of bin ends; we enjoyed a wonderful 1997 Regaleali from Sicily for £25. The prompt arrival of flavoured breads, a bundle of fresh own-made grissini and a creamy olive and herb dip kept us happy until we received our starters. The first to arrive was a large serving of bresaola with rocket and Parmesan, followed by a delightful risotto of courgettes and whitebait. Main courses of roast lamb with dry stuffed vegetables and an excess of lemony breadcrumbs, and swordfish with citrus flavours were less impressive; maybe we should have opted for the terrific-looking pasta instead. However, Grissini redeemed itself with wondrous fresh strawberry and balsamic soup enhanced with light lime jelly, and a chocolate- and coffee-flavoured cake. Macchiato was delicious but pricey at £3.50, and with 75cl of San Pellegrino at £4.50, we left with the feeling that we had paid a little too much for the upmarket location.
Babies and children welcome; high chairs. Booking advisable. Disabled: toilet in hotel. Entertainment: live music 12.30-3.30pm Sun. Dress: smart casual. Separate room for parties, seats 50. **Map 12/10F.**

Isola ★

145 Knightsbridge, SW1 (020 7838 1044/1055). Knightsbridge tube. **Lunch served** noon-3pm daily. **Dinner served** 6-10.45pm Mon-Sat; 6-9pm Sun. **Main courses** £17-£22. **Set menu** £10 for 8 dishes noon-7pm Mon-Sat. **Service** 12½%. **Credit** AmEx, DC, JCB, MC, V.
It's not as if Oliver Peyton has anything left to prove – his previous ventures Atlantic Bar & Grill, Coast and Mash have already changed the face of London dining for ever by mixing glamour with a tongue-in-cheek aesthetic. But Isola – which Peyton describes as 'a modern power dining room' – still stuns, this time in a *Thunderbirds*-meets-opulent-Moscow-dining-circa-1985 way (lush red leather banquettes and curvaceous white chairs, chrome-framed tables and vast globular chandeliers). It will please readers of irony-laced magazine *Wallpaper** and scare the living daylights out of those who like unobtrusive, low-key dining. Our verdict? – it's both vaguely surreal and totally fabulous. But the best thing about Isola is the food. Particularly memorable was a starter of tuna carpaccio roll, served with fresh fennel, avocado and a citrus dressing or an intensely flavoured main-course roast fillet of lamb flavoured with orange and sautéed with aubergines, capers and balsamic vinegar. Other equally delectable choices might include quail stuffed with cotechino and cabbage, served with egg and spinach raviolo, or desserts such as apricot sorbet with fresh raspberries and prosecco. For a more informal experience try Osteria d'Isola in the basement (*see p219* **Wine Bars**). A resounding victory for Peyton and his burgeoning Gruppo empire.
Babies and children admitted; high chairs. Disabled: toilet. Dress: smart-casual.
Map 12/9F.

Monte's

164 Sloane Street, SW1 (020 7235 0555) Knightsbridge or Sloane Square tube.
Lunch served noon-2.15pm Mon-Fri. **Dinner served** 7-10.45pm Mon-Sat. **Main courses** £6-£18.50. **Set lunches** £16 two courses, £22 three courses. **Service** 12½%. **Credit** AmEx, DC, MC, V.
For the last five years Monte's has been a creditable but fogeyish private members' club for cigar-lovers. It needed rejuvenation. It needed street cred. It needed Jamie Oliver. But Jamie isn't in the gaff all the time: he gets his chum and former River Café colleague Ben O'Donoghue to rustle up the tucker. The menu is brief (a good thing) and very River Café – even down to the pricing. And yes, the nosh is wicked. Antipasti verdura was a wodge of sourdough bruschetta blackened on the grill, with a lug of excellent olive oil and some lovely jubbly buffalo mozzarella. However, neither menu nor waiter mentioned that our next dish, fritto misto, contained sweetbread – slipping offal into something that a non-meat eater might order isn't pukka at all. Next, cappellacci was slithery but lovely pasta envelopes filled with ricotta, while seared Scottish scallops were also spot on, served with more olive oil on some peas, broad beans and chopped samphire. A pud of red berry crumble even had that trendy home-style dribble of red juice down the side of the bowl. The wine list offers a good choice, but mark-ups are high, so don't come looking for bargains. Really this place shouldn't work, but the charisma seems strong enough to pull it off.
Babies and children admitted lunch. Booking advisable. Disabled: toilet. Separate room for parties, seats 14. **Map 12/9F.**

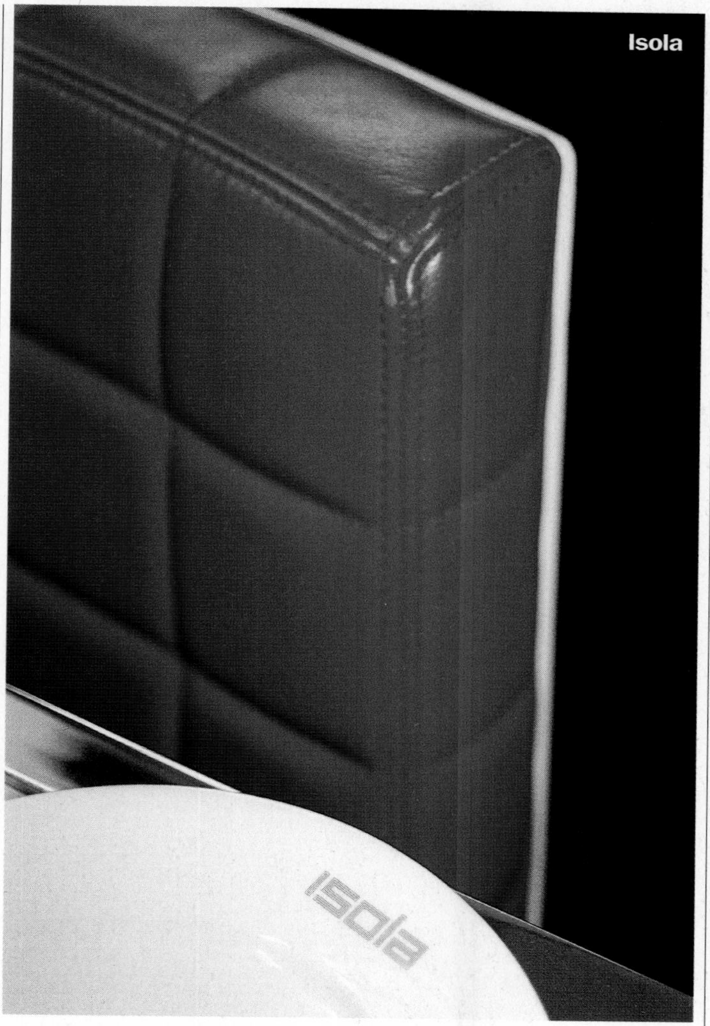

Isola

Monza

6 Yeoman's Row, SW3 (020 7591 0210). Knightsbridge tube. **Lunch served** noon-2.30pm Tue-Sun. **Dinner served** 7-11.30pm daily. **Main courses** £11-£17. **Set lunch** £11 two courses. **Cover** £1.50. **Credit** AmEx, DC, JCB, MC, V.
Appropriately enough you can hire a Ferrari through Monza, which provides a clue to this restaurant's usual clientele. Actually, we were surprised by the absence of medallions and chest-wigs – perhaps the dress code requires customers to keep them hidden at meal times. The main menu is supplemented by a huge list of daily specials, which the waiter recites to you. There is no way of knowing what these dishes cost unless you ask and that's not the done thing. Amazingly, the waiter turned quite huffy when we refused the bottle of wine he had brought to the table, preferring to choose our own from the wine list. The high point of the meal was an excellent mixed grill of swordfish, prawns, scallops, salmon and tuna with a rocket salad, well worth its £17.50. Less successful were some rather stodgy arancini (rice balls), an octopus salad buried under piles of raw onion and squid ink pasta that tasted as if it had been reheated. There's a great deal of motor memorabilia on the pastel yellow walls, which gives Monza a bit of character, but the whole place feels rather dated, underlined by the '80s music that plays loudly in the background.
Babies and children welcome. Book dinner. Tables outdoors (6, pavement). **Map 12/10E.**

San Lorenzo

22 Beauchamp Place, SW3 (020 7584 1074). Knightsbridge or South Kensington tube.
Lunch served 12.30-3pm, **dinner served** 7.30-11.30pm Mon-Sat. **Main courses** £14.50-£22.50. **Cover** £2.50. **Credit** £$TC.
If it wasn't for its menu and its eclectic interior design, San Lorenzo would be difficult to distinguish from a posh Pizza Express. The clientele may be wealthy, the restaurant may be very crowded, but the swanky atmosphere has dissipated over the years and the kitchen is now among the least exciting of London's pricey Italian venues. On our visit the £2.50 cover charge produced a small dish of dry chewy olives and one piece of bread each. The long menu majors on Italian culinary clichés – Parma ham with melon among the starters, for instance. We opted to start with salad of raw artichoke and Parmesan (a stingy portion but OK-tasting), and penne with tomato sauce topped with cubes of creamily pungent mozzarella. Main-course fritto misto di mare was also decent enough but not cheap at £16.50. One of three specials of the day – grilled swordfish with fresh borlotti beans and new potatoes (also £16.50) – was very simply, even plainly cooked and presented. Venezia Giulia Pinot Grigio 1998 proved to be a good guess from the unhelpfully arranged wine list. We finished with fabulous coffee plus tasty desserts of zabaione and meringue, both served with perfect fresh raspberries, and left with mixed feelings.
Babies and children welcome; high chairs. Booking essential. Dress: smart casual; no shorts. **Map 12/9F.**
For branch see index.

Zafferano ★

15 Lowndes Street, SW1 (020 7235 5800). Knightsbridge tube. **Lunch served** noon-2.30pm, **dinner served** 7-11pm daily. **Set lunches** £18.50 two courses, £21.50 three courses. **Set dinners** £29.50 two courses, £35.50 three courses, £39.50 four courses. **Credit** AmEx, DC, MC, £TC, V.
Georgio Locatelli may now be a highly paid consultant to Marks and Sparks but you'll still find him slaving at his stove or meeting and greeting the Knightsbridge ladies who lunch at his friendly, intimate restaurant. Zafferano produces food that succeeds in every way. The menu is inspirational, seasonal and comforting, with dishes you simply do not find elsewhere. Examples include spinach with cabernet sauvignon and smoked Ricotta (a bold bitter-sweet, smoky combination of flavours), yellow bean, chive and potato salad with summer black truffles (simple, fresh and fabulously tasty) or char-grilled pork stuffed with herbs and fried courgettes (an inspired seasonal take on sausage and chips). Pasta is own-made, unctuous and buttery, which is why it seemed so tragic that our feather-light gnocchi could have been smothered with too much tomato sauce. Puddings are just one indulgence too many if you've already pigged your way through three courses, but many will be unable to resist the likes of chocolate soufflé torte with liquorice ice-cream. The all-Italian wine list is exemplary, with big-bucks bottles admirably complementing real bargains. In a head to head with the much hyped and much pricier River Café we think Zafferano would come out on top.
Babies and children welcome; high chairs. Booking essential, at least a week in advance for lunch, 4-6 weeks for dinner. **Map 12/9G.**

Marble Arch W2

Al San Vincenzo

30 Connaught Street, W2 (020 7262 9623). Marble Arch tube. **Lunch served** 12.15-1.45pm Mon-Fri. **Dinner served** 7-9.30pm Mon-Sat. **Set meals** £25 two courses, £31 three courses. **Service** 12½% for parties of five or more. **Credit** MC, £TC, V.
Leafy tomato bushes line the front window of this quiet, charming local restaurant close to, yet far removed from, bustling Edgware Road. The service is especially friendly and welcoming, though not particularly Italian. Neither is the set-price menu (£31 for three courses), which instead offers a pleasing mix of modern and conventional ideas. A starter of seared scallops, for example, was served with a salsa of orange and fresh ginger, while smoked salmon came with strawberries and fresh basil, laced with rich, syrupy balsamic vinegar. For main courses, however, we reverted to tradition, choosing calf's liver with gnocchi and garlicky spinach, and a wonderfully light mix of veal escalope, artichokes and plump green olives. Of the other dishes on offer, a special of sautéed clams and risotto with broad beans, fresh peas, mint and mascarpone were also tempting. The wine list is all Italian and a bottle of rosé, Feudi di San Gregorio, was £16 worth of intense fruity pleasure. Desserts were less impressive but perfectly adequate – pannettone bread-and-butter pudding was a bit dry. Service was unhurried and the atmosphere was so relaxing that we would happily have stayed all night.
Booking essential. **Map 2/6F.**

Marylebone W1

Ibla

89 Marylebone High Street, W1 (020 7224 3799). Regent's Park tube. **Lunch served** noon-2.30pm, **dinner served** 7-10.15pm, Mon-Sat. **Main courses** lunch £9, dinner £14. **Set lunch** £15 two courses, £18 three courses. **Set dinner** £23 two courses, £27 three courses. **Credit** AmEx, MC, V.
Having dinner in the front room of Ibla is like sitting in a giant bowl of olives, all shiny black and green, but preferable, we think, to a table in

the Mafioso-red section behind. Even the staff seem slightly sinister in their black uniforms. Despite previous good meals here, the cooking on this visit was disappointingly bland. The kitchen has good ideas but presents food in an orchestrated nouvelle-cuisine style that can seem mean rather than stylish – a main course of monkfish tempura with leeks, sun-dried tomatoes and saffron-flavoured lemon sauce looked more like a starter. Although the menu price is set at £27 for three courses, many dishes required a £3 supplement, including a very dreary plate of almost tasteless crab ravioli. Better was the tepid white bean soup served with an 'urchin' (actually three curled fillets) of Dover sole and some punchy veg. The global wine list includes some good whites by the glass. Impressive too was the annotated cheese menu. For dessert, Grand Marnier cassata was dry but well flavoured, and chocolate cake with figs and sorbet was fine. The Illy coffee, on the other hand, was excellent. Ibla's worth a try but it could be (and has been) so much better.
Babies and children admitted. Booking advisable. **Map 2/5G.**

Mayfair W1

Alloro
19-20 Dover Street, W1 (020 7495 4768). Green Park tube.
Bar **Open** noon-10.30pm Mon-Sat.
Restaurant **Lunch served** noon-2.30pm, **dinner served** 7-10.30pm Mon-Sat. **Set lunch** £18 two courses, £21 three courses. **Set dinner** £21 two, £25 three. **Credit** MC, V.
Two rooms make up this appealing new restaurant. One, a small 'baretto', has a short menu and a beautifully designed panel behind the bottles; the other holds the main dining room and has a big window with a view of the street. The effect is light, elegant and comfortable, posh but not intimidating. Alloro is from the same stable as Zafferano (the chef has worked there, too) and the menu offers the same type of attractive modern Italian dishes. Everything we tried was a success: sweetbreads with artichokes; marinated anchovies with meltingly sweet onions in a starter; even a slightly overcooked John Dory with black olives and potatoes was still a wonderful combination of tastes and textures. The jury's still out on an olive oil ice-cream with strawberries, but this is the only oddity on the dessert list. Cocktails are good, and there are plenty of wines by the glass. Service was charming, if a tiny bit slow. The customers are Mayfair through and through – swinging it ain't – as you'd expect from the location.
Booking advisable. **Map 13/7J.**

Diverso
85 Piccadilly, W1 (020 7491 2222). Green Park tube. **Lunch served** noon-3pm Mon-Sat. **Dinner served** 6.45-11.30pm Mon-Sat; 6.30-11pm Sun. **Main courses** £10-£18.50. **Cover** £2. **Service** 12½% for parties of 8 or more. **Credit** AmEx, DC, JCB, MC, £TC, V.
Diverso's wood and stone decor is catch-all rustic – squint and you could just as easily be in a Greek, Balinese or Mexican venue. It is situated opposite Green Park but the ground-floor room isn't high enough to benefit from the location nor does the Piccadilly traffic make for a relaxing ambience. Nevertheless, the location seems to be justification enough for prices that are almost double that of comparable but less central restaurants. A starter of asparagus and lime dressing had excellent long spears but none of the anticipated citrus tang. Prosciutto and pears with salad was fine, but overpriced at £10.80. More reasonable was the generous entrecôte steak with mushrooms, marsala and raisins: not too sweet and not too expensive at £14. We were also tempted by duck in acacia honey and pasta with scampi, saffron sauce and artichokes. The very good mixed Mediterranean grill included prawns, white fish, salmon and langoustine, flavoured with balsamic, lemon, oil and mixed herbs. Included in the £2 cover charge was a bountiful choice of three breads, a generous bowl of chopped tomatoes and basil, and tasty tapenade for dipping. In retrospect, we should have enjoyed these, skipped the starters and left room for one of the desserts.
Babies and children admitted. Booking advisable dinner. Dress: smart casual. **Map 6/8H.**

Marquis
121A Mount Street, W1 (020 7499 1256). Bond Street or Green Park tube. **Lunch served** noon-3pm Mon-Fri. **Dinner served** 6-10.45pm Mon-Fri. **Average** £26. **Set meal** £14.50 two courses, £17.50 three courses. **Service** 12½%. **Credit** AmEx, DC, JCB, MC, £TC, V.
This is a strange restaurant, on the one hand smart and modern with spruce blond wood furnishings and pleasant staff, but at the same time completely lacking in character. It's almost reminiscent of a film set; it doesn't feel permanent. The menu promised fine ingredients and dishes that sounded tantalising but the reality was disappointing. One exception was an excellent starter of meaty crab and diced tomato bruschetta, which was a match made in heaven for our chosen tipple of nicely chilled muscadet. Sadly, though, the glow of contentment was short-lived. A main course of osso bucco with saffron risotto had been so heavily seasoned with salt that each mouthful had to be swiftly followed by a cooling draught of water. Grilled breast of chicken wrapped in pancetta with mozzarella and porcini stuffing was dry as a bone and had also suffered a severe salt assault. We no longer fancied pudding nor could we risk further dehydration at the hands of the coffee pot, so our meal ended there. Perhaps this is a reasonable bet for a Mayfair business lunch but those on low-sodium diets, at least, should avoid it like the plague.
Babies and children welcome. Book lunch. Dress: smart casual. Separate rooms for parties, seating 24 and 30. **Map 2/7H.**

Teca
54 Brooks Mews, W1 (020 7495 4774). Bond Street tube.
Bar **Open** noon-midnight Mon-Sat.
Restaurant **Lunch served** noon-2.30pm Mon-Fri. **Dinner served** 7-10.30pmMon-Sat. **Set lunch** £18 two courses, £21 three courses. **Set dinner** £19 two courses, £23.50 three courses, £27 four courses. **Service** 12½%.
Both **Credit** AmEx, MC, £TC, V.
Don't let the dreary views of a 1960s office block deter you from visiting Teca. Having survived the first flush of fashionability, this stylish modern restaurant is really beginning to show its calibre. Even reclusive celebrities from nearby Claridges hotel dare a visit (we spotted Steve Martin sneaking out). The food is simple and seasonal with the accent on pasta and fish. A dish of home-made tagliatelle with vegetables, smoked ricotta and basil came with a scattering of tiny, colourful spring vegetables, while feather-light gnocchi stuffed with artichoke purée was deliciously simple. Swordfish was served on mash rich with olive oil and sea bream came in a light broth of courgettes; everything retaining its own taste and texture. Prices are more than reasonable for this part of town, but you could easily blow the budget on the lavish all-Italian wine list or on the unusually good selection of cigars. Puddings are not the forte here: a concoction of cream, grappa and amaretti biscuit was far too rich, while an otherwise excellent orange tart was marred by soggy pastry. Order an espresso and a grappa instead and the amiable staff will bring you some excellent petits fours.
Babies and children welcome; high chairs. Booking advisable. Dress: smart casual. **Map 2/6H.**

Sartoria
20 Savile Row, W1 (020 7534 7000). Oxford Circus or Piccadilly Circus tube.
Bar **Open** noon-11pm Mon-Sat; 6-10pm Sun. **Set lunch** £15 two courses.
Restaurant **Lunch served** noon-3pm Mon-Sat. **Dinner served** 6.30-11pm Mon-Sat; 6-10pm Sun. **Main courses** £15-£18.50.
Both **Service** 12½%. **Credit** AmEx, DC, JCB, MC, £TC, V.
Despite an uncluttered bookings schedule and our early arrival, staff at Sartoria seemed desperate to get our visit over with as quickly as possible. Within a few minutes of sitting down we were asked three times if we were ready to order. The sommelier, however, was most impressive and recommended an excellent 1996 Rocca Guicciarda Barone Ricasoli chianti classico to bridge the flavours of a diverse meal. This began with roast vitello, char-grilled courgette and bagna cauda and a plate of cured meats from Valle d'Aosta. There are around four choices in each of the pasta, risotto, pesce and carne sections of the menu. We enjoyed Gressingham duck with zucca and cime di rapa and linguine marinara. Side dishes, such as cicoria with anchovy and garlic, and braised Castelluccio lentils, were interesting. Desserts tend towards classics with a twist, such as apple crostata with rum and raisin ice-cream. There are also four individual cheese plates, plus a selection for £7 that comes with carta da musica. However the final bill at Sartoria never seems to match the calibre of the product. Whether it's down to the location or wittier-than-thou design affectations, the pricing arrogantly overestimates the merits of a meal here.
Babies and children welcome; high chairs. Booking advisable, essential lunch. Disabled: toilet. Separate rooms for parties, both seating 16. **Map 13/7J.**

Pimlico SW1

Como Lario
22 Holbein Place, SW1 (020 7730 2954/ 9046). Sloane Square tube. **Lunch served** 12.30-2.45pm, **dinner served** 6.30-11.30pm Mon-Sat. **Main courses** £10-£15. **Cover** £1.50. **Credit** AmEx, DC, JCB, MC, £TC, V.
You could almost believe you're in Italy in Como Lario. Not so much from the Technicolor murals of Lake Como on the walls but from the very Italian banter that goes on. *Goodfellas* types, still wearing dark glasses at nine in the evening, mingle with mahogany-tanned regulars; everyone is greeted like a long-lost friend. No wonder the place was packed. The food is not exceptional but it's reasonably priced for this part of town. A plate of buffalo mozzarella with char-grilled vegetables came inexplicably scattered with pieces of grated carrot; warm rolls of Parma ham with smoked mozzarella and rocket was a strange idea but it worked well. Veal escalopes with cream and mushrooms were a touch chunky, but home-made cannelloni stuffed with crab meat and scampi was an excellent old Italian dish. The highlight of the meal, though, was nougat ice-cream with a show-stopping chocolate sauce. There's an endearing eccentricity about the wine list, which includes half a dozen Moroccan wines, but on a hot, sticky summer evening, a rustic rosé (£11) went down a treat.
Babies and children welcome; high chairs. Booking advisable. Dress: smart casual. Separate room for parties, seats 16. **Map 12/11G.**

Soho W1

Il Forno
63-64 Frith Street, W1 (020 7734 4545). Tottenham Court Road tube. **Lunch served** noon-3pm Mon-Fri. **Dinner served** 6-10.45pm Mon-Sat. **Main courses** £7-£9. **Service** 12½%. **Credit** AmEx, JCB, MC, V.
It seems odd that the very fine, very upmarket yet reasonably priced Frith Street restaurant should have closed to make way for something so completely different – what was the problem? According to Claudio Pulze, the man behind the change, Frith Street was just too food-oriented and pricey for the Soho market, whereas Il Forno, on the other hand, Pulze sees as offering good food at affordable prices. Certainly our visit didn't cast any major doubts on this assertion but, when compared to its sister restaurant, Al Duca, Il Forno didn't shine quite so brightly. Ingredients and cooking are good, make no mistake: a huge scoop of top-quality buffalo mozzarella atop a disc of grilled aubergine and basil was a delicious beginning. Soft organic polenta was a little too soft and porridge-like for our taste; the topping of chicken livers and baby onions was fine, but the agrodolce (sweet and sour) balsamic vinegar dressing was a touch too sour. There are also some excellent and huge pizzas with imaginitive toppings such as smoked swordfish, main courses of fish – pan-fried, roasted or char-grilled – for under a tenner, and luscious desserts of lemon tart, tiramisu and the like. Busy at most sittings, it seems Il Forno has hit the Soho spot.
Babies and children admitted; high chairs. **Map 13/6K.**

Little Italy
21 Frith Street, W1 (020 7734 4737). Leicester Square or Tottenham Court Road tube. **Meals served** noon-4am Mon-Sat; noon-11.30pm Sun. **Main courses** £7.80-£15.10. **Cover** £1. **Credit** AmEx, JCB, MC, £TC, V.
A multi-levelled bar and restaurant in the heart of Soho, Little Italy is neither little nor, apart from the dishes on the menu, particularly Italian. Probably a better place to end an evening than to begin one (the full menu's available till very late), it has an industrial-chic metal stairway leading to an interior balcony crammed with tables above the bustling bar area. Staff are generally switched-on and always friendly, although muddled orders and dozy waitresses are not unheard of. We got the ball rolling with a nicely flavoursome plate of char-grilled vegetables dressed in oil and balsamic, and an equally moreish and generous salad of rocket and Parmesan. By contrast, a plate of pasta with broccoli and sun-dried tomatoes was OK but little more than filler food. A main course of beef carpaccio was a generous serving and went surprisingly well with a very simple accompaniment of chips. The dessert list encompasses popular classics such as cheesecake, tiramisu and sorbets, all very reasonably priced at £3.50. Little Italy is very noisy and very crowded; in fact, if you're not in a group, you'll probably end up willing them to turn the tables and get you out as quick as possible.
Babies and children admitted Sat. Tables outdoors (4, pavement). **Map 13/6K.**

Signor Zilli
40 & 41 Dean Street, W1 (restaurant 020 7734 3924/bar 020 7734 1853). Piccadilly Circus or Tottenham Court Road tube.
Bar **Open** noon-midnight, **meals served** noon-11pm Mon-Sat. **Main courses** £7.50-£16.50.
Restaurant **Lunch served** noon-3pm Mon-Fri. **Dinner served** 6-11.30pm Mon-Sat. **Main courses** £7-£19. **Service** 12½%.
Both **Credit** AmEx, DC, JCB, MC, V.
It's hard to fathom quite why Signor Zilli is so fashionable. The Zilli in question is celebrity chef Aldo and the Dean Street location is in the heart of media land, but that doesn't quite seem enough to lure types such as Chris Evans into the public eye – clearly it is, though, as there he was, on the other side of the restaurant. Of course, the food isn't bad, and the fish dishes are generally very good. A garlicky starter of char-grilled squid, for instance, was done to perfection and pappardelle with smoked salmon, asparagus and mascarpone sauce was fresh and tasty, as was a salad of smoked mozzarella and Parma ham. Only Zilli's spaghetti lobster, ridiculously priced at £19, failed to impress: a pointlessly large plate of very ordinary tomato sauce with a load of lobster chucked in. The desserts are averagely good renditions of Italian standards – say, tiramisu or vin santo with cantuccini. All in all, Zilli's is a perfectly enjoyable restaurant as long as you're prepared to put up with smarmy Italian waiters and their infernal pepper mill. Weather permitting, the front tables in the entrance or on the street are undoubtedly the best.
Babies and children welcome. Booking advisable. Separate room for parties, seats 40. Tables outdoors (10, pavement). **Map 13/6K.**
For branches see index.

Spiga
84-86 Wardour Street, W1 (020 7734 3444). Leicester Square, Oxford Circus, Piccadilly Circus or Tottenham Court Road tube. **Lunch served** noon-3pm daily. **Dinner served** 6-11pm Mon,Tue, Sun; 6pm-midnight Wed-Sat. **Main courses** £8-£13.50. **Service** 12½%. **Credit** AmEx, MC, £TC, V.
Designed in muted retro tones and with a 'best of Italian' menu, Spiga brings current restaurant sensibilities to bear on honest home-style cooking, but a trattoria this is not. Rather, it is an extremely pleasing restaurant serving fresh, appetising food at a higher quality than its moderate prices would imply. The menu is modern Italian, with all the usual rocket and Parmesan additions and some seasonal flourishes. Mixed meats with fennel was a fine dish, simply presented and served (like many of the dishes) either in starter or main-course sizes. The pastas were cooked à point with nicely judged partners. Ravioli with goat's cheese and butter herb sauce was subtle yet intense, and spaghetti with a prawn sauce was especially savoury and not mean on the seafood. Alluring puddings included roast peach with almond mascarpone, which not only tasted good but looked beautiful with its angelica garnish and pink lake of juice. La Spiga is generally calm in both décor and atmosphere, but for premium privacy, ask for one of the brown leather booths.
Babies and children welcome; high chairs. Booking advisable. Disabled: toilet. **Map 13/6K.**

Vasco & Piero's Pavilion
15 Poland Street, W1 (020 7437 8774). Oxford Circus or Tottenham Court Road tube. **Lunch served** noon-3pm Mon-Fri. **Dinner served** 6-11pm Mon-Fri; 7-11pm Sat. **Main courses** lunch £9.50-£15.50. **Set dinner** £16.50 two courses, £17.50 three courses. **Credit** AmEx, DC, JCB, MC, £$TC, V.
Although its name never hits the headlines Vasco & Piero's is a favourite media haunt, so you can tune in to some good gossip about photo shoots as you fork up your tagliatelle. The staff have the blasé air of those who have seen it all before, a nonchalance that extends to the menu descriptions, which bear little relation to what actually arrives on the plate. Gazpacho was in fact a chilled tomato and red pepper soup. Similarly, char-grilled ham with radicchio and Parmesan tasted not the slightest bit char-grilled. A torte of spinach and ricotta even turned out to be a large raviolo. But none of that mattered because everything that arrived was first rate. Equally good (and accurately described) was a dish of monkfish, tomato and

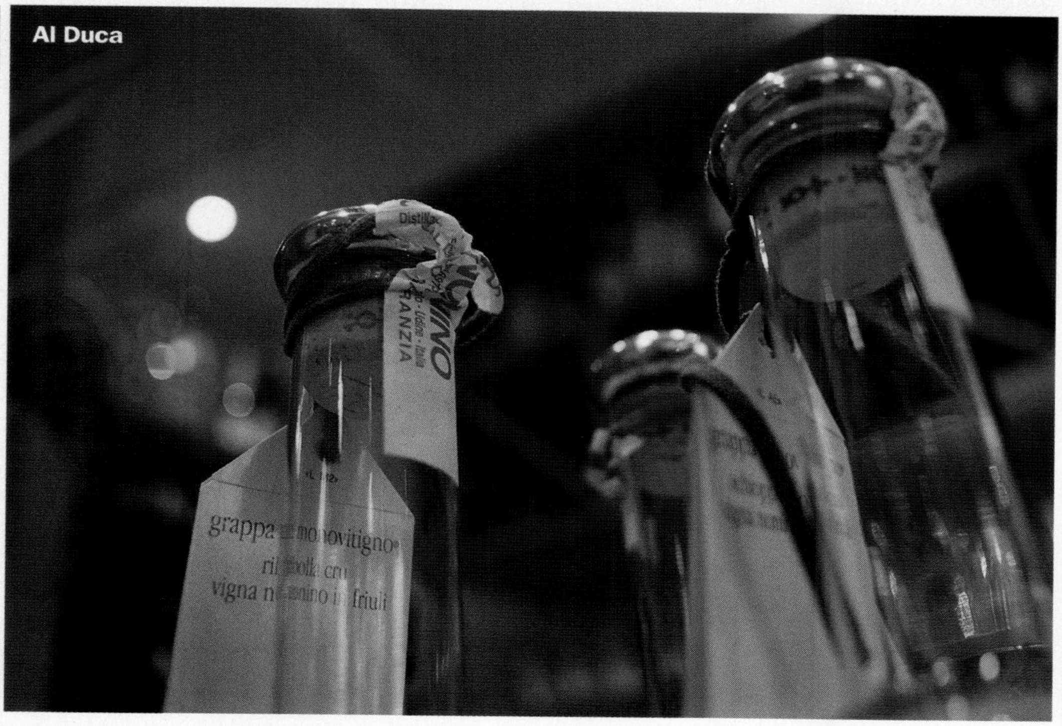

Al Duca

lentils. In addition to the idiosyncracies of the menu, there are also occasional lapses in presentation: the tiramisu looked more like a bowl of muesli, but did at least taste home-made. The decor is an artful compromise between trad and modern Italian, with soothing ochre-coloured walls. A safe place to meet someone you don't know very well and/or want to impress without being too flash.
Children admitted. Book lunch. Separate room for parties, seats 35. **Map 13/6J**.

St James's SW1

Al Duca ★

4-5 Duke of York Street, SW1 (020 7839 3090). Green Park or Piccadilly Circus tube. **Lunch served** noon-2.30pm Mon-Fri; 12.30-3pm Sat. **Dinner served** 6-10.30pm Mon-Thur; 6-11pm Fri, Sat. **Minimum** £15 (lunch), £18 dinner. **Set lunch** £15.50 two courses, £18.50 three courses, £21.50 four courses. **Set dinner** £18 two courses; £21 three courses; £24 four courses. **Service** 12½%. **Credit** AmEx, JCB, DC, MC, V.

A lot less stuffy than its St James' location suggests, Al Duca serves up-to-the-minute Italian food in surroundings of pared-down, 1970's-esque chic. It's part of the Cuisine's Collection group, which is run by the irrepressible Claudio Pulze and Raj Sharma. At dinner, the set meals represent amazing value for the quality of the food on offer. We were particularly impressed by a splendidly flavoursome line-up of linguini with clams, sweet chilli and parsley, followed by pan-fried monkfish with pumpkin purée and aromatic leaves, and coconut sorbet with chocolate sauce. Other tempting options were a starter of cured pork with baby onions and balsamic salad, main-course char-grilled fillet of sea bass with rocket, tomato and tapenade or a dessert of white chocolate mousse served with raspberries. Chef Michele Franzolin has spent time at Zafferano, and it shows. In fact, the menu has a very encouraging little codicil that reads, 'As our produce is purchased freshly each day, please be understanding if certain dishes are not available.' Roughly translated this means: if you like uncomplicated, well-executed Italian food then Al Duca is a good place to know.
Babies and children admitted. Dress: smart casual. Tables outdoors (2, pavement). **Map 13/7J**.

West

Bayswater W2

L'Accento

16 Garway Road, W2 (020 7243 2201). Bayswater or Queensway tube. **Lunch served** noon-2.30pm Mon-Sat. **Dinner served** 6.30-11.15pm daily. **Main courses** £12-£14. **Set meal** £12.50 two courses. **Service** 12½%. **Credit** AmEx, JCB, MC, V.

Busy and buzzy L'Accento is a good bet if you're after simple food with a shot of style and plenty of noise and brio thrown in. But if you're more in the mood for a romantic or relaxing evening, the ear-splitting decibel levels make this place a non-starter. The front room opens out on to the street and is rusticly chic; out back is initially uninviting but there is a lovely leafy garden outside that can be glimpsed through the tiny windows and through the ingenious overhead canopy. The tempting à la carte menu features lots of pasta and shellfish, with the option of a two-course menu for £12.50 – pretty good value for this part of town. From this, we chose a starter of broccoli and taleggio risotto, which looked plain but tasted great, and own-made beetroot and spinach ravioli with poppy seeds, which was swamped by an oily butter sauce. From the à la carte, grilled squid with rocket, and lobster taglioni with a rich tomato and basil sauce both proved fine choices. Desserts tend to be hearty favourites like apricot and almond tart and rich chocolate torte. The wine list is also reasonably priced – an Oleandro Alghero rosé 1999 was an excellent choice at £13.50.
Babies and children admitted. Booking advisable. Separate room for parties (garden room with removable roof), seats 26. **Map 11/6B**.

Chiswick W4

Grano ★

162 Thames Road, W4 (020 8995 0120). Gunnersbury tube/rail/Kew Bridge rail. **Lunch served** 12.30-3pm Sun. **Dinner served** 7-10.30pm daily. **Main courses** £15. **Set meals** £19 two courses, £24 three courses, £27.50 four courses. **Service** 12½%. **Credit** AmEx, DC, JCB, MC, V.

Judging by the abundance of couples on our Saturday night visit (ranging from retirement age down to first-daters), Grano is a popular spot for a romantic celebration. It's easy to see why, with its impressive but relaxed ambience and a multi-choice set-price (not to mention mouth-watering) menu that can be extended to a gastronomic procession of four courses for just £27.50. Seasonal ingredients are very much the pivot of the cooking here. We began with a delicious plate of grilled vegetables and seared scallops, and a generous serving of salad. Main courses were also impressive: pappardelle with Italian sausage, broad beans and peas was satisfyingly rich, and grilled rib-eye steak had been perfectly judged and was simply accompanied by rocket salad. A side dish of wonderful sautéed potatoes with rosemary was also well worth its £2.50 price tag. The wine list offers plenty of good drinking at the cheaper end. Add super coffee, a hearty bread basket and excellent friendly service and you have a very good reason to make a reservation.
Babies and children welcome; high chair. Book dinner. Dress: smart casual. Separate room for parties, seats 30.

Riso

76 South Parade, W4 (020 8742 2121). Chiswick Park tube. **Dinner served** 7-11pm Mon-Sat; 7-10.30pm Sun. **Set meals only** £14.50 two courses; £18.50 three courses; £23.50 four courses. **Service** 12½%. **Credit** MC, V.

With large shopfront windows offering splendid views of the park, Riso is a spacious, brightly coloured restaurant. It's deservedly popular – full, during our visit, of beautiful couples, who were much easier on the eye than the hideous modern art on the walls. Given the name, we expected some stonking risottos on the set menu, but there were none. Of the starters, bresaola with goat's cheese dressing had fine ingredients but the meat overpowered the cheese. Better was the attractively garnished cold cream of tomato soup. Meaty main courses such as herb-crusted chicken and grilled lamb with balsamic mash were offered on a specials board, while the printed menu concentrated on pasta and huge pizzas. Very good was the black pasta with scallops and garlicky herb sauce. Unfortunately desserts of baked peaches with amaretti mascarpone and chocolate parfait had been sitting in the fridge too long; the icy-cold plates arrived studded with lumps of congealed icing sugar. Service was a bit scatty: the main courses arrived so swiftly after the starter that we barely had time to swallow and orders were forgotten. But the staff were genuinely apologetic and sweet with it, so none of that detracted from a highly enjoyable evening.
Babies and children admitted; high chairs.

Hammersmith W6

River Café

Thames Wharf, Rainville Road, W6 (020 7381 8824). Hammersmith tube/211, 220, 295 bus. **Lunch served** 12.30-3pm daily. **Dinner served** 7-9.30pm Mon-Sat. **Main courses** £21-£28. **Service** 12½%. **Credit** AmEx, DC, JCB, MC, £TC, V.

The River Café is suddenly looking a bit retro. The place that launched a thousand cookbooks and a TV series is stuck in an early '90s time-warp, with its blue panelling, acres of mirrors and irritatingly dinky designer halogen lamps. Sub-Habitat wicker chairs and paper tablecloths smack too much of laurel-resting, especially at these prices (allow at least £130 for two people with a modest bottle of wine). The toilets are claustrophobic and odorous, and 'a local planning restriction' means that everybody has to be shooed out by 11pm. That said, the food does make up for these annoyances. The tagliatelle with asparagus and Parmesan fonduta was a perfect meld of flavours, as was a wood-roasted turbot with capers and marjoram, roast fennel and radicchio. The cappe sante (scallops) were huge Scottish mutants, not the delicate Venetian variety, but by and large, the Café's take on classically modern northern Italian cuisine is convincing and authentic. Dessert lacked something in presentation but, once in the mouth, valpolicella sorbet with lemon and Ricotta ice-cream was spectacular. Service was efficient but on the arrogant side of cordial. If only they would sort out the trimmings – and the prices – so we can enjoy the food unreservedly.
Babies and children welcome; high chairs. Booking essential, at least two weeks in advance. Disabled: toilet. No cigar or pipe-smoking. Tables outdoors (16, terrace).

Holland Park W11

Orsino

119 Portland Road, W11 (020 7221 3299). Holland Park tube. **Meals served** noon-11.30pm daily. **Main courses** £12.50-£15.50. **Set meals** (noon-3pm, 5.30-7pm, 10-11.30pm) £11.50 two courses, £15.50 three courses. **Credit** AmEx, MC, £TC, V.

For a large and busy restaurant on a quiet residential street, Orsino is easy to miss. The building is a triangular, warehouse-like structure at the point of Portland Road and Penzance Place. Its dimly lit interior makes the most of the beautifully designed tall wooden shutters but, apart from the décor and the clientele (at the trendier end of Sloaniness), there is little to distinguish this venue from its progenitor, Orso, in Covent Garden. A starter of seared scallops with rocket, cherry tomatoes and balsamic was very pleasing; ditto main-course grilled corn-fed chicken with lemon, rosemary, spinach and hot peppers. Tubular pasta with pancetta, broccoli, capers and green olives might also have been a tasty dish but overcooked pasta and unwarranted quantities of salt held it back. Beetroot and ricotta ravioli, served with a sage and butter sauce, was much better. Interesting side veg included a combination of yellow beans, onion and pancetta, and buttered Jersey royals. Desserts are a fiver; ours were nothing special. Still, Orsino is a useful late-evening venue with a practical set menu of two-courses for £11.50. The staff make up in friendliness for what they lack in efficiency.
Babies and children admitted. Booking advisable. No-smoking tables. Separate room for parties, seats 36. **Map 11/7Az**.

Maida Vale W9

Green Olive

5 Warwick Place, W9 (020 7289 2469). Warwick Avenue tube/6 bus. **Lunch served** 12.30-2.30pm Mon-Fri, Sun. **Dinner served** 7-10.30pm daily. **Main courses** £14-£17. **Set meals** £22 two courses, £24.50 three courses, £28 four courses. **Credit** AmEx, MC, £TC, V.

Something was seriously amiss at the Green Olive when we last visited. The food was, as it always has been, impeccable in both execution and presentation, but the standard of service had fallen to an unacceptable level and one very much at odds with its sibling restaurants (Red Pepper, Purple Sage et al). Our evening began badly; we had to repeatedly ask for the wine list and were then made to wait for ages to order our food. The chef, like the rest of the staff, is also a recent arrival but happily he actually knows what he's doing: starters of courgette flowers filled with crab meat on tomato sauce (£3 supplement), and foie gras terrine with cherry (another £3 supplement) were faultless. Equally good were the main courses, such as lamb cutlet stuffed with mushroom and served with cabbage and aubergine timbale and garlic sauce (£4 supplement). Desserts – strawberry coulis and coconut ice-cream, and a selection of Italian cheeses (£3 supplement) – were also very moreish, but the espressos we ordered failed to materialise. Naturally, there was another interminable wait for the bill, which was riven with various supplements when it did arrive, somewhat undermining the concept of a prix-fixe menu. Once a safe bet for fine Italian food, the Olive seems to have lost its way.
Booking essential dinner. Tables outdoors (7, conservatory). **Map 1/4C**.

Notting Hill W8, W11

Assaggi

The Chepstow, 39 Chepstow Place, W2 (020 7792 5501). Notting Hill Gate tube. **Lunch served** 12.30-2.30pm, **dinner served** 7.30-11pm Mon-Sat. **Main courses** £15.50-£18.25. **Credit** AmEx, DC, MC, JCB, £TC, V.

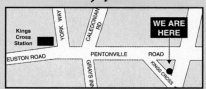

The hype surrounding Assaggi often centres on its showbiz visitors but around half the tables on our recent visit were taken up with people from the food industry – Raymond Blanc included – demonstrating the esteem this restaurant commands for its high-calibre cooking. Our meal was delicious but rather aggressive and haughty service put a dampener on things. The menu is all in Italian and demands translation from the maitre d', though this has its charms. Starters included a tasty salad of scallops and squid. Taglioni with walnuts and herbs, presented in an elegant but generous cylinder, was delightful. Mains started at £15.50 for calf's liver and maxed out at £18.25 for turbot. Fish of the day, grilled tuna, was a moderate portion cooked to medium-rare perfection. This was not so true of the puréed potatoes, which were the consistency of very thick soup. Super desserts of almond and fig tart and bitter chocolate tart put the kitchen back on the right track and we finished with great coffees. Assaggi seems to deserve its culinary reputation and the prices are reasonable for this standard of cooking; the chief reason for the long advance booking requirement seems to be that this is a small room with only a few tables.
Booking essential; six weeks in advance for dinner. **Map 11/6B**.

The Ark
122 Palace Gardens, W8 (020 7229 4024) Notting Hill Gate tube. **Lunch served** 12.30-3pm Tue-Sun. **Dinner served** 6.30-11pm Mon-Sat. **Main courses** £11-£17.50. **Service** 12½%. **Credit** AmEx, MC, V.
The Ark is more than just a wooden shack resting in the eddies of Notting Hill Gate's one-way system. Once a rite of passage for waitressing debutantes putting the finishing touches to their hosting skills, the Ark was then seized by Jean-Christophe Novelli on his ascent to culinary stardom and sadly relinquished by him on the way back down. Now, in its latest taupe and shocking pink incarnation, this trailer-like restaurant has turned Italian. Riccardo Isolini, who used to be chef at Islington local Maremma (now closed), is the man behind the stoves. Prices are high but, we felt, justifiably so given the standard of cooking. A starter of mixed salamis was prime dried pork served with colourful own-made pickled vegetables on a wooden platter. Risotto al verde was a dreamy, creamy consistency, made with seasonal courgette and French beans. Main courses (we never made it that far) sounded equally alluring: sautéed rabbit, grilled veal with truffle oil, char-grilled swordfish. Puddings such as fresh peach with amaretti and amaretto sauce are, again, all proper Italian stuff. The wine list is 100 per cent Italian, offering well-chosen gems from top producers throughout the country. Well worth rediscovering.
Babies and children welcome; high chairs. Booking advisable. **Map 11/7B**.

Mediterraneo
37 Kensington Park Road, W11 (020 7792 3131). Ladbroke Grove or Notting Hill Gate tube/52 bus. **Lunch served** 12.30-3pm Mon-Fri; 12.30-4pm Sat; noon-3.45pm Sun. **Dinner served** 6.30-11.30pm Mon-Sat; 6.30-10.30pm Sun. **Main courses** £9-£15. **Service** 12½%. **Credit** AmEx, JCB, MC, £TC, V.
Saturday lunchtimes are understandably frantic at this casually well-to-do corner venue – it's only a short walk from Portobello Road and seems to catch a lot of the market traffic. Even so, we were irritated that, having booked and arrived fashionably late, we were still asked to stand at the bar – where there is no room to stand – until a table became available. But in spite of our rather gruff welcome, the list of daily specials perked us up. Lobster salad or half a dozen oysters would have been the sensible choice, it being a hot day, but we couldn't resist vitello tonnato (cold veal coated in a rich tuna mayonnaise). The main courses were a mixed success: grilled tuna steak arrived unappetisingly cold in the centre, but the grilled beef was satisfyingly well cooked. Sadly, the dessert list showed no signs of the seasonal fruits available in the nearby market; instead there was a poor selection of rich, heavy items. Indeed, panna cotta turned out to be rubbery and almost tasteless. Still, Mediterraneo is clearly popular with the well-heeled locals, and a grown-up alternative to nearby Osteria Basilico.
Babies and children welcome; high chairs. Booking essential evenings. Tables outdoors (5, pavement). **Map 11/6Az**.

Osteria Basilico
29 Kensington Park Road, W11 (020 7727 9372). Ladbroke Grove or Notting Hill Gate tube. **Lunch served** 12.30-3pm Mon-Fri; 12.30-4pm Sat; 12.30-3.15pm Sun. **Dinner served** 6.30-11pm Mon-Sat; 6.30-10.30pm Sun. **Main courses** £6.50-£14.50. **Service** 12½%. **Credit** AmEx, MC, £TC, V.
There is a more intimate downstairs area but on the whole this is a bustling, unpretentious and hugely popular neighbourhood restaurant (booking is essential and couples may be asked to share the larger tables). Soup of the day, generally a please-all variety such as mushroom, is around £4.80 with other starters under £7 and pasta or pizza a popular choice at about £6 to £8. On our visit the day's special pizza was topped with Italian sausage and broccoli. We were also tempted by the antipasta buffet, the bruschetta of artichoke, tomato and Pecorino, and the warm salad of smoked mozzarella and Parma ham. A main course of veal was well matched with its salad of fennel, radicchio, oil and lemon but, while the menu is enticing, the quality of cooking is not always top-notch. For example, a plate of pasta with ricotta and tomato sauce was unimaginatively presented and had little flavour beyond that you'd find in a supermarket ready meal. Desserts such as panna cotta and tiramisu are pretty ordinary, too. The service is informally professional but we felt under pressure to eat up and make way for the next sitting.
Babies and children welcome. Book two days in advance; bookings not accepted lunch Sat. Tables outdoors (4, pavement). Takeaway service (pizza only). **Map 11/6Az**.

Olympia W14

Cibo
3 Russell Gardens, W14 (020 7371 6271/2085). Olympia tube/rail/Shepherd's Bush (Central Line) tube. **Lunch served** noon-2.30pm Mon-Fri, Sun. **Dinner served** 7-11pm Mon-Sat. **Main courses** £9.50-£23.50. **Set lunch** (Mon-Fri) £12.50 two courses. **Set Sunday lunch** £14.95 two courses, £17.95 three courses. **Service** 12½%. **Credit** AmEx, DC, JCB, MC, £TC, V.
This fine upmarket local offers several generous touches such as appetisers, petits fours and plentiful servings that add up to great-value eating. Plates of fat black and green olives are brought immediately to the table accompanied by pizza slices and bread baskets filled with ciabatta, focaccia and carta da musica. The menu offers plenty of choice, but shellfish seems to be a particular favourite. We began with a fresh-tasting dish of artichokes cooked in white wine, and an equally enjoyable helping of lightly fried calamari and whitebait. Main courses included a collection of crustacea, fish and molluscs cooked in wine and tomatoes, alongside dishes like baked rack of lamb with baby artichokes. The long dessert list offers, primarily, variations on an ice-cream theme, plus Italian classics such as budino and panna cotta. The baked cherries with ricotta ice-cream were divine. Alternatively, round off a meal with excellent coffee and petits fours, which may include chocolate-coated cherries, tartlets and truffles. We ate leisurely to a relaxing jazz soundtrack, grateful for the fact that, even on a Friday night, Cibo does not push customers out of the door in order to profit from an extra sitting.
Babies and children admitted. Booking advisable, essential dinner Fri, Sat. Separate rooms for parties, seating 10 and 16. Tables outdoors (5, pavement).

Westbourne Grove W2

Zucca
188 Westbourne Grove, W11 (020 7727 0060). Notting Hill Gate tube/23 bus. **Brunch served** 11.30am-3.30pm Sun. **Lunch served** 12.30-3pm Mon-Fri; 12.30-3.30pm Sat. **Dinner served** 7-11pm Mon-Sat; 7-10.30pm Sun. **Main courses** £7.75-£13.50. **Set lunch** £12.50 two courses, £14.50 three courses. **Service** 12½%. **Credit** MC, £TC, V.
Service has improved tremendously at Zucca since our last visit, the posturing and sulking has been replaced by well-meaning friendliness, even if menus, bills and so on take a little long to arrive. Also impressive was a swift no-quibbles refund following our complaint that two of the four mussels in our main course pasta dish were unopened. Otherwise our meal was very good and reasonably priced. Zucca's menu ranges from populist, ginormous pizzas to vegetable treats for calorie-counters, such as a fine starter of globe artichoke filled with wilted spinach and balsamic dressing. The offending pasta dish redeemed itself with superb large prawns and a tasty sauce, while our other main course of smoked haddock and spring onion risotto boasted excellent flavour and texture. Brandy and orange gelato was a beautifully simple and refreshing choice for dessert. A plate of young Taleggio, pear and toast was an astute offering let down only by chilled food regulations that do no favours to cheese. The wine list is seductively annotated, easy to understand and reasonably priced. The open kitchen at the end of the split-level dining area provides some theatre but, while the room is light and airy, it would benefit from a no-smoking section.
Babies and children welcome; high chairs. Booking essential dinner; not accepted lunch Sat. Tables outdoors (2, pavement). **Map 11/6A**.

South West

Barnes SW13

Riva ★
169 Church Road, SW13 (020 8748 0434). Barnes Bridge rail. **Lunch served** noon-2.30pm Mon-Fri, Sun. **Dinner served** 7-11pm Mon-Thur; 7-11.30pm Fri, Sat; 7-9.30pm Sun. **Main courses** £9.50-£16.50. **Service** 10%. **Credit** AmEx, MC, £TC, V.
On a busy day, Riva is best sampled at lunch, as the room can turn quite stuffy and noisy in the evenings and the normally discreet, efficient staff can become fraught. Some believe this to be London's best Italian restaurant but in our experience the cooking can be patchy; the meal on this visit was a typical example. Traditionally, combinations of pasta and shellfish are a safe bet here, and a fine starter of linguine with prawns, clams, tomato and chilli was delicious proof of that, as was a dish of tiny calamari with a pungent tangle of grilled fresh herbs. Unfortunately, though, a bowl of bland and stodgy gratinated spinach pasta tossed with crab was a total let down. However, best-ever steak accompanied by shoestring fries and crisp, fine slices of courgettes was a simple dish masterfully cooked. Desserts, too, were sublime – a dish combining cinnamon ice-cream with acacia honey and balsamic vinegar was particularly lovely. A chilled bottle of Bardolino Chiaretto La Vigne San Petro rosé 1998 from the interesting but concise wine list was a highly drinkable accompaniment and, despite a lunch bill of around £90 for two, the event was so enjoyable we left resolved to visit Riva more often.
Babies and children welcome; high chairs. Booking essential. No cigars or pipes. Tables outdoors (3, pavement).

Fulham SW10

La Famiglia
7 Langton Street, SW10 (020 7351 0761/020 7352 6095/www.lafamiglia.sageweb.co.uk). Sloane Square tube then 11, 22 bus/31 bus. **Lunch served** noon-2.45pm, **dinner served** 7-11.45pm daily. **Main courses** £10.50-£20.50. **Cover** £1.75. **Minimum** £18.50 dinner. **Credit** AmEx, DC, JCB, MC, £$TC, V.
There is a palpable sense of theatre at La Famiglia; the many waiters, every one of them dressed in old-fashioned white jackets, apply their comic shtick with near professional pride. And the bread, oil and delicious olive paste that arrived at our table almost as soon as we did seemed to justify the £1.75 cover charge. The extensive menu offers several unusual meat and game dishes, plus simple classics and a short selection of tempting daily specials. Carpaccio of tuna was a delightfully presented and tastily garnished starter but it was a starter-sized portion of tagliatelle dressed with truffle oil and Parmesan that stole the show. Main course fusilli with broccoli and garlic sauce looked small but was highly satisfying thanks to the superbly rich quality of the pasta; a side order of sautéed potatoes was also delicious. The dessert trolley looks spectacular and we were not let down by our choice of heavenly torta all nonna studded with pine nuts. Italian coffees are superb, and there's a reasonable wine list that, like everything here, is priced at the premium end. Admittedly, the bill was more than we'd hoped but the distinctly Italiano occasion of dining here was probably worth it.
Babies and children welcome; high chairs. Booking essential dinner and Sun. Separate room for parties, seats 35. Tables outdoors (35, garden). **Map 5/13C**.

Putney SW15

Del Buongustaio
283 Putney Bridge Road, SW15 (020 8780 9361/020 8789 9659). East Putney tube/ Putney rail/14, 220 bus. **Lunch served** noon-3pm Mon-Fri; 12.30-3.30pm Sun. **Dinner served** 6.30-11pm Mon-Sat; 6.30-10.30pm Sun. **Main courses** £9.90-£13.95. **Set lunch** £9.50 two courses. **Set dinner** £22.50 five courses. **Cover** 90p. **Service** 10% for parties of six or more. **Credit** AmEx, MC, V.
While Del Buongustaio is invariably a charming place to visit, with relaxing atmosphere and superb service, the calibre of the cooking is doubtful. Much of the menu is given over to obscure traditional recipes, which have usually been left to gather dust for a reason, as demonstrated by one poor starter, salad of mushrooms sautéed with pears and white wine. It's not often you wish you'd ordered cauliflower soup instead, but on this occasion it was a smooth and tasty bowlful. Mains of pasta with spring vegetables and a huge rectangular lobster pie with saffron sauce also proved to be good choices. To round off the meal we enjoyed desserts of chocolate espresso mousse and macedonia of fruit and ice-cream. The restaurant has recently opened an opulently furnished coffee lounge and pasticceria next door to compete with Putney's high proliferation of cafés. The pasticceria serves rustic breads and creamy pastries, but sadly, despite some good coffee, the baking isn't the best in town.
Babies and children welcome; children's menu. Book dinner.

Enoteca Turi
28 Putney High Street, SW15 (020 8785 4449). East Putney tube/Putney rail/14 bus. **Lunch served** 12.30-2.30pm Mon-Fri. **Dinner served** 7-11pm Mon-Sat. **Main courses** £12.50-£13.50. **Credit** AmEx, DC, MC, V.
Matching wines with food is a special feature of the mouth-watering menu at this deservedly popular restaurant. Several excellent Italian wines are available by the glass (£3.75-£4.25) and each dish on the printed menu has one recommended as an accompaniment. In addition, there is a blackboard menu of daily specials: on our visit, crispy duck leg salad with quince preserve and a parsley and red onion dressing or lemon-braised poussin with roast sweet potatoes and Parmesan green beans. We opted for a salad starter of rocket, baby artichokes and salted ricotta, and some own-cured duck with rocket and Parmesan. Unfortunately the latter arrived icy-cold but tasted excellent after it had been left to warm slightly. Of the main courses, pasta with mussels and borlotti beans was good, but excellent home-made beetroot ravioli with mascarpone and poppy-seed dressing was even better. This was deliciously nutty and crunchy and would alone justify a return trip. Desserts included a rustic Neapolitan with fresh strawberries and cream, and a fine panna cotta with a rich sticky confit of Sicilian oranges. Polite and attentive service perfectly rounded off an enjoyable lunch.
Babies and children admitted. Book dinner. Separate room for parties, seats 80.

South

Battersea SW11

Cantinetta Venegazzù
31-32 Battersea Square, SW11 (020 7978 5395). Clapham Junction rail/19, 49, 319, 237, 345, 349 bus. **Lunch served** 12.30-3pm Mon-Sat; 12.30-3.30pm Sun. **Dinner served** 7-11pm Mon-Sat, 7-10.30pm Sun. **Main courses** £9.50-£15.50. **Set lunch** (Mon-Fri) £5.90 two courses. **Credit** AmEx, DC, JCB, MC, £TC, V.
Seafood lovers will find plenty to catch their interest in this simple rustic eaterie on Battersea Square – it's almost impossible to have pasta here without it containing some kind of fishy element. One starter, however, that won the undivided attention of a commited carnivore in our party was a plate of Venetian salumeria that included tasty ham, coppa and salami. Another particularly enjoyable starter was a dish of tiny scallops lightly topped with herbs and breadcrumbs, then oven baked. For main courses, we chose fresh crab and a platter of herby grilled fish and shellfish, both of which were generous, fresh and well executed. Side orders such as mixed vegetables and sautéed potatoes were also nicely done and not too pricey at £2.50. Similarly, a bottle of Bolla Bordolino Chiaretto 1998 was a very reasonable £14.50. Tables for two are small here, a little too close together as well, but the place is rarely packed. Service is friendly – the owner is particularly enthusiastic, even if the staff seemed rather weary on our visit.
Babies and children admitted. Booking advisable dinner, essential weekends. Dress: smart casual. Tables outdoors (28, terrace).

Metrogusto
153 Battersea Park Road, SW8 (020 7720 0204). Battersea Park rail/44, 344 bus. Restaurant **Lunch served** noon-2.45pm

Mon-Fri; noon-3.30pm Sat, Sun. **Dinner served** 6.30-10.45pm Mon-Sat. **Main courses** £6.50-£14.50. **Service** 10%. **Credit** MC, £TC, V.
We were treated to a formal bow from the elegantly besuited manager as we arrived at this spacious, stylish eaterie. The courteous and efficient waiters continued to pamper us as they delivered hearty portions of robustly flavoured dishes to our table. We started with a glass of the house red and munched on bread and oil before ordering a deep-fried pasta pillow served with an admittedly rather bland tomato sauce and a truffley pasta dish of the day. Beef steak was a simple dish expertly cooked, but the chef's innovative leanings were revealed in a duck burger stuffed with beetroot and served with jerusalem artichoke sauce. Desserts included 'homage to Sicily' (a mix of whey cheese, candied peel and pistachios) served with balsamic vinegar and orange ice-cream, and a board of Neal's Yard cheeses. We opted for the desserts of the day: a large chocolate pot unrestrainedly flavoured with rosewater; and a rich, chewy compote of over-roasted fruit served with delicious saffron ice-cream. Despite some lapses in the cooking, it was a highly enjoyable evening. Metrogusto is a tremendous asset to Battersea.
Babies and children welcome; high chair. Booking advisable. No-smoking tables.
For branch see index.

Osteria Antica Bologna

23 Northcote Road, SW11 (020 7978 4771). Clapham Junction rail/35, 37, 319 bus. **Lunch served** noon-3pm Mon-Fri. **Dinner served** 6-11pm Mon-Thur; 6-11.30pm Fri. **Meals served** 10am-11.30pm Sat; 11am-10.30pm Sun. **Main courses** £6.75-£15.90. **Set lunch** (Mon-Sat) £8.50 two courses. **Service** 10%. **Cover** 90p. **Credit** AmEx, MC, £TC, V.
Lunchtimes are increasingly busy at this rustic Northcote Road institution, as locals have finally twigged the brilliant value of the two-course, two-choice set menu. Just £8.50 buys one of the restaurant's vibrant soups or something piquant and salady, then a hearty bowl of pasta or a seasonal dish such as roast lamb or char-grilled cuttlefish with Italian vegetables. In the evening, the venue can be noisy, stuffy and claustrophobic – tables in the mid-section are jammed too close together, and sitting out back feels like you're in school detention, so aim for the front area if possible. The menu is lengthy but the kitchen handles it with panache. Starters and glamorous nibbles for sharing begin under a fiver, and several items can be scaled up for a main course, while secondi are based on diverse ingredients such as goat (Sicilian-style goat cooked with tomato and almond pesto, served with grilled polenta) and rabbit (casseroled with fennel, thyme, onion, olives and wine). Bonuses include excellent bread and Sicilian house wine, popularly ordered in pottery jugs. Desserts are worth having; we were tempted by chocolate and date tart with vanilla ice-cream, and baked stuffed peaches with amaretti ice-cream. At the weekends there's a good-value, sophisticated brunch menu.
Babies and children admitted. Book dinner. Tables outdoors (5, pavement).

Pepe Nero

133 Lavender Hill, SW11 (020 7978 4863). Clapham Junction rail. **Lunch served** 12.15-2.30pm, **dinner served** 6.45-11.30pm Tue-Sun. **Main courses** £9.50-£11.95. **Credit** MC, £TC, V.
Situated opposite a church, Pepe Nero has a better view than most other venues on Lavender Hill. The decor is a subtly updated version of traditional rustic, with plenty of wooden furnishings and a cosy bar area at the back of the split-level dining room. The menu is also a deft modern take on classic Italian cooking, with dishes such as crab and lobster ravioli with truffle oil and grilled scallops with broad bean purée among the starters. Both these dishes were good, though the broad bean purée was a little too bitter. Of the mains, cod steamed in vermouth with mussels and a selection of delicately turned vegetables was pretty as a picture and very enjoyable. Equally tasty was a sliced grilled steak with rocket and basil. Unfortunately, the same cannot be said of a dessert of apple cake 'pepe nero' with vanilla ice-cream; profiteroles proved to be the better choice. We were also annoyed at having to pay £1 extra for a decidedly ordinary basket of bread. On the whole, though, if you live locally, Pepe Nero is a good place for relaxed meals at sensible prices.
Babies and children admitted; high chairs. Book dinner. No-smoking tables. Separate room for parties, seats 14. Tables outdoors (4, pavement).

Clapham SW4

Tuba

4 Clapham Common Southside, SW4 (020 7978 3333/www.tuba.com). Clapham Common tube. **Lunch served** 11.30am-6pm Fri-Sun. **Dinner served** 5pm-11.30am daily. **Main courses** £4.95-£11.95. **Service** 12½%. **Credit** AmEx, MC, V.
Tuba is to restaurants what Steps are to pop music – fun but lacking substance. It's a busy and vibrant venue, but beware of tables near the front window, where traffic noise is almost overwhelming. The main menu is supplemented by daily blackboard specials and, although dishes are primarily Italian, stray ingredients such as Cajun spices, soy and hoi sin sauces do make an appearance. From the brief and very competitively priced wine list we chose a superb Giacosa Fratelli Barbera d'Alba 1996 for £16.95. An initial special of sautéed wild mushrooms in soy sauce turned out to be very unspecial; own-made spinach and ricotta ravioli with sage butter sauce was far tastier. Main course baked lamb with cracked pepper, garlic, oregano and lemon-roasted potatoes, though tender and richly sauced, failed to exploit any of its flavourings. Better (and cheaper) was 'estiva' pizza, imaginatively topped with smoked salmon, rocket, deep-fried capers and crème fraîche. Dessert took ages to arrive: chocolate torta was excellent; summer berry sorbet was well flavoured but sadly half melted. Choose carefully from the menu and Tuba can be a good, reasonably-priced evening out.
Babies and children welcome; high chairs. Booking advisable weekends. Takeaway service.

Tooting SW17

Ferrari's

225 Balham High Road, SW17 (020 8682 3553). Tooting Broadway tube. **Lunch served** noon-3pm daily. **Dinner served** 6-11pm Mon-Sat; 6-10.30pm Sun. **Main courses** £5.95-£13. **Set lunch** £5.95 pasta or pizza and drink. **Service** 10%. **Credit** DC, MC, V.
It's not themed around Jeremy Clarkson's bonnet bulge, and there's not even a hint of screaming V12s in the place; Ferrari's is merely a smart-looking new restaurant. There's so little to choose from in this part of the world that every new eaterie is descended upon with glee by Heaver Estate dinkies. Pizza, pasta, salads, steaks and chicken dishes dominate. Penne siciliana was unlike any found in Sicily, where the tomatoes used are fresh; this tomato sauce was strangely glutinous. Sautéed chicken livers (fegatini Ferrari's) were minced with onion to the extent that the liver flavour was barely perceptible. Pollo sorpresa was an even bigger let down, as the aubergine slice stuffed inside the chicken breast was so undercooked it was inedible. At least the swordfish was of decent quality and nicely cooked, served with artichokes. Finally, cassata was a strange confection of frozen colours, closely resembling a bought-in dessert. Ferrari's has many good things going for it – prompt and friendly service, the family atmosphere, the light-filled room; but it's as if they've just said 'Right, let's do Italian', without sourcing real Italian staff or making an effort with the menu. And it shows.
Babies and children admitted; high chairs. Disabled: toilet. No-smoking tables.

South East

Bermondsey SE16

Arancia

52 Southwark Park Road, SE16 (020 7394 1751). Bermondsey tube/Elephant & Castle tube/rail then 1, 53 bus/South Bermondsey rail. **Dinner served** 7-11pm daily. **Main courses** £8.80-£9.20. **Set meal** £10 two courses. **Credit** DC, JCB, MC, £TC, V.
The sandwich board sign with a funky logo is the only suggestion that this shabby orange corner restaurant could be worth a punt. Indeed, the cramped low-lit room tends to be populated by south-east London's grooviest twenty- and thirty-somethings speaking in hushed tones. Staff are pleasant but not the most experienced in town but then with a decent little wine list with nothing over £17.80, who's complaining? The experimental menu is also wallet-friendly and contains a large number of vegetarian dishes. A cheesy potato frittata, and pumpkin and blue cheese on doughy own-made bread, made good, piquant first courses. A main course of cold tomato tart with thick, crisp pastry was accompanied by rocket and nearly converted a committed carnivore. Good too was the garlic and olive oil mash. Side salads such as tomato and basil or rocket and Parmesan are offered, though with the high veg content of most of the dishes these may not be necessary. Coffees are not the best you can buy but despite this, and the fact that we had to ask for the bread, we liked it here. A friendly wave from the kitchen accompanied our departure with satisfyingly low credit card slip in hand.
Babies and children admitted. Book dinner. **Map 8/11S.**

Tower Bridge SE1

Tentazioni

2 Mill Street, SE1 (020 7237 1100). Bermondsey or Tower Bridge tube/Tower Gateway DLR/London Bridge tube/rail. **Lunch served** noon-2.30pm Tue-Fri. **Dinner served** 7-10.45pm Mon-Sat. **Main courses** £10-£17. **Set dinner** £35 five courses. **Service** 12½%. **Credit** AmEx, DC, JCB, MC, £TC, V.
The excessive formality to the service and tableware at Tentazioni transforms what could be easily a fun, modern space into a wannabe temple of gastronomy in which the cooking doesn't quite live up to the ambition. There's a 'degustazione' menu (a reasonable £35 for five courses), which cherry-picks the best of the à la carte. From this we chose a delicious starter of puréed chickpea and rosemary soup, prettily topped with shrimp. Next came pungent goat's cheese ravioli with aubergine and tomato sauce, and strongly flavoured roast mullet with broad bean purée. Another main course of roast duck was accompanied by a powerful demi-glace, perfect wilted spinach, truffle-flavoured mash and succulent foie gras ravioli. Strawberry tart with balsamic syrup would have been a superb end to the meal had our coffee (plus a generous selection of expertly made petits fours) not arrived at the same time. Water and wines are expensive, although a bottle of Le Meridiane Merlot 1996 was delicious and worth every penny of its £22 price tag. Tentazioni should have been busier on a Friday evening. If they could just lose the fancy crockery, change the damask interior, encourage the staff to dress casually and stop mucking about with the cutlery, this place could be terrific.
Babies and children admitted. Book dinner. Dress: smart casual, no shorts. Separate room for parties, seats 45. **Map 8/9S.**

East

Shoreditch EC2

Great Eastern Dining Room

54-56 Great Eastern Street, EC2 (020 7613 4545). Old Street tube/rail.
Bar **Open** noon-midnight Mon-Fri; 6pm-midnight Sat. **Main courses** £3.50-£6.50.
Restaurant **Lunch served** noon-3pm, **dinner served** 6.30-10.45pm Mon-Fri. **Main courses** £7.75-£10. **Service** 12½%.
Both **Credit** AmEx, DC, JCB, MC, V.
Two small rooms of a shopfront have been converted into a black-painted bare boards bar and a dark wood-veneered dining room. Staff are young and able, and the Italian-with-a-twist menu changes weekly and offers plenty of flexibility. We tried a tiny but perfectly formed plateful of swordfish carpaccio that contained delicate blobs of saffron aïoli, decorative sprigs of lamb's lettuce and slivers of radish. Altogether heartier were three spicy slices of cotechino served with green lentils spiked with red onion. The simple, bold combinations of the main dishes demand the freshest of ingredients and can turn up disconcertingly al dente. Slices of duck breast came with a dash of pomegranate and (strangely) a salad of raw fennel and red onion; a nicely crisp fillet of sea bass was served with a chickpea and aubergine salad and more of the same onion. For pudding there might be a boozy ice-cream and chocolate affogato, a textbook tiramisu or perhaps some panna cotta. Don't let the self-consciously fashionable reputation of this Shoreditch new media haunt put you off; go and watch the young hopefuls earnestly plotting their start-ups on the back of a napkin.
Babies and children admitted. Booking advisable. **Map 17/4R.**

North East

Highbury N5

San Daniele de Friuli

72 Highbury Park, N5 (020 7226 1609). Highbury & Islington tube/rail/4, 19 bus. **Lunch served** noon-2.30pm Tue-Fri. **Dinner served** 6.30-10.45pm Mon-Fri; 6-10.45pm Sat. **Average** £20. **Set lunch** £7.50 two courses incl coffee. **Service** 10%. **Credit** MC, £TC, V.
The imitation Italian stone exterior makes this corner restaurant (named after the owner's family home) seem rather pompous at first glance. But once you're inside, the airs and graces vanish: maps, flags and travel pictures hang on the walls, while traditional wooden chairs with woven seats and red vinyl tablecloths complete the old-school image. The long menu offers pizza, pasta and salad staples with an additional four pasta al forno dishes and three risottos. The substantial list of daily specials yielded some interesting dishes, such as delightful carrot and ricotta gnocchi in cheese sauce, and pan-fried sea bass, perfectly cooked and served with a choice of lemon and basil or garlic and rosemary sauces. Porcini risotto was also packed with seductive flavours and textures. An irritating slip in standards, though, was the bread basket – £1.20 worth of dried-out white rolls that were almost impossible to break with the fingers. A dessert of pannetone filled with crème patissière and soaked in orange liqueur was nicely flavoured but heavy; marinated oranges with caramelised zest and yummy vanilla ice-cream was a much better dish. The wine list, which specialises in the Friuli region, is affordable with no bottles over £30.
Babies and children admitted; high chairs. Booking essential, dinner Fri, Sat. Disabled: toilet. No-smoking tables.

North

Camden Town & Chalk Farm NW1

Black Truffle

40 Chalcot Road, NW1 (020 7483 0077). Chalk Farm tube. **Lunch served** 12.30-2.30pm Sat, Sun. **Dinner served** 6.30-10.45pm Mon-Sat; 6.30-9.30pm Sun. **Set meals** £19.50 two courses; £20.50 three courses; £24.50 four courses. **Service** 12½%. **Credit** AmEx, JCB, DC, MC, V.
A success from the moment it opened in January 2000, the Black Truffle has an air of confidence about it. An unusual layout (a ground floor mezzanine overlooking an open-plan basement) is groovily decorated in shades of chocolate brown, with smooth limestone floors and retro-sleek tubular steel lights. Food is similarly stylish and a notch above the familiar hearty-yet-refined style of cooking that you'll find in sister restaurants White Onion, Red Pepper, Green Olive and Purple Sage. The menu is divided into starters, pasta and risotto dishes, meat and fish, and puddings. The likes of tuna carpaccio, ricotta dumpling with taleggio and rocket, and ravioli of pheasant with black truffle, followed by roast duck breast with sautéed radicchio and endive, and grilled venison fillet with roast vegetables all perform well on looks and taste. Puddings – notably a heavenly dark chocolate tart – make any meal end on a high note. There are also some decent wines supplied by Enotria, an importer known for its good Italian list. In all, Black Truffle is a super neighbourhood hangout.
Babies and children admitted. Disabled: toilet. **Map 10.**

Vegia Zena

17 Princess Road, NW1 (020 7483 0192/ www.vegiazena.com). Chalk Farm tube/274 bus. **Lunch served** noon-3pm Mon-Sat. **Dinner served** 7-11pm, Mon-Sat. **Meals served** noon-10.30pm Sun. **Main courses** £10.25-£12.95. **Set lunches** (Mon-Fri) £4.95 one course, £7.45 two courses, incl glass of wine or beer. **Credit** AmEx, DC, JCB, MC, £TC, V.
This Primrose Hill local is a handy spot for good, reasonably priced Italian food, but with its tired decor and overstretched staff it's not really worth going out of your way for. We were led downstairs to a table in the rather shabby basement, through which waiting staff traipse to and from an open kitchen peopled by a stressed-out gaggle of chefs. What they produce, however, is perfectly competent: a shared starter of trenette pasta, potatoes and beans tossed in pesto sauce was fresh and tasty, with just the right degree of oiliness. Likewise, there was nothing to fault in mains of grilled leg of lamb with roast courgettes and peppers and mint dressing and carne del giorno (rabbit with artichokes, potatoes and red onion). A dessert of chocolate cake with chocolate sauce was fine. The waitresses were not really on the ball, though, with one or two of them far from fluent in English. The all-Italian wine list boasts some fine, competitively priced bottles.
Babies and children admitted. Book dinner and weekends. Separate room for parties, seats 20. Tables outdoors (12, garden; 3, pavement).
Map 10.

Crouch End N8

Florians

4 Topsfield Parade, Middle Lane, N8 (020 8348 8348). Finsbury Park tube/rail then W7 bus/91 bus.
Wine bar **Open** noon-11pm Mon-Fri; 11am-11pm Sat; 7-10.30pm Sun. **Main courses** £6.50. **Set meal** £8.50 two courses.
Restaurant **Lunch served** noon-3pm daily. **Dinner served** 7-11pm Mon-Sat; 7-10.30pm Sun. **Set meal** £15.95 two courses before 9pm. **Main courses** £9.50-£11.75. **Minimum** £15.
Both **Credit** MC, £TC, V.
Once you've walked through Florians' rowdy front bar the mellow dining area comes as something of a surprise, with its Mediterranean-style white walls and fine outdoor terrace. The food, while not particularly outstanding, is nevertheless very good value for money, although the abundant portions might be a bit too challenging for some. For starters we opted for what turned out to be a somewhat bland risotto of the day (mixed fish and courgettes) and a more flavoursome dish of black tagliatelle with calamares, prawns and tomatoes, though the prawns tasted a little less than fresh. A main course of grilled rib-eye steak with an enormous pat of spicy garlic butter and gigantic herby roasted potato wedges was fine, if off-puttingly enormous; calf's liver with sage and fried marinated courgettes was tasty, though the sage wasn't sufficiently in evidence and the courgettes came with lots of unadvertised mint. Panna cotta with summer berries was spot on; creamy but firm. The all-Italian wine list is extensive but not expensive, with bottles ranging from £9.95 to £47.50.
Babies and children welcome; high chairs. Booking advisable. Tables outdoors (8, patio).

North West

Golders Green NW2

Philpotts Mezzaluna

424 Finchley Road, NW2 (020 7794 0455). Golders Green tube. **Lunch served** noon-2.30pm Tue-Fri, Sun. **Dinner served** 6.30-11pm Tue-Sun. **Set lunch** £10 pasta or risotto, glass of wine and coffee; £14 two courses, £18 three courses, £22 four courses. **Set dinner** £18 two courses, £23 three courses, £28 four courses. **Credit** AmEx, MC, V.
The scent of truffles and a blackboard announcing the recent takeover by popular north London chef David Philpott greeted our arrival at this Finchley Road venue, but sadly no staff member did. Things did not improve when we were finally led to our seats: an appetiser of courgette and mushroom pizza arrived promptly but 20 more minutes elapsed before our order was taken; longer still before drinks and bread arrived. The Italian-with-a-twist menu is clearly set out. We started with asparagus minestrone with truffle oil, and a fishy rather than creamy saffron risotto topped with grilled prawns. In both cases the food arrived so extraordinarily hot it had to be left to cool before eating – more waiting. Next came sweet and tender roast lamb (with plenty of fat) and accompaniments of pea purée and potatoes. A second main of basil pasta with wilted rocket and black olives was overly salty and disappointingly bitter. Philpott did redeem himself, though, with a fine dessert of crisp apple tart topped with crumbly lemon and ricotta ice-cream, served with custard sauce and sultanas. Great petits fours furthered his recovery. French windows opening out onto the busy road lend a somewhat relaxing ambience to the noisy tiled room, but the inefficient waiting staff and close conditions made the evening frustrating. We wound up very keen to leave.
Babies and children welcome. Book dinner. Tables outdoors (4, terrace).

Villa

38 North End Road, NW11 (020 8458 6344). Golders Green tube. **Lunch served** 12.30-2pm daily. **Dinner served** 6.30-11.30pm Mon-Sat; 6.30-10.30pm Sun. **Main courses** £9.90-£16.50. **Set meals** £14.50 two courses, £18 three courses (not Sat dinner). **Credit** AmEx, DC, MC, V.
There's been a restaurant here since 1980 and its latest incarnation has the same owner, Carlo Barbieri, who opened the place two decades ago. Villa has clearly secured a place in the hearts and stomachs of local customers (there were loads in attendance during our Sunday lunchtime visit), which is at least partly due to the professionalism

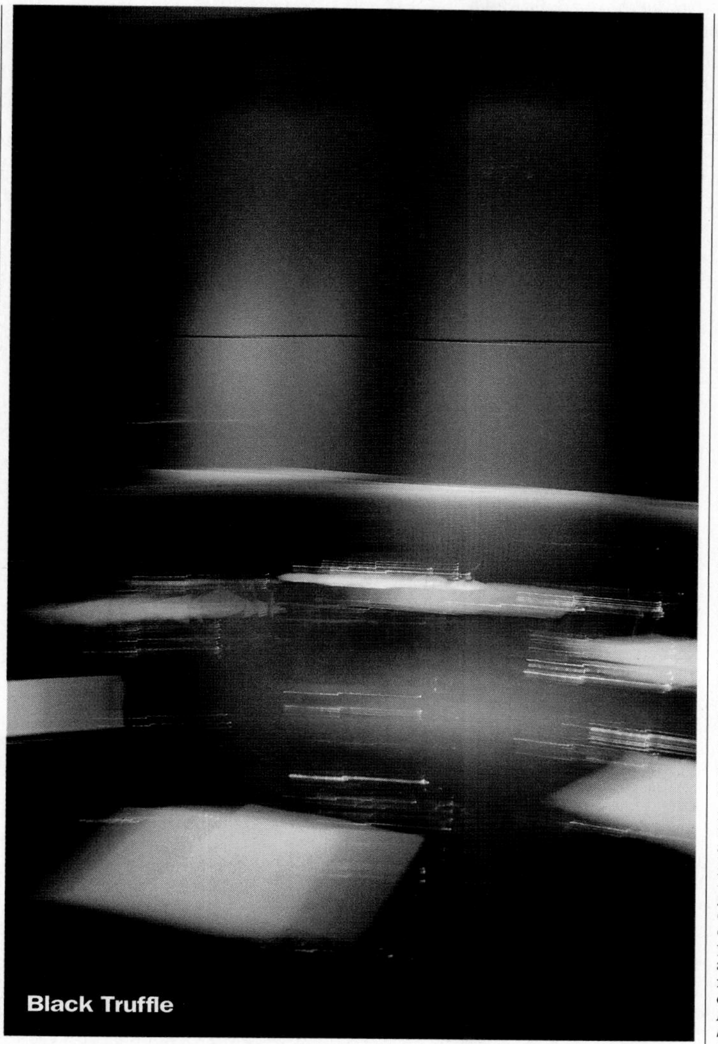
Black Truffle

and hospitality of Mr Barbieri. The decor has been given the slick, modernist once-over, now sporting smart terracotta floor tiles and streamlined furnishings. The chef, Nicola Zanoni, not long since arrived from Italy, has created a menu that nimbly straddles old and new – usually with success. Summer minestrone was light and generous, while another starter of octopus carpaccio was a technical marvel, even if the portion of octopus was vanishingly small and the accompanying tomatoes tooth-achingly cold. Main courses of vegetable lasagne and rotolo di crespella (rolled pancake with ricotta and spinach) were both sound. Dessert was the real highlight, though, with a fabulous lemon tart of melting texture and soothing richness. Side dishes weren't so impressive (french beans came completely unadorned and in a mean portion) but the wine list is interesting and affordable. Not worth schlepping across town for, perhaps, but a great local nonetheless.
Babies and children admitted; high chairs. No-smoking tables. Entertainment: live music Sat evenings.

Queen's Park NW6

The Park

105 Salusbury Road, NW6 (020 7372 8882). Queen's Park tube.
Bar **Open** noon-11.15pm Mon-Sat; noon-10.30pm Sun. **Main courses** £6.
Restaurant **Brunch served** 11am-6pm Sat, Sun. **Lunch served** noon-6pm Mon-Fri. **Dinner served** 6-11.15pm daily. **Main courses** £6-£11. **Set lunches** (Mon-Fri) £7.50 two courses, £9.50 three courses. **Service** 12½%. **Credit** AmEx, MC, V.
Newly groovy Queen's Park is an apt setting for this modern restaurant, with its sassy retro decor, multicoloured fabrics and competent, relaxed new management team. The menu's base of traditional Italian dishes is also supplemented by a more modish selection of international flavours and a short blackboard list of daily specials (wood-roasted sea bass stuffed with fennel and served with garlic potatoes featured on our visit). We got off to a good start with tasty dishes of chicken Caesar salad, white bean soup with chorizo and coriander, and a frighteningly moreish order of garlic pizza bread. Next, marinated lamb steak with a tomato and olive compote was generous in size and flavour but needed our side order of wood-roasted vegetables to provide the balance. Finally, panna cotta had an excellent texture but was slightly overpowered by a sickly sweet roast plum compote; but the ice-cream was delicious. As the evening wore on and the restaurant got busier, service did slow down and we were never offered coffee, but then again, we weren't shooed out of the door either. There are weekly wine deals, while the list itself like the menu reaches beyond Italy and is helpfully categorised by light, medium and full-bodied wines.
Babies and children admitted before 7pm; high chairs. Disabled: toilet. No-smoking tables. Separate room for parties, seats 16. Tables outdoors (5, pavement).

St John's Wood NW8

Rosmarino

1 Bleinham Terrace, NW8 (020 7328 5014). St John's Wood tube. **Open** 10.30am-2.30pm Mon-Fri; 10.30am-3pm Sat, Sun. **Dinner served** 7.30-10.30pm daily. **Set lunch** £16 two courses, £19 three courses. **Set dinner** £19.50 two courses, £24 three courses, £26.50 four courses. **Service** 12½%. **Credit** AmEx, JCB, MC, V.
The gastronomic renaissance in St John's Wood continues apace with this fabulous if pricey new restaurant. Décor is restrained with white-washed walls and cream trimmings concealed behind the handsome wood balcony and the capacious awning. Cooking is top-notch classical Italian with some French touches and a modern twist. At first glance, the menu seemed good if basic, but we soon discovered there is more to Rosmarino than meets the eye. An exquisite swordfish carpaccio was worth its £3 supplement for the presentation alone (wrapped around a small bush of rocket), while home-made taglierini propped up huge fresh clams in a light garlic and sweet chilli sauce, and chicken and truffle oil pasta parcels arrived in an enticing consommé. Much excited thus by our starters, we were raring for our mains. Chestnut pappardelle with girolles and black truffles sauce (again a £3 supplement) was rich but subtle, and grilled lamb steak with spinach was surpassed only by the perfectly charred fillet steak (another supplement, this time £4) To finish, excellent tiramisu, fresh raspberries served with a memorable mascarpone ice-cream, and beautifully light lemon cake. The many supplements did bump up the bill but the food was a treat and the service faultless.
Babies and children admitted; high chairs. Tables outdoors (10, patio). **Map 1/2C.**

West Hampstead NW3

Zuccato

Unit 8A, O_2 Complex, 225 Finchley Road, NW3 (020 7431 1799). Finchley Road tube.
Meals served 10.30am-midnight Mon-Sat; 10.30am-11pm Sun. **Main courses** £5.50-£11. **Credit** AmEx, DC, LV, MC, £TC, V.
High above Finchley Road in the O_2 Complex, Zuccato feels pleasingly remote, its wall of windows providing an extensive view but not the noise or smog of the busy street. The laminated menu boasts 13 pizzas, with a further list of antipasti, pasta and risotto, all of which are available as starters or mains. A starter of grilled mushrooms was juicy and herby, accompanied by nicely charred polenta. A main course of char-grilled salmon with endive proved to be another robust, tasty dish (despite its unappetisingly dry appearance). Other typical mains are breast of chicken wrapped in Parma ham, sautéed with sage and served with mash. Tempted as we certainly were by the large range of waffles on the dessert menu, we opted instead for apple tart with cinnamon ice-cream, a valiantly full-flavoured effort that was sadly let down by soggy pastry. With red and white house wines a reasonable £2.35 per glass and good, large coffees at around £2, Zuccato is definitely a good choice for pre-or post-cinema dining. Surely there are few other reasons to find yourself in this tacky mall of chain restaurants, although Zuccato's bar and special deals on food may offer a lunch hour of sophistication for local office workers.
Babies and children welcome; children's menu; high chairs; nappy-changing facilities. Disabled toilet. No-smoking tables. Tables outdoors (5, patio). Takeaway service.

Outer London

Richmond, Surrey

Caffè Mamma

24 Hill Street, Richmond, Surrey (020 8940 1625). Richmond tube/rail/33 bus. **Meals served** noon-midnight daily. **Main courses** £5.25-£6.95. **Service** 10%. **Credit** AmEx, LV, MC, £TC, V.
This long-established eaterie, known for its trompe l'oeil decor depicting a Neapolitan side street, has decided to get a bit groovy out front with new chairs and a purple and lemon yellow paint job. The laminated menu, however, does not seem to have changed. Fruit juice cocktails arrived heavily garnished and looking like something Del Boy would drink, which suited the Ricky Martin background music perfectly. Blackboard specials of the day included lentil soup and spaghetti with smoked salmon and creamy tomato sauce. Antipasto misto was a good-value meal in itself, jammed with savoury morsels including marinated mushrooms, tuna, prawns, mortadella, milano salami and more. Next, a rather garlicky dish of spaghetti neri with fresh calamari and piquant herb sauce demonstrated admirably the kitchen's potential, but lasagne verdi was dull in flavour. To finish there were pancakes with strawberries, caramel sauce, almonds and ice-cream, and profiteroles that had been strangely contorted into the shape of bishops' hats. With more attention to detail – better quality bread and butter, a good brand of coffee – and a little more care, Caffè Mamma could be a fine destination for traditional Italian fans.
Babies and children welcome; high chairs. Bookings accepted for large groups only. No-smoking tables. Separate room for parties, seats 45. Takeaway service.

Japanese

K-10

When it comes to Japanese dining in London, there's no shortage of good-value meals and a fair smattering of upmarket treats to be had. **Kulu Kulu** (which serves conveyor-belt sushi), **Sushi-Hiro** (out in Ealing), **Ramen Seto** (much more than a noodle bar), **Ikkyu** (on Tottenham Court Road), **Misato** and **Tokyo Diner** continue to champion the budget end of the market. For posh nosh, you still can't beat traditional old warhorse **Suntory** and newfangled **Nobu**. And if it's sheer entertainment value you're after, there's always teppanyaki showtime at Rocky Aoki's **Benihana** chain.

Newcomers over the past year have added nicely to a healthy scene, but they have made little impact in terms of either culinary innovation or format changes. They include: generalist **Miyabi**, which is a small part of Terence Conran's awfully big venture, Great Eastern Hotel; **Seabar**, which is one of three restaurants in Ian Schrager's chic St Martin's Lane hotel; and **K-10**, yet another (and a very fine) addition to London's growing kaiten clan. Nothing, however, on the scale of **Nobu**.

On a minor but niggling point: although fusion cuisine can be a very good thing, as practised by Nobu and **Itsu** (*see page 149* **Oriental**), we would like to lodge a protest against the use of cheese. This western interloper has been creeping inappropriately on to certain menus. We chose not to sample **Miyabi**'s nasu miso cheese yaki, but **Jin Kichi**'s prawn-and-Edam spring roll and **Café Japan**'s gooey sesame-flavoured beancurd served in a cheese sauce were proof, as if any were needed, that cheese does not work in Japanese cooking. This madness should be stopped – now.

Central

Bloomsbury WC1

Abeno
47 Museum Street, WC1 (020 7405 3211). Holborn or Tottenham Court Road tube. **Open** noon-10pm Mon-Sat; noon-8pm Sun. **Main courses** £4.80-£15. **Set lunch** £7.95 two starters, main course, drink. **Set dinner** £8.95 two starters, main course, drink. **Credit** DC, JCB, V.
High quality, low prices and a warm welcome are the attractions at Abeno, with an element of theatre thrown in for free. The operation moved to Bloomsbury from Oriental City in Colindale (*see p118*), taking over the site of the much-lamented Museum Street Café. The layout hasn't changed, the unobtrusive Japanese decor is pleasant, and details (such as the crockery) are lovely. The restaurant specialises in Okonomiyaki. Egg, dough and batter are mixed with cabbage, and with fillings of your choice, then fried on the teppan. The pancakes come in two sizes; we ate a small-size (about 5in diameter) 'Tokyo mix' (with pork, squid and prawn) and a variant called negi-yaki (spring onions instead of cabbage), which made an adequate lunch for two. There are also a few noodle dishes and teppanyaki on offer, along with some diminutive, delicious titbits for starters. The wine list is another surprise: both inexpensive and well-chosen. Within weeks of its opening, in autumn 1999, Abeno had already attracted a steady stream of locals.
Babies and children admitted; high chairs. No-smoking tables. Takeaway service. **Map 14/5L.**

Chinatown W1, WC2

Ikkyu of Chinatown
7-9 Newport Place, WC2 (020 7439 3554). Leicester Square or Piccadilly Circus tube. **Meals served** noon-10.30pm Mon-Wed, Sun; noon-11.30pm Thur-Sat. **Main courses** £7.70-£22. **Set meals** £7.70-£11.50 per person (minimum two) incl miso soup, rice & pickles; eat as much as you like (5-10pm) £13.50. **Credit** AmEx, MC, £TC, V.
An interloper to Chinatown, offering Thai as well as Japanese food, Ikkyu of Chinatown is perhaps a bit of a fish out of water. Although the decor is authentic right down to the tatami mats and pine-effect furniture, we got the feeling the Chinese staff had never eaten real Japanese food and didn't care. From the wide selection of reasonably priced 'Big Bowl Noodles' we chose gyoza ramen; the gyoza were adequate, but the noodles weren't ramen, and were almost inedibly hard. Hoping for more from the tempura and seafood deluxe set lunch, we were pleasantly surprised by a generous portion of grilled just-so salmon steak. The tempura, however, bore more resemblance to what you might get at a local chippy. The miso soup it came with was fine, but the practical non-existence of substance (bar a few slivers of spring onions) seemed ludicrous. Upstairs is an 'eat as much as you like' restaurant, which interestingly foregoes a buffet in favour of set menus that are made to order. On weekdays, set lunches seem a bargain. Ikkyu is adequate for food, less so for authentic Japanese food.
Babies and children admitted. Book Fri-Sun. Separate rooms for parties (3), each seating 12. No-smoking tables. Takeaway service. **Map 13/6K.**

Misato ★
11 Wardour Street, W1 (020 7734 0808). Leicester Square or Piccadilly Circus tube. **Lunch served** noon-2.45pm, **dinner served** 5.30-10.30pm daily. **Main courses** £4.60-£11.80. **Set lunches** £5-£6.80 incl brown tea, miso soup, rice & pickles. **No credit cards.**
No fast food is quite as fast as Japanese fast food. Misato specialises in rapid lunches at rock-bottom prices, and crucially does this without any loss of quality – although it isn't a place with an atmosphere conducive to toying over your teriyaki. Bento box meals are £8.20 for tempura, £8.60 for sushi/sashimi, and come with the usual frills (pickles, rice, fried chicken, Japanese omelette); but Misato manages to undercut these prices with its own set lunch menu. The saké shio lunch included miso soup, pickles, a hijiki (seaweed) appetiser, salad and a sumo-sized bowl of rice to accompany a decent fillet of salt-grilled salmon; it came to just £6.60. The sushi equivalent costs £7, and a sweet, fresh side-order of maguro (£2 for two pieces; all fish sushi the same price) suggested this might be a worthwhile option. Tucked away at the west end of Chinatown, the restaurant is airy and bright, the Japanese-ness confused by the half-beamed ceiling and faux-gas lamps left behind by some previous restaurant incarnation.
Babies and children admitted. Bookings not accepted. No-smoking tables. Takeaway service. **Map 13/7K.**
For branch see index.

Tokyo Diner ★
2 Newport Place, WC2 (020 7287 8777). Leicester Square tube. **Meals served** noon-midnight daily. **Main courses** £3.90-£14.50. **Set lunches** £5.90-£12.90 incl green tea, miso soup, rice. **Credit** JCB, MC, V; no cheques accepted.
The trouble with kaiten bars is that you spend all night watching the sushi go round and round, like tourists lost on the Circle line. After all, there are nights when you might want to gaze into the eyes of your companion, rather than the back-end of a turbot. Help is at hand. At Tokyo Diner the customers (not the food) are the ultimate centre of attention. Few of London's Japanese venues can boast such unfailingly polite and friendly service – and these are not characteristics in short supply at Japanese restaurants. The food isn't so

unfailing, but then it can seem as if London Japanese food only has two price settings (cheap eat and splurge) and Tokyo Diner is no splurge. 'Donburis range from £3.90 (tamago, or egg) to £6.60 (chicken katsu); bento meals start at £8.30 (vegetarian) and top out at £12.90 (salmon teriyaki). Sushi is fresh but not prime; teriyaki is well-sauced but overcooked. The decor is mock-Meiji in a way that is authentically modern Japan. A fine doorway to duck into.
Babies and children admitted. Bookings not accepted. No smoking (ground floor). **Map 13/7K.**

Zipangu ★
8 Little Newport Street, WC2 (020 7437 5042). Leicester Square tube. **Meals served** noon-11.30pm Mon-Sat; noon-10.30pm Sun. **Main courses** £3.30-£7.70. **Set lunches** £5.50-£12.50 incl miso soup, rice & pickles. **Set dinners** £9-£13.50 incl miso soup, rice, dessert. **Credit** MC, V.
The menu at Zipangu quotes Marco Polo on Japan: 'They have delicious dishes in greater abundance than in any other country of the world.' Fortunately these days you don't have to rediscover the Orient to get a decent bowl of ramen: just pop down to Chinatown. Around the corner from Tokyo Diner, Zipangu is less stylish than its neighbour, but serves a similar quality of food at similar prices, and has a wider menu. Japan's adopted dishes – ramen, gyoza, and kim chee – make a tasty combination: ramens start at £4.40 and rise to £5.50, depending on garnishes. From the older Japanese dishes, the bentos here (chicken teriyaki, salmon shio, ebi fry) have Tokyo Diner flat beat for price, and include agedashidofu; while assorted sushi include turbot. There are also three varieties of vegetarian sushi, of which maguro kanpyou (soy-cooked gourd: a roll cut into six pieces) is the main attraction.
Babies and children admitted. Bookings not accepted. Separate room for parties, seats 20. Takeaway service. **Map 13/7K.**

City EC2, EC4

Aykoku-Kaku
Bucklersbury House, 9 Walbrook, EC4 (020 7236 9020/www.japanweb.co.uk/ak). Bank tube/DLR/15, 16, 25, 43, 76 bus. **Lunch served** 11.30am-2.30pm Mon-Fri. **Dinner served** 6-10pm. **Main courses** £10-£50. **Set lunches** £8-£25 incl miso soup, green tea and dessert. **Set dinner** £13.20-£28 incl miso soup, green tea and dessert. **Credit** AmEx, DC, JCB, MC, £TC, V.
It's almost a shock to see that one of London's most prestigious Japanese restaurants also has a brisk bento takeaway service. The owners are obviously making the most of their captive audience of Japanese expats working in nearby banks. Passing the takeaway, and going downstairs, you find yourself in an unexpectedly large maze of rooms and dining areas. Lunches range from £8 to £13.50 and are of nearly foolproof quality. The curry-rice (somewhat like Anglo-Indian curries) came piping hot, on a Fuji-like pile of rice. A staple of rushed Tokyo office workers, it was utterly authentic. The sushi teishoku, with a good selection of firm and visibly fresh cuts of salmon, hamachi, tuna and prawns, also kept us happy. Three ultra-fresh, flavour-packed king-sized prawns came with the usual assortment of aubergines, shiitake and sweet potato in the tempura teishoku and were deep-fried to perfection. The only blips were a slightly too salty miso soup, and for dessert a rather floury apple. We'd have preferred a mouthful of the intriguing-sounding honey and sesame ice-cream. The windowless black and white interior is reminiscent of 1980s minimalist chic, but the consistently good, authentic food and unobtrusive service make this a reliable spot for a quality meal in the City.
Babies and children admitted. Booking advisable. Entertainment; karaoke (on request). Separate room for parties, seats 4, 8, 150. Takeaway service (lunch only). Vegetarian menu. **Map 4/7P.**

City Miyama
17 Godliman Street, EC4 (020 7489 1937). St. Paul's tube/11, 15, 23 bus. **Lunch served** noon-2.30pm Mon-Sat. **Dinner served** 6-10pm Mon-Fri. **Main courses** £5-£25. **Set lunch** £19 incl miso soup, rice & pickles, green tea and dessert. **Set dinner** £35 incl miso soup, rice & pickles, green tea and dessert. **Credit** AmEx, DC, JCB, MC, £TC, V.
If you like Japanese food but are tired of the lunchbox basics, the next place to go is a sit-down restaurant. City Miyama isn't the best in town, but like its Piccadilly sister, it is consistent without being exorbitant. Both restaurants are well into their second decades – the decor is beginning to show its age – but only City has managed to retain that oriental classic, the half-translated menu. Many of the best options are listed only in Japanese. Unagi kabayaki appears in English, but the more spectacular unajyu is squirrelled away in the Japanese section, and costs only £2.50 more (at £18). There's a good selection of winter dishes – including the epic kaisen nabe – but none of the nabemono has been translated. On the other hand, the staff are friendly and ready to help. Salmon skin maki were deliciously crunchy at heart, and shabu shabu was a delight, the waitress gradually adding Scottish beef and eight vegetables to a subtle and increasingly rich stock. We finished with a chilled glass of umeshu (plum wine), the most refreshing after-dinner drink in the world. Probably.
Babies and children admitted. Separate room for parties, seats 10. Vegetarian menu. **Map 4/6O.**
For branch (Miyama) see index.

K-10 ★
20 Copthall Avenue, EC2 (020 7562 8510/www.k10.net). Liverpool Street or Moorgate tube/rail. **Lunch served** 11.30am-3pm, **dinner served** 5-9.30pm Mon-Fri. **Main courses** £1-£3.50. **Credit** AmEx, DC, JCB, MC, V.
If there's one thing that epitomises the popularity of Japanese food, it's the rise of the kaiten. Professional scientists estimate there are now more raw fish on conveyer belts in London than passengers on the Underground. There's a bar for every taste, from the cacophony of the Yo!s to the quiet quality of Kulu Kulu, but K-10 is the kaiten of choice. The dining hall is elegant, and never more so than at the moment you enter. From the staircase you look down on the bright spectacle of sushi rotating ten feet below, bright spots of colour in a setting of neon and chrome. The menu is innovative in a way that other kaitens have often attempted and failed to achieve: no dodgy melon slices here. Salmon sashimi ceviche with olive oil and chives (an innovation first tried at **Nobu**, *see p115*) was gone before it hit the table; octopus salad with pine nuts and fennel seeds sprouted chopsticks; duck in cucumber pancakes with fresh plum sauce was a fine variation on a theme. Sushi rice had the luxuriant softness that only comes with hand-rolling, and the miso soup was exceptional. Don't expect to pay much less than £20 if you're hungry – otherwise, just sit back and enjoy the ride.
Babies and children admitted. Disabled: toilet. No bookings accepted. No smoking. Vegetarian menu. **Map 4/6Q.**

Miyabi
Great Eastern Hotel, Liverpool Street, EC2 (020 7618 7100). Liverpool Street tube/rail. **Lunch served** noon-2.30pm, **dinner served** 6-10.30pm Mon-Fri. **Main courses** £7-£14. **Set lunches** £12.50-£21.50 incl miso soup, rice & pickles. **Service** 12½%. **Credit** AmEx, DC, JCB, MC, V.
Although Miyabi is an outpost of the Conran empire, there's not much to this small but neatly formed component of the Great Eastern Hotel bar/restaurant complex (*see also p54* **Fish** and *p131* **Modern European**). The almost coffin-like dining room is lined with dark wood, while furnishings are smart but sparse. The menu is

Menu

For a more comprehensive explanation and translation of the ingredients and dishes found in Japanese cuisine, Richard Hosking's *A Dictionary of Japanese Food: Ingredients & Culture* (Prospect Books 1996, £12.99) is highly recommended.

Agedashidofu: tofu coated with katakuriko (wheat flour), deep-fried, sprinkled with shaved fish and served in a shoyu-based broth with grated ginger and daikon (qv).
Amaebi: sweet shrimps.
Anago: see Unagi below
Bento: a meal served in a compartmentalised box.
Calpis or **Calpico**: a sweet soft drink derived from milk, similar in taste to barley water. Dilute to taste and serve ice-cold.
Chawan mushi: savoury egg custard served in a tea tumbler (chawan).
Daikon: a long, white radish (aka mooli), which is often grated or cut into fine strips.
Dashi: the basic stock for Japanese soups and simmered dishes. It's made from dried bonito (a type of tuna) flakes and konbu (kelp).
Dobin mushi: a variety of morsels (prawn, fish, chicken, shiitake, ginkgo nuts) in a gently flavoured dashi-based soup, steamed (mushi) and served in a clay teapot (dobin).
Donburi: a bowl of boiled rice with various toppings, such as beef, chicken or egg.
Edamame: fresh soy beans boiled in their pods and then sprinkled with salt.
Gari: pickled ginger, usually pink and thinly sliced. Served with sushi to cleanse the palate between courses.
Gohan: rice.
Gyoza: soft rice pastry cases stuffed with minced pork and herbs; northern Chinese in origin, cooked by a combination of frying and steaming. Usually eaten as an accompaniment to ramen.
Hamachi: young yellowtail or Japanese amberjack, commonly used for sashimi and also very good grilled.
Hashi: chopsticks.
Hiyashi chuka: Chinese-style (chuka means Chinese) ramen served cold (hiyashi) in tsuyu (qv) with a mixed topping that usually includes shredded ham, chicken, cucumber, egg and beansprouts.
Ikura: salmon roe.
Kaiseki ryori: a multi-course meal of Japanese haute cuisine that originally followed the Japanese tea ceremony.
Kaiten zushi: 'revolving sushi' (on a conveyor belt).
Katsu: breaded and deep-fried meat, hence tonkatsu (pork katsu) and katsu curry (tonkatsu or chicken katsu with mild vegetable curry).
Maki: the word means 'roll' and this is a style of sushi (qv) where the rice and filling are rolled inside a nori (qv) wrapper.
Mirin: a sweetened rice wine used in many Japanese sauces and dressings.
Miso: a thick paste of fermented soy beans, used in miso soup and some dressings. Miso comes in a wide variety of styles, ranging from 'white' to 'red', slightly sweet to very salty and earthy, crunchy or smooth.
Miso shiru: classic miso soup most commonly containing pieces of tofu and wakame (qv).
Nabemono: a class of dishes cooked at the table and served directly from the earthenware pot or metal pan.
Natto: fermented soy beans of stringy, mucous consistency.
Nimono: vegetables boiled in a stock, often presented 'dry'.
Noodles: second only to rice as Japan's favourite staple. Noodles are served hot or cold, dry or in soup, and are sometimes fried. There are many types, but the most common are: ramen (Chinese-style egg noodles), udon (thick white wheat-flour noodles), soba (buckwheat noodles); and somen (thin white wheat-flour noodles, usually served cold as a refreshing summer dish – hiyashi somen – with a chilled dipping broth).
Nori: sheets of dried seaweed.
Okonomiyaki: Japanese pizza; in fact, more like an overstuffed omelette, which is usually cooked in front of diners on a teppanyaki (qv) hotplate.
Ponzu: Usually short for ponzu joyu, a mixture of citrus fruit juice and soy sauce used as a dip, especially with seafood and chicken or fish nabemono (qv).
Robatayaki: A kind of grilled food, generally cooked in front of the customer, who makes their selection from a large counter display.
Saké: a rice wine of between 15% and 162% alcohol. It's usually served warm or hot, but in the summer may be chilled.
Sashimi: raw fish.
Shabu shabu: originally a peasant dish designed to capture all possible nourishment from the little food available. A pan of stock is heated at the table and plates of thinly sliced raw beef and vegetables are cooked in it piece by piece. The broth is then portioned out and drunk.
Shiso: perilla or beefsteak plant. A nettle-like leaf of the mint family that is often served with sashimi (qv).
Shochu: Japan's answer to vodka. It is colourless and distilled from a variety of raw materials including wheat, rice and potatoes.
Shoyu: Japanese soy sauce.
Sukiyaki: pieces of thinly sliced beef and vegetables that are boiled at the table on a portable stove, then taken out and dipped in raw egg, which semi-cooks on the hot food.
Sunomono: seafood or vegetables marinated (but not pickled) in rice vinegar.
Sushi: combination of raw fish, shellfish or vegetables with rice – nearly always with a touch of wasabi (qv). Sugar-sweetened vinegar is added to the rice, which is then cooled before use. There are different sushi formats: nigiri (lozenge-shaped), futomaki (thick-rolled), temaki (hand-rolled), gunkan makinigiri (with a nori wrap) and chirashi (scattered on top of a bowl of rice).Hand-rolled is best.
Tare: general term for shoyu-based cooking marinades, typically on yakitori (qv) and unagi (eel).
Tatami: a heavy straw mat, traditional Japanese flooring. A tatami room in a restaurant is usually a private room where you remove your shoes and sit on the floor to eat.
Tea: black tea is fermented, while green tea (ocha) is heat-treated by steam to prevent the leaves fermenting. Matcha is powdered green tea, which has a high caffeine content. Bancha is the coarsest grade of green tea that has been roasted; it contains the stems or twigs of the plant as well as the leaves, and is usually served free of charge with a meal. Hojicha is freshly toasted bancha. Mugicha is barley tea, served iced in summer.
Teishoku: set meal.
Tempura: fish, shellfish or vegetables dipped in a light batter and deep-fried. Served with tsuyu (qv) to which you add finely grated daikon (qv) and fresh ginger.
Teppanyaki: 'grilled on an iron plate', or originally 'grilled on a plough share'. In modern Japanese restaurants, a chef standing at a hotplate (teppan) is surrounded by six to eight diners. Slivers of beef, fish and vegetables are cooked with a dazzling display of knife work and deposited on to your plate.
Teriyaki: a sauce made of a thick reduction of shoyu (qv), saké (qv), sugar and spice. It is also the name of the cooking method in which meat is marinated in shoyu and wine (mirin, qv, or saké), then grilled and served in this sauce.
Tokkuri: saké flask – usually ceramic, sometimes bamboo.
Tofu or **dofu**: soy beancurd used fresh in simmered or grilled dishes, or deep-fried (agedashi dofu), or sometimes eaten cold and uncooked (hiyayakko).
Tonkatsu: katsu (qv).
Tsuyu: a general term for shoyu/mirin-based dips, served both warm and cold with various dishes ranging from tempura (qv) to cold noodles.
Unagi: freshwater eel, whereas anago is the saltwater conger eel.
Wafu: Japanese style
Wakame: a type of seaweed most commonly used in miso (qv) soup and kaiso (seaweed) salad.
Wasabi: a fiery green 'mustard' that is often compared to horseradish, grated from the root of an aquatic plant. It is eaten in minute quantities (tucked inside sushi, qv), or diluted into shoyu (qv) for dipping sashimi (qv).
Yakitori: grilled chicken (breast, wings, liver, gizzard, heart), served on skewers.
Yakimono: 'grilled things'.
Zarusoba: soba (qv) served cold, usually on a bamboo draining mat, with a dipping broth.
Zensai: appetisers.

Miyabi.
See page 111.

also simple, running to three or four choices in each section: sushi, sashimi, tempura and 'main' dishes, along with assorted side dishes. Predictability is relieved by the odd adventurous concoction, such as hotate no wasabi mayonnaise yaki, a succulent titbit of scallop slivers on soft sliced onion under a coating of wasabi-tinged mayo, served on a scallop shell; or nasu miso cheese yaki (deep-fried aubergine topped with cheese and bean paste) – we steered clear of that one. Our meal was nicely bookended by zensai san ten mori (chef's selection of appetisers, which involved three twists on the art of sashimi) and the superb ginger nama choco ('velvet finished ginger chocolate mousse'), both of which outshone the 'main' dishes. Prices might appear modest, but the portions are petite so the bill swiftly mounts up. The service can seem overwhelming on a quiet evening, and the distant toilets are nigh-on impossible to find. There's also a choice of four reasonably priced lunchtime takeaway bentos, but note: 'orders should be placed by 3pm for next-day collection'.
Babies and children admitted. Takeaway service (noon-7pm Mon-Fri). **Map 4/6R.**

Moshi Moshi Sushi
Unit 24, Liverpool Street Station, EC2 (020 7427 3227/www.moshimoshi.co.uk) Liverpool Street tube/rail. **Meals served** 11.30am-9pm Mon-Fri. **Set meals** £4.90-£8.50 incl miso soup and rice. **Credit** JCB, MC, V.
At its best, kaiten sushi is quick, fun and healthy. At its worst it can be a kind of Dantean Circle of Hell for Fish, where dodgy mullet rotate endlessly under the bored gaze of jaded eaters. Where Moshi Moshi rests between these two extremes depends on the time you arrive and the method by which you order. As at all kaiten bars, it's worth remembering you can ask the chefs to make any sushi that aren't already circulating – that way you'll get your fish fresher. Here, it's also worth arriving early: the merchandise tires noticeably as the afternoon progresses. Sit at stools by the conveyor belt and take in the surroundings: the large glass-domed roof (the restaurant is on the top floor of a shopping centre); the giant photos of Tokyo neonscapes; the industrial, almost makeshift decor. It is hard to be churlish about Moshi Moshi, who first brought kaiten eating to London, but the chain currently lags behind some competitors in terms of quality and imagination. Even so, the basic ingredients are generally fine, and kaiten is kaiten: it's more fun than a poke in the eye with a blunt fish. Usuzukuri (red snapper sashimi topped with salmon roe) and kakuni (marinated cooked tuna) were the best dishes we tried: both were ordered direct from the sushimeister.
Bookings not accepted. No smoking. Takeaway service. Vegetarian menu. **Map 4/5R.**
For branches see index.

Noto Ramen House ★
Bow Bells House, 7 Bread Street, EC4 (020 7329 8056). Mansion House or St Paul's tube/Bank tube/DLR. **Meals served** 11.30am-8.45pm Mon-Fri. **Main courses** £5.80-£7.60. **Set lunch** £6.50 incl miso soup rice & dumplings. **Unlicensed. Credit** £TC.
At the centre of Noto Ramen House is a noodle bar surrounded by seats, from where to watch chefs create myriad noodle dishes. The basic shoyu and shio (salt) ramen are good value at £5.80, with miso ramen coming in slightly more expensive at £6.80. Noto claims to be the only restaurant that imports noodles direct from Japan (from Sapporo, which in Japan is to noodles what Scotland is to whisky) and they certainly are a cut above the rest. The miso wun tun noodles were perfect comfort food: six tasty prawn and pork wun tun with crunchy beansprouts and spinach. Piping hot, the miso stock was perfect too. We did notice, though, that the noodles were cut up into smaller sections than usual (to stop slurping, perhaps?). This aside, everything was as authentic as they come. Other toppings include seafood, char siu pork and sweetcorn. If you've a Godzilla-like appetite, order a large bowl of noodles for an extra £2. Noto gets crowded between noon and 1pm, so go later to avoid having to queue outside. Even homesick Japanese tourists, ravenous for ramen, beat a path to Noto's door. It must be good.
Babies and children admitted. Takeaway service. **Map 4/6P.**
For branches see index.

Fitzrovia W1

Ikkyu ★ ★
67 Tottenham Court Road, W1 (020 7636 9280). Goodge Street tube. **Lunch served** noon-2.30pm Mon-Fri. **Dinner served** 6-10.30pm Mon-Fri, Sun. **Main courses** £6.50-£10. **Set lunches** £6-£9.50. **Set dinners** £10-£14. **Service** 10%. **Credit** AmEx, DC, JCB, MC, V.
The entrance to Ikkyu (not to be confused with Ikkyu of Chinatown, which is under different ownership) is quite easy to miss. Don't – this is one of the best and most reasonable Japanese restaurants in town. A welcome injection of cash has brought about a marked improvement in the place. Where once it felt almost down-at-heel, it's now on a par with other London restaurants similarly focusing on robatayaki food. The yakitori includes all the standards, as well as more interesting fare such as okra, and even whelks. Those we tried (heart, tongue and chicken wings) were a triumph. Most impressive was the offal, which managed to be tender and juicy at the same time as retaining a good texture. Foregoing raw conger eel, and the intriguing-sounding cuttlefish vermicelli, we chose salmon roll and California roll. The fish was a treat, fatty and succulent, but the rice was a little too wet and overly vinegared. We had one more small gripe: when the agedashidofu arrived, the tofu hadn't been coated in flour before deep-frying, so it lacked the required glutinous texture. This said, the broth it came in was a perfect balance of salty dashi and sweet mirin. Particularly easy on the pocket, and more so on the mouth was the large plate of fried chicken (karaage). Behind the bar is a kitchen full of people engaged in furiously chopping, grating and slicing; on request, they can usually accommodate off-menu excursions. Friendly, fast waiting staff are a boon, too.
Babies and children admitted. Book dinner Wed-Fri. No-smoking tables. Separate room for parties (tatami), seats 12. Takeaway service. **Map 3/5K.**

Leicester Square WC2

Seabar
St Martin's Lane, 45 St Martin's Lane, WC2 (020 7300 5588). Leicester Square tube. **Lunch served** noon-2.30pm Mon-Fri. **Dinner served** 6pm-midnight; 6pm-1am Thur-Sat; 6-10.30pm Sun. **Main courses** £14.50-£34. **Credit** AmEx, DC, MC, V.
Tucked away at the back of the quirkily minimalist St Martin's Lane hotel, the Seabar looks like a big square fridge with its whiteout decor and a central counter of underlit ice bejewelled with shellfish and crustacea – particularly when the air-conditioning is cranked up to full blast. The sushi/sashimi half of the incredibly short menu doesn't mess about. Choose from nine nigiri, if you don't mind coughing up £5.50 for two pieces (whether the finest hamachi, ubiquitous salmon or boring old egg). Hamachi nigiri were exceedingly fresh with delicate colouring and a full flavour; scallop nigiri were passable but a bit weedy and crunchy. More substantial offerings include seven futomaki (thick sushi rolls), and a bento box that includes a dessert. The bento failed to impress, with mean cuts of tuna and salmon sashimi, and three mediocre nigiri (ebi, salmon and sea bass). The best bit was the compartment containing two fat, juicy, piping-hot ebi katsu (prawns in breadcrumbs). These cropped up again in the misnamed but more satisfying 'shrimp tempura uramaki': ebi katsu, cucumber and crabstick wrapped in nori and rice speckled with black sesame and orange flying-fish roe. At first, the service seemed to be in tune with the chilly surroundings. On arrival, we could see two chefs working behind the counter but nary a waiter in

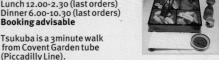

sight. Eventually things warmed up, with a friendly face and helpful explanations, but dining here is something of a heartless experience.
Babies and children welcome; high chairs. Booking essential. Dress: smart casual. Disabled: toilet. **Map 14/7L.**

Marylebone W1

Yumi ★

110 George Street, W1 (020 7935 8320). Baker Street, Bond Street or Marble Arch tube. **Dinner served** 5.30-10.30pm daily. **Main courses** £18-£22. **Set dinners** £38-£85. **Service** 12½%. **Credit** AmEx, DC, MC, £TC, V.
After 15 years in operation, Yumi (meaning an archery bow) remains a top-class restaurant that rarely fails to deliver. The high prices mean it is mainly the preserve of Japanese expense-accounters. There are three set dinners: the wafu (£39), the sushi dinner (£44) and the kaiseki (a formal banquet at a whopping £70). Each course comes impeccably presented on the most beautiful of pottery and porcelain, that changes in shape and texture with each dish. Oblong for the heavenly starter of asparagus with plum, sliced smoked goose and a thimbleful of Chinese leaves, with mashed sardine and sweet miso on top. It was a riot of flavours, and beautiful to behold. Next was a similarly excellent fried chicken encased in a crunchy batter. In a similar vein, deep-fried prawn balls from the Japanese menu (larger than the English) were a lesson in all things culinary, as were the scallops wrapped in nori. We lingered over steamed slices of daikon and carrot wrapped in chicken that was swimming in an ambrosial mustard and sesame sauce. Strangely, the main sushi and sashimi dish failed to entice. The maguro, which dominated over salmon, hamachi and a few other fish, was a dull scarlet and not perfectly fresh. We found refuge in a comforting sesame ice-cream. Even though the main focus of our meal failed to please, Yumi is without parallel in terms of quality, breadth of menu and service (impeccably performed by kimono-clad waitresses).
Booking advisable. Separate rooms for parties (3), seating up to 14. Takeaway service (sushi only). **Map 2/5G.**

Mayfair W1

Benihana

37 Sackville Street, W1 (020 7494 2525/www.benihana.co.uk). Green Park or Piccadilly Circus tube. **Lunch served** noon-3pm daily. **Dinner served** 6-11pm Mon-Thur, Sun; 6pm-midnight Fri, Sat. **Main courses** £14-£60. **Set lunches** £8.50-£24 incl salad, rice, mushrooms, grilled vegetables, green tea. **Set dinners** £14-£60 incl Japanese onion soup, salad, prawn appetiser, grilled vegetables, rice, green tea. **Service** 12½%. **Credit** AmEx, DC, JCB, MC, £TC, V.
The Piccadilly branch of Benihana is one of three restaurants in London, and many around the world, started by ex-Olympic wrestler 'Rocky' Aoki. More than somewhere simply to enjoy teppanyaki mixed with American pzazz, here you come for the whole Benihana 'experience'. We were seated with six strangers round a large steel hot-plate. Dinners range from £10, through mid-price sets like teriyaki chicken (£16) or hibachi steak (£17), to the seafood combo including lobster, king prawns, scallops and more (£40), and the rather kinky-sounding 'string of pearls' at £50 (sashimi, tempura as well as seafood teppanyaki). The starter on all set menus is onion soup (actually consommé) and was sweet to taste, containing slices of onion and bits of onion tempura. After this our cook for the evening began the show. When not frying and chopping food before our eyes he charmed us with cheesy banter, juggling with salt and pepper pots, and for a finale flipping the uneaten prawn tails from plate, to chef's hat, to the small disposal unit set in the hot-plate. You can carry on the eating-meets-entertainment theme by checking out the authentic pachinko machine façades in the bar, while sipping a Banana Benihana, or even a Wou Wou. Particularly cringeworthy are the photos of 1980s celebs posing with Rocky – a bouffant George Michael is not to be missed. If you don't expect wonders from the food, and don't mind high prices, Benihana certainly makes for a novel night out.
Babies and children welcome; high chairs. Booking advisable. Separate room for parties, seats 8. **Map 13/7J.**
For branches see index.

Nobu ★

19 Old Park Lane, W1 (020 7447 4747). Hyde Park Corner tube. **Lunch served** noon-2.15pm Mon-Fri. **Dinner served** 6-10pm Mon-Thur; 6-11pm Fri, Sat; 6-9.30pm Sun.

Seabar.
See page 113.

Main courses £13.50-£27.50. **Set lunch** £24.50 incl rice, miso soup & salad. **Set sushi lunch box** £25. **Set dinner** (omakase) £50 incl green tea. **Service** 12½%. **Credit** AmEx, DC, MC, £TC, V.
Since Nobu opened first in New York and then London, the restaurants (which are part-owned by Matsuhisa Nobuyuki and Robert De Niro) have made a tsunami-sized splash on the food scenes of both cities. Mr Nobu has lived in Japan, Peru and the US, a fact reflected in a menu that takes the basics of Japanese cuisine and melds them with influences from the Americas. Such daring doesn't always succeed, but the dishes that disappointed us were the most Japanese in origin. Sashimi salad turned out to be tuna tataki, around a pillar of lettuces and carrot, crowned with a pansy. Fresh tuna, ever so slightly seared, was delicious with its sesame and garlic dressing. Recommended to try a new-style sashimi we ordered the salmon. Hot olive and sesame oil had been dribbled on top, with sesame seeds, garlic and fire-red peppercorns added. Nice – but the flavourings overpowered the delicate flavour of the fish. Shojin tempura came in a heavy batter, and looked anaemic. However, rock shrimp ceviche was beautifully tart, and restored our faith, as did the scallop in garlic sauce (browned outside, succulent inside). A divine dessert, chocolate harumaki, had chocolate goo and nuts on the inside of the roll, complemented by a passion fruit and shiso jelly. Expert staff guide you (sometimes with too firm a hand) round the menu. In the ultra-swish Metropolitan Hotel, Nobu comes at a price, but can't be beaten for its panache.
Babies and children welcome; high chairs. Book three weeks in advance. Disabled: toilet. Dress: smart casual. No-smoking tables. Separate room for parties, seats 40. **Map 6/8H.**

Piccadilly W1

Yoshino

3 Piccadilly Place, W1 (020 7287 6622). Piccadilly Circus tube. **Lunch served** noon-2pm Mon-Fri, noon-2.30pm Sat. **Dinner served** 6-10pm Mon-Sat. **Set lunches** £5.80-£19.80 incl miso soup, green tea and dessert. **Set dinner** £19.80-£35 incl miso soup, green tea and dessert. **Credit** AmEx, DC, JCB, MC, £TC, V.
Piccadilly Place suffers the indignity of not making it on to the A to Z – it's 100m down from the Circus on the right – but at ten yards plus Yoshino, it's barely a Place at all, more of a Pl. The interior of the restaurant is odd, the super-cool decor offset by a stuffed sturgeon hanging from the roof; chairs are wrapped in sashed towelling, as if they are just getting ready for bed. Continuing the theme of pleasant eccentricity, the menu is entirely built around the rough-and-ready stockpot oden, an ex-peasant winter dish as simple and delicious as coq au vin. The price of a pot depends entirely on its ingredients, from boiled egg (90p) to yam noodles (£1.50). Sashimi was also extremely good, the tuna fresh and thick-cut as chunks of watermelon. Yoshino serves only fish and vegetables, and this specialisation shows in the quality of ingredients. Other idiosyncrasies were a mixed blessing: there's brown hojicha tea but no green, only four kinds of sashimi, and plum wine arrived frozen solid in the glass. Yoshino is a weird and wonderful experience – if you can find it.
Babies and children admitted. Booking advisable. No-smoking tables. Separate room for parties, seats 20-30. Vegetarian menu. **Map 13/7J.**

Soho W1

Donzoko

15 Kingly Street, W1 (020 7734 1974). Oxford Circus or Piccadilly Circus tube. **Lunch served** noon-2.30pm, **dinner served** 6-10.30pm daily. **Main courses** £4.50-£8. **Set lunches** £4.50-£18 incl miso soup, rice & pickles, service. **Credit** AmEx, MC, £TC, V.
At Donzoko, you could almost feel you were in Japan. From the large number of Japanese diners, to the many dishes from the menu listed on bunting-like strips of paper on the walls, it has nearly all the ingredients of a typical local izakaya (Japanese-style tavern). The only thing missing on the night we went were the crowds of people pumping up the noise level (*de rigueur* in downtown Tokyo). Instead we were met with a rather sober and thoughtful assortment of fellow eaters, leaving us fearful of offending with even the slightest outburst. A wide selection of small tapas-like dishes is the focus of the menu, and all are of a high quality. Particularly to be recommended is the aubergine with white miso (one of the few things that might appeal to vegetarians). All the standards like grilled fish, tempura, yakitori (well worth trying), sushi, and so on, appear on the menu, plus stranger concoctions such as taro and duck nimono. Prices can rise alarmingly so, if you can, supplement the smaller dishes with the more substantial teishokus. Service is unobtrusive, with the exception of the rather brusque 'head-waitress cum mama-san' who has been here for years. Situated just behind Regent Street, this is a useful restaurant for the exhausted shopper.
Booking advisable. Takeaway service. **Map 13/6J.**

Hi Sushi

40 Frith Street, W1 (020 7734 9688). Piccadilly Circus tube. **Meals served** noon-10.30pm Mon-Wed, Sun; noon-11.15pm Thur-Sat. **Main courses** £5-£8.80. **Set meals** £5.50-£7 incl miso soup, rice & salad. **Service** 10%. **Credit** MC, V.
Of all the sushi bars in all the cities of the world, we had to walk into Hi. The second weirdest thing here is that sushi is the weakest point of the menu: noodles and tempura are both better prepared and priced. The first weirdest thing is the downstairs decor, where – for perhaps the first and last time – kaiseki dining meets clubland grunge. The sunken tables are malformed plaques, like blobs in a lava lamp, while diners sit on scuffed floor cushions under living-dead warehouse lighting. The waiters seemed to be on another planet, but it was 9pm (it's worth remembering that some sushi bars wind up early). Food was mixed. Nigiri were overdosed with wasabi, and prices begin at £1.70 a piece for your basic salmon (almost triple the price at Kulu Kulu) rising to £2 for anago eel (the poor relation of unagi) and reaching £2.50 for uni (sea urchin, with a lovely delicate shellfish flavour); all with a minimum order of two. In contrast, the ten zaru (zarusoba and tempura prawns) was great, the prawns light and fluffy, and the chilled buckwheat noodles deliciously refreshing on on our summer night visit.
Babies and children admitted. Book dinner Thur-Sat. No-smoking tables. Takeaway service. **Map 13/6K.**
For branch see index.

Kulu Kulu

76 Brewer Street, W1 (020 7734 7316). Piccadilly Circus tube. **Lunch served** noon-2.30pm Mon-Fri; noon-3.45pm Sat. **Dinner served** 5-10pm Mon-Sat. **Main courses** £1.20-£3. **Credit** JCB, MC, £TC, V.
The secret of kaiten zushi bars is the balance of supply and demand: the fish shouldn't wait around and nor should the customers. At Kulu Kulu – so good they named it twice – nothing waits, and consequently quality is high. The time limit for a meal may be 45 minutes (enforcers tend to appear after an hour), but the result is fresh fish and fast and friendly service. The clientele is Japanese until about 6.30pm and becomes increasingly Theatrelandish thereafter, but the food remains excellent. Two-piece plates start at £1.20 (salmon nigiri; natto maki for the adventurous), rise through £1.80 (fine tuna nigiri, soy-fried aubergine) to £2.40 (unagi eel, sweet prawn, salmon eggs, scallops) and £3 (salmon sashimi). Practically every plate is a West End bargain at the price, and the sashimi possesses the iced-fruit sweetness of the freshest fish. The selection is more varied than this, but the kitchen is less handy with the other available dishes: don't be tempted by tempura or chawan mushi, this isn't the place to try them.
Babies and children admitted. No smoking (1 smoking table). Takeaway service. **Map 13/7J.**

Ramen Seto ★

19 Kingly Street, W1 (020 7434 0309). Oxford Circus tube. **Lunch served** noon-2.45pm, **dinner served** 6-10pm Mon-Sat. **Main courses** £4-£7. **Set meals** £4.50-£5.80 incl miso soup, rice & pickles. **Credit** MC, V.
Exceptionally low prices and a position just behind Regent Street ensure a brisk lunchtime trade for Ramen Seto. Its no-nonsense menu and notably helpful staff (who didn't tire of our various demands) are further attractions. The

Donzoko.
See page 115.

menu is divided into simple sections. We ate some good gyoza, and a chicken spring roll that was scaldingly hot on arrival. Of the good-value set lunches, the tempura is an absolute winner, comprising three king prawns, a mountain of veg accompanied by miso shiru, rice and a small dish of pickles. The salmon and sashimi set was also generous to a fault, with six slices of salmon and three of maguro, but the tuna was a bizarre Day-Glo pink, the likes of which we'd never seen before. The location means the place fills with a cosmopolitan mix of Japanese trendies, office workers and tourists out to try something new. All was well on our visit this year – just don't ask for Chinese beer as one of our fellow diners did; Ramen Seto is as pukka as Pokémon.
Babies and children welcome; high chairs. Booking advisable lunch. Separate room for parties, seats 25. **Map 13/6J.**

Ryo ★
84 Brewer Street, W1 (020 7287 1318). Piccadilly Circus tube. **Meals served** noon-midnight Mon-Wed, Sun; noon-1am Thur-Sat. **Main courses** £4.50-£8.50. **Set meals** £7.50-£10. **No credit cards.**
The noodle bar formerly known as Hamine is under new management, but does the same old menu. Which is a good thing, especially as prices have barely edged upwards over several years. The gyoza and the hiyashi chuka (summer only) remain excellent; probably the best in town. Although miso ramen didn't quite match up to its previous record (it had been overdosed with miso and unnecessary chilli), it was still palatable, and enormous as ever. The simple monochrome decor is a little worse for wear, but this is still a fine and genuine Japanese noodle bar, even if it doesn't do karaoke upstairs any more. The late opening hours make Ryo a perfect post-pub/theatre/gig venue, if you want something cheap, quick (you pay first and service is usually fast) and filling.
Babies and children welcome. Separate room for parties, seats 25. Takeaway service. **Map 13/7J.**

Satsuma
56 Wardour Street, W1 (020 7437 8338). Piccadilly Circus tube. **Meals served** noon-11pm Mon, Tue; noon-11.30pm Wed, Thur; noon-midnight Fri, Sat; noon-10pm Sun. **Main courses** £5.20-£15.50. **Set lunches** £5-£12 incl miso soup, rice & pickles. **Credit** AmEx, DC, JCB, MC, £TC, V.
Anyone who has ever slurped noodles at Wagamama will recognise where Satsuma gets its inspiration. Classroom-style, Scandinavian pine benches and tables, a large selection of authentic and not-so authentic noodle dishes, plus primary colours and loud thumping music are the deal here. The style is highly popular, as shown by the large numbers of diners on the Saturday night of our visit. User-friendly menus, English and European staff, and modern decor make eating easy for novices to Japanese food. Noodle dishes (ramen, udon and soba) seemed to be what most people had plumped for. The spicy fried ramen with fresh crunchy beansprouts, ginger, chicken pieces stir-fried with Japanese Worcester sauce, certainly spiced up our life. Then came chicken teriyaki with roasted garlic slices, which made a nice change from the norm, and finally a salmon roll: a good cut of salmon, clean-tasting and satisfyingly fatty. Satsuma has a wide range of sakés, fruit juices, plum wines and beers. The Kirin beer comes in a magnificent frosted glass with Japanese writing down the side. It's amazing how competent and friendly the staff are, in such a hectic environment. A good place for a no-nonsense fairly priced intro to Japanese food.
Babies and children welcome; high chairs. Disabled: toilet. No smoking. Takeaway service. **Map 1. Map 13/6K.**

Ten Ten Tei
56 Brewer Street, W1 (020 7287 1738). Piccadilly Circus tube. **Lunch served** noon-2.30pm Mon-Fri; noon-4pm Sat. **Dinner served** 5-10pm Mon-Sat. **Main courses** £1.80-£7. **Set lunches** £6.50-£12 incl green tea, miso soup, rice & pickles. **Set dinners** £13.80-£17.80 incl green tea, miso soup, rice & pickles, dessert. **Service** 10% dinner. **Credit** JCB, MC, £TC, V.
Ten Ten Tei is nothing much to look at on ground level, but downstairs the restaurant has a surprisingly large area of semi-partitioned dining tables. A largely Japanese crowd eats here. The usual sushi, tempura, yakitori and so on are offered, though ramen is the speciality – we counted 25 kinds of noodle dishes on the menu. However, we plumped for tonkatsu teishoku, which came mini creaking at the seams of its red and black bento box. The pork cutlet had been deep-fried in breadcrumbs to perfection. Also in the box were a few slices of sashimi, which weren't as fresh as they could have been. The pièce de resistance came in the humble form of a few slices of chicken teriyaki. The chicken had been char-grilled before cooking in teriyaki sauce and both flavours complemented each other to tear-jerking excellence. All the other dishes we ordered – such as fried oysters, and agedashidofu – also attested to the split-second timing and experience of the kitchen. Service can seem idiosyncratic at times, but don't let it put you off, as this place is one of the minor stars of the Japanese food scene.
Babies and children admitted. Book Fri, Sat. Takeaway service. **Map 13/7J.**

Yo! Sushi/Yo! Below
52 Poland Street, W1 (Yo! Sushi 020 7287 0443/Yo! Below 020 7439 3660/ www.yosushi.com). Oxford Circus tube.
Yo! Sushi **Meals served** noon-midnight daily. **Main courses** £1.50-£3.50. **Credit** AmEx, DC, JCB, MC, £TC, V.
Yo! Below **Meals served** noon-1am Mon-Sat; noon-10.30pm Sun. **Bar snacks** £3-£5. **Set bento** £6.50. **Credit** MC, V.
If variety is the spice of life, then Yo! is a 'red-hot chilli-pepper, flaming-Lamborghini' kind of dining experience. On the ground-floor Yo! Sushi, you can hardly see the food for gizmos; and when you do, the food looks like a procession of gizmos itself. There are gunkan (nigiri in flyaway seaweed wraps, including chilli tuna); lobster and avocado hand rolls the size of ice-cream cones; more than ten vegetarian sushi; and, famously, drinks-trolley robots that bump into one another and whinge about it. There's also some fairly good food, although sushi rice is machine-packed (making it a little hard and cold), and late-night sashimi is best avoided: closing time may be midnight in Poland Street, but the kitchens wind down two hours earlier. Two children (aged up to 12) eat free with every adult spending a minimum of £10 (Mon-Fri). Yo! isn't the best conveyer of conveyor-belt sushi in town, but it's certainly the most entertaining. The newer basement operation, Yo! Below, is more of a drinking den. Down here, seating is at sunken tables, beer is served from a help-yourself tabletop tap, and there are novel cocktails as well as a wide range of flavoured sakés. Food includes basic sushi, noodle dishes, bento boxes and bar snacks. Tarot card reading takes place on quieter nights (Sun-Wed); there's also a masseur, DJs, and staff who perform on the karaoke machine (thankfully, customers aren't permitted to).
Yo! Sushi *Babies and children welcome; children's menu. No smoking. Takeaway service; delivery service (minimum order £10; £4 central London-£6 suburbs).*
Yo! Below *Bookings not accepted. Entertainment: staff karaoke cabaret daily; DJs Wed-Sat; musicians Sun. Tables outdoors (3, pavement). Takeaway service.* **Map 13/6J.**
For branches see index.

St James's SW1

Matsuri ★
15 Bury Street, SW1 (020 7839 1101/ www.matsuri-restaurant.com). Green Park or Piccadilly Circus tube. **Lunch served** noon-2.30pm, **dinner served** 6-10.30pm Mon-Sat. **Main courses** £10-£22 lunch, £15-£28 dinner. **Set lunches** £6.50-£40 incl green tea, miso soup, rice & pickles. **Set dinners** £13-£70 incl green tea, miso soup, rice & pickles, dessert. **Credit** AmEx, DC, JCB, MC, £TC, V.
'Matsuri' means festival, which is about right – this is a place for the special occasion. The decor is muted, but offset by bright echoes of Japanese seasonal festivities: man-sized papier mâché masks and photographs of street fairs. The theme is well chosen and executed, and so is each stage of the meal, from raw ingredients through preparation and presentation to the knowledgeable and unpretentious service. The menu includes simpler lunchtime choices such as edamame and a great range of sushi, but the speciality here is teppanyaki, and the greater part of the restaurant is laid out for that purpose. The chefs are a floorshow, the diners looking on with big eyes as their neighbours' lobster tail, scallops and Scottish sirloin are skilleted. Matsuri also makes some brave attempts to break with the traditions of Japanese cuisine, and many of its 'modern' dishes are successful: we found the salmon tartare with wasabi sauce a worthwhile variation on an old theme.
Babies and children welcome; high chairs. Booking advisable. Disabled: toilet; stair lift. No-smoking tables. Separate rooms for parties (teppanyaki), seating 8-18. **Map 13/7J.**

Suntory
72-73 St James's Street, SW1 (020 7409 0201). Green Park or Piccadilly Circus tube. **Lunch served** noon-2pm Mon-Sat. **Dinner served** 6-10pm Mon-Sat; 6-9.30pm Sun. **Main courses** £5-£47. **Set lunches** £15-£35 incl green tea, miso soup, rice & pickles, dessert, service. **Set dinners** £50-£93 incl green tea, miso soup, rice & pickles, dessert, service. **Credit** AmEx, DC, JCB, MC, £$¥TC, V.
One of the oldest Japanese restaurants in London, Suntory is just round the corner from the Japanese Embassy. It has a fearsome reputation for stratospheric prices, so we were pleasantly surprised at the reasonable cost of the set lunches. Dinner, though, comes at a premium. Dishes such as grilled tuna with balsamic sauce, and fillet of sea bass, foie gras and aubergine attest to the fact that, although the food is essentially Japanese, the chefs are not averse to taking on board international influences. Everything we ordered from the three-course lunch menu was beyond reproach. The tempura was light and crispy, the sushi bristling with freshness and the sashimi salad with miso sauce (misoae), a perfect combination of sweetness, saltiness and, with a dash of rice wine vinegar, piquancy. The use of cashew nuts in the dish added another layer of taste and texture. From the à la carte we ordered uni gunkan maki (sea urchin on sushi rice wrapped in seaweed), which at £5 for one is steep, but the creaminess and flavour made it almost worthwhile. Boneless grilled eel on a bed of rice was a melt-in-the-mouth experience. Suntory attracts an international crowd, matched in part by the international nature of the staff. The Japanese waitresses wear kimonos, which certainly adds to the upmarket ambience Suntory exudes.
Children over ten years admitted. Booking advisable. Dress: smart casual. Separate rooms for parties (3 tatami, 1 teppanyaki), seating 4, 7, 8 and 14. Takeaway service. **Map 13/8J.**

West

Ealing W5

Momo
14 Queen's Parade, W5 (020 8997 0206). Ealing Common, North Ealing or West Acton tube. **Lunch served** noon-2.30pm, **dinner served** 6-10pm Mon-Sat. **Main courses** £5-£15. **Set lunches** £7.50-£16 incl miso soup, rice & pickles, green tea, dessert, service. **Set dinners** £15-£25 incl miso soup, rice & pickles, green tea, dessert. **Service** 12½%. **Minimum** £10 dinner. **Credit** AmEx, DC, JCB, MC, £TC, V.
Not to be confused with the W1 restaurant of the same name (*see p144* **North African**), Momo is a comfortable suburban restaurant with the casual looks of a smalltown Japanese bar: large saké bottles and 1970s lounge decor predominate. The menu is broad, with an unusually heavy emphasis on the Portuguese influence in Japanese cuisine – there are four kinds of tempura, a wide range of breaded cutlets, deep-fried crumbed crab, tofu and prawns, and a wild and not quite wonderful experiment called umeshisokatsu (pickled-plum and shiso deep-fried cutlet). Other choices were better. Dobinmushi was sweetly delicate, mentaiko chazuke (chilli cod roe in green tea soup) rich and heartening, and unajyu (with misoshiru) a luxury meal in itself: a whole side of eel, grilled with kabayaki sauce, sprinkled with sansho (aromatic Japanese pepper) and laid on a bed of rice in its own bento box. Go eeling in Ealing. You know you want to.
Babies and children welcome; high chairs. Booking advisable. Takeaway service.

Sushi-Hiro ★ ★
1 Station Parade, Uxbridge Road, W5 (020 8896 3175). Ealing Common tube. **Lunch served** 11am-1.30pm, **dinner served** 4.30-9pm Tue-Sun. **Average** £8 lunch, £10 dinner. **Set lunches** £5-£12 incl green tea, miso soup. **Set dinners** £5-£12 incl green tea. **No cheques or credit cards.**
One of the strengths of Japanese restaurants is their specialisation: a place might serve little except eel, but it'll serve it perfectly. In London the tendency is less pronounced, but Sushi-Hiro is faithful to the pattern. As minimalist as Wakaba, this bright-white bar serves almost nothing except some of the best sushi in town. Quality is high, prices low. The chefs work over their square-inches of fish with the care of watchmakers. From the nigiri menu, glittering flying-fish roe, salmon roe, sea urchin, red clam, and sea bass were all superb, while raw quail's egg melted in the mouth to a marvellous sweetness. Along with inarizushi (rice-stuffed pockets of sweetened, fried slices of tofu), there are five vegetarian maki; umeboshi-shiso, and kanpyou (gourd) were more than good. Nigiri sets start at just £3, as do the chirashi bowls. But the character of the bar is caught best by its miso soup, which comes enriched with clams in the shell, and costs all of 50p. Directly opposite Ealing Common tube, Sushi-Hiro is a Travelcard well spent any day of the week.
Takeaway service.

Kensington W8

Koi
1E Palace Gate, W8 (020 7581 8778). Gloucester Road or High Street Kensington tube. **Lunch served** noon-3pm daily. **Dinner served** 6-11pm Mon-Sat; 6-10.30pm Sun. **Main courses** £10.50-£33.50. **Set lunches** £7.50-£13.50 incl miso soup, rice & pickles. **Set dinners** £25.50-£60. **Service** 12½%. **Credit** AmEx, MC, £$TC, V.
Palace Gate is Embassy Country, which explains why, for a little place, Koi charges some large prices. The epicurean specialities here include teppanyaki foie gras (£18 per 100g), soft-shell crab maki (£9 a roll) and, when in season, black cod with miso (£18.50). This is Japanese Suntory-style, where the naturally fresh, clean flavours of the cuisine are made dense and super-rich: sushi meets Gascony. It's not a development that's to everyone's taste, but on the other hand, the foie gras was selling like hot cakes when we visited. Koi somehow manages to squeeze a sushi bar, tatami room, group tables, teppanyaki floor and fishpond inside its narrow split levels, and still looks uncluttered. We opted for teppanyaki menus Koi and A: eight courses each, including turbot for the former and scallops and sirloin steak for the latter. The high point was the beef, tender and piping-hot from the skillet, with ponzu sauce for dipping. An appetiser that tasted and looked like spam represented the low. The food at Koi isn't worth every penny, but it suits its regulars; and the regulars are always right.
Babies and children welcome; high chairs. Book Fri-Sun. No-smoking sushi counter. Separate room for parties (tatami, karaoke), seats 20. Takeaway service. **Map 5/9C.**

South West

Putney SW15

Chosan ★
292 Upper Richmond Road, SW15 (020 8788 9626). East Putney tube/Richmond Road rail. **Lunch served** 11.30am-2.30pm Sat, Sun. **Dinner served** 6.30-11pm daily. **Main courses** £16-£17. **Set lunch** £10 incl miso soup, green tea. **Set dinner** £15 incl miso soup, green tea, dessert. **Service** 10%. **Credit** JCB, MC, V.
A small, family-run affair on an uninspiring stretch of road, Chosan opened in 1998 and, judging from the meal we had, has been wowing Putney residents ever since. On the monster menu, covering the whole gamut of Japanese food, sushi and sashimi take pride of place. If you're dining alone, sit at the bar and watch the itamae-san (sushi chef) perform his craft. Dotted around the place are colour menus with pictures and explanations of the various sushi and sashimi. Only a restricted menu is offered for weekend lunch, though you can supplement this with orders from the bar. Both the tempura and sashimi set lunch came with three large blocks of agedashidofu in heavenly dashi. Fresh tofu, textured as well as tasty, set the scene for the perfect meal to follow. The sashimi was so fresh it nearly jumped, and all the slices of tuna, salmon, mackerel and hamachi were generous to a fault. Similarly the tempura was light and crisp, and the king prawns were juicy and succulent. Not wishing the meal to end we ordered toro (the fattiest cut of tuna) with spring onions, which again was a cracker of a dish. Service is efficient, and the staff are more than happy to proffer suggestions to the unsure or undecided. Plastic sushi, Japanese prints, stuffed puffer fish – the decor is an eclectic mixture of kitsch and cool.
Babies and children admitted. Disabled: toilet. Separate room for parties, seats 22. Vegetarian menu.

North

Camden Town & Chalk Farm NW1

Asakusa
265 Eversholt Street, NW1 (020 7388 8533/020 7388 8399). Camden Town or Mornington Crescent tube. **Dinner served** 6-11.30pm Mon-Fri; 6-11pm Sat. **Main courses** £2-£12. **Set dinners** £5.20-£18 incl miso soup, rice & pickles. **Service** 12%. **Credit** AmEx, DC, MC, £TC, V.
Tucked away on an unassuming row of shops behind Mornington Crescent tube, Asakusa has a longish menu covering the basic robatayaki favourites, supplemented by extra dishes listed on the wall (though only in Japanese script). Food has a pleasingly homemade feel, but on our last couple of visits we've witnessed the ever-decreasing size of portions and the odd culinary slip. Seaweed salad was an object lesson in taste (succulent sesame sauce) and colour (verdant greens, and even a purple one) but there was so little of it, we wondered if something had been forgotten. A delicious butanokakuni (stewed pork) practically crumbled to the touch, attesting to long hours of slow cooking. Particularly authentic was the generous blob of Japanese mustard that came with it. Yet all the yakitori we ordered was as tough and dry as the proverbial boot. Mackerel tatsuta-age had been over-fried and lacked all trace of the seasoning required. The chef redeemed himself however with fightingly fresh nikunira moyashi itame (stir-fried garlic shoots, beansprouts and chicken) with pungent nira (Chinese chives). The old-fashioned decor at Asakusa – with the odd splash of Japanese kitsch (porcelain cats and flying herons) – is endearing rather than uplifting, but the service, fast and furious, makes up for it. There's a wide range of cheap, and not so cheap sakés – including regional varieties. Always a reliable bet in the past, we hope Asakusa improves for next year.
Babies and children admitted. Book dinner Fri, Sat. Separate room for parties (basement with karaoke machine), seats 25. Takeaway service. **Map 2/2J.**

Swiss Cottage NW3

Wakaba
122A Finchley Road, NW3 (020 7586 7960). Finchley Road tube. **Dinner served** 6.30-11pm Mon-Sat. **Main courses** £5.70-£18.80. **Set dinners** £23.60-£33 incl green tea, miso soup, rice & pickles, dessert, service. **Credit** AmEx, DC, JCB, MC, £TC, V.
Depending on your desires and inclinations, you might think any of the following about Wakaba: it's a restaurant with a mission, offering good Japanese food without the hidebound traditions of the cuisine; it's a very nice place to have on the Finchley Road, thank you; or it's got a cheek charging £4.80 for an undercooked bowl of edamame, and in Zone Two too. Wakaba looks like the kind of thing architects build for themselves – all white and perennially unfinished – but the food is the complete product. Sukiyaki was a wonderfully rich two-course affair, and from the vegetarian sushi menu, pickled burdock maki and umeboshi-shiso maki were exceedingly good fakes. The only drawback here is price, and this is at its most excessive at the lowest end of the menu. Yakitori (£4.50 for two) were OK, but not that OK. Engawa natto ae (turbot and fermented soybeans, £5.90) was an interesting but overpriced tablespoonful. The moral may be to come here when you mean to have something extravagant. For sushi and soup, there's a Yo! across the road.
Babies and children admitted. Booking advisable. Dress: smart casual. Takeaway service.

North West

Colindale NW9

Oriental City Food Court
Oriental City, 399 Edgware Road, NW9 (020 8200 0009). Colindale tube/32, 142, 204, 292, 303 bus. **Meals served** 10am-10pm Mon-Sat; 10am-8.30pm Sun. **Main courses** £3.50-£7.50. **No credit cards.**
It might not be worth the trek out to Colindale just to eat at this shopping mall, but if you're stocking up on Japanese groceries at the supermarket or playing around in the Segadome games centre, Oriental City's Food Court makes for a cheap, easy and really not bad meal break. On the Sunday afternoon we went, the central area was thronging with families and couples, mostly oriental, but there were easily enough canteen-style tables and chairs to go around. The main Japanese choices are the generally reliable and good-value Noto Ramen (*see also p113* **Noto Ramen House**) for noodles, Atami for variable lunchboxes (around £5-£7), and Noto Sushi for exactly what it says – the sushi costs a little more here but tends to be of better quality than Atami's. We contrasted our hearty miso ramen set meal (which included decent though not very hot gyoza) with a box of salmon maki from Noto Sushi; takeaway rates are slightly cheaper than prices for dining at the counter, which is situated opposite the supermarket rather than facing on to the Food Court. If you're not in the mood for Japanese food, take your pick instead from the Malaysian, Indonesian, Vietnamese, Thai, Singaporean and Chinese stalls.
Babies and children welcome; high chairs; nappy-changing facilities. Disabled: toilets. No-smoking tables. Takeaway service.

Kensal Green NW10

Murasaki
43 Chamberlayne Road, NW10 (020 8964 3939). Kensal Green tube/Kensal Rise rail. **Lunch served** 1-3pm daily. **Dinner served** 6-10.40pm Mon-Thur, Sun; 6-11.30pm Fri, Sat. **Main courses** £6.50-£11.50. **Credit** AmEx, MC, V.
The name means purple but the place is less self-consciously so now, having discarded some of the colour co-ordinated trimmings on show when it opened a couple of years ago. Even if the Notting Hill trendies seem to have moved on, Murasaki has retained a healthy vibe, with cool staff who put customers at their ease. Forced table-sharing is a problem, though, due to the flawed seating design: half a dozen fixed tables (seating up to six each) backed on to each other and against the walls, which can only be accessed from one side. It looks good, but isn't user-friendly. Sushi (hamachi nigiri, tekka maki) was done well, apart from the rice being a bit chewy. However, the cooked dishes (yakitori, ebi tempura, and gyoza) didn't ring true in taste or texture, especially the gyoza, which contained a rather strong-flavoured kind of sausage stuffing and, with their heavy casings, were more reminiscent of Cornish pasties than Chinese dumplings. Nevertheless, trade looked brisk on the delivery side of the operation, judging by the succession of orders whizzing out of the door. Overall, culinary shortfalls here are compensated for by a comfortable atmosphere and assured service. Occasionally, there's the added attraction of an all-you-can-eat buffet lunch for £8.50 (phone to find out when the next is scheduled).
Babies and children welcome; high chairs. Bookings accepted for parties of 4 and over. No-smoking tables (2). Separate rooms for parties, seating 8 and 14. Takeaway service.

Golders Green NW11

Café Japan ★
626 Finchley Road, NW11 (020 8455 6854). Golders Green tube/13, 82, 139 bus. **Lunch served** noon-2pm Wed-Sun. **Dinner served** 5.30-10.30pm Tue-Sun. **Main courses** £5-£19.50. **Set lunches** £3.90, £5.90. **Set dinner** £18.50, £19.50. **Credit** MC, V.
On the back of the menu, a message reads: 'We will try our best to please all of you to your hearts' contents.' And they do. Even if orders occasionally get confused, staff are unstinting in their efforts to get it right. There are usually a couple of eye-openers on the weekly specials list, at the front of the long but straightforward menu: we didn't see gindara misozuke yaki (grilled marinated black cod) or satoimo uni dengaku (fried Japanese potato with sea urchin sauce), but amaebi shiso age (deep-fried sweet prawn with Japanese herb) was brought to our table by mistake and looked stunning; and age hamachi uramaki (crispy fried yellowtail inside-out roll) was deliciously robust and tangy with firm, clean-tasting flesh wrapped in nori, and rice lined with spring onion mayo that betrayed a hint of chilli. The Café Japan set dinner (£18.50) is excellent value – as long as your appetite is big – taking in sashimi, yakitori and tempura as well as any main dish from the menu costing up to £8, plus ice-cream for dessert. The choice of grilled stuff is unusually varied, including the likes of marinated tuna, fried beancurd and spicy prawns. Sashimi and sushi are good and fresh and, well, 99% of the food is difficult to fault. Regularly and deservedly packed out, Café Japan delivers on every front now the decor has been spruced up with a lick of yellow paint and some hi-tech lighting.
Babies and children admitted. Booking essential. No-smoking sushi counter. Takeaway service.

Hampstead NW3

Jin Kichi ★
73 Heath Street, NW3 (020 7794 6158). Hampstead tube. **Lunch served** 12.30-2pm Sat, Sun. **Dinner served** 6-11pm Tue-Sat; 6-10pm Sun. **Main courses** £6.90-£11.80. **Set lunches** £6.90-£11.80 incl green tea, miso soup, rice & pickles. **Credit** AmEx, DC, JCB, MC, £TC, V.
This Hampstead old hand continues to excel at the art of grilling. The stunning array of tasty morsels lined up on the central counter ranges from staples such as chicken and onion, to less common nibbles: the likes of cuttlefish tentacles, quails' eggs and ginkgo nuts. A good starting point is to share a grilled set, priced £7.90 or £9.80. The latter comprised two sticks of chicken, one of shiitake, asparagus and pork, tsukune (chicken meatballs), pork and shiso roll, and a whole prawn. However, leave space for something else, as the menu runs to virtually every kind of Japanese cuisine. Salmon sashimi was succulent, creamy and absolutely fresh. There's also a specials menu, from which we sampled with mixed results: ultra-tender chicken breast with shiso and umeboshi proved a sublime combination of flavours refreshing and sour; yet a harumaki (spring roll), containing prawn, asparagus and Edam (!), could definitely have done without the cheese. There's little room for manoeuvre between tables, but the atmosphere is one of cosiness rather than claustrophobia, amid lanterns, posters and signed celebrity photos on the walls. We saw plenty of 'reserved' cards on neighbouring tables, which were duly taken up by Japanese businessmen, families, western couples and a foursome of Americans – all clearly appreciative of the perfectly prepared food and attentive service.
Babies and children admitted. Book Fri-Sun. Takeaway service. **Map 9.**

Willesden NW2

Sushi-Say ★
33B Walm Lane, NW2 (020 8459 2971/7512). Willesden Green tube. **Lunch served** noon-2.30pm Sat, Sun. **Dinner served** 6.30-11pm Tue-Sun. **Main courses** £3.80-£18.85. **Set dinners** £17.70-£27.90 incl miso soup, rice & pickles, dessert. **Credit** AmEx, JCB, MC, £TC, V.
There's a reassuring air of care and attention here, from the meticulously prepared food to the considerate young waitresses – ours bothered to ask in which order we wanted our dishes to arrive. Serving staff are marshalled by the friendly and efficient Yuko Shimizu – one half of the husband-and-wife partnership behind Sushi-Say – hubby Katsuhara Shimizu (formerly of **Wakaba** *see p117*) handles the all-important sushi, on duty behind the fish counter, looking very much the part in his bandana. We opened with straightforward salmon sashimi, seven generously cut, succulent chunks accompanied by what seemed to be real wasabi (freshly grated rather than rehydrated powder). Perfectly steamed and fried gyoza also benefited from the home-made touch, boasting a slightly looser texture and gentler flavour than usual. Set meals aren't cheap, but in the case of the Sushi-Say Dinner (£27.60), you get more than enough to eat, and it's all of a very high quality. Interestingly, the annotated wine list includes an organic saké, though you might think twice about it at £28 for 720ml. The long, low-slung dining space is decked out in simple black and cream, with a sprinkling of Japanese knick-knackery on the walls. The place was encouragingly full for a midweek night. Customers were predominantly non-Japanese couples, but there's no doubting the authentic touch here.
Babies and children welcome; high chairs. Booking advisable. Takeaway service.

Jewish

Bagel shops

Brick Lane Beigel Bake
159 Brick Lane, E1 (020 7729 0616). Liverpool Street tube/rail/8 bus. **Open** 24 hours daily. **Main courses** 45p-£2.10. **No credit cards.**
The late-night pit stop for Hoxtonites and old-timers alike is still going strong, at its prime position at the Bethnal Green Road end of Brick Lane. You can get all the classic bagel fillings, and the prices haven't changed since last year: egg (45p), smoked salmon (95p), chopped herring, and tuna. Racks of plain loaves (chollah and rye) fill the back wall, while cakes (danish pastries, strudel, cheesecake and the like) are piled high in the glass counter. Salt beef (£1.60 for a bagel, £2.10 for a sandwich) rounds off the range.
Takeaway service. **Map 4/4S.**

Carmelli
128 Golders Green Road, NW11 (020 8455 2074). Golders Green tube. **Open** 7am-1am Mon-Thur; 7am-one hour before sabbath Fri; one hour after sabbath Sat-1am Mon. **No credit cards.**
A spick-and-span white-tiled interior contains the big Golders Green bakery, which has some claim to being the jewel in the crown of kosher bread-and-cakedom. Filled bagels (smoked salmon, £1.40; egg mayo, £1.20; smoked salmon and cream cheese, £1.60), chollah and black bread fill up the left-hand side of the shop, while rows of cheesecakes, biscuits and cakes throng the other counters. There's a hot counter on the right containing slices of kosher pizza (£1.30), while a couple of towering wedding cakes loiter in the corner.
Kosher supervised (Beth Din and Kedassia). **For branch see index.**

Daniel's Bagel Bakery
12-13 Hallswelle Parade, Finchley Road, NW11 (020 8455 5826). Golders Green tube. **Open** 7am-9pm Mon-Thur, Sun; 5am-one hour before sabbath Fri. **No credit cards.**
Filled bagels come in all the customary shapes and sizes here – smoked salmon (£1.40), egg mayo (£1.20), tuna mayo (£1.20), and smoked salmon and cream cheese (£1.60). Plain (26p), sesame, onion and rye (35p), and chollah are also available. There's a huge range of cakes and pastries, too. You can buy biscuits by the pound, as do several Temple Fortune locals.
Kosher supervised (Beth Din).

Hendon Bagel
55-57 Church Road, NW4 (020 8203 6919). Hendon Central tube. **Open** 7am-11pm Mon-Thur; 7am-one hour before sabbath Fri; 11pm Sat-11pm Sun. **No credit cards.**
A popular outlet in north-west London, so much so that Church Road seems permanently blocked with parked cars at post-sabbath high points. Filled bagels are the mainstay, with smoked salmon (£1.40), tuna (£1.40), egg (£1.20), cream cheese (£1.20), and smoked salmon and cream cheese (£1.50) all up for grabs. There are cakes aplenty, too; the owner was talking up a cinnamon rugela (bun) he'd just started selling.

Manhattan Bagel Bakery
31 Seven Sisters Road, N7 (020 7263 9007). Holloway Road tube/Finsbury Park tube/rail. **Open** 7am-11pm Mon-Thur, Sun; 24 hours Fri, Sat. **No credit cards.**
A reliable bakery complemented by friendly staff, offering the usual selection of plain and filled bagels (chopped herring, smoked salmon, salt beef). Staff are happy to take orders in advance, including requests for 'fancy' bagels (cinnamon, raisin, and so on) and the pastry range. The manager proudly announced he'd managed to lower prices in the doughnut (30p-50p) and danish (65p) departments. Good for early-hours weekenders in north London.

Shalom Hot Bagel Bakery
35 Woodford Avenue, Ilford, Essex (020 8551 5503). Gants Hill tube. **Open** 7am-midnight Mon-Fri; 5pm-2.30am Sat; 5am-midnight Sun. **No credit cards.**
Shalom's bagels come with the usual cream cheese, smoked salmon, egg, and chopped herring fillings; chollahs and other breads are sold separately. There's a big range of pastries and biscuits, too, from apple strudel to jam-topped cookies. Extra incentive to scoff is provided by a well-stocked deli counter, offering everything heimishe from viennas to chopped liver.

Restaurants

Central

Clerkenwell & Farringdon EC1

The Knosherie ★
12-13 Greville Street, EC1 (020 7242 5190/ www.theknosherie.sageweb.co.uk). Chancery Lane tube/Farringdon tube/rail. **Meals served** 24 hours daily. **Main courses** £2.90-£7.90. **Credit** AmEx, MC, £TC, V.
Taken over a year ago by a former director of the now-defunct Whitechapel Bloom's, the Knosherie is making a bit more effort to attract Hatton Gardenites. It still presents itself as 'kosher style', but the ultra-religious sticklers won't be crowding anyone out. The decor hasn't changed much either (electric-pink plastic table coverings, round-back metal chairs that look like patio furniture), except for the increasing number of framed jigsaws on the walls. The menu has been trimmed down since the takeover, with all the curries banished and only a few chicken-and-chips standards still around. Our starters were excellent: a plate of mixed sweet rollmop herrings; and chunky, thick barley and bean soup. The salt beef sandwich (on rye) was reliable, if somewhat unconventionally cut into quarters; while the 'Bloom's Viennas' and two fried eggs gave us a sizeable dose of cholesterol. Tzimmes was a disappointment: diced carrots and a plain dumpling covered in a sticky sauce that rendered it largely inedible. After such a blow-out, only one of our party could manage dessert: a lokshen pudding which, frankly, wasn't the world's greatest, especially as it was graced with a dollop of plain white sugar. The Knosherie makes no claims for great cuisine – it offers fuel for local traders and market workers, and for that it's perfectly adequate.
Babies and children admitted. Takeaway service. **Map 3/5N.**

Knightsbridge SW1

Harrods Famous Deli
Ground floor, Harrods, Knightsbridge, SW1 (020 7730 1234 ext 2997). Knightsbridge tube. **Open** 11am-7pm Mon-Fri; 10am-7pm Sat. **Main courses** £10-£12.95. **Minimum** £8 noon-3pm. **Credit** AmEx, DC, JCB, MC, £TC, V.
Admittedly, Saturday afternoon during the summer sales isn't the best time to visit Harrods, with its throngs of awestricken tourists and crawling shoppers. However, the 'Famous' deli, wedged into a corner of one of the food halls, doesn't really make the grade except as a pit stop for trippers. Twenty bar stools ranged around a counter is the extent of the establishment. There's no queuing system, so hopeful eaters have to circle like sharks to nab the next free spot – not the most relaxed start to any meal. Once you're seated, the service is efficient and friendly; the straw-hatted and aproned counter staff are alert and quick with the foodstuffs. The Reuben (Gruyère cheese on a salt beef sandwich) is still the star offering; we also had a salt beef sandwich, from the small 'custom made' selection. The salt beef wasn't a wow (barely warm and a little fatty) even though it was freshly carved from a slab behind the bar; at £10.95 you expect better. Latkes hadn't improved from last year's visit (stodgy and rubbery, though they did come with cream and apple sauce). To drink there's kosher lager, but we had an Old Fashioned Lemonade (very sweet, and a hefty £2.95) and a glass of champagne (Harrods own, £8.50). We were going to sample

The Knosherie

the cheesecake, but the bill got slapped down before we had a chance to order. Popular it might be, but hardly worth the trip.
Babies and children admitted. Bookings not accepted. Disabled: toilets. No smoking. Takeaway service. **Map 6/9F.**

Marylebone W1

Reuben's

79 Baker Street, W1 (020 7486 0035). Baker Street tube.
Deli/café **Open** 11am-10pm Mon-Thur, Sun; 11am-3pm Fri.
Restaurant **Lunch served** noon-3pm Mon-Fri. **Dinner served** 5-10pm Mon-Thur. **Meals served** 11am-10pm Sun. **Main courses** £9.95-£18.95. **Minimum** £10.
Both **Credit** MC, V.
Long considered the classiest of London's kosher restaurants, Reuben's proved a mixed bag on our visit. The interior of the downstairs waiter-service section has been given a makeover, with a minty-green decor that extends to coordinated tableware. The service was enthusiastic, too: in fact, a little too enthusiastic, which meant the dishes were served almost as soon as they were ordered. Starters were generous, with plenty of flavour: chicken liver pâté, an imaginative twist on a classic concept, came with rye bread (though we had to ask for more); deep-fried mushrooms were tangy; and gefilte fish was almost a meal in itself. Main courses – a decent mix of trad Jewish and more conventional brasserie-type meals – also came in chunky servings. Salt beef and tongue was succulent; steak au poivre was a huge hunk of tender meat, smothered in a peppery sauce; unfortunately an identical liquid was employed in the lamb with pepper sauce. Prices aren't low, and vegetables cost an extra £2.25 a serving. Nevertheless, it's incredibly filling fare, and meant none of our party could face pudding.
Babies and children welcome; high chairs. Booking advisable (restaurant). Kosher supervised (Sephardi). No-smoking tables. Tables outdoors (4, pavement). Takeaway service. **Map 2/5G.**

North West

Golders Green NW11

Bloom's ★

130 Golders Green Road, NW11 (020 8455 1338). Golders Green tube. **Meals served** noon-11pm Mon-Thur, Sun; noon-3pm Fri; *winter* 90 minutes after sabbath-4am Sat. **Main courses** £5.20-£11.50. **Credit** AmEx, MC, £TC, V.
From the moment you step inside Bloom's, the experience is a delight. Gone is the crusty attitude of old; the white-jacketed waiters are so solicitous it's positively embarrassing. There's a self-conscious air of nostalgia about the place, from the 1950s-drab fittings to the foul wall-length frieze depicting scenes that lie somewhere between a shtetl (village) and *West Side Story*. The food's good too: we kicked off with chopped liver plus egg and onion (nice and heavy), and beetroot borscht and potato (of the pale pink and sweet variety). Next came a plate of gedempte (steamed; boiled, really) meatballs, served with rice or chips, and a club sandwich. This last turned out to be a triple-decker doorstep of cold salt beef, sliced turkey and worscht sausage. Latkes were crisp and non-oily. Despite the meat-eating frenzy, we forced down a dessert. Lokshen pudding avoided the glutinous texture that often afflicts this Jewish equivalent of bread-and-butter pud, while the strudel was suitably rich and appley.
Babies and children welcome; children's menu (£5.95); high chairs. Booking advisable. Kosher supervised (Beth Din). Takeaway service.
Map 12/9F.

Dizengoff's

118 Golders Green Road, NW11 (020 8458 7003). Golders Green tube. **Meals served** noon-11.30pm Mon-Thur, Sun; noon-3pm Fri; 6pm-11:30pm Sat. **Main courses** £3.50-£14. **Credit** MC, V.
Named after Tel Aviv's famous boulevard (and decorated with poster-sized photographs of the town), Dizengoff's is a friendly landmark on the Golders Green strip. The decor – chrome chairs, pink tablecloths – contains a little of the Middle Eastern garishness common to Israeli-influenced restaurants, but is positively restrained compared to the gold-and-pink yuckiness of the nearby non-meat café Milk 'n' Honey. The menu, as you'd expect, is the usual compendium of kebabs, falafels and pitta (there's nary a slice of rye to be found), but our waitress was very friendly, plonking down unasked-for extras with proprietorial enthusiasm. We started with the eternal tester: chopped liver, of the chicken variety. It turned out to be adequate, but not fantastic. The bean soup was better, practically solid and very tasty. The main dishes we tried were most notable: baked lamb, which came with chips and salad, was tender and almost fell off the bone; chicken Dizengoff was a large marinated-and-grilled slab that retained all the flavour you would want. Great plus point: though we couldn't manage dessert (those generous portions again), our waitress, again unasked, supplied a plate of freshly cut orange slices to complete the meal.
Babies and children welcome; high chairs. Tables outdoors (3, pavement). Takeaway service. Vegetarian menu.

Solly's

148A Golders Green Road, NW11 (ground floor and takeaway 020 8455 2121/first floor 020 8455 0004). Golders Green tube.
Ground floor **Lunch served** 11.30am-3pm Fri. **Meals served** 11am-11.30pm Mon-Thur, Sun; one hour after sabbath-1am Sat. **Main courses** £8.50-£13. **Set meal** £20 three courses.
First floor **Dinner served** 6.30-11.30pm Mon-Thur; *winter* one hour after sabbath-11.30pm Sat. **Meals served** noon-11pm Sun. **Main courses** £8.50-£14. **Set dinner** £20 four courses.
Both **Credit** AmEx, DC, MC, £TC, V.
Maybe it was just an off day, but the first time we tried to secure a table at this well-known Lebanese Jewish restaurant, we were repelled with an astonishing level of rudeness by one (apparently senior) member of staff. Such is Solly's reputation, though, we felt we should try again. Second time around, all was sweetness and light. There are three separate arenas competing for customer attention: a restaurant on the first floor, bar stools downstairs (by the takeaway grill), and a diner-style group of tables at the back. We opted for the last-named, which lays on the Middle Eastern charm, with ornate hanging lamps and the like festooned around the place. The menu is of the Middle-Eastern variety, too. We started with delicately flavoured tabouleh, and Moroccan merguez, a particularly flavour-packed spicy lamb sausage. From the choice of grills, steaks and kebabs, we tried lamb shawarma (a heaped plateful of cinnamon-infused meat and rice), and lamb chops (grilled to perfection). The house wine was, as usual, some forgettable kosher vintage, but at least it came from France.
Babies and children welcome; high chairs. Booking advisable. Kosher supervised (Beth Din). No-smoking tables (upstairs). Separate room for parties, seats 100. Takeaway service.

Hendon NW4

The White House

10 Bell Lane, NW4 (020 8203 2427). Hendon Central tube. **Meals served** noon-11.30pm Mon-Thur, Sun. **Main courses** £11-£18. **Credit** AmEx, JCB, MC, £TC, V.
The focal point of a serious-minded Jewish neighbourhood, this is a strictly kosher joint (where all but one of the male customers, on a midweek evening, sported a yarmulka). However, the service, from cheerful Israelis, was friendly – if a tad amateurish (no ice in the water, orders needed repeating: that sort of thing). The menu is a mix between traditional Yiddish-inflected dishes, and occasionally unfamiliar Middle Eastern items. Tasty houmous and mushrooms, a nicely textured chopped liver (which, at £4.25, should have come with bread, but didn't), and a respectable chicken soup with kneidlach kicked things off. Iraqi pitta arrived fresh from the oven in the back. We also tried cigarim, cigar-shaped pastry stuffed with mince. Main courses were large (and, again, with prices over the odds for kosher meat, they ought to be). Lamb casserole was perfectly enjoyable; a plate of tongue was piled thickly with a tender cut; and the salt beef was well up to scratch. All came with a choice of potatoes or rice (or both). Desserts weren't memorable: fresh fruit salad was heavy on the apple, as was apple strudel. Past experience of kosher wines led us to stick to water, but if you've a craving for the unknown, try one of the Golan Heights vintages.
Babies and children welcome; high chairs. Booking advisable. Kosher supervised (Beth Din). No-smoking tables. Tables outdoors (2, pavement). Takeaway service; delivery service.

St John's Wood NW8

Harry Morgan's ★

31 St John's Wood High Street, NW8 (020 7722 1869). St John's Wood tube. **Meals served** noon-9.30pm daily. **Main courses** £6.50-£9.95. **Service** 10%. **Credit** AmEx, MC, TC, V.
Long established in the heart of London's most prosperous Jewish colony, Harry's knows it has a lot to live up to. And it succeeds quite impressively. The clean, white-walls-and-stripped-wood interior boded well. As is often the way in Jewish eateries, the starters were the best part of the meal. Gefilte fish came finely minced and delicately flavoured; chopped liver was as good as it gets, with a generous egg topping; and borscht (which arrived with a big boiled potato floating in its midst) was sweet and eminently drinkable. A big basket of ultra-fresh rye bread came without request, along with a box of matzo. Next was the platter of salt beef and tongue, made with meat of genuine tenderness – but it came on its own, so a side dish of vegetables of the day (spinach, £1.90) was a necessity. Meatballs and rice was served smothered in a rich, tangy ratatouille sauce, while the stuffed pepper 'Hungarian style' turned out to have rice and mince in the middle, with the same rich tomato-based sauce ladled on top. Service was hampered by lack of staff the night of our visit, but, to her credit, the manageress pitched in to help.
Babies and children welcome; high chairs. Tables outdoors (5, pavement). Takeaway service. **Map 1/2E.**

Outer London

Edgware, Middlesex

Aviv

87 High Street, Edgware, Middx (020 8952 2484). Edgware tube. **Lunch served** noon-2.30pm Mon-Thur, Sun. **Dinner served** *Oct-Apr* 6-11pm Mon-Thur, Sat, Sun; *May-Sept* 6-11pm Mon-Thur, Sun. **Main courses** £7-£12. **Set meals** £12.95 three courses, £16.95 four courses. **Service** 10%. **Credit** AmEx, MC, V.
Recently expanded to accommodate a new raft of tables, Aviv remains a popular venue for the local community. It's rather more Israeli than European Jewish, with a preponderance of vaguely Middle Eastern dishes on the menu (kebabs, moussaka and so on), rather than the traditional salt beef and cholent staples; the only bread available was pitta. Chopped liver (coarse-cut and heavy in a wonderfully old-fashioned way), houmous and hot mushrooms (a bit on the dry side) and a toothsome coriander-flavoured bean soup made up the starters. Service, however, was polite and prompt. Main courses were pretty unspectacular, offering weak variants of the kind of thing done much better in Greek and Turkish restaurants. Moussaka was a bland concoction of mince, aubergine and potato; kevas batanur (lamb on the bone) was big but not especially tender. Chicken Kiev was nothing to write home about, either. All dishes came with rice or chips, though you could have salad (shredded red cabbage, basically). The relaxed, unintimidating atmosphere is Aviv's strong point; there's a happy, contented buzz here.
Babies and children welcome; children's set meal (£4.95); high chairs. Booking advisable. Kosher supervised (Beth Din). Tables outdoors (4, patio). Takeaway service.

B&K Salt Beef Bar ★ ★

11 Lanson House, Whitchurch Lane, Edgware, Middx (020 8952 8204). Edgware tube.
Lunch served noon-3pm, **dinner served** 5.30-9pm, Tue-Sun. **Main courses** £3.50-£9.50. **Unlicensed. Corkage** no charge. **Credit** MC, £TC, V.
An unpromising location in a bleak shopping parade disguises this purveyor of top-notch nosh, family-run and generous with it. B&K has only eight tables, making it a tight squeeze, especially as the place, on a Sunday night, is stuffed with elderly locals who are clearly regulars; they seem to know the menu off by heart. There are proper tablecloths, too. We started with rollmop herring, chopped liver (nice and eggy, with a couple of mini matzas stuck in like wafers), and bean and barley soup; all were just as momma would make them. A big stack of rye bread came with the order. Ordinary sandwiches aren't served to diners at the weekends, so we went straight into the plates of meat: hot salt beef, salt beef and viennas, and salt beef and tongue. All came piled high and were the real deal. Side dishes included grilled tomatoes, pickled sweet and sour cucumber, and perfectly fried latkes. So large were the servings, however, that none of us could finish the meal. Without being asked, the manager offered us all doggy-bags. In a spirit of blow-out we forced down an apple strudel; it was adequate, if not quite the equal of what had gone before.
Babies and children welcome. Bookings not accepted. No smoking. Takeaway service (11.30am-9.15pm).

Menu

See also the menu in **Middle Eastern** (*page 129*).

Bagels: ring-shaped rolls of sweet, heavy bread. The dough is boiled or steamed, then glazed and baked.
Baklava: a many-layered pastry stuffed with nuts and soaked in a rose-scented syrup.
Blintzes: pancakes, most commonly filled with cream cheese, but also with sweet or savoury fillings.
Borscht: a classic beetroot soup served hot or cold, often with sour cream.
Bulka: a loaf made of chollah dough.
Cholent: a stew of meat and beans, traditionally cooked overnight and eaten on the sabbath.
Chollah: egg-rich, slightly sweet plaited bread.
Chopped liver: either chicken or calf's liver is fried with onions, coarsely chopped and then mixed with hard-boiled egg whites to form a paste. It is then served cold, moistened with chicken fat and topped with a hard-boiled egg.
Chrain: a pungent sauce made from grated horseradish and beetroot. Used as a relish with fish.
Falafel: spicy deep-fried balls of ground chickpeas, often served with houmous and pitta bread.
Gefilte fish: traditionally a fish stuffing made from carp or pike; now a mixture of flaked white fish, onion, celery, carrots, egg and meal, rolled into balls. These are boiled or fried and usually served cold.
Heimishe or haimische: Jewish home-cooking, East European in style.
Kuba, kouba or **kibbeh**: Middle Eastern dish of deep-fried minced meat and crushed wheat balls, stuffed and cooked with meat, onions, spices and pine kernels.
Kishka: a vegetable (but not vegetarian) haggis made of flour, barley, onions, carrot and chicken fat, stuffed in intestines, boiled and baked.
Kneidlach: matzo meal dumplings served in soup, often chicken.
Kreplach: pockets of noodle dough filled with meat and served in soup, or with sweet fillings, eaten with sour cream.
Kugel: a baked savoury made with potato, onions and chicken fat, eaten with meat dishes.
Latkes: grated potatoes, eggs and flour shaped into small pancakes and fried until crisp. A side dish eaten with meat or fish.
Lokshen: egg pasta noodles used in puddings and soups. Lokshen pudding is stodgy but deliciously cinnamon-flavoured.
Lox: smoked salmon.
Matzo meal: unleavened bread that has been ground to a flour; traditionally used to coat fish for frying.
Platzels: a type of white bread roll, which can be flavoured with onion.
Tzimmes: a sweetened compote of vegetables and fruits, usually carrot with apple, served as a side dish alongside meat.

Korean

Korean restaurants have been in business in London since the late 1970s. It wasn't, however, until a few years back that many of them began to make serious efforts to cater to London's local, mixed clientele – the start of the economic crisis in Korea in 1998 provided the impetus.

In the past, most custom had come from Korean and Japanese businessmen, who in turn enjoyed priority service and use of the karaoke facilities. There was no need to cater for the seemingly more complex local clientele. Yet when the crisis started, and the number of Koreans in London suddenly plummeted, it became necessary to do just that. Ever since, many welcome changes have been made. Menus and service were improved, and variety increased. The Barbican Centre's **Young Bin**, in particular, earns an honourable mention for the transformation it has made since reopening in 1999.

The economic crisis now being a thing of the past, the number of Koreans in London is again growing rapidly. This includes Koreans from Yanbian, the Korean autonomous prefecture in China's Jilin Province. Many workers from Yanbian are employed at London's Korean restaurants, which might explain the odd misunderstanding between staff.

Although the influx of Koreans should boost the quality of London's Korean restaurants, it is unlikely to curb prices. However, this shouldn't deter anyone looking for extraordinary and authentic food. Fans of the cuisine should make the trip to New Malden, Europe's largest 'Korea Town'. The overall quality of food is better in this south-western suburb than in central London, the prices are lower, and, as in Korea, at the New Malden restaurants you'll get a number of panch'an (side dishes) free of charge with your main course. Panch'an commonly include pickled vegetables, but may also comprise tofu, fish, seaweed or beans. We review **Chisshine** below, and also **Kkach'ine** (arguably the leader of the pack in terms of quality of food served) in nearby Raynes Park.

The menu

Chilli appears at every opportunity on Korean menus. Other common ingredients include soy sauce (different to both the Chinese and Japanese varieties), sesame oil, sugar, sesame seeds, garlic, ginger and various fermented soy bean pastes (chang/jang). Until the late 1970s eating meat was a luxury in Korea, so the quality of vegetarian dishes is high. Try pibimbap – steamed rice topped with seasoned or pickled vegetables and (or without, if preferred) a fried egg.

Given the spicy nature and the overall flavour of Korean food, drinks such as chilled lager or the vodka-like soju are the best matches. A wonderful non-alcoholic alternative which is always available but not listed on the menu is barley tea (porich'a). This tea has a light dry taste that perfectly matches Korean food, and it is still served free of charge at all the restaurants we list.

Central

Barbican EC2

Young Bin

3 St Alphage High Walk, EC2 (020 7638 9151/020 7628 0492). Moorgate tube/rail. **Lunch served** 11.30am-2.30pm, **dinner served** 5.30-10pm Mon-Fri. **Main courses** £6-£25. **Set buffet lunch** £8.50. **Set dinner** £10. **Credit** JCB, MC, V.

Young Bin ('VIP Room') reopened under a new owner in 1999. Since then, many improvements have been made to the food and the menu. On the whole, more time is now given to the preparation of dishes: meat is better marinated and soups are made with a higher-quality stock. The only letdown is that the restaurant has retained its hotel-foyer interior, with little being done to create a Korean atmosphere. Since summer 2000, however, Young Bin has inaugurated a buffet that might just increase its appeal. The buffet includes as many as 25 truly different dishes, such as sushi and savoury fruit salads. The quality is high and the variety is wonderful, allowing you to have a completely vegetarian or practically salt- or spice-free lunch. The best dishes included pulgogi (very well-seasoned and made with high-quality meat), sweet and sour chicken (t'angsuyuk), and the savoury fruit salad. Battered pork was a bit too greasy and chapch'ae was far from the real thing, being clumsily mixed and containing too few vegetables. A strongly spiced sea-snail dish (kolbaengi) served as evidence that Korean customers are among the regulars. When dishes ran out or overheated, the waiters hurried to replace them. If the restaurant manages to keep up this quality, the only empty seats will be those reserved for VIPs.

Babies and children admitted. Book lunch. Separate room for parties, seats 12. Takeaway service (noon-3pm Mon-Fri). **Map 4/5P.**

City EC1

Arana

116 Newgate Street, EC1 (020 7600 1134/ 020 7606 2320). St Paul's tube. **Lunch served** noon-2.30pm, **dinner served** 6-11pm Mon-Fri. **Main courses** £10-£30. **Set lunch** £8, £10, three courses. **Set dinner** £19, £24, three courses. **Service** 12½%. **Credit** AmEx, £TC, V.

Still the weirdest-looking restaurant in town, Arana resembles something between a Korean-run Irish pub and a Dutch pancake restaurant. In the past, the owner and the waitresses seemed at odds with each other, but both parties appear to have resolved their differences, and this is reflected in the service. The cooking has improved, too. The menu still boasts raw fermented crab (kejang), but, as on our previous visits, it had run out – a great pity, as it is one of Korea's little-known wonders. The menu lists a series of fine lunch deals all under £10; we ordered tolsot pibimbap, yukhoe pibimbap, and pokkeum udong (stir-fried noodles). All full of fresh ingredients and very rich in flavour, though the same couldn't be said of the small 'soups' that accompanied them. Fortunately, the pickles that came as part of the lunch deal were perfect: fresh and uncompromisingly spicy, with just the right amount of sweetness. Uniquely in central London, the pickles were refilled at no extra cost. With quality and prices like this, it is remarkable that we were the only non-Koreans present.

Entertainment: karaoke 9pm (booking essential). Separate room for parties, seats 20. **Map 15/6O.**

Clerkenwell & Farringdon EC1

New Seoul

164 Clerkenwell Road, EC1 (020 7278 8674). Chancery Lane tube/Farringdon tube/rail. **Lunch served** noon-3pm, **dinner served** 6-10.30pm Mon-Fri. **Main courses** £4.50-£10. **Set meals** £14-£18 per person (minimum two). **Credit** AmEx, MC, V.

A bright, simply decorated, somewhat Japanese-looking place, New Seoul is furnished with light brown tables, chairs and floors, and white walls with scant decoration. At lunchtime, western businessmen eat here; in the evenings Koreans crowd the place. For dinner, however, some may find the atmosphere a little flat. The service is attentive, but staff can seem rushed during busy periods. The menu is clearly written and lists a wide selection of mostly standard Korean dishes. We started off with noktu cheon (another name for pindaetteok) and p'ajeon. Both were a delight: crisp, light and full of flavour. Modeum namul, on the other hand, was old and bland, as was kkaktugi, which seemed palpably beyond its sell-by date. At the other extreme, pulgogi teoppap was fresh and made with high-quality beef. Compared to this, an otherwise blameless saengseon gui (fried mackerel) was a little boring. Kimch'i chigye (Korea's most popular soup, and a good measure of the quality of a kitchen), was enjoyable too, with plenty of flavour and freshness. New Seoul is certainly worth a visit; prices are very reasonable and portions large, but the chef needs to work a little harder on preparing pickles.

Babies and children admitted. Book lunch. Takeaway service. **Map 15/4N.**

Covent Garden WC2

Nam Dae Moon

56 St Giles High Street, WC2 (020 7836 7235). Tottenham Court Road tube. **Lunch served** noon-2.30pm Mon-Sat. **Dinner served** 5.30-10.30pm Mon-Sat; 5-10pm Sun. **Minimum** £6. **Set dinners** £20-£24. **Service** 15% dinner. **Credit** JCB, MC, £TC, V.

Namdaemun (the South Gate) is one of South Korea's National Treasures, but inside Nam Dae Moon (the restaurant), the feel is not as distinctively Korean as such a name would suggest. It is subtly decorated with thin black woodwork and white walls. In the basement are a few karaoke rooms, where young ladies entertain Korean and Japanese businessmen. The women often appear upstairs, seemingly to escape the many off-key notes. The restaurant, mercifully, is quiet. Our cheery waitress patiently helped us make up our minds. To start, we ate a brilliantly complex pindaetteok, and fresh yet bland deep-fried squid and deep-fried cod. We then ordered two large servings of ojingeo pokkeum and kimch'i pokkeum; both of them arrived fresh and with a perfect balance of flavours thanks to plenty of vegetables and thinly sliced pork respectively. However, two barbecued meat dishes – pulgogi and kalbi – were disappointingly dry, and appeared to have been seasoned with just sugar and soy sauce. Overall, the food here is good and the service memorably cheerful, but the restaurant doesn't quite merit its high prices.

Babies and children admitted. Book dinner. Entertainment: karaoke 8pm-2am Mon-Sat. Takeaway service. **Map 14/6K.**

Fitzrovia W1

Han Kang ★

16 Hanway Street, W1 (020 7637 1985). Tottenham Court Road tube. **Lunch served** noon-3pm, **dinner served** 6-11pm Mon-Sat. **Main courses** £5.90-£8. **Set lunch** £5.90. **Service** 10% (dinner). **Credit** AmEx, DC, JCB, MC, £TC, V.

Han Kang, named after the river that runs through South Korea's capital, has maintained trade despite the continuous building work on Hanway Street over the last couple of years. The quality of the food and the fair prices are the attractions. Tables are set on two little stages which, along with the dim lighting, serves to conceal the lack of space. The restaurant is popular with young Korean students, who come for the noraebang (Korean-style karaoke) in the basement. Special low-priced lunches are served, but it is worth spending a little more. We started with kkaktugi and modeum namul, which came in large portions and were wonderfully fresh and flavoursome, the only letdown being unwanted slices of cucumber in the latter. Our next dish, p'ajeon, was well-filled, and light, despite its many ingredients. Pulgogi and kalbi were tender and well marinated, even though the small lettuce leaves didn't warrant the £2.50 charge. Other dishes sampled, such as ojingeo pokkeum and pibimbap, were also a delight; they, too, came in such generous portions we almost felt embarrassed to have ordered them all. However, it's not just the size of the portions that puts Han Kang at the top of our list of Korean restaurants in central London – it's the winning combination of service, food and ambience.

Babies and children admitted. Entertainment: karaoke 8pm-midnight Mon-Sat. Takeaway service. **Map 13/5K.**

Mayfair W1

Kaya

42 Albemarle Street, W1 (020 7499 0622/ 0633). Green Park or Piccadilly Circus tube. **Lunch served** noon-3pm Mon-Sat. **Dinner served** 6-11pm daily. **Main courses** £4.80-£20. **Set lunches** £13-£15. **Cover** £1 dinner. **Service** 15%. **Credit** AmEx, DC, JCB, MC, V.

On the surface, Kaya has class. It's a stylish restaurant with large round flypaper lanterns softly illuminating the light-brown wooden furniture and off-white walls. The friendly waitresses, who by night are clad in traditional costume (hanbok), shuffle past to the beat of Korean folk music. The problem is that they usually shuffle past (rather than towards) you. The menu has been changed and now has a few special offers on the first page. We tried one of them, kimch'i cheon, a delicious savoury pancake ill-explained on the menu as a 'pan-fried' dish. The seasoned raw squid (cheotkal) isn't described well either; it is not 'fried', but simply seasoned to perfection. Yukhoe pibimbap looked pretty, but was boring: the meat wasn't seasoned at all, which meant the dish relied on the flavour of the rather bland vegetables. In contrast, a large serving of assorted seasoned vegetables (modeul namul) was brilliant and provided some of the flavour we'd been looking for in the rice dish. We enjoyed our lunch, but expected more of the service when it is charged at 15%.

Booking advisable. Entertainment: karaoke 8pm-2am Mon-Sat. Separate rooms for parties, seating 8 and 12. **Map 13/7J.**

Soho W1

Arirang

31-32 Poland Street, W1 (020 7437 9662/ 6633). Oxford Circus tube. **Lunch served** noon-3pm Mon-Sat. **Dinner served** 6-10pm daily. **Set buffet** (noon-3pm) £5.50. **Service** 15%. **Credit** AmEx, DC, JCB, MC, V.

If you saw only the outside of Arirang, you'd be forgiven for taking the restaurant to be one of those tourists-only places where speed and simplicity come first and quality second. An 'eat as much as you want' lunch buffet is still offered here, but our initial excitement over this has waned. The buffet now consists mostly of fried or deep-fried dishes, and lacks anything fresh or juicy. Usually the choice is limited to sweet and sour chicken, mixed fried noodles, chickpea pancake (pindaetteok), pickled peppers, pulgogi, soup, fried sweet potato and deep-fried drumsticks. On our visit all fried dishes were overly dry and tough, and some seemed reheated. Pulgogi was well seasoned, but the meat was of such poor quality that it needed to be. What meat we found on the drumsticks was also very tough. The pickled peppers could have provided fresh relief, but they were too salty. A late order of pickles off the full menu came quickly and turned out to be very good. Kimch'i and seasoned spinach (shigeumch'i namul) were fresh and very rich in both sweetness and spice. Toenjang chigye also helped wake up our taste buds – a perfect rich stock retained all the flavour of the many fresh ingredients. It's a shame most customers opt for the buffet; food from the full menu is much better, and if need be, helpful waitresses will guide you through the list.

Babies and children welcome; high chairs. Separate room for parties, seats 15. Takeaway service. **Map 13/6J.**

Jin

16 Bateman Street, W1 (020 7734 0908). Leicester Square tube. **Lunch served** noon-2.30pm Mon-Sat. **Dinner served** 6-11pm daily. **Main courses** £5.20-£7.50. **Service** 12½%. **Credit** AmEx, DC, JCB, MC, V.

Set in the centre of Soho, Jin manages to offer Korean food in remarkably relaxed surroundings. It's a dark, posh-looking restaurant that, because of its basement location, is not popular at lunchtime in summer. The owner has been in business some time – as partly shown by the lacquer peeling off some of the furniture. He unfailingly distrusts his waiters (to deal with whatever he can handle himself) and his customers (to know what they want). Ignoring his appeal to choose the barbecued squid, we ordered barbecued ox tongue (sohyeo kui), and beef (pul kalbi), both of which were nice and tender, though the tongue came in a small portion. As on our previous visit, the cold noodle dish (naengmyeon) was unavailable. We opted for tolsot pibimbap, which, an overdose of pepper notwithstanding, was boring as it lacked any distinctive ingredients. A rather small yukkaejang came with too few vegetables, but had a nice stock; we did, however, wonder about its freshness. A cold side dish of seasoned bracken stems (kosari namul) was the saving grace: unusual, highly tasty and very fresh. Jin is worth trying, but hit and miss.

Takeaway service. **Map 13/6K.**

Myung Ga

1 Kingly Street, W1 (020 7287 9768). Oxford Circus tube. **Lunch served** noon-3pm Mon-Sat. **Dinner served** 5.30-11pm Mon-Sat; 5.30-10.30pm Sun. **Main courses** £6.90-£7.90. **Set lunches** £9.50-£12.50. **Set dinners** £25-£35. **Service** 10%. **Credit** AmEx, DC, MC, £TC, V.

Myung Ga thrives on shoppers and trendy Japanese students. It's a chic place, with soft wooden chairs and white tables with built-in grills. Space is limited, but the large tables and the tinted glass between them create a sense of privacy, which is underpinned by soothing Korean pop ballads. The tranquil effect, however, seems to work on the customers only. The waitresses look stressed, edgy and in fear of the boss. Food, though, is above average. Although an order of kimch'i was disappointing (too little salt), another starter, p'ajeon, was wonderful: plenty of spring onion, perfectly fried and virtually no oil. At the other extreme, ojingeo kui (grilled slices of squid) seemed old; it was lightly grilled but remained extremely tough. The dipping sauce provided no relief either, as the customary sweet variety of koch'ujang had been replaced by a bland one. However, kalbi had a rich flavour and was surprisingly tender. Another redeeming factor was the highly enjoyable, if a little sticky, chapch'ae. The only smile we got from the owner was when we asked for the bill.

Separate room for parties, seats 14. **Map 13/6J.**

Shilla

58-59 Great Marlborough Street, W1 (020 7434 1650). Oxford Circus tube. **Lunch served** noon-3pm Mon-Sat. **Dinner served** 6-11pm daily. **Set lunches** £11-£16. **Set dinners** £22-£32. **Credit** AmEx, DC, JCB, MC, £TC, V.

Shilla is arguably London's grandest Korean restaurant. It's a bright, spacious place with large, tasteful pictures of national cultural treasures on one wall, and colourful modern art on the other. Tables are placed at comfortable distances from each other; waitresses are attentive and this year (unlike on previous occasions) they gave equal consideration to a few students, as to two large groups of businessmen. The menu lists many Japanese-style dishes; the two set menus offer little out of the ordinary, simply a selection of noodles and barbecued meat dishes. The stir-fried noodles (chapch'ae), however, were among the best we've eaten, with plenty of fresh vegetables. Ojingeo pokkeum was excellent, too, with well-fried but tender fresh squid. Kyeojach'ae (jellyfish salad with sweet mustard dressing) contained too little jellyfish, yet its otherwise generous portion and perfect seasoning made up for it. Pickled cucumber (oi kimch'i) was fresh and uncompromisingly spicy, but a little too salty. The fact our tea was served in a plastic cup that smelled of chlorine forced us to order soft drinks instead. These, however, were the only hiccups in an otherwise perfect dinner.

Babies and children welcome; high chairs. Booking advisable. Entertainment: karaoke 8pm-2am Mon-Sat (basement). **Map 13/6J.**

South West

Raynes Park SW20

Kkach'ine ★

34 Durham Road, SW20 (020 8947 1081). Raynes Park rail. **Lunch served** noon-3pm, **dinner served** 5-11pm Tue-Fri. **Meals served** 11am-11pm Sat, Sun. **Main courses** £4.50-£15. **Set dinner** £15 three courses. **Unlicensed. Corkage** no charge. **No credit cards.**

Han Kang

The interior of Kkach'ine is a mix of light brown wooden furniture and white walls, the latter full of cool Korean scribblings of special offers. Tables are a bit too close together for comfort. Staff are unfailingly helpful and fast. The only dishes that took some time to arrive were the free panch'an, which included beans in sweet soy sauce, kimch'i and kkaktugi. It seems the panch'an are always served late so as not to stop customers ordering extra dishes off the menu – but we shouldn't complain about a wonderful free service. The food here is of the highest quality. Don't miss yukhoe pibimbap: lots of vegetables (all keeping their distinct flavours) and a generous portion of fresh raw beef with pear juice on top. Elsewhere, the koch'ujang served with this dish adds some necessary flavour, but at Kkach'ine the dish can do without. Tak pulgogi was an instant pleaser, with plenty of flavour and ingredients, but seolleongt'ang (beef-stock soup with rice) for some reason had the wrong pepper taste. The cold noodles dish with fish (hoenaengmyeon) was reassuringly perfect, though. No wonder nearby competitor Sarangbang has given up.

Babies and children welcome; high chairs. Booking essential. Separate room for parties, seats 20. Takeaway service.

North

Finchley N3

Yijo

1 Station Road, N3 (020 8343 3960). Finchley Central tube. **Lunch served** noon-3pm Sat, Sun. **Dinner served** 6-11pm daily. **Main courses** £4-£17. **Set meal** £25 per person (minimum two). **Service** 12½%. **Credit** AmEx, DC, JCB, MC, £TC, V.

Yijo is a bright, white place simply decorated with black woodwork and golf paintings (which have been on sale for at least the past five years). The 6ft-high paper on the windows nicely shields the room from the outside world. The atmosphere created is scarcely exotic, as western classical music plays and the only Korean decorations are a pot of ginseng liquor and an incense holder. The food usually makes up for the lack of Korean-ness, but not so on our visit. Kimch'i looked pretty, but tasted dull. Taktchim also looked the part, though comprised two whole chicken thighs that were too lightly cooked in an overly mild sweet soy sauce; the red peppers and mushrooms in the sauce consequently had more flavour than the chicken, which was difficult to eat and seemed under-done. Kun mandu (deep-fried dumplings), on the other hand, were fresh and well-filled. Yach'ae t'wigim (deep-fried vegetables and strips of sweet potato) was crisp and, again, beautiful to behold, while maintaining the natural flavour of the vegetables. However, the slight sweetness of this dish only added to that of the chicken. Barbecued meat dishes, pulgogi and kalbi, partially saved the day, being well seasoned and rich in flavour.

Babies and children welcome; high chairs. Book weekends. Takeaway service.

Holloway Road N7

Busan

43 Holloway Road, N7 (020 7607 8264). Highbury & Islington tube/rail. **Lunch served** noon-2.30pm Mon-Fri. **Dinner served** 6-11pm Mon-Thur; 6-11.30pm Fri, Sat; 6-10pm Sun. **Main courses** £5.90-£19.95. **Set dinners** £14.75-£19 per person. **Service** 10%. **Credit** MC, £TC, V.

One of London's oldest Korean restaurants, Busan is a homely-looking place with many plants, candles and typical Korean decorations. It's a favourite with locals, despite the service, which is best described as frank. Once again we noticed a single diner ordering against the advice of the waitress, who, when he was unable to finish it, triumphantly noted: 'I told you so'. The waitress seemed rushed (despite the absence of many customers), even pulling the menu out of our hands before we'd finished ordering. Pickles are worth trying here. Oi much'im (seasoned cucumber) was refreshing and full of flavour. That couldn't be said of kaji chorim (boiled aubergine), a pretty mini hot-pot that failed to bring out the aubergine's natural flavour. Pimbimbap contained lots of Chinese cabbage, making the dish taste and look like a refurbished leftover. Kimch'i pokkeum was drowned in sweet koch'ujang causing it to be overly heavy. As with other fried dishes, it came with too much oil on a burning oven plate, rendering parts of it black. Sadly, all this evoked feelings of déjà vu in us. Remember: we told you so.

Babies and children welcome; high chairs. Booking advisable. Takeaway service. Vegetarian menu.

Outer London

New Malden, Surrey

Chisshine

74 Burlington Road, New Malden, Surrey (020 8942 0682). New Malden rail. **Lunch served** 11.30am-3pm, **dinner served** 6-11pm Tue-Sun. **Main courses** £4.50-£6. **No credit cards.**

For food, Chisshine is among the best Korean restaurants in London, but service-wise we'd put it at the bottom of the list. We've felt very uncomfortable here in the past, but were pleasantly surprised last year to find ourselves not stared at by customers and staff. On our most recent visit, however, we couldn't get any attention at all from the waitress, let alone a smile. Questions were left unanswered, and our queries more than once received a chilly stare. The fact there was no music exacerbated the ordeal, leaving all customers (most of them Korean) somewhat miffed. What a shame, considering Chisshine produces such good tteokpokki, a ridiculously cheap (£5.50) gourmet dish where vegetables, sausages and bars of compressed rice (tteok) are fried in a chilli sauce on a hot-plate. Samgyeopsal (uncured bacon, for a minimum of two people), came with small slices of garlic, seasoned spring onion salad, toenjang and lettuce. Although the lettuce was a little old, the meat was tender and came in a large portion. Garlic and salad added some welcome freshness. Tubu kimch'i (kimch'i, unsmoked bacon and soft tofu) contained too little meat, leaving the sourness unbalanced and off-putting. The restaurant also offers the best free panch'an in town; this time it included sliced potato salad, kimch'i and pickled cucumber. How easy it should be to serve this great food with a smile.

Babies and children welcome; high chairs. Takeaway service.

Korean etiquette

- Chances are you won't find soy sauce on your table. If you do it is to be used as a dip and not put over your meal to improve the flavour.
- Unlike in neighbouring countries China and Japan, in Korea it is considered rude to lift the rice bowl from the table.
- Korean chopsticks (thin strips of metal) and a spoon are all you need in the way of cutlery. It is perfectly acceptable to eat your rice using a spoon,but NEVER stick your chopsticks in the rice pointing upwards, as this symbolises death.
- Don't be surprised if the waiter/waitress comes and cuts up your meat or noodles with a large pair of scissors. Even in the best restaurants in Seoul this is perfectly acceptable practice.
- Slurp your noodles! There's no other way to do it in Korea. It is considered bad manners to shake off your food above your soup bowl, even when you want to prevent drops of soup from dripping on to your shirt or table. Bow over your soup.
- When eating pulgogi, you should first hold the lettuce in your left hand. Then with your chopsticks put some rice and meat, dip, and so on, on top of this. Finally, wrap the parcel up with both hands, and pop it in your mouth. Many Koreans also eat slices of raw garlic with it, sometimes after burning the garlic slightly on the barbecue. Try it, but make sure your partner does likewise...
- When drinking with Koreans always fill other people's glasses, never your own. They in turn will fill your glass – even when you can no longer lift it yourself.

Menu

There are many variations in the spelling of Korean dishes; we have listed the most common.

Bokum: a stir-fried dish, usually with chilli.
Chapch'ae, **chap chee** or **jap chee**: mixed vegetables and beef cooked with transparent vermicelli or noodles.
Cheon or **jon**: the literal meaning is 'something flat'; this can range from a pancake containing vegetables, meat or seafood, to thinly sliced vegetables, beancurd, and so on, in a light batter.
Chigae or **jigae**: a hot stew containing fermented bean paste and chillies.
Gim or **kim**: dried seaweed, toasted and seasoned with salt and sesame oil.
Gu shul pan: a traditional lacquered tray with nine compartments containing individual appetisers.
Hobak chun, **hobak jun**: sliced marrow in a light egg batter.
Jjim: fish or meat stewed for a long time in soy sauce, sugar and garlic.
Kalbi or **kalbee**: beef spare ribs, marinated and barbecued.
Kimch'i, **kimchi** or **kim chee**: pickled vegetables, usually Chinese cabbage, white radishes, cucumber or greens, served in a small bowl with a spicy chilli sauce.
Koch'ujang: hot red bean paste.
Kkaktugi or **kkakttugi**: pickled radish.
Kook, **gook**, **kuk** or **guk**: soup; Koreans have an enormous variety of soups, from consommé-like liquid to heavy, meaty broths with noodles, dumplings, meat or fish.
Ko sari na mool or **gosari namul**: cooked bracken stalks dressed with sesame seeds.
Mandu kuk, **man doo kook**: clear soup with steamed meat dumplings.
Na mool or **namul**: vegetable side dishes.
Ojingeo pokkeum: stir-fried squid in chilli sauce.
P'ajeon: flour pancake with spring onions and (usually) seafood.
Panch'an: side dishes; they usually include pickled vegetables, but may also comprise tofu, fish, seaweed or beans.
Pap, bap, bab or **pahb**: rice.
Pibimbap or **bibimbap**: rice, vegetables and meat with a raw or fried egg dropped on top, often served on a hot stone.
Pindaetteok: a lentil pancake.
Pokkeum or **pokkm**: stir-fry; cheyuk pokkeum is a pork stir-fry with lots of chilli sauce; yach'ae is a vegetable stir-fry, and so on.
Pulgogi or **bulgogi**: slices of marinated beef barbecued at the table and then sometimes rolled in a lettuce leaf and eaten with vegetable relishes.
Shinseollo, shinsonro, shinsulro or **sin sollo**: the 'royal casserole', a meat soup with seaweed, seafood, eggs and vegetables, cooked at the table.
Soju: strong Korean rice wine, often drunk as an aperitif.
Toenjang: seasoned (usually with chilli) soybean paste
Tolsot pibimbap: tolsot is a sizzling hot stone bowl that makes the pibimbap (qv) a little crunchy on the sides.
Teoppap or **toppap**: 'on top of rice' for example, ojingeo teoppap is squid on rice.
Tteokpokki: bars of compressed rice (tteok) fried with vegetables and sausages in a chilli sauce on a hot-plate.
Twaeji: pork.
T'wigim, **twigim** or **tuigim**: fish, prawns or vegetables dipped in batter and deep-fried until golden brown.
Yukhoe, yukhwoe or **yukhwe**: shredded raw beef, strips of pear and egg yolk, served chilled.
Yukkaejang: spicy beef soup.

Malaysian, Indonesian & Singaporean

There are 50,000 eating places in Singapore: four times as many as in London, in a city a quarter of the size. Imagine 16 times the shish kebabs, 16 times the Terence Conrans. It's a culinary tradition that is not so much national as urban. Like London, Singapore is a place where food is entertainment, a bright crossroads of regional cuisines. Malay coconut and chilli, Indonesian dried fish and cooked fruit, Indian, Hokkien and Thai come together in an oriental equivalent of Modern European cuisine. For the Malaysian Straits Chinese community, Singapore is the place their cooking blossomed into a recognised cuisine, Nonya. Fusing the saltier tendencies of Chinese food with the sweetness of South-east Asian dishes, Nonya specialities are still a rarity in London. On the whole, though, the places to look for them are Singaporean outlets such as both branches of **Singapura**.

All this lies in sharp contrast to the culinary traditions of Singapore's neighbours. Particularly in Indonesia, the vending of food has always been a low-status trade. There is no heritage of court cuisine, as in China. The dishes you'll find in a London Malaysian or Indonesian restaurant are often based on home cooking or street food; there isn't much in between. The nearest these cuisines come to a restaurant culture is the Indonesian rijsttafel banquet – and this is a 1930s Dutch invention, a Sunday pig-out, as artificial as a gigantic ploughman's lunch.

On the whole, the cosiest local places in this section are Malaysian or Indonesian, while those that feel most comfortable about food as extravagance and excitement tend to be Singaporean, whether the food leans south to Indonesia or north to Malaysia, Thailand and China.

Central

City EC2, EC4

Singapura
1-2 Limeburner Lane, EC4 (020 7329 1133). St Paul's tube. **Meals served** 11.30am-10.30pm Mon-Fri. **Main courses** £7.50-£13.95. **Set meals** £18-£25. **Service** 122 %. **Credit** AmEx, DC, JCB, MC, V.
The dining room is spare and elegantly monotone, and so are the executive diners. Sinatra and Satchmo take turns on the sound system. The food ranges across the Malaysian archipelago and up through Thailand and Laos to southern coastal China. Here as elsewhere in London, popiah was a low point – you'll get better spring rolls at your local chippy – but siput (mussels with lemongrass, lime leaves, ginger, and sherry) was richly, sweetly, aromatically delicious. Terong combined aubergine with turmeric and coconut milk – signature Nonya ingredients, each flavour strong and dense enough to match the next. Itek sio (duck with star anise and galangal) was also enjoyable, the meat delicately cooked with spices that might easily have overwhelmed it. One of London's better Singaporean restaurants.
Disabled: toilet. Separate rooms for parties, seating 10-30. Tables outdoors (15, pavement). Takeaway service. **Map 15/6O.**

Singapura EC2
31 Broadgate Circle, EC2 (020 7256 5044). Liverpool Street tube/rail. **Meals served** 11.30am-9.30pm Mon-Fri. **Main courses** £7.50-£13.95. **Set meals** £18 two courses, £25 three courses, £30 four courses. **Service** 122 %. **Credit** AmEx, DC, JCB, MC, V.
When in the City, pay as the City does. The average price here may be £30, but if you want the freedom of the menu you'll exceed that without effort. Not that freedom isn't worth extra. Tucked away in the stone circle of Broadgate Circus, this restaurant was formerly known as Suan Neo. The menus of the two Singapuras have become identical, although at EC2 you get the benefit of the head chef's direction. Larb, a fine Laotian speciality, combined minced chicken breast with coriander, lemongrass and chilli. Chap chye (vegetable stir-fry) came piping hot and enriched with wood-ear mushrooms and lily flowers. It's worth trying the more prosaic choices here, too; char kway teow was perfect, tasty fish cakes and prawns embedded in chewy rice noodles and sweet soy. Only the service left us wanting anything more. The waitress was sharp-eyed but unsmiling and uncommunicative. Still, perhaps good food and mechanistic service is better than vice-versa.
Book lunch. Dress: smart casual. Takeaway service. **Map 4/5Q.**

Covent Garden WC2

New Jakarta
150 Shaftesbury Avenue, WC2 (020 7836 2644). Leicester Square or Tottenham Court Road tube. **Lunch served** noon-2.15pm Mon-Fri; noon-2pm Sat. **Dinner served** 6-11.30pm Mon-Sat; 5-10.30pm Sun. **Main courses** £5-£6.95. **Set lunch** £5.50 three courses. **Set dinner** £20 per person (minimum two) three courses incl bottle wine. **Credit** AmEx, JCB, MC, V.
You know you're in a dodgy restaurant when the house white tastes better than any of the food. New Jakarta didn't quite fit this bill, but it threatened to. Indonesian food can be cooked in many ways – char-grilled, steamed, boiled. Here, the only thing that wasn't fried was the soup. Emping crackers arrived dripping from the chip pan. Murtabak udang had been deep-fried instead of properly griddled, the prawn and egg parcels varnished with grease. Char kway teow came with a circle of prawn crackers planted in it like a sodden pink Stonehenge, but once these were removed the rice noodles themselves were good. A step east of Cambridge Circus, New Jakarta is well-placed for post-theatre dining. Although staff wouldn't take a booking later than 10pm, customers were still being seated at 11pm. Oil or no oil, customers remained at midnight, at which time the weary staff changed the Indonesian muzak to dire 1990s soul, then pumped up the volume.
Babies and children welcome; high chairs. Book weekends. Takeaway service. **Map 14/6K.**

Edgware Road W2

Bali
101 Edgware Road, W2 (020 7262 9100/020 7723 3303). Marble Arch tube. **Meals served** noon-11.15pm daily. **Main courses** £5.50-£6.30. **Set meals** £17, £19 per person. **Credit** AmEx, DC, MC, V.
Around the Arabic quarter of Edgware Road is a handful of Further Eastern restaurants, including a few Malaysians. Of these, **Selasih** is the best and Bali not the worst. Past reviews have noted the quality of the satay; those we tried were excellent. Prawn satay was lightly charred but tender, the sauce sour-rich with tamarind. Other dishes did their best to avoid the attention of the tastebuds. They also looked as unappetising as possible, as if they had been bred to survive. Several of them did. Nasi goreng had no chilli, garlic, soy, onions or shrimp paste that could be tasted with the naked tongue; in their absence the rice, shrimps and a renegade diced carrot were left to fend for themselves. Singapore laksa and gado gado were rendered as sweetly monotonous comfort foods. Rojak was better, and a glass of cendol was wonderfully refreshing, but satay is what Bali does best. Stick to the sticks.
Takeaway service; delivery service. **Map 2/6F.**

Mawar ★
175A Edgware Road, W2 (020 7262 1663). Edgware Road tube.
Café **Meals served** noon-10.45pm Mon-Sat; noon-10.30pm Sun. **Main courses** £4-£5.
Restaurant **Dinner served** 6-10.45pm daily. **Main courses** £5.50-£18 (for two).
Service 10%.
Both **Unlicensed. Corkage** no charge. **Mineral water** 90p small bottle. **Credit** MC, TC, V; cheques over £10 accepted.
Mawar is reached down Axminster- and dust-clad metal stairs that boom as you descend. By the time you reach the bottom you feel like a cross between Darth Vader and Quentin Crisp. In the dining room, an electric fan democratically distributes the smell of damp between tables. Up to this point it's hard to say a good word for the place, but from the moment you sit down, critical thoughts dissipate. The set menu (£4.50) got us rice, vegetables and three main dishes from a hotplate selection including beef rendang, curried tuna steak and sambal udang. From the carte, kangkung belacan and sambal tumis ikan bilis (dried anchovies in chilli sauce) were satisfying. Why be snobbish? This cheerful canteen serves adequate food at great prices, and both the waiters (Indonesian English students) and the clientele (Indonesian English students) know it.
Babies and children welcome; high chairs. Booking essential weekends. Takeaway service. **Map 2/5E.**

Marylebone W1

Selasih
114 Seymour Place, W1 (020 7724 4454/www.selasih.co.uk). Edgware Road tube. **Lunch served** noon-3pm Mon-Sat. **Dinner served** 6-10.30pm daily. **Main courses** £4.95-£7.95. **Set lunch** £4.95 one course. **Set meals** £10 (vegetarian), £15 per person (minimum two). **Credit** AmEx, DC, MC, V.
'Selasih' is basil, but at Selasih basil isn't the half of it. Daging rendang was typical of the depth of the cooking: beef stewed with galangal and lemongrass, ginger and lime leaf, fresh chilli, onion and desiccated coconut. The red meat had been patiently simmered to dissolution, its deep earthy flavours offset by the aromatics and the bite of the spices. Just as good was kangkung goreng belacan, the delicious, burdock-like flavour of the vegetable edged with chilli and garlic. Sup pantai Timur and nasi ulam got split votes: the soup was hearty but glutinous in a monosodium glutamate kind of way, while the rice with fish flakes and herbs seemed interesting to one of our party but, 'tasted like fish food' to another. Service was friendly. The main room is beautiful – high ceiling, old mouldings – and every table was full. Even the room hidden away in the basement beside the toilets was packed. If you're booking for the weekend, specify upstairs.
Babies and children welcome; high chairs. Book weekends. No-smoking tables. Separate room for parties, seats 12. Takeaway service. **Map 2/5F.**

Soho W1

Melati
21 Great Windmill Street, W1 (020 7437 2745). Piccadilly Circus tube. **Meals served** noon-11.30pm Mon-Thur, Sun; noon-12.30am Fri, Sat. **Main courses** £5.95-£7.85. **Set meals** £16.50, £19.50, £21.50, £24.50 per person (minimum two). **Credit** AmEx, JCB, LV, MC, TC, V.
Squirrelled away at the 'Live Girls' end of Great Windmill Street, Melati has been quietly getting on with the business of cooking good Indonesian food for decades. The dining rooms are kitted out in 1970s wood and raffia, and the food somehow matches the décor: down-to-earth, hearty portions, and plenty of rijsttafel. Spicing can be erratic; 'refreshing' sayur assam was too light with the tamarind and too savage with the chillies, which makes soups particularly hard-going. But the staple dishes are hard to knock.

Pavillion.
See page 123.

Menu

Some common terms and dishes – spellings vary:

Acar: assorted pickled vegetables such as carrots, beans and onions, often spiced with turmeric and pepper.
Assam: tamarind, makes a sour-tasting sauce.
Ayam: chicken.
Bergedel or **pergedel**: a spiced potato cake.
Belacan or **blacan**: dried fermented shrimp paste; it smells unpleasant raw, but adds a piquant fishy taste to dishes.
Bumbu Bali: a rich, chilli-hot sauce from the island of Bali.
Char kway teow or **char kwai teow**: stir-fry of rice noodles with meat and/or seafood with dark soy sauce and beansprouts. A Hakka Chinese-derived speciality of Singapore.
Daging: beef.
Ebi: shrimps.
Gado gado: a salad of blanched vegetables with a peanut-based sauce on top.
Galangal: often called Laos root or blue ginger, this spice gives a distinctive flavour to many South-east Asian dishes.
Goreng: wok-fried.
Ikan: fish.
Ikan bilis or **ikan teri**: tiny whitebait-like fish, often fried and made into a dry sambal (qv) with peanuts.
Kari: curry.
Kambing: lamb.
Kangkung: water convolvulus, or swamp cabbage. An aquatic plant often steamed and used in salads with a spicy sauce.
Kelapa: coconut.
Kecap manis: sweet dark Indonesian soy sauce.
Kemiri: candlenuts. Used in Indonesian and Nonya cooking, they are a little like macadamias in taste.
Kerupuk: like prawn crackers.
Laksa: a noodle dish with either coconut milk or (as with Penang laksa) tamarind as the stock base; indigenous to all of South-east Asia.
Lemang: sticky Indonesian rice that is cooked in bamboo segments.
Lenkuas: Malaysian name for galangal (qv).
Lumpia: deep-fried spring rolls filled with meat or vegetables; like poh pia (qv).
Masak lemak: anything cooked in a rich, red spice paste with coconut milk.
Mee: noodles.
Mee goreng: fried egg noodles with meat, prawns and vegetables.
Mee hoon: rice vermicelli noodles.
Murtabak: an Indian/Malaysian pancake fried on a griddle, with a savoury filling.
Nasi lemak: coconut rice on a plate with a selection of curries and fish dishes topped with ikan bilis (qv).
Nasi goreng: fried rice with shrimp paste, garlic, onions, chillies and soy sauce.
Nonya: the name referring to both the women and the dishes of the Straits Chinese community, derived from Indonesian and Thai influences with some Chinese elements spiced up.
Otak otak: a Nonya speciality made from eggs, fish and coconut milk.
Peranakan: literally meaning 'born of the soil' in reference to Chinese settlers who first came to Malacca (now Melaka), a seaport on the Malaysian west coast, in the seventeenth century. Generally applied to those born of Sino-Malay extraction who adopted Malay customs, costume and cuisine, the community being known as 'Straits Chinese'. The cuisine is also known as Nonya (qv).
Petai: a pungent, flat green bean used in Malaysian cooking.
Poh pia, popiah: dumplings or spring rolls, steamed or fried, their innards spread with black bean, hoisin or plum sauce. Common throughout South-east Asia, they are called lumpia (qv) in Indonesia and the Philippines.
Rempah: generic term for the fresh curry pastes used in Malaysian cookery.
Rijsttafel: an Indonesian set meal of several courses; it means 'rice table' in Dutch.
Rendang: meat cooked in coconut milk; a 'dry' curry.
Rojak: fruit and vegetables in a spicy sauce.
Roti canai: a south Indian Malaysian breakfast dish of fried round, unleavened bread served with a dip of either chicken curry or dahl.
Sambal: there are several types of sambal, often made of fiery chilli sauce, onions and coconut oil; served as a side dish or used as a relish. The suffix 'sambal' means 'cooked with chilli'.
Satay: there are two kinds, terkan (minced and moulded to the skewer) and chochok ('shish'). In London you are most likely to encounter the whole-meat version. The traditional choice of beef or chicken often now extends to prawn. Satay is served with a rich spicy sauce made with onions, lemongrass, galangal, chillies in tamarind sauce, sweetened and thickened with ground peanuts.
Sayur: vegetables.
Soto: soup.
Soto ayam: a classic spicy Indonesian chicken soup, often with noodles.
Sotong: squid.
Tahu: tofu, beancurd.
Telor: egg.
Tempeh: an Indonesian fermented soy bean product similar to tofu, but with a more varied texture; it can resemble peanut butter in appearance.
Terong: aubergine
Tersai or **trassie**: alternative names for belacan (qv).
Udang: prawns.

Desserts

Cendol: mung bean flour droplets, coloured and perfumed with the essence of pandan (screwpine) leaf and served in a chilled coconut milk and palm sugar syrup.
Es: ice; a prefix for the multitude of desserts made with combinations of fruit salad, agar jelly cubes, palm syrup, condensed milk and crushed ice.
Es kacang: shaved ice and syrup mixed with jellies, red beans and sweetcorn.
Gula melaka: palm sugar, an important ingredient with a distinctive scent added to a sago and coconut-milk pudding of the same name.
Kueh: literally, 'cakes', but a general term for many desserts.
Pisang goreng: banana fritters.

Satay udang (£7.75 for a generous five sticks) came with a delectably crunchy sauce; kangkung was garnished with dried-and-cooked anchovies – a wonderful contrast of textures. Cumi cumi istemewa was a kind of cephalopod Sunday lunch: a squid the size and colour of a roast chicken, glazed with kecap, and stuffed with spiced potato. Colonel Sanders eat your heart out.
Babies and children welcome; high chairs. Book weekends. Separate room for parties, seats 35. Takeaway service. **Map 13/7K.**

Minang ★

11 Greek Street, W1 (020 7287 1408). Leicester Square tube. **Lunch served** noon-3pm, **dinner served** 5.30-11.30pm Mon-Sat. **Main courses** £5.65-£8.65. **Set lunch** £5 per person (minimum two). **Set meals** (rijsttafel) £16.50-£24.50. **Credit** AmEx, DC, JCB, MC, £TC, V.
A menu of 100 items should be a hint of another dodgy restaurant: except somehow, at Minang, it isn't. The five dishes we tried were all carefully prepared and planned, yet nothing tasted perceptibly of the freezer. Satay udang was as good as fresh grilled prawns on sticks will always be; cumi cumi bakar (grilled baby squid) came delicately charred, the bodies stuffed with savoury potato, the coronets of tentacles infused with soy and garlic. The chef here is Padang Indonesian, and a few specialities of the regional Nasi Padang cuisine appear on the menu. Rendang Padang was beautifully flavoured, though the slow-cooked beef had been allowed to dry out a little. The highlight of the meal, however, was palai ikan: a whole plump jack mackerel (enough for two), wrapped in banana leaves and grilled with turmeric and coconut. The fish was sweet, unfishy and full of flavour. It could almost have been dock-fresh; Minang must have an ocean in the garden. Catch them while you can.
Babies and children welcome; high chairs. Book dinner. Separate room for parties, seats 30. Takeaway service. **Map 13/6K.**

Nusa Dua

11-12 Dean Street, W1 (020 7437 3559). Tottenham Court Road tube. **Lunch served** noon-2.30pm Mon-Fri. **Dinner served** 6.30-11.30pm Mon-Thur; 6.30pm-midnight Fri, Sat; 6.30-10.30pm Sun. **Main courses** £5.10-£7.65. **Set meals** £15.50, £17.50 incl 2 bottle of house wine, per person (minimum two). **Credit** AmEx, MC, V.
Nusa Dua looks like a cross between a pet fish shop and a Balinese tourist agency, but the service is good, the aquariums' occupants look well-fed, and there are worse things to read than hotel brochures while you're waiting for a table. The restaurant has staff connections with the Indonesian Embassy, and the menu makes efforts to present a national cuisine, with several good Javanese and Balinese numbers. Kerupuk udang (prawn crackers) cost £2.75 for a plate of two; this may seem steep until they arrive – each is a foot long and four inches wide, like gigantic rashers of bacon. Sayur assam was equally huge: a ramen-sized bowl of vegetables in a clear and refreshing soup flavoured with tamarind. No wonder the guppies look happy. Other dishes were less successful, however. Sambal tahu (french beans and tofu in salted bean chilli sauce) could have done with less oil, while gulai kambing (Javanese lamb curry) came with its meat cunningly disguised as fat with bits on. Nusa Dua may be a cheap restaurant, but it's not that cheap.
Booking advisable. Braille menu. Separate room for parties, seats 14. Tables outdoors (4, pavement). Takeaway service. **Map 13/6K.**

West

Bayswater W2

Pavillion

Holiday Villa Hotel, 37 Leinster Gardens, W2 (020 7258 0269). Bayswater or Queensway tube. **Breakfast served** 7-10am Mon-Fri; 7.30-10am Sat. **Lunch served** noon-3pm, **dinner served** 6-10pm daily. **Main courses** £4-£8. **Service** 10%. **Credit** AmEx, DC, MC, V.
There is your basic kitsch; then there is your Bayswater hotel-bar kitsch. Pavillion not only serves decent Malaysian food, but it does so under the ranked illumination of a dozen chandeliers modelled on the Taj Mahal. Shop dummies in traditional Malaysian gold lamé watch you eat your kangkong belacan udang (hot and nicely shrimpy). Ikan bakar Langkawi (whole marinated and char-grilled mackerel) tastes all the better under a ceiling tiled in tortoiseshell-effect mirror. All this combined with friendly service makes the overall feel of Pavillion lovely. The mackerel was a highlight, the sweetness of dried-and-soaked chilli sauce extracting every ounce of flavour from the fish. Nasi lemak antarabangsa could have done without the addition of deeply deep-fried Dixie chicken, but the coconut rice, chilli prawns, and dry-fried anchovies were good. The menu is 50/50 Malaysian/English breakfast, but the number of South-east Asians eating here is an encouraging sign.
Babies and children welcome: high chairs. Separate room for parties, seats 100. Takeaway service. **Map 1/6C.**

Ladbroke Grove W10

Makan ★

270 Portobello Road, W10 (020 8960 5169). Ladbroke Grove tube. **Meals served** 11.30am-7.30pm Mon-Sat. **Main courses** £4.25-£5.50. **Minimum** (12.30-2.30pm Fri, Sat) £2.50. **Unlicensed** no alcohol allowed. **Credit** LV, TC.
A restaurant under a flyover might not sound like your cup of tea, but come market-day Makan might turn out to be just your bowl of laksa. This is a clean and colourful canteen-cum-takeaway, open to the air on a summer afternoon. The menu stretches from Malaysian roots as far as Morocco, taking in a good vegetarian range on the way. Main courses top out at £5.50 in/£4.50 out, including a choice of rice or noodles. If the shopping has left you too hot to be hungry, try the very decent coffee (though a £2.50 minimum charge applies on Friday and Saturday lunchtimes). From the hotplate, we sampled trevally lemak and aubergine sambal: the Australian mackerel was juiced up with coconut milk and lemongrass; the aubergine was heavy on the kecap, light on the chilli. It's a pity the place doesn't go on serving in the evening, but really this is a place that comes alive for Portobello market.
Babies and children welcome. No smoking. Takeaway service. **Map 11/5Az.**

Paddington W2

Satay House

13 Sale Place, W2 (020 7723 6763/www.satayhouse.com). Edgware Road tube/ Paddington tube/rail. **Lunch served** noon-3pm, **dinner served** 6-11pm daily. **Main courses** £4.50-£9.30. **Set meals** £12, £15, £22, per person (minimum two). **Service** 10%. **Credit** AmEx, DC, JCB, MC, V.
Satay House is owned by the same group that runs **Selasih** and **Mawar**, and resembles the former more than the latter in terms of quality and price. A handsome little restaurant in a handsome little street, this is an eat-in/takeaway with ambition: the menu is unusual, the food above average. Petai – a Malaysian speciality – features in many of the dishes. Sambal ikan bilis petai (dried anchovies in chilli petai sauce) could have done with less oil, but coulai tempayak (fermented durians with petai, anchovies and turmeric leaves) was an exceptional dish, each powerful ingredient bringing out unexpected subtleties in the whole. From the more regular choices, turmeric-yellow udang galah goreng was a pleasure to look at and to eat, and kangkung belacan was tasty as always, and hot in every sense of the word.
Book weekends. Entertainment: karaoke (£3 per person). Takeaway service. **Map 2/5E.**

South

Brixton SW9

Satay Bar

447-450 Coldharbour Lane, SW9 (020 7326 5001). Brixton tube/rail.
Bar **Open** noon-11pm Mon-Thur; noon-2am Fri, Sat; 1-10.30pm Sun.
Restaurant **Lunch served** noon-3pm Mon-Fri. **Dinner served** 6pm-midnight Mon-Thur; 6pm-2am Fri. **Meals served** 1pm-2am Sat; 1-10.30pm Sun. **Main courses** £4.25-£7.75. **Set meal** (rijsttafel) £11.95 per person (minimum two). **Service** 10%. **Credit** AmEx, MC, V.
It's hard to review a restaurant evenly when Mike Tyson turns up halfway through your sayur kari (mixed vegetables in 'mild' chilli soup – hot enough to exfoliate your tonsils). One minute the capacity of this restaurant was 60, the next, the whole of Brixton was trying to watch people trying to get signatures. Not that the place was empty beforehand. Three-quarters cocktail bar, one-quarter satay restaurant, Satay Bar is stylish and popular. Seven nights a week, it does a roaring trade in beef on sticks and sticks in drinks: the drinks are better than the beef, but the beef is better than most bars could hope for. Ikan kukus (salmon steak with lemongrass and soy) was tasty and generously apportioned. Mee goreng was decent, but had lost contact with the advertised squid and was instead accompanied by two sad prawns battered in brown Hammerite. The man with three ears left looking well-satisfied; we left well-tanked and well-fuelled.
Babies and children admitted. Book weekends. Tables outdoors (7, covered porch). Takeaway service. **Map 18.**

North

Crouch End N8

Satay Malaysia

10 Crouch End Hill, N8 (020 8340 3286). Finsbury Park tube/rail then W7 bus. **Dinner served** 6-10.45pm Mon-Thur, Sun; 6-11.45pm Fri, Sat. **Main courses** £3.70-£5. **Set dinners** £11-£13, per person (minimum two). **Credit** £TC.
Confusing Crouch End Hill with nearby Crouch Hill, we arrived late for our booking to find it the only table still free. Satay is booming in Crouchland where, cut off from all modern forms of transport except the mythical W7 bus, a decent local restaurant is worth its weight in gold. The décor at Satay Malaysia is some kind of national treasure: the ceiling overhung with fishing nets, raffia and plastic sunflowers and

Malay House

carnations, as if a drunken and misguided fisherman drowned his misfortunes in laksa and left behind all his worldly possessions. The chef here is Malaysian, the food Chinese-oriented and good at its best. Keyo (aubergine and shrimps in a delicate sauce) was excellent. Sambal tofu came with a generic sweet and sour sauce, which also starred in sri Penang squids. On the whole, the dishes were generous and tempting, and so was the bill, which not only failed to arrive but was replaced by somebody else's change.
Babies and children admitted. Book weekends. Takeaway service.
For branch (Satay Raya) see index.

Swiss Cottage NW6

Singapore Garden ★
83 Fairfax Road, NW6 (020 7624 8233). Swiss Cottage tube. **Lunch served** noon-2.45pm daily. **Dinner served** 6-10.45pm Mon-Fri. 6-11.15pm Sat, Sun. **Main courses** £5-£20. **Set lunch** £7 two courses £8.50 three courses. **Minimum** £10. **Service** 122 %. **Credit** AmEx, DC, JCB, MC, V.
The chefs are Chinese and Vietnamese, and there isn't any garden, but never mind. What Singapore Garden does have is a bright modern interior, tables out front in summer, and food that exhibits all the eclecticism of Singaporean cuisine. The menu has a great range, with a fair-sized section dedicated to Malaysian specialities, a spread of Cantonese, Hakka and Hokkien styles, and the usual Thai favourites. Among all this are some of the most interesting Singaporean dishes. Whole fresh crab in mild chilli sauce exceeded even a side order of spare ribs, in terms of delicious messiness. Steamed chicken in light soy and sesame oil subtly drew out the natural flavours of the meat. Ho jien (oyster omelette) was a meal in itself, rich as its smoked-salmon western equivalent. The pavement tables are a bonus: Fairfax Road doesn't see too much evening traffic, and there are shrubs to sit under while you suck at your chosen crustacean. Singapore Garden's Gloucester Road counterpart closed in the past year, leaving this branch alone near the top of the Singaporean tree.
Babies and children welcome; high chairs. Booking essential weekends. Tables outdoors (20, pavement). Separate room for parties seats 6.

Turnpike Lane N8

Penang Satay House
9 Turnpike Lane, N8 (020 8340 8707). Turnpike Lane tube/29 bus. **Dinner served** 6-11pm Mon-Sat. **Main courses** £4.20-£8.50. **Set meals** £12.50, £13.50, per person (minimum two). **Credit** MC, V.

Despite its name, the chef at this pleasant Turnpike Lane fixture is Singaporean, and the menu is more Singaporean fusion than Malaysian. Archipelago and Nonya dishes jostle for space with Thai and Cantonese, and the dips and sauces owe as much to five-spice and Chinese wine as to peanuts and coconut. The place was packed on a midweek evening, and there was plenty of how's-your-fathering going on between regulars and the friendly staff. Penang asam laksa was a perfectly adequate Thai-style broth of tamarind and lemongrass, chicken and prawns. Lo bak (chicken fried in tofu skins, with a wine-and-soy dipping sauce) was a fine, sweet accompaniment to the hot and sour flavours of the soup. Sambal udang came with okra and a well-judged chilli spiciness. The decor verges on parody – never in the history of noodles can so many batiks have furnished the tables of so few – but the dishes are generous and inventive.
Babies and children welcome; high chairs. Takeaway service. Vegetarian menu.

Outer London

Croydon, Surrey

Malay House ★ ★
60 Lower Addiscombe Road, Croydon, Surrey (020 8666 0266). East Croydon rail then 197 or 410 bus. **Lunch served** noon-3pm, **dinner served** 6-11pm Tue-Sun. **Main courses** £3.20-£4. **Set lunch** £3.90. **Unlicensed. Corkage** £1 per glass. **Credit** MC, V.
If you've never been beyond Penge, or seen the skyline of Croydon at sunset, now's your chance. Malay House is an excellent reason to spend more time in London's third city. This is one of those unassuming local restaurants that serve better food at lower prices than any number of contentedly tired West End operations. The dining room is pine and chrome, the sushi-bar spareness offset by bright murals and place settings. Similar thought goes into the presentation of food. Nasi lemak arrived on a celadon-green dish: aromatic coconut rice and scarlet chilli prawns accompanied by a garnish of dried anchovies. Lamb murtabak was skillet-fried, delicately seasoned, and came with a delicious Malaysian-Indian dahl dip. To finish, sago gula melaka was a kind of superior tapioca pudding, flavoured with the maple bitter-sweetness of palm syrup. Even with corkage you'd be pushed to spend £7.50 a head here, and that for one of the best new Malaysian restaurants in town.
Babies and children welcome; high chairs. Booking essential. Takeaway service.

Mediterranean

Central

Soho W1

Aurora
49 Lexington Street, W1 (020 7494 0514). Oxford Circus tube. **Lunch served** noon-3.30pm, **dinner served** 6-11pm Mon-Sat. **Main courses** £6.95-£12.50 lunch; £9.75-£12.50 dinner. **Service** 12½%. **Credit** MC, £TC, V.
A lunchtime visit found this low-key Soho bistro buzzing with media types. Its faded yellow walls and stripped wood floors create an impression of space but the close-knit, chunky wooden tables leave little room for intimate conversation (the patio's a more spacious alternative). Having surveyed the large portions, we decided to opt for two starters and share a main course. Starter number one, chunky pea and ginger soup was bland, with only the slightest trace of ginger, but king prawns served with a tangy dressing were a decent size and very juicy. A predictably generous main of tagine consisted of chunky vegetables and prunes in an intensely rich sauce. The accompanying brown rice was perfectly cooked but a side order of mixed leaf salad lacked dressing. Full though we were, we could not resist a slice of chocolate and cocoa tart, which managed to be both decadent and light and went perfectly with a cup of full-flavoured coffee. Service is friendly (but slow) and, although the food at Aurora is sometimes below average, its relaxed atmosphere gives it a certain novelty value in the heart of Soho.
Separate room for parties, seating 20. Tables outdoors (6, garden). **Map 13/6J.**

Mezzo Café
100 Wardour Street, W1 (020 7314 4000). Picadilly Circus tube. **Meals served** 8.30am-11pm Mon-Sat; 11am-11pm Sun. **Main courses** £2.50-£4.95. **Credit** AmEx, DC, MC, £TC, V.
This less showy sister café to Conran's Mezzo restaurant is aiming to attract a quick lunchtime trade and casual evening diners. The concept is good – cocktails and fresh fruit juices at the bar, and an open kitchen serving freshly made paninis, skewers, salads and meze – but there's little atmosphere. Despite having recently undergone refurbishment, the large, two-level room appears to be suffering from an identity crisis: wooden floors clash with black and white tiles, while blue chairs reminiscent of *Play School* and tables too low to fit legs under look like the ill-matched leftovers of a Habitat sale. This is a shame because the Middle-Eastern-inflected Mediterranean food is well conceived and carefully executed, and the prices are refreshingly reasonable for this part of town. A starter of baba ganoush dip was gloriously smoky while marinated mushrooms were juicy, lemony and garlicky. A skewer of five huge chunks of salmon was cooked to perfection, and a roast vegetable panini was rich in flavour and well matched with tabouleh. Café Mezzo has the potential to be a popular place for post-work drinks and informal eating but it's not quite there yet.
Takeaway service. **Map 13/6K.**

Trafalgar Square WC2

Crivelli's Garden
National Gallery, WC2 (020 7747 2869). Charing Cross tube/rail. **Meals served** 10am-5pm Mon, Tue, Thur-Sun; 10am-8pm Wed. **Set meals** £13.50 one course, £14.50 two courses, £17.50 three courses. **Set afternoon tea** £4.95. **Credit** AmEx, DC, JCB, MC, V.
What's happening to museum and art gallery restaurants? Once you could rely on them canteen catering, but lately galleries have gone upmarket. The National is a case in point. The catering has been taken over by the Red Pepper Group (of White Onion, Black Truffle fame), who have created a new café-bar (serving pert salads, fresh pasta and piping-hot pizza) and a smart restaurant with cooking that's startlingly refined. The large dining room, with its low ceilings and scattering of window seats overlooking Trafalgar Square, is a rather unceremonious space, unlike the restaurant's north Italian and Provençal-style dishes, which look very pretty. A red pepper mousse, for instance, was topped with discs of caramelised red pepper and marinated chicken, then hidden under a tangle of frisée. Effective flavour combinations haven't been forgotten either: pan-fried calf's liver was successfully matched with a grey-green purée of globe artichoke and crisps of sweet potatoes. Couscous topped with salmon tartare wasn't so good; the fish was less than fresh and pairing this with harissa wasn't one of the chef's better ideas. There's also an unusual pricing structure, presumably to discourage nibblers: £13.50 for one course, but £14.50 for two (and £17.50 for three).
Babies and children welcome; high chairs. Disabled: toilet. No smoking. **Map 14 /7K.**

West

Brook Green W6

Snow's on the Green
166 Shepherd's Bush Road, W6 (020 7603 2142). Hammersmith tube. **Lunch served** noon-3pm Mon-Fri. **Dinner served** 6-11pm Mon-Sat. **Main courses** £10.50-£14.50. **Set meals** £13.50 two courses, £16.50 three courses (6-8pm). **Credit** AmEx, DC, MC, V.
Light terracotta walls, deep green banquettes, well-spaced tables and huge windows give Snow's a sunny feel. The global wine list has a good selection of wines by the glass and the extensive menu encompasses nine starters, 13 mains, 11 side orders and five dishes that can be served as a main or starter. Artichoke, fava bean and rocket salad was simply dressed and came with generous shavings of Parmesan. More complex was a starter of salt cod and crab ravioli with a basil pistou which was restrained, balanced and delicate. Two large fillets of flaky, fresh sea bass with pea purée and girolles was attractively presented and packed with flavour and texture. Mediterranean food is the forte here but a faultless main course of roast sea scallops with buckwheat linguine and cucumber, coconut and ginger proved that the kitchen has a wider remit. The only slight disappointment was a bitter apricot tarte tatin. When we visited early in the week there were only a few other diners – we hope this is not always the case because Snow's deserves to do well.
Babies and children welcome. Booking advisable. Separate room for parties, seats 25.

Westbourne Grove W11

Beach Blanket Babylon
45 Ledbury Road, W11 (020 7229 2907). Notting Hill Gate or Westbourne Park tube.
Bar **Open** noon-11pm Mon-Sat; noon-10.30pm Sun.
Restaurant **Brunch served** noon-5pm Sat, Sun. **Lunch served** noon-3pm Mon-Fri. **Dinner served** 7-11pm Mon-Thur; 7-11.30pm Fri, Sat; 7-10.30pm Sun. **Main courses** £10-£13.25. **Set lunch** £15 three courses.
Both **Credit** AmEx, DC, MC, £TC, V.
Design certainly takes precedent over content at this outlandish Notting Hill restaurant. It divides into three levels, all of which sport the same surreal mix of Gaudi-esque design and medieval dungeon trappings – false stonework, skylights, heavy chains and mosaic tiles. The staff are dressed to fit in with the overall aesthetic but it was soon clear that most of them hadn't been (and wouldn't remain) in the job very long. As for the food, the eclectic menu turned out to be something of a lucky dip. Pan-fried foie gras with roasted pear on brioche was a wonderfully harmonious combination, as too was the butter bean salad with fried chorizo, rocket and coriander dressing. Mains were not so good: rabbit loin wrapped in bacon, for instance, even raised doubts as to whether the meat really was rabbit, whereas slow-roasted shoulder of lamb with garlic, anchovies, rosemary and shallots was decent, but not the freshest or the best-cooked we've ever tasted. Desserts (pavlova and fig clafoutis) were adequate. The wine list, on the other hand, was wide-ranging and well-priced. Not a venue for serious gastros but BBB has what it takes for a lively night out.
Babies and children welcome. Booking advisable. Tables outdoors (4, patio). **Map 11/6A.**

South West

South Kensington SW3, SW7

Bistrot 190
190 Queensgate, SW7 (020 7581 5666). Gloucester Road or South Kensington tube.
Bar **Open** 11am-1am daily (members only after 11pm).
Bistro **Meals served** 7am-midnight Mon-Fri; 7.30am-midnight Sat; 7.30am-11.30pm Sun. **Main courses** £9.50-£14.95. **Service** 12½%.
Both **Credit** AmEx, DC, MC, £TC, V.
This townhouse address also houses a smart hotel and the more formal **Downstairs at 190** (*see p57* **Fish**), as well as this charming bistro. The latter occupies a light room with tall ceilings, large windows and cream walls strewn with paintings and mirrors. The atmosphere is neither formal nor scruffy, just wonderfully relaxed. The eclectic wine list adopts a similarly laid-back approach, with a range of eight wines available in two-glass pichets, accessibly priced at £6. On paper, the food sounds straightforward, with a good showing of fish and vegetarian dishes, but in some cases it turned out to be just plain ordinary. Summer vegetable minestrone with oregano pesto and truffle oil was light, balanced and full of flavour but crab terrine with smoked salmon and basil tartare was too dense and lacked any distinct crab flavour. Similarly, crab and salt cod fish cake, despite its fluffy texture, was nothing special. The highlight of the meal was a tender, pepper-rubbed spatchcock served with an intensely nutty chorizo and wild mushroom risotto. Generous portions meant we could only manage one pudding, a rich, crumbly blackcurrant tart. Culinary glitches aside, excellent service, reasonable prices and unbeatable atmosphere meant we left smiling, not grumbling.
Babies and children admitted. Booking advisable. Separate room for parties, seats 24. **Map 12/9D.**

Brompton Bay
96 Draycott Avenue, SW3 (020 7225 2500). South Kensington tube.
Bar **Open** noon-2.30pm, 5.30-11.30pm, Mon-Sat; noon-4pm Sun.
Restaurant **Lunch served** noon-2.30pm Mon-Fri; noon-3pm Sat; noon-4pm Sun. **Dinner served** 7-10.30pm Mon-Sat. **Main courses** £9-£16. **Service** 12½%.
Both **Credit** AmEx, DC, MC, JCB, V.
In one of the capital's swankier locations, Brompton Bay does more to gratify its customers' sense of style than their tastebuds. Well-spaced tables, cream walls and floor-to-ceiling arched windows create a sense of space that borders on the impersonal. Given the area and the potential to hike up prices, we were pleasantly surprised by the well-thought-out, simple wine list. There seemed, however, to be insufficient staff to cover all the tables. From the well-balanced menu we chose a starter of deliciously succulent squid, which was sadly overpowered by an overly sweet and raw-tasting chilli jam. Similarly, juicy fresh scallops were not enhanced by a soggy rice cake. A main course calf's liver with coppa and mash had been hanging about in the kitchen until it was barely warm and slightly tough, which spoiled an otherwise good combination. Another mismatch was faultlessly cooked cod and greasy aïoli potatoes. We hoped that a pudding of berries with sabayon would redeem the meal but, served with a heavy sponge, it did not. Given the prices and the area, Brompton Bay does not deliver the goods.
Babies and children welcome; high chairs. Booking advisable dinner. Separate room for parties (seats 22). Tables outdoors (1, garden; 3, pavement). **Map 12/10E.**

Daphne's
112 Draycott Avenue, SW3 (020 7589 4257). South Kensington tube. **Lunch served** noon-3pm Mon-Sat; 12.30-3.30pm Sun. **Dinner served** 7-11.30pm Mon-Sat; 7-10.30pm Sun. **Main courses** £7-£16 lunch, £7.50-£25 dinner. **Service** 15%. **Credit** AmEx, DC, JCB, MC, £TC, V.
On a swelteringly hot day we arrived at Daphne's for lunch looking dishevelled, sweaty and entirely out of place among the ranks of coiffed, coutured and manicured customers. The brusque manner of the head waiter didn't help, but air-conditioning and large bottles of water soon cooled us down and we were able to take in the surroundings: flagstone floors, spectacular flower arrangements, an outside patio with retractable roof and olive trees, and a claustrophobic arrangement of white linen-covered tables. To keep us going, we started with an extremely generous mountain of thin, perfectly battered courgette fritters. We were hoping to be dazzled by a second £9 starter of octopus salad with grilled peppers but it was oily, bland and unremarkable. Gutsy fava bean and fennel soup was better, as was goat's cheese and tomato galette, which came with a creamy, smoky aubergine paste. Next, Caesar salad was pretty ordinary but seemed a bargain when compared to the daily special (beetroot pasta with a dry broad bean, asparagus and prawn sauce) which cost a staggering £16.50. Defeated both morally and financially, we skipped dessert. For those with more money than sense.
Babies and children admitted. Booking essential, several days in advance. Dress: smart casual. **Map 12/10E.**

South East

London Bridge SE1

Blue Olive
56-58 Tooley Street, SE1 (020 7407 6001). London Bridge tube/rail.
Bar **Open** 10am-11pm Mon-Sat.
Café & restaurant **Lunch served** noon-3pm Mon-Fri. **Dinner served** 6-11pm Mon-Sat. **Main courses** £7-£12 (restaurant), £8 (café).
Both **Credit** AmEx, DC, MC, £TC, V.
Though it hasn't changed hands, the Blue Olive (formerly Café dell'Ugo) has undergone something of a makeover. The upstairs of this railway arch now feels more spacious, with an abundance of cream and wood offset by an intriguing chandelier made from blue-painted tree branches. Fresh flowers, excellent bread and casually efficient waiters made us feel welcome from the outset and the menu, while not exactly daring, offers fresh ingredients and reasonable prices. Both starters – char-grilled squid salad with lime slices and chilli, and beef carpaccio – were fine, despite the sameness of the 'pile the rocket high' school of presentation. Main course pan-fried Pacific cod was crispy on the outside and moist in the centre, nicely balanced by polenta and a fresh tomato and caper sauce, while ballotine of chicken skilfully combined delicacy with heartiness. Dessert-wise, summer pudding with mint sauce was better than it sounded and panna cotta with grappa was so delicious we wanted another one. The wine list is predominantly Italian and French and we were very happy with a slatey bottle of pinot grigio. Not the most cutting edge restaurant in the area but a reliable and economical option.
Babies and children admitted. Book lunch. **Map 8/8Q.**

Tower Bridge SE1

Cantina del Ponte
Butlers Wharf Building, 36C Shad Thames, SE1 (020 7403 5403). Tower Hill tube/London Bridge tube/rail/Tower Gateway DLR. **Lunch served** noon-3pm Mon-Fri; noon-4pm Sat, Sun. **Dinner served** 6-11pm Mon-Sat; 6-10pm Sun. **Main courses** £6.95-£14.95. **Minimum charge** £10 per person. **Service** 12½%. **Credit** AmEx, DC, JCB, MC, £TC, V.
The USP of this restaurant, as you might guess from the pretentious name, is its view of Tower Bridge. Other than this, the caff by the bridge is fairly unremarkable, both in terms of food and furnishings. It's a cavernous, plain restaurant with booming acoustics and slap-dash service, which might be explained (although not excused) by the fact that we visited on a particularly busy night. The menu, which includes a selection of six pizzas, was tempting enough if not wildly exciting. A smoky and light starter of own-made taramasalata was spoiled by the accompanying deep-fried squid, which was thick and tough; salt cod fish cakes were too dense and lacked flavour. Mains were not much of an improvement: tuna was overcooked and served with a raw-tasting piperade, and lamb osso bucco was completely unremarkable. Things slightly improved with a decent pudding – poached plums in red wine with zabaglione. Perhaps we visited on a duff night but shabby service, average food and tired decor conspired to create an entirely forgettable evening.
Babies and children welcome; children's menu £8, lunch Sat, Sun; high chairs. Booking essential. Tables outdoors (19, terrace). Takeaway service (pizzas noon-3pm, 6-10pm daily). **Map 8/9S.**

East

Shoreditch EC2

Cantaloupe ★
35 Charlotte Road, EC2 (020 7613 4411). Bus 55, 242. **Lunch served** noon-3pm Mon-Fri. **Dinner served** 6-11.30pm Mon-Fri; 7-11.30pm Sat. **Main courses** £9-£12.50. **Service** 12½%. **Credit** AmEx, JCB, MC, TC, V.
Situated on a raised platform at the back of a large, exceedingly loud and trendy Hoxton bar (*see p209* **Bars**), this restaurant is surprisingly cosy and

relaxed. The decor combines urban warehouse style with deep red walls, red leather booths and yellow Formica tables. The excellent wine list offers mostly French labels, with a wide choice of styles and prices, while the menu is predominantly inspired by the sun-drenched flavours of Spain, Greece, southern France (olives, feta, aubergine and capers feature prominently). Saffron and ginger cured salmon with coriander and honey dressing sounded an unlikely combination but worked well. A second starter of chicken livers, warm lentils and ciabatta was hearty and flavoursome. A main course salad of asparagus, butternut squash, walnuts, olives and goat's cheese was dressed in a light lemony dressing, and swordfish with spiced chickpeas, lime and aubergine was fresh, generous and full of flavour. A choice of five desserts, including Picos de Europa (Spanish blue cheese from the Pyrenees), was tempting but by this time we were stuffed. Despite our initial misgivings on entering the noisy, packed bar, this proved to be a decent meal served by unfailingly helpful and informed young staff.
Babies and children admitted. Booking advisable. **Map 17/4R**.

North East

Stoke Newington N16

Mesclun
24 Stoke Newington Church Street, N16 (020 7249 5029). Bus 73. **Dinner served** 6-11pm daily. **Main courses** £7.95-£11.95. **Set meals** (before 7.30pm) £11.95 two courses, £13.95 three courses. **Service** 10%. **Credit** MC, £TC, V.
Such is the popularity of this restaurant with its thirty-something regulars that we had difficulty getting a mid-week table. Deep ochre walls, a huge mosaic mirror and seascape photographs give a Mediterranean air, but faultless service, starched linens and sparkling wine glasses make for a smart, albeit rather cramped, dining area. The menu has an ample choice of starters and mains but there's a tendency towards rich, over-complicated cooking. A starter of deep-fried aubergine and smoked cheese in a red pepper sauce arrived as a stunning black, red and white tower but was too heavy for a hot summer evening. Better suited to the season were salmon fish cakes, which contained big flakes of salmon and were well complemented by a garlicky tsatsiki. A main course of cod, couscous and caramelised orange was well presented but the flavours simply didn't work together, while pork stuffed with cheese and herbs served with creamy oyster mushroom sauce was delicious but overpowering. Surprisingly, sticky toffee pudding proved to be as light as it was intense, and the highlight of the meal. Mesclun deserves to do well but a less complicated and more balanced menu might help.
Babies and children welcome; high chairs. Booking advisable.

North

Islington N1

Café Med
370 St John Street, EC1 (020 7278 1199). Angel tube. **Open** noon-midnight Mon-Sat; noon-10.30pm Sun. **Main courses** £8.95-£12.50. **Service** 12½%. **Set lunch** (noon-5pm Mon-Sat) £8.50 two courses, £10.95 three courses. **Pre-theatre menu** (5-7pm Mon-Sat) £10.95 two courses, £12.95 three courses. **Credit** AmEx, DC, MC, TC, V.
The wooden floors and terracotta walls of this spacious bar-cum-restaurant might have lost their zeitgeist appeal back in the 90s, but top-quality ingredients, a well-conceived wine list and efficient service make this a good destination for casual dining. Freshly baked bread, marinated olives and aromatic oils – very reasonably priced at £1 – sustained us while we browsed the extensive menu. It's simple, unpretentious stuff. A starter of five large, thick slices of marinated haloumi, was perfectly complemented by a coriander leaf salad. Continuing the good work, a grilled swordfish main was unmistakably fresh, very generous and came with a big dollop of fresh herbs, capers and gherkins. Similarly, the pasta of the day – penne with tomato, capers, basil and fruity olive oil – though uncomplicated, was made with top-quality ingredients. Although the food at Café Med is not trying to make any bold culinary statements, a commitment to integrity of ingredients, cooking to order, generous portions and reasonable prices work very well in its favour.
Babies and children welcome; children's menu; high chairs. **Map 3/3N**.
For branches see index.

White Onion
297 Upper Street, N1 (020 7359 3533). Angel tube. **Lunch served** 12.30-3pm Sun. **Dinner served** 7-10pm daily. **Set lunch** £14.95 two courses, £17.95 three courses. **Set dinner** £21.50 two courses, £24.50 three courses. **Credit** AmEx, JCB, MC, £TC, V.
White Onion is rather gloomy: the walls are painted dark green, which seems to absorb all the light and, despite the fact it was only a third full and we'd booked, we were shown to the worst table in the house, next to the kitchen and far from the windows. The food is slightly above average in quality and in price. For starters, asparagus with Parmesan cheese crackling and gazpacho dressing was nicely seasonal; marinated grilled Mediterranean vegetables with deep-fried ricotto ravioli and buffalo mozzarello seemed to have lost its way. Maybe we should have tried the own-made potato gnocchi with roasted tomato, Parmesan, pesto sauce and crispy onion, but again that sounded an ingredient too many. Main courses redeemed matters. Particularly good was fritto misto of fish and vegetables with rocket and lemon dressing. The chef hadn't fallen into the trap of including too many calamares, and the effect was light and tasty. There was also a very good pud; billed as a pear sorbet, it came with a slice of cheese (maybe Lancashire) and a wedge of pear: delicious.
Booking advisable.

Stroud Green N4

La Ventura
28 Crouch Hill, N4 (020 7281 5811). Finsbury Park tube/rail then W2, W7 bus. **Open** 10.30am-1am daily. **Meals served** 10.30am-10.30pm daily. **Main courses** £7.95-£12.95. **Set meals** £9.95 two courses, £13.50 four courses. **Service** 12½%. **Credit** AmEx, MC, TC, V.
When we visited on a wet Sunday lunchtime, La Ventura was less than half full and was looking slightly shabby. Granted, in the evenings the chipped maroon walls might be less obvious and in a dimmer light the long room with well-spaced tables and stained glass windows might appear more atmospheric. The menu is predominantly Mediterranean but some dishes venture farther afield, with questionable results. A main course of pan-fried chicken breast with green beans and mushrooms came on a bed of what tasted like stale instant noodles, for example. Other dishes were much better: a starter of artichoke heart with Russian salad was prettily presented and delicate, and a generous main course of pan-fried sea bass was perfectly cooked and accompanied by a restrained balsamic dressing. Summer pudding with clotted cream was OK. Our fellow Sunday-lunchers were a mix of regulars and families who had come for the bargain Sunday roast special – choice of roast with all the trimmings for £6.95. La Ventura may not be the most polished restaurant but it has a pleasant, unpretentious appeal.
Babies and children welcome; children's menu Sat, Sun; play area; high chairs; under-12s half-price Mon-Fri. Disabled: toilet.

North West

Hampstead NW3

Base
71 Hampstead High Street, NW3 (020 7431 2224). Hampstead tube. **Lunch served** noon-3pm Mon-Fri; noon-4pm Sat, Sun. **Dinner served** 6.30-11pm daily. **Main courses** £11-£13. **Set lunch** £12.95 two courses. **Service** 12½%. **Credit** AmEx, DC, MC, V.
French-Algerian chef Pierre Khodja makes his mark at this relaxed and airy Hampstead restaurant by adhering strictly to Mediterranean principles of cooking. The wine list is understated but perfectly adequate, with four red and four white wines by the glass and a good selection of bottles priced under £15. The menu is similarly straightforward, with an emphasis on first-class ingredients and strong, fresh flavours, simply presented. Pan-fried goat's cheese with pretty roasted vegetable quenelles, and a generous tuna carpaccio served with olive tapenade and roast pepper salsa got the meal off to a bright start. To follow, swordfish with a delicate fennel, orange and lime salad was faultlessly fresh. The only slight disappointment was a heavy main course of roasted duck cake but it was redeemed by a refreshing beetroot marmalade. Pudding sounded convoluted – poached pear with lemon and mascarpone tarte and vanilla ice-cream – but on delivery provided a sensible balance of flavours. There is a busy café adjacent to the restaurant, serving breakfast and quality sandwiches and wraps. Staff are friendly and efficient.
Babies and children admitted. Booking advisable. No-smoking tables. Tables outdoors (5, pavement). **Map 9**.

Middle Eastern

Central

Clerkenwell & Farringdon EC1

Midi
140-142 St John Street, EC1 (020 7250 0025). Farringdon tube/rail/55 bus. **Meals served** noon-midnight Mon-Sat. **Main courses** £7.50-£9.80. **Credit** AmEx, DC, JCB, MC, £TC, V.
Le Midi is an unusual thing: a Lebanese fusion restaurant. Spacious, modern, white and airy, with widely spaced tables, the restaurant looks attractive. Staff are pleasant, too. The meze dishes we tried weren't really up to scratch, though. Balila (warm chickpeas in oil) was fine but ordinary, baba ganoush lacked flavour, while a peppery salad (shanklish) was much better: crumbly feta cheese, plenty of spices and crunchy salad. Sujuk (Lebanese sausages) are never a low-fat dish, but Midi's version are over-laden with oil and not spicy enough. We went fusion with one of our main courses, samak (fish) kebab. The portion was generous: a large tuna steak and piece of halibut. But the problem was in the cooking; both the fish were boringly lacking in flavour. Their only accompaniment was a selection of ketchup-like salsas served burger-style in pots. Lamb sultan (skewers of minced lamb in a tomato salsa) was better; the rare-cooked meat complemented the zesty, young tomato sauce well. The very fresh and delicate pastries we ate with coffee were good too, but overall we felt Le Midi scored higher on decor than on food.
Babies and children welcome; high chairs. Booking advisable. Separate room for parties, seats 60. Takeaway service. **Map 15/4O**.

Edgware Road W1, W2

Al-Dar
61-63 Edgware Road, W2 (020 7402 2541). Edgware Road or Marble Arch tube. **Meals served** 8am-1am daily. **Main courses** £8. **Service** 10%. **Unlicensed**. **Credit** AmEx, MC, £TC, V.
A great Edgware Road hangout, where many customers choose to sit outside (fumes permitting) to smoke sheesha and have a coffee. Al-Dar's other speciality is freshly squeezed fruit juices, which come in large glass tumblers and in an enormous range, including melon, orange and carrot juices and fruit cocktail, all priced at £2.50. In the spacious interior, a full Lebanese menu of grills, meze and cakes is served. The meze dishes we opted for tended towards the bland, however. Green broad beans (fuul bil zeit) was lukewarm, rather squidgy and flavourless, with none of the tang of lemon and coriander expected. Loubieh bil zeit was similarly disappointing – french beans in a watery tomato sauce. Better were the thick slices of rare-cooked basturma (smoked beef) and fatayer bi sabanek (spinach pastries), which came in soft pastry rather than the usual filo, but the spinach had some lemon-induced kick. All rather lacklustre, but Al-Dar functions better as a café than a full-scale restaurant.
Babies and children welcome. Booking advisable. Tables outdoors (10, pavement). Takeaway service. **Map 2/6F**.
For branch see index.

Iran the Restaurant
59 Edgware Road, W2 (020 7723 1344). Marble Arch tube. **Meals served** noon-midnight daily. **Main courses** £6.95-£13.95. **Service** 15%. **Credit** AmEx, DC, JCB, MC, £TC, V.
Glass-fronted and with a light, rather clinical interior, Iran the Restaurant hadn't attracted many customers the evening we visited – just us, in fact. The formality is tempered slightly by the front counter where staff make fruit juices and prepare flat bread to be cooked in the oven at the front of the restaurant. The menu covers kebabs, Persian stews and biriani-style dishes, plus rice flavoured in various ways. Starters, too, are wide ranging and include dishes rarely found in London restaurants. We tried some lovely warm bread, along with a rather tedious salad shirazi (mixed salad) and halim bademjon, a flavoursome aubergine dip. Khoresht fesenjon is a Persian special-occasion dish: chicken in a pomegranate and walnut sauce. Too sweet and it can be overpowering; too fruity and it can be acidic; but this dense, smooth, chocolate-brown version hit the nail right on the head. The taste was superb – strong yet with subtle layers of flavour – but the three small pieces of chicken it contained made a stingy portion for a dish costing £11.95. Sultani chicken kebab contained far more chicken, marinated for softness with perfectly cooked saffron rice: good, but not the best, and very expensive at £13.95. We finished with a refreshing though very sweet rosewater ice and vermicelli. With coffee and a bottle of wine our bill came to £87 – and the restaurant doesn't accept credit or debit cards.
Babies and children welcome; high chairs. Booking advisable. Entertainment: pianist (phone for details). No-smoking tables. Tables outdoors (4, pavement). Takeaway service. **Map 2/6F**.

Kandoo
458 Edgware Road, W2 (020 7724 2428). Edgware Road tube. **Meals served** noon-midnight daily. **Main courses** £4.20-£7.75. **Unlicensed**. **Corkage** no charge. **Credit** MC, V.
Kandoo means 'beehive' in Persian – like the shape of the blue mosaic-covered tandoor oven where the naan breads are baked. This Kandoo is a smart Persian kebab shop at the 'wrong' end of Edgware Road (the bleak traffic artery with cheap shop units lining it). But this keeps prices down, and as the restaurant has a 'bring your own bottle' policy, it makes an excellent cheap feed. Dishes seem to be brought as soon as they're ready, which in this case meant virtually all at once. 'Starters' of large, crisp, sesame-dusted naan were served with mint and mixed pickles, plus fresh tarragon which imparts a cooling, slightly aniseed flavour. A paste of chopped egg, potato, chicken, pickled cucumber, mayonnaise and olive oil (salad olivieh) was a surprisingly appealing combination, a bit like coronation chicken. Seconds later, the mains arrived. Persian-style kebabs can be served with bread or a fluffy mound of rice with knobs of butter. Minced lamb kebabs are much the same as the Turkish and Arabic versions, and these were fine specimens. Kandoo doesn't offer the refined Persian cooking of legend, but then its prices reflect this. Tables in the small rear garden are an additional pull on balmy evenings.
Babies and children welcome; high chairs. Tables outdoors (8, garden). **Map 1/4D**.

Lebanese Restaurant
60 Edgware Road, W2 (020 7723 9130). Marble Arch tube. **Meals served** noon-midnight daily. **Main courses** £10. **Cover** £1.60. **Credit** AmEx, MC, £TC, V.
This place is just what its name suggests, a completely standard Lebanese restaurant, but one whose kindly staff and good food make it a popular Edgware Road haunt. We were impressed for two reasons: the place was full of babies and children who were treated solicitously; and, as the French house wine was not available, the staff substituted it with a (more expensive) Lebanese bottle at no extra cost. 'Fine renditions of classic dishes, without surprises' sums up the food. A crunchy fattoush (salad vegetables with little pieces of crisp fried Lebanese bread: like croûtons but flat) was pepped up with a sprinkling of sumac spice. If fattoush is left hanging around too long it goes soggy, but ours was straight from the chopping board. Other hits were a dense and garlicky houmous, and a robust fuul, which tasted great mashed into the good olive oil poured on top of the dish. Sawda daja (fried chicken livers in a lemony sauce) was the only dish that was below par, as the livers were a bit tough. A main course of shish taouk, however, was fine, if unexceptional. As traditional Lebanese restaurants go, this is a good one; a meal here is a relaxing and leisurely experience.
Babies and children welcome; high chairs. Booking advisable. Takeaway service. **Map2/6F**.

Maroush ★
21 Edgware Road, W2 (020 7723 0773). Marble Arch tube. **Meals served** noon-1.30am daily. **Main Courses** £10. **Cover** £2 noon-10pm. **Minimum** £48 incl £6 cover after 10pm. **Credit** AmEx, DC, JCB, MC, £TC, V.
The first in the Maroush chain (which now boasts four main branches serving Lebanese food, as well as a couple of cafés), this is the kind of restaurant to visit for a night out. There's a long bar and a few tables on the ground floor, but the action takes place in the low-ceilinged, dimly lit but spacious basement. Wanting to enjoy conversation as well as the entertainment, we opted for a table some distance from the electric piano and mike. On our visit, the singer plumped for songs of the *Strangers in the Night* school; perhaps there were some Arabic songs later. At weekends a belly dancer performs. We opted for a meze spread, plus a couple of meat dishes. The food was all enjoyable: the usual big bowl of salad vegetables; a bowl of thick houmous; a mushy fuul with plenty of high-quality olive oil; some very spicy batata hara (like Spanish patatas bravas); moutabal that was a little nondescript; a zesty tabouleh; some grilled halloumi; and sujuk, discs of spongy, spicy sausage. Our main courses were generous portions of perfectly grilled meat. Too full for pudding, we were given a large plate of complimentary fruit, not to mention some cakes (sadly past their prime) to go with Arabic coffee. As we left, the place was filling up with a mix of Arab and European diners, settling in for a late night of entertainment and good food.
Babies and children admitted lunch. Booking essential after 10pm Fri, Sat. Dress: smart casual. Entertainment: musicians and singer 9.30pm-2am nightly; belly dancer (phone for details). Takeaway service. **Map 2/6F.**
For branches see index.

Patogh ★
8 Crawford Place, W1 (020 7262 4015). Edgware Road tube. **Meals served** 1pm-midnight daily. **Main courses** £5-£9.50. **Unlicensed. Corkage** no charge. **Mineral water** £1.50 small bottle. **Credit** £TC.
A delightful and informal restaurant on two small floors, with rag-rolled brown walls, wooden tables and bench seating. Groaning plates of Iranian kebabs emerge from the cooking area (sited in a corner of the ground floor), often as not accompanied by huge portions of sabzi – branches of mint and fennel with a square of feta. We decided to bypass starters and go straight to a chicken chelo kebab: lots of well-cooked chicken, although grilled plainly, not marinated to the softness found in some Iranian restaurants. It came with a huge mound of saffron rice, perfectly cooked, served with butter. Although we'd not ordered starters, the waitress brought us a little plate with some houmous and garlic yoghurt – which added loads of flavour to the food. Patogh's good, no-nonsense cooking and jovial atmosphere ensure its popularity with a young, largely Persian, clientele.
Booking advisable weekends. Takeaway service. **Map 2/5E.**

Ranoush Juice Bar ★
43 Edgware Road, W2 (020 7723 5929). Marble Arch tube. **Meals served** 9am-3am daily. **Main courses** £3-£3.50. **Unlicensed. No credit cards.**
There's always a hub of activity around Ranoush. It is popular as a takeaway for fruit juices and snacks like shawarma sandwiches (sliced meat or chicken with garlic sauce, wrapped in flat bread, £3), but is also a café with marble-topped tables that run alongside the long glass counter. Here you can enjoy the same food along with meze dishes and cakes. Most of the meze dishes cost £3.50. They include a full range of standards such as fuul, tabouleh and loubieh bil zeit (green beans in a tomato sauce), all displayed behind the counter. Pay first, then take your ticket to the right section where staff will fill your order.
Babies and children welcome. Takeaway service. **Map 2/6F.**
For branches see index.

Safa
22-23 Nutford Place, W1 (020 7723 8331). Edgware Road or Marble Arch tube. **Meals served** *winter* noon-midnight daily; *summer* noon-2am daily. **Main courses** £7-£12. **Set meal** £14.50 per person (minimum two) three courses incl ½ bottle of wine. **Cover** 50p. **Service** 10%. **Credit** JCB, MC, £TC, V.
An unusual mix of Turkish, Iranian and Arabic dishes make up Safa's menu. This is a small establishment, modest beside its Edgware Road neighbours, with a dark interior brightened by a few desultory artefacts. The food isn't up there with the best of Iranian or Arabic cooking, but Safa has its saving graces. One is the very relaxed atmosphere and laidback staff. Our waitress went to every effort to ensure we enjoyed our al fresco lunch. A glass of house white was removed from our uncomplaining lips because she said it wasn't cold enough; otherwise, we were left to enjoy our meal in peace. We tried a mixture of Iranian and Arabic meze dishes: a coarsely chopped and not very subtle tabouleh; a better, creamy moutabal; plus ultra-thick yoghurt flavoured with spinach and garlic, which made a good accompaniment to the flat, almost crispy Iranian bread. A main course of chicken Safa, a poussin with sultanas and pine nuts, was a tender bird, but neither particularly fruity nor flavoursome; and chicken taouk could have done with at least a modicum of seasoning. But it's worth coming to Safa for dessert alone – fabulous Iranian ice-cream, flavoured with rosewater and made with clotted cream. It was fragrant, creamy but never overpoweringly rich. Just add Turkish coffee and sunshine for a perfect afternoon.
Babies and children welcome; high chairs. Book dinner in summer. Tables outdoors (16, pavement). Takeaway service; delivery service. **Map 2/5F.**

Dish Dash

Fitzrovia W1

Dish Dash
57-59 Goodge Street, W1 (020 7637 7474). **Lunch served** 11.30am-3.30pm daily. **Dinner served** 6-11pm Mon-Sat. **Main courses** £6.70-£12. **Set lunch** £10 one mazza, two beers and bread (two people). **Credit** MC, V.
There's nothing of the faux-bazaar look about this new Anglo-Persian outfit – just minimal decoration with bench-style seating and utilitarian touches such as diner-style dispensers of paper napkins. Chef John Goodall's menu is laudably flexible, beginning with 'mazza' which can be ordered singly or in groups of five (£10) or seven (£15). After that come four soups, then grills, then side dishes and 'mish-mash' – main courses. Desserts finish off, apart from a caviar menu. A decent lunch for two (without wine, with service) cost just £30. From our selection of five mazzas, we'd recommend the 'Persian cheese' (more like yoghurt) and pumpkin kibbeh (delicately fried pumpkin patties). Grilled halloumi salad with grilled peppers, assorted greens and an especially fine vinaigrette was a delight. Special mention should be made of the soups, from which we tried (and loved) the duck and pomegranate: sharp and meaty. Whatever you do, order the Yemeni chips with sumac as a side dish, but avoid the (yucky) coffee. Dish Dash is pushing itself as a bar-restaurant, and the cocktail list is long and ambitious; in contrast, the wine list is short and to the point. Service sometimes wobbled, but it was unfailingly friendly. In all, a promising start.
Babies and children admitted. Booking advisable. Entertainment: bands or DJs Sat evenings (bar). Separate room for parties, seats 40. **Map 2/5J.**

Knightsbridge SW1

Al Bustan ★
27 Motcomb Street, SW1 (020 7235 8277). Knightsbridge tube. **Meals served** noon-11pm daily. **Main courses** £10-£15. **Set lunch** £13 three courses. **Cover** £2. **Credit** AmEx, DC, MC, £TC, V.
Deep in the heart of Knightsbridge, Al Bustan is an exclusive (read 'expensive') restaurant serving very good Lebanese food. It's a formal, but comfortable place, with intimacy added by plants and trellises dividing the room. Staff were very helpful on our visit. They were greatly concerned after spilling water over a leather jacket (it was given a good wipe-down and taken away to be hung up). One might expect this in such a classy joint, but following us to the pub with a forgotten briefcase was kind beyond the call of duty. Food came in large portions and was all enjoyable. Particular favourites were: soudat dajaj (perfectly soft chicken livers in a lovely thin lemony sauce); makdus (pickled aubergines stuffed with walnuts); and another nutty dish, muhamara (chopped nuts in a spicy tomato sauce). We balanced this with a very fresh and green tabouleh, and a smooth moutabal (baba ganoush). Our only vague reservations were over fattoush, which came with tiny bits of bread instead of the usual crispy toasted squares. A main course mixed grill provided ample tender lamb and chicken to share (as well it might at £15), and a bottle of Ksara red Lebanese wine made a great accompaniment to an excellent meal.
Babies and children welcome; high chairs. Book dinner. Tables outdoors (5, pavement). Takeaway service. **Map 12/9G.**

Marylebone W1, NW1

Al Fawar ★
50 Baker Street, W1 (020 7224 4777). Baker Street tube. **Meals served** noon-midnight daily. **Main courses** £11. **Set meal** £25 three courses incl coffee. **Cover** £2. **Credit** AmEx, DC, JCB, MC, £TC, V.
A huge expanse of white-clothed tables; swathes of red velvet; fountains in the window; and wall paintings depicting scenes from Lebanon – all adding more than a touch of kitsch – set the scene for this upmarket Lebanese restaurant. The palatial air did nothing to dampen our enjoyment of Sunday lunch. Charming staff left us plenty of time to choose, and we ordered a feast of dishes that were, almost without exception, among the best we've tasted. The basics were all there, including solid, smoky houmous with a well of good olive oil in the middle; a flavoursome fuul that mashed to a delicious mush with the oil; a zesty tabouleh; and a delicately fragrant fuul akhdar tara (broad beans with coriander in a thin, creamy sauce). We branched out with some hot meze dishes too: fish sausages were a tad dry and not very fishy, the meal's only low point. Beid ghanam (lamb's testicles), on the other hand, were a treat: tender, and served in a thin, piquant lemony sauce. We had a single main course, a respectable shish taouk. For afters, the cakes we picked were perfect – baby pancakes, filled with ricotta. But food in top Lebanese restaurants doesn't come cheap. An ingenuous request for 'an orange' was answered by a beautifully presented plate of fresh fruit, and an extra £4 on the bill. Staff are nice to children; painted hard-boiled eggs (for Easter) came along with the high chair.
Babies and children welcome; high chairs. Book dinner. Dress: smart casual. Takeaway service. Vegetarian menu. **Map 2/5G.**

Ali Baba ★
32 Ivor Place, NW1 (020 7723 7474/5805). Baker Street tube/Marylebone tube/rail. **Meals served** noon-midnight daily. **Main courses** £5-£7. **Service** 10%. **Unlicensed. Corkage** no charge. **No credit cards.**
There's nowhere quite like Ali Baba. At the front is a takeaway section; beyond is the carpeted 'hasn't changed since the 1970s' restaurant, with murals that scream 'Egypt': kitsch peasant girl at her toils, a medieval Cairene scene, plus the odd bit of papyrus. The food is Egyptian home cooking, with a few Lebanese meze dishes thrown in. Among the Egyptian dishes are koshary (a mix of pasta, rice and lentils with caramelised onions), bamia (okra with meat in a tomato sauce) and saiadi (fish in a hot sauce: not available when we visited). We tried molokhia, made with lamb. The stew had the right distinctive, almost sticky consistency created by the leaves of molokhia. It came with a huge pile of rice, sadly not cooked by the Egyptian method of frying in butter first with a few strands of vermicelli. The meal was plain, filling, comfort food – just as expected. We decided to be greedy with Om Ali, a good-sized portion of this Egyptian version of bread and butter pudding, sweetly spiced and with plenty of raisins and nuts. Ali Baba is a family-run restaurant, and on our lunchtime visit the family was much in evidence, gathered around the restaurant TV, but this didn't distract from their welcoming attitude or polite, friendly service.
Babies and children admitted. Booking advisable. Separate room for parties, seats 30. Table outdoors (1, pavement). Takeaway service. **Map 2/4F.**

Fairuz ★
3 Blandford Street, W1 (020 7486 8108/8182). Bond Street or Baker Street tube. **Meals served** noon-11.30pm daily. **Main courses** £9.95-£15.95. **Set meals** £15.95 meze with arak, £24.95 two courses. **Credit** AmEx, DC, MC, TC, V.
Warmly hued and intimate, Fairuz serves first-rate classic Lebanese cooking without the glacial formality of some of its rivals. That's not to say it's not smart – you'll find the usual snowy-white

Levant

tablecloths, shiny glassware and formal service – but these accoutrements are tempered by Arabic music, bonhomie (from both staff and customers), not to mention great food. The meze list isn't London's longest, but all the well-loved standards are here. Tabouleh was zesty and bursting with lemon juice and herbs; foul moukaaka (broad beans with olive oil, lemon and coriander) was so fresh and lively it almost jumped off the plate, with coriander that had left the chopping board only seconds before appearing at our table. Moutabal was suitably dense and smoky, and arayes (grilled pitta bread dusted with herbs) was spicy and warm. As is often the case, there's not much to say about the meat – a mixed grill that was tender if a touch tedious. A Lebanese Kefraya red was a fine companion to an all-round enjoyable meal.
Babies and children admitted. Tables outdoors (3, pavement). Takeaway service. Map 2/5G.

Levant
Jason Court, 76 Wigmore Street, W1 (020 7224 1111). Bond Street tube.
Bar **Open** noon-3pm, 5.30-11pm Mon-Sat. **Bar snacks** £3-£4.50.
Restaurant **Lunch served** noon-3pm Mon-Fri. **Dinner served** 6-11pm Mon-Sat. **Main courses** £11.50-£16.50. **Set lunch** £12.50 two courses, £15.50 three courses. **Service** 12½%.
Both **Credit** AmEx, DC, JCB, MC, V.
This new restaurant looks good. Diners descend down concreted stairs, through a large double door to a beautiful modern interior in brown and cream: gleaming bar area, polished stone floors, sleek curved lines. It all looks perfect. We got off to a fine start with the food, too. Levant is aiming at a kind of Levantine fusion: Middle Eastern dishes (like mahashi, stuffed vegetables), along with creative use of Middle Eastern ideas (roast sea bream with red pepper and walnut sauce) and more eclectic dishes. While we looked at the menu we tried one of the 'Levant purée' appetisers, mohamara, an unusual but delicious version of

the Lebanese classic, mixed to a paste and marvellously spiced, served with lovely bread dusted with spices and oil. It was downhill from here. A starter of watermelon, pomegranate and feta looked a picture on the plate, but didn't come together as a combination. Almond-crusted deep-fried squid with lemon and parsley was similarly disappointing, lacking in lemon. Next, a chicken stew with preserved lemons and olives (a Moroccan classic) contained a generous portion of chicken, a few olives and no discernible pickled lemons in a wildly over-salted sauce. The service did nothing to redeem our eating experience, main courses following starters at breakneck speed, then a long wait for the bill. We felt it wise to skip pudding, but the restaurant had run out of mint for mint tea and a cup of filter coffee was truly grim.
Babies and children welcome. Separate room for parties, seats 10. Vegetarian menu. Map 2/6G.

Mayfair W1

Fakhreldine
85 Piccadilly, W1 (020 7493 3424). Green Park tube. **Meals served** noon-midnight daily. **Main courses** £13. **Meze** £26 three courses incl coffee. **Minimum** £15. **Cover** £2. **Credit** AmEx, DC, JCB, MC, TC, V.
All smoked glass, velvet-covered chairs and 1970s light fittings, this large, well-established restaurant continues to trade on its great view from first-floor premises overlooking Green Park. In the past, we've found that some of the touches let the food down, but this time what we ate was spot on. The usual plate of salad vegetables was accompanied by good juicy olives. A fattoush salad was fresh, with crispy pieces of bread and freshly sprinkled sumac spice. Fuul was just how we like it: soft and malleable, a perfect consistency for mashing into the accompanying olive oil. Houmous was thick and punchy. We also enjoyed some fresh and flavoursome warak einab (stuffed vine leaves), but the shish taouk was not particularly tender and rather pricey at

£13. Service was professional and friendly. Late at night Fakhreldine was buzzing with the chatter of wealthy tourists.
Babies and children welcome; high chairs. Booking essential. No-smoking tables. Takeaway service. **Map 6/8H.**
For branch see index.

Al Hamra
31-33 Shepherd Market, W1 (020 7493 1954). Green Park or Hyde Park Corner tube. **Meals served** noon-11.30pm daily. **Main courses** £11-£18. **Cover** £2.50. **Minimum** £20. **Credit** AmEx, DC, JCB, MC, TC, V.
Al Hamra was full to bursting with summer tourists on our last visit, but the numbers hadn't affected the quality of the food, and, contrary to a past experience, the service was cheery too. We decided to choose from the long meze list (this is a highly traditional Lebanese restaurant) and to opt for filling café-style food. To this end we chose hot and tasty batata hara (cubes of spicy fried potatoes) along with crispy falafel with not a drop of excess oil, a robust fuul where the beans were soft enough to mash into decent olive oil, and sujuk bi beid (little spicy sausages cut into discs, mixed with beaten eggs and baked in the oven: a very typical dish, but not one we've tried before in an upmarket restaurant like this). A real downhome Middle Eastern meal, but we couldn't resist accompanying it with a bottle of good Lebanese house white.
Babies and children welcome; high chairs. Book dinner. Dress: smart casual. Tables outdoors (150, pavement). Takeaway service. **Map 6/8H.**

Al Sultan
51-52 Hertford Street, W1 (020 7408 1155/1166). Green Park or Hyde Park Corner tube. **Meals served** noon-midnight daily. **Main courses** £10-£18. **Cover** £2. **Credit** AmEx, DC, MC, £TC, V.
With the formal furnishings and hotel-like atmosphere of so many of its ilk, Al Sultan is a reliable restaurant for high-quality Lebanese food. It is popular during summer months with wealthy Mayfair tourists. Most of the dishes we tried were well up to standard. We particularly liked a peppery shanklish (spicy cheese crumbled into a salad with a dusting of sumac spice added), a warm moujadara (softly spiced lentils and rice with caramelised onions) and a lovely mushy fuul. In contrast, tabouleh was fresh and had a good lemony tang. Only fuul makala, beans with coriander and lemon, was slightly below par – a touch bland and lacking in zest. Farruj meshwi (a spatchcocked, grilled poussin), on the other hand, was tender and came with plenty of garlicky mayonnaise. Like the restaurant, staff are formal, but service was pleasant and efficient.
Babies and children welcome; high chairs. Book dinner. Tables outdoors (4, pavement). Takeaway service. **Map 6/8H.**

Soho W1

Tarboush
11 Wardour Street, W1 (020 7287 1220). Leicester Square or Piccadilly Circus tube. **Meals served** noon-2am Mon-Thur; noon-3am Fri, Sat; noon-11pm Sun. **Main courses** £6.95-£15. **Set lunches** £4.95 (meze), £7.95 two courses, £14.95 three courses. **Cover** 75p. **Credit** MC, TC, V.
Tarboush was pretty frenetic on a Friday night, and about as different from a typical Lebanese restaurant as one can imagine. We were escorted past the first-floor Insomnia bar (painted black) to the second-floor restaurant, which was somewhat quieter. The food is less expensive than in most Lebanese restaurants, but of a lower quality too. A meze dish of batata hara was tiny, but tasted OK; a fattoush salad was rather elderly, with soggy pieces of toasted bread; and bamia biziet (okra with tomato sauce) was very ordinary and underspiced. A shish taouk was fine, though: a large portion with tender pieces of chicken. But our other main course of stuffed lamb was simply a shank with rice, and none of the expected bulgar wheat stuffing in evidence. Staff clearly aim to attract tourists, and sometimes eagerness to pull in the punters can make service suffer. We were not happy to be asked to move to another table between courses so another party could be squeezed in (we refused). The appearance of a belly dancer fortunately distracted us from a 1970s-style, rather meagre fruit salad.
Babies and children admitted. Book Fri, Sat. Entertainment: belly dancer (restaurant) 9.30-10pm Fri, Sat; DJ (bar) from 10pm Thur-Sat. Separate room for parties, seats 60. Takeaway service. Vegetarian menu. **Map 13/7K.**
For branch see index.

West

Kensington W8

Phoenicia
11-13 Abingdon Road, W8 (020 7937 0120). High Street Kensington tube. **Meals served** noon-midnight daily. **Main courses** £9.90-£15. **Minimum** £16.30 dinner. **Meze** £16.80. **Set lunch** (12.15-3.30pm Mon-Fri) £9.95 two courses, £11.95 three courses. **Set buffet lunch** (12.15-2.30pm Sat) £10.95; (12.15-3.30pm Sun) £12.95. **Set meals** £16.80-£30. **Cover** £1.90. **Credit** AmEx, DC, JCB, MC, TC, V.
Looked at from a certain angle, Phoenicia is a completely standard Lebanese restaurant – formally dressed staff; wouldn't know a trend if one hit it in the face; traditional menu at high prices – but we always find our visits here a delight. One reason is the staff, who go out of their way to make a meal a pleasant occasion. Then there's the plant-filled, split-level decor, which adds some level of intimacy to what is actually a large restaurant. The food is generally of a high standard. We had a shanklish salad (peppery cheese crumbled into salad, with added sumac), fuul bil zeit (this one fell a bit short of the mark, with limp beans and elderly coriander), a lovely, rich fuul, and crispy hot fatayer with cheese. Highlight of the meal, though, was samak harra, a beautifully tender cod baked in a fairly hot sauce with tomatoes and peppers. Arabic coffee, with refills poured from a brass coffee-maker, came with complimentary little sugar-ball cakes.
Babies and children welcome; high chairs. Book weekends. Dress: smart casual. No-smoking tables. Separate room for parties, seats 35. Takeaway service. Vegetarian menu. **Map 5/9A.**

Olympia W14

Alounak ★
10 Russell Gardens, W14 (020 7603 7645). Olympia tube/rail. **Meals served** noon-midnight daily. **Main courses** £5.20-£9.80. **Unlicensed. Corkage** no charge. **Mineral water** £1 small bottle. **Credit** MC, V.
The brickwork interior is done out with kilims, mirrors, and other paraphernalia; huge multi-coloured glass lanterns hang from the ceiling. However, this is no theme restaurant – rather, it's the home of some of the best Persian food in London. Flat Iranian bread is brought to the table straight from the front-of-house oven; with it we tried boorani (spinach and yoghurt dip, the spinach unbelievably fresh), hallim badgemoon (a tomatoey aubergine dip) and a good, beany houmous. We've always found both kebabs and Persian stews excellent here. This time, we were in kebab and rice mood. Both joojeh kebab makshoos (chicken kebab) and chelo kebab chenjeh and kubideh (lamb and kofta kebab) were melt-in-the-mouth meat, perfectly cooked, full of flavour. The rice deserves a eulogy of its own; cooked the Persian way (soft, made with saffron, served with a knob of butter), it tasted just about as good as it gets: especially when given a good dusting of sumac spice. We managed some Iranian rosewater ice-cream for pudding, creamy and tasting like Turkish delight. The place was already busy at 8pm on a Thursday; by 9.30pm there was a big queue.
Babies and children welcome (lunch only); high chairs. Booking advisable. Tables outdoors (2, pavement). Takeaway service.
For branch see index.

Chez Marcelle
34 Blythe Road, W14 (020 7603 3241). Olympia tube/rail/9, 10, 27 bus. **Meals served** noon-11pm Tue-Sun. **Main courses** £6-£7.50 incl £1.50 cover restaurant, £10 café. **Credit** JCB, MC, £TC, V.
The parlour-like basement dining room was closed for refurbishment on our most recent visit, so we had to eat in the ground-floor café/takeaway area. Simply furnished with wooden benches and tables, the place seems pleasant enough by day, but suffers from harsh fluorescent lighting by night. Our grills took a while to prepare – a rather torturous wait under the punishing lights. In the meantime, we tried a mixed bag of meze dishes: moutabal, fattoush (which had an over-abundance of mint and salt) and some very moreish batata harra (spicy hot fried potatoes). The grills were both chicken dishes. One, described as 'boneless', came with bones and wings; the other, a shish taouk, can only be described as an acquired taste – very disappointing. And neither the house white wine nor the bottle of Lebanese beer was as cold as we would have liked.
Babies and children welcome; high chairs. Book weekends. Takeaway service.

Yas
7 Hammersmith Road, W14 (020 7603 9148/3980). Hammersmith tube/Olympia tube/rail/9, 10 bus. **Meals served** noon-5am daily. **Main courses** £7-12. **Service** 15%. **Credit** AmEx, DC, MC, TC, V.
Late-night opening, and first-class Persian stews and kebabs ensure Yas's continuing popularity. At lunchtime, this small, orange-coloured restaurant is popular with families; at night it's laid-back. Staff were unfailingly helpful and friendly. We began with dips (mast o mousir, very thick yoghurt with shallots), kashke badjeman (aubergine mixed with whey and herbs – you either love it or hate it), plus a plate of sabzi (herb leaves with feta cheese). They were accompanied by hot flat bread straight from the oven at the front of the restaurant. Stews – such as khoresh gheime badjeman (lamb cooked with aubergines, split peas, tomatoes and lime) – and kebabs are reliably good. On our last visit, we opted for chelo kebab kubideh, a large portion of well-flavoured minced chicken with near-perfect Iranian-style rice.
Babies and children welcome; high chairs. Booking essential. Separate room for parties, seats 40. Takeaway service.

Paddington W2

Isfahan
3-4 Bouverie Place, W2 (020 7460 1030). Paddington tube/rail. **Meals served** noon-midnight daily. **Main courses** £6.50-£7.45. **Set lunch** £9.95 two courses incl a drink. **Set meal** £15 two courses incl coffee. **Credit** AmEx, DC, JCB, MC, £TC, V.
Isfahan sustains itself on a loyal clientele of Persians and locals who wouldn't dream of being bothered by the retro decor (cartwheels on the ceiling, bare stonework and incongruous Spanish-style tiles). Instead they come to enjoy long evening meals often accompanied by Arabic or Iranian musicians. The menu is quite ambitious, comprising a full range of Persian stews as well as kebabs and biriani-style rice dishes. We started our meal in classic Persian style with panir o sabzi: fresh herbs (predominantly mint), with the odd radish and cube of feta, served with a huge, freshly baked piece of Iranian bread. Other starters can fall short of perfection; salad shirazi was a rather boring, finely chopped mixed salad. For mains we opted for a Persian stew and a kebab. Chicken kebab (kebab morgh) was the better choice – meat marinated to melt-in-the-mouth tenderness – although the rice was mundane. Fesenjoon morgh came as pieces of chicken with a huge amount of dense, dark sauce of pomegranates and walnuts. For our taste, the balance of the dish was skewed, with the tart tang of the fruit too dominant. So rich and strong was the sauce, we could only eat a small amount, and the flavour of the chicken and walnuts was lost. We don't want to be too harsh on Isfahan, but it's probably better to stick to the kebabs.
Babies and children welcome; half-price dishes for under-12s; high chairs. Book dinner. Entertainment: Arabic and Iranian music, belly dancers, 8-11.30pm daily. Tables outdoors (6, pavement). Vegetarian menu. **Map 1/5E.**

Westbourne Grove W2

Fresco ★
25 Westbourne Grove, W2 (020 7221 2355). Bayswater tube. **Meals served** 9am-11pm daily. **Main courses** £4.50-£7.95. **Unlicensed. Credit** DC, MC, £TC, V.
A cheery Lebanese café with great juices and milkshakes, Fresco also serves a selection of meze dishes and the odd kebab. Juices are the speciality. They come in many combinations, from a straight orange, mango, apple, melon or grapefruit (£1.90) to combinations (all £2.50), including strawberry, mango and banana and a super-healthy carrot, celery and ginger. Banana and strawberry milkshake was a large, creamy, fruity glassful. We also picked a few meze dishes – loubieh (french beans cooked in olive oil with onions and garlic), some falafel and baba ganoush (all meze dishes are £3.25). It wasn't

Menu

See also the menu in **Turkish** *(page 171).*

Soups
Ash-e-reshteh: a Persian soup containing noodles, spinach, pulses and dried herbs.
Harira: a Moroccan soup usually based around chickpeas, tomatoes and noodles.

Meze dishes
Baba ganoush: Egyptian name for moutabal (qv).
Basturma: smoked beef.
Falafel: a mixture of spicy chickpeas or broad beans rolled into balls and served with houmous or tahini (sesame seed sauce). Tamaya is the Egyptian name.
Fatayer: a soft pastry with fillings of cheese, onions, spinach and pine kernels.
Fattoush: fresh vegetable salad containing shards of toasted pitta bread and sumac, an astringent and fruity-tasting spice made from dried seeds.
Fuul, fu'l or **fu'l medames**: brown broad beans seasoned with olive oil, lemon juice and garlic, sprinkled with parsley and often served with hard-boiled eggs.
Kalaj: halloumi cheese on pastry.
Kibbeh: highly seasoned mixture of minced lamb, cracked wheat and onion. For meze it is often served raw (kibbeh nayeh) or deep-fried in balls. Also served baked as a main course, or stewed in yoghurt.
Labneh: Middle Eastern cream cheese made from yoghurt.
Masto musir: (Iranian) shallot-flavoured yoghurt.
Moujadara: lentils, rice and caramelised onions mixed together.
Moutabal: a purée of toasted aubergines mixed with sesame sauce, garlic and lemon juice.
Muhamara: spiced mixed crushed nuts.
Sabzi: (Iranian) a plate of fresh herb leaves (usually mint and fennel) often served with a cube of feta.
Salad olivieh: (Iranian) a bit like a Russian salad, with chopped potatoes, chicken, eggs, peas and gherkins, mixed with olive oil and mayonnaise.
Sambousek: small pastries filled with mince, onion and pine kernels.
Sujuk or **sojuk**: spicy Lebanese sausages.
Tabouleh: a mixture of chopped parsley, tomatoes, crushed wheat, onions, olive oil and lemon juice.
Warak einab: rice-stuffed vine leaves.

Meat
Fesenjon: (Iranian) a puréed walnut and pomegranate sauce that usually accompanies meat.
Kofta, kafta or **kufta kebab**: minced lamb or beef mixed with spices, eggs and onions, shaped into sausages and then barbecued.
Lahim meshwi (shish, or sheesh, kebab): cubes of marinated meat grilled on a skewer, often with tomatoes, onions and sweet peppers. Served either in pitta bread or with rice.
Molokhia: a soupy stew made with meat and molokhia (mallow) leaves.
Shashlik: skewered, marinated meat and vegetables.
Shawarma or **sharwerma**: slices of meat (usually lamb) marinated then grilled on a spit and sliced kebab-style.
Shish taouk: marinated and grilled chicken cubes served with garlic and lemon sauce.

Desserts
Baklava: filo pastry interleaved with pistachio nuts, almonds or walnuts, and covered in syrup.
Konafa or **kadayif**: cake made from shredded pastry dough, filled with syrup and nuts, or cream.
Ma'amoul: variously shaped pastries filled with nuts or dates.
Muhallabia: a milky ground-rice pudding with almonds and pistachios, flavoured with rosewater or orange blossom.
Om Ali: bread and butter pudding.

Le Mignon

Le Mignon

Lebanese Cuisine

the best Lebanese food around, but pleasant enough. The falafel were heated up in the microwave, then the man behind the counter went to town on presentation, arranging everything beautifully on one plate and drizzling the falafel with tahini.
Babies and children welcome; high chairs. Takeaway service. **Map 11/6B.**

Hafez
5 Hereford Road, W2 (020 7221 3167/020 7229 9398). Bayswater, Notting Hill Gate or Queensway tube/7, 23, 27, 28, 31, 70 bus. **Meals served** noon-midnight daily. **Main courses** £4.50-£12.90. **Service** 10%. **No credit cards.**
On a Saturday lunchtime, Hafez was doing a roaring trade with (mostly) Iranian families tucking into one of the things Persian cooking does best – the kebab. Chicken chello kebab was as good as we had expected: lovely tenderised meat. But meat is only part of the story with a Persian kebab. As usual, it came with rice (some cooked with saffron, lending a colourful white and yellow pattern to the plate) that was served with a knob of butter, and a grilled tomato. Make your plate even more colourful by adding lashings of red sumac spice, and you have a plate of rice that could almost be a meal in itself. Salmon also came with the fab rice, although the fish itself was a fairly ordinary grill. But with flat Iranian bread (made to order in the oven in the front of the restaurant), and some tasty yoghurt and garlic dip to go with it, we didn't feel we had much to complain about. Hafez also has some Persian stews, such as chello ghaime (lamb in a tomato, saffron and split-pea sauce), on its menu.
Babies and children welcome; high chairs. Book Thur-Sun. Tables outdoors (3, pavement). Takeaway service. **Map 11/6B.**
For branch see index.

Al Waha ★
75 Westbourne Grove, W2 (020 7229 0806). Bayswater or Queensway tube. **Meals served** noon-midnight daily. **Main courses** £8-£14. **Set meal** £18 three courses, incl coffee. **Cover** £1.50. **Credit** AmEx, DC, MC, £TC, V.

Small and square, on two levels, and painted a warm yellow, Al Waha is a pleasant and intimate space in which to enjoy first rate, traditional Lebanese cooking away from the acres of floorage and formal atmosphere of restaurants of a similar standard. We stuck mainly to meze, and there wasn't a duff dish among our choices. We particularly liked fuul moukala (a perfect blend of firm green broad beans, lemon and coriander); a creamy labneh with lashings of good olive oil in a well in the middle; and a very thick, garlicky houmous. These went very well with batata harra (spicy fried potatoes) and manakiesh jebna (grilled halloumi cheese on Arabic bread, sprinkled with herbs). Our sole main dish, a shish taouk, was plenty for two. The staff were professional and pleasant, the Kefraya Lebanese wine a good accompaniment to a highly enjoyable meal.
Tables outdoors (8, pavement). Takeaway service. **Map 11/6B.**

South West

Gloucester Road SW7

Soraya
36 Gloucester Road, SW7 (020 7589 4060). Gloucester Road tube. **Meals served** 11am-midnight daily. **Main courses** £5.95-£12.50. **Service** 10%. **Credit** DC, JCB, MC, £TC, V.
It advertises itself as the longest established Persian restaurant in London, but Soraya has been overtaken by newer places. The menu is pretty complete, listing kebabs, 'Persian specialities' and 'Soraya specialities' (Persian-inspired inventions such as 'Oasis' – chicken on a bed of rice garnished with sultanas and onions). There's also a tell-tale section of grilled fish: salmon, trout, sole, prawns and sea bass. The fact that not all dishes are authentic doesn't necessarily imply criticism; the problem was that on our visit the cooking simply wasn't up to much. We had some reasonable starters: mirza ghessemi (a salad of aubergine, tomato, egg and garlic), and a plate of sabzi (herb leaves with a feta cheese cube). However, baghali polow

(chicken with rice steamed with dill and broad beans) was simply bland, while a vegetarian platter (more Lebanese than Persian, comprising falafel, houmous, baba ganoush and tabouleh) was far below the standards found in other places. On top of that, the restaurant has covered its walls with some unappealing works of art that are for sale (we suspect they're the same ones that were there last year), and service is slow. Soraya continues to do reasonable business, but, as far as the food goes, we feel it has lost its way.
Babies and children welcome; high chairs. Entertainment: belly dancer and Persian singer Thur, Fri dinner. Separate room for parties, seats 70. Takeaway service. **Map 5/9C.**

South

Battersea SW8

The Village
34 Queenstown Road, SW8 (020 7720 1161). Battersea Park rail. **Meals served** 11am-midnight Tue-Sun. **Main courses** £12-£15. **Meze** £15 per person (minimum two). **Cover** £2. **Credit** JCB, MC, £TC, V.
One of a string of restaurants on this patch of Queenstown Road, the Village has all the accoutrements of a good neighbourhood eaterie: a relaxed ambience, friendly staff and fine food for less than you'd pay in central London. Trendy it certainly isn't. White roughened plasterwork dominates, along with a few pine fittings, but once we'd tucked into some superbly light and fresh dishes on a Saturday lunchtime, we felt very positive about the place. Lebanese food can be perfect for a summery lunch if you choose wisely. We had tabouleh (quite coarsely chopped but suffused with flavour), some lemony, tender sawda dajaj (fried chicken livers), a smooth baba ganoush, and 'Village fries' (a Village original): fried vegetables in a light batter, cooked just right, so the vegetable flavours were retained. The only duff dish was shanklish, which came with little

cubes of bland, rubbery cheese scattered over threds of lettuce rather than the expected peppery, crumbly cheese and spiced-up salad. Next came a shared main-course shish taouk: a large portion, well-grilled, with lashings of garlic sauce. We finished our meal with Arabic coffee, and a plateful of complimentary (and fresh) Arabic pastries.
Babies and children welcome; high chairs. Book dinner. Disabled: toilet. No-smoking tables. Tables outdoors (3, terrace). Takeaway service; free local delivery.

North

Camden NW1

Le Mignon ★
9A Delancey Street, NW1 (020 7387 0600). Camden Town tube. **Meals served** noon-midnight Tue-Sun. **Main courses** £7.50-£14. **Credit** AmEx, DC, MC, V.
Though it's simply a Camden neighbourhood restaurant in appearance – with dark terracotta paint, wooden floors, and wine racks along the back wall – Le Mignon creates food that is pure Lebanese, and very good, too. Cooking takes place in a little kitchen behind the wine racks; on our visit the chefs turned out some great meze dishes. Among them were a super-fresh tabouleh with lashings of lemon juice; moussaka (like the Greek dish, but made with tomatoes and aubergine only); warm cheese sambouseks (feta cheese encased in good filo pastry); sawda djaj (superbly tender chicken livers in a thin sauce with just the right amount of lemon); a tomatoey and very tasty fuul that was great when mashed into the accompanying oil; hommos shobar (hot chickpeas cooked in oil; not to mention some of the best fries in town. The restaurant is a relaxing spot. Prices here aren't much lower than in top-rank central London establishments, but the cooking is as good, portions are large, the staff hospitable and the enjoyment factor very high.
Tables outdoors (2, pavement). Takeaway service. Vegetarian menu.

Modern European

Central

Barbican EC2

Searcy's
Level 2, Barbican, Silk Street, EC2 (020 7588 3008). Barbican tube/rail. **Lunch served** noon-2.30pm Mon-Fri, Sun. **Dinner served** 5-11pm Mon-Sat; 5-7pm Sun. **Main courses** lunch £13; dinner £16.25-£19. **Set meal** £18.50 two courses, £21.50 three courses. **Credit** AmEx, DC, MC, £TC, V.
In truth, you're never going to make a journey into the heart of the Barbican for a meal unless you: a) live in the complex, b) work locally, or c) are attending a show there. But should you pay it a visit, Searcy's can oblige with more-than-competent cooking (at a price), friendly, efficient service and agreeable second-floor views out over the church of St Giles where Oliver Cromwell was married. The menu du jour (three choices at each course) offers considerable savings on the carte. We embarked upon it but were disappointed by a bland chilled cucumber, mint and mascarpone soup. In contrast, an earthy poached breast of chicken filled with black pudding and served with watercress, new potato, chorizo salad and fig jus provided a fine sweet and savoury main course. From the carte, there was a subtle oriental air to air-cured duck breast, cut into tiny slices and accompanied by a delicate salad of broad bean, orange, radish, alfalfa sprouts and star anise; and a big Mediterranean punch to olive oil-poached swordfish, topped with a tomato, aubergine and black olive sauce and roast artichokes. It was back to Blighty for desserts with a superb sticky toffee pudding and a big plate of first-rate British cheeses and chutneys.
Babies and children welcome. Booking advisable. Disabled: toilet. No-smoking tables.
Map 4/5P.

Bloomsbury WC1

AKA
18 West Central Street, WC1 (020 7836 0110). Covent Garden or Holborn tube.
Bar **Open** 6pm-3am Tue-Fri; 7pm-3am Sat.
Bar snacks £3.50-£7.
Restaurant **Dinner served** 6-11.30pm Tue-Thur; 6pm-1am Fri, Sat. **Main courses** £9-£14.50. **Service** 12½%.
Both **Credit** AmEx, DC, JCB, MC, £TC, V.
With its smoky, warehouse atmosphere and bouncers at the door, AKA is a curious hybrid. The ground floor is a club, complete with DJ, bar and frenetic twentysomethings on the pull. Upstairs, in a spotlit annexe with purple banquettes, is a restaurant serving unexpectedly good food. We decided to splash out on three courses, although most of our achingly trendy fellow diners were sharing dishes or barely eating. Slices of tuna with ginger and soy sauce was attractively presented and beautifully balanced. Equally successful was the riotously colourful salad of artichokes, plum tomatoes and Dolcelatte. Main courses took a while, but were worth the wait. The coquelet with wild mushrooms was delicious, if a little fiddly, and we enjoyed the scallops with Parma ham. Desserts were very slow to arrive, but we were consoled by glasses of muscat on the house. A lovely apple crumble was spiced with cloves and came with apple purée and crème fraîche. We drank a crisp, tangy La Serre sauvignon blanc from an unremarkable wine list with short tasting notes. Service is attentive, but we could hardly hear ourselves speak above the din of dance music from below. A shame, as the food, though slow to materialise, was of a high quality – go at lunch.
Booking advisable. Disabled: toilet. Entertainment: DJs 11pm-3am Thur-Sat.
Map 14/6L.

City EC3

1 Blossom Street
1 Blossom Street, E1 (020 7247 6530). Liverpool Street tube/rail. **Lunch served** noon-3.30pm, **dinner served** 5.30-9.30pm Mon-Fri. **Main courses** £12.75-£17.50. **Service** 12%. **Credit** AmEx, JCB, MC, £TC, V.
Located in a pokey basement beyond Old Spitalfields Market, 1 Blossom Street is in that minority of City restaurants you can use for fun as well as business. It has many City trappings – a comfortable bar, well-spaced large tables, private rooms, power breakfasts, even a courtyard garden – but cooking and service surpass the City norm. Staff match professionalism and attentiveness with a friendliness that isn't too in-yer-face; little touches such as amuses-gueules and chocolates with the coffee arrive unbidden. There are simple but well-made dishes such as watercress soup as well as luxury ingredients like foie gras – in this case, caramelised and served as a starter on a fatty toasted brioche with Madeira jus and candied orange. Many dishes are French-inspired (magret of duck was pan-fried, then served on rich black pudding with a blackcurrant sauce) and some are more challenging than you'd expect. Underneath a crisp fillet of sea bass, a couple of lambs' tongues added a powerful, offal-like flavour, complemented by a red wine jus. A pear blancmange was completely unlike English school-dinner food, being light and not overly gelatinous. The wine list is surprisingly short for such a classy kitchen, but there are enough good bottles of interest. Prices here are substantial, yet both the cooking and service are of a standard that puts some higher-profile City places to shame.
Babies and children admitted. Booking advisable. Disabled: toilet. Separate room for parties, seats 10-25. Tables outdoors (garden).
Map 17/5R.

Prism ★
147 Leadenhall Street, EC3 (020 7256 3888). Monument tube/Bank tube/DLR.
Bar **Open** 11am-11pm Mon-Fri. **Main courses** £5-£10.
Restaurant **Lunch served** 11.30am-3pm, **dinner served** 6-10pm Mon-Fri. **Main courses** £12.20-£22. **Service** 12½%. **Credit** AmEx, DC, JCB, MC, £TC, V.
The airy grand hall of a former bank provides the setting for Prism, a stately, classical, even forbidding arena, but one where top-notch cooking is touted. The menu follows the fashion for seemingly simple dishes (watercress soup, sardines on toast, Cumberland sausage), yet rarely misses a tantalising trick. Sweet potato, chilli, coconut and crab soup was a deliciously rich concoction, while Carpegna ham, Parmesan and savoy cabbage salad was a great example of imaginative simplicity. Most mains have French infrastructures, except for Chinese-style duck breast, noodles, pak choi and soy broth. Char-grilled red bream, spiced chorizo and tomato couscous was perfectly flaky, light and balanced. At £22, roast fillet of beef, Lyonnaise potatoes and périgourdine sauce needed to punch above its weight. It was indeed a knock-out example of marbled fillet, with the thinnest, crispiest charred crust and a lush sauce. We finished with a dangerously rich Dime Bar cheesecake and a superlative rhubarb and banana crumble. Service was impeccable. The highly trained waiters were studiously attentive to a companion's gluten allergy, while a formidable wine waiter skippered us through the high seas of the giant wine list, plotting every course with fine flavours at acceptable prices. You pay for this executive treatment (£115 for two, including less than £30 on drinks), but for once it was worth it.
Babies and children welcome; high chairs. Booking essential, two weeks in advance. Disabled: toilet. Dress: smart casual. Separate rooms for parties, seating 30 and 50.
Map 4/6Q.

Terminus Bar & Grill
40 Liverpool Street, EC2 (020 7618 7400). Liverpool Street tube/rail. **Meals served** 11am-11.45pm daily. **Main courses** £9.50-£14.50. **Service** 12½%. **Credit** AmEx, DC, MC, V.
You could be forgiven for not realising this adjunct to the Great Eastern Hotel is a restaurant. Look behind the bar full of young City types guzzling champagne like milk, however, and you'll discover tables and an open-plan kitchen. The space is noisy, minimalist and monochrome, while the good service, big portions and busy mix

1 Blossom Street

Terminus Bar & Grill.
See page 131.

of diners and drinkers set an American tone. Starters seemed comparatively expensive, but both of ours (a richly dressed Caesar salad with avocado and marinated anchovies, and a rare roast beef and rocket salad with Parmesan and a mild horseradish sauce) were substantial snacks in themselves. Mains were no less ample, and bore the character of gastropub cuisine, with dishes such as seared tuna niçoise and char-grilled Great Eastern burger and chips. Both the roast chump of lamb with garlic mash and marjoram jus, and the fillet of red snapper with crushed new potatoes, artichokes and olives were sturdy, well-judged dishes, nicely complemented by unusually good house wines. We arrived with a sharp appetite, but after such hearty portions, desserts were impossible, although we were tempted by coconut tapioca and lilikoi sorbet with seasonal fruits. By 9.30pm, most of the City whizz kids had lurched home; however, this busy venue is worth the rest of us checking out, too.
Babies and children admitted; high chairs. Disabled: toilet. Dress: smart casual.
Map 4/6R.

Clerkenwell EC1

Smiths of Smithfield

67-77 Charterhouse Street, EC1 (020 7236 6666/www.smithsofsmithfield.co.uk). Farringdon tube/rail.
Ground Floor Bar **Meals served** 7am-11pm Mon-Sat; 10.30am-10.30pm Sun. **Bar snacks** £2.25-£5.50.
Dining Room **Lunch served** noon-3pm, **dinner served** 6-11pm daily. **Main courses** £9.50-£10.50. **Credit** AmEx, MC, V.
The ground floor bar and café at Smiths of Smithfield has that utterly contemporary look of strip-down, knock-through, tear-up-the-carpets, concrete and industrial-tech utility. A graffitied car bonnet hangs on the wall; brown leather sofas huddle around formica tables laid with HP sauce and Heinz salad cream; and a train station announcement board summons diners upstairs to their tables. It's worth hanging around downstairs, though, to sample the exemplary all-day fry-ups, fish finger butties and Cornish pasties. On the first floor there's a plush, red cocktail bar harbouring a few suits – the dress code elsewhere is dot.com casual and designer workwear. Above that you'll find the brasserie (second floor) and the fine dining room (*see p34* **British**), both presided over by Aussie TV chef John Torode. Ingredient quality is high, with much organic produce on the daily-changing menus. Torode seems best at simple European dishes, but also likes dabbling with Asian-style food. Starters in the brasserie include the contrasting delights of smoked haddock with Old Spot bacon and mustard, and lucky squid with chilli jam and choi sum. Of the mains, belly of pork with mashed potato was squidgy and unappetising, but Welsh black rib steak with fat chips and mustard mayonnaise was superb.
Babies and children admitted. **Map 15/5O.**

Covent Garden WC2

Axis

One Aldwych, 1 Aldwych, WC2 (020 7300 0300). Covent Garden or Temple tube. **Lunch served** noon-3pm Mon-Fri. **Dinner served** 6-11.30pm Mon-Sat. **Main courses** £12.50-£22. **Set lunch** £15.75 two courses, £19.75 three courses. **Service** 12½%. **Credit** AmEx, DC, JCB, MC, £TC, V.
In the basement of the ultra chic and much lauded One Aldwych hotel, Axis has scored a prime location. But it suffers (perhaps because of its subterranean position or hotel pedigree) from a disturbing lack of atmosphere. Maybe it's the hard acoustics, the pale modern minimalism of the decor, or the bland (though perfectly efficient) service. The menu is encouraging enough, offering plenty of eclectic options. There might be a crispy duck noodle salad or a creamy, lemon-infused scallop risotto to start, followed by grilled fillet of sole with cheese, cauliflower and lentils, or venison with pasta, ceps and sugar snaps. A smoked salmon starter with horseradish, crème fraîche and blinis was the only real disappointment of the meal; the blinis were dry and cold and the horseradish scarcely made its presence felt. You can choose from a list of daily grills cooked to order – a huge hunk of char-grilled sirloin came with cheesy mash, green beans and spinach – or have pasta as a starter or main course. A plateful of prawn linguini had plenty of grilled and garlicked king prawns. Though not recommended for a boisterous night out, Axis probably won't let you down for a business lunch. *See also below* **Indigo**.
Babies and children admitted. Booking advisable. **Map 14/7M.**

Bank

1 Kingsway, WC2 (020 7234 3344). Holborn tube. **Breakfast served** 7.30-11.30am Mon-Fri. **Brunch served** 11.30am-3.30pm Sat, Sun. **Lunch served** noon-3pm Mon-Fri. **Dinner served** 5.30-11.30pm Mon-Sat; 5.30-10pm Sun. **Main courses** £9.50-£19. **Set meal** (5.30-7pm Mon-Sat; 10-11pm Mon-Fri) £13.90 two courses, £17.50 three courses. **Service** 12½%. **Credit** AmEx, DC, MC, TC, V.
Maybe the owners called this restaurant Bank because they're laughing all the way there. The interior sports an open-plan kitchen behind a long glass wall stretching from chi-chi cocktail bar to noisy, overcrowded restaurant decorated with murals of Coney Island at the rear. Food is served round the clock, with power breakfasts, super-power lunches and world domination dinners. All the Modern European favourites you can think of are here, from gazpacho to seared tuna salad. Pasta and risotto are particularly expensive at £10-£13, but the sauces are made of ceps, crab and baby artichokes. Still, with grilled calf's liver, bacon, sage and onion mash at £16.50 and Bank fish and chips at £18.50, you don't need to eat caviar (£41.95-£87) to run up an overdraft. The prix fixe is less inflationary; on our visit it included a hearty potato, salmon and celery soup, and a juicy magret duck, sweetly served with baby carrots and game jus. Elsewhere, summer pudding was perfectly rendered, while rhubarb soup and peach sorbet showed evidence of creative minds investing bright ideas. House wines are relatively modestly priced, but bottles rise to a comedic £260.
Babies and children welcome; children's brunch menu; high chairs; nappy-changing facilities. Booking advisable. **Map 14/6M.**

Café du Jardin

28 Wellington Street, WC2 (020 7836 8769). Covent Garden tube. **Lunch served** noon-3pm daily. **Dinner served** 5.30pm-midnight Mon-Sat; 5.30-11pm Sun. **Main courses** £9.50-£14.50. **Set lunch** £9.95 two courses, £13.50 three courses, incl coffee. **Set dinner** (5.30-7.30pm, 10-11.30pm) £9.95 two courses, £13.50 three courses, incl coffee. **Service** 15%. **Credit** AmEx, DC, JCB, MC, V.
The tasteful decor and extensive menu has made this Covent Garden eaterie popular with both post-business suits and pre-theatre casuals. The restaurant is light and airy, the starters likewise, although the gnocchi on this particular evening struggled to lift itself free of its blanket of cheese sauce. For our other starter we settled for buffalo mozzarella with ratatouille and roast peppers (an excellent combination), although we had also been tempted by lemon and ginger 'tempura' chicken, and spinach salad with blue cheese. A main course of steamed salmon with braised vegetables was well prepared and enlivened by a high-quality basil aïoli, but the swordfish steak with ribbon courgettes and a black olive dressing would have benefited from a minute or two's more grilling and less olive oil. However, any reservations about the food melted along with the delectable lemon tart and the poached pear with bitter chocolate sauce. Service was attentive and friendly.
Babies and children admitted. Booking advisable. Entertainment: pianist 8pm-midnight Mon-Sat. Tables outdoors (6, pavement). **Map 14/6L.**

Indigo

One Aldwych, 1 Aldwych, WC2 (020 7300 0400). Covent Garden tube. **Breakfast served** 6.30-11am, **lunch served** noon-3pm, **dinner served** 6-11.15pm daily. **Main courses** £13.75-£17.50. **Set meals** £15.50 two courses, £19.50 three courses. **Service** 12½%. **Credit** AmEx, DC, JCB, MC, V.
You'd expect the restaurants in the superflash One Aldwych hotel to have style, and the lounge bar-like Indigo – decked out in muted tones, with architectural flower arrangements – certainly looks the part. There are, though, a few fraying edges: the backs of the comfy throne-chairs were worn, and someone appeared to have taken a nibble from the corner of a large artwork made up of multiple slices of toast. The globally-influenced menu is one of those tempters where almost everything appeals. We went for a daily special of chilled (and rather bland) cucumber soup, paired, surprisingly but effectively, with a superb, fresh and crunchy spring roll. There was more oriental influence in the moist crab cakes with a corn relish (spiked with star anise) and a beautifully dressed little pile of red chard. To follow, prawn risotto had an almost rice-puddingy creaminess and plenty of warmth and bite, while seared tuna was sea-fresh, came perfectly cooked (medium rare, as requested) and was served with citrus potatoes (not noticeably citric). The high standard was maintained in desserts of rhubarb with a citrus parfait and a biscuit with stem ginger; and gratin of blueberries, strawberries and raspberries in a wonderfully light sabayon. Credit is also due to the first-rate, well-informed service. *See also above* **Axis**.
Babies and children welcome. Booking advisable. Disabled: toilet in hotel. Separate rooms for parties, seating 45 and 48.
Map 14/7M.

The Ivy

1 West Street, WC2 (020 7836 4751). Covent Garden or Leicester Square tube. **Lunch served** noon-3pm Mon-Sat; noon-3.30pm Sun. **Dinner served** 5.30pm-midnight daily. **Main courses** £9-£23.50. **Set lunch** (Sat, Sun) £15.50 three courses. **Cover** £1.50. **Credit** AmEx, DC, MC, £TC, V.
As of October 2000, Jeremy King and Chris Corbin are leaving the Ivy (and Le Caprice and J Sheekey – all owned by the Belgo group). What effect this will have on the mini-chain, no one can tell, but given the pair's almost obsessive attention to detail, it's hard to imagine that things will be quite the same. At the time of writing, and for a good many years, the Ivy has been the stage, screen and media's first choice of restaurant, serving up a menu of crowd-pleasing dishes in an atmosphere of gentle privilege (it's very hard indeed for mere mortals to get a table – booking six weeks ahead is the norm) and gentlemen's club decor. The diamond-patterned jewel-coloured windows shield diners from the world outside while throwing a very pretty light into the room. Well-drilled staff serve dishes such as steak tartare, corned beef hash, lobster salad, and salmon fish cake on spinach with sorrel sauce, from a menu that lists the occasional new dish but mainly sticks to a much-loved formula. The not-so-secret ingredient is the former owners, however, and it will be interesting to see what happens next.
Babies and children welcome; high chairs. Booking essential, well in advance. Separate room for parties, seats 25-60. **Map 14/6K.**

Fitzrovia W1

Mash

19-21 Great Portland Street, W1 (020 7637 5555). Oxford Circus tube.
Bar **Open** 11am-1am Mon-Fri; noon-1am Sat.
Restaurant **Brunch served** noon-4pm Sat. **Lunch served** noon-3pm Mon-Fri. **Dinner served** 6-11pm Mon-Sat. **Main courses** £9-£15. **Service** 12½%. **House wine** £12.50 bottle, £4.30 glass. **Mineral water** £3 bottle, £1.20 glass. **Credit** AmEx, DC, MC, V.
Oliver Peyton's Mash continues to pull in the crowds, both in the ground-floor bar (*see p207* **Bars**) and in the first-floor restaurant. The two large rooms are decorated in a '1960s vision of the space age' sort of way and neither seems to have any form of sound absorption. Perhaps these factors are meant to distract diners from the food, which although OK, was nothing to write home about. The assemblies worked best – a plate of Italian charcuterie (a starter) and an interesting cheese plate, featuring Isle of Mull cheddar, grapes, and onions pickled in balsamic vinegar. Cookies and chocolate brownies weren't bad either. However, the Mash salad was large but not particularly distinguished, chips were average, roast salmon with pak choi and sweet chilli dressing was nicely flavoured but overcooked, as was an otherwise tasty grilled marlin (with crushed new potatoes, spinach and tapenade). Grilled rump of lamb, with ragout of peppers, lima beans and Swiss chard, was a rather mean, over-fatty portion. Maybe we hit an off day; there is much here to praise. Service was perky and pleasant; the micro-brewery beers are worth ordering (tasting glasses of each of the four beers cost £3.20); and the place certainly has a buzz about it.
Babies and children welcome (lunch); high chairs. Book dinner. Disabled: toilet. Separate room for parties, seats 28. **Map 13/6J.**

Knightsbridge SW1

The Fifth Floor ★

Harvey Nichols, Knightsbridge, SW1 (020 7235 5250). Knightsbridge tube.
Bar **Open** 11am-11pm Mon-Sat; noon-6pm Sun.
Restaurant **Lunch served** noon-3pm Mon-Fri; noon-3.30pm Sat, Sun. **Dinner served** 6.30-11.30pm Mon-Sat. **Main courses** £11-£36.25. **Set lunch** £20 two courses, £24.50 three courses. **Service** 12½%. **Credit** AmEx, DC, JCB, MC, £TC, V.

The classy, if cacophonous, café and busy branch of Yo! Sushi on Harvey Nicks' fifth floor are what you'd expect from the sleekest, chicest department store in town. Cocooned from the din by a glass wall, the well-mannered, relaxed restaurant is more of a surprise. Henry Harris's long association with the Fifth Floor Restaurant is as evident in the agreeable ease of the staff as in the assured touch of the cooking. Here is a menu of perfect balance and many temptations. From the three-course lunch selection, we sampled a classic vitello tonnato (ultra-thin slices of cold veal with a tuna and caper sauce) and a more unusual, but entirely successful, confit of wild salmon with preserved duck, served with an artichoke and fennel salad and held together by a subtle caramelised sauce. The mains were equally impressive: rare roast aiguillette of beef with mushroom, red onion and bone marrow croûte and red wine jus; and the intriguing, Indian-spiced grilled chicken tjiske, with new potatoes, spring onion and coriander. The wine list is a beauty: the Little List reels off more than 40 fine bottles; the Big List is oenophile heaven.
Babies and children welcome; nappy-changing facilities. Booking advisable lunch; essential dinner. Disabled: toilet. Vegetarian menu. **Map 6/8G.**

Leicester Square WC2

Seven

1 Leicester Square, WC2 (020 7909 1177). Leicester Square tube. **Lunch served** noon-2.45pm Mon-Fri. **Dinner served** 6-11.45pm Mon-Sat. **Main courses** £12-£24. **Set lunch** £14.50 two courses, £17.50 three courses. **Pre-theatre meal** (6-7pm) £17.50 three courses. **Credit** AmEx, JCB, MC, £TC, V.
We had high hopes for this newish venue above the nightclub Home. Certainly the setting is spectacular and the balcony tables are worth fighting for in summer. Service is both charming and efficient and the set lunch reasonable value. The pan-European menu combines ingredients and influences regardless of any geographical boundaries. There might be gazpacho andaluz, prosciutto with figs and basil, or parfait of foie gras to start, then smoked haddock with Welsh rarebit, beef with béarnaise sauce, or hake with chorizo and white beans to follow. Lunch got off to a joyous start with a perfect mushroom and asparagus risotto. But it was downhill thereafter. A salad of duck breast came with dull, limp leaves, spirals of cucumber and not enough plum dressing. Salmon with tagliatelle was similarly uninspiring, while a stuffed chicken breast with greasy and limp potato rösti was undercooked and inedible. Unwisely passing on the strawberries and cream for pudding, we tried some spring rolls stuffed with ginger, pine nuts and fresh figs. These came with almost tasteless blueberry ice-cream, which proved an uneasy combination. Perhaps our lunch was an aberration; other meals here (particularly in the evening) have garnered praise. Our advice? Choose carefully, and watch this space.
Babies and children welcome; high chairs. Disabled: toilet. Tables outdoors (11, balcony). Vegetarian menu. **Map 13/7K.**

Marylebone W1

Orrery ★

55 Marylebone High Street, W1 (020 7616 8000/www.orrery.co.uk). Baker Street or Regent's Park tube. **Lunch served** noon-3pm, **dinner served** 7-11pm daily. **Main courses** £14.50-£24. **Set lunch** £23.50 three courses. **Set Sunday dinner** £28.50 three courses incl glass of champagne. **Service** 12½%. **Credit** AmEx, DC, JCB, MC, £TC, V.
An Orrery is a mechanical model of the solar system. Sure enough we thought we had died and gone to the heavens on our last visit here. The decor is very much à la Conran, but the cooking is light years away from some of the mass-produced fodder in his other kitchens. For starters, carpaccio of tuna, 'fines herbs' and wasabi dressing was a gorgeous set of translucent ruby circles orbiting a lightly dressed salad, while cannelloni of native lobster, vine tomatoes, fines herbs and lobster essence was a creamy roll of lobster flakes blended with tarragon. For mains, baked sea bass cost a startling £24, but was superbly delicate and served with a rich, almost meaty sauce. Sea scallops and John Dory in a bouillabaisse sauce was light, fresh and divine. The glorious trolley of cheese was aromatically sky high, but we went straight to desserts for an immaculate raspberry soufflé and a creamy cylinder of mango ice-cream. The wine list is like an international socialite's filofax; some of the prices read like telephone numbers. We went from the sublime to the mellifluous when an American at the next table gave us a taste of her breathtaking £100 burgundy. A £204 bill for three, including two inexpensive bottles of wine, brought us down to earth with a bump, but then again, gastronomy and space travel ain't cheap.
Babies and children welcome; high chairs. Booking essential. Disabled: toilet. Tables outdoors (10, roof terrace, for bar menu). **Map 2/4G.**

Stephen Bull ★

5-7 Blandford Street, W1 (020 7486 9696). Baker Street or Bond Street tube. **Lunch served** 12.15-2.30pm Mon-Fri. **Dinner served** 6.30-10.30pm Mon-Sat. **Main courses** £7.95-£15. **Credit** AmEx, DC, MC, V.
Mr Bull, one of the founding fathers of Modern European cooking in London, has closed his branches in St John Street and St Martin's Lane, but this, the sole survivor, keeps the Bull flag flying proudly. We went with a long-serving food fanatic who commented that the meal took him back to a time in the London restaurant scene when quality counted more than media hype; he's right. The room is modern but comfortable, and if spartan touches like paper over the tablecloth help keep prices down, then paper's fine with us. We ate some amazing food here, especially haggis fritters with curry gravy, and duck tournedos with figs and a red onion tarte tatin (most chefs would proudly serve the tarte on its own). Leg of lamb with garlic, rosemary and flageolet beans was a large tranche of superior meat, sauced with a reduction so good we asked for a spoon in order to scoff every drop. Desserts are beautifully presented and balance luxury with manageability. Only a poorly timed starter (undercooked wild-mushroom ravioli) kept the meal from being perfect. The wine list, arranged by style, is mercifully short, unfailingly well chosen, and fairly priced. Friendly service, tip-top espresso and a lower-than-expected bill were the finishing touches to a wonderful meal. This place is treasure – and a serious bargain.
Babies and children admitted. **Map 2/5G.**

Mayfair W1

Greenhouse

27A Hay's Mews, W1 (020 7499 3331/3314). Green Park or Hyde Park Corner tube. **Lunch served** noon-2.30pm Mon-Fri; 12.30-3pm Sun. **Dinner served** 6.30-11pm Mon-Sat; 6.30-10pm Sun. **Main courses** £8 lunch, £12.50-£19 dinner. **Set lunch** £10.50 two courses, £14.50 three courses. **Set Sunday lunch** £22.50 three courses. **Cover** £1. **Credit** AmEx, DC, JCB, MC, £TC, V.
The Greenhouse has long been an example of substance over style. Sure, the service is formal, efficient and friendly; the dishes are artistically arranged on the plate; and the lingua franca of the staff is cutely accented franglais. But, set as it is in a rectangular room on the ground floor of an apartment block and decorated with dull gilt-framed still-lifes on cream walls, Greenhouse probably doesn't draw its clientele from admirers of interior design. Instead, courting couples and a regular stream of business diners (especially Japanese on our visits) come here for the fine food. Starters such as potato-topped seared scallops on peperonata, or cream of puy lentil and smoked bacon with sautéed foie gras, show that there's invention in the kitchen. The lobster ravioli with ginger was capped with a glorious shallot, fennel and carrot fricassee. Mains were equally imaginative: pan-fried sea bass on saag aloo, onion bhaji and tomato pickle; and pot au feu of black-leg chicken with root vegetables and bone marrow dumplings. Wholesome roast beef came on a bed of crisp noodles and pak choi with a miso and coriander broth. Although such delights come at a hefty price, in less than palatial surroundings, you're likely to potter off from the Greenhouse feeling well satisfied.
Babies and children welcome; high chairs. Booking advisable. Dress: smart casual. Vegetarian dish. **Map 2/7H.**

Langan's Brasserie

Stratton Street, W1 (020 7491 8822). Green Park tube. **Meals served** 12.15-11.45pm Mon-Fri. **Dinner served** 7pm-midnight Sat. **Main courses** £13.25-£14.95. **Cover** £1.50 **Service** 12½%. **Credit** AmEx, DC, JCB, MC, TC, V.
Restaurants like Langan's really have very little to prove, but they should try to maintain standards – Langan's is a shadow of its former self. Its fail-safe formula of posh bistro decor, slick service and competently rendered classic brasserie dishes has kept the punters pouring through the doors for decades. Our most recent meal here was something of a curate's egg. Caesar salad was generously proportioned and impeccably dressed. It was followed by faultless liver and bacon with spinach on the side. Carpaccio of beef, though, was submerged under an unnecessarily mountainous stack of rocket and Parmesan; and tagliatelle with prawns, squid and chilli was oily, flavourless and gave every impression of having been kept hot for too long on the plate in the kitchen. The short wine list is dated and unlikely to impress, and prices are pretty steep for basic bistro food, but you're paying for the Mayfair setting and the long-since vanished glamour of Langan's heyday.
Babies and children admitted. Booking advisable. Entertainment: band from 10pm nightly. **Map 2/7H.**
For branch see index.

Morton's

28 Berkeley Square, W1 (020 7493 7171/020 7499 0363). Bond Street or Green Park tube. **Lunch served** noon-2.30pm Mon-Fri. **Dinner served** 7-11.30pm Mon-Sat. **Main courses** £13-£19.50. **Set lunch** £19.50 two courses, £22.50 three courses. **Set dinner** £26.50 three courses. **Service** 15%. **Credit** AmEx, DC, MC, £TC, V.
They were having an unspecified nightmare in the kitchen at Morton's on the day of our lunchtime visit. Not that we had any hints from the decor or menu, both of which express the exclusivity and assurance suitable to a former gentlemen's club overlooking Berkeley Square. The broad square room is imperiously furnished, and balcony seats take pole position on sunny days. Prices are equally serious; a set two-course lunch offering only two starters and two mains costs £19.50. Of these, salad niçoise was a self-assembly kit, with the traditional elements artfully arranged on a broad platter, while lamb's liver with bacon and mash was on the verge of being rubbery and cold. À la carte there's a fatter selection beginning with the likes of smoked salmon, dandelion and sauce ravigote, and prosciutto with ripe black figs. Mains take a detour into Eurasian fusion, but breast of chicken, borlotti beans, porcini and gremolata was an unremarkable alliance. In contrast, raspberry and blueberry trifle was a gorgeously rich sponge with fluffy cream in a glass. As for that nightmare in the kitchen, it took our starters an hour to arrive, with the mains following half an hour after that. We were appeased by a glass of classy Chablis off an impressive and expensive wine list, but with pungent loos, a restaurant less than half full and service at 15%, you had to raise your eyebrows.
Babies and children admitted. Booking advisable; essential dinner. Dress: smart casual. Tables outdoors (4, balcony). **Map 2/7H.**

Nicole's

158 New Bond Street, W1 (020 7499 8408). Green Park tube. **Open** 10am-10.45pm Mon-Fri; 10am-6pm Sat.
Bar **Meals served** 11.30am-5.30pm Mon-Sat.
Restaurant **Breakfast served** 10-11.30am Mon-Sat. **Lunch served** noon-3.30pm Mon-Fri; noon-4pm Sat. **Tea served** 3-6pm Mon-Sat. **Dinner served** 6.30-10.45pm Mon-Fri. **Main courses** £16.25-£19.75. **Cover** £1 noon-4pm, 6.30-10.45pm Mon-Sat. **Minimum** £15.
Both **Service** 12½%. **Credit** AmEx, DC, JCB, MC, £TC, V.
Ladies who lunch favour this restaurant in the basement of Nicole Farhi's shop on New Bond Street. It's an elegant, creamy room, beautifully lit, with pink gerberas on each table. On a quiet weekday evening, service was friendly and accommodating; three waiters danced attendance on us, creating confusion in the kitchen. A starter of chorizo with spinach and soft boiled egg was stylish and beautifully executed. Goat's cheese and pear salad was also faultless. Baked sea bream and monkfish was a rich, meaty affair, full of flavour and texture, and greatly enhanced by the hot harissa sauce that accompanied it. The perfectly sized portion of sea bass with clams, mashed potato and spinach was less imaginative, but delicious in its simplicity and restraint. To finish, fruit salad was pretty to look at and very tasty; and rhubarb tart was creamy, sensationally chunky, and quickly demolished. The bill was steep, even for the area, but we enjoyed the elegance of the surroundings, and left feeling relaxed and pampered.
Babies and children welcome. Book lunch. Dress: smart casual. No-smoking tables. **Map 2/7H.**

Smiths of Smithfield

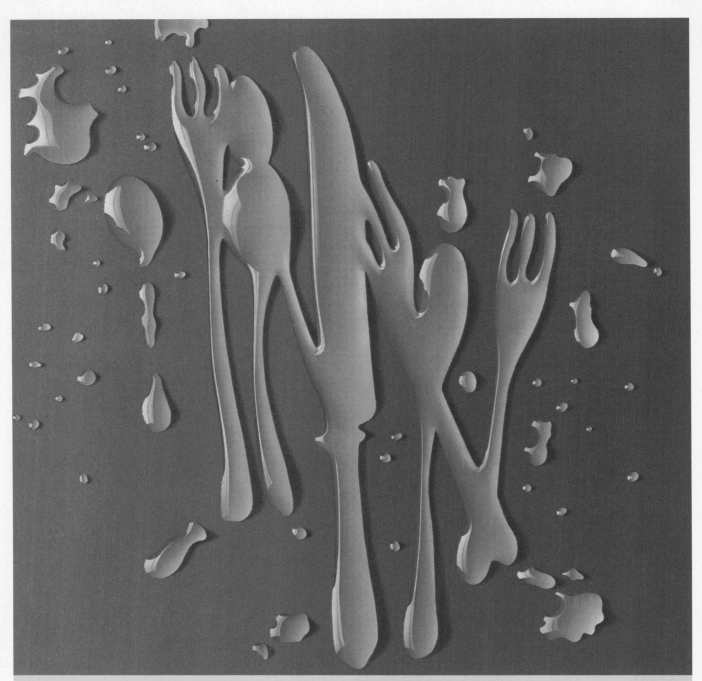

THOMAS & WORTH
executive search

THE CATERING SOLUTION

Progressive Recruitment Solutions for Restaurant Management,
Accounts and Finance Personnel, Senior Hotel Management and Chefs.

36/37 Maiden Lane, Covent Garden, London WC2E 7LJ

Tel: 020 7836 0200   Fax: 020 7836 1500

www.thomasworth.com

noble rot

3-5 Mill Street, W1 (020 7629 8877). Oxford Circus tube. **Lunch served** noon-3pm, **dinner served** 6-11pm Mon-Sat. **Main courses** £12.50-£25. **Service** 12½%. **Credit** AmEx, DC, JCB, V.

'Less is more' seems to be the design creed of this new Mayfair restaurant, part of Søren Jessen's small but growing London empire. An L-shaped space is kitted out with wooden venetian blinds, austere shades of green, the dimmest possible lighting, an obtrusive, eclectic soundtrack, starched white linen and low potted candles. In contrast, the dishes are elaborate culinary sculptures with sometimes bizarre flavour-pairings: smoked salmon collides with cassis and eucalyptus; foie gras does battle with chocolate. An entrée of crab meat salad came with a blob of lemon sorbet on top and a recommendation that we should 'try to get all the flavours in the same mouthful' – it just about worked. A main course of roast John Dory with borlotti beans, chorizo, piquillo pepper and houmous, on the other hand, tasted as if it had been drawn up by a well-meaning UN committee. Pan-braised sea bass with scallops was more delicate and more convincing. Service from the lean, urbane and uniformed waiters was prompt and charming, though the first bottle of white wine arrived warm after 20 minutes. There's a good dessert wine list, with around 40 bottles costing from £12.50 to £385. The desserts themselves, including a mellifluous apricot crème brûlée, provide a fitting accompaniment. There is undoubted talent in the kitchen, but noble rot could do with taking a couple of steps back from the precipice of pure style.

Babies and children admitted. Dress: smart casual. Tables outdoors (10, terrace). **Map 2/6H.**

Sotheby's Café

34-35 New Bond Street, W1 (020 7293 5077). Bond Street tube. **Open** 9.30am-5pm Mon-Fri. **Closed** last two weeks of August and two weeks at Christmas. **Breakfast served** 9.30-11.30am, **lunch served** noon-3pm, **tea served** 3-4.45pm Mon-Fri. **Main courses** £9-£15. **Set teas** £4.95, £9.50, £14.95 (with champagne). **Credit** AmEx, DC, MC, £TC, V.

It seems strange to find a café in the middle of Sotheby's – occupying a small, white-walled annexe and half a corridor on the way to the main auction house – but the enthusiastic, highly groomed staff and the impressive cooking quickly make you forget you're not in a purpose-built restaurant. After a while, the only reminder of the corporate setting is the PC screen across the corridor, showing a live feed from Sotheby's website – the heavy-lunching, heavily groomed clientele can be seen fingering their purses wistfully. The lunch menu proffers just three starters and mains, but it's not exactly standard café fare. A celeriac and rosemary soup was thick, hearty but a shade bland; while slices of seared pigeon breast on bitter leaves and muscat grapes was a great combination of sweet and sour. We had a slightly dull moment with the day's risotto (field mushrooms and thyme), but grilled lamb cutlets on a very piquant black olive tapenade, and chunky, succulent, haddock and chive fish cakes with salad and peas were both superb and flavour-packed. The wine list is just as snappy; all wines are by the glass and we were happy with a lovely unoaked Sicilian chardonnay, Le Vigne, for £15. Thank goodness we didn't try too hard to resist the lemon meringue pie made with brown sugar. As tea-time arrives (there's no dinner served) the lunchers' places are taken by Japanese tourists and a desirable-looking spread of cakes and sandwiches.

Babies and children welcome. Book lunch. Disabled: toilet. No smoking. **Map 2/6H.**

Piccadilly W1

Atlantic Bar & Grill

20 Glasshouse Street, W1 (020 7734 4888). Piccadilly Circus tube.
Bar **Open** noon-3am Mon-Sat; 6-10.30pm Sun.
Restaurant **Lunch served** noon-3pm Mon-Fri. **Dinner served** 6-11.30pm Mon-Sat; 7-11pm Sun. **Main courses** £12.50-£17. **Set lunch** £14.50 three courses. **Set dinner** (6-7pm Mon-Fri) £14.50 two courses, £16.50 three courses. **Service** 12½%. **Credit** AmEx, DC, MC, £TC, V.

Yes Sir I Can Boogie was warbling on the stereo when we walked into the Atlantic Bar & Grill, but there were few people to enjoy it on that Monday night. The room is stunning – like a luxury cruise ship – and even if the 'it-crowd' has moved on, there's a sense of occasion to the place. The food is accessible, unintimidating and has a bold, epic quality that suits the setting and the clientele perfectly. We enjoyed the starters of roasted Mediterranean vegetables, and artichoke hearts, although both were a little over-elaborate. Main courses of roast halibut and roast Gressingham duck were both well executed, if unexciting, and side dishes of summer vegetables and sticky mash were fine (although we resented paying extra for them). The pudding list was a catalogue of old favourites: raspberry ripple cheesecake; Atlantic chocolate box with dark Belgian chocolate. We opted for the simple, but sensational fruit platter: a gorgeous array of ripe tropical fruit with three dipping sauces (raspberry, mango and crème fraîche). We drank a lovely, ripe Argentinian malbec from a long, seductive wine list. Although the bill, at over £100 for two, was accurately labelled 'The Damage' and the service was rather amateurish, we enjoyed ourselves here. The Atlantic has matured gracefully.

Babies and children admitted (in restaurant until 10pm). Booking essential. Separate room for parties, seats 70. Vegetarian dishes. **Map 13/7J.**

Red Room

Basement, Waterstone's, 203 Piccadilly, W1 (020 7851 2464). Piccadilly Circus tube. **Meals served** noon-8.30pm Mon-Sat. **Main courses** £8.95-£11.50. **Set meals** £15.50 two courses, £18.50 three courses. **Service** 12½%. **Credit** AmEx, MC, V.

The Red Room's owners will have to be more proactive if they're going to save this large, smart restaurant from seeming like a sleepy afterthought at the rear of Waterstone's stylish Simpsons building. Its menu contains a batch of simple dishes for those wishing to refuel quickly after browsing in the shop, including leek and potato soup, Caesar salad, mushroom risotto, and sausage and mash. There are also afternoon snacks such as Welsh rarebit or a club sandwich and crisps, which can be served at the bar. We, however, got stuck into the set menu. Among four starters, the artichoke, green bean and shallot salad was fresh but ordinary, while the rough-cut pork terrine was pleasantly creamy and mild. Rump of lamb (our choice from four main courses) was tender and juicy, though its bed of couscous was a touch sticky. By contrast, breast of chicken Kiev was a sophisticated pub lunch, served with chips that were awesome in size and flavour. For dessert, summer fruit fool was simply summer fruits with double cream. The wine list seemed no more inspired, despite an enticing range by the glass and half bottle. Perhaps because business was slow, service was slow. However, a two-and-a-quarter-hour lunch is not well suited to contemporary office culture.

Babies and children welcome; high chairs. Disabled: toilet. No-smoking tables. Separate rooms for parties, seating 14, 20, 60 and 150. **Map 13/7J.**

St James's SW1

The Avenue

7-9 St James's Street, SW1 (020 7321 2111). Green Park tube.
Bar **Open** noon-11pm Mon-Sat; noon-10pm Sun.
Restaurant **Brunch served** noon-3.30pm Sun. **Lunch served** noon-3pm Mon-Sat. **Dinner served** 5.45pm-midnight Mon-Thur; 5.45pm-12.30am Fri, Sat; 6.30-10pm Sun. **Main courses** £12.75-£17.25. **Set lunch** £17.50 two courses, £19.50 three courses. **Set dinner** (5.45-7.30pm, 10.15pm-midnight) £14.50 two courses, £16.50 three courses. **Service** 12½%. **Credit** AmEx, DC, MC, £TC, V.

Invariably packed and buzzing, this smoothly run St James's eaterie has settled down into a well-oiled groove. Punters are a mix of business diners, opulent tourists and family groups, rather than the young fashion types who used to pack the place. The restaurant has the air of a prestigious art gallery on opening night. Service remains impeccable, the lighting low and the decoration minimal and modern. A seasonally changing menu offers decent choice in the Modern Euro mould, backed up by a Francophile wine list. Perhaps it would be nit-picking to say that the food doesn't always taste as good as it looks, but something was lacking. A starter of seared scallops with squash and bacon was a merely so-so combination, while a tiny plateful of cheese 'beignets' with asparagus salad was weird but moreish. Main courses scored more of a success. Tender slices of veal loin were arranged on a plateful of french bean, anchovy and caperberry salad, while a moist risotto cake from the daily specials list was rich with wild mushrooms, chive butter and a poached egg. For pudding, the @venue chocolate feast tasted strangely un-chocolatey, though it looked worthy of a page from a glossy food magazine. Despite the occasional lack of joie de vivre in the food, the Avenue remains a sleek spot.

Babies and children welcome. Booking advisable. Disabled: toilet. Entertainment: pianist from 8pm Mon-Sat; brunch Sun. **Map 13/8J.**

Le Caprice

Arlington House, Arlington Street, SW1 (020 7629 2239). Green Park tube. **Lunch served** noon-3pm Mon-Sat; noon-4pm Sun. **Dinner served** 5.30pm-midnight Mon-Sat; 6pm-midnight Sun. **Main courses** £9.75-£21.75. **Cover** £1.50. **Credit** AmEx, DC, MC, £$TC, V.

Unlike at its sister restaurant the Ivy, ordinary mortals can still secure a table at Le Caprice (though you'll probably need to book a couple of months ahead for dinner). Do it. This is a classic London dining experience. The interior still sports its matt black, 1980s-and-proud-of-it interior, but there's a huge buzz to the place and a remarkably relaxed atmosphere thanks to the zippy yet chilled service. Like the Ivy, the menu is packed with timeless, not overly fancy stomach-pleasers, with more than a few nods to 1970s bistro cuisine. Baby peppers with halloumi and tabouleh provided a clean, fresh opening, while a seriously pricey but seriously divine lobster and tarragon risotto with samphire was generous with the meat. To follow, there was more crustacean to enjoy in a fine baby lobster salad, and plenty of earthy bite in a more humble plate of grilled lambs' kidneys with mustard mash (a bit heavy on the Dijon) and broad beans. The signature dessert of Scandinavian iced berries with white chocolate sauce never fails to please, yet we were a touch disappointed that the meringue of the baked Alaska wasn't hot, despite flaming impressively at the table. Wines are a joy, and fairly priced: a rich, chocolatey Ormah shiraz 1998 caused purrs of contentment. There's changes afoot at the top (*see p132* **The Ivy**) but let's hope the rest of the operation rolls smoothly on.

Babies and children admitted. Booking essential several weeks in advance. Entertainment: pianist 8pm-midnight nightly. **Map 13/8J.**

Quaglino's

16 Bury Street, SW1 (020 7930 6767). Green Park tube.
Bar **Open** 11.30am-1am Mon-Thur; 11.30am-2am Fri, Sat; noon-11pm Sun.
Restaurant **Lunch served** noon-3pm daily. **Dinner served** 5.30pm-midnight Mon-Thur; 5.30pm-1am Fri, Sat; 5.30-11pm Sun. **Main courses** £12-£24. **Set meal** (noon-3pm, 5.30-6.30pm) £12.50 two courses, £15 three courses.
Both **Credit** AmEx, DC, JCB, MC, £TC, V.

Regulars here attest to their ability to recite the 'canteen' menu from memory, such is the predictable nature of the place. Quaglino's offers a multi-coloured, postmodern take on the 1930s ocean-liner, a straightforward dining-by-numbers experience; but it's probably no worse than any other restaurant of its size. Our three starters of thick gazpacho, sautéed squid, and rocket and Parmesan salad were perfectly agreeable. However, shoulder of pork with crackling and apple sauce would have been good, but for its strong gravy, while overpriced scallops came with a stingy portion of salade niçoise. Only char-grilled swordfish with aubergine compôte stood out. To finish, crème brûlée had the consistency of extra-thick clotted cream, while raspberry pavlova was a Freudian dome of crunchy meringue benippled by an unappetising dollop of crème fraîche and a few raspberries. The wine list, meanwhile, told a revealing story: too few bottles under £20, then sky-rocketing to £240. These prices are way out of step with the unexceptional food and impersonal service. Quaglino's is best left to Bond Street shoppers and expense-account diners – the rest of us can do better elsewhere.

Babies and children welcome; children's menu; high chairs. Disabled: toilet. Entertainment: singer/pianist 9pm-1am Mon-Thur, Sun; jazz trio 10pm-2am Fri, Sat. Separate room for parties, seats 44. **Map 13/7J.**

Soho W1

Alastair Little

49 Frith Street, W1 (020 7734 5183). Tottenham Court Road tube. **Lunch served** noon-3pm Mon-Fri. **Dinner served** 6-11pm Mon-Sat. **Set lunch** £25 two courses incl coffee. **Set dinner** £33 three courses. **Credit** AmEx, JCB, MC, £TC, V.

Attractive modern art is pretty much the only decoration in this small Soho institution. The set-price menu and global wine list are similarly pared down. Helped by sensitive service, there's a pleasant, low-key atmosphere (that vanished near the end of our evening visit when a slightly incongruous office party appeared). Great bread raised expectations of the Italian-biased menu, which starters pretty much fulfilled: pizzetta with potato, mozzarella and truffled leaves was almost too much of a good thing (we had to leave some); a dressed baby artichoke was a finely judged blend of acid and sweet. Mains – slightly tough spinach and ricotta ravioli, and a so-so John Dory – were less pleasing. Puddings continued the slide: Venetian rice pudding (with pine nuts and raisins) was a worthy affair, while panna cotta with raspberry coulis was a run-of-the-mill example. We're very fond of this restaurant, but at these prices, it has to put in a more impressive performance. *See p139* for the W11 branch.

Babies and children welcome. Booking essential. Separate room for parties, seats 25. **Map 13/6K.**

Andrew Edmunds

46 Lexington Street, W1 (020 7437 5708). Oxford Circus or Piccadilly Circus tube. **Lunch served** 12.30-3pm Mon-Fri; 1-3pm Sat, Sun. **Dinner served** 6-10.45pm Mon-Sat; 6-10.30pm Sun. **Main courses** £7.50-£12.50. **Service** 12½% for bills over £50. **Credit** AmEx, MC, V.

This tiny place poses a mystery. The food is nothing special, the decor is stuck in a 1980s wine-bar timewarp, and the surroundings are dark and cramped, apart from at the coveted window tables. Yet you can't get a table for dinner without booking several days in advance. What's the explanation? First an office-crowded location near Oxford Circus. Second, user-friendly prices and atmosphere. And third, a wine list that's simply amazing, with fine, boldly chosen bottles sometimes selling at little more than retail prices. The menu changes daily, with specials on the blackboard, but from the evidence of our lunchtime visit, the wines outshine the food as completely as the sun outshines a 40-watt lightbulb. A starter of toasted focaccia with Dolcelatte, roast tomatoes and black olive paste was woeful, served at room temperature so the skimpy topping of melted cheese had hardened into a lifeless crust. A main course of gnocchi with bacon and sausage was pork-overkill in a humdrum tomato sauce. Chilled tomato, lemon and basil soup had good flavour but could have done with a finer sieve to remove the crunchy seeds. Courgette and rocket pesto cake with tomato salsa and mixed leaves was a large portion of a misconceived idea. We might go back, but only if we could get a window table and order the simplest possible food to show off the vino. Countless others, it should be stressed, don't share our lack of enthusiasm.

Babies and children admitted. Booking essential (no more than one week in advance). Tables outdoors (2, pavement). **Map 13/6J.**

Circus

1 Upper James Street, W1 (020 7534 4000). Piccadilly Circus tube.
Bar **Open** noon-1.30am Mon-Wed; noon-3am Thur, Fri; 6pm-3am Sat. **Set meal** £10.50 two courses, £12.50 three courses.
Restaurant **Lunch served** noon-3pm, **dinner served** 5.45pm-midnight Mon-Fri. **Main courses** £11.50-£17.50. **Set lunch** £17.50 two courses, £19.50 three courses. **Set meal** (lunch; 6-7.15pm, 10.45pm-midnight) £10.50 two courses, £12.50 three courses. **Credit** AmEx, DC, MC, £TC, V.

Circus is more than three years old but still looks utterly contemporary, with its expanses of white space, clean lines and sheets of reflective glass. The basement bar claims to be open to all, but we've been turned away in the past with the excuse that it's a private members' bar. On this occasion we found it lightly peppered with besuited blokes on the pull, so were relieved to take refuge in the ground-floor restaurant. The set menu has always been great value; the more elaborate carte offers Modern European dishes that have become standards. Some dishes were delectable, such as a starter of pan-fried risotto with smoked haddock and soft-poached egg; others were less successful, such as the only vegetarian main course of potato rösti with fried chunks of globe artichoke and mushrooms. Best were the starter of pan-fried chicken livers with braised shallots; and a lip-smacking parkin (ginger-flavoured) pudding with butterscotch sauce. Circus plays safe, and therefore mostly gets it right. Service was pleasant and helpful, if not always attentive. The wine list is interesting, but expensive, with very little choice below £20.

Babies and children admitted. Booking advisable; essential lunch. Dress: smart casual. Entertainment: DJ (bar) 10pm-3am Thur-Sat. Separate room for parties, seats 16. **Map 13/6J.**

French House Dining Room

First floor, The French House, 49 Dean Street, W1 (020 7437 2477). Leicester Square, Piccadilly Circus or Tottenham Court Road tube. **Lunch served** noon-3pm, **dinner served** 6-11.15pm Mon-Sat. **Main courses** £9.50-£12. **Service** 12½% for parties of five or more. **Credit** AmEx, DC, MC, £TC, V.

The small, first-floor room has become a bit of a Soho fixture. Tables are close together, and although a huge mirror on the end wall and large windows give plenty of light during the day, the effect is essentially snug. This and the food (guinea fowl and lentils; lambs' sweetbreads with carrots and turnips) make this a top winter venue. Highlights from a recent lunch included a splendid garlic, spinach and potato soup, and excellent bread. Also good were a superior roast chicken with watercress and dauphinoise potatoes that was slightly too salty but very moreish; and a plate of spring vegetables with green sauce (a mint sauce) – a beautiful heap of assorted colours (baby carrots, beetroots, broad beans, peas) marred by some slightly bitter (baby) turnips. The French House is the companion restaurant to St John (*see p33* **British**), a link that's easy to spot on the daily-changing menu (pickled pigeon and cucumber, or kipper pâté, for example) and has the same charming but unobtrusive service and easy companionability. A bit of a gem, especially when measured against big, brash mega-restaurants.
Babies and children admitted. Booking advisable. **Map 13/6K.**

The Lexington

45 Lexington Street, W1 (020 7434 3401). Oxford Circus or Piccadilly Circus tube. **Lunch served** noon-3pm Mon-Fri. **Dinner served** 6.30-11pm Mon-Sat. **Main courses** £9.75-£12.95. **Service** 12½%. **Credit** AmEx, DC, JCB, MC, V.

Not exactly a gastronomic wonderland, the Lexington is a lively stomach-liner for twentysomethings on the razzle. Plain wooden tables line the edges of a long dark room; they are pushed together for parties or pulled apart for couples. On the night of our visit, inter-table banter came with polite, informal service. Starters – cautiously ambitious dishes – hover around £5. Asparagus with a soft-boiled egg was exactly that. The most alluring choice, lobster and scallop mousseline, was turgid but edible. Greek and couscous salads can be starters or light main courses. Otherwise, mains cover a popular range, from Tuscan risotto to sirloin steak, with fish cakes and snapper in between. 'Noble' guinea fowl breast wrapped in zucchini with saffron mash was fine, but fell short of its aristocratic title, while artichoke and mushroom filo parcel with lemon, tomato and basil pesto was in essence a gigantic, garlicky spring roll. Classic desserts are youthed-up with jazzy spins: lemon and lime crème brûlée, for instance, or banana tiramisu. The short wine list sums up the place – aimed at consumers not connoisseurs.
Book lunch. Entertainment: saxophonist 8-11pm Mon, Sat. No-smoking tables. **Map 13/6J.**

Mezzo

100 Wardour Street, W1 (020 7314 4000). Leicester Square, Piccadilly Circus or Tottenham Court Road tube.
Bar **Open** noon-1am Mon-Thur; noon-3am Fri, Sat; noon-11pm Sun.
Restaurant **Lunch served** noon-3pm Mon-Fri; 12.30-3pm Sun. **Dinner served** 6-11.30pm Mon-Thur; 6pm-12.30am Fri, Sat; 6-10.30pm Sun. **Main courses** £11.50-£16.50. **Set lunch** £12.50 two courses, £15.50 three courses. **Pre-theatre meal** (6-7pm) £15.50 three courses. **Music charge** £5 after 10pm Wed-Sat.
Both **Service** 12½%. **Credit** AmEx, DC, JCB, MC, V.

People often turn their noses up at Conran's huge Soho eating emporium, but even if it is a noisy impersonal space, its fixed menus offer respectable value. Starters are Tuscan bean soup, or pancetta, or duck and pork terrine; for mains there's pasta, or shoulder of pork, or gently spiced roast salmon, pak choi and lentils; for desserts, there's chocolate mousse, oeufs à la neige, or ice-cream and sorbet. Going à la carte accelerates the cash register, but starters are mostly at the bottom end of the £5.50 to £12 range. The speciality is seafood, with three types of caviar, four types of oyster and five species of crustacea. So relatively speaking, a dozen fleshy Loch Fyne rock oysters at £15.50 between two didn't seem excessively extravagant. Main courses show some enterprise and encompass a classic range, from braised rabbit leg with cumin-spiced aubergine, to a good swordfish steak with caponata and basil. Decent wines and top coffee are further attractions. We had no complaints about food or service, but the subterranean, artificial ambience may be off-putting to some, and music nights are a cue for a good old-fashioned dinner and dance – be warned.
Babies and children welcome; high chairs. Booking advisable. Entertainment: see p209 Eating & Entertainment. Separate room for parties, seats 44. **Map 13/6K.**

The Sugar Club ★

21 Warwick Street, W1 (020 7437 7776). Oxford Circus or Piccadilly Circus tube. **Lunch served** noon-3pm Mon-Sat; 12.30-3pm Sun. **Dinner served** 6-10.30pm daily. **Main courses** £13.80-£19.90. **Service** 12½%. **House wine** £10.50 bottle, £3.50 glass. **Mineral water** £3 bottle, £1.80 glass. **Credit** AmEx, DC, JCB, MC, TC, V.

Fusion cooking is a dangerous game. When it works it can be dazzling; when it doesn't it's meaningless gimmickry. Luckily the Sugar Club is one of the most successful practitioners of this eclectic approach. The menu dances between Europe and Asia, bringing together ingredients and cooking methods from radically different culinary traditions. Barely flash-grilled scallops with sweet chilli sauce and crème fraîche were sumptuously tender and brought an irresistible 'mmm' to our lips. An impeccably sourced Spanish antipasti platter offered a playful juxtaposition of titbits: creamy Garrotxa cheese, Leon chorizo, serrano ham, piquillo peppers, guindilla chillies, caperberries, delicate Lucque olives and Marcona almonds. Roast Trelough duck breast on vanilla flageolet beans with grilled baby leeks and piquillo pepper dressing was magnificent: the subtle, teasing thread of vanilla flavour quite inspirational. Sweet potato gyoza was also a successful ensemble, with contrasts of texture, colour and flavour. Finally, a pineapple millefeuille wowed us with its Sichuan-pepper fragrance and luscious scatterings of passion fruit curd. The pale walls, minimal furniture and atmosphere of studious cool at the Sugar Club don't match up to the playful inventiveness of the food, but staff are relaxed and friendly, and didn't try to rush us through the meal despite the imminence of the second sitting. Very impressive.
Babies and children admitted. Booking advisable. No-smoking tables. Separate room for parties (lunchtime only), seats 40. Vegetarian dishes. **Map 13/7J.**

Sugar Reef

41-44 Great Windmill Street, W1 (020 7851 0800). Piccadilly Circus tube.
Bar **Open** noon-1am Mon-Fri; 6pm-1am Sat.
Restaurant **Lunch served** noon-3pm, **dinner served** 6-11.30pm daily. **Main courses** £10.50-£23.95. **Set meal** (lunch, 6-7pm Sat) £14.95 two courses, £17.95 three courses. **Service** 12½%. **Credit** AmEx, DC, JCB, MC, V.

Sugar Reef had a problematic opening in late 1999 – the original chef, Kenny Miller, was replaced in the first week by Garry Hollihead. Things have settled down since and punters have piled in to eat amid the kitsch cocktail bar surroundings. The waterfall feature gave off an occasional whiff of chlorine that didn't encourage our appetites. Staff take your credit card number when you book a table; you're charged £15 per person for not turning up. For starters, three sea scallops came perfectly cooked, but with two less-than-inspiring dips. King crab with garlic hollandaise had large hunks of (shelled) crab in a lovely rich sauce. For mains, an upmarket surf'n'turf had a great herby, buttery drizzle over the lobster and a fine fillet of steak cooked to perfection. But the roast sea bass and crab risotto proved far too creamy and sickly to finish. A shared, sublime chocolate truffle with marshmallow and peanut butter ice-cream made an appropriately decadent finish. The bill topped £100: too much for fine, but certainly not fantastic food. After the meal we retired to the basement bar, joined by many of the besuited workers who had been dining upstairs. A final question: do restaurants such as this really need attendants in their toilets?
Babies and children admitted; high chairs. Disabled: toilet. Dress: smart casual. **Map 13/7K.**

Teatro

93-107 Shaftesbury Avenue, W1 (020 7494 3040). Piccadilly Circus tube. **Lunch served** noon-3pm Mon-Fri. **Dinner served** 6-11.45pm Mon-Sat. **Main courses** £8.50-£18.95. **Set lunch** £15.50 two courses, £18 three courses. **Pre-theatre meal** (6-7.30pm) £15 two courses, £18 three courses. **Cover** £1.50. **Service** 12½%. **Credit** AmEx, MC, £TC, V.

Though it's known as much for its celeb owners – actress Leslie Ash and footballer Lee Chapman – and punters as its food, Teatro is remarkably low key. The United Designers interior is muted and masculine, with an olive and red colour scheme and Rothko-esque prints; the atmosphere's pretty subdued, too. Stuart Gillies' food is still a draw, though on our visit the food wasn't blow-you-away brilliant. Except, that is, for a dish of small eastern starters (tiger prawns, sushi rolls, beef with teriyaki sauce, a mozzarella and tomato parcel and saké sorbet): a wonderful explosion of flavours, and big enough to share. In contrast, salmon fish cakes were nothing special. Potato gnocchi with artichokes was a nice-enough dish, with a light, creamy tomato sauce, but roast loin of suckling pig with wilted Asian greens was a pretty ordinary piece of pork in soy sauce. We regretted not choosing the whole roast Canadian lobster with garlic butter and chips. Portions are large, so we didn't have room for a delicious-looking chocolate fondant with black cherry ice-cream. The wine list is extensive, but pricey. Teatro takes your credit card details when you book and charges £20 per head for a no-show. We didn't mind the lack of star-spotting, but at these prices you expect a little more dazzle from the food. Maybe the fixed-price menus are a better bet.
Babies and children welcome; high chairs. Book dinner. Disabled: lift, toilet. **Map 13/6K.**

Titanic

81 Brewer Street, W1 (020 7437 1912). Piccadilly Circus tube. **Dinner served** 5.30-11pm Tue-Sat. **Main courses** £8.50-£24.95. **Service** 12½%. **Credit** AmEx, DC, MC, TC, V.

If you don't mind dining in a disco (complete with nine massive revolving glitterballs), then Marco Pierre White's huge restaurant and bar, modelled very approximately on the White Star Line's infamous liner, still looks impressive. The menu makes good reading, containing the sort of global bistro food that the Ivy does so well. But this isn't the Ivy, and the execution here veered from the competent to the clueless. Tuna sashimi was good, but onion frittata seemed no more than an onion omelette. It came on two slices of rock-hard toast, which were inexplicably affixed to the plate by a glob of mashed potato, and surrounded with a smear of unpleasantly pungent sauce piperade. Mains were similarly odd. Chicken with ketchup and herb vinaigrette came in two pieces: one was fine, the other looked like a piece of mangled road-kill. The chips and mushy peas in the fish and chips were decent, but the fish was desperately flaccid. This mixed tone continued with desserts. The cheeses on the cheese plate were of a high quality, though too cold; while the pecan pie was a poor, dry specimen, but was topped by superb peanut butter ice-cream. When you add in the uninterested service, the many empty tables and the cacophonous yet buzz-free atmosphere, you get the overwhelming feeling this bloated leviathan is rudderless and drifting. What's that big white thing just ahead?
Babies and children admitted. Booking essential. Entertainment: DJs dinner Thur-Sat. **Map 13/7J.**

Trafalgar Square WC2

The Portrait Restaurant

National Portrait Gallery, St Martin's Place, WC2 (020 7312 2490). Leicester Square tube. **Open** 10am-6pm Mon-Wed; 10am-10pm Thur, Fri; 10am-6pm Sat, Sun. **Lunch served** 11.45am-2pm, **dinner served** 5.30-8.30pm daily. **Main courses** £6.50-£10.75 (lounge menu); £10.75-£14 (restaurant menu). **Service** 10%. **Credit** AmEx, JCB, MC, V.

Searcy's has come a long way since its days as a banqueting caterer in the City's guild halls. This stylish new venue on the top floor of the National Portrait Gallery is one of several high-profile restaurants around town (including **The Red Room** in Waterstone's, Piccadilly, *see p135*) to benefit from the firm's involvement. The trouble is that profit margins are hampered by the closing hours of the establishments Searcy's serves, so lunch can seem pricey. Several visits here confirm that, while the view of Nelson on his column and the rooftops surrounding Trafalgar Square make a delightful panorama, the bare tables and variable cooking standards can leave even the most enthusiastic art lovers dissatisfied. Honey-cured salmon was no more or less than two slices of fatty fish; the attendant lavender dressing tasted less of the flower than of citrus. Still, ham knuckle with green beans and shallots was an excellent take on an old-fashioned cut, if an expensive starter at £6.95. Mrs Kirkham's Lancashire cheese tartlet with ceps, tarragon, leeks and rocket melted into

Zander. *See page 138.*

the mouth (buttery pastry included) and was topped by a poached egg – an addendum also appreciated in oven-baked smoked haddock with macaroni cheese. A side dish of french beans and shallots was way above average, yet a dessert of brown sugar meringue with roast banana ice-cream was dry and hard to chew. There's much here worth trying and commending, but the café atmosphere sits ill with the high prices.
Babies and children admitted. Booking essential. Disabled: toilet. No smoking (restaurant). **Map 13/7K**.

Victoria SW1

Ebury Wine Bar & Restaurant

139 Ebury Street, SW1 (020 7730 5447). Sloane Square tube/Victoria tube/rail. **Open** 11am-11pm Mon-Sat; noon-3pm, 6-10.30pm Sun. **Lunch served** noon-3pm daily. **Dinner served** 5.30-10.30pm Mon-Sat; 6-10pm Sun. **Main courses** £9.75-£16. **Service** 12½%. **Credit** AmEx, DC, MC, £TC, V.

This neck of Victoria, on the wrong side of Sloane Square, has ideas above its station (Victoria Coach Station in this instance). Ebury Wine Bar reflects the area's aspirations: a corner pub turned Mod Euro eaterie with jocular trompe l'oeil frescoes that feel a mite claustrophobic in such a confined space. But the Ebury has two things going for it. First, the wine list: a small but carefully chosen range of bottles from three continents, at prices ranging from £11.50 to £25, plus around 12 by-the-glass options. And second, the cooking of Australian chef Josh Hampton, which is excellent when it eschews over-fussy combinations of flavours. A starter of fried goat's cheese in hazelnuts with tapenade got the balance just right. A second course of baked cod, Mediterranean garnishes and aïoli was less convincing, partly because the promised aïoli was little more than a thin salad dressing. Far more persuasive was the char-grilled tuna with pak choi and soy – although the strength of the dish was in the excellent cooking of the main turn, rather than the merely adequate supporting cast. Desserts play to the gallery. A Mars Bar spring roll was a startling sight on the menu, let alone on the plate, but due to the selfless sacrifice of a ten year-old, we can reveal it to be 'yummy'.
Babies and children admitted. Booking essential. **Map 6/10H**.

Zander

45 Buckingham Gate, SW1 (020 7378 3838). St James's Park tube/Victoria tube/rail.
Bar **Open** noon-11pm Mon-Sat; noon-10.30pm Sun.
Restaurant **Lunch served** noon-2.45pm daily. **Dinner served** 5.30-11pm Mon-Sat; 5.30-9.30pm Sun. **Set meals** £12.50 two courses, £15.50 three courses (lunch, 5.30-7pm, 10-11pm). **Main courses** £10-£32. **Service** 12½%. **Credit** AmEx, DC, JCB, MC, V.

From the people behind **Bank** (*see p132*), comes another monolith, this time featuring one of the longest bars in town. Fantastically and unbearably loud in the evenings, this curvaceous creation is not recommended to those looking for a quiet night out. The restaurant behind, however, is a haven of peace by comparison, with an equally impressive setting. Architect Julyan Wickham has created a striking circular glass conservatory that provides an unexpected but entertaining view over the internal courtyard of a block of Victorian mansion flats. The menu is long and brasserie-like. Choices range from the familiar (Caesar salad; sausage, mash and onion gravy; grilled calf's liver; sole meunière) to more contemporary combos (beetroot tarte tatin; swordfish with salsa verde and pak choi; duck breast with spring greens, lime and ginger). It's all fairly expertly done with only the occasional slip; Greek salad with over-battered squid was disappointing. But we can recommend the foie gras and ham terrine, the seared tuna with peppers, the scallops with black bean salsa and crisped seaweed, and the white chocolate cheesecake without hesitation. There's also a page-long well-thought-out wine list. If you can stand the racket in the bar, Zander could prove a welcome newcomer in an otherwise surprisingly ill-served area.
Babies and children welcome; high chairs. Disabled: toilet. No-smoking tables. **Map 6/9J**.

West

Chiswick W4

The Chiswick

131 Chiswick High Road, W4 (020 8994 6887). Turnham Green tube. **Lunch served** 12.30-2.45pm Mon-Fri; noon-3pm Sun. **Dinner served** 7-11pm Mon-Sat. **Main courses** £8.50-£15. **Set meal** (12.30-2.45pm, 7-8pm) £9.50 two courses, £12.95 three courses, incl coffee. **Credit** AmEx, MC, £TC, V.

This busy neighbourhood restaurant is obviously popular with locals, though it's hard to see why. The low ceilings and dark turquoise walls make for an oppressive and noisy dining experience, and the food is not worth the high prices. Portions are generous, yet in some contexts size really doesn't matter. For starters, we had an indifferent gazpacho, and warm baby artichokes stuffed with goat's cheese, which were pleasant but on the tough side. Things improved somewhat with main courses. Herb-crusted monkfish with curry sauce was a surprisingly delicate and successful combination, while couscous and tagine were fine accompaniments to tender chunks of lamb, although the addition of tsatsiki was a bit unnecessary. Pappardelle with peas, broad beans and mint was overpoweringly minty and, frankly, inedible. So thank heavens for the chips: perfect fat chunks with a lovely garlicky aïoli. Even the desserts disappointed. Hot chocolate pudding was dried out and powdery, and came with a mouth-puckeringly acidic lemon ice-cream. There's a decent and lengthy wine list. Staff do their job but seem disinterested in both customers and the food – given our overall experience of the place, it's not hard to see why.
Babies and children welcome. Book dinner. Tables outdoors (4, pavement).

Ealing W5

Gilbey's

77 The Grove, W5 (020 8840 7568). Ealing Broadway tube/rail. **Lunch served** 12.30-3pm Wed-Sun. **Dinner served** 7-10pm Tue-Sat. **Main courses** £9.95-£15.95. **Set meal** (lunch daily; dinner Mon-Thur, Sun) £10.50 two courses. **Service** 10%. **Credit** AmEx, DC, MC, £TC, V.

A bright little neighbourhood restaurant on a quiet, tree-lined street in Ealing, Gilbey's serves classy food in an unpretentious, easy-going atmosphere. Presentation is spot-on and the service is young, charming and unfailingly professional. The pleasing main room is a bright conservatory with yellow walls and pale wooden floors. In summer you can eat in the small garden at the back, surrounded by walls dripping with ivy. Everything we ate was delicious, subtle and beautifully presented. We couldn't fault buffalo mozzarella and Parma ham, or the lemony fish terrine. Thyme and pumpkin risotto was creamy and irresistible. Only the veal escalope failed to excite. For dessert, lemon tart and brioche bread and butter pudding were both superlative. We were also bowled over by the ambitious, admirably priced, all-French wine list which featured 100 or so wines, many at under £10 a bottle. We left in high spirits – Gilbey's is a real local treat.
Babies and children welcome; half-price children's portions; high chairs. Booking adviasable dinner; essential weekends. No cigar or pipe smoking; no smoking (conservatory). Separate room for parties, seats 28. Tables outdoors (4, garden; 3, pavement).

Parade

18-19 The Mall, W5 (020 8810 0202). Ealing Broadway tube/rail. **Lunch served** noon-2.30pm Mon-Fri; 12.30pm-3pm Sat, Sun. **Dinner served** 7-10.30pm Mon-Wed; 7-11pm Thur-Sat. **Main courses** £16.50-£19.50. **Set lunch** £12 two courses, £15 three courses. **Set dinner** £23.50 three courses. **Credit** AmEx, JCB, MC, £TC, V.

Don't be put off by the cheap frontage or clinical-looking eating area as, despite these design errors, Parade offers a pleasurable dining experience. The menu lacks surprises but delivers cooking that is substantial and full of flavour, if not revelatory. We started with (slightly overcooked) gnocchi smothered in an appetising trio of red peppers, olives and goat's cheese, and a more adventurous ballottine of duck rillettes and foie gras. The smooth, light pâté and rich own-made chutney provided a delightful contrast to the texture of the duck. Corn-fed chicken with Parma ham was more than satisfactory: cooked until tender and set off by a delicious bed of beans, spinach and juicy wild mushrooms. A lighter option, sea trout, was perfectly prepared and beautifully presented, swimming in a delicate mustard seed and chive sauce. Finally we enjoyed a smooth, creamy iced white chocolate and praline parfait, but passion fruit crème brûlée was too sweet to finish. Parade offers casual surroundings in which to relax; service is attentive, but not intrusive; it's easy to settle in here for a whole evening. A welcome addition to the area.
Babies and children welcome; high chairs. Booking advisable; essential weekends. Disabled: toilet. Separate room for parties, seats 10-45. Vegetarian menu.

Holland Park W8

The Belvedere

Off Abbotsbury Road, Holland Park, W8 (020 7602 1238). Holland Park tube. **Lunch served** noon-2.30pm Mon-Sat; noon-3.30pm Sun. **Dinner served** 6-11pm Mon-Sat; 7-10.30pm Sun. **Main courses** £12.50-£22.50. **Set lunch** £14.95 two courses, £17.95 three courses. **Set Sunday lunch** £19.50 two courses. **Service** 12½%. **Credit** AmEx, DC, JCB, MC, V.

What with the haughty cries of the peacocks, the strains of opera from the open-air theatre and the captive market of well-to-do residents, Holland Park always deserved a good restaurant. Since the summer of 2000 it has had one – though not a place many people could afford to visit often. Despite his protestations to the contrary, the new improved Belvedere has Marco Pierre White's stamp all over it, from the suede seating and monumental vases of flowers to the smooth, French-style service and complex modern cuisine. Indeed it's a sort of Mirabelle-in-the-park, with the added dimension of noisy family lunches on Sundays. The cooking is always competent, though some of the combos are ill-judged. A risotto of calamares, for example, was more buttery than fishy, and the deep-fried, battered calamares strewn on top were rather reminiscent of breakfast cereal. Langoustine tagliatelle was exemplary pasta with fat shellfish in a good, if not superb sauce. Sea bass with tomatoes, olives and sauce vièrge was fresh and tasty, but honey roast duck was overly sweet. It's rare to pay £7.50 for desserts, yet the Belvedere's classic renditions are worthwhile. Prune and Armagnac ice-cream was creamy and alcoholic; apple tart very fine, with perfect pastry and razor-thin slices of fruit. The wine list is grand, with few good bottles under £30.
Babies and children welcome; high chairs. Tables outdoors (5, patio).

Kensington W8

Clarke's ★

124 Kensington Church Street, W8 (020 7221 9225). Notting Hill Gate tube. **Lunch served** 12.30-2pm, **dinner served** 7-10pm Mon-Fri. **Set lunch** £14.50 one course, £22 two courses, £30 three courses, incl coffee, service. **Set dinner** £44 four courses incl coffee, service. **Credit** AmEx, DC, JCB, MC, £TC, V.

Sally Clarke's respected establishment has a fresh feel to it. Immaculately turned-out staff are attentive and enthusiastic without being intrusive; the simple layout, of white-clothed tables, white walls and, downstairs, an open-plan kitchen displaying trays of vegetables, fits into the sedate, but professional ambience. This is a place where food is taken seriously, and where the freshness of ingredients dictates the daily changing menu. For although at lunch there's some element of choice (with all starters at £8, mains at £14.50 and desserts at £7.50), dinner here means simply accepting Clarke's choice for the evening. (If you have an aversion to the set menu, the kitchen may be able to accommodate you, but it is best to ring in advance to be sure you're happy with the day's dishes.) We began with courgette flowers deep-fried in crisp, light batter, wetted by a sauce of roast vine tomatoes, basil and wild rocket. The main course was a gently roasted salmon steak, topped by a relish of olives, tarragon and chives, surrounded by a selection of slightly overdone autumn vegetables. Then it was on to the cheese course – Appleby's Cheshire and goat's cheese with exquisite oatmeal biscuits – and finally a dessert of white peaches and shortbread swimming in a vin d'orange sauce. Each dish was carefully presented and thoughtfully constructed, the only drawback being that the hand-written menu was barely legible. But that doesn't really matter when there's no choice anyway.
Babies and children admitted. Booking advisable, essential weekends. No smoking (dinner). **Map 11/7B**.

Kensington Place

201 Kensington Church Street, W8 (020 7727 3184). Notting Hill Gate tube. **Lunch served** noon-3pm Mon-Fri; noon-3.30pm Sat, Sun. **Dinner served** 6.30-11.45pm Mon-Sat; 6.30-10.15pm Sun. **Main courses** £13-£18. **Set lunch** (Mon-Fri) £14.50 three courses. **Credit** AmEx, DC, JCB, MC, £TC, V.

At any time of the day or week you'll have to squeeze your way through the packed tables and penetrating voices of this ever-so Kensington hangout. Space-age pillars do battle with overbearingly puce walls and a sub-1930s riverside mural; only the old parquet floor gleams soothingly. The inconsistency of the decor is brought into sharp relief by the consistency of the food. Borlotti bean purée with peppers, olives and Parmesan crisp was too processed, lacking texture and character; it reminded us of mushy refried beans. Fried squid with crème fraîche and chilli jam had descended into bland wodginess due to the thick batter encasing the squid and the lack of any sign of chilli in the jam. Main courses scarcely lifted our spirits: baked smoked haddock with leeks and Parmesan was overpoweringly strong; while wild salmon with horseradish and chives looked withered and tasted underwhelming. Gooseberry fool was fragrant in aroma, but had the consistency of wallpaper paste, which meant the high point of the meal was an enjoyable trio of ice-creams. There's an extensive wine list, and staff were unfailingly polite (and adept at weaving their way through the gesticulating cigarettes). Kensington Place will doubtless continue to thrive, but we found it pricey, posey, and well past its sell-by date.
Babies and children welcome; high chairs. Booking advisable, essential weekends. Disabled: toilet. Dress: smart casual. Separate room for parties, seats 40. **Map 11/7A**.

Launceston Place

1A Launceston Place, W8 (020 7937 6912). Gloucester Road or High Street Kensington tube. **Lunch served** 12.30-2.30pm Mon-Fri; 12.30-3pm Sun. **Dinner served** 7-11.30pm Mon-Sat. **Main courses** £15-£18.50. **Set lunch** £15.50 two courses, £18.50 three courses. **Service** 12½% for parties of ten or more. **Credit** AmEx, JCB, MC, £TC, V.

The Launceston stretches its handsome curving frontage around a picturesque corner of South Ken, thick with bijoux kidswear shops and antique dealers. There's something immediately welcoming about the space, which is broken up into a number of intimate rooms with huge gilded mirrors and a handful of tables. Service is attentive and unaffected, though we had to wait almost 40 minutes between our first course and our main course on a busy Thursday evening. The menu is traditional English with exotic frills; the results are certainly competent, but the dishes tend to get stuck somewhere between the Anglo and the exotic. A roast chump of lamb, for example, was served with a mint 'jus' that was crying out to be mint sauce. An entrée of spiced Malaysian noodles with roast butternut squash looked adventurous on the menu, but was not so on the plate. Chilled watercress and pea soup with mint, on the other hand, was just right, and a main course of seared salmon with gooseberry sabayon was pleasing enough. The ambience is so urbanely sociable that cutting-edge cuisine is hardly the main point. A good wine list, strong on burgundies, aids distraction. However, prices are on the high side, away from the lunchtime and early evening prix fixe menus.
Babies and children admitted. Booking advisable. Separate room for parties, seats 14. **Map 5/9C**.

The Terrace

33C Holland Street, W8 (020 7937 3224). High Street Kensington tube. **Lunch served** noon-2.30pm Mon-Sat; 12.30-3pm Sun. **Dinner served** 7-10.30pm Mon-Sat. **Main courses** £11.50-£20. **Set lunch** £12.50 two courses, £14.50 three courses. **Pre-theatre dinner** (5.45-7pm June-Sept) £17.50 two courses. **Service** 12½%. **Credit** AmEx, DC, JCB, MC, £TC, V.

A small, welcoming neighbourhood restaurant with tables outside for warm weather. However, by 'neighbourhood' we mean the point where Notting Hill meets Ken High Street, so the prices are higher than you'd expect from a local place. Starters range from £5.50 for soup to £11 for pan-fried foie gras with grape and watercress salad and Sauternes jus; mains are from £11.50 for wild mushroom risotto to £20 for grilled tuna with a fennel, orange, olive and parsley salad. Moreover the food is just too variable to justify the West End prices. Terrace salad was a dreadfully misconceived mix of crunchy pulses, cherry tomatoes and gooey melted goat's cheese, but a roasted tomato soup was truly brilliant. Sloppily presented honey-roasted duck breast was flavourful, but served with undercooked and excessively bitter Swiss chard. Risotto was reasonably successful but rather stodgy, while overcooked calf's liver was almost too salty to eat. The wine list is fair to people on limited budgets, but in all, the Terrace isn't a place we'll come back to in a hurry.
Babies and children welcome. Booking advisable. Tables outdoors (7, terrace). **Map 11/8B**.

Ladbroke Grove W11

Alastair Little ★

136A Lancaster Road, W11 (020 7243 2220). Ladbroke Grove tube. **Lunch served** 12.30-2.30pm Mon-Fri; 12.30-3pm Sat. **Dinner served** 7-11pm Mon-Sat. **Main courses** £8-£12 lunch. **Set dinner** £23.50 two courses, £27.50 three courses. **Credit** AmEx, DC, MC, V.

The muted, pale light seems to come from nowhere in this minimalist space. Fortunately (considering the prices), portions are far from minimalist and the food is superb. The fixed-price menu offers around half a dozen choices for each course. Caesar salad with avocado was piled high with rocket, crispy croûtons and great chunks of the slippery green pear. The fresh pea soup with clotted cream – bright in colour and light in taste, its green depths concealing crunchy watercress – was so good we wanted it all over again. So, expectations were high for the main courses. Neither baked plaice with prawn sauce and mash, nor breast of corn-fed chicken with wild mushroom, disappointed. Fish flesh and bone parted easily, the prawn sauce was exquisitely flavoursome, and the mash smooth and buttery. The chicken was tender and succulent, and the fungi had a gritty authenticity. Portions were so generous we couldn't have done justice to a third course, but diners on all sides were slipping into restrained, W11 rhapsodies over their pear tarte tatin with vanilla ice-cream, and panna cotta with raspberry sauce. Staff were polite and friendly, if a little slow to get going. Though £80 for two people seems a lot amid the scruff and tat of Ladbroke Grove, we'd fed very well. *See also p135.*
Babies and children welcome. Booking advisable (dinner). Tables outdoors (4, pavement). **Map 11/5Az.**

Notting Hill W11

192

192 Kensington Park Road, W11 (020 7229 0482). Ladbroke Grove or Notting Hill Gate tube/15, 52 bus. **Lunch served** 12.30-3pm Mon-Fri; 12.30-3.30pm Sat, Sun. **Dinner served** 6.30-11.30pm Mon-Sat; 7-11pm Sun. **Main courses** £8.50-£16. **Set lunch** (Mon-Fri) £11.50 two courses incl coffee. **Set Sunday lunch** £12.50 two courses incl coffee. **Credit** AmEx, DC, MC, £TC, V.
Despite the boom in rival eateries, 192 still leads the field for west London's media hounds. The food sticks to well-established East-West formulas, while wines continue to offer good value and varietal coverage. However, like the strong, increasingly unfashionable 1990s colour scheme, the flavours in the free-ranging cuisine are on the loud side. Steamed mussels with tomato and cardamom sauce was noisily spiced, while risotto of truffled Pecorino, olive and bacon was volubly smoky and not too sticky. The broad range of starters also includes solid seasonal favourites such as various pastas. Next, pan-fried black bream with Asian noodle broth and pickled lime was again rowdily flavoured, with the fish a touch too soft; pan-fried liver with braised cabbage and pancetta came in a vivid, rich sauce. Our burgundy was marginally corked; to the staff's great credit, our diagnosis was instantly confirmed and the bottle replaced. It's hard to find fault in 192's set-up and mid-range standards.
Babies and children admitted. Booking advisable dinner. Tables outdoors (4, pavement). **Map 11/6Az.**

Nosh Brothers

12 All Saints Road, W11 (020 7243 2808). Notting Hill Gate or Westbourne Park tube. **Lunch served** 12.30-3pm Mon-Sat; 12.30-4pm Sun. **Dinner served** 7-11pm Mon-Sat. **Main course** £10-£14. **Service** 12½%. **Credit** AmEx, DC, MC, V.
Restaurants come and go on this tricky site, but if any epitomises the new face of Notting Hill this is it. Service is super-casual, led, on our visit, by a shaggy-haired dude and a statutory surly girly. Bob Dylan and other bohemian rhapsodisers completed the aural deal. The corpulent 'brothers', the erstwhile TV chefs who run the joint, circulated discreetly with their books conspicuously for sale. Plain bright decor gives the place a Gap-like appearance, but neither the menu nor the world wine list is mass market. Set Sunday lunch offers a choice of four dishes for each course. For starters, grilled asparagus risotto was vibrantly fresh and minty, if under-seasoned, while cecinna (Spanish cured beef) with artichoke, baked tomato, olive, caper and rocket salad was a typical fusion of fashionable ingredients. Mains included a nice, flaky piece of cod wrapped in Bayonne ham, served with a wonderfully rich mash. A pink, tender, juicy rump of lamb on couscous (with harissa-spiced jus and a date and cumin relish) gave a bold North African spin to a Sunday roast – though was a little sweet to the tooth. For dessert, pear and custard tartlet was pleasant but small, while British cheeses were under-ripe and came with challenging hunks of bread. Nevertheless, the Nosh Brothers seem to have got their teeth stuck well into Notting Hill's bloated eating scene.
Babies and children admitted. Booking advisable. **Map 11/5Az.**

Pharmacy Restaurant & Bar

150 Notting Hill Gate, W11 (020 7221 2442). Notting Hill Gate tube.
Bar **Open** noon-3pm, 6pm-1am Mon-Thur; noon-3pm, 6pm-2am Fri, Sat; 11.15am-3pm, 6-10.30pm Sun.
Restaurant **Lunch served** 12.30-3pm daily. **Dinner served** 7pm-midnight Mon-Sat; 7-10.30pm Sun. **Main courses** £11.50-£23. **Set lunch** £15.50 two courses, £17.50 three courses.
Both **Service** 12½%. **Credit** AmEx, DC, MC, TC, V.
People love to hate Pharmacy, but this sniffiness seems merely dyspeptic. Although some of the fittings look a little tired, overall the room remains light and airy with surprisingly dramatic views of Notting Hill Gate. This lightness of touch is reflected in the collection of Damien Hirst's butterfly paintings. Food, too, is very much what the doctor ordered. From the set menu, Waldorf salad with Bayonne ham was a mouthwatering opener, while the main course of pan-fried skate with burnt caper butter was as delicate as the side dish of french beans was al dente. À la carte, the fresh Med theme continued, with top-quality asparagus made exquisite by beetroot and a fine, aged balsamic vinegar. The list of main courses has fish and chips with tartare sauce rubbing shoulders with pea and artichoke risotto with lemon oil, the latter a perfect balance of richness and freshness. Desserts couldn't be resisted and although the lemon tart was less refined, sunken chocolate soufflé with apricots was cocoa-packed to the point of crumbling. The wine list, too, is something to email home about, with a dozen unusual and affordable Pharmacy selections supplemented by a pricier (£20-£300) choice. Graciously wined and dined, we required no further medication for the belly-aching that this establishment often attracts.
Babies and children admitted. Booking advisable. Entertainment: DJ from 7pm Fri, Sat (bar). **Map 11/7A.**

Shepherd's Bush W6, W14

Blythe Road

71 Blythe Road, W14 (020 7371 3635). Hammersmith or Shepherd's Bush tube. **Lunch served** 12.30-2.30pm Mon-Fri. **Dinner served** 7-10.30pm Mon-Sat. **Main courses** £11.50-£13.50. **Service** 12½% for parties of six or more. **Credit** AmEx, DC, MC, £TC, V.
Blythe Road isn't the most adventurous of restaurants but does offer some of the freshest food in town. An unpretentious local with a sunny yellow interior and folding front, it has a down-to-earth atmosphere. There might be lapses of taste in the pictures and photos on the wall, but this is otherwise a well-judged operation. The menu is fresh and trim and put together with an imaginative twist. Ceviche of salmon was a delicate swollen fillet, while smoked mackerel, with beetroot, horseradish and crème fraîche salad, was a summery combination. The warm salad of endive with roasted almonds, avocado, bacon and Stilton is a Blythe Road classic. However, not all combinations are so successful. Oak-smoked haddock really didn't need its accompanying grilled Cheddar, which completely obscured the tomatoes, endive and chive dressing. Equally, we were mystified by the presence of a tandoori chicken breast with vegetable korma, basmati rice and raita, which belonged in an Indian restaurant at half the £12 price tag. However, pork tenderloin with sweet potato and chorizo mash, mangetout and grain mustard sauce was a dignified example of meat and two veg. To finish, a hot tarte tatin dessert owed more to Anglo-Saxon heartiness than French finesse. The short wine list is shrewdly assembled and sensibly priced, but the bill came to £75 for what was hardly an extravagant meal for two.
Babies and children welcome. Booking essential. Tables outdoors (8, pavement).

Brackenbury

129-131 Brackenbury Road, W6 (020 8748 0107). Goldhawk Road or Hammersmith tube. **Lunch served** 12.30-2.45pm Mon-Fri, Sun. **Dinner served** 7-10.45pm Mon-Sat. **Main courses** £7.50-£13.75. **Set lunch** (Mon-Fri) £9.50 two courses, £12.50 three courses. **Service** 12½% for parties of six or more. **Credit** AmEx, MC, £TC, V.
Estate agents call the district Brackenbury Village, but there's no green decorated with cider drinkers and their dogs, just this persistently popular local. Filled with resident yuppies and BBC personnel, the two goldfish-bowl rooms with IKEA-like furnishings can feel cramped, so on warmer, drier days the pavement terrace beckons. The menu is seasonally adjusted. There was a surprisingly minty undertone to the yellow split-pea soup with chilli and coriander butter, while asparagus with shaved Parmesan was blown away by a Branston Pickle-like balsamic vinaigrette. Among the main courses, popular ideas take precedence over execution: grilled sea bass with fennel, new potatoes and french bean salad was overcooked and soft. Pea and mint risotto with Parmesan and green salad proved the better, fresher buy. In deference to the Brackenbury's public school clientele, desserts are as numerous as mains and starters (six in total, all around £5). Chocolate mousse and crème fraîche, served with 1970s throw-back brandy snaps, was rich but light. If you can't find something on the 50-strong wine list (£9.75-£55) you're probably teetotal. Service can lag behind demand, but this is no place to snap your fingers.
Babies and children welcome; high chair. Booking essential. Tables outdoors (8, pavement).

Cotto ★

44 Blythe Road, W14 (020 7602 9333). Goldhawk Road tube/Olympia tube/rail. **Lunch served** noon-3.30pm Mon-Fri. **Dinner served** 7-10.30pm Mon-Sat. **Main courses** £9-£14. **Set lunch** £12.50 two courses, £15.50 three courses. **Service** 12½%. **Credit** MC, V.
Occupying a corner location opposite the vast edifice of Blythe House, Cotto is a beautifully cool, white-walled, Tardis-like space that extends further back than you at first realise, as well as underground. If it weren't for the tables and chairs you'd think it an art gallery (indeed, the abstract paintings that add colour are all for sale). Black-clad waiters hovered as we sat down; staff will do anything for you, whether you want them to or not. Fortunately, the food is superb. We started with ballottine of oxtail and aubergine with onion purée and onion rings, and ragout of snails, garlic confit, green olives, pasta and baby artichokes. These creations were marked by subtle, delicate yet distinct flavours. From a choice of six main courses, we tried deliciously gamy roast partridge, and poached Dover sole (which came deboned and coiled, with mussels, spinach, carrots, shallots and parsley). Both dishes were perfectly cooked and exquisitely presented. To finish, chocolate dough-nuts with mascarpone sorbet was very good, while apricot and peach strudel with apricot ice-cream produced restrained moans of pleasure. We enjoyed a bottle of Two Mile Creek Australian chardonnay with the meal and finished with a glass of the wonderfully syrupy Monbazillac. Once Cotto gets into its stride and the waiters learn to back off, it will be hard to beat. It's not cheap though: our bill was just £15 shy of a ton. Treat yourself.
Babies and children admitted. Booking advisable. Separate room for parties, seats 40. Tables outdoors (4, pavement).

South West

Barnes SW13

Sonny's ★

94 Church Road, SW13 (020 8748 0393). Barnes Bridge rail. **Lunch served** 12.30-2.30pm Mon-Sat; 12.30-3pm Sun. **Dinner served** 7.30-11pm Mon-Sat. **Main courses** £10.50-£15. **Set lunch** £13 two courses, £16 three courses. **Set Sunday lunch** £18.50 three courses. **Credit** AmEx, DC, MC, V.
The well-heeled burghers of Barnes know a good thing when they see it, and Sonny's is packed most nights of the week. In fact, it's hard to fault on any level. The all-white decor, plate-glass frontage and glass-brick wall in the back room provide a light, serene and relaxed atmosphere. Tables are ideally spaced and the acoustics are perfect. The white-aproned staff are impeccable, and always advise on whether or not you need side dishes. And the food – which follows the stacking school of cuisine, with everything artfully arranged as a little tower – is very, very good. A starter of ricotta, figs, baby artichokes, dandelion leaves and purple basil was an inspired combination of tastes and textures, and crab with guacamole and confit potatoes was stunning. New potato, black olive and watercress salad was a superb contrast to a perfectly cooked main course of flaky brill. Tender chicken breast was pleasingly herby and accompanied by a mouthwatering cep and onion tart, although the side dish of french beans was too salty. We shared a delicious, raspberry-filled baked Alaska for dessert; nice to see that 1970s favourite revived for the 21st century. The bill totalled a less-than-expected £60 (including a bottle of Beaujolais Villages rosé and coffee): good value for such a repast. There are also bargain-priced set menus every lunchtime. Lucky Barnes.
Babies and children welcome; high chairs. Booking essential Wed-Sun. Separate room for parties, seats 24.

Chelsea SW3

Bluebird

350 King's Road, SW3 (020 7559 1000). Bus 19, 22, 49.
Bar **Open** noon-11pm Mon-Sat; noon-10.30pm Sun.
Restaurant **Brunch served** 11am-3.30pm Sat, Sun. **Lunch served** noon-3.30pm Mon-Fri. **Dinner served** 6-11pm Mon-Sat; 6-10.30pm Sun. **Main courses** £9.50-£23.50. **Set Sunday lunch** £17.50 three courses. **Set meal** (lunch, 6-7pm) £12.75 two courses, £15.75 three courses. **Service** 12½%. **Credit** AmEx, DC, JCB, MC, TC, V.
We were gobsmacked by the beauty of this huge room at lunchtime, with light pouring in through the skylights. We were also delighted by the warm welcome our party of three children and one adult received, and by the good value of the set lunch/pre-theatre dinner menu: £15.75 for three courses. Both Thai fish cakes with Asian cabbage, and wild mushroom tart with rocket and Pecorino were thoroughly dreary, but the rest of the food ranged from decent to utterly brilliant. The best thing was a mountain of linguine with tomato and basil sauce from the children's menu. Pommes frites were crisp, brown and delicious. Desserts were uniformly fine. The problem with Bluebird, as with other Conran restaurants, is the ease with which you can run up an enormous bill. Spending less than £100 for a full meal for two is difficult without cutting corners, and if you get reckless – with lovely fruits de mer or pricier meat dishes, such as chateaubriand at £19.50 per person – you can find yourself staring at a bill for £150. There's too much inconsistency to justify that expenditure. But at lunchtime, just try to keep us away.
Babies and children welcome; children's menu (weekends); high chairs. Booking essential several days in advance. Disabled: toilet. Dress: smart casual. Entertainment: pianist, dinner nightly. Separate room for parties, seats 25. **Map 5/13C.**

Parsons Green SW6

The Mission

116 Wandsworth Bridge Road, SW6 (020 7736 3322). Fulham Broadway or Parsons Green tube/28, 295 bus. **Dinner served** 7-11pm Mon-Sat. **Set meals** £24 two courses, £28 three courses. **Credit** JCB, MC, £TC, V.
The arrival of a new chef, Phillip Lamb from the Lanesborough, has transmogrified this once very ordinary wine bar into a top-notch restaurant. Art deco windows and mirrors give the interior a refined, elegantly simple feel, entirely in keeping with the beautifully presented food. Our meal began with a mouthwatering seafood tartare with sweet pickled vegetables and 'voodoo sauce' (an unusual and effective sweet and sour combo). Tamarind quail with oriental slaw and mango and papaya salsa was a second perfectly cooked, well-balanced starter. Next, red mullet with fennel purée, vermicelli rösti and a sweetcorn and vanilla emulsion sounded downright complicated but worked well. Roast rabbit with broad beans, sweetbread and sorrel sauce was also well cooked and very tasty. The highlight of the desserts was a stunning strawberry and black pepper tart with a lemon and basil sorbet. Staff are knowledgeable and friendly and the well-chosen wine list has a number of wines by the glass. Food of this standard doesn't come cheap, but at £28 a head for three courses (including olive bread, salmon mousse hors d'oeuvres and own-made chocolates) the Mission isn't extortionate, but is a treat.
Babies and children admitted. Book weekends. Tables outdoors (14, patio).

Putney SW15

Phoenix Bar & Grill

162-164 Lower Richmond Road, SW15 (020 8780 3131). Putney Bridge tube/22, 265 bus. **Lunch served** 12.30-2.30pm Mon-Sat; noon-3pm Sun. **Dinner served** 7-11.30pm Mon-Sat; 7-10pm Sun. **Main courses** £9.50-£13. **Set Sunday lunch** £18.50 three courses incl coffee. **Set meal** (lunch Mon-Sat; 7-7.45pm daily) £12 two courses incl coffee, £15 three courses. **Credit** AmEx, DC, MC, £TC, V.
The Phoenix has an enticing terrace with outdoor heaters and swish waterproof parasols, while inside, an airy, modern room benefits from french windows and lots of space. Staff are young and smiling, the menu is modern and well-composed and wines are not over-priced. So what is it about the Phoenix that doesn't quite stack up? A lack of intensity in the flavours has something to do with it. Despite ample chunks of potato, yellow pepper, bacon, carrot and celery, clam and bacon chowder was so light on the clams that it tasted of little more than cream. Squid, chorizo and

The Mission.
See page 139.

chickpea salad tasted only of sausage, and left a lake of paprika-flavoured oil on the plate. Yet two large ravioli stuffed with broad beans, ricotta and mint and sprinkled with pine nuts were a treat, with or without their brown butter dressing. They came with a plate of crisp, fresh leaves that made the 'summer vegetables' secreted under another main course – new season's lamb – seem paltry. Desserts exhibited the same technical competence but lack of passion as the starters. Apricot and almond tart was little more than sponge on (quite hard) pastry; chocolate brownie with vanilla ice-cream was dark and chewy, yet had an under-taste of raw cake mix. We left wondering why service was so slow in a restaurant that was only half-full.
Babies and children welcome; children's menu; crayons and comics; high chairs. Book dinner. Disabled: toilet. Tables outdoors (16, terrace).

Sheen SW14

Redmond's

170 Upper Richmond Road West, SW14 (020 8878 1922). Barnes or Mortlake rail then 33 bus. **Lunch served** noon-2.30pm Mon-Fri, Sun. **Dinner served** 7-10.30pm Mon-Sat. **Express lunch** £10 two courses, £12.50 three courses. **Set lunch** £12.50 one main course or two starters, £16.50 starter and main course, £21.50 three courses. **Set Sunday lunch** £17.50 three courses. **Set dinner** £22 two courses, £25 three courses. **Service** 10% for parties of six or more. **Credit** JCB, MC, £TC, V.
Sheen may not be London's most hip neighbourhood, but its well-off citizens enjoy the finer things in life, as this accomplished restaurant shows. A one-room affair with a dark pink and white design, it's a rather subdued place, despite the garish abstract paintings and the busy Upper Richmond Road outside. The food is excellent. We started with an exquisite warm mushroom and rosemary tart, and an equally good char-grilled aubergine, fennel, courgette and tomato salad. For mains, char-grilled wild sea trout, though overcooked, worked very well on its bed of samphire, 'spaghetti' cucumber and runner beans, surrounded by a delicate basil sauce. Pan-fried calf's liver with horseradish and parsley rösti was also a fine rendition, though the pretty ring of carrot purée added nothing to the taste. Both dishes were served far too hot, and we could have done with some side orders of veg. We finished with a generous selection of Neal's Yard cheeses, and a cherry and almond tart with melt-in-the-mouth pastry and Marsala ice-cream. Staff were friendly and knowledgeable, especially about the wine (try the pear-flavoured Menetou-Salon). Extra touches, such as the free appetiser of chicken and foie gras terrine, and chocolates with coffee, are what makes Redmond's stand out. It was only half full on a midweek evening, but deserves to be busier.
Babies and children welcome. Booking advisable; essential weekends. No pipe or cigar smoking.

South Kensington SW3, SW7

Bibendum

Michelin House, 81 Fulham Road, SW3 (020 7581 5817/www.bibendum.co.uk). South Kensington tube. **Lunch served** noon-2.30pm Mon-Fri; 12.30-3pm Sat, Sun. **Dinner served** 7-11.30pm Mon-Sat; 7-10.30pm Sun. **Set lunch** (Mon-Fri) £23 two courses, £27.50 three courses; (Sat, Sun) £27.50 three courses. **Main courses** £14.50-£22.50. **Service** 12½%. **Credit** AmEx, DC, MC, £TC, V.
The elements that have now become the hallmarks of a Conran restaurant (see Quaglino's, Le Pont de la Tour and numerous others) were pretty much pioneered at Bibendum. Elegantly housed in the restored former HQ of the Michelin tyre company, and still presided over by stained-glass images of the tubby tyre man, the restaurant continues to attract cosmopolitan business diners with its classic French-based cuisine and exquisitely handled nostalgia. Matthew Harris's menu sticks fairly firmly to the classics: foie gras, escargots de Bourgogne and chateaubriand with béarnaise all feature, and there's even a classy version of fish and chips with tartare sauce. Our meal produced satisfied smiles rather than raves. A smoky brochette of oysters wrapped in salty bacon with a hollandaise sauce, and a rather dull roast tomato salad with crème fraîche, mint, sweet onions and a saffron-infused sauce proved an uninspiring start. Much better were mains of rabbit flavoured with fresh young rosemary tendrils, white and purple garlic and a glossy white wine jus, and sea bass with broad beans and girolles. Fresh raspberries folded into thick cream and topped by a chewy macaroon was the essence of a summer pudding. The average price per head is £50, even before choosing from the formidable wine list. Service is efficient and impersonal. Perhaps now so many venues plough a similar course, Bibendum has lost some of its lustre, but it remains a pretty faultless operation.
Babies and children admitted. Booking essential (two weeks in advance for dinner). **Map 12/11D.**

Hilaire

68 Old Brompton Road, SW7 (020 7584 8993). South Kensington tube. **Lunch served** 12.15-2.30pm Mon-Fri. **Dinner served** 6.30-11pm Mon-Sat. **Set lunch** £18.50 two courses, £21.50 three courses. **Set meal** £23.50 two starters, £33 two courses, £37.50 three courses. **Service** 12½%. **Credit** AmEx, DC, MC, £TC, V.
This veteran is a charming local restaurant we'd all kill to have round the corner. It's comfortably furnished in a nicely old-fashioned way (though some find the tables cramped) and the menu leaves you drooling over almost every line. What's more, we've never had less than an excellent meal here. The menu has its feet firmly on the Franco/Spanish/Italian ground, avoiding fiddliness in favour of classic combinations and maximum flavour. Jambon persille with sauce ravigote; gazpacho; and pigeon, artichoke and french bean salad all feature among the starters. Mains might be char-grilled wild salmon with sorrel sauce, steak au poivre, or calves' kidneys served with risotto. Fish has always been a strong point, as have delicious puddings. The only niggle about Hilaire is the expense of eating here, especially at dinner. But this is South Ken, after all. The restaurant helps out us non-millionaires by offering flexible options (two courses for £33), and lunch is much cheaper at £21.50 for three courses. The wine is pricey, but decent house wines soften the blow. Expect to spend serious money; but expect to get serious food in return.
Babies and children welcome. Booking advisable. Separate room for parties, seats 24. **Map 12/10D.**

South

Battersea SW8, SW11

Ransome's Dock

35-37 Parkgate Road, SW11 (020 7223 1611). Bus 19, 49, 319, 345.
Bar **Open** 11am-11pm Mon-Sat; noon-3.30pm Sun.
Restaurant **Meals served** 11am-11pm Mon-Fri; 11am-midnight Sat; 11.30am-3.30pm Sun. **Main courses** £9.50-£18.50. **Set lunch** (Mon-Fri) £12.50 two courses. **Service** 12½%. **Credit** AmEx, DC, MC, V.
If you're lucky with the weather you can dine al fresco by the dock side at this upmarket Battersea favourite, but even on less clement days the glass-sided, blue-painted dining room (hung with a disparate collection of pictures) is a lovely spot in which to eat. The monthly-changing menu (supplemented by a few specials) is one of those cannily simple less-is-more affairs where almost every dish appeals. Crab and saffron tart was gloriously light, but could have done with a bit more bite; field mushroom with goat's cheese and red peppers was altogether more earthy. Trelough duck came crispy on the outside and perfectly tender within, served with new potatoes and a complementarily tangy red onion marmalade. Juicy pink cutlets of lamb were accompanied by dauphinoise potatoes, spinach and carrots. We could manage no more for dessert than a fine strawberry jelly with fresh strawberries and organic vanilla ice-cream. The excellent wine list is thoughtfully divided by grape and style and (in summer) daringly suggests the chilling of some reds. The only duff note was the sweet-natured but dippy service; several staff repeated questions already asked by colleagues, and, even so, several of our requests were forgotten.
Babies and children welcome; high chairs. Booking essential (weekends two days in advance). Tables outdoors (10, terrace). **Map 6/13E.**

Stepping Stone

123 Queenstown Road, SW8 (020 7622 0555). Queenstown Road rail/137 bus. **Lunch served** noon-2.30pm Mon-Fri, Sun. **Dinner served** 7-10.30pm Mon; 7-11pm Tue-Sat. **Main courses** £11.25-£13.75. **Set lunch** (Mon-Fri) £12.50 two courses. **Set Sunday lunch** £16.50 three courses. **Set dinners** (7-9pm Mon-Fri) £12.50 two courses, £15 three courses. **Credit** DC, MC, £TC, V.
Much thought seems to have gone into creating the dining experience at this bright, modern and reassuringly comfortable haven from the thunderous traffic of Queenstown Road. Waiters are genuinely welcoming; fixed-price and à la carte menus cater to most pockets; and the cuisine is akin to home-cooked food, stylishly presented. Haddock salad incorporated a slice of toast as well as green leaves, a poached egg and some beurre blanc – a wonderfully unctuous, if salty beginning. Another starter, feta salad, was a pleasing mix of onions, aubergine and tomato in a colourful and tasty mound. Next, grilled tuna came up nicely rare on a sizeable bed of mildly spiced stir-fried tagliatelle of vegetables. Rabbit arrived partly on the bone, with wholesome accompaniments of creamy mash, buttery cabbage and al dente carrots. There are other unpretentious and caring touches, too, such as the box of (somewhat inadequate) tasting notes for the brief wine list. To finish, chocolate macaroon with chocolate mousse was chewy in the middle and timidly flavoured, while summer pavlova disappointingly offered more meringue than fruits. But on the whole, Stepping Stone deserves plaudits. A thoroughly agreeable restaurant.
Babies and children welcome; high chairs; nappy-changing facilities. Book dinner. No-smoking room. Vegetarian dishes.

Clapham SW4

Polygon

4 The Polygon, SW4 (020 7622 1199). Clapham Common tube/35, 37, 345 bus. **Brunch served** 11am-5pm Sat, Sun. **Lunch served** noon-3pm Mon-Fri. **Dinner served** 6-11pm Mon-Sat; 6-10.30pm Sun. **Main courses** £7.50-£14.75. **Early set meal** (6-11pm Mon, 6-7.30pm Tue-Sun) £10 two courses. **Service** 12½%. **Credit** AmEx, MC, £TC, V.
When Polygon opened in 1997, it set the pace for restaurants in Clapham with its design consciousness and air of metropolitan cool, but on the evidence of this visit it has slipped from pole position. The food hit the target more often than it missed, but the service was often slow and forgetful. A bottle of Australian riesling only materialised after a long bout of arm-waving, by which time we had nearly finished a bland shared starter of roast butternut squash with trevisse (a chard-like Italian leaf vegetable) and sugar-cured tomatoes. Things improved with the main courses, however. Roast marinated lamb rump with chickpea tagine was beautifully cooked to a state of soft succulence, while grilled scallops with broad beans, mint and black pepper (a pricey starter at £8.25) displayed a pearly translucence and a subtle but delicious flavour. Spicing for both dishes was spot on. Although tempted by flourless chocolate cake with mocha sauce and white coffee bean ice-cream, we instead shared a portion of Neal's Yard cheese with pickled figs. This was a mistake, as we were presented with a mere sliver of Cheddar and two tiny bits of another cheese that neither we nor the waiter could identify. Polygon can still impress, but with so much high-quality (and often better-value) competition nearby, it needs to sharpen up.
Babies and children welcome; high chairs. Book dinner. Disabled: toilet.

The Sequel

75 Venn Street, SW4 (020 7622 4222). Clapham Common tube.
Bar **Open** 4.30-11pm Mon-Fri; 11am-11pm Sat; noon-10.30pm Sun.
Restaurant **Lunch served** 10.30am-4pm Sat; 11.30am-5.30pm Sun. **Dinner served** 6-11.30pm Mon-Sat; 6.30-11pm Sun. **Main courses** £7-£12.50.
Both **Credit** AmEx, DC, MC, V.
The Sequel was a runner-up in the Best Local Restaurant category of the 2000 *Time Out* Eating & Drinking Awards. It looks like part of the Picture House next door – the huge screen playing films silently above the small bar accentuates this suspicion. It isn't, but it is connected to the Rapscallion on the other side of Venn Street (Justin Savage owns both). Dining here is always a bit of an adventure. The cross-pollination of cuisines can

be confusing. It can be hard to distinguish where one dish starts and another finishes on the menu. 'It's comedy food,' said our dining companion on viewing the menu. She had a point: the place does try a little too hard. On our most recent visit, a shark steak was disappointing (more like a genetically modified fish finger) while a chicken and mango salad was light, zesty and enjoyable. Desserts are works of art and help make a visit memorable. Previously we have feasted here on a fetching and flavoursome tian of aubergines with tomatoes, avocado and houmous and a paw-paw salsa, followed by an 'open' lasagne nero with swordfish and Parma ham. The background soundtrack of high-quality lounge tunes is another bonus. A meal for two with wine will set you back around £60.
Babies and children welcome; cartoons on video wall (weekends). Booking advisable. Disabled: toilet. No-smoking tables. Tables outdoors (4, pavement).

Kennington SE11

Kennington Lane Restaurant & Bar

205-209 Kennington Lane, SE11 (020 7793 8313). Kennington or Oval tube. **Lunch served** noon-3pm Mon-Fri; noon-5pm Sat, Sun. **Dinner served** 6-10.30pm Mon-Sat. **Main courses** £9.50-£14.95. **Set meal** (noon-3pm, 6-7.30pm Mon-Fri) £13.50 two courses, £15.75 three courses. **Service** 12½%. **Credit** MC, V.
This laurel-green corner restaurant, adorned with smart awnings and topiary bay trees, has a handsome enclosed terrace at the back and a small bar by the entrance. The restaurant is uncompromisingly modern, with bare tables, white walls and carefully colour-coordinated abstract art. Yet the menu shows no parallel clarity of purpose. Staff describe it as French, Italian and British, but the result seems to be anything you fancy, as long as it isn't too difficult to cook. To start, £7.50 was steep for four slices of lomo iberico, one slice of supermarket goat's cheese, a spoonful of tapenade and a cold herb pancake (socca). Potato pancake, on the other hand, was excellent – crunchy on the outside, creamy within – and came with smoked salmon and crème fraîche (we had to remind staff about the promised Mujjol caviar). Wild salmon was a tad overcooked, but had none of the fattiness of farmed fish, and sat on steamed samphire and sautéed new potatoes with a blob of horseradish cream. Seared scallops came with good black risotto and spinach, subtly flavoured with anchovy. Desserts deserve high plaudits: strawberry tart was rough, fresh and simply delicious; torta caprese turned out to be rich chocolate and nut cake served with pistachio ice-cream. Wines are helpfully divided by character and cover a sensible price range. It's not hard to see why young locals are pleased with the place, but it's irritating to pay such inflated prices.
Babies and children admitted lunch and weekends. Tables outdoors (14, patio).
Map 7/12M.

Waterloo SE1

Oxo Tower Restaurant, Bar & Brasserie

Oxo Tower Wharf, Barge House Street, SE1 (020 7803 3888). Blackfriars or Waterloo tube/rail.
Bar **Open** 11am-11pm Mon-Sat; noon-10.30pm Sun.
Brasserie **Lunch served** noon-3.30pm daily. **Dinner served** 5.30-11.30pm Mon-Sat; 6-10.30pm Sun. **Main courses** £14.75-£23.50. **Set meal** (lunch, 5.30-7pm, Mon-Fri) £20 two courses incl glass of wine, coffee.
Restaurant **Lunch served** noon-3pm Mon-Sat; noon-3.30pm Sun. **Dinner served** 6-11.30pm Mon-Sat; 6.30-10pm Sun. **Main courses** £15-£21.50. **Set lunch** £27.50 three courses.
All **Service** 12½%. **Credit** AmEx, DC, JCB, MC, £TC, V.
Views from restaurants don't come much better than that from the top floor of the Oxo Tower – a staggering sweep over the Thames to St Paul's and beyond. So it's to the management's credit that there's a great deal more to this establishment. The management in question is Harvey Nichols, so what you also get is an interior of sweeping, minimalist style, a lithe and white-coated serving crew, a menu that almost oozes olive oil, and an impressive, modish wine list. Windows ring the three, roughly partitioned rooms (restaurant, brasserie, excellent bar). If the weather's fine you can take a table on the terrace. The food is light and ingredients are top quality. On our latest trip to the brasserie we relished the £20 set lunch, starting with a neat, flavourful plate of shaved smoked swordfish on vine tomatoes, sheep's milk ricotta and 'torn' basil. A main of fregola sarda (Portuguese risotto with clumps of clams, more swordfish, mussels and salmon) was just as tasty, but a fraction heavy. No such problems with the whole fried sea bass off the carte: seared to perfection and offset by a feisty Thai dressing. Cooking tends towards this fashionable ecleticism (Portugal was firmly on the map on our visit), but the simple things are also done well. Our neighbours' heap of chips was fabulous, which in our experience is typical of a place that manages to generate a good-time atmosphere among its clientele of office workers and meejah babes.
Babies and children admitted. Booking essential. Disabled: toilet. Entertainment: pianist/singer from 7.30pm nightly (brasserie). Tables outdoors (27, restaurant terrace; 34, brasserie terrace). Vegetarian dishes.
Map 3/7N.

The People's Palace

Level 3, Royal Festival Hall, South Bank Centre, SE1 (020 7928 9999). Waterloo tube/rail. **Lunch served** noon-3pm, **dinner served** 5.30-11pm daily. **Main courses** £12-£16.50. **Set dinner** (5.30-7pm Mon-Sat) £15.50 two courses, £20.45 three courses. **Set Sunday meal** (noon-3pm, 5.30-11pm) £15.95 two courses, £20.90 three courses. **Credit** AmEx, DC, MC, TC, V.
The great river view that hits you through the large picture windows of this high-ceilinged and spacious restaurant is a romantic bonus. Service is slick and professional, but after the concert rush, waiters hovered unnecessarily when all we wanted to do was sit back in the comfy seats. Food for the most part is pretty good and seems to be improving. A delicious double-baked Bleu d'Auvergne soufflé with spiced pear and rocket wasn't too cheesy, but was still full of flavour. Chilled tomato and cracked pepper soup made an ideal summer dish and had a pleasant peppery kick, although less olive oil would have been a plus. Baked salmon with a basil and anchovy crust was a flavourful fish, but the accompanying tomato sauce felt watered down. We enjoyed the lovely piece of pan-fried sea bass with piperade and fennel confit, despite a heavy hand on the piperade. Puddings included a melt-in-your-mouth chocolate tart with chantilly cream and raspberry coulis; and an exotic crumble made with a pleasing selection of kiwi, pineapple and mango. A French waiter steered us away from New World wines (on a well-chosen list that has numerous choices by the glass) to an excellent white burgundy (Morgon) that worked well with the fish.
Babies and children welcome; high chairs. Booking advisable. Disabled: toilets (in Royal Festival Hall). No-smoking tables.
Map 7/8M.

South East

Blackheath SE3

Chapter Two

43-45 Montpelier Vale, SE3 (020 8333 2666). Blackheath rail. **Lunch served** noon-2.30pm Mon-Sat; noon-3.30pm Sun. **Dinner served** 6.30-10.30pm Mon-Thur; 6.30-11pm Fri, Sat; 7-9.30pm Sun. **Set lunch** £14.50 two courses, £18.50 three courses. **Set dinner** (Mon-Thur, Sun) £16.50 two courses, £19.50 three courses; (Fri, Sat) £22.50 three courses. **Service** 12½%. **Credit** AmEx, DC, JCB, MC, V.
Overlooking the heath, Chapter Two prides itself on its food and service, rather than its nondescript, predominantly brown decor. Grilled scallops with pea purée and a glossy rocket salad were luscious if a bit meagre. Basil risotto had a perfect texture and a winning combination of warm balsamic vinegar, goat's cheese and basil. A fine tender piece of sea bass with crisped skin arrived on a bed of lively greens, including pak choi and a hint of ginger, with salsa verde adding extra oomph. But roast cod with peas, asparagus and pasta was less pleasing: doused in a sub-hollandaise yellow sauce, with limp ribbons of pasta inexplicably strewn over the plate. For dessert, a dish of chocolate cookie with vanilla ice-cream and raspberry compote was composed like a sweet but unimaginative traffic light, while strawberries with excellent vanilla panna cotta and clotted cream arrived similarly dotted across a large plate. There's a fair choice of interesting wines. We've heard of unhappy experiences at Chapter Two, and our latest meal certainly had its low points. However, if you ignore the faint pretensions, the food is generally fine and the service is eager to please. A better than average local with reasonable prices.
Babies and children welcome; high chairs. Booking essential. Disabled: toilet.
For branch see index.

Lawn

1 Lawn Terrace, SE3 (020 8355 1110). Blackheath rail/53 bus. **Brunch served** 11.30am-2.30pm Sat; 11.30am-6pm Sun. **Lunch served** noon-2.30pm Tue-Fri. **Dinner served** 6-10.30pm Mon-Sat. **Main courses** £9.95-£15.50. **Set meals** (lunch; dinner Mon-Wed; before 7.30pm Thur-Sat) £11.95 two courses, £15.50 three courses. **Service** 12½%. **House wine** £13.50 bottle, £3.40 glass. **Mineral water** £2.50 bottle, £1 glass. **Credit** AmEx, DC, JCB, MC, V.
Lawn made the last six of the *Kids Out* Best Family Restaurant category of the 2000 *Time Out* Eating & Drinking Awards, thanks to its relaxed atmosphere and kiddy-friendly extras. However, this backstreet hideaway has plenty to satisfy its child-free clientele, too. The capacious first-floor industrial conversion has groovy glass panels, dimmed lighting and outré boucle chairs; the menu stays sensibly with recent modern European staples, and the cooking looks and tastes like fine food rather than modern sculpture. The meal started promisingly with impeccable char-grilled vegetables with a mozzarella bruschetta and pesto dressing. Thai fish and crab cakes with sweet chilli sauce were moist and fragrant, with a not unpleasant springy texture. Main courses excited us further. Char-grilled tuna came perfectly medium-rare (as requested), bedded on a rich aubergine and red onion compote. Fish and chips with mushy peas was a near perfect incarnation: a lavish piece of excellent cod with golden chips and dreamy mushy peas. Desserts both looked and tasted wonderful. Every mouthful of the raspberry and elderflower jelly with clotted cream recalled distilled summer evenings, while a passion fruit biscuit and strawberry millefeuille was greeted with rapturous squeaks. The wine list divides wines by character. Service was pleasant and efficient, if ever-so-slightly too swift.
Babies and children welcome; children's menu (£6.95 two courses); colouring books; high chairs; nappy-changing facilities. Book Fri, Sat. Disabled: toilet. Entertainment: jazz musicians (phone for details). Separate rooms for parties, seating 12 and 30.

Borough SE1

Cantina Vinopolis

1 Bank End, SE1 (020 7940 8333). London Bridge tube/rail.
Wine bar **Open** 10am-10pm Mon-Fri; 11am-9pm Sat, Sun.
Brasserie **Lunch served** noon-2.45pm Mon-Sat; noon-3.45pm Sun. **Dinner served** 6-10.15pm Mon-Sat.
Main courses £11.50-£13.50. **Service** 12½%. **Credit** AmEx, DC, MC, V.
Think of Cantina Vinopolis and you think about wine, which is hardly surprising as the list boasts some 400 bins, all of them available by the glass. But the food is an attraction in itself: a thoroughly modern French and Italian menu, with abundant New World influences, and prices that make spending much more than £25 on food impossible. What's more, it's cooked with a level of attention unmatched in some restaurants charging far more. Another major attraction is the group of brick-vaulted dining rooms, with ceilings that soar skywards. We loved starters of carpaccio with a good rocket salad and creamy horseradish sauce, and full-flavoured, precisely cooked Mediterranean vegetables with delicious buffalo mozzarella. A main course of own-made spaghetti with confit tomatoes, mozzarella and pesto was let down by overcooking, but cured salmon was a delight: crisp outside, pink inside, and poised on top of a fine salad featuring outstanding cherry tomatoes. A shared dish of British and Irish cheeses featured five varieties of impeccable pedigree in perfect condition. Vinopolis (the permanent exhibition of wines from around the world) wasn't busy when we visited, but with all the activity in this booming area, the Cantina looks set to do just fine. For **Vinopolis Wine Wharf** *see p222* **Wine Bars**.
Babies and children admitted. Booking advisable. **Map 8/8P.**

Shakespeare's Globe

New Globe Walk, SE1 (020 7928 9444). Mansion House tube/London Bridge tube/rail. **Lunch served** noon-2.30pm, **dinner served** 6-10pm daily. **Main courses** £12.50-£16.50. **Set meals** £17 two courses, £21.50 three courses. **Credit** AmEx, DC, JCB, MC, £TC, V.
The restaurant next to the Globe is also Elizabethan in architectural style – the early part of Elizabeth II's reign, that is. It's a light-filled, cream-painted room with a spectacular view of St Paul's Cathedral. Staff are friendly, the tables aren't too close together, it's not noisy and no-one is going to feel too old or unfashionable. The menu also aims for this happy middle ground, with dishes that are more than competently prepared without being cutting edge. On a summer's evening with the windows thrown open to the Thames' air, it was good to see seasonal produce on the menu (slightly overdone salmon with samphire and crushed potatoes, and a fruit jelly for pudding). We also gave the thumbs up to pea and asparagus risotto cake with mint and lemon dressing, and crisp duck breast with peas and caramelised onions. A very pleasant experience all round, the Globe is one to remember for a meal with a view, particularly given the cost and attitude of certain riverside restaurants.
Babies and children admitted; high chairs. Booking essential dinner Fri. Disabled: toilet. Separate rooms for parties, seating 100 (2) and 250. **Map 4/7O.**

Sixty-two

62 Southwark Bridge Road, SE1 (020 7633 0831). Borough or Southwark tube/London Bridge tube/rail. **Lunch served** noon-3pm Mon-Fri; noon-4pm Sun. **Dinner served** 6-10.30pm Mon-Sat. **Main courses** £10.95-£12.50. **Credit** AmEx, DC, LV, MC, £TC, V.
First impressions don't bode well. For one, Sixty-two is blandly named, like far too many bars and restaurants these days, after its street number. For two, it's attached to the Southwark Playhouse, and eateries adjoining theatres are rarely anything to write home about. However, stick with it, as Sixty-two is well worth seeking out, even if you're not of a dramatic bent. The menu at this modish space – arty photographs hang on the plain, coloured walls, with light wooden floorboards beneath your feet – changes monthly, and comprises about half a dozen starters, mains and desserts. After a lovely egg and spinach pie, we moved on to tender confit of duck with dauphinoise potatoes and roasted plums: a great combination. The fillet of beef, served atop a gorgeous slab of polenta and ringed with rocket, was similarly delicious and cooked to perfection. Following above-average desserts – an apple tarte tatin and a moreish Bailey's parfait – we left, replete. Service was fine, the wine list was better, and we'll be going back.
Babies and children welcome. Book lunch. Disabled: toilet in theatre. No-smoking tables.

Dulwich SE21

Belair House

Gallery Road, SE21 (020 8299 9788). West Dulwich rail. **Lunch served** noon-2.30pm Mon-Sat; noon-3pm Sun. **Dinner served** 7-10.30pm Mon-Thur; 7-11pm Fri, Sat; 7-10pm Sun. **Set lunch** £17.50 three courses. **Set Sunday lunch** £25.95 three courses. **Set meal** £25.95 three courses. **Service** 12½%. **Credit** AmEx, DC, JCB, MC, TC, V.
Surprisingly, perhaps, wealthy Dulwich isn't overburdened with classy eating options, so this gleaming white, reconstructed Georgian mansion holds the monopoly. The grandness of the exterior is, thankfully, tempered inside with sunflower-yellow walls, contemporary artworks and an agreeable air of modernity. There's no great invention on the set-price menu, which provides around seven choices at each course, but the quality is usually sound. A plate of Italian charcuterie was perfectly paired with a sharp, crunchy green bean salad and honey-dressed mustard figs. Little smoked haddock fish cakes were finely textured (but not noticeably smoky) and came with a herb salad and good tomato-based dipping sauce. We followed these with an excellent grilled breast of chicken with black olive pasta and buttery tomato and thyme sauce, and sliced chump of lamb on creamed spinach with a comforting confit aubergine ravioli, given bite by the inclusion of capers. Desserts were less impressive. Champagne-poached fruits with vanilla ice-cream didn't taste much better than their tinned cousins, although summer pudding with cucumber and apple sorbet was a fine seasonal dish. Despite the general culinary competence, there's a slight air of chill about Belair House; perhaps it's the slightly disengaged service, or the 'almost, but not quite' food – it just seems to be missing its mark.
Babies and children welcome; high chairs. Booking essential. Separate room for parties, seats 85. Tables outdoors (11, terrace).

Greenwich SE10

Time

7A College Approach, SE10 (020 8305 9767). Cutty Sark DLR.
Bar **Open** noon-midnight Mon-Sat; noon-10.30pm Sun.
Restaurant **Lunch served** noon-2.30pm Mon-Sat; noon-3.30pm Sun. **Dinner served** 7-10.30pm Mon-Sat; 7-10pm Sun. **Main**

courses £11-£15.50. **Set dinner** £23.50 three courses. **House wine** £11.50 bottle, £2.50 glass. **Mineral water** £2.95 bottle, £1.10 glass. **Credit** AmEx, MC, V.
Not before time, this funky addition to Greenwich's eating possibilities has been widely welcomed. It is perched overlooking the covered market, and most of its space is given over to a relaxed bar with chunky modern sofas and old wooden floors. Dinner happens on the upstairs balcony overlooking the bar; on our visit we shared the room with an avant garde slide show. Food is solidly Modern European in character. We happily shared a starter of tender seared scallops and then moved on to the mains. Poached halibut was a rather lacklustre piece of fish, revived by the cauliflower and parsley purée. Char-grilled monkfish with red onion marmalade was a more robust contribution, while a side order of creamy mash helped things along nicely. Light lemon cheesecake with summer fruits coulis, and a hot chocolate brownie with praline parfait and chocolate sauce were both highly acceptable without being stunning. House chardonnay, too, was unexceptional. We liked the friendly waitress; a mistake in the bill was swiftly rectified after hearty apologies. Given the laid-back, louche feel of the bar, such a formal restaurant seems a little incongruous; a broader menu of simpler food might fit this likeable place better. That said, Time's cooking shines besides Greenwich's usual offerings. The booking procedure needs work, however: a reader has complained of being 'bumped' to make way for a party booking – not very professional.
Babies and children admitted; high chairs; toys. Booking advisable; essential weekends. Entertainment: jazz (phone for details). Dress: smart casual Fri, Sat. Vegetarian dishes. **Map 19.**

London Bridge SE1

Delfina
50 Bermondsey Street, SE1 (020 7357 0244). London Bridge tube/rail. **Open** 10am-5pm, **coffee served** 10am-noon, 3.30-5pm, **lunch served** noon-3pm Mon-Fri. **Main courses** £9.50-£14.50. **Service** 12½%. **Credit** AmEx, DC, JCB, MC, £TC, V.
Eating at Delfina is a real treat. It's not exactly a typical restaurant – it's also a gallery space – and the combination of its daytime-only opening hours and the trendy London Bridge location provide it with an interesting assortment of customers. Inside is all open-plan, with plenty of space between tables and massive canvases hanging on the walls. The eponymous proprietress supplies her restaurant with wine and olive oil from her estate; a pungent little bowl of the latter speedily arrived accompanied by good fresh bread. Maria Elia's food is imaginative but not fussy, relying on the quality and freshness of the ingredients to do all the work. We began with a mini mountain of juicy crab meat dotted with shaved fennel and ceps and drizzled with vanilla oil. Smoked anchovies with rocket, Parmesan and spaghetti was another excellent starter. Mains of tender pink snapper (the 'Australian fish of the day') and tarragon-stuffed corn-fed chicken with serrano ham, lemon myrtle noodles and a fresh herb and crème fraîche broth were also deeply delicious. A rather bland chocolate lasagne made a slightly drab end to the meal, but Delfina's wonderfully fruity house wine was a welcome accompaniment throughout.
Babies and children welcome. Booking advisable; essential Thur, Fri. Disabled: toilet. Separate rooms for parties, seating 20-400. **Map 8/9Q.**

Tower Bridge SE1

The Apprentice
Cardamom Building, 31 Shad Thames, Butlers Wharf, SE1 (020 7234 0254). Tower Bridge tube//Tower Gateway DLR/London Bridge tube/rail. **Lunch served** noon-1.30pm, **dinner served** 6.30-8.30pm Mon-Fri. **Set lunch** £10.50 two courses, £13.50 three courses. **Set dinner** £15.50 two courses, £18.50 three courses. **Main courses** £8.50-£12.50. **House wine** £10.25 bottle, £2.50 glass. **Mineral water** £2.50 bottle, £1 glass. **Credit** AmEx, DC, JCB, MC, £TC, V.
It seems that no component of the Conran restaurant empire is devoid of marketable potential; the furniture, the cutlery, even the trainee staff have found their place in the money-spinning process. Everyone at the Apprentice, both in and out of the kitchen, is a student at the Butlers Wharf Chef School. It's not exactly a glam venue (imagine a drab-looking meeting room stretched to restaurant dimensions), but prices have been accordingly tweaked and, more importantly, the food is good. A starter of Thai squid contained a well-judged medley of flavours,

and its accompanying prawn risotto was nice and creamy. Main-course poached smoked haddock was done just right and arrived with a comforting trio of pea cream, a perfectly poached egg and sticky saffron rice. Fruit-stuffed pork fillet with radicchio, château potatoes and red onion vinaigrette was another well-judged dish. There's also an interesting selection of desserts, such as vanilla brûlée with tamarillo sorbet. The service, however, is priceless: fresh-faced waiters and waitresses deliver food to the table as if accepting a prize at the local eisteddfod, all downcast eyes and blushes, before bolting back to the safety of the kitchen.
Babies and children welcome. Booking advisable. Disabled: toilet. No-smoking tables. Separate room for parties, seats 50. **Map 8/8R.**

Blue Print Café ★
Design Museum, Butlers Wharf, SE1 (020 7378 7031). Tower Hill tube/Tower Gateway DLR/London Bridge tube/rail/47, 78 bus. **Lunch served** noon-2.45pm daily. **Dinner served** 6-10.45pm Mon-Sat. **Main courses** £11-£16.50. **Minimum** £10. **Service** 12½%. **Credit** AmEx, DC, JCB, MC, £TC, V.
Perfectly poised overlooking the Thames and Tower Bridge, the Blue Print Café sails gracefully on as one of London's most reliably enjoyable places to eat. The ideal is to catch a sunny day on the balcony, and soak up the cool design, adept staff and confident cooking. We enjoyed a vibrant chilled spinach and watercress soup, zingy in taste and colour. Crostini with broad beans and tapenade amazed us with its curved sculptural crostini, but was slightly overwhelmed by a pungent tapenade. Main courses lifted ordinary ingredients into a new class. Fegato alla veneziana was mouthwateringly succulent calf's liver, white hake with beetroot, horseradish and chives was a revelatory and much fought-over combination. Accompanying roast potatoes, fragrant with garlic and rosemary, were almost a meal in themselves. Pure greed forced us into desserts: a daunting-looking but surprisingly light almond tart with Jersey cream, and an irresistible blueberry and raspberry trifle. The wine list hits the same note of ease and authority without pomp, that characterises this most likeable of Conran enterprises. The Blue Print Café continues to justify its excellent reputation.
Babies and children admitted; high chair. Booking advisable; essential dinner Fri, Sat. **Map 8/9S.**

Le Pont de la Tour
Butlers Wharf Building, 36D Shad Thames, Butlers Wharf, SE1 (020 7403 8403). Tower Hill tube/Tower Gateway DLR/London Bridge tube/rail/47, 78 bus. **Bar and grill Open** 11.30am-11.30pm Mon-Sat; noon-11pm Sun. **Main courses** £9.50-£14.50. **Set meal** (noon-3pm, 6-8pm Mon-Fri) £15 two courses. *Restaurant* **Lunch served** noon-3pm Mon-Fri, Sun. **Dinner served** 6-11.30pm Mon-Sat; 6-11pm Sun. **Main courses** £17-£27. **Set lunch** (Mon-Fri) £28.50 three courses. **Set dinner** (6-6.45pm, 10.45-11.30pm Mon-Sat; 6-6.45pm Sun) £19.50 three courses. *Both* **Service** 12½%. **Credit** AmEx, DC, JCB, MC, £TC, V.
The best thing about Le Pont de la Tour is, and always has been, the view on a sunny day. Or a clear night, for that matter. Located right on the river, the pretty room is overshadowed by the attractions outside its big windows. It was a shame, then, that on a miraculously clear August day, with all the windows open, the food didn't come even half-way to matching the quality of the view. The weekday set lunch offers a fair choice of dishes, but though they were good, the standard just wasn't high enough to justify the price. A quickly seared tranche of smoked salmon sat on a rather tough potato galette; tomato consommé with buffalo mozzarella featured good cheese and good vegetables, but failed to excite us, while a main course of half a cold lobster with mayonnaise was chewy and bland. Three small portions of wonderfully flavourful cheese and a delicious chocolate tart proved to be the highlights of the meal. The lengthy wine list is no friend to anyone but the wealthy. With dinner costing from around £31 à la carte, and the average spend (before drink) at about £40 a head, there just isn't enough quality to make us recommend this place wholeheartedly. Despite the view, there are more memorable meals to be had elsewhere.
Babies and children welcome; high chairs. Booking essential. Dress: smart casual. Entertainment: pianist nightly; 1-4pm Sun. Separate room for parties, seats 20. Tables outdoors (22, terrace). Vegetarian menu. **Map 8/8S.**

North

Camden Town & Chalk Farm NW1

Odette's

130 Regent's Park Road, NW1 (020 7586 5486). Chalk Farm tube/31, 168 bus. **Wine bar Open** 12.30-2.30pm, 5.30-10.30pm Mon-Sat; 12.30-2.30pm Sun. *Restaurant* **Lunch served** 12.30-2.30pm Mon-Fri. **Dinner served** 7-11pm Mon-Sat. **Main courses** £10.50-£17.50. **Set lunch** (Mon-Fri) £12.50 three courses. **Credit** AmEx, DC, MC, V. Odette's offers a slightly old-fashioned experience, in that service is pleasant, rather than too smoothly professional; decor is interesting and easy-on-the-eye rather than modern or flash; and the atmosphere is relaxed. The prices, however, are up to the minute, but the standard of cooking is excellent. Summer minestrone looked processed but tasted full of flavour; even better was salad of asparagus, sugarsnap peas, rocket, mascarpone and own-made penne, with balsamic dressing. Grilled halibut with greens was a simple but excellent main course; Gressingham duck breast with caramelised endive, glazed peaches and citrus zest also won praise. Blackberry sorbet was less appealing, being slightly sour and having a strange texture; steamed gooseberry pudding might have been a better choice. The splendid wine list is helpfully divided into 'full bodied aromatic white wines', 'medium bodied red wines' and so on, with clear notes for each bottle. At Odette's the emphasis is placed on the enjoyment of the customer, not the convenience of the staff. *Babies and children admitted. Booking essential. Dress: smart casual. Separate rooms for parties, seating 8 and 30. Tables outdoors (3, pavement).*

Islington N1

Euphorium

203 Upper Street, N1 (020 7704 6909). Highbury & Islington tube/rail. **Lunch served** noon-2.30pm Mon-Sat; noon-3.30pm Sun. **Dinner served** 6-10.30pm daily. **Main courses** £6.50-£12.50. **Service** 12½%. **Credit** AmEx, JCB, MC, £TC, V. Amid Upper Street's frenzied restaurant scene, Euphorium has begun to seem like a stable fixture, and is certainly holding its own with the competition. The dining room has been extended and lightened, so that long pink balloon lights now sway over the bar and in the bamboo-filled back yard. However, the cheerful staff continue to serve slightly overpriced and slightly hit-and-miss cooking to the youngish crowd that packs in every night. Both starters had imperfections; goat's cheese tart with roasted onion and globe artichoke was rather heavy, while balsamic-based dressing and capers swamped the delicate flavour of the confit salmon. Things began to look up with the main courses. Slow-roasted shoulder of lamb with puy lentils and mustard fruits was delicious, even if the lamb was a puzzlingly perfect box shape. Pan-roasted cod with skordalia and chermoula (one of which contained almonds) was worth trying, too. The big chips were sublime, and the vegetable mix of pak choi, Thai aubergine and fennel was an appetising accompaniment. Puddings won out overall, though. Cape gooseberry brûlée with pear compote had a satisfyingly dense topping and was refreshingly tart inside, and the vanilla panna cotta with strawberry soup was blissful. *Babies and children welcome. Book dinner; lunch Sun. Tables outdoors (15, garden).*

Granita ★

127 Upper Street, N1 (020 7226 3222). Angel tube. **Lunch served** 12.30-2.30pm Wed-Sat; 12.30-3pm Sun. **Dinner served** 6.30-10pm Tue-Sun. **Main courses** £10-£14.50. **Set Sunday lunch** £12.50 two courses, £14.95 three courses. **Credit** MC, £TC, V. This very simply decorated, pared down restaurant is still the best in Islington. The lack of frills and furbelows concentrates attention on the food on a short, daily-changing menu. There are six or so choices per course, and all dishes are cooked with confidence and packed with flavour. A typical meal might be runner bean, rocket, black fig, Manchego and chive salad followed by char-grilled chump of lamb with okra and tomato, cumin, lemon and rocket, finished by nectarine and almond tart. Recent stand-out dishes were asparagus, char-grilled with sweet potato, dill and sour cream (a starter); and spinach fatayer with feta, cos, olive and parsley salad (a light, refreshing reworking of a Middle Eastern classic). Service, like the rest of the establishment, is unfussy but assured. A shining light on a street full of tawdry eateries. *Babies and children welcome. Booking advisable. Vegetarian dishes.* **Map 16/1O.**

Kavanagh's

26 Penton Street, N1 (020 7833 1380/ www.kavrestaurant.co.uk). Angel tube. **Brunch served** noon-3.30pm Sun. **Lunch served** 12.30-2.30pm, **dinner served** 6-10.30pm Tue-Sat. **Main courses** £9-£13.50. **Set meals** (lunch; 6-7pm Tue-Sun) £10 two courses, £12.95 three courses. **Service** 12½% for parties of six or more. **Credit** MC, £TC, V. Very much the laid-back local, Kavanagh's provides a ray of sunshine in an Islington backwater. The small ground-floor room is painted in primary-school bright colours, with stripped-pine floors and furniture and an open kitchen at one end. The atmosphere and the staff are friendly and easy-going. In keeping with this modest operation, the menu and wine list are very short, but also reasonably priced. The food may not scale great culinary heights, but dishes (mostly in the modern Mediterranean mould) are well thought out and come nicely presented. Southern European influences show up in dishes such as a char-grilled aubergine salad with nutty lemon tahini dressing and coriander, and prawns grilled with lashings of garlic and a lemon and lime dressing. A warm fungi salad packed with ginger and garlic would have warmed the cockles of Carluccio's heart, although some overcooked risotto served as a main course with rocket, Parmesan and too many spring onions was less of a hit. Puddings – including a raspberry crème brûlée and tarte tatin with Calvados cream – came lightly dusted with icing sugar and decorated with berries. A local worth supporting. *Babies and children welcome. Booking advisable. Tables outdoors (2, pavement).* **Map 3/2N.**

Lola's

The Mall Building, Camden Passage, 359 Upper Street, N1 (020 7359 1932). Angel tube. **Brunch served** noon-3pm Sat, Sun. **Lunch served** noon-2.30pm Mon-Fri. **Dinner served** 6-11pm Mon-Sat. **Main courses** £10.75-£16.50. **Set lunch** £10 two courses, £15 three courses. **Service** 12½% for parties of five or more. **Credit** AmEx, DC, JCB, MC, TC, V. At the end of a chilly Bank Holiday weekend, Lola's seemed downbeat. The menu is short and attractively eclectic; prawn cocktail, and Caesar salad stand proud amid other starters of marinated artichoke focaccia with Pecorino and caperberries (a nice idea, but not entirely successful), and a delicious Roquefort, rosemary and red onion pizza. For main courses, the lobster and tarragon risotto won high praise for its generous helping of lobster, but the rocket pesto with cavatelli pasta was not as rocket-peppery as we'd hoped, and its accompanying tomato and shallot salad never arrived. Perhaps the fresh pea and goat's cheese risotto would have been a better bet. Puddings range from palate-refreshers to comfort food such as sticky date and chocolate pudding with butterscotch sauce. The wine list provides some unusual treats. Our main gripe, then, was with the slow, unfriendly and inefficient service. The general feeling of flatness wasn't helped by melancholy piano music and ill-conceived decor. Given that a meal for two including service came to over £90, Lola's must try harder. *Babies and children welcome. Booking advisable; essential weekends; bookings not accepted for parties of 9 or more. Entertainment: pianist nightly; jazz brunch Sun.* **Map 16/2O.**

North West

Hampstead NW3

Cucina

45A South End Road, NW3 (020 7435 7814). Hampstead Heath rail/24, 168, C11 bus. **Lunch served** noon-2.30pm Mon-Sat; noon-3pm Sun. **Dinner served** 7-10.30pm Mon-Thur; 7-11pm Fri, Sat. **Main courses** £10.50-£15.95. **Set lunch** (Mon-Sat) £8.50 two courses. **Set Sunday lunch** £12.95 two courses, £15.95 three courses. **Set dinner** £16.95 three courses. **Credit** AmEx, MC, £TC, V. After a slow start, it seemed that the entire population of Hampstead had rolled in to Cucina, greeting waitresses and commenting on the revamped decor (a bizarre combination of Donald Duck meets Renaissance meets circuit-board sculpture). Meanwhile, we were tucking into a warm and carefully put together assembly of char-grilled squid, crunchy pancetta, spinach and herbs, and a second starter of roast quail, served searingly hot with legs-akimbo on a nice warm lentil salad. Unfortunately, salsa verde, designed to complement the two dishes, alienated

The New End.
See page 144.

them both with its harsh capers. Main courses were also a mixed bag. The first few mouthfuls of chunky salmon fillet with pickled ginger, caramelised onions, fresh asparagus and a sweet sake dressing were delicious, but by the end the dish tasted more like a fishy dessert. The one vegetarian option, mushroom and feta pie, successfully combined crisp thin flaky pastry, with layers of spinach, leeks and pine nuts, but could have done with a more moist sidekick than beansprouts and watercress. Puddings, brimming with calories, included a weighty chocolate, mascarpone and gingernut cheesecake with toffee bananas, and crêpes filled with shredded coconut and palm sugar, served with fresh pineapple and five-spice ice-cream. The wine list is reasonable and descriptive; the staff are friendly and informative. A pleasant place.
Babies and children welcome; high chairs. Booking advisable; essential weekends. Takeaway service. **Map 9.**

Gresslin's

13 Heath Street, NW3 (020 7794 8386). Hampstead tube. **Lunch served** noon-2.30pm Tue-Sun. **Dinner served** 7-10.30pm Mon-Sat. **Main courses** £12.50-£16.50. **Set Sunday lunch** £15.95 two courses, £18.95 three courses. **Set dinner** (Mon-Thur) £15.95 two courses, £18.95 three courses. **Service** 12½%. **Credit** AmEx, MC, TC, V.
Gresslins is a local restaurant that manages to provide both skilled cooking and comfortable surroundings – in a long narrow room with a modern feel to it. While we were perusing the menu (Modern European with an oriental touch), the friendly and attentive staff offered a selection of great bread, made in-house. A raw fish fix of salmon sashimi with coriander and sesame was mouthwatering and excellent value from the set menu, while marinated tuna, rocket and squid salad was equally enticing, coming with a moreish balsamic syrup on the side. Pan-fried guinea fowl with yam galette and tamarillo salsa was a pleasing combination, featuring tender meat and an unusual yet effective salsa made of summer fruits. Marlin with a herb, tomato and caper crust and mussel sauce vièrge was also excellent, with the marlin cooked to perfection. A dessert of caramelised lemon tart with minted raspberries was just right, too. However, we were blown away by a black rice pudding with peaches and coconut – simply superb, and surely helped by a glass of Monbazillac from the well-chosen wine list. Worth a trip.
Babies and children welcome; high chairs. Booking advisable; essential dinner and weekends. No smoking. Takeaway service. **Map 9.**

The New End

102 Heath Street, NW3 (020 7431 4423). Hampstead tube. **Lunch served** noon-3pm Wed-Sun. **Dinner served** 6-11pm Tue-Sun. **Main courses** £16.50-£19.50. **Set meal** £18.50 two courses, £21.50 three courses. **Credit** AmEx, MC, V.
Having had no quality restaurants for years, Hampstead now has several. The New End is the latest. The inside is light, airy, sleek and minimal; quarry tiles, white plaster, bare brick and flower photos lead to a finely carpentered serving bar. The cooking isn't bad either, offering a simple fixed-price menu of four starters and mains, all with thoughtfully combined flavours that are echoed in an alluring wine list (£14-£50 a bottle). Wild sea trout tartare with a small dollop of crème fraîche and caviar couched in greenery was deliciously refreshing, while cured dried beef with rocket and Manchego cheese was a delightful nest of surprising flavours. Breast of free-range chicken with fondant potato and wild mushrooms was juicier and livelier than it sounds, while a baked cod fillet arrived nicely accompanied by artichokes and lightly garlicked parsley mash. Service seemed tentative, but any complications over a chocolate fondant dessert were vitiated by the chocolate cake with a gooey middle that arrived. In the days when the gravy train has replaced the gravy boat, the set meal here provides great value.
No-smoking tables. **Map 9.**

Outer London

Kew, Surrey

The Glasshouse ★

14 Station Parade, Kew, Surrey (020 8940 6777). Kew Gardens tube/rail. **Lunch served** noon-2.30pm daily. **Dinner served** 7-10.30pm Mon-Thur; 6.30-10.30pm Fri, Sat. **Set lunch** £19.50 three courses. **Set Sunday lunch** £21.50 three courses. **Set dinner** £25 three courses. **Service** 12½%. **Credit** AmEx, MC, £TC, V.
Home of possibly the nicest waiters and front-of-house staff in town, the Glasshouse has swiftly built up a loyal following in Kew and beyond. Diners can hear themselves think in this light-filled, pleasantly decorated room (enlivened by flowers and a few abstract art works), and the atmosphere is welcoming and unjudgmental. All this, and the food is good. Own-cured salmon with a salt-cod fish cake and pickled cucumber was a great blend of flavours, though in another starter, sauce gribiche slightly emasculated the deep-fried Rossmore oysters with which it was paired. Next, we eschewed ravioli paysanne with roast vegetables and cep broth, and roast loin of pork with black pudding, split green peas and grain mustard, in favour of ragout of monkfish with crème fraîche, chives and baby leeks; and braised rump of lamb with rosemary and creamed white beans – lovely spring dishes. Prince among puddings was a fabulous combo of rhubarb, yoghurt, pistachio ice-cream and madeleines. All together a good-natured venture that richly deserves its full house, and a deserved finalist in the Best New Restaurant category of the *Time Out* Eating Awards.
Babies and children admitted lunch; high chairs. Booking essential.

Surbiton, Surrey

Luca ★

85 Maple Road, Surbiton, Surrey (020 8399 2365). Surbiton rail. **Lunch served** 11.30am-2.30pm Sun. **Dinner served** 6.30-10.30pm Tue-Sat. **Main courses** £9.90-£14. **Set meal** (6.30-7pm Mon-Sat) £12.95 two courses, £15.95 three courses. **Credit** JCB, MC, V.
Elegantly chic decor in shades of cranberry and sage green, charming service and a fusion menu masterminded by a Sugar Club alumna create a winning formula at Luca. Annie O'Carroll combines the best ingredients with an expert touch on a short menu that offers just six choices in each course. This is a restrained version of fusion cooking, produced with panache. Start the adventure with lamb's sweetbread linguine with peas and almond pesto, perhaps, or warm potato and goat's cheese terrine with rocket and balsamic onions. Next, Australian reef fish with udon noodle vegetables, crispy garlic and fresh coconut chutney is one of the most outré offerings among main courses that might also include black bean chilli, guacamole, cornbread and sour cream; or breast of wood pigeon, grilled salami, cauliflower cheese and watercress. Flavours continue to surprise with desserts such as the chocolate, ricotta and black pepper tart, though if you've had enough excitement for one meal, comforting pairings like orange and almond cake with cinnamon custard beckon. Winner of Best Local Restaurant category in the *Time Out* Eating Awards.
Babies and children admitted; crayons; high chairs. Booking essential; one week in advance for weekends, two days for week days. No-smoking tables. Tables outdoors (2, pavement). Vegetarian dishes.

Twickenham, Middlesex

Brula

43 Crown Road, Twickenham, Middx (020 8892 0602). St Margarets rail. **Lunch served** 12.30-2pm Tue-Fri. **Dinner served** 7-10.30pm Tue-Sat. **Main courses** £9.50-£11. **Set lunch** (Tue-Fri) £8 two courses, £10 three courses. **House wine** £9.50 bottle, £2.50 glass. **No credit cards.**
Brula has crossed the road to larger premises at the heart of St Margarets village and the transition has been well worthwhile. Retaining some of the original bistro intimacy, the restaurant's decor includes a mirrored wall, modern prints, stained-glass windows, large brass ceiling fans and a beautifully carved wooden panel. With four choices for each course, we started with a succulent pork terrine, admirably complemented by onion marmalade, and whole grilled sardines tastily set off by a cabernet sauvignon vinaigrette. Provençal beef stew, served on pasta and topped with strips of orange peel was satisfyingly flavoursome and tender, while a subtle mixture of vegetables and goat's cheese in crispy samosas, served with red pepper sauce, turned out to be a mildly spicy classic. To round off we chose an ideal combination of luxurious chocolate mousse and cream, and a slightly disappointing crème brûlée. Bottles of wine range from £9 to £25 and the house red and white can be ordered by the glass or carafe. Though the crowding of tables resulted in us getting an occasional buffeting from busy members of staff, this is a new and improved version of a popular formula. Book early.
Babies and children admitted. Booking essential dinner. Separate room for parties, seats 10.

North African

Restaurants in this section are all inspired by the cuisine of the Maghreb – Morocco, Tunisia and Algeria. For Egyptian restaurant **Ali Baba**, *see page 127* **Middle Eastern**. Sudanese, Ethiopian and Eritrean restaurants are included in the **African & Caribbean** chapter.

The North African vogue may have reached its zenith now, with many a restaurant premises converted to a loose interpretation of a generic Maghrebi kasbah. Some such places have little to offer, but others, like the newly refurbished and renamed **Kyma** and the new outfit **Maghreb**, are giving Londoners a taste of the best in Maghrebi cooking, combined with the odd European touch. A few North African restaurants, such as **Ayoush** and **Souk**, have found a niche as party venues; still others (usually the most expensive and fashionable) continue along the fusion route, in which North African cooking influences European dishes and vice-versa. One (**Mô**, the tea room attached to **Momo**) functions as a bazaar as well as a café serving little samples of brilliant Moroccan fusion food. And don't forget the old-guard restaurants, such as **Laurent** and the **Royal Couscous House**, which continue to turn out fine tagines and couscous dishes. London's North African restaurants are nothing if not diverse.

Central

Leicester Square WC2

Souk

27 Litchfield Street, WC2 (020 7240 1796). Leicester Square tube. **Meals served** noon-11.30pm daily. **Main courses** £7.50-£8.50. **Set meal** £15 three courses incl mint tea. **Service** 10%. **Credit** MC, £TC, V.
This is not the sort of place you drop into by chance – tucked away as it is in a basement near to the Ivy. Souk used to be Bunjies folk club; its low ceilings (watch your head) and shady corners maintain an intimate, club-like feel. The service is helpful. Staff were happy to prepare another table after we asked to be moved from our low-slung leather cushions next to a speaker. This isn't a venue for a quiet evening. On our visit a large gang of West End workers was out celebrating a birthday. The waiters helped the occasion along with bongos and a cake. We were spared any belly dancers, although some diners had a game go. After perusing the pleasing fur-covered menus and supping Moroccan beers (Casablanca), we tucked into a mixed meze for two that was well-presented, fresh and filling. Main course tagines (lamb with prunes and almonds; and spinach, feta cheese and roast onion) were rich, but retained a subtlety of flavour. Fresh mint tea to finish was a welcome restorative. Souk's set three-course dinners are good value, particularly if you're after a 'Badouin-style' evening.
Booking essential. Separate room for parties, seats 35. Takeaway service. **Map 14/6K.**

Marylebone W1

Ayoush

58 James Street & 77 Wigmore Street, W1 (020 7935 9839). Bond Street tube. **Meals served** 11am-11pm Mon-Sat. **Main courses** £5.50-£15.50. **Set lunch** (noon-4pm) £8 three courses. **Minimum** £25 (restaurant, dinner). **Service** 12½%. **Credit** AmEx, DC, JCB, MC, TC, V.
Ayoush is a party restaurant. Diners descend from the airy ground-floor café to a dimly lit basement, transformed into an orientalist's vision of the kasbah, with eastern-style lanterns and arches leading into secluded, cushioned alcoves for large groups. We were only two, so were stuck on one of the few tables in the middle of the restaurant. A starter of Moroccan carrot salad was warmly spiced and just right, but a salad mechouia (grilled peppers, chillies, tomato and garlic with herbs and olive oil) was too vinegary. By the time we'd finished our starters the music had been cranked up and some groups had taken to the dance floor. From then on, unable to converse above the noise, we found ourselves involuntarily eating to the beat of the Arabic rhythms. Chicken couscous consisted of a large portion of poultry with plenty of vegetables. It wasn't particularly flavoursome, but the couscous was light and fluffy. Tagine de viande (lamb with prunes and almonds) came with a rich sauce just the right side of fruity: a fine rendition of a Moroccan classic. We couldn't quite make it on to the dancefloor, but instead opted for some mint tea and a smoke at the sheesha pipe. The food doesn't really warrant the prices charged, but at Ayoush you pay for the party atmosphere.
Booking advisable. Children admitted. Dress: no caps, jeans or trainers. Tables outdoors (5, pavement). Takeaway service. **Map 2/6G.**

Original Tajines

7A Dorset Street, W1 (020 7935 1545). Baker Street tube. **Lunch served** noon-2.30pm Mon-Fri. **Dinner served** 6-10.30pm Mon-Sat. **Main courses** £8.95-£11. **Credit** MC, V.
Now with a new name (it used to be Tajine), Original Tajines has become a highly popular restaurant. The interior is pleasant – with round Moroccan-style mosaic tables, candlelight and North African artefacts. On our most recent visit, the food was enjoyable, but not stunning. A pepper salad starter consisted of warmly spiced strips of pepper in olive oil. Tabouleh Moroccan-style differed widely from the Lebanese version, consisting of large amounts of couscous with chunks of tomato and cucumber. It lacked the delicacy of flavour found in the best Lebanese restaurants. We spiced it up with a side dish of harira sauce with olives. Main course fish tagine was a large portion of juicy, perfectly cooked salmon in a nicely piquant sauce, with olives and onions. Chicken tagine with peppers was adequate, but again lacked flavour. It didn't help that the bread accompanying the tagines was not the freshest. A nice touch, though, was the plate of flavoured bulgar wheat and a Greek salad that come with all main courses. Service varied; a waitress was grim-faced, but the man who served the splendid, dry Moroccan wine was charm itself.
Babies and children admitted. Tables outdoors (5, pavement). Takeaway service. **Map 2/5G.**

Mayfair W1

Momo

25 Heddon Street, W1 (020 7434 4040). Piccadilly Circus tube. **Brunch served** 12.30-2.30pm Sat, Sun. **Lunch served** 12.30-2.30pm Mon-Fri. **Dinner served** 7-11.30pm Mon-Sat. **Main courses** £9.75-£15.50. **Set brunch** £15 four courses. **Set lunch** £12 two courses, £15 three courses. **Service** 12½%. **Credit** AmEx, DC, MC, £TC, V.
For a younger generation of restaurant-goers, Momo is now firmly established as a place to be seen in. It's certainly lively; the closely packed tables, well-lubricated diners and loud Arabic music make sure of that. It has also retained its looks, with stunning North African themed decor and attractive staff. But we weren't so sure about the food. Our dinner was good, though it didn't quite produce the exquisite fusion of North African and European elements that previous visits had led us to expect. The best dish was a starter of seared tuna with a sharp preserved-lemon marmalade and oily mushrooms: a skilful combination of succulent fish and fruitiness. Mechouia (roast peppers, tomatoes with garlic and cumin) was OK, but unadventurous. It was followed by a vegetable tagine (one of only two vegetarian main courses, and steep at £9.50) that proved a bit too much of the same. For our other main course, we eschewed fusion dishes such as roast monkfish tail with walnut butter and dried fruits, opting instead for couscous Momo with a shank of lamb, merguez sausages and grilled chunks of lamb. The shank

was beautifully tender and melted away from the bone, the sausages were suitably spicy, but the grilled lamb lacked that touch of class. The fluffy, flagrant and delicate couscous, though, was impossible to fault. Gripes aside, Momo remains a great place for a special night out.
Babies and children admitted. Booking advisable. Tables outdoors (2, patio; 6, pavement). Map 13/7J.

Mô
23 Heddon Street, W1 (020 7434 4040). Piccadilly Circus tube. **Meals served** 11am-11pm Mon-Sat. **Credit** AmEx, DC, MC, £TC, V.
The artfully arranged artefacts in Mô are for sale, giving the place the appearance of a bazaar (albeit a very quiet one). Its ambience is deeply relaxing: so peaceful that one could happily sit for hours daydreaming over a glass of mint tea. In these respects it could hardly be more different from its sleek and stylised sister **Momo** next door. Mô sells sandwiches with a Moroccan flavour, but we opted for 'l'assiette de 4 specialities' (£4.95 for four vegetarian dishes, £5.80 if you choose one meat option): a choice of four from 14 dishes. Our selection, put together as one beautifully presented small plateful, was close to being exquisite: all our choices combined well; every little dish was put together with consummate skill and care. Among our favourites were a tomato and mustard tart (super-soft pastry, filling with a touch of piquancy) and seared tuna marinated with thyme, lemon and ginger (slim slices that had just touched the grill and melted in the mouth, drizzled with balsamic vinegar – wonderful). Other dishes were more traditionally Moroccan, but made to a standard several notches above the norm; they included zaalouk (aubergine purée), green beans with sesame seeds, and grilled peppers. We couldn't resist pudding, and had Berber pancake in a sea of honey along with mint tea. Mô modestly describes itself as a 'salad bar, tea room and bazaar' – if only more salad bars were like this.
Babies and children admitted. Tables outdoors (5, terrace). Takeaway service. **Map 13/7J.**

West

Hammersmith W6

Azou
375 King Street, W6 (020 8563 7266). Stamford Brook tube. **Lunch served** noon-2.30pm Mon-Fri. **Dinner served** 6-11pm daily. **Main courses** £6.90-£13. **Set meals** £12.50, £15, three courses. **Service** 12%. **Credit** DC, MC, V.
One of three recently opened North African places on this stretch, Azou looks the most promising with its rai music and Berber-inspired interior (even if our waitress appeared to be Polish). Azou's menu mixes the Maghreb with a few Middle Eastern meze dishes, but we stuck to the North African food. Brik was a delight: a large parcel of fried, filo-wrapped, soft-cooked egg, with potato and tuna. A version of harira (the soup often eaten to break the Ramadan fast) had a glutinous and rich lamb stock, which worked well with the pulses and vegetables. Traditional tagine combinations – such as lamb with prunes, apricots and almonds; or chicken with olives, preserved lemons and almonds – simply can't be improved upon, so we were pleased to find Azou's versions hadn't been tampered with; they were right on target. The couscous, too, was some of the fluffiest we'd tasted. Azou is a simple neighbourhood restaurant, so don't go expecting Momo. Nevertheless, this is a decent place to explore North African food.
Babies and children admitted. Entertainment: belly dancing (phone for details).

Shepherd's Bush W12

Adam's Café
77 Askew Road, W12 (020 8743 0572). Hammersmith tube, then 266 bus or Shepherd's Bush tube, then 207 bus. **Set dinner** £9.95 one course incl mint tea or coffee, £12.95 two courses, £14.95 three courses. **Credit** AmEx, DC, MC, V.
Adam's Café has been sticking to its successful formula for several years now, and the formula still works. The husband-and-wife team serve down-to-earth, mainly Maghrebi food (with some French influences) from a fixed-price menu. All meals begin with moreish little meatballs, olives and pickled vegetables. Tunisian brik au thon (tuna and egg encased in filo pastry) is a favourite starter, but this time we went for a good bisque-like fish soup, and whole prawns in a warmly flavoured chilli and tomato sauce. The prawns were big and juicy, but they were quite difficult to eat: we had to make extensive use of the fingerbowl. Main course couscous merguez was a generous portion of spicy sausages with couscous (not the fluffiest ever, but

Kyma

refills were supplied) and the requisite harira and vegetable broth as accompaniments. Lamb tagine with prunes was a well-balanced version, with just the right degree of sweetness, although the lamb was perhaps a tad overcooked. Puddings were a highlight: a lovely tarte au citron, and Berber pancakes doused in a delicious honey sauce. A fine neighbourhood restaurant that attracts a band of local regulars, Adam's is hard to beat for price.
Babies and children admitted. Book weekends. Separate room for parties, seats 24.

Westbourne Grove W2

Kyma
84 Westbourne Grove, W2 (020 7792 2207). Bayswater or Queensway tube. **Dinner served** 6pm-midnight Mon-Sat; noon-11pm Sun. **Main courses** £6.75-£9.95. **Service** 10%. **Credit** AmEx, JCB, MC, £TC, V.
The restaurant formerly known as Agadir has undergone a major refit and a revolution in the kitchen. What had been an old-fashioned place with adequate, vaguely North African cooking has become spot-on in the food stakes. A large plate of Moroccan meze to share included warmly spiced carrots and peppers among the authentic tasting vegetable salads: a fine mix of flavours with good Maghrebi-style use of spices. Barkouk (lamb with plum sauce) was superb. The meat was tender and plentiful and the balance of flavours just so. Chicken couscous with caramelised onions and raisins was less spectacular, but perfectly acceptable, with tender chicken and feather-light couscous. For pudding, beautifully presented dried figs came with a dribbling of Grand Marnier and a dusting of icing sugar. The obvious care that goes into the food here is matched by a modern, ethnic (but not over-the-top) look and by attentive service from pleasant staff. Kyma deserves to succeed.
Babies and children welcome; half-price children's portions. Book weekends. Entertainment: belly dancers 9-11pm Fri, Sat. Separate room for parties, seats 70. Takeaway service. **Map 11/6B.**

South West

Gloucester Road SW7

Pasha
1 Gloucester Road, SW7 (020 7589 7969/ www.pasha-restaurant.co.uk). Gloucester Road tube/10, 49, 52 bus. **Lunch served** noon-3pm daily. **Dinner served** 6-11.30pm Mon-Sat; 6-10.30pm Sun. **Main courses** £9.90-£18.50. **Service** 15%. **Credit** AmEx, DC, MC, TC, V.
Pasha's oriental-inspired but original decor still looks stunning. A sweeping stairway leads to the lower level, which is decked out with a centrepiece mosaic fountain, lantern lighting, low tables and uncomfortable boudoir-style chairs. Such extraordinary furnishings exude an aura of specialness that one assumes will continue in the food, but although there were flashes of brilliance in the dishes we chose, our enjoyment of the meal was marred by mismatching ingredients or lack of attention to detail. An outstandingly tangy seafood tagine was served with a flatbread fussily infused with olive oil and dusted with herbs: completely useless for mopping up the tagine's tasty sauce. A prawn chermoula starter contained fat, juicy prawns and herby, very buttery sauce. It tasted great, except when combined with the accompanying rocket. Another starter, prawn brigout, was filled mainly by slightly spicy mashed potato, with a rather low prawn quota. A main course crab cake was better, but again, not very inspiring. Accompanying aubergine chips, however, were a great concept, having a proper chip-like texture and a good taste; they weren't at all greasy. Pleasing puddings were turkish delight brûlée (pure indulgence) and chocolate brownie (a fine example). A crisp Gris de Guerrouane Moroccan white was excellent, too, and good value at £13. A mixed bag.
Babies and children admitted. Booking advisable. No-smoking tables. **Map 5/9C.**

South

Clapham SW4

Kasbah
73 Venn Street, SW4 (020 7498 3622). Clapham Common tube. **Meals served** 6-11.30pm Mon-Fri; 10am-11.30pm Sat; 10am-10.30pm Sun. **Main courses** £6.50-£8.95. **Credit** AmEx, MC, V.
Sandwiched between two of the brighter stars of Clapham's eaterie firmament (the Sequel and Gastro) Kasbah struggles to shine. It's a pleasant enough place, with simple, authentic-looking decor and wooden floors and furniture giving it a comfortable feel. On our visit, however, the food was too bland to be memorable. Complimentary warm bread, olives and a (very hot) chilli dip made a promising start, but main courses – royal couscous, and beef tagine with almonds – both had a sparsity of spice. The one-dimensional nature and lack of freshness in the flavours made both dishes a battle to finish. Maybe the daily specials (chick pea purée and chicken tagine) would have proved a better bet. A decent bottle of beefy Moroccan red wine did enhance the dining experience, though. The front room at Kasbah was pretty full for a Monday; there's a large back room for busier nights or for party bookings.
Babies and children admitted. Booking advisable.

North

Camden Town & Chalk Farm NW1

Yima
95 Parkway, NW1 (020 7267 1097). Camden Town tube. **Meals served** noon-10pm Mon-Sat; 1-7pm Sun. **Main courses** £4.50-£6.95. **Unlicensed. No credit cards.**

There are some tables on the ground floor at Yima, but many diners opt for the comfortable ethnic-look basement, with its sofa seating, soft lighting, low tables and abundance of artefacts. Starters consist of classic Maghrebi salads (carrot, aubergine and pepper), all of which were tasty and enjoyable. We particularly liked the distinctive warm piquancy of the carrot salad. Main courses are hearty portions of straight-down-the-line traditional Maghrebi cooking, but we were less impressed with the results. Tagine with lamb, prunes and almonds was bland and stew-like, while couscous with chicken and onions was also under-flavoured, although the chicken was tender and the couscous well cooked. Reservations about the cooking aside, Yima is a really pleasant place to spend time. We stayed for hours, drinking mint tea and chatting, tended by charming, helpful staff.
Babies and children admitted. Booking advisable. No-smoking tables. Separate room for parties, seats 35. Tables outdoors (2, pavement). Takeaway service.

Finsbury Park N4

Yamina

192 Stroud Green Road, N4 (020 7263 6161). Finsbury Park tube/rail then W2, W3, W7 bus. **Dinner served** 6-11.30pm Tue-Fri. **Meals served** 11am-midnight Sat, Sun. **Main courses** £4.50-£7.90. **Credit** DC, MC, V.

Adorned with cushions and artefacts for that Moroccan look, Yamina is a pleasant space. We began our meal on the deck-like upper area at the front of the restaurant, but had to move when a party arrived to take up its reservation, because the tables were impossibly close together. The menu is wide-ranging and includes dishes not often found in London restaurants, such as Moroccan white bean stew with tomatoes, garlic, harissa and coriander; and orzo salad (pasta with dill, lemon and olive oil). After a meze platter of nicely flavoured salads (including spicy carrot and roast peppers), we moved on to lamb tagine with prunes and almonds. The chef had gone overboard on the prunes, rendering the sauce thick and over-sweet; the flavours of the tender meat were masked. Seafood bastilla wrapped in filo pastry and dusted with icing sugar – a variation on traditional bastilla, which is made with pigeon – was less sweet, but a touch bland. In fact, mint tea and Moroccan pastries turned out to be the best parts of the meal.
Babies and children welcome; high chairs. No-smoking tables. Tables outdoors (3, pavement).

Holloway N7

Royal Cous-Cous House

316 Holloway Road, N7 (020 7700 2188). Holloway Road tube. **Dinner served** 5-11pm Tue-Sun. **Main courses** £5.95-£9.95. **Credit** AmEx, JCB, MC, £TC, V.

Holloway Road is a small hub for London's Moroccan community, with a few Moroccan shops alongside the Royal Couscous House. The restaurant is devoid of pretensions: its interior has patterned carpet with plastic pine-look walls on which the occasional desultory artefact is hung; the welcome is warm; food comes in generous portions and is very good. Marinated sardines were larger than average fish in a warmly spiced tomato sauce. Salads of smoked peppers and a roughly mashed smoky aubergine paste were a great accompaniment, as was the fresh, warm bread (probably from the local Turkish shop, and just what you need for mopping up tagines). Royal tagine (lamb with prunes, almonds, sesame seeds and boiled eggs) got the sweet to savoury ratio just right: there was plenty of thickish sauce, not so sweet that you couldn't taste the meat, and full of fruity flavour. Marrakesh couscous was also a fine rendition, consisting of two large hunks of chicken with plenty of raisins and the flavour of cinnamon (but lacking the usual bowl of accompanying broth). Puddings were out of the question, but we had Moroccan coffee – sweet and milky and served in a glass.
Babies and children welcome; high chairs. Booking advisable weekends. Student discount (10%). Takeaway service (Tue-Thur, Sun).

Islington N1

Maghreb

189 Upper Street, N1 (020 7226 2305). Angel tube/Highbury & Islington tube/rail. **Dinner served** 6-11.30pm daily. **Main courses** £5.95-£11.95. **Set meal** (Mon-Wed, Sun) £8.95. **Service** 12½% for parties of six or more. **Credit** AmEx, MC, V.

Maghreb is clearly aiming for a spot in the upper echelons of the burgeoning North African restaurant scene. It looks handsome – deep-yellow walls, red hanging lamps, velvet-covered chairs in jewel colours – and brims with confidence. The fusion menu places adaptations of traditional dishes alongside tagines and couscous. When the cooking's good it's very good, but the spicing was unpredictable, veering between over-enthusiastic and almost absent. A starter of fresh sardines with chermoula was fine, if not inspired, while an aubergine salad (like a ratatouille in consistency, but without tomatoes) was completely overloaded with hot spices. In contrast, Maghreb's lamb tagine was a revelation. Tender lumps of meat in a thick but delicate prune sauce, spiced to a level of smoky, fruity perfection. It was a hard act to follow, and sea bream (a substitute for the advertised sea bass) didn't quite make the grade. The generous chunk of fish was beautifully cooked, but the promised chermoula was barely in evidence and the preserved lemon couldn't rescue the dish from blandness. 'Moroccan' coffee also disappointed: hardly-sweetened filter coffee, with a bizarre and overpowering flavour of ginger and perhaps the tiniest touch of cardamom. A Moroccan rosé wine was far better. We hope Maghreb finds its feet, since the staff are charming, the mood is relaxing and, when the food hits the bull's-eye, it reminds you just what Moroccan cooking is all about.
Booking advisable. Babies and children admitted; high chairs. No-smoking tables. Entertainment: belly dancer (9pm Thur).

Kentish Town NW5

Le Petit Prince

5 Holmes Road, NW5 (020 7267 3789). Kentish Town tube/rail. **Lunch served** noon-2.30pm Tue-Fri. **Dinner served** 7-11pm Tue-Sun. **Main courses** £6.90-£10.90. **Service** 10% (dinner). **No credit cards.**

Le Petit Prince serves an idiosyncratic combination of 'French provincial cuisine and North African couscous'. Starters are very much in the Gallic vein, with the likes of coquille de poisson, salade niçoise and duck pâté. The only starter from the Middle East was tabouleh, which was heavy on the bulgar wheat and lacked the flavour of fresh herbs and lemon that gives this dish its bite. Gazpacho also lacked zing. Along with some French main courses there are numerous varieties of couscous. We plumped for couscous imperial to share. The plentiful couscous (you can ask for more) was served with braised lamb, chicken, two lamb cutlets, one kebab, two merguez sausages and a traditional vegetable broth. Both meat and couscous had been well cooked, but neither were outstanding versions. However, it would be a shame to be too dismissive of this place; it's bright and cheerful, furnished in light pine, with illustrations from the tale of the *Little Prince* on the walls. Staff are most welcoming (babies are accommodated without hesitation) and every effort is made to make you feel at home.
Babies and children welcome. Booking advisable weekends.

North West

Golders Green NW2

Laurent

428 Finchley Road, NW2 (020 7794 3603). Golders Green tube then 13 bus. **Lunch served** noon-2pm, **dinner served** 6-11pm Mon-Sat. **Main courses** £7-£11.50. **Credit** AmEx, MC, £TC, V.

The sign outside reads 'couscous', and couscous is what you get, with no pretensions added. Laurent was here years before enterprising interior designers and restaurateurs decided that the ethnic look was the way to go, and it continues to serve a loyal local clientele. The room is painted white, with red-and-white checked tablecloths adding colour. In addition to couscous, the menu lists a solitary starter of brique à l'oeuf (a Tunisian dish of filo pastry wrapped around a soft egg) and puddings of ice-cream, crème caramel and crêpe suzette. Couscous comes in the usual variations of lamb, merguez, chicken, fish and vegetables. We were hungry enough to go for the couscous royal with shank of lamb, lamb chop, brochette of lamb and merguez sausage, served with plenty of vegetable broth. This was robust, high-protein comfort food: the meat was tender; the couscous was light; the quantity was more than ample. May Laurent never change.
Babies and children welcome. Booking advisable, essential weekends. Takeaway service.

Oriental

Central

City EC2, EC4

Pacific Oriental

1 Bishopsgate, EC2 (020 7621 9988). Bank tube/DLR/Liverpool Street tube/rail/ 8, 26, 149, 242 bus.
Bar **Open** 11.30am-11pm Mon-Fri. **Main courses** £9.95-£17.95.
Restaurant **Lunch served** 11.30am-3pm, **dinner served** 6-9pm, Mon-Fri. **Main courses** £9.95-£17.95.
Both **Service** 12½%. **Credit** AmEx, DC, MC, V.

Conceived when the fiery cooking of the Pacific Rim was still trading on its novelty value, Pacific Oriental is a City haunt, so be prepared for the downstairs bar to be awash with excitable suits. This was certainly the case on the Friday evening we visited, but, despite the bustle of the bar, we were practically alone in the restaurant above. Unlike the extensive New World wine list, the menu sticks to the Pacific Rim part of Asia, relying on the busy open grill for around a third of the dishes. We passed over a rather bitty-sounding salmon and lime quesadilla with chilli oil, in favour of sushi and sashimi, which tasted just as it should – super-fresh. Part one of the next course, seafood linguine with tomato and fennel, was sweet, gungy and a bit unexciting, whereas Thai chicken with green papaya slaw (actually small strands of garnish) was spicily barbied and further boosted by delicious wok-fried greens. Citrus brûlée and chocolate ginger mousse were both good endings to an enjoyable meal. Service was attentive and presentation fantastic, but expense-account prices don't necessarily mean top-of-the-range cooking.
Babies and children admitted. Disabled: toilet. Separate rooms for parties (4), seating from 20. Takeaway service 11.30am-9pm.
Map 4/6Q.

Tao

11-11A Bow Lane, EC4 (020 7248 5833). Mansion House tube.
Bar **Open** 11.30am-11pm Mon-Fri.
Restaurant **Lunch served** 11.30am-3pm Mon-Fri. **Dinner served** 6-10.30pm Mon-Fri. **Main courses** £7.25-£15.25. **Set meals** £15, £25.
Both **Service** 12½%. **Credit** AmEx, DC, LV, MC, £TC, V.

Tao's menu is dominated by oriental-inspired dishes, but with dashes of more global influences. Hence tempura seafood, herb and Gorgonzola pears, and bang bang chicken are among the starters, while main courses include penne with grilled asparagus, crispy chilli beef, and 'grilled smoking carpet bag rib-eye steak' (stuffed with smoked oysters). There's also a notable wine list. The decor – glass bricks, mirrors, industrial piping, oriental lacquer and carving, colour washes and weird plaster friezes – tries a bit too hard to please. To start, a prawn and avocado salad was a light mix of prawns and avocado purée topped by a crispy pancake; sesame shrimp toast was plump and crisp. Next, sesame crusted salmon (with mustard sauce, broccoli and steamed rice) was good, but the presentation (on a rectangular plate) made it resemble an in-flight meal, albeit business class; roast rump of lamb on cumin potato rösti was rich and caramelised. Service came across as pushy, with two waiters hovering around us like flies. At 9.30pm they told us the kitchen was closing and chivvied us through the rest of our meal. Desserts are scarcely oriental, but a chocolate and raspberry pie was worthy of a Belgian pâtissier. The cooking at Tao is well managed, if rather corporate-style, yet at such high prices, we expected to be able to enjoy it in peace.
Babies and children welcome. Booking advisable. Dress: smart casual. Entertainment: DJs 7-11pm Thur, Fri. No-smoking tables. Separate room for parties, seats 18. Tables outdoors (35, garden). Takeaway service.
Map 4/6P.

Clerkenwell & Farringdon EC1

Cicada

132-136 St John Street, EC1 (020 7608 1550). Farringdon tube/rail/55 bus. **Lunch served** noon-3pm Mon-Fri. **Dinner served** 6-11pm Mon-Sat. **Main courses** £6.50-£10. **Service** 12½%. **Credit** AmEx, DC, JCB, MC, £TC, V.

Only at the third attempt did we succeed in securing a table at Cicada, which surprised us as we'd assumed the trendy types would have long moved on. However, this bar-restaurant is still heaving with young media office workers. By 9pm, there's a nightclub feel – and it's so loud our order had to be shouted. Food comes from an open kitchen at the back of the room. Starters, beautifully presented, were a success if small. Asian broth with fish balls had a gutsy, fishy stock with fish-filled wun tuns; and asparagus summer rolls with green nam jihm sauce were fresh with a foliage of herbs. From the large dishes, snapper with sweet soy and holy basil was only a very small piece of fish, padded out with the usual vegetables, though it was tasty. Thai red vegetable curry could have been spicier, but had a good selection of veg, raw and cooked, and tofu. Barbecued Thai baby chicken, with som tam salad and a superfluous coconut dressing, was a delicious whole bird on authentic som tam (hot and sour papaya salad) which suffered from being on a stupid rectangular tile plate from which bits kept falling off. A crisp grenache blanc was a good choice from the extensive wine list, although most customers were quaffing cocktails or champagne and giggling at the grilled bananas which come in a very phallic-looking tower.
Babies and children admitted. Booking advisable. Tables outdoors (5, pavement).
Map 15/4O.

Fitzrovia W1

Birdcage

110 Whitfield Street, W1 (020 7323 9655). Goodge Street or Warren Street tube. **Lunch served** noon-2.30pm Mon-Fri. **Dinner served** 6-11.15pm Mon-Sat. **Set lunch** £26.50 three courses. **Set dinner** £38.50 three courses. **Credit** AmEx, DC, JCB, MC, £TC, V.

If all the world's a stage, then the Birdcage is the ethnic props cupboard. The room is full of ornithological knick-knacks, nudes, Buddhas, and slide projections of risqué poems. Moth-eaten peacock feathers sprout from every table, and the waitresses are covered in glitter. Not the most relaxing place, but certainly fun. The drinks list features garden vegetable juices, Eritrean incense coffee, organic hot chocolate with silver leaf, and 15 champagnes. After delightful reindeer and peacock egg canapés, served with spicy bread and a delicious yoghurt, green tea and wasabi dip, we got on to starters. Grapefruit and cardamom vichyssoise was spiced with hot chilli muted by a yoghurty base. Goat consommé was deeply rich with strange but lovely Irish moss lurking in the bottom and a clumsy wakame tartlet on the side. A main dish of seaweed, porcini and hemp risotto was competent but unexceptional, while honeyed Hungarian chilli pig came with fabulously fresh-tasting broth and green beans. A neat square of rice and tiger nut pesto accompanied the main dishes. For dessert, filo-wrapped pear cigarillos came with gingery ice-cream and an outrageously perfumed jasmine anglaise, which pulled the dish together into a sparklingly original whole. Alas, excellent gumleaf créme brûlée was ruined by the wheatgrass milk poured over its freshly caramelised topping. The Birdcage's stated aim is to provide 'unparalleled service, food, integrity, innovation and fun'. It succeeds in many areas, but the jury's still out on the food.
Babies and children admitted. Booking advisable. Dress: smart casual. Entertainment: magician 9-10pm Mon. No-smoking tables. Tables outdoors (2, patio).
Map 2/4J.

Busaba Eathai

Noho
*32 Charlotte Street, W1 (020 7636 4445).
Goodge Street tube.* **Meals served** noon-
11.30pm Mon-Sat; noon-11pm Sun. **Main
courses** £6.25-£7.95. **Credit** DC, JCB, MC,
£TC, V.
For those who don't know, it stands for 'north of
Soho'. This kind of contraction might suit the tidy
grid of New York, but London? That said,
however, this restaurant fits in well with the
Charlotte Street scenery. It gives a convivial first
impression with its raised pavement terrace and,
once inside, there's plenty of natural light and
white space in which to slurp your noodles. From
the list of starters, known here as 'intros', we chose
Thai fish cakes (four well-spiced but slightly
rubbery cakes, with the authentic cucumber, chilli
and peanut dipping sauce) and burn-the-mouth
hot and crispy spring rolls. A substantial main
course of ho fun – flat rice noodles with beef,
broccoli, mushrooms and oyster sauce – was
oriental food at its most earthy, sticky and filling.
Thai vegetable green curry with jasmine rice was
a lighter option, with a soupy yet authentically
flavoured sauce. Too full, we skipped the 'outros'
(that's pudding to most people), despite the exotic
allure of rambutan and the homely stodge of
banana fritters. The short wine list also offers sake,
Asian beers and fresh juices.
*Babies and children admitted. Booking
advisable. Tables outdoors (4, terrace).
Takeaway service.* **Map 2/5J.**
For branch (Noho 2) see index.

Silks & Spice
*23 Foley Street, W1 (020 7636 2718). Goodge
Street tube.* **Meals served** noon-11pm Mon-
Fri; 5.30-11pm Sat; noon-3pm, 5.30-10.30pm
Sun. **Main courses** £4.50-£11.95. **Set lunch**
£14.50 per person (minimum two), three
courses. **Set meals** £17.50-£22 per person
(minimum two), three courses. **Service** 10%.
Credit AmEx, MC, £TC, V.
Colonial bamboo, carved wood and red and gold
swathes make Foley Street a slightly overwhelming branch of this group of Thai-Malaysian

café-bars. Outside seating is pleasant enough,
though, and the long menu offers plenty of exotic
twists and turns. From an interesting list of
starters, we chose sesame prawn toasts (very
succulent and tasty) and veg spring rolls
(comparatively dull). There's also a selection of
soups and salads. Main courses are divided into
house specials, stir-fries and curries. Lobster
noodles, from the house specials, was half a
hacked-up crustacean that had been dumped on a
plate with noodles and pak choi, topped with an
unceremonious pile of whole garlic cloves and huge
lumps of ginger, and drowned in soy sauce. More
impressive chuchee goong offered butterfly-style
king prawns in a curry sauce with loads of coconut
milk and lime leaves. The menu is varied enough
to appeal to vegetarians and omnivores alike and
the set menus are unusually good value. For
dessert, coconut and sweet molasses wrapped in a
pandan leaf pancake and served with coconut ice-
cream was enjoyable but heavy. Service was
prompt and pleasant, if slightly corporate.
*Babies and children admitted. Booking
advisable. Separate room for parties, seats 40.
Tables outdoors (10, pavement). Takeaway
service.* **Map 2/5J.**
For branches see index.

Knightsbridge SW1

Vong ★
*The Berkeley, Wilton Place, SW1 (020 7235
1010). Hyde Park Corner or Knightsbridge tube.*
Brunch served 11.30am-2pm Sat, Sun. **Lunch
served** noon-2.30pm Mon-Fri. **Dinner served**
6-11.30pm Mon-Sat; 6-10.30pm Sun. **Main
courses** £14.50-£31.50. **Set lunches** £17.50
two courses, £21 three courses. **Set dinner** (6-
7.30pm, 10.30-11.30pm) £19.50 two courses.
Service 12½%. **Credit** AmEx, DC, JCB, MC, V.
We were dismayed to hear that the Berkeley hotel
had closed down the brilliant Minema Cinema in
order to extend its premier eating place. Like the
neighbouring Nobu, Vong started life in New York
among the smart set. The clientele is now mostly
expense-account diners and well-heeled hotel

residents, but the food, a Thai/French fusion, is still
spot on. To start with, two could share the Black
Plate, made of bite-size snacks from across the
menu. We decided to go solo, however, with starters
of prawn satay (huge juicy prawns marinated in a
mix of chilli and Thai spices), and chicken
dumpling (a steamed dim sum filled with chicken
and foie gras in a rich truffle sauce: every smidgen
was licked up). These followed a complimentary
creamy peanut dip with rice crackers. Next came
turbot, tenderly cooked and laid on a bed of
spinach with a fragrant lemongrass sauce with
pearl onions and kumquats. A dish of rabbit was
more hearty. A leg, breast in breadcrumbs, and
kidneys on a cocktail stick were arranged on a plate
in a coconutty, mildly spiced yellow curry sauce
with braised carrots – everything going together
very well. For pudding, we'd been tipped off about
the Valrhona chocolate cake: a heavenly concoction.
With an accompanying bottle of Chablis (£24 from
the pricey wine list), the meal was a treat. Staff
were faultless, too. We left determined to return to
try Vong's new weekend brunch menu.
*Babies and children welcome; high chairs.
Booking essential. No cigars or pipes in dining
room. No-smoking tables. Vegetarian menu.*
Map 12/9F.

Marylebone W1

Wagamama ★
*101A Wigmore Street, W1 (020 7409 0111).
Bond Street or Marble Arch tube.* **Meals
served** noon-11pm Mon-Sat; 12.30-10.30pm
Sun. **Main courses** £4.80-£7.35. **Set meals**
£8.50-£9.95. **Credit** AmEx, DC, JCB, MC, V.
The Wagamama empire shows no signs of waning.
Dabblers in the increasingly fashionable field of
Japanese cooking might dismiss the firm as a
supplier of unauthentic, stylised noodle bars, but
the three Japanese students we shared a bench with
seemed happy enough. The menu, more than just
ramen, soba and udon noodles, usefully lists the
ingredients of all dishes (rice makes its presence
strongly felt). Chicken tama rice, for instance, was
just as the menu told it: a mound of sticky rice

topped with char-grilled slices of chicken, with a
few chunks of courgette and mushroom in a ginger,
egg and wine sauce. Salmon korroke (fish cakes)
came in a tamarind sauce with salad – hardly very
Japanese, but bearing the signature clean, fresh
touch. In the absence of any starters or puds, we
filled up on side dishes of yasai gyoza (healthy-
tasting steamed dumplings with a soy-based
dipping sauce) and ebi gyoza (fried to a golden
crisp, and with an infinitely more interesting filling
of succulent prawn). Even with miso soup and
pickles, a cleansing raw juice and a glass of
delicious plum wine and soda, the bill was still
more canteen than haute cuisine. We left feeling
satisfied but virtuous.
*Babies and children welcome; high chairs;
nappy-changing facilities. Bookings not
accepted. Disabled: toilet. No smoking.*
Map 2/6G.
For branches see index.

Mayfair W1

Cassia Oriental
*12 Berkeley Square, W1 (020 7629
8886/www.cassiaoriental.com). Green Park
tube.* **Lunch served** noon-3pm, **dinner
served** 6-11.30pm Mon-Sat. **Bar snacks**
£3.80. **Sushi** £2.20-£5. **Set meals** £18 two
courses, £22 three courses. **Service** 12½%.
Credit AmEx, DC, MC, V.
Lawrence Leung, who founded the Zen group, has
gone for the nouveau-plush look in his new
restaurant. A designer-suited greeter sweeps you
up a grand staircase lit by scented candles. Drinks
and Chinese dough balls were brought while we
perused the menu. We started with the highlight of
our meal: twin summer and autumn rolls. Summer
was represented by prawns and mint leaves, served
cold in a light, fresh rice wrapper; autumn consisted
of mushrooms, vegetables and noodles in a deep-
fried wrapper to provide an earthy contrast. The
oriental selection of starters, however, was hit and
miss; little pieces of fried fish, rolled to look like
sushi were flavoursome, but deep-fried pork tasted
like pork scratchings. All main course dishes were

enjoy 6 oriental cuisines at wok·wok

140 fulham road SW10
tel 020 7370 5355

10 frith street, soho W1V
tel 020 7437 7080

51-53 northcote road
clapham SW11
tel 020 7978 7181

67 upper street
islington N1
tel 020 7288 0333

7 kensington high street W8
tel 020 7938 1221

4th floor, harrods ltd
knightsbridge SW1
tel 020 7225 5951

30 hill street richmond
surrey TW9 1TW
tel 020 8332 2646

34 duke street, brighton
sussex BN1 1AG
tel 01273 735 712

92-94 high street
marlow, bucks SL7 1AQ
tel 01628 488 544

wok·wok

beautifully presented, but the cooking wasn't up to scratch. Japanese grilled sea bass fillets came with greasy deep-fried vegetable cakes, medicinal-tasting noodles and egg-fried rice. A trio of chicken – rolled chicken with prawn mousse, spicy crispy chicken fillets and chicken wings filled with spring onions and ginger – was no better. While savoury dishes were all far too salty and greasy, puds were all soapily sweet. We shared green tea and sesame ice-cream with rambutan fruit and almond mousse: quite refreshing in a Badedas kind of way. With two Tiger beers, two mineral waters, two mint teas and one dessert, the bill came to over £60. It was our tastebuds that felt cheated.
Babies and children admitted. Booking advisable. Entertainment: pianist 5.30-8.30pm Mon-Sat. Separate room for parties, seats 22. **Map 2/7H.**

Soho W1

Busaba Eathai
106-110 Wardour Street, W1 (020 7255 8686). Piccadilly Circus tube. **Meals served** noon-11pm Mon-Thur; noon-11.30pm Fri, Sat; noon-10pm Sun. **Main courses** £4-£8. **Credit** AmEx, MC, V.
Combining the name of a Thai flower with a fusion of the words 'eat' and 'Thai', Busaba Eathai serves noodle dishes, curries, stir-fries and side dishes. According to the blurb, in this 'Thai casual dining venue' you 'define yourself by the way in which you approach food'. We settled ourselves on to the teak stools and tried to look both casual and intelligent while tucking into bubbly strips of deep-fried squid with ginger, garlic and peppercorns; substantial tod maan prawns in breadcrumbs with a tasty pineapple and lemongrass relish; and an unbearably hot green papaya salad. A main-course bowl of tom ka salmon with fresh baby spinach and rice noodles in a coconut and galangal soup was comforting if bland, but the green vegetable curry was wholly disappointing. Not only was our request for extra prawns turned down (leading us to believe that food is pre-cooked), but the flavours of basil, lemongrass and coconut milk were overpowered by chilli. We tried to cheer ourselves up with tom yam jay (stir-fried veg, tofu and noodles in a spicy sour soup), but again were struck by the unauthenticity of its assembly. Busaba Eathai is popular for its stylish decor, accessible location and speedy delivery, and on another occasion we had a much better meal (nicely moist fish cakes; fried squid with a zingy ginger, garlic and peppercorn dip; and an ample portion of pad Thai), so we'll have to see whether style or substance wins the day at Busaba.
Babies and children admitted. No-smoking tables. **Map 13/6K.**

Mezzonine
100 Wardour Street, W1 (020 7314 4000). Piccadilly Circus tube. **Lunch served** noon-3pm Mon-Fri; noon-4pm Sat. **Dinner served** 5.30pm-1am Mon-Thur; 5.30pm-3am Fri, Sat. **Main courses** £4.75-£10.95. **Set meal** (noon-3pm, 5.30-7pm) £8.90 two courses. **Service** 12½%. **Credit** AmEx, DC, JCB, MC, TC, V.
The dining area beside the upstairs bar in this Conran eaterie was pretty empty when we visited on a Tuesday evening, although the DJ was still going full tilt. The menu divides into small and large dishes instead of starters and mains, with quicker alternatives like 'ordinaries' (Caesar salad or perhaps a steak) or 'soups and noodles' (laksa, pad Thai and the like). Our first starter of shredded duck, spring onion, plum sauce and crispy pancake needlessly overcomplicated a perfectly simple dish by piling bite-sized (not shredded) chunks of duck between two popadom-like pancakes. Prawn and ginger wun tuns also defied traditional wisdom by sandwiching their filling between two flat, soggy wrappers. Things picked up with a main of roast duck with Thai red curry sauce and fragrant rice (delicious), but seared salmon on Thai-inspired bean stew was no more than comfort food. A side order of garden salad was also ordinary, with just the inclusion of some beansprouts to keep the eastern theme going. Pavlova and chocolate marquise were a final sweetener and went nicely with the last sips of a fruity Chateau La Croix rosé. As you'd expect from the M&S of London restaurants, food here isn't wildly exciting, but it is pretty tasty.
Babies and children welcome; high chairs. Booking advisable. Disabled: toilet. Separate room for parties, seats 44. Vegetarian dishes. **Map 13/6K.**

Wok Wok
10 Frith Street, W1 (020 7437 7080). Piccadilly Circus or Tottenham Court Road tube. **Meals served** noon-11pm Mon-Wed; noon-midnight Thur-Sat. **Dinner served** 5.30-10.30pm Sun. **Main courses** £5.95-£11.95. **Set lunch** (Mon-Fri) £6.95 two

courses. **Set meals** £14.50-£19.20 per person (minimum six). **Service** 10% for parties of six or more. **Credit** AmEx, DC, JCB, MC, £TC, V.
Reading like a whistle-stop tour of South-east Asia, the menu at Wok Wok raids China, Japan, Indonesia, Malaysia, Vietnam and Thailand to bring a kaleidoscope of flavours to this smartly-designed Soho branch. Dishes are assembled in an open kitchen. A decent range of cocktails, Asian beers, fresh juices and New World wines make for good accompaniments to the frenetic wok action. First came a shared starter of four large, nicely misshapen and flavoursome Thai fish cakes. Then nothing. Cut to 40 minutes later and, still without our main courses, we have clearly been forgotten (although the staff do seem genuinely apologetic, offering us compensatory desserts and drinks on the house). Late arrival number one was wun tun mee, a flavoured bowl of stock with good chicken dumplings, slightly dry pork, greens and thin, coarse noodles, but just too delicately flavoured to be memorable. Not so a special of Thai green vegetable curry, though, which successfully combined crunchy veg with rich coconut creaminess (but missed that holy basil and citrus tang). Desserts of lychee, pineapple and mango sorbet and yoghurt mousse with mixed berries were light and refreshing. Perhaps a few more staff would make this a stronger link in the chain.
Babies and children welcome; children's menu; high chairs. Booking essential, lunch; bookings accepted for parties of 8 or more only, dinner. Takeaway service. **Map 13/6K.**
For branches see index.

West

Maida Vale W9

Southeast W9
239 Elgin Avenue, W9 (020 7328 8883). Maida Vale tube/31 bus. **Meals served** noon-11pm Mon-Sat; noon-10pm Sun. **Main courses** £4.50-£7.95. **Credit** AmEx, MC, V.
Situated directly opposite Maida Vale tube, this restaurant was absolutely packed on the evening of our visit. It certainly has a wide culinary appeal, with a menu that visits more parts of South-east Asia than a gap-year back-packer – Thailand, Cambodia, Vietnam, Burma, Singapore, Laos and Malaysia to be exact. The decor is white, bright and functional, punctuated by a few vibrantly colourful paintings. The spine-deadeningly hard metal chairs, however, belong in the Marquis de Sade camp of ergonomic design. We began our meal with a quick jaunt into Thai territory (good crunchy prawn spring rolls with sweet chilli dip), then on to Malaysia (bog standard chicken satay). Next stop Laos, for spicy beef with aubergine and basil, followed by a Thai dish of prawns fried with ginger, chilli and vegetables. The prawns certainly beat the beef, which was dry and overcooked; copious galangal (as opposed to the advertised ginger) gave the whole dish zing. Accompanying coconut rice was excellent, containing all the fragrance of fresh coconut without being over-powering. To drink, bottles of crisp Asahi beer seemed more inviting than anything on the limited wine list. Staff are friendly and efficient.
Babies and children admitted. Book dinner. No-smoking tables. Tables outdoors (2, pavement). Takeaway service. Vegetarian dishes. **Map 1/3C.**

Notting Hill W11

Uli
16 All Saints Road, W11 (020 7727 7511). Ladbroke Grove tube. **Meals served** 6.45-11.15pm daily. **Main courses** £6.25-£8.50. **Set meal** £15 three courses incl coffee. **Credit** MC, V.
Perhaps this area suffers from an excess of eateries, but on a Saturday lunchtime a few streets away from Portobello market, Uli was dead. Offering a combination of Chinese, Malaysian and Thai cooking, the menu is presided over by owner Michael Lim, a cheeky chappie with a story to accompany every dish. We ordered sautéed calamares from the two-course lunchtime menu, and hot and sour soup from the main list of starters. The strips of calamares came fresh from the pan, spitting with chilli and garlic, while the soup was a hearty brown broth packed with strips of vegetables, tofu and chicken, but so heavily doctored with pepper and chilli we could barely eat it. A green vegetable curry that came next was also quite hot but had a delicious balance of flavours and a fine selection of delicately cooked veg. Baked spicy fish, however, came with a layer of red-hot chilli paste that rendered it almost unapproachable to our soup-damaged mouths. We wished we'd ordered stir-fried lamb with spring onions, or Malay chicken curry instead. There's a good wine list, but we found that a couple of Tiger beers fitted

the bill exactly. A small outdoor eating area is popular with locals when the weather is right. Staff are among the most congenial in west London. *Babies and children admitted. Booking advisable. Tables outdoors (6, patio). Takeaway service.* **Map 11/5Az.**

South West

Fulham SW6

Jim Thompson's
617 King's Road, SW6 (020 7731 0999). Fulham Broadway tube. **Meals served** noon-11pm Mon-Sat; noon-10.30pm Sun. **Main courses** £4.45-£9.95. **Service** 10%. **Credit** AmEx, DC, MC, £TC, V.
JT's is to oriental cooking what Terry Wogan is to the art of interviewing: the product has been passed through the blanderiser so many times that it has reached a higher level of innocuousness. Inside, the place has a Disneyesque feel, the many pseudo-Eastern artefacts and bits of furniture giving it the look of an Aladdin's Cave theme pub (there are wooden seats in the shape of large upturned hands, for example: as comfortable to sit in as, well, big wooden hands). The bulk of the menu consists of set meals for two people or more, although individual portions of curries, stir-fries and the like are also available. We opted for the 'spice merchant platter'. In fact it wasn't spicy at all; the first wave of spring rolls, chicken satay, sesame prawn toast and fish cakes was almost entirely devoid of real flavour. The fish cakes were the exception – firm, full of fish and flecked with fresh coriander. Main course duck red curry only seemed OK in comparison to the gloopy chicken with cashews and the harmless stir-fried pork with chilli. All around us, a loud Fulham crowd washed down their own fodder with pints of Stella while intermittently squawking into their mobiles. *Babies and children welcome. Book dinner. Tables outdoors (9, patio). Takeaway service. Vegetarian menu.* **Map 5/13B.**
For branches see index.

South Kensington SW3

Itsu ★
118 Draycott Avenue, SW3 (020 7584 5522). South Kensington tube/49 bus.
Bar **Open** 5pm-midnight Mon-Sat; 5-10pm Sun.
Restaurant **Meals served** noon-11pm Mon-Sat; noon-10pm Sun. **Main courses** £2.50-£3.50.
Both **Credit** AmEx, JCB, MC, £TC, V.
'It's time for a different type of place', says the leaflet that accompanies your chopsticks and, for more than a year now, Itsu has striven to provide just that. You don't need to book, just turn up and find a seat in the slick conveyor-belt eaterie on the ground floor, or head upstairs to the bar area (where you can smoke). The food is a sushi hybrid (more of an oriental tapas, really) and comes in a range of colour-coded dishes; gold plates are the most expensive at £3.50. We tried ten between two of us, including a summer-roll-like spicy crab wrap, very moreish chicken and coconut soup, dainty slices of seared tuna, and ikura tartare with pretty-looking fish eggs. This made for a beautifully presented, delicious and perfectly proportioned meal. If it all sounds too healthy, fear not, three puds were also doing the rounds (the grilled pineapple with butterscotch sauce is particularly recommended). Serve yourself a bottle of Asahi from the ice-packed chiller, or flick a switch and a waiter will appear, to take your order for sake or cocktails. When you're finished, just add up the cost of your plates and glasses. Convenient and classy. *Babies and children welcome. Bookings not accepted. No smoking (smoking allowed in first-floor bar). Vegetarian dishes.* **Map 12/10E.**

South

Brixton SW9

Fujiyama
7 Vining Street, SW9 (020 7737 2369). Brixton tube/rail. **Meals served** noon-11pm Mon-Thur, Sun; noon-midnight Fri, Sat. **Main courses** £5-£6. **Service** 10%. **Credit** MC, V.
Fujiyama is a noodle bar Brixton-style. It's cramped, dark, loud and has no ceremony about it whatsoever. Customers must shove up along wooden benches and learn to make friends with strangers. We sat in the back room and pitched in to the general melée by shouting across at each other. The menu makes it clear that side dishes are to accompany your main meal. Staff treat them as starters but plonk down your next choice when you're halfway through. We chose yasai salad: straight from the health food shop and masquerading as something oriental, but tasty enough with sultanas, pumpkin and sunflower

Southeast W9

seeds nestling in the lettuce and tomato; the dressing was of lemon, honey and coriander. Yakitori (chicken and vegetable skewers) 'with a mouth-watering aroma' attracted much attention up and down the table. Mains are split into curry noodles, pan-fried noodles, ramen, miso, bento, donburi ('rice bowls') and rice dishes. The only problem is in choosing while the trendy Japanese waitress does an impatient little dance beside you. Yaki udon (with chicken, prawns, fish cake, leeks, shiitake mushrooms, red peppers, beansprouts and egg in curried oil) was a fair copy of a Wagamama fave, with lots of pockets of interest among the white udon noodles. Tuna chilli men was a huge pile of steamed noodles with a small topping of chilli sauce and char-grilled tuna steak. To finish, smoothies should satisfy the craving for something sweet. *Babies and children admitted. Book dinner Fri, Sat. No-smoking tables. Separate room for parties, seats 30-40. Takeaway service. Vegetarian dishes.* **Map 18.**

South East

Herne Hill SE24

Lombok
17 Half Moon Lane, SE24 (020 7733 7131). Herne Hill rail. **Dinner served** 6-10.30pm Tue-Sun. **Main courses** £5.50-£7.95. **Service** 10%. **Credit** MC, V.

Lombok has proved itself a welcome and hugely popular addition to the area. Impressive carved wooden dragons on the pale clapboard walls and a reclining Buddha on top of the bar are the only clues to the style of the menu, which is Thai-based, but sprinkled with dishes from other South-east Asian countries. Sugar cane prawns (minced prawns wrapped around sugar cane, and usually grilled) are a Vietnamese speciality, although the rather flavourless version here appeared to have been deep-fried; better was zingy salt and pepper squid. On another occasion, our duck salad was far too heavy on the cloying hoi sin sauce (obviously bottled) and the duck was deep fried rather than roasted. Main courses were the stars, however. Rejecting such extravagances as Singapore chilli crab and such oddities as char-grilled teriyaki chicken with fresh asparagus, we instead feasted on a beautifully marinated tamarind duck served on juicy pak choi, and cleanly flavoured chicken with Thai basil. For pudding, a coconut custard and mango sorbet certainly didn't need the addition of horrible squirty cream. The wine list offers some interesting bottles among its six reds and six whites. Such is Lombok's popularity that the tables are packed too tightly and service can get a little frazzled towards the end of the evening – but don't let that put you off. *Babies and children admitted. Booking advisable; essential weekends. Takeaway service.*

North East

Stoke Newington N16

Barracuda ★
125 Stoke Newington Church Street, N16 (020 7923 7488). Stoke Newington rail/73 bus. **Lunch served** June-Sept 1-4.30pm Sat, Sun. **Dinner served** 6.30-11pm Mon-Thur, Sun; 6.30-11.45pm Fri, Sat. **Main courses** £7.50-£9.50. **Service** 10%. **Credit** MC, V.
This oriental brasserie was empty when we pitched up at 8pm on a Tuesday, but Barracuda has stalwart regulars and much to commend it. If you don't fancy eating in the street-level area at the front, try the pleasant wood-floored room at the back which leads to a balcony and garden. There's also a jazz cellar at weekends. The menu has been put together with care; many dishes sound tempting. To start we could have had taro rolls (yam in tofu pastry with sweet chilli sauce) or sea empress (grilled scallops with sweet chilli sauce and crème fraîche), but plumped for chicken parcels wrapped in fragrant leaves with sesame and soy: we needed to unravel the leaf to reveal the succulent chicken, but it was worth it. We also sampled paper prawns wrapped in just the right amount of crispy rice paper. Mains all come with either rice, couscous or potato wedges. Garlic aubergine in black bean salsa with lemon and coriander couscous sounded enticing, but we opted for pumpkin and chickpea red curry with rice, and tamarind lamb. The curry had fresh chunks of interesting veg with a discernible red curry kick, and the lamb was a juicy fillet dressed with sweet tamarind and deep-fried basil leaves and paired with soy broccoli and coconut rice. Puddings included a varied selection of ices (lemongrass sorbet for instance), but the trad option of bitter chocolate satisfied us, as did the entire meal. *Babies and children admitted. Entertainment: jazz musicians from 9.30pm Fri, Sat. Tables outdoors (9, garden).*

Itto ★
226 Stoke Newington High Street, N16 (020 7275 8827). Stoke Newington rail/67, 73, 76, 106, 149, 243 bus. **Lunch served** noon-3pm, **dinner served** 5-11pm Mon-Sat. **Main courses** £3.30-£5.50. **No credit cards.**
A good Stoke Newington snack spot, Itto has an orange dining area that's both bright and relaxed. The long menu is drawn from pan-South-east Asian references, but is simplified into easy-to-understand soup, noodle and rice sections, with practically a score of side dishes for good measure. Most dishes cost around £5. We ordered the Vietnamese spring rolls to share, while we perused the expanse of noodle dishes. The spring rolls were fat with a minced pork and noodle filling, although the deep-fried wrapping was a little heavy. Seafood fried udon came packed with prawns, squid, crabstick, fish cake and vegetables (and unfortunately part of a plastic kitchen container), but needed a bit of chilli to give it zing. The Itto chicken ramen soup was a good flavoursome stock, pungent with coriander and stuffed with grilled chicken, greens, crabstick, tofu, fish cake, spring onions and noodles. Maybe so many ingredients are needed to fuel a Japanese 16-hour working day, but it was too much for us. Cheery staff are happy to pack up anything you can't eat into a takeaway carton. There's also a good choice of beers and juices, including Sapporo at £2.10. Cheap and cheerful. *Babies and children welcome. No smoking. Takeaway service.*

North

Camden Town & Chalk Farm NW1, NW3

Café de Maya ★
38 Primrose Hill Road, NW3 (020 7209 0672). Chalk Farm or Swiss Cottage tube/31 bus. **Dinner served** 6-11pm daily. **Main courses** £4.45-£6.75. **Service** 10%. **Credit** JCB, MC, £TC, V.
It may be off the usual Primrose Hill restaurant track, but this homely little place has a loyal local following; many diners were greeted by name on the Sunday night of our visit. Service comes with a smile. Pink walls are hung with pictures and South-east Asian knick-knacks; towers of CDs are arranged around an old piano. The menu is a mix of Thai, Malaysian and Chinese food. From the starter section the tom yum hed soup was sweet with tomatoes and spicy with chilli; lime leaves lay at the bottom of the bowl and just-poached mushrooms floated on top. Spring rolls were tasty, but more like winter rolls in their heaviness. The curry section offers mainly Thai red and green varieties, but we opted for Hawaiian pineapple

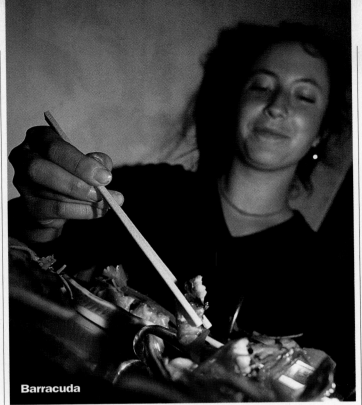
Barracuda

chicken, which was light and fruity with peppers, basil, onion and (unfortunately tinned) pineapple, set off by a deliciously fragrant coconut rice. Spicy fish was much less subtle: deep fried and covered with an unexpected sweet and sour orange sauce that made us wonder whether the chef had made a mistake. The dessert menu is notable for this style of restaurant. Coconut ice-cream with strawberries and syrup, and fresh fruit salad, rounded off the meal nicely.
Babies and children welcome; high chairs. No-smoking tables. Takeaway service. Vegetarian menu.

Lemongrass ★ ★
243 Royal College Street, NW1 (020 7284 1116). Camden Town tube/Camden Road rail. **Dinner served** 7-10.30pm Mon-Sat. **Main courses** £4.30-£7.90. **Set dinner** £13.80 per person (minimum two). **Credit** MC, £TC, V.
As the menu explains, this little local relies on just one chef and his three woks to produce all the food, so expect to wait for it. The Cambodian-influenced cooking is certainly worth it, though, and an equally industrious front-of-house performance (there was only one waitress on a Saturday night) ensures that it reaches the table still hot. Our starters of vegetable spring rolls (deliciously freshly filled) and leek cake (steamed and green in the middle and crisp on the outside) both arrived with tangy dipping sauces. Next, a recommended 'classic Khmer colonial dish' of lok luk steak (cubes of tender meat with onions and peppers) was refreshed by a fantastic side order of mango salad with coriander, lemon and onion. Another main of king prawn curry provided a spicy contrast to its creamy coconut milk sauce. Sadly, banana cake was off the menu, so we singed our eyebrows with banana flambés instead – fritters liberally doused in Grand Marnier, served with ice-cream. Even with the more-than-fair prices, ingredients were never less than fresh and of hand-selected quality. The whole Lemongrass experience was one that we will undoubtedly repeat.
Booking advisable weekends. No smoking. Vegetarian menu. **Map 10.**

Hampstead NW3

dim T café
3 Heath Street, NW3 (020 7435 0024). Hampstead tube. **Meals served** noon-11pm daily. **Main courses** £4.50-£6.25. **Credit** MC, V.
dim T café claims to offer a 'totally new dining concept', but the only novelties to distinguish this Chinese-oriented eatery are that it serves dim sum in the evenings and has a good list of teas, some of which are served 'using the traditional Chinese tea ceremony method' (others, like our gunpowder tea, come in a traditional teabag). The dim sum's pretty good by suburban standards, though it doesn't approach the finesse of most Chinatown specialists. Steamed dim sum are brought round on a trolley ready-cooked, but ours were fresh enough. Steamed rice buns had a perfect consistency and well-textured fillings, but seafood dumplings were stuck to the base of their basket and fell apart on removal. The grilled dim sum platter was a bad choice: not really dim sum at all, but rather bar food nibbles, including greasy spring rolls and a stuffed and fried piece of red pepper. If dim sum's not your bag, try the noodle dishes (choose your noodle, meat, and topping and have them stir-fried or in soup), or dishes such as chicken satay or vegetable tempura. There's also a blackboard of daily specials; our Malaysian curry plate was fine. Regardless of whether it's a 'new dining concept' or not, dim T is good value, and Hampstead could do with more places like it.
Babies and children admitted; high chairs. No-smoking tables. Separate room for parties, seats 30. Tables outdoors (2, pavement; 2, patio). Takeaway service. **Map 9.**

Islington N1

Yellow River Café
206 Upper Street, N1 (020 7354 8833). Angel tube/Highbury & Islington tube/rail. **Lunch served** noon-3pm Mon-Sat. **Dinner served** 5.30-11pm Mon-Wed; 5.30-11.30pm Thur-Sat. **Meals served** noon-10.30pm Sun. **Main courses** £5.50-£9.50. **Bento box** £11.80. **Credit** AmEx, DC, MC V.
TV chef Ken Hom is consultant to this smart chain of oriental eateries and his picture's on the menu, beaming away. The motto is 'strength through eating' (artificial additives and MSG are strictly forbidden). This branch has an easy, laid-back feel, with traditional lacquer and lanterns offsetting the stark, urban decor of the bar. It was manically busy when we visited on a Monday night, thanks to a special £10.95-a-head buffet (also available on Sunday nights) that offers basic dishes from the menu. Among them, sweetcorn soup was tasty but gloopy, while other starters like chicken and beef satay were fine, but of only supermarket standard. Main courses offered stronger flavours, with the likes of Thai green chicken curry, or stir-fried beef with black bean sauce. As well as the buffet, we sampled a meal box (a selection from the menu served in a lacquered box). The spicy Thai fish cakes were rubbery and oily, but prawn curry with coconut was both delicate and spicy; good stir-fried vegetables, noodles with beansprouts and prawn crackers made this the preferable option. Desserts – mango pudding, tropical fruit salad, and lime sorbet, for instance – are delicious and the special children's menu is also worth knowing about.
Babies and children welcome; children's menu; high chairs; toys. No-smoking tables. Takeaway service; delivery service.
For branches see index.

Portuguese

One of the genuine pleasures about going Portuguese in London is that you feel, however briefly, you've become part of the community. This is because most of the cafés, pâtisseries (pastelaria) and restaurants are much more than simply places in which to feed. The capital's sizeable Portuguese population of around 80,000 (living mainly in the west and south-west of the city) use their eateries as meeting place, TV room, community centre and homesickness palliative, all rolled into one.

The cafés in particular offer a through-the-day experience. From the morning opening to chairs-on-the-table time, you could get breakfast, lunch and dinner without having to move. These are places to linger in, venues to take the rush out of the day. Men drift in to catch the football or news on satellite TV, while kids scamper around and older folks chat at length over a coffee. This easygoing atmosphere is a real bonus. With a little poetic licence, it's not hard to imagine yourself in a winding backstreet of Lisbon's Bairro Alto district, or by the harbour in Porto.

The atmospheric charm is helped along by the fact that the food isn't half bad either. Don't go expecting nouvelle cuisine. Similarly, dedicated vegetarians will find little to chew on. The recipes are straightforward and without frills, the portions in all courses are usually very generous and filling (a point to remember when pacing yourself for dessert).

At first, a typical menu can seem limited in range, but you soon realise that where any restaurant makes is mark is on its take on tried and trusted favourites. Starters are seafood-heavy, with gambas (prawns), mussels, sardines and clams the old faithfuls, alongside vegetable soups and spicy chouriço sausage. With main courses, fish, seafood and meat are equal partners, and occasionally even join together on the same plate. Carne de porco à alentejana – pork with clams, a festival dish from the southern interior – is about as traditional as they come. Otherwise it's steak, lamb, chicken (often in hot piri-piri or chilli sauce) and a range of fish – from bacalhau (salted cod) through tuna and swordfish to tamboril (monkfish). Look out, too, for the Portuguese paella, arroz com mariscos, and various mixed espetadas (skewers) of meat or fish. Desserts are a real bonus and, with the famous pastries (such as the custard tarts, pasteis de nata), are well worth holding out for. Try chocolate mousse, crème caramel (pudim) or rice pudding (arroz doce), accompanied by one of the range of local brandies, the famous ports (of course) or flavoursome coffees – a milky galão is sometimes a pudding in its own right. For snacks, alongside the great cakes is normally a range of fish and meat rissoles, tapas and filled rolls. Eating Portuguese needn't be expensive, but don't forget that you pay a cover charge of a pound or so per head for any bread, olives and so on that you consume.

The national wines are certainly worth trying – not that you'll have any choice but to do so at most venues. Some have won awards in recent years, with many vineyards undergoing a rejuvenation after employing new techniques. Vinho verde (a good seafood accompaniment) offers a traditional and especially refreshing glass.

Pastelaria

West

Ladbroke Grove W10

Lisboa Patisserie
57 Golborne Road, W10 (020 8968 5242). Ladbroke Grove tube. **Open** 8am-8pm daily. **No credit cards**.
Part of a mini empire of outlets – including a deli and bookshop of the same name on Golborne Road and another pâtisserie in Chelsea – this hugely popular venue can seemingly do no wrong with the mixed community of Portobello. We arrived on the crest of a sudden influx of hungry locals, but just managed to secure a table in the frantically busy interior, the pavement to either side thronging with people munching contentedly. Savouries are fine; cheese croissants, filled rolls and various rissoles and pasties cost about £1 each, but it's the cakes that do the business. Pasteis de nata, coconut buns and apricot pastries were all excellent, as were the bica (espresso) and the atmosphere. A great vindication of a vibrant multicultural area.
Babies and children admitted. Tables outdoors (3, pavement). Takeaway service. **Map 11/4Az.**
For branch see index.

Oporto Patisserie
62A Golborne Road, W10 (020 8968 8839). Ladbroke Grove tube. **Open** 8am-8pm daily. **No credit cards** cheques accepted over £5 only.
If popularity is the best gauge of a place, then this Golborne Road pastelaria rivals the Lisboa. On a midweek mid-afternoon visit Oporto was packed, with standing room only – even outside. Large bread trays were turned into makeshift chairs and it felt like summer had come early. Inside there's not much of aesthetic value, just white walls and seating, but there is some serious Portuguese action. Low-end prices on cakes, pastries, rolls, rissoles, salads and omelettes made it hard for us to choose. The service is friendly and there's a buzz you can't buy. Pasteis de nata have a flaky authenticity, and an extra-strong galão (milky coffee), delivered in a scalding glass, was just what the doctor ordered. Dreadlocked Home Counties boys share tables with Lusaphone Africans and old folks from Portugal – it's a west London wake-up call to the full benefits of multicultural living.
Babies and children admitted. Takeaway service. **Map 11/4Az.**

Restaurants

Central

Knightsbridge SW3

Caravela
39 Beauchamp Place, SW3 (020 7581 2366). Knightsbridge or South Kensington tube. **Lunch served** noon-3pm Mon-Sat. **Dinner served** 7pm-1am Mon-Sat; 7pm-midnight Sun. **Main courses** £8-£12. **Set lunch** £7.95 two courses incl glass of wine. **Cover** £1.25. **Service** 12½%. **Credit** AmEx, DC, JCB, MC, £TC, V.
Half full on a Monday night, Caravela (galleon) exploits the marine associations of its name in full. It's a relaxed basement set-up, and feels a little like a ship's cabin. Blue-washed walls and boat ephemera set the scene for a menu strong on fish and seafood. For starters, gambas a guilho (prawns in a spicy sauce) were particularly good, and the portion of mussels with garlic and white wine was generous. Espetada à transmontana (barbecued skewer of pork fillet) was mostly tender and mild, but moved from rare to burned

along its length. Espetada de tamboril (monkfish) was flavourless, and the rice with it pretty flat. Chocolate mousse, however, was exceptionally rich. An extensive wine list includes a crisp half-bottle of house white for £6.95. Service was friendly and attentive – a complimentary brandy and a delicious almond liqueur were thrown in. Given the location, prices are very competitive.
Babies and children admitted. Book dinner. Entertainment: guitarists from 8pm Wed-Sun. **Map 12/10F.**

O Fado
49-50 Beauchamp Place, SW3 (020 7589 3002). Knightsbridge or South Kensington tube. **Lunch served** noon-3pm, **dinner served** 6.30pm-1am daily. **Main courses** £7.20-£14.50. **Service** 10%. **Credit** AmEx, MC, £TC, V.
O Fado's position as London's oldest Portuguese restaurant, together with its Knightsbridge locale, lead to high expectations. These are on the whole met reasonably well. A formal but not off-putting basement, it shows its heritage primarily through wall mountings, has several feature arches and a fine bar. A guitar abandoned on one of the few empty tables promised music that never materialised. A traditional menu is offered, along with restrained but friendly service. One starter, a mountain of mussels in garlic and white wine, could have kept two of us quiet. As it was, our other order of gambas (prawns) also came in abundance. A main course of tuna steak in tomato and onion delivered as expected. The unpredictably enormous arroz de tamboril (rice and monkfish) was delicious, but so large we felt guilty at having to leave so much. To finish, banana a Fado is a house speciality. The good wine list includes a fresh house white, but we had hoped for more than three ports on parade. Expensive starters pushed our bill up, but other courses kept the total below what you might expect to pay somewhere so close to Harrods.
Babies and children welcome. Book dinner weekends. Separate room for parties, seats 75. Takeaway service. **Map 12/9F.**

West

Ladbroke Grove W10, W11

Café Algarve ★
129A Ladbroke Grove, W11 (020 7727 4604). Ladbroke Grove tube. **Meals served** 8am-8pm Mon-Sat. **Unlicensed. No credit cards.**
Run by probably the most enthusiastic Portuguese family in London, this tiny café is popular way beyond its size. It has a handful of tables on the pavement, at basement level and in the crowded front room, but wherever you eat you'll feel like you're in someone's home. There's no space for a queue: customers just try and get noticed. Despite the crush, you're perfectly at liberty to spend an hour nursing a single bica (espresso coffee). The Saturday afternoon we went, football was on live from Lisbon, confusing attendance even more. The brightly coloured main space is packed with national products, from endless juices and biscuits to interlopers such as variety pack cereals. English breakfast is served, alongside the usual Portuguese snacks (most of them around £1). Sardines were thin and not very warm, but prego (steak in a roll) was superb and a bargain at £2.50. We ordered coffees but they never showed. It wasn't a particular problem, however; it was fine just being here.
Tables outdoors (3, pavement). Takeaway service. **Map 11/6Az.**

Casa Santana
44 Golborne Road, W10 (020 8968 8764). Ladbroke Grove tube/7, 23 bus. **Meals served** noon-11pm daily. **Main courses** £5.50-£11.25. **Credit** MC, V.
Being the only customers on our lunchtime visit meant at least that service (friendly enough) was fast in this slightly ramshackle but airy Portobello venue. A dozen tables in neat rows look on to a large scenic mural. There's a cabin-like feel to the place. Several items (including one of the low-price trademark soups) were unavailable, so we settled for gambas (pricey at £6.95). The prawns were certainly king-sized, but the visual promise of their garlic and herb sauce didn't translate into taste. Similarly the bacalhau main, while nicely flaky, was a little too bony – and the potatoes and salad both lacked flavour. Most desserts were off, but the waiter assured us things would pick up for the evening. Generous glasses of wine cheered us a little, but it was hard to ignore the fact that the details which could lift a meal were missing. For somewhere that looks like a bargain find, Casa Santana has some realignments to make.
Babies and children welcome. Book weekends. Takeaway service. **Map 11/4Az.**

South

Stockwell SW8

O Cantinho de Portugal
135-137 Stockwell Road, SW9 (020 7924 0218). Stockwell tube/Brixton tube/rail/2, 322, 345, 355 bus.
Bar **Open** 11am-11pm daily.
Restaurant **Meals served** noon-midnight daily. **Main courses** £4-£9. **Cover** 50p. **Credit** £TC.
Another example of a split bar/restaurant operation, O Cantinho is a popular location in the heart of Portuguese territory. It's not fancy but works very well as a place to indulge in a long, Mediterranean-style lunch. The busy road outside doesn't impinge on a decent-sized dining area that has a relaxed atmosphere to complement the service. Gambas (prawns in their shells, £5) continued to work their slightly pricey charm, but the prawn salad was bland. We tried a mains special, pork and chickpeas. It was a little too close to ragout, quite fatty, but came with a decent sauce. Squid in wine and garlic worked better: very filling and pleasantly free of the excessively rubbery texture usually found. A fruity house red kept us going through standard desserts (caramel custard, chocolate mousse and the like) and up to a fine brandy. Try O Cantinho as a bar: there's a supportive tapas list.
Babies and children welcome; high chairs. Book weekends. Takeaway service. **Map 18.**

Gira-Sol ★
176A Wandsworth Road, SW8 (020 7622 7526). Stockwell tube/Vauxhall tube/rail/77, 77A bus. **Open** 11am-11pm Tue-Sat; 11am-10.30pm Sun. **Tapas** £3.50-£5.50. **No credit cards.**
The first thing you notice about this easygoing café (beyond the fact it provides instant relief from the pollution and roar of the Wandsworth Road) is the well-stocked bar and the friendly demeanour of the owner. Our midweek afternoon visit unfortunately just missed the lunchtime sitting (which finishes at 2pm), so we relied on the snack cabinet. Chouriço came piping hot and genuinely spicy, while a selection of seafood – prawn pasties, fish cakes and crab claws in potato and batter – could all have done with more warming. But there was no arguing about the prices of the drinks, with Super Bock beer, Sumol orange and a strong galão all cheaper than usual. It wasn't hard to spend an hour or so here and eavesdrop on a lively discussion about the 'state of the game'. Not worth a special trip, perhaps, but if you're in the neighbourhood, Gira-Sol is a decent option.
Babies and children admitted. Book weekends. Tables outdoors (2, pavement). Takeaway service.

Vauxhall SW8

Bar Estrela
111-115 South Lambeth Road, SW8 (020 7793 1051). Stockwell tube/Vauxhall tube/rail. **Meals served** 11am-midnight daily. **Main courses** £7-£10.50. **Credit** MC, V.
Estrela's highly popular bar, with its packed pavement tables, might obscure the fact that a pleasant restaurant also lurks within. Up some stairs to one side, the room is a little dark towards the back but reasonably ornate – and it's certainly easier to get served there. Large, tangy gambas, and slightly charred but rich sardines, set the tone. The main courses didn't disappoint, either. Arroz de mariscos was generous and varied, full of seafood and nicely soupy in texture. Porco à alentejana (pork with clams) had a richly infused flavour, the meat was lean and the potatoes well-seasoned. Desserts (all the usual Portuguese batch, including chocolate mousse and crème caramel pudim) were fine, as were coffees and wine, the Terras d'el Rei white being particularly crisp. A decent range of tapas and a games room in the basement widen Bar Estrela's attraction.
Babies and children welcome; high chairs. Tables outdoors (8, pavement). **Map 7/13L.**

O Barros
168A Old South Lambeth Road, SW8 (020 7582 0976). Stockwell tube/Vauxhall tube/rail.
Bar **Open** noon-midnight Mon-Sat; noon-10.30pm Sun.
Restaurant **Lunch served** noon-3pm, **dinner served** 6-11.45pm Mon-Sat. **Meals served** noon-10.30pm Sun. **Main courses** £6.50-£13. **Credit** AmEx, MC, V.
Friday lunchtime found this quiet sidestreet restaurant almost empty except for a couple of locals and the Portuguese parliament (via satellite). Such a scarcity of customers didn't get in the way of a good meal, however. Indeed, the seriously laidback air to the place took us a long way from South Lambeth. We pitched up near the

Pescador

bar, as the back dining area appeared too gloomy for a day sitting. Chouriço came flaming, soaked (unannounced) in aguardente. Both mains – beef madeirense, and calamares – were large portions, with the meat winning in the taste stakes, being perfectly tender and free of any fat. Desserts (usually based around crème caramel) were off the menu, but coffees were fine. A good tapas menu and a well-maintained bar mean there are serious snack possibilities, too. Worth a diversion, O Barros shouldn't be overlooked in favour of its more visible neighbours up the road.
Babies and children welcome; high chairs. Separate room for parties, seats 150. Tables outdoors (2, pavement). Takeaway service. **Map 7/13L.**

Café Portugal
5A-6A Victoria House, South Lambeth Road, SW8 (020 7587 1962). Vauxhall tube/rail/ 2, 88 bus.
Café/bar **Open** 10am-11.30pm daily.
Restaurant **Lunch served** noon-3pm, **dinner served** 7-11pm daily. **Main courses** £8.50-£13. **Cover** £1. **Service** 10%.
Both **Credit** AmEx, JCB, LV, MC, £TC, V.
Café Portugal is double-fronted, giving both bar and restaurant sides plenty of light. An archway joins the two, and when we visited, the handful of bar tables were occupied. The restaurant proper has a simple charm, with a ladder strapped to the wall acting as a recipe bookshelf. Starters include a larger than usual number of vegetarian options, veering away from Portuguese cuisine. Garlic mushrooms of the flat variety were great steaks, superb in a parsley dressing. Similarly Provençal-style broad beans were tangy and fresh. There were six fish mains (all around £12) with bacalhau Vivien a mixed affair: the cod was appetising and effective, but the prawn sauce didn't seem fresh and the vegetables disappointed. Arroz com mariscos was a good portion of rice and seafood, and surprisingly chilli-hot. However, arroz doce (rice pudding) was a high point, with distinct flashes of lemon alongside the cinnamon. A dozen each of red and white wines (£8.50-£20) should cover most tastes and wallets. According to the dapper patter of the waiter, the white Beiras 'keeps the patron alive'. Apart from the overpriced main courses, Café Portugal is a good all-rounder.
Babies and children welcome; high chairs. Book dinner. Takeaway service. Vegetarian menu. **Map 7/13L.**

The Gallery
256A Brixton Hill, SW2 (020 8671 8311). Brixton tube/rail/45, 109, 118, 123, 250 bus. **Dinner served** 7-10.30pm Mon-Sat. **Meals served** 1-10pm Sun. **Main courses** £9.50-£12. **Credit** JCB, MC, £TC, V.
Don't be put off by the confusing frontage. The restaurant – dinner opening hours only, and very traditional in approach – lies through a door in the corner of the all-day fast-food piri-piri chicken operation. Once inside, you'll find the place distinctive, with murals predominant and a wood-banistered dining gallery above the main space. The well-stocked bar at one end supports an extensive wine list. Our meal was significantly uneven, however. Starters veered from £2-£8.50. We settled in the mid-price range for shared gambas house-style, which meant a spicy sauce and finger bowls (making a rare appearance in London). Mains were a disappointment: monkfish and prawn espetada was overpriced at £12.50, too salty, and had the prawns grilled to tastelessness; the bacalhau experienced similar problems. Things picked up with dessert – a huge wedge of crème caramel – and coffee, but the overall tone was much at odds with the huge blow-up review in the front window.
Babies and children welcome; high chairs. Book weekends. Takeaway service 12.30-11pm Mon-Sat; 12.30-10.30pm Sun. **Map 18.**

North

Camden Town & Chalk Farm NW1

Pescador ★
33 Pratt Street, NW1 (020 7482 7008). Camden Town tube. **Dinner served** 6-11.30pm Tue-Fri. **Meals served** 1-11.30pm Sat; 1-10pm Sun. **Main courses** £6-£11.90. **No credit cards.**
On our arrival one Sunday evening, this attractive new restaurant was so quiet that the waiter could get personal with the napkin placement. By the time we left, however, it was full but relaxed, and seems to have developed a mixed clientele in the year since opening. The clean, marine theme involves blue and white walls, nets and fish plates, but the menu also incorporates meat – and everything is fairly priced. Starters (sardines, mussels, and mozzarella salad) were all fresh and well-presented, as were the mains. Arroz de mariscos was packed with seafood; porco à alentejana (pork with clams) was rich and memorable. Desserts (all £2) are notable examples of Portuguese favourites (including pudim, or crème caramel). The house white wine was refreshing and light. Friendly service and an attentive chef, who came out to see how things were going, helped make a very enjoyable meal.
Babies and children admitted. Tables outdoors (2, pavement). Takeaway service. **Map 10.**

North East

Dalston E8

Nando's ★
148 Kingsland High Street, E8 (020 7923 3555/www.nandos.co.uk). Dalston Kingsland rail. **Meals served** noon-11.30pm Mon-Thur, Sun; noon-midnight Fri, Sat. **Main courses** £4.75-£6.95. **Credit** DC, MC, V.
Belying its location on a busy main junction, the Dalston branch of the international piri-piri chicken chain is light and airy, offering a take-away counter and a large dining area, decked out in wood and brightly coloured murals. Afro-Brazilian pop adds to the nicely uptempo atmosphere. Nando's is home to some seriously spicy sauces – freely circulating Medium, Hot and Very Hot. You select both heat and chicken part. Chilli nuts got us in the mood, along with pitta bread sauce-tasters. The chicken is char-grilled; breast in a roll was soft and succulent, and came as a good-sized portion with fries. There are also steak rolls and organic beanyburgers to be had, alongside competitively priced wines and beer. Pudim de limão (lemon pudding) had a real zest, and the galãos came with floating coffee beans. Friendly service and a clean environment made Nando's much more than a fast-food experience.
Babies and children admitted; high chairs. Disabled: toilet. Entertainment: salsa classes 9-10pm Thur. Takeaway service.
For branches see index.

Outer London

Wembley, Middlesex

O Galinheiro ★
414 High Road, Wembley, Middx (020 8903 0811). Wembley Central tube/18, 82, 83, 273 bus. **Meals served** 9am-11pm daily. **Main courses** £3.50-£9. **Credit** MC, £TC, V.
If outdoor tables on Wembley High Road seem unlikely, then the confusion increases once inside this café-restaurant/fast-food hybrid. The rather staid wood-panelled interior with inset vase cubby-holes seems entirely at odds with the pumping salsa-pop and menu declaration that 'piri-piri chicken is the best natural aphrodisiac'. The Ireland logo above the till remains a mystery. Chicken and seafood dominate. A calamares starter was fine if unremarkable, but the mains were a surprise. Chicken espetada (spit-roasted) was lean and succulent, with great fries, and the tuna steak was sizeable and well grilled. Desserts were not available (though chocolate mousse is usually a fixture), service was pretty slow and the place feels overpriced for the district. That said, both waitress and venue were friendly.
Babies and children welcome; children's menu. Takeaway service.
For branch see index.

Spanish

Centro

After one more burst of expansion, Spanish food in London seems to have reached yet another of its plateaus. For many people the cuisine still automatically suggests the neighbourhood tapas bar; cheap, handy and with straightforward, fun food to go with it. However, London has attracted some highly skilled and very imaginative young Spanish chefs who, at **Cambio de Tercio**, **Las Brasas** and **Gaudí**, present subtle, contemporary dishes that give the cuisine a completely different dimension. And, meanwhile, at **Moro**, Spanish culinary traditions provide the main basis for young British cooks' vibrantly original and ultra-popular pan-Mediterranean experiments.

Central

Belgravia SW1

Flamenco

54 Pimlico Road, SW1 (020 7730 4484). Sloane Square tube/Victoria tube/rail. **Lunch served** noon-3pm, **dinner served** 6-11.30pm Mon-Sat. **Main courses** £6.50-£15.25. **Tapas** £2.50-£7.90. **Service** 10%. **Credit** AmEx, DC, JCB, MC, TC, V.

A snugly comfortable tapas bar and restaurant, with dark wooden beams and brown plush booths in the bar area. It has a certain timeless quality that is reflected in the menu; the list of tapas – at slightly higher prices than the norm – includes good versions of all the classics, plus a few interesting departures such as pimientos de piquillo con setas (piquillo peppers stuffed with oyster mushrooms, £5.50) and rather luxurious tapas such as solomillo troceado al ajillo (chunks of steak cooked in garlic, £7.90). The main menu is similarly reliable, with a wide and, again, traditional choice of meat and seafood dishes, including an excellent rape al ajo (monkfish in garlic, £11.95) and solomillo de cerdo a la Murciana (pork steak cooked in tomatoes, onions and peppers, £9.50). The wine list suits the food, with plenty of robust, traditional Spanish labels. The Flamenco has a distinctly secluded feel for much of the time, but has been known to develop a livelier atmosphere on weekend evenings. It draws a diverse crowd – local regulars, after-work couples, lunching suits, even a few of the young and trendy. What keeps them coming back – as well as the food and comfort – is the service, which is exceptionally warm, personal and attentive.

Babies and children welcome; high chairs. Book dinner. No-smoking tables. Separate room for parties, seats 50. Takeaway service. **Map 6/11G.**

City E1, EC3

Barcelona Tapas Bar y Restaurante

15 St Botolph Street – entrance in Middlesex Street, EC3 (020 7377 5111). Aldgate tube/ Liverpool Street tube/rail. **Meals served** 11am-11pm Mon-Fri. **Happy hour** 5-7pm Mon-Fri. **Tapas** £3.25-£13.95. **Credit** AmEx, DC, MC, V.

This big, two-level bar sits behind wide plate-glass windows at the foot of a giant Aldgate office block. With striking decor of Gaudi-inspired mosaics and metalwork, it's smart and very much oriented to a suited City clientele. Staff buzz about efficiently in neatly stylish tunics. The long menu – all tapas, except for a choice of paellas and fideuàs (from £9.95 per person, minimum two) – offers a very wide choice, with some Catalan dishes such as esqueixada (salad of salt cod, red peppers, tomatoes, onions and olives, £4.95) and escalivada (£3.75) as well as tapas standards and a larger-than-usual choice of Spanish cold meats and cheeses. Food sometimes promises more than it delivers, and tapas prices are significantly higher than usual. This doesn't seem to bother most of the regular clientele that much, and to compensate there's an impressively comprehensive modern Spanish wine list (also quite pricey), including such London rarities as the much-admired Finca Dofí Priorat (£75) or, at the other end of the scale, the smooth Camparrón red from the rising wine region of Toro (£14.50). There's also an unusually large choice of cavas and Spanish dessert wines, and a hefty list of spirits and cocktails to soothe the after-office brow (from £3.95).

Babies and children admitted. Booking advisable. Separate room for parties, seats 80. Tables outdoors (4, pavement). Takeaway service. **Map 4/6S.**

For branches see index.

Leadenhall Wine Bar

27 Leadenhall Market, EC3 (020 7623 1818). Monument tube. **Open** 11.30am-11pm, **meals served** noon-10pm Mon-Fri. **Tapas** £2.95-£5.50. **Credit** AmEx, DC, JCB, MC, £TC, V.

An atypical bar occupying two shady, attractive old wooden-floored rooms above the Victorian splendour of Leadenhall Market. Curiously, this rather Dickensian space has for some years housed a tapas bar. It's a pleasant place to take refuge from the City bustle and linger over a drink, especially after the lunchtime rush has receded. There's a relatively short list of under 20 tapas, plus some chalked-up specials; food here can be erratic, varying from satisfyingly flavoursome to dead bland, but when they come out right the seafood specials in particular (around £5) and interesting tapas such as wild rice salad with peppers and nuts (£3.35) and chicken in a saffron and garlic sauce (£4.35) offer plenty to enjoy. The wine list makes no attempt to headline Spanish bottles but instead wanders happily around the world, with French, Italian, Australian, Chilean and even English labels as well as Iberian ones. In similar vein, the beer selection includes brands such as Pilsner Urquell as well as Spanish beers (from £2.50). Outside the rush, service is calm and laid back.

Babies and children admitted. Separate room for parties (top floor), seats 60. **Map 4/7Q.**

Mesón Los Barriles

8A Lamb Street, E1 (020 7375 3136). Aldgate East tube/Liverpool Street tube/rail. **Meals served** 11am-11pm Mon-Fri; 11am-4pm Sun. **Closed** three weeks Aug. **Main courses** £8.50-£17.50. **Tapas** £2.50-£18.90. **Credit** AmEx, JCB, MC, V.

Redevelopment proceeds apace at one end of Old Spitalfields Market, and so too does the burgeoning success of Los Barriles at the other end, as its tables continue to fill up with City workers during the week and market-goers on Sunday. Conventional tapas figure on the menu, but the best thing to go for are the larger fish and seafood specials (mostly £6.50-£11), market-fresh and often simply grilled. Dishes like this naturally vary with the quality of the ingredients, but the Barriles crew are skilled seafood buyers and, at their best, specials such as langoustines in oil and garlic or mussels marinière are utterly delicious, and as good as the offerings of far more elaborate establishments. The smaller tapas (mostly £2.50-£5) can be a mixed bag: on a recent visit, chipirones al ajillo offered a good, punchy mix of crustacean ink and garlic, and a standard Spanish salad (lettuce, tomato, onion, olives – nothing fancy), was nicely fresh, but patatas bravas were disappointingly mushy. As with the specials, seafood is often a good thing to go for. Tables are spread between a conservatory looking out on to the market and the large, cool and shady dark wood-and-brick interior; service is brisk, which adds to the bustling feel. Ice-cold Spanish beers (from £2.30) go perfectly with the food, but there's also a decent wine list.

Babies and children welcome; high chairs. Bookings not accepted 1-6pm. **Map 17/5R.**

Clerkenwell & Farringdon EC1

Las Brasas ★

63A Clerkenwell Road, EC1 (020 7250 3401). Farringdon tube/rail/55, 243 bus.
Bar **Open** noon-1am Mon-Fri; 6pm-1am Sat.
Restaurant **Lunch served** noon-2.30pm Mon-Fri. **Dinner served** 6.30-10pm Mon-Thur; 6.30-9.30pm Fri. **Main courses** £6.25-£9.95. **Set lunch** £7.50 two courses. **Credit** AmEx, MC, V.

Like the adjacent Gaudí, Las Brasas occupies part of the Turnmills building; it offers similarly sophisticated and inventive modern Spanish cooking, only this time applied to small, tapas-sized dishes, at much lower prices (referred to on the oddly misspelt menu as 'nibbles' or raciones, the word tapa apparently being seen as a no-no here). Occasional lapses aside, preparation, presentation and quality of ingredients are all on a different level from the tapas-bar norm. The menu changes frequently, but of dishes we've tried recently, two classics, ensaladilla and potatoes allioli (both £2.95) were subtly, smoothly flavoured, while a mixed platter of cold meats with toast (£5.50) included good serrano ham and great lomo (marinated pork); in escalibada (£2.95) the vegetables were memorably fresh and juicy. While waiting for the food to arrive, you can lay into fresh bread and garlic butter that could be a draw in themselves (garlic is not a flavour Las Brasas shies away from). There is also a range of main course-sized dishes, of which the biggest hits seem to be the barbecued mixed grills of meats, fish and seafood or vegetables (£6.50-£9.50), served sizzling hot. The wine selection is not as distinctive as the cooking, but among the fairly standard Spanish labels there are some less usual offerings (such as a crisp Gran Bazán Galician verde, very like Portuguese vinho verde, £15.50) and a good range of quality cavas. The Turnmills decor reflects its club origins with a postmodern-operatic style that's a tad wild for a bar-restaurant, and the dining area generates a powerful echo when it fills up with after-work groups, but it's also a pleasantly airy, roomy space (sit by the door to lessen the boom). Service is smoothly efficient.

Babies and children admitted. No-smoking tables. Separate room for parties, seats 60. Tables outdoors (4, pavement). **Map 15/4N.**

Gaudí ★

63 Clerkenwell Road, EC1 (020 7608 3220). Farringdon tube/rail/55, 243 bus. **Lunch served** noon-2.30pm, **dinner served** 7-10.30pm Mon-Fri. **Main courses** £14.50-£16. **Set lunch** £10 two courses, £15 three courses. **Service** 12½%. **Credit** AmEx, DC, MC, £TC, V.

A corner of the Turnmills building is an unusual location for a first-rank restaurant. However, this restaurant, with its convoluted, rather grandiose Gaudí-based decor, is the current base of one of the ablest young chefs in London, Nacho Martínez Jiménez, who arrived in 1997 after winning many awards in Spain. His cooking shows great flair, and yet is strongly rooted in traditional Spanish styles; inventive combinations of powerful and lighter flavours and textures are a trademark. A lasagne of goat's cheese with ceps, courgettes and aubergine in a saffron bechamel with spinach, pine kernels and sultanas (£10) was a deliciously varied, rich mix; a salad of fine Spanish ham with figs, melon and tomato and garlic bread (£12) offered sparer, but still stimulating flavours. Of our mains, a brochette of fillet steak with soft cheese, melon, dried apricots and sherry sauce (£15.50) was another audacious mix, while grilled swordfish and cockles in garlic with potato purée and field mushrooms (£15.75) had a more upfront, traditional strength. Special mention has to go to the fabulous desserts (all £5); anything with chocolate is heavenly, but other things, such as a manchego cheese mousse with quince jam, walnuts and honey, have a similarly orgiastic quality. The wine list offers a precise, well-chosen range of fine Spanish labels; service doesn't miss a step. Prices here may be high, but for a special occasion, Gaudí doesn't disappoint.

Babies and children welcome. Booking advisable. Separate room for parties, seats 45. **Map 15/4N.**

Moro ★

34-36 Exmouth Market, EC1 (020 7833 8336). Farringdon tube/rail.
Bar **Open** noon-11pm Mon-Fri; 6.30-11.30pm Sat.
Restaurant **Lunch served** 12.30-2.30pm Mon-Fri. **Dinner served** 7-10.30pm Mon-Sat. **Main courses** £10.50-£14.50.
Both **Credit** AmEx, MC,TC, V.

Being lauded on every side and elevated to celebrity chef-dom can be an instant recipe for complacency and overstretch, but thankfully this has never happened with cooking duo Sam & Sam (Samantha and Samuel) Clark and their crew. Moro's service, too, has never gone snotty on us but, the odd glitch aside, remains an exemplary mix of professionalism, friendliness and efficiency. The Clarks' eclectic but well-centred cooking style, based in Spanish traditions but borrowing freely from North Africa and other parts of the Mediterranean, has clearly struck exactly the right note with London diners. The menu changes daily. Of recent starters, prawn tortillitas with rocket and lemon (£6) was a deliciously balanced seafood and egg mix. With girolle mushrooms marinated in sherry vinegar and oregano (£5.50), the radical powerful dressing at first seemed too much for the mushrooms, but actually combined with it remarkably well. Staples among the mains are char-grilled lamb and monkfish, but with a constantly changing range of other elements, as in lamb with cos lettuce and a nuttily savoury mix of braised green beans and walnuts (£13.50). To finish up, yoghurt cake with pistachios (£4) made an equally special and enjoyable dessert. Outstanding throughout is the use of high-quality Spanish and Mediterranean ingredients with wonderfully clear, sharp flavours; the wine list is also expertly selected. Moro has now answered the requests of many by opening for dinner on Saturdays, although it's still necessary to book well ahead. Complaints? Well, the postmodern-minimal decor means that when it's full (most of the time) it gets powerfully loud.

Babies and children admitted. Booking essential. Disabled: toilet. **Map 15/4N.**

Fitzrovia W1

Costa Dorada

47-55 Hanway Street, W1 (020 7636 7139). Tottenham Court Road tube.
Tapas bar **Open** 7.30pm-3am Mon-Sat. **Set tapas meal** £18 per person (minimum ten).
Restaurant **Dinner served** 7.30pm-2.30am Mon-Sat. **Set dinner** £29.95 per person (minimum ten), three courses incl two bottles wine, coffee.
Both **Service** 10%. **Credit** AmEx, DC, MC, V.

In some parts of the London restaurant world, fashion just doesn't count. The floor-shatteringly loud, twice-nightly-except-Sunday live shows at London's only full-scale flamenco venue are perennially popular, with hen nights and Christmas parties a speciality. Between and after the shows there's dancing to favourite Latin tunes, cheesily rendered on an electronic keyboard, and the decor covers all the Costa-whatta clichés. This popularity comes in spite of the fact that the food – which is really secondary to the partying – is rarely anything above ordinary in quality, and distinctly pricey for what you get; a plate of chorizo costs £4.75 and a large-ish tapa of fried calamares is £6.75. The stage can be seen from the main restaurant area and (with a slightly reduced view) from the tapas bar alongside, and staying with tapas also allows you to keep prices a bit more under control. It's also better to stick to classic tapas and simpler dishes,

such as straightforward meat or fish grills (mostly around £10, with vegetables extra), which are more reliable than the more elaborate variations offered by the very long menu. Drink prices are again well above average, with Spanish beers at £3, hefty mark-ups on all wines except the basic house, jugs of sangría at £12.90 and standard Freixenet cava at an eye-popping £24. *Babies and children admitted. Book Fri, Sat. Entertainment: flamenco shows 9.30pm, 11.30pm, Mon-Thur; 10pm, 12.30am, Fri, Sat.* **Map 13/6K.**

Navarro's

67 Charlotte Street, W1 (020 7637 7713). Goodge Street tube. **Lunch served** noon-3pm Mon-Fri. **Dinner served** 6-10.30pm Mon-Sat. **Tapas** £2.20-£12.50. **Credit** AmEx, DC, MC, V.
Many London Spanish bar-restaurants seem to offer virtually interchangeable menus, but Navarro's has for several years followed a far more distinctive path by presenting a consistently interesting, original and sophisticated range of dishes, often based on less familiar traditional Spanish recipes. Salads, such as the ensalada bética (lettuce, beans, onions and avocado, £2.20) or remojón (seville oranges, tuna and onions, dressed in olive oil and wine vinegar, £3.25) are especially good, and make great summer lunches. Also memorable are moros y cristianos (black beans and rice, without the more usual bacon to make it vegetarian-friendly, £2.95) and the often superb setas con langostinos (langoustines with wild mushrooms, £5.75). For cooler times of year there's a rich fabada (£3.25), chorizo al coñac (in brandy, £3.85) and other robust offerings. Alongside the tapas, another house speciality is the range of brochettes (£9.05-£12.50), served sizzling hot at your table. Desserts are equally non-routine, with such choices as flan (crème caramel) with raspberry sauce (£2.95). The main wine list offers a well-selected range including good labels rarely seen in London such as a Basque Txomin Etxaniz white (£16.95) and a nicely crisp Enate rosé (£13.50). Navarro's also has a fine wine collection, available on request, which includes some of the most highly regarded of all recent Spanish vintages. The counterpoint to the fine food and wines is provided by the sometimes cranky or even brusque service, which is almost as much a regular feature of the place. Nevertheless, Navarro's is an original that deserves to be acknowledged.
Babies and children welcome; high chairs. Booking advisable. **Map 2/5J.**

Sevilla Mía

22 Hanway Street, W1 (020 7637 3756). Tottenham Court Road tube. **Open** 7pm-2am Mon-Sat; 7pm-midnight Sun. **Credit** (except Sun) AmEx, DC, MC, £TC, V.
Tucked away on Hanway Street is the quirky corner of London Andalusia that is the Sevilla Mía. It's housed in a cramped basement, reached via a shabbily anonymous entrance corridor; decor is basic seating, tourist posters and a few other Andalusian knick-knacks. The place is owned by the same people as the Costa Dorada, and the flamenco performers often come over after their shows there to play at the Sevilla Mía – usually in more relaxed style. A late licence and the bar's special hidden-dive feel have made it a late-night favourite with a diverse bunch of after-work drinkers, students, local Spaniards and other night owls, who hole up here till closing time. Drinks are as expensive as at the Costa Dorada (Spanish beers £3, jugs of sangria £12.90). Food consists of a limited range of tapas, brought across from the Costa Dorada kitchen and then microwaved; simpler tapas, though, such as tortilla or patatas bravas, make effective fillers, and according to the barman's mood, can come in large portions. A bar that should be saved for posterity.
Entertainment: flamenco singer, musicians 8.30pm-12.30am nightly. **Map 13/5K.**

Holborn WC1

Centro

93 Gray's Inn Road, WC1 (020 7242 2252). Chancery Lane tubel.
Bar **Open** 6-10.30pm Mon-Fri. **Tapas** £2.50-£3. *Restaurant* **Lunch served** noon-4pm, **dinner served** 6-10.30pm Mon-Fri. **Set meal** £20 (paella for two). **Main courses** £9.50-£10. **Service** 12½%.
Both **Credit** AmEx, DC, JCB, MC, V.
Opened in early 2000, Centro is a bright, relaxed bar-restaurant with a stripped-down modern decor – wooden floors, grey walls – that deliberately shuns tapas bar clichés. The menu (predominantly tapas and not as adventurous as those of London's first-rank Spanish restaurants) offers a contemporary take on Spanish dishes without losing touch with their traditional earthy strengths. Of tapas we tried, ham croquettes (£3) and spinach tortilla (£2.50) were both competently done. More original dishes often feature on a blackboard of daily specials, from which green beans with chorizo, cooked exactly to the right point, and cuttlefish with allioli (both £3.50) hit all the right notes. There are also a few full-size main courses listed on the printed and specials menus, such as char-grilled sea bass with a romesco sauce (£11.50) and sautéed vegetables with garlic (£7). The wine list is short and to the point, but includes a few quality Spanish and New World labels among the standards. Friendly service adds to Centro's likeable feel, and prices are unusually low for the area, even though the service charge does push them back up a bit. An attractive arrival.
No-smoking tables. Tables outdoors (4, pavement). **Map 3/4M.**

Mayfair W1

El Pirata

5-6 Down Street, W1 (020 7491 3810). Green Park or Hyde Park Corner tube. **Meals served** noon-11.45pm Mon-Fri; 6-11.45pm Sat. **Main courses** £8.50-£12.50. **Tapas** £2.20-£5. **Service** 10%. **Credit** AmEx, DC, JCB, MC, V.
Elegantly decorated in black and white, with two levels and prints by Picasso, Miró and other Spanish artists around the walls, the Mayfair Pirata has a smart look and style, but is actually one of the most reasonably priced and best-value places to eat in an area well supplied with very expensive ones. The tapas list is extensive, with some more refined tapas than usual such as a salad of fresh asparagus with manchego cheese and a tarragon vinagrette (£5.50), prawns in olive oil with peppers and wild mushrooms (£4.75) and a crêpe of mixed vegetables (£3.95) as well as more familiar favourites. Flavours, for the most part, are fresh and clear. The two set tapas menus are best kept for an occasion, since although they can be ordered by two people they provide an enormous amount of food. The wine list is also substantial and varied, as is the range of cocktails and liqueurs. Helpful and charming service adds to the comfortable feel of the bar.
Babies and children admitted. Booking advisable. Entertainment: Latin/Spanish musicians 9-11.30pm Fri. Separate room for parties, seats 60. Tables outdoors (16, pavement). Takeaway service. **Map 6/8H.**

Pimlico SW1

Goya

34 Lupus Street, SW1 (020 7976 5309). Pimlico tube/24 bus. **Meals served** noon-11.30pm daily. **Main courses** £8.50-£12.90. **Tapas** £1.50-£9.50. **Credit** AmEx, DC, MC, V.
The Goya seems to have established a peculiar place in the heart of Britain's political class, particularly the Tory element. In early 2000, the *Observer* reported a 'tapas plot' hatched by young Tory hopefuls around its tables to replace Billy Hague with that Castilian rascal Don Miguel Portillo, and when General Pinochet was let off the hook, this was the place hired by a bunch of Chilean rightists and their British chums for a celebratory bash. Apart from its proximity to Westminster, just why the Goya should have won this status isn't clear, but it does cater to a wide range of ages and tastes. The neat, white basement dining room – with intimate alcoves for conspiring in – tends to be preferred by an older, well-heeled clientele; the pretty, airy bar upstairs caters to a younger, international but still flush crowd, especially in summer when it overflows onto a very attractive pavement terrace. A wide range of classic tapas and larger dishes are available. Food has been surprisingly erratic at times, but on a recent visit two meat tapas – lomo adobado (marinated pork, £4.20) and costillas (lamb cutlets, £5.80) – were succulently juicy and excellently cooked, and calamares (£4.90) and an ensaladilla (£3.20) also hit all the right notes. The main menu includes substantial offerings such as the tournedo Goya (beef fillet in a wine sauce with peppers and artichokes, £12.90), plenty of fish, pastas and a range of paellas. The Spanish wine list features a few good newer labels among the old standards; and service is bustling and sharp, in a slightly haughty sort of way.
Babies and children admitted. Book dinner. Tables outdoors (8, pavement; 8, terrace). Takeaway service. **Map 6/11J.**
For branch see index.

Soho W1

Café España ★

63 Old Compton Street, W1 (020 7494 1271). Leicester Square tube. **Meals served** noon-midnight Mon-Sat; noon-11pm Sun. **Main courses** £6.25-£11. **Credit** MC, £TC, V.
One of the busiest places in Soho is this bright, resolutely straightforward little restaurant, offering Spanish home cooking at low prices. Its fare is not sophisticated, but portions are (sometimes very) large, flavours are satisfying and meat grills, in particular, such as lamb chops (£8.95), are often as good as you would find in far more imposing establishments. Fish and seafood dishes, such as bacalao a la vizcaína (salt cod with potatoes and onions in a tomato sauce, £5.95) seem to be less reliable, but still come in hefty platefuls. In addition to main courses, there's a list of classic tapas, also at decent prices (mussels a la marinera, £4.20; patatas bravas, £2.20), salads and daily specials. Drinks are equally accessible, with several reasonable Spanish labels for under £15. Service can seem curiously deadpan at first, but this is soon got over by the completely varied crowds of Soho-ites who fill the España's tables for lunch and dinner, all in search of a convivial, bargain meal.
Babies and children admitted. Bookings not accepted. Separate room for parties, seats 30. Takeaway service (weekends). **Map 13/6K.**

Café Latino

25 Frith Street, W1 (020 7287 5676). Leicester Square tube. **Open** noon-1am, Mon-Sat; 1pm-10.30pm Sun. **Meals served** noon-midnight Mon-Sat; noon-10.30pm Sun. **Happy hour** 5.30-7.30pm daily. **Main courses** £6.25-£9.95. **Tapas** £2.50-£4.50. **Service** 12½% on bills over £20. **Credit** AmEx, DC, JCB, MC, V.
Café Latino seems to have an ambition to become the archetypal Soho after-work good-times venue. It's spread over three stylishly designed floors, with a striking, vaulted basement bar that turns into the 'Latin Underground' as the evening wears on, with Latin and Caribbean DJs and live acts most nights of the week. Consequently, most of the punters who cram around its tables seem to be drawn by the big cocktail range (from £4.75), or the happy hour than by the cooking. The Latino's food, though, has become more than just something to help the alcohol go down. Over the last year the menu has offered a completely pan-Latin and sometimes hit-and-miss mix of dishes from across the Hispanic world (Argentina, Ecuador and Colombia have all featured). But in summer 2000 the restaurant introduced an all-new, much more Spanish-oriented menu that promises a good deal, with interesting tapa-sized dishes such as Mallorcan tumbet (casserole of baked aubergine, peppers, tomato, goat's cheese and basil, £3.25), brandada of salt cod in bruschetta (£3.95), mussels in white wine (£3.80) and chorizo with potatoes (£3.50) as well as a few transatlantic 'Latino' staples like chicken fajitas (£3.50). When it's not too full, the upstairs room, with its balcony view of Old Compton Street, is actually a peacefully relaxing, tranquil space.
Book Fri, Sat one week in advance. Entertainment: percussionist and DJ 6-10.30pm Sun. Tables outdoors (10, pavement). Takeaway service. **Map 13/6K.**

El Pirata

West

Brook Green W6

Los Molinos

127 Shepherd's Bush Road, W6 (020 7603 2229). Hammersmith tube. **Open** noon-midnight Mon-Fri; 6pm-midnight Sat. **Lunch served** noon-3pm Mon-Fri. **Dinner served** 6-11pm Mon-Sat. **Raciones** £7.80-£10.40. **Service** 10%. **Credit** AmEx, DC, JCB, MC, V.
Full tables on most nights of the week attest to the popularity of this small tapas local. It's attractively decorated, with not over-cutesy Spanish-rustic fittings and an interesting display of traditional ceramics. The menu is very long and varied and, unusually, many dishes can be ordered as tapas (£1.95-£5.50) or larger raciones (£3-£11). As well as an interesting mix of Spanish specialities, there are dishes with other influences, such as couscous with almonds and sultanas (£3.50/£7) or arepas (polenta cakes) with Mexican salsa (tapa only, £3.95). With so much to choose from, ups and downs in quality are hard to avoid, although recently a filloa al pescador (seafood pancake, £4.80/£9.60) and oyster mushrooms sautéed with ham (£4.50/£9) were cleverly put together and enjoyable. The well-priced Spanish wine list is complemented by an equally varied collection of fine sherries, spirits and liqueurs. Service sometimes gets a bit confused, but then it's always a struggle to fit many tapas dishes onto the intimately small tables.
Babies and children admitted; high chairs. Book Thur-Sat. Separate room for parties, seats 45.

Ladbroke Grove W10

Galicia

323 Portobello Road, W10 (020 8969 3539). Ladbroke Grove tube. **Lunch served** noon-3pm, **dinner served** 7-11.30pm Tue-Sun. **Main courses** £7.20-£13. **Tapas** £2.75-£5. **Set lunch** £7 three courses. **Credit** AmEx, DC, MC, £TC, V.
The Galicia began life as one more piece of home for the west London Galician/northern Spanish community, but because of where it is, at the top of Portobello by Golborne Road, it has also been taken up by a boho and sometimes distinctly upscale clientele of trendy Notting Hillites. The bar's style has scarcely changed to accommodate them, and the inimitably grumpy owners don't seem to care much who comes through the door, which all adds to the ambience (although, on a recent visit, one of the waiters was actually quite jolly). The quality of the tapas served in the bar (mostly £2.50-£5) can meander, but on the right day, traditional, earthy tapas such as juicy gambas al ajillo or chorizo al vino have all the right strong, punchy flavours, with no holding back on the garlic, and the freshly made tortillas (easily enough for two, £4.90) are great. The main menu served at the tables at the back and on the balcony upstairs offers a mix of Galician specialities such as pulpo a la gallega (£5), and London-Spanish restaurant favourites like fried hake (£9.20) and steak flamed in brandy (£10.75); it's an old-fashioned list, but meat grills we've tried recently such as lamb cutlets (£8.10) and veal in a sherry sauce (£8.90) have been excellent, with very good meat cooked exactly right. High points in the short wine list are the quality Galician whites for £15-£16, and special mention should go to the coffee, which is a lesson for all those who acquire espresso machines but seem to think they actually work automatically.
Book dinner. **Map 11/5Az.**

Maida Vale NW6, NW8

Don Pepe

99 Frampton Street, NW8 (020 7262 3834). Edgware Road tube.
Tapas bar **Open** 6pm-1am Mon-Sat. **Tapas** £2-£6.50.
Restaurant **Lunch served** noon-3pm, **dinner served** 7pm-1am Mon-Sat. **Main courses** £7.50-£13.10. **Set meal** £13.95 three courses. **Service** 12½%.
Both **Credit** AmEx, DC, MC, TC, V.
Anyone devoted to the most traditional Spanish restaurant staples, such as a creamy own-made flan, or merluza a la gallega, served in a rather old-fashioned style, would do well to make for Don Pepe, London's oldest Spanish restaurant. It's decorated in Galician country-inn style, with dark, heavy wooden beams and furniture in the bar,

which leads into a small, neat dining room. Tapas (£2.50-£5) are mostly nicely done, especially the robust classics – a revuelto (scrambled egg) with mushrooms and garlic was deliciously full-flavoured. Other fixtures on the list are 'winter warmers', full-strength versions of northern Spanish stews like fabada or caldo gallego (potato, mixed greens, bacon and black pudding), both £3.50. The main menu offers a similarly wide choice of hearty and satisfying Galician-based dishes, served in ample portions, with fish and seafood a mainstay; to finish up, there are very smooth own-made traditional pastries (£2.50) as well as flan. The wine list leaps rather abruptly from some good quality but accessible Spanish labels to a reserve stock of fine Riojas at over £100 a bottle. Unlikely to become a fashionable restaurant, but it is consistently good value.
Babies and children welcome; high chairs. Booking advisable, essential weekends. Entertainment: Spanish musicians 8.30pm-midnight nightly. Takeaway service. **Map 1/4D.**

Mesón Bilbao ★
33 Malvern Road, NW6 (020 7328 1744). Maida Vale or Queen's Park tube. **Lunch served** noon-3pm Mon-Fri. **Dinner served** 6-11pm Mon-Thur; 7-11.30pm Fri, Sat. **Closed** three weeks Aug. **Main courses** £8.90-£13.75. **Tapas** £1.50-£2.50. **Credit** JCB, MC, £TC, V.
Mesón Bilbao is consistently one of London's best, as well as most individual, Spanish restaurants. It attracts a clientele that runs from students and locals to well-heeled business lunchers, drawn by the skills of Basque owner José Larrucea and his family, who are expert fish and seafood cooks and even better seafood buyers. Even in off-season periods they seem able to track down quality seafood in a city where crustacean quality can be notoriously patchy. It pays to follow the day's recommendations, such as the chalked-up main course specials – the likes of sea bass in garlic and oil (£13.75), grilled swordfish (£8.90) or the traditional Basque dish merluza a la koskera (hake simmered with olive oil, onions and clams, £19.75 for two). The Bilbao also offers a very superior paella. Standing out among the smaller, tapa-sized dishes are Larrucea's spectacularly good own-recipe mussels 'al pepe' (£3) and chipirones en su tinta (baby squid in their own ink); some non-seafood tapas, such as fresh tortillas (£3) are also excellent. The restaurant has its quirks, however: meat dishes are generally less impressive than seafood ones, and some things – occasional sauces, some salads, the often nondescript patatas bravas – are surprisingly casually put together. Still, that's individuality for you. Service can also be off-centre at times, but is bluffly friendly. There's a smallish but sensible wine selection.
Book dinner Fri, Sat. Entertainment: Spanish guitarist 8-11pm Thur-Sat (Sept-Apr). Tables outdoors (7, pavement). **Map 1/3A.**

Paddington W2

Los Remos
38A Southwick Street, W2 (020 7723 5056/020 7706 1870). Paddington tube/rail. Tapas bar **Open** noon-midnight Mon-Sat. *Restaurant* **Lunch served** noon-3pm, **dinner served** 7pm-midnight Mon-Sat. **Set lunch** £9.95 three courses incl coffee. **Service** 10%. *Both* **Credit** AmEx, DC, MC, £$TC, V.
Los Remos's attractive little basement tapas bar is a snugly tranquil hideaway from the city with a loyal lunchtime clientele, which adds to its relaxed, neighbourhood feel. The long tapas list (mostly £2.50-£5) stays authentically within Galician tradition, so seafood is a strong point, particularly anything marinated. Boquerones a la vinagreta (£3.50) are wonderful, without any excess acidity and a model of a simple dish beautifully done; seafood salads, which frequently figure among the day's specials (around £5), can make a refreshing lunch. Service is charmingly low-key; the bar is hardly ever crowded, but it's a place that deserves to be cherished. More visible from the street is the ornately old-fashioned upstairs restaurant, with a suitably old-fashioned menu of heavily sauced (and heavy) meat and seafood dishes. Service is very correct, again in an old-fashioned style. Los Remos can also boast one of London's most extensive Spanish wine lists, with a very comprehensive selection of the more traditional Spanish labels.
Babies and children welcome. Book Thur-Sat. Entertainment: guitarist 8pm-12.45am Thur-Sat. Separate room for parties, seats 25.
Map 2/ 5E.

Shepherd's Bush W12

La Copita ★
63 Askew Road, W12 (020 8743 1289). Goldhawk Road tube. **Dinner served** 7pm-midnight Mon-Sat. **Tapas** £1.85-£3.75. **Service** 10%. **Credit** AmEx, MC, V.
La Copita has been an established port of call at the western end of Shepherd's Bush for several years now. It's small, narrow and snug, with little tables crammed around the bar and in a lower-level room at the back – this is not a place for anyone who likes to wave their arms around. The set menu is popular, providing a choice of any three tapas, plus garlic bread, or bread with olive tapenade and allioli, for £9.90. The list of around 30 tapas, plus daily specials, is strongest in seafood and vegetarian dishes such as squid cooked in their ink (£3.50) or vegetable paella in a gazpacho coulis (£3.50). There are also a few meat choices such as the long-running speciality of pepes (potatoes, onions and chorizo cooked together, £3.50). Some dishes have pleasurably strong flavours, while others can be dull. Service often seems very slow at busy times, but there's a convivial buzz most nights, and the current wine list strikes some interesting notes with a Scala Dei Priorat red for an unusually low £13.95, and an intriguing Latin American selection that even includes a Bolivian red, La Concepción (£14.75).
Babies and children welcome; children's set meal £6.50. Booking advisable. Separate room for parties, seats 26.

South West

Chelsea SW3

El Blasón
8-9 Blacklands Terrace, SW3 (020 7823 7383). Sloane Square tube. **Lunch served** noon-3pm, **dinner served** 6-11pm Mon-Sat. **Main courses** £3-£22.50. **Credit** AmEx, DC, JCB, MC, £TC, V.
A distinctive local tapas bar-restaurant for a distinctive neighbourhood. Just off Sloane Square, El Blasón is Chelsea through and through, a place where ladies lunch and multi-national executives take their families. Service is smoothly correct, which, with the old-fashioned upper-crust decor (thick pastel-green carpet, pink and white linen), adds to the discreet and tranquil atmosphere. The tapas menu includes decent versions of all the standards, plus some more elaborate additions including a succulently garlicky pinchito (skewer) of monkfish and Spanish bacon. More than usual care is given to presentation and prices are also higher than usual, with most tapas costing £4 or more. The main menu offers a wide range of Spanish-based dishes, majoring on seafood, with a similarly opulent note in the cooking, as in crab and mixed seafood in fennel with a cheese sauce (£15.90), roast suckling pig (£16.90) or, two of the house specialities, scallops in champagne (£10.50) and snails in a cream sauce (£9.60 for 12). The lengthy wine list is also distinguished, and expensive. El Bláson is a pleasant place for a peaceful, rather old-fashioned meal, but the prices soon mount up – not that this seems to bother most of the regular clientele.
Babies and children admitted. Booking essential. Disabled: toilet. Separate room for parties, seats 50. **Map 12/11F.**

Lomo
222-224 Fulham Road, SW10 (020 7349 8848). Bus 14. **Meals served** noon-midnight Mon-Sat; noon-11pm Sun. **Tapas** £3.50-£7.50. **Set lunch** (noon-6pm) £5 three tapas. **Credit** AmEx, DC, MC, £TC, V.
A style-tapas bar, with a slick, hip approach befitting its Chelsea locale, Lomo opened to considerable applause in 1999 as London's latest effort to showcase quality, contemporary Spanish food in a modern context. Decor is sleek: mostly metal and terracotta-red, with an undulating bar and tall, round drinking and talking tables (and just four ordinary-height tables, which cannot be booked). Service is chattily speedy. Blackboard specials supplement a varied menu of small dishes (referred to, as in several similarly style-conscious establishments, as raciones, the word 'tapa' apparently having the stain of naffness). Food here, though, has become a bit of a mixed experience. One of the bar's signature dishes, an open sandwich of steak hogazas (chunks) with rocket and manchego cheese (£6.95), was still delicious, with wonderful meat; a mixed salad (£3.75) was a refreshing combination of Mediterranean leaves. But while that old favourite of squid rings with allioli (£5.95) had an extremely smooth and refined garlic mayonnaise, the batter on the calamares seemed to have too much flour; a plate of mixed charcuterie (£5.95), came with decent lomo, but excessively salty ham and a deeply ordinary chorizo – a real come-down for a bar that used to stand out for its sourcing of Spanish ingredients. For dessert we were urged to try the day's special cheesecake (£4.50), which turned out to be heavy and chewy, and the espresso coffee that followed it was burnt to death. Maybe attention has been distracted away from the food by the popularity of the bar's cocktail list (£4-£6.50), happy hours (5-7pm) and so on. For more serious drinkers the wine list offers some fine labels, such as a Condado de Haza Ribera del Duero red (£20), a superior Albariño white (£19.50) and French and New World labels.
Babies and children admitted. **Map 5/12C.**

Fulham SW6

El Metro
Metropolitan Centre, Beadon Road, W6 (020 8748 3132). Hammersmith tube. **Meals served** noon-11pm Mon-Thur, noon-midnight Fri, 3pm-midnight Sat. **Main courses** £3.95-£10. **Set meal** £5.95 two courses. **Credit** AmEx, DC, JCB, MC, £TC, V.
The two branches of the Metro are quite different in appearance, but both go down the same fun-bar route in the evenings. The original Metro off Fulham Broadway has the prettiest location, in a cottage-like little house with a very attractive leafy patio at the front, but such has been the noise created by all that partying that it's no longer allowed to have tables outside after 8pm. El Metro II, in the arcade approaching Hammersmith Metropolitan line station, is less striking but has fewer problems with neighbours, and becomes a Latin dance-bar with admission payable on the door on weekend nights. In this kind of good-times bar food rarely impresses and, true to form, on a recent visit to Metro II albóndigas (£3) came in a production-line tomato sauce, patatas bravas (£2.50) were soggy and a portion of tortilla (£2.50) was too dry; wild mushrooms in garlic (£3), on the other hand, were much better, with all the right flavours. The menu also offers a large range of other choices in addition to tapas, and things such as baguette sandwiches (from around £4.50) are often a better bet. Staff are amiably unprofessional. Spanish beers cost from £2.50, and there are decent wine and cocktail lists. Go at lunchtime and you'll find a completely different atmosphere, and the food may well be better taken care of too.
Babies and children welcome; high chairs. Book evenings, weekends. Separate room for parties, seats 50. Tables outdoors (12, pavement). Vegetarian menu.
For branch see index.

The Rock
619 Fulham Road, SW6 (020 7385 8179). Fulham Broadway tube. **Lunch served** 11am-3pm, **dinner served** 6pm-midnight daily. **Main courses** £6.50-£12.50. **Tapas** £2.50-£5.75. **Service** 10% at weekends and for parties of ten or more. **Credit** MC, £TC, V.
One of London's more idiosyncratic local tapas bars, the Rock has retained its amiably laidback, street-corner bar feel despite a rather bland smartening up of the main bar a few years ago. The owners are from Gibraltar (hence the name) and inimitably deadpan, but friendly with it, and the other staff were likeably obliging in handling late orders. At the back of the bar there is a surprisingly large dining room, which occasionally hosts live entertainment, where you can order from an unchanging menu of hefty main courses such as grilled pork chops (£6.50) or trout meunière (£7.50), all served in giant portions with abundant chips and veg. They're hearty fillers first and foremost, but for anyone with a powerful appetite they are very good value. For anyone who isn't that hungry it's probably best to stay with tapas in the bar, the list of which also never varies, and includes all the classics plus some less usual, gutsy specialities such as two traditional Spanish ways of cooking tripe, and snails in red wine (all £3.75). Recently, we tried a pinchito moruno (£2.50) – enjoyable, juicy meat – and patatas bravas (£2.50), which caught us out by being hot enough to face down a vindaloo, and should maybe come with a warning.
Babies and children welcome; high chairs. Book dinner Fri, Sat. No-smoking tables. **Map 5/13A.**

La Rueda
642 King's Road, SW6 (020 7384 2684). Fulham Broadway tube. **Lunch served** noon-3pm, **dinner served** 6.30-11.30pm Mon-Fri. **Meals served** noon-11.30pm Sat; 1-10.30pm Sun. **Main courses** £9-£15. **Set meal** (Fri, Sat) £17 three courses. **Credit** AmEx, MC, V.
The three Ruedas are the most prominent of London's older-style, Galician-run Spanish restaurants, and sometimes one or other of them seems to be the one Spanish place in town that everybody has been to at least once. The big Clapham and Chelsea branches are pretty much alike, with dark, old-Spanish style woodwork, slightly rustic-looking bar areas and neater dining areas with pink linen-clad tables. Both are restfully quiet by day, but fill up at night and at weekends with big, noisy bunches of after-workers, students and other partiers. The Wigmore Street Rueda is smaller and more sedate, but still popular with local workers looking for a good-value lunch. All three share the same menu, and, with such a successful formula, no one feels the need for innovations. The long tapas list includes all the standards and a few more; really traditional northern-Spanish meat dishes are often done well here – fabada (£3.95) and pollo al ajillo (£3.50) that we tried recently both had lots of earthy flavour. Fish and vegetable dishes tend to be more so-so, but any dips in the cooking can be offset by the low prices and easygoing buzz. Less popular than the tapas but always available is a substantial main menu, with an old-fashioned list of often pretty heavy Anglo-Spanish favourites such as battered hake (£10.95) and meat grills. The wine list is as well-priced as the food. Despite all the bustle, things are kept going smoothly thanks to amiably gruff waiters who look as if they've had things under control for years.
Babies and children welcome; high chairs. Book dinner Fri, Sat. Entertainment: Spanish musicians 8-10pm Tue; DJ and Latin American dancing from 11.30pm Thur-Sat. Separate room for parties, seats 50. Tables outdoors (6, pavement). **Map 5/13B.**
For branches see index.

Parsons Green SW6

El Prado
764-766 Fulham Road, SW6 (020 7731 7179). Putney Bridge tube. **Lunch served** noon-2.30pm daily. **Dinner served** 7-11pm Mon-Sat; 7-10.30pm Sun. **Main courses** £8.50-£15. **Set lunch** £9.95 three courses. **Set meal** £14.95 three courses. **Service** 12½%. **Credit** AmEx, DC, JCB, MC, £TC, V.
The Prado's success has allowed it to spread into the next-door building, which has been knocked together with the original restaurant to create a much larger dining room that now fills a whole street corner. The decor and linen, mostly in pink, are traditional, and the walls are suitably decorated with prints by Goya, Velázquez and other artists featured in the Prado museum in Madrid. The clientele tends to be a little older than is the norm for tapas bar-restaurants. Tapas do feature on the menu, but for once they are given less emphasis than the main courses, and particularly the specialities of chef Antonio Ruíz, who produces some of London's best versions of powerful Spanish classics such as cordero asado (Segovian slow-roasted lamb, cooked in its own juices, £10), a platter of langoustines (£11), marmitako (a Basque stew of fresh tuna with paprika, onions, potatoes and peppers, £10) or his own-recipe 8oz solomillo steaks (£12). Ruiz is an expert meat cook, and roasts, above all, are succulently tender. Smaller offerings can be ordered separately as tapas, or as starters; they're much less distinctive than the mains, but a few blips aside, dishes such as revuelto con setas (scrambled egg with mushrooms, £4) or ham croquettes (£4.50) are generally enjoyably satisfying. The wine list headlines on Riojas, which go excellently with the roasts. Staff are charming, presided over by owner Félix Velarde, a very energetic and welcoming host.
Booking essential. Entertainment: guitarist 8pm-midnight Fri, Sat. Separate room for parties, seats 80.

Putney SW15

La Mancha
32 Putney High Street, SW15 (020 8780 1022). Putney Bridge tube. Tapas bar **Open** noon-11pm Mon-Thur; noon-11.30pm Fri, Sat; noon-10.30pm Sun. **Main courses** £8.95-£10.50. **Tapas** £3.60-£5.95. **Service** 10%.
Restaurant **Dinner served** 7-11pm Mon-Sat; 7-10.30pm Sun. **Set lunch** (Mon-Fri) £7.50 two courses. **Set dinner** £15.95 two courses. **Service** lunch 10%; dinner 12½%.
Both **Credit** AmEx, DC, JCB, MC, £TC, V.
Like many Spanish establishments around town, Putney's La Mancha is a game of two halves. On the ground floor there is a large tapas bar, which when busy (which seems to be most evenings) is a candidate for London's noisiest eating space. The current decor – sultry tequila sunrise colours and a black ceiling – seems to magnify the boom still further. The tapas menu offers a wide variety, and there are a few larger dishes such as breast of duck with a cherry sauce (£9.90); of tapas we've sampled, escalopinas de pollo (chicken escalopes with ham and cheese in a tomato sauce, £4.90), hit the right notes with plenty of flavour, and a piece of tortilla (£3.80) was enjoyably fresh, but a tapa-sized portion of paella (£3.75) was very dull. Service was fast to the point of being irritatingly abrupt and impersonal. Drinks, though, are a plus. There is a varied wine list with some New World (mostly Latin American) as well as Spanish bottles, and, for once, an excellent sangría (£11.25, 1 litre jug) that's subtly refreshing rather than head-banging or over-sweet. On the floor above is the main restaurant, in similar colours but much

more sedate, which is popular with local families. The two-course set menu is Spanish-international, including interesting dishes such as a serrano ham, goat's cheese and mango starter or pork knuckle with herbs on a bed of lentils. The cooking often has nice touches, even though the set-price formula may not be as cheap as it looks once wines, desserts and coffees are added.
Babies and children welcome; high chairs. Entertainment: guitarist 8-11pm Mon-Sat; pianist 8-10.30pm Sun.

South Kensington SW5

Cambio de Tercio ★
163 Old Brompton Road, SW5 (020 7244 8970). Gloucester Road tube. **Lunch served** 12.30-2.30pm daily. **Dinner served** 7-11.30pm Mon-Sat; 7-11pm Sun. **Main courses** £9-£15. **Service** 12½% for parties of six or more. **Credit** AmEx, MC, V.
Cambio de Tercio doesn't set out to grab your attention, but has regularly produced some of the best examples of sophisticated modern Spanish food to be found in London. It's smart and stylish, even though some of the bullfight-theme accessories are now looking a bit faded; the menu once used to also offer its first courses as 'tapas', but now this unnecessary pretence has been dropped, and it's a restaurant-only list. Exceptionally able chef Diego Ferrer's cooking is streets away from the earthy clichés about Spanish food; it is innovative and yet still true to its roots. Piquillo peppers stuffed with salt cod brandada (£7.50) was a beautifully delicate sweet and savoury mix; serrano ham croquettes (£6) were very smooth. Of the mains, rabo de toro caramelizado con salsa de vino tinto (glazed bull's tail in a red wine sauce, £13.90), was an expert refinement of a traditional Andalusian classic, combining subtle flavourings with all the earthiness of the basic meat; in Galician-style gratinated scallops with a spring onion cream sauce (£13.50) the shellfish were a tad disappointing, but the sauce was luxuriously, delicately rich. Desserts, such as a hot chocolate soufflé (£5.50), are just as striking. Service is intelligent, smooth and attentive. A much-expanded wine list now offers an impressively broad selection of the most prestigious – and newly acclaimed – Spanish wines. A class act.
Babies and children admitted. Book dinner. Dress: smart casual. Entertainment: Spanish guitarist 8-11pm Wed, Thur. Separate rooms for parties, seating 18 and 30. Tables outdoors (3, pavement). **Map 5/11C.**

South

Battersea SW11

Castilla
82 Battersea Rise, SW11 (020 7738 9597). Clapham Junction rail. **Open** 6.30-11.30pm Mon-Thur; 6.30pm-2am Fri, Sat. **Main courses** £8.40-£16. **Tapas** £3.20-£6.20. **Service** 10%. **Admission** £5 after 10.30pm Fri, Sat. **Credit** AmEx, JCB, MC, £TC, V.
Battersea's Castilla has a very traditional Castilian-inn look, with dark-wood panelling and a heavy, curving bar, snugly comfortable seating and heraldic symbols around the walls. The restaurant's strengths lie not in any great surprises on the menu but in classic Spanish tapas done very well: dishes such as pimientos de piquillo stuffed with fish in a spicy sauce (£4.60), revuelto de esparragos (scrambled eggs with asparagus, £3.80), rajo (with chips, £4.20) or salmon croquettes (£3.90). There's also a sizeable list of main courses including a mixed fish and seafood grill (£16) and lamb cutlets with honey and apple (£12.60). The Spanish wine list is varied and decently priced. However, problems we had heard about at the Castilla became evident on a Saturday night visit: food took an age to arrive, orders were lost, and one big group on another table had been waiting so long they decided to walk out. Despite heroic efforts by the waiting staff, it was clear the kitchen could scarcely cope. It's a shame: regulars seem willing to forgive the restaurant this 'eccentricity', but others might not want to give it so much slack.
Babies and children welcome. Book Thur-Sat. Separate room for parties, seats 35. Tables outdoors (12, terrace).

San Miguel's on the River
Molasses House, Plantation Wharf, Battersea Reach, SW11 (020 7801 9696). Clapham Junction rail. **Open** noon-11pm Mon-Sat; noon-10.30pm Sun. **Main courses** £9.50-£15.75. **Tapas** £1.50-£6.75. **Set tapas meal** £6.95. **Service** 10%. **Credit** AmEx, DC, JCB, MC, V.
A large, comfortable bar-restaurant in a Thames-side wharf redevelopment, with panoramic views over the river from big bay windows. The decor and fittings in light wood are neat and slightly old-fashioned, and service is smoothly welcoming, but despite the smartish look of the place, prices – for tapas – are low. There are no radical departures on the tapas list, but this is an excellent place to come to find all the classics done well, with plenty of robust flavour: dishes such as chorizo al vino (£2.75), boquerones in vinagrette (£1.95) or a moreish guisadito en cazuela (meat and vegetable casserole, £2.75). There is also an extensive and relatively pricier restaurant menu, with many hefty specialities such as caldo gallego (a heavy, wintery meat and vegetable broth, £3.50), trout with almonds (£9.50), loin of pork marinated in red wine and peppers (£8.95) and giant mixed grills (£30 fish and seafood, £29 meat, both for two). The wine selection includes a very crisp Galician Albariño white for £19.95. A pleasant place for a relaxing lunch beside the river, whether you want to eat a lot or little.
Babies and children admitted; high chairs. No-smoking tables. Takeaway service.
For branch see index.

Cambio de Tercio

Clapham SW4

Carmen ★
6 Clapham Common Southside, SW4 (020 7622 6848). Clapham Common tube. **Dinner served** 6pm-midnight Mon-Thur. **Meals served** noon-midnight Fri-Sun. **Tapas** £2.75-£5.95. **No credit cards.**
A pleasantly airy, easygoing little tapas bar beside Clapham Common, Carmen makes a handy standby for a relaxed evening meal or a Sunday afternoon snack. The tiles and bare-wood decor tends towards Spanish-rustic, but the list of around 40 tapas is new- rather than old-style, with a large number of vegetarian options and a choice of five salads. Some of the tapas don't turn out to be as good as they sound, but the best ones have plenty of lively flavour, and even standard tapas often come with imaginative original touches. Moreish ones to go for include the lipsmacking croquetas de cabrales (croquettes of Asturian cabrales goat's cheese, £3.95), generously sized boquerones (£3.85) and chorizo al vino (£3.30); there's also an enjoyably light gazpacho (£3.95). The wine list is shortish but very well-priced, and the range of Spanish fruit liqueurs and brandies (from £2) is a house speciality. Coffee, too, is above average.
Babies and children welcome; high chairs. Bookings not accepted weekends.

El Rincón Latino
148 Clapham Manor Street, SW4 (020 7622 0599). Clapham North tube. **Open** 10am-midnight Mon-Fri; 11am-midnight Sat; 11am-11pm Sun. **Lunch served** 11.30am-3pm, **dinner served** 6.30-11.30pm Mon-Fri. **Meals served** 11am-11.30pm Sat; 11am-10.30pm Sun. **Main courses** £8-£11. **Tapas** £2.50-£5. **Credit** AmEx, MC, V.
This bright, long-popular Clapham local went through a bad patch a couple of years ago, but under its young and energetic current owners it has bounced right back. The quality of the welcome deserves special mention, as an important part of the likeable buzz: on a busy night, with people asking for extra places at booked tables, turning up late and so on, staff remained unfailingly cheerful and helpful throughout, sometimes against the odds. There's a list of around 50 tapas, so there's plenty of variety: the best we've tried are the croquetas de cabrales (goat's cheese croquettes) and revuelto de ajos tiernos (scrambled egg with wild garlic), both £3.50, along with the house albóndigas (£4), which come in a very dunk-worthy sauce. Some others, however, such as slices of aubergine in batter (£4) and an ensaladilla (£3) have been a little on the dull side. A few Colombian specialities remain on the menu from the days when the place was Colombian-owned; they include a gutsy Colombian chorizo with fried plantain (£4.50) and, among the short list of substantial main courses, tamal colombiano (cornmeal and meat patty, served with rice, £8). Spanish and Mexican beers cost £2.20-£2.40, and there's the usual ample range of cocktails (all £3.75). Drinkers can also find a few quality Spanish wines on the list, at very decent prices.
Babies and children welcome; high chairs. Booking essential.

Vauxhall SW8

Rebato's
169 South Lambeth Road, SW8 (020 7735 6388). Stockwell tube.
Tapas bar **Meals served** 5.30-10.45pm Mon-Fri; 5.30-7.45pm Sat. **Tapas** 75p-£11.75.
Restaurant **Lunch served** noon-2.30pm Mon-Fri. **Dinner served** 7-10.45pm Mon-Sat. **Set meal** £15.95 three courses.
Both **Credit** AmEx, DC, MC, £TC, V.
From one year to the next, the only things that are likely to change at Rebato's, one of London's longest-established Spanish-run tapas restaurants, are the prices – and those don't change much, either. But why change a winning formula? Rebato's is a consistent favourite with a multifarious clientele that runs from elderly couples and wandering Spaniards to students. It's a rather grand-looking establishment, with ornate mouldings, tiled floors, big mirrors behind the bar and plush seats. The younger crowd generally prefers to stay in the bar, where a wholly traditional range of tapas (mostly £2.50-£4.50) is available. These can sometimes be lacklustre, but for the most part dishes such as pulpo a la gallega (£4), riñones al jerez (£2.95) or ensaladilla (£2.75) have plenty of spark and flavour. Continue past the bar and you'll come to the smart dining room, where the ample fixed-price menu is served, combining satisfying versions of Spanish dishes such as lamb chops with (great) allioli and fresh fish specials with old-style international standards like chicken supreme. It's very good value, if you're hungry enough. Also fine value is the wine list, although many customers don't notice it, since they stay with the exceptional bargain of the house wines, good Torres labels at well below usual prices.
Booking advisable (restaurant). Entertainment: Spanish musicians 8.30-11.30pm Wed-Sat.

Waterloo SE1

Mesón Don Felipe
53 The Cut, SE1 (020 7928 3237). Southwark tube/Waterloo tube/rail. **Meals served** noon-11pm Mon-Sat. **Tapas** £2.50-£4.50. **Service** 10%. **Credit** MC, V.
We tried to get into Don Felipe on several nights and were unable even to make it through the door, such is the ongoing popularity of one of London's best-known tapas bars. In appearance and style it combines Spanishness, Englishness, modernity and traditional touches, and the clientele are a similarly broad mix. The menu is tapas-only (£1.95-£4.50), and offers a sizeable variety organised into fish, vegetable and meat dishes. Food here seems to go through highs and lows. When we finally managed to gain entry, albóndigas were nicely meaty, with a good rich sauce, and the mint in habas con jamón y menta (broad beans with ham and mint) gave a pleasant tang to the other ingredients. But espinacas con piñones (spinach with pine kernels and raisins) were a little soggy, and tuna croquettes could have done with some more fish. Almost an established 'eccentricity' of the restaurant is its service, by an ever-changing flow of young Spaniards, some of whom are very competent, while others clearly have very little idea of what they're doing. The Don Felipe's greatest plus, on the other hand, is its truly exceptional Spanish wine list, certainly among the best in London, with a very fine selection of reserva Riojas together with high-quality labels from Ribera del Duero, Navarra, Rueda and up and coming regions such as Somontano and Galicia's Rías Baixas, all at fair prices. Alternatively, there's also quite a special choice of cavas, and fine sherries.
Babies and children admitted. Booking advisable. Entertainment: guitarist 8.30-11pm nightly. No-smoking tables. **Map 7/8N.**

South East

Blackheath SE3

El Pirata
16 Royal Parade, SE3 (020 8297 1770/1880). Blackheath rail. **Open** noon-11.30pm Mon-Sat; noon-10.30pm Sun. **Lunch served** noon-2.45pm Mon-Fri; noon-3.45pm Sat. **Dinner served** 6-11.15pm Mon-Sat. **Meals served** noon-10.15pm Sun. **Service** 10%. **Set meals** £19.50, £17.75 tapas selection (minimum two). **Credit** AmEx, DC, JCB, MC, V.
El Pirata is a spacious bar-restaurant, with idiosyncratic decor of rag-rolled walls with things about pirates written on them, an ornate stained-glass central lamp and multi-coloured cushions along the walls. On previous visits we'd been impressed by the fast and obliging service, but on a recent Sunday lunchtime staff seemed distinctly semi-detached, despite the place being nowhere near full. There are no real surprises on the tapas menu, but prices seem on the high side for a tapas local, and the set tapas meals are also quite expensive (£35.50 or £39 for two). Albóndigas (£4.25) were nicely meaty, if a tad overcooked, and an ensaladilla (£3.70) offered a pleasant, fresh balance of tuna and veg; chicken croquetas (£3.50) could have done with more flavour but were nicely crunchy. Best of the tapas we tried was an excellent revuelto (scrambled egg) with spinach, mushrooms and garlic (£4.25), really more like a spinach tortilla, in which every element combined perfectly together. The wine list is straightforward but reasonably priced, and there's the option of some often quite gooey desserts (from around £2.95).
Babies and children welcome; high chairs. Entertainment: Spanish music Tue. Separate room for parties, seats 46. Tables outdoors (3, pavement). Vegetarian menu.

East

Bethnal Green E2

Laxeiro
93 Columbia Road, E2 (020 7729 1147). Bus 26, 48, 55. **Meals served** noon-3pm, 7-11pm Tue-Sat; 9am-3pm Sun. **Tapas** £2.95-£5.95. **Credit** AmEx, DC, JCB, MC, V.
An easygoing neighbourhood local during the week, Laxeiro does its biggest business on Sunday mornings, when the Columbia Road market-goers flock in and it becomes a struggle to get a table. The colourful decor suits the laidback style, with Keith Haring-ish painted tables. The week's menu is written up on a blackboard; for such an unpretentious little place the standard of food has been impressively high, but on recent visits things seem to have slipped a fair bit back towards the ordinary. Patatas allioli were decently tangy, and mixed salad featured a good mix of fresh leaves (both £2.95). However, garlic prawns (£5.95) and chorizo al vino (£3.50) were both distinctly bland, and made with pretty lacklustre ingredients. Service, too, has been reported as going beyond relaxed to just plain slow. How much this matters may depend on whether you're in any kind of hurry; to ease the wait there's a quite well-varied and low-priced wine list, and Spanish beers for £2.
Babies and children admitted. Booking essential weekends. Takeaway service.

Docklands E14

Baradero ★
Turnberry Quay, off Pepper Street, E14 (020 7537 1666). Crossharbour DLR. **Open** 11am-11pm Mon-Fri; 6-11pm Sat. **Main courses** £11.50-£16.50. **Tapas** £1.95-£5.25. **Service** 12½%. **Credit** AmEx, DC, JCB, LV, MC, £TC, V.

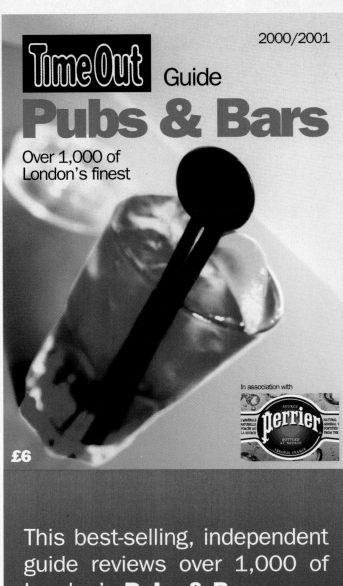

Some may think that Docklands empties out straight after work, but the lively Baradero is there to disabuse them of this notion. A big, airy, two-floor space, it has a great location beside Millwall Dock, with views over the water and a quayside terrace that's a fine location for a relaxing lunch. The tapas menu stays mainly with Spanish standards, but the staff are a Spanish-Latin American mix, who run the place with flair. An ensaladilla rusa (£4.25) was an excellently fresh-flavoured version of a dish that's often sloppily done, and garbanzos al pisto (chickpeas in a sauce of peppers, onion, garlic and oregano, £3.95) had lots of good-tastings ingredients that blended together well; more impressive still was a delicious bowl of mejillones a la marinera (moules marinière, £4.50) and a succulent vuelta de carne (pan-fried steak medallions with garlic, peppers and parsley, £4.95), with first-rate meat. Occasional larger specials supplement the tapas list, and for those settling in for a long session there are extremely ample set tapas menus (£19.50 per person, minimum two). Baradero also has a serious Spanish wine list, with an especially good range of new and up-and-coming labels for under £25; Spanish beers are a modest £2.50, including the heavier-than-usual Voll Damm. Plus there's a big range of liqueurs, spirits and the like, and on Friday and Saturday night Latin DJs move in.
Babies and children admitted; high chairs. Dress: smart casual. Entertainment: DJs dinner Fri, Sat. Separate room for parties, seats 50. Tables outdoors (18, terrace). Vegetarian menu.

Leytonstone E11

Elche

567-569 Leytonstone High Road, E11 (020 8558 0008). Leytonstone tube. **Lunch served** 12.30-2pm Tue-Sat. **Dinner served** 6.30-11pm Mon-Thur; 6.30pm-midnight Fri, Sat. **Meals served** 12.30-10pm Sun. **Main courses** £7.50-£15.50. **Sunday buffet** (12.30-4pm) £10 incl ½ bottle of wine or sangria. **Credit** AmEx, DC, MC, V.

At many times over the last ten years, Elche has served up some of the most interesting and enjoyable Spanish food in London, with imaginative and skilfully prepared variations on traditional and contemporary dishes using high-standard ingredients. More recently, its fare has been more conventional, and sometimes inconsistent in quality, but at its best it's still a good cut above the norm. In addition to familiar classics, the tapas menu offers attractive versions of escalivada (£4.95), warm goat's cheese salad (£4.25), piquillo peppers stuffed with monkfish (£6.50) and an often-delicious espinacas a la catalana (spinach with pine kernels, garlic and raisins, £4.50). The short list of main courses includes a seafood fideuà (£9.50) and a hefty mixed grill (£15). From Sunday to Thursday you can have your choice of any three tapas for £10, and a very popular event with locals is the all-you-can-eat Sunday buffet lunch, also £10, half-jug of sangria included. There are any number of well-prepared dishes to choose from, including a great, classic paella, made with good shellfish that retains its proper flavours. The wine list runs through all the more familiar Spanish regions, at very reasonable prices; service is quietly welcoming.
Babies and children welcome; high chairs; half-price sunday buffet. Book dinner Fri, Sat. Takeaway service.

North East

Stoke Newington N16

Bar Lorca

175 Stoke Newington High Street, N16 (020 7275 8659). Stoke Newington rail/73 bus. **Meals served** noon-midnight Mon-Thur; noon-1am Fri, Sat; noon-11pm Sun. **Main courses** £7.20-£11.50. **Tapas** £2.20-£5.80. **Credit** (for bills over £10) MC, V.

The party heart of Stoke Newington, with salsa classes, flamenco nights, funk, Latin and other DJs and occasional surf-lounge bands on different nights of the week, the Lorca also functions, when it's less busy, as a more general local hangout, with a big, airy space and high windows for people watching. Its popularity as a good-time spot and boozer hasn't encouraged the staff to pay great attention to the quality of the food, which tends to be patchy: classic Spanish tapas such as gambas al ajillo (£5.20), albóndigas (£4.20) or mushrooms in garlic (£3.70) can be enjoyably well-flavoured, or dull and sloppily put together. There are group menus to ease tapas ordering (£9.95 a head, minimum four), a recently-introduced family-friendly kids' menu, some larger dishes such as grilled hake with chips and salad (£8.95), and a few fruity and chocolatey desserts (from £3.20). Service, like the food, can get hit-and-miss when the crowds stream in. For partygoers, there's an extensive and recently revised cocktail list; wines seem relatively expensive for this kind of place, beginning at £10.50 a bottle, but Spanish beers cost £2.30-£4. The Lorca's success has led to it opening a branch offering the same formula in Brixton.
Babies and children admitted before 8pm; children's menu. Book Thur-Sun. Entertainment: musicians, DJs, from 10pm nightly (admission £4 after 10pm Fri, Sat); big screen showing Spanish football.
For branch see index.

North

Camden Town NW1

Bar Gansa ★

2 Inverness Street, NW1 (020 7267 8909). Camden Town tube. **Open** 10am-12.30am Mon-Sat; 10am-11.30pm Sun. **Breakfast served** 10am-5pm daily. **Meals served** 10am-midnight Mon-Sat; 10am-11.30pm Sun. **Service** 10%; 12½% for bills over £30. **Credit** MC, TC, V.

Camden is, of course, a place where trendy eating venues come and go, but Bar Gansa has, over more than a decade, settled into being an almost immovable, even archetypal, model of a hip, laidback (sometimes extremely so) local hangout. It's staffed by a regularly changing bunch of young Spaniards, who just as regularly get orders mixed up, but they're generally pretty sweet about it (except when things are really busy). In the last couple of years the bar has also opened for breakfast. We recently tried the 'French' (a full English breakfast, with Toulouse sausage instead of bacon, £3.95) and the 'Spanish' (ditto, with serrano ham). Both were good-value wake-ups – even though the not-bad serrano was perhaps wasted with a fried egg and mushrooms – and we were impressed by the quality of the freshly squeezed orange juice (£1.75). Tapas (mostly £2.50-£4) are a bit pot-luck, and can be enjoyably full of flavour, or on the dull and routine side; there are also a few main courses, such as the requisite paella. Still, the wine list offers a good range of Spanish and some other- nationality labels for under £16; beers are also decently priced at around £2 and the espresso coffee is well above average. If you want more, you're probably in the wrong place.
Babies and children admitted. Book dinner Thur-Sat. Entertainment: Spanish guitarist 8-11pm Tue. Tables outdoors (2, pavement).
Map 10.

El Parador

245 Eversholt Street, NW1 (020 7387 2789). Camden Town or Mornington Crescent tube. **Lunch served** noon-3pm Mon-Fri. **Dinner served** 6-11pm Mon-Thur; 6-11.30pm Fri, Sat; 7-10.30pm Sun. **Tapas** £2.90-£4.80. **Service** 10% for parties of five or more. **Credit** MC, £TC, V.

There are three parts to El Parador: a leafy, walled garden at the back (the best bit – bookings are at a premium each summer), a bright, airy main dining room facing Eversholt Street, and a rather dark basement, to which it's quite easy to find yourself confined due to a rather inflexible policy under which bookings for two are not accepted. The all-tapas menu has been extensively revised recently, and along with a few of the classics – patatas bravas (£3), fried calamares (£4.90) – it offers an unusually wide-ranging, imaginative and sometimes globetrotting mix that includes swordfish sautéd with garlic, coriander and vine tomatoes (£4.80), morcilla de Burgos (blood sausage fried with bacon, potatoes and tomatoes, £3.90) and, among the several vegetarian choices, hinojo al pil-pil (fennel roasted with chilli, £3.90) and champiñones del Parador (a mix of shiitake, oyster and chestnut mushrooms with tomato, chilli, coriander and sherry, £3.90). There are sometimes blips in the cooking, but in general the mix of flavours is very well-balanced. Service is generally friendly and efficient, but gets pressured at busy times. The wine and drinks list is not over-long but offers a well-selected variety with several good, lesser-known labels, although Spanish beers (Cruzcampo, Estrella) are a tad expensive at £2.60.
Babies and children admitted. Booking advisable; bookings accepted for groups of three or more only. Separate room for parties, seats 30. Tables outdoors (9, terrace).

Crouch End N8

La Bota

31 Broadway Parade, Tottenham Lane, N8 (020 8340 3082). Finsbury Park tube/rail then W7, 91 bus. **Lunch served** noon-2.30pm Mon-Fri; noon-3.30pm Sat, Sun. **Dinner served** 6-11.30pm Mon-Sat; 6-11pm Sun. **Main courses** £6.50-£10.75. **Tapas** £1.80-£6. **Credit** AmEx, JCB, MC, £TC, V.

A cheerful local tapas bar that manages to appeal to a broad range of publics: mothers with kids by day, couples in the evenings, a more boisterous, hipper crowd on weekend nights. A while ago it seemed to have hit a low patch, with both food and service off-form, but on a recent visit things look to have picked up again. Service was welcoming and helpful. Foodwise, chicken in garlic (£2.95) was nicely pungent, lamb cordobesa (£3.25) came in a fragrant, juicy sauce, spinach with chickpeas (£2.75) was enjoyably well-cooked; La Bota's patatas allioli (£1.85) was as great as usual. Best of all this time, though, was sepia (cuttlefish) cooked in its ink (£3.25), well tenderised, with a rich, dark flavour. A few larger dishes are available as well as tapas. Spanish beers (Estrella) are still £2, but there's also a respectable Spanish wine list.
Babies and children welcome; high chairs. Book dinner Fri, Sat.

Harringay N4

La Viña

3 Wightman Road, N4 (020 8340 5400). Manor House tube/Harringay rail/29, 341 bus. **Open** 5pm-midnight Mon-Sat; 5-11.30pm Sun. **Main courses** £8.75-£9.75. **Tapas** £3-£5. **Set meal** (Mon, Tue) £5 paella. **Credit** MC, V.

La Viña has established a loyal following by providing reliable food at very reasonable prices, along with unfussily charming service. The bar is comfortable and pretty, with only a few tapas-bar accoutrements on show; the atmosphere is unhurried. An ensaladilla (£3) surprisingly came without the usual tuna, but otherwise featured a refreshing mix of veg, pimientos asados (baked peppers with tomatoes and onions, £3.50) made an excellent, unusual tapa, with all the elements very ably cooked together. Classic fried calamares (£4) did everything they needed to do, and fabada (£3.75) was a fine, rich mix. As well as around 40 tapas, the menu also offers, main courses such as chicken in avocado sauce (£7.75), paellas (from £11.50 per person, minimum two) and grilled swordfish with rice and salad (£9.75). As well as the basic house wine there's a decent house Rioja, Otoñal, for £11, and a brief but varied list of other Spanish bottles at similarly accessible prices.
Babies and children welcome; high chairs. No-smoking tables. Separate room for parties, seats 28.

Menu

Much of London's Spanish community hails from Galicia, in north-western Spain, and most older-style Spanish bars and restaurants are Galician owned. Fish and seafood is a major feature of Galician cooking; other food tends to be rich and hearty. Dishes may be spelt in various ways on menus, due to their being written in Spanish, Galician (Gallego) or, sometimes, Catalan.

Cooking styles

Al ajillo:with olive oil and garlic.
A la cazuela: a stew or casserole.
Al jerez: cooked in sherry.
A la marinera (fish or seafood): cooked with garlic, onions and white wine.
Al pil-pil: a Basque way of cooking seafood, very quickly in earthenware dishes with oil, garlic and chilli. Should be served still sizzling hot.
A la parrilla: grilled.
A la plancha: griddled on a hot-plate.
A la romana: fried in batter.
Asado: roast.
En su tinta (seafood): in their own ink.
Ración: a plateful, larger than a traditional individual tapa but smaller than a main course; most tapas served in London are more like raciones.
Relleno: stuffed.

Dishes & ingredients

Ajo: garlic.
Albóndigas: meatballs.
Almendras: almonds.
Almejas: clams.
Anchoas: anchovies.
Atún or **bonito**: tuna.
Bacalao:salt cod.
Berberechos: cockles.
Besugo: sea bream.
Boquerones: marinated anchovies, whitebait.
Calamares: squid.
Callos:tripe.
Cerdo: pork, pig.
Chipirones: baby squid.
Chocolate con churros: a traditional breakfast treat – sticks of sweet batter, with thick hot chocolate to dunk them in.
Chorizo: there are many varieties (and grades of quality) of the standard Spanish sausage, but all divide into two: for eating cold (in slices), or for cooking.
Chuletas: chops.
Cigalas: crayfish or langoustines, although in London it often means scampi.
Cochinillo: roast suckling pig.
Cordero: lamb.
Costillas: ribs.
Crema catalana: custard with a burnt sugar top; similar to crème brûlée, but should be more eggy and less creamy than the French equivalent.
Ensaladilla rusa: salad of potatoes, onions, red peppers, tuna and maybe other ingredients, in mayonnaise; now as Spanish as flamenco, but curiously still called a Russian salad.
Escalivada or **Escalibada**: char-grilled or roasted peppers, aubergines, onions and maybe other Mediterranean vegetables.
Espinacas a la catalana: spinach with pine kernels, raisins and garlic.
Estofado de ternera: veal and potato stew.
Fabada: from Asturias, a rich stew of butter-beans, chorizo, morcilla, onions and garlic.
Fideos: noodles.
Fideuà: a Catalan dish of mixed ingredients cooked together similar to a paella, but made with noodles instead of rice.
Flan: crème caramel.
Gambas: prawns.
Garbanzos: chickpeas.
Habas: broad beans.
Jamón: ham.
Jamón Ibérico: ham from the native Iberian breed of pig. An increasingly rare and expensive delicacy.
Jamón serrano: dry-cured ham, similar to Parma ham.
Judías: beans; judías verdes are green beans.
Lenguado: sole.
Lomo: loin of pork.
Mariscos: shellfish.
Mejillones:mussels.
Merluza: hake; merluza a la gallega is hake poached in white wine with potatoes, peppers and shellfish.
Morcilla: a black, blood sausage.
Patatas bravas: chopped potatoes in a hot pepper sauce; they should always be fried crisp, not just boiled.
Pimientos: red peppers; pimientos de piquillo are a specially sweet variety.
Pincho moruno or **pinchito**: a small kebab of peppered meat, usually pork.
Pisto: a mix of Mediterranean vegetables similar to ratatouille.
Pollo: chicken.
Pulpo: octopus; pulpo a la gallega is chopped octopus with hot pepper, olive oil, lemon, salt and sometimes garlic.
Rajo or **Raxo**: loin of pork marinated in wine.
Rape: monkfish; rape a la gallega is monkfish poached in white wine with potatoes, peppers and shellfish.
Revuelto: scrambled egg, usually with other ingredients (mushrooms, chorizo) mixed in.
Riñones: kidneys.
Salpicón: a cold chopped salad, often with shellfish.
Setas: wild mushrooms.
Ternera: veal – if it is real Spanish ternera, it is not as young as most veal, and so is in fact closer to beef.
Tortilla: potato and onion omelette.
Vieiras: scallops.
Zarzuela: fish and seafood stew.
Zorza: pork marinated in wine and herbs, similar to rajo (qv).

Holloway N7

El Molino
379 Holloway Road, N7 (020 7700 4312). Holloway Road tube. **Meals served** 11am-10.30pm Mon-Sat. **Main courses** £6.50-£10.50. **Tapas** £2.20-£5.20. **Credit** AmEx, DC, MC, V.
Low prices, convenience and an easygoing atmosphere have made El Molino a favourite drop-in for students and staff from the University of North London, just down the Holloway Road. There are no great surprises on the menu, which has a long, traditional list of classic tapas such as fried boquerones (whitebait, £2.75), chickpea salad (£2.75) and zorza (£3.20). Among the main courses, as well as Spanish restaurant standards – such as monkfish in a spicy sauce (£8.95), pollo riojana (chicken with a sauce of tomato, peppers, mushrooms and white wine, £6.95) and paella (£9.75 per person, minimum two) – there are a few pasta dishes such as spag bol (£5). The cooking predictably has its ups and downs; tapas can be dull and carelessly assembled, but on a good day meat tapas such as albóndigas (£3), in particular, are nicely satisfying. The wine selection is short but a real bargain, with several above-average Spanish labels – Callejo Ribera del Duero red, even a reserva cava – for under £15.
Babies and children admitted. Book weekends. Entertainment: guitarist 8-11pm Fri, Sat. Takeaway service.

Islington N1

The Finca
96-98 Pentonville Road, N1 (020 7837 5387). Angel tube. **Open** 5pm-midnight Mon; noon-midnight Tue-Sat; 2pm-midnight Sun. **Meals served** noon-11.30pm Mon-Thur; noon-1.30am Fri, Sat; noon-11.15pm Sun. **Tapas** £2.95-£5.50. **Credit** MC, £TC, V.
Those great survivors, the two Fincas, above and below the river in Islington and Kennington, have been purveyors of good times since the late '80s, but now function in slightly different ways. Both have clubs attached: the one above the Islington Finca, Tiempo, is one of London's best salsa venues, while Tanit in Kennington is now more funk-oriented, with DJs several nights a week. The Kennington branch has also taken on a more contemporary decor; the Islington Finca, however, has kept its now time-honoured daft theme-park Spanish meets Wild West decor. The menu in Islington has recently been revamped, though, and now includes novelties such as pintxo de cabrales (cabrales goat's cheese, tomato and red peppers, grilled and served on French bread, £3.95) and bolas de espinacas (deep-fried balls of spinach, onions and herbs with a bechamel sauce, £3.75) as well as the traditional seafood salad (£4.70), pincho moruno (£4.25) and Sunday paella (£8.95 per person, minimum two). Food here has always been inconsistent: it can be quite good, but standards are often stretched when tables are busy; the same thing goes for the service. There's a big drinks selection, including a recently improved wine list and all the usual cocktails; among the beers there's a very good Mexican brew, Negra Modelo, for just £2.75. Happy hours (5-7pm Mon-Fri, 6-8pm Sat) are an important part of the evening, but note that there is sometimes an extra charge on drinks after midnight on Fridays and Saturdays.
Babies and children admitted. Entertainment: Latin rhythms, jazz, flamenco guitarists Thur, Sun; salsa club and bands upstairs from 9pm Wed-Sun (admission: £4-£6); salsa classes upstairs 7-9pm nightly. **Map 3/2N.**
For branch see index.

Muswell Hill N10

Cafe Loco
206 Muswell Hill, N10 (020 8444 3370). Highgate tube then 43 or 143 bus. **Meals served** 11am-2am Sat; 11am-1am Sun. **Dinner served** 6pm-2am Mon-Fri. **Tapas** £2.25-£4.75. **Service** 10%. **Credit** MC, V.
Just how loco, one asks. Well, the decor is pretty wacky, with a multi-coloured sort-of Mexican rather than Spanish theme, and it builds up a party atmosphere on busy weekend nights, but on a Sunday lunchtime we found things were much quieter, with a scattering of laidback Muswell Hill diners who have clearly taken to this well-priced, recently opened local. The menu plays fast and loose with Spanish spelling, a reasonable indication that authenticity is not a primary consideration, but the list features most of the tapas favourites. Of those we tried, fried calamares (£3.25) were decent, but an ensaladilla (£2.95) was over-dry; better were chorizo with beans (£3.95) and especially a lamb pinchito with herb mayonnaise (£3.25), which featured well-flavoured, juicy meat and a good, strong kick of garlic. To complement the tapas there's the obligatory short selection of main courses, with such dishes as paella (£8.95) and rib-eye steak in a brandy sauce (£9.45). The wine list is very short, but cheap; most of the beers, perhaps to match the paintwork, are Mexican (Sol, Dos Equis, both £2.75). There's a range of alcohol-charged coffees if you feel like settling in. Service matches the feel of this easygoing bar.
Babies and children admitted; high chairs. Separate rooms for parties, seating 15 and 30. Entertainment: Spanish music (Wed).

Southgate N14

La Paella
9 The Broadway, N14 (020 8882 7868). Southgate tube. **Lunch served** noon-2.30pm Tue-Sat. **Dinner served** 6-10.30pm Tue-Thur; 6-11.30pm Fri, Sat. **Meals served** noon-10pm Sun. **Main courses** £7.95-£13.50. **Tapas** £1.95-£4.95. **Credit** MC, £TC, V.
From its name to its decor and fittings (dark wood, traditional ceramics, fans and similar bits and bobs around the walls), Southgate's Paella fits the mould of an archetypal neighbourhood tapas bar, and well-occupied tables on a weekday evening testify to its local popularity (despite the fact that we've also heard that service can get erratic at times). The menu covers all the traditional tapas-bar bases at decent prices. Raxo with chips (£3.50) came in a heftily un-tapa-ish portion and was full of flavour, while spinach with almonds (£1.95) made an enjoyable vegetable alternative. Main courses naturally include a range of mixed, seafood, meat and vegetarian paellas (£11.95-£17.95 per person, minimum two). There are also interesting fish dishes such as trucha al jerez (trout in an almonds, ham and sherry sauce, £7.95) and substantial meat options. Desserts are another high point, with own-made traditional Spanish pastries and a very correctly made crema catalana (£2.95), with a nicely crunchy crust. To drink, most people seem to stay with the house wines, Spanish beers (£2.20) or jugs of sangría (£10.75), but the list also offers a wide-ranging choice of quality Spanish labels.
Babies and children admitted. Book Fri, Sat. Takeaway service.

Outer London

Richmond, Surrey

Don Fernando's
27F The Quadrant, Richmond, Surrey (020 8948 6447). Richmond tube/rail. **Open** noon-3pm Mon, Tue. **Meals served** noon-3pm, 6-11pm Mon, Tue; noon-11pm Wed-Sat; noon-10pm Sun. **Main courses** £6.95-£12.50. **Tapas** £2.95-£5.95. **Credit** MC, £TC, V.
A big, bright and successful tapas restaurant that caters to a variety of needs. The long and very varied menu makes excellent provision for families, with lots of things for kids; there are plenty of vegetarian options; anyone wanting to linger over a meal can inspect an admirably adventurous Spanish wine list; and there are lots of cocktails, liqueurs and the like for the young people who pack the bar at weekends. Very long menus can be an indication of trying to do too much, but dishes we've tried here have kept up an impressive consistency of quality, from specialities such as langostinos borrachos (king prawns sautéed in white wine, chilli and garlic, £5.95) or garbanzos Don Fernando (a stew of chickpeas and other veg with white wine, £3.75) to standards like tortilla (£3.25) or fish croquettes (£4.25). Main courses include the requisite range of paellas (£6.95-£11.75 per person, minimum two), and some original options such as lomo al orégano (marinated pork with herbs, £7.95) and the moreish pinchito marino (skewers of mixed grilled seafood with rice, £8.50). Despite the virtually-no-bookings policy, energetic and skilful service seems to ensure that no one ever has to wait for long.
Babies and children welcome; high chairs. Bookings accepted for parties of ten or more (deposit required); no bookings accepted at weekends. Tables outdoors (6, pavement).

Thai

Central

City EC4

Sri Thai
Bucklersbury House, 3 Queen Victoria Street, EC4 (020 7827 0202). Mansion House tube/Bank tube/DLR/8, 35, 242 bus. **Meals served** 11.30am-10pm Mon-Fri. **Main courses** £7.50-£10.95. **Set meals** £15.99-£29.99. **Service** 12½%. **Credit** AmEx, DC, MC, £TC, V.
Early on a Friday evening the nearly empty restaurant struggled to compete with the loud bassy music and local City slickers in the bar, letting off steam after a hard week at the office. The service was friendly but very slow and we were grateful for the complimentary basket of prawn crackers. The menu covers all the old favourites plus a selection of set meals ranging in price from £15.99 to £29.99 per person, including a five-course vegetarian meal. At £6.50, the merely adequate kai bai teoy seemed pretty pricey for four nuggets of chicken wrapped in pandan leaves accompanied by tamarind sauce. However, the peek kai yadsai (chicken wings stuffed with minced pork and chicken) were simultaneously crispy and juicy as hoped. Kanom jeep (Thai dim sum) was tasty but pretty unremarkable. The main courses were a little more exciting: pla pao bai tong was a char-grilled fillet of trout wrapped in banana leaves served with a chilli and plum sauce, while 'weeping tiger' or sai rong hai was slices of rare, melt-in-your-mouth beef cooked with mint and coriander, with a delicious lime and chilli dressing. All in all, quality was a little lacking for a restaurant in this price range.
Babies and children admitted (dinner). Booking advisable lunch. Entertainment: guitarist 5.30-9.30pm Wed. Takeaway service.
Map 4/6P.
For branches (Sri Siam City, Sri Siam) see index.

Clerkenwell & Farringdon EC1

Thai Jen
10-11 Clerkenwell Road, EC1 (020 7490 4041). Farringdon tube/rail/19, 38, 55, 341 bus. **Lunch served** noon-3pm Mon-Fri, Sun. **Dinner served** 6-11pm daily. **Main courses** £5.50-£28.90. **Set lunch** £5.50. **Set dinner** £18.50. **Credit** AmEx, MC, V.
Thai Jen is a collaboration between a Thai chef and a Chinese manager, which the menu reflects with an inspiring selection of the best of both cuisines, including six set dinners of vegetarian, Peking, Thai and mixed dishes. Things got off to a good start with a complimentary basket of prawn crackers that was refilled while we contemplated the ample menu. We chose the mid-range four-course Thai royal banquet (£16.50 each, minimum two people). Less greedy options included delicious sweet and sour chicken and spicy chicken or beef penang. The banquet's starters were a selection of perfectly executed appetisers, including scrumptious pickled vegetables, Thai prawn cakes, stuffed chicken wings, crispy pork dumplings and delicately marinated satay. This was followed by a tasty but uninspiring special Thai barbecue chicken (kai yang fai dang). The excellent third course consisted of kai phad bai kapro (succulent chunks of chicken with basil and chilli), nueo gang kiew wan (a rich full flavoured green beef curry, accompanied by al dente Thai mixed vegetables) and a large plate of fried rice with seafood. Inexplicably the Banquet dessert (toffee apple or banana and ice-cream) never appeared but hot towels and slices of orange completed the meal Chinese style. A decent local in an area with few oriental restaurants.
Babies and children welcome; high chairs. Booking advisable; essential dinner. Disabled: toilet. Separate room for parties, seats 20. Takeaway service. Vegetarian menu.
Map 15/4O.

Covent Garden WC2

Manorom
16 Maiden Lane, WC2 (020 7240 4139). Covent Garden tube/Charing Cross tube/rail. **Lunch served** noon-2.30pm Mon-Fri. **Dinner served** 6-11pm Mon-Sat. **Main courses** £5-£10.95. **Set lunch** £10.95 two courses. **Set dinner** £16 three courses. **Service** 10%. **Credit** AmEx, MC, V.
Located between the Strand and Covent Garden, this small Thai restaurant continues to offer intimate dining in sedate surroundings. The recently opened restaurant Manorom Too in nearby Southampton Street shares the same good-quality, no-surprises menu as its parent . From a selection of starters, the Manorom hors d'oeuvres (£11.50 for two people) was a winning combination of beef satay, spring rolls, fish cakes, stuffed chicken wings, chicken wrapped in pandan leaves and a spicy vermicelli salad; a delicious departure from the minced meat and deep-fried fare usually found in mixed starter platters. Gaeng phet ped yang – a red curry with coconut milk and a generous amount of duck – was a smooth, rich taste sensation. Pla phao – a fresh, flaky whole fish marinated then grilled in banana leaves and served with a chilli dressing – also exceeded expectations. In fact the only disappointment was the brusquely efficient service; maybe arriving for lunch at 2.15pm, just before the kitchen closed, didn't contribute to the waiting staff's good humour. Flawless food but service without a smile.
Babies and children admitted. Booking advisable dinner. Takeaway service.
Map 14/7L.
For branch see index.

Thai Pot
1 Bedfordbury, WC2 (020 7379 4580). Covent Garden tube/Charing Cross tube/rail. **Lunch served** noon-3pm Mon-Sat. **Dinner served** 5.30-11.15pm Mon-Sat. **Main courses** £4.50-£8. **Set lunch** £11 two courses incl coffee. **Set dinner** £15 three courses, £18 four courses incl coffee. **Credit** AmEx, DC, MC, £TC, V.
High ceilings and cream walls mean that this stylish Thai maintains a light spacious feel even when it's crowded to capacity with those who work and play in Covent Garden. It was certainly buzzing on our Friday lunchtime visit and we were glad to have booked (even though it didn't guarantee us a prime location). The casually cool staff sport Thai Pot T-shirts with jeans and flip flops and get the job done in an unhurried but efficient manner. The menu is pretty standard and includes most people's hot favourites. For starters we sampled the kai ho bai toey, usually nuggets of chicken wrapped then deep fried in pandan leaves, only this version used spinach leaves in an interesting (and cheaper) variation. The tom yam goong (spicy prawn soup) was a wonderfully hot, tangy tapestry of lime, chilli, coriander and lemon grass. Next we had the gai pad hed, large chunks of succulent chicken sautéed in soy sauce with fresh mushrooms, baby corn and spring onions, accompanied by pad poh tak, a mixture of lightly fried seafood in a fragrant sauce of lemon grass, chilli, garlic and basil leaves that flawlessly balanced these key Thai flavours. A highly pleasurable experience.
Booking advisable; essential weekends. No-smoking tables. Separate room for parties, seats 25. Takeaway service (10% discount).
Map 14/7K.
For branch (Thai Pot on The Strand) see index.

Fitzrovia W1

Vow Thai
53 Cleveland Street, W1 (020 7580 7608). Goodge Street or Oxford Circus tube. **Lunch served** noon-3pm Mon-Fri. **Dinner served** 5.30-11pm Mon-Wed, Sat, Sun; 5.30-11.30pm Thur, Fri. **Main courses** £4.95-£8.90. **Set lunch** £4.95 one course, £6.50 two courses. **Set dinner** £12 (vegetarian) two courses, £15 (meat) three courses, £17 (meat and seafood) four courses, all incl tea or coffee. **Credit** MC, V.

Batik tablecloths have replaced the vinyl of yesteryear, but Vow Thai still lacks ambience and feels like a cheap café rather than an evening venue. To be fair though, the prices reflect this, with starters from £2.95 to £4.50 for the king prawn satay, soups from £2.95 and mains for £4.50 to £8.90 for the sizzling platter of jumbo prawns. The menu has over 100 dishes, including a respectable vegetarian selection. The shrimp satay starter was reportedly 'divine'; squid royal (tender pieces of squid deep fried in tempura batter with a chilli sauce) was equally good. We sampled tom kha kai (an above average version of the creamy aromatic chicken soup); gaeng ped phed yangb (tender slices of roast duck in a rich red curry and coconut sauce with pineapple); and penang beef (slices of beef in a rich flavoursome curry) that had a sublime balance of quintessential Thai flavourings. On the night of our visit service was slow and the staff elusive. Bonus marks, though, for the ornate vegetable garnishes, which are carved on the premises (many other Thai restaurants just buy them in). *Babies and children admitted. Separate rooms for parties, seating 30 and 40. Takeaway service.* **Map 2/5J.**

King's Cross WC1

Paolina Café & Thai Restaurant ★
181 King's Road, WC1 (020 7278 8176). King's Cross tube/rail. **Lunch served** noon-3pm Mon-Fri. **Dinner served** 6-10pm Mon-Sat. **Main courses** £3.45-£7.50. **Unlicensed. Corkage** 50p per person. **No credit cards.**
At night, Paolina generates a buzz, as punters squeeze themselves in for some tasty, cheap and cheerful nosh and BYO booze. Obviously a greasy spoon in a former incarnation, the restaurant has a mix of built-in mismatched furniture, Formica tables, fake flowers and obligatory portraits of Thai royals and the Grand Palace on the walls; there's no room for pretension here. The kitchen area is in full view behind the serving counter, with the lunch menu conveniently pasted on the opposite wall, so you can order before finding a seat in the back room. There is a good range of dishes, with starters from £2.75 to £3.40, plus a mixed platter for two (a bargain at £6.50). Mains cost between £2.95 and £4.95, with the exception of three whole fish dishes at £7.50 each. Chicken satay was moist and tender, and served with a moreish peanut sauce, while Thai dumplings with minced pork and prawn were rich in texture and taste, and topped by a pile of crispy toasted garlic. Mains were equally pleasing: a portion of soft, succulent squid in a sweet, fiery basil and chilli sauce; plus a fine example of pad Thai. Surprisingly good food at bargain prices.
Babies and chidren admitted. Takeaway service. **Map 3/3M.**

Knightsbridge SW3

Patara
9 Beauchamp Place, SW3 (020 7581 8820). Knightsbridge tube/14, 74, C1 bus. **Lunch served** noon-2.30pm, **dinner served** 6.30-10.30pm daily. **Main courses** £8-£15. **Set lunch** £9.95 two courses. **Service** 12½%. **Credit** AmEx, DC, MC, £TC, V.
Patara's long, narrow dining room has cream walls and white linen tablecloths that whisper understated sophistication; the only decorations are lavish arrangements of orchids and a collection of framed Thai textiles. The appetisers are a standard selection of fried and steamed goodies or soup, ranging in price from £5.75 to £6.50, while the main course menu lists around 30 dishes for between £9.75 and £12.95, including quail's eggs, clams, New Zealand lamb and venison, plus typical Thai chicken, pork, beef, prawn and fish dishes. As starters we sampled tom yam goong (hot and spicy prawn soup with a fragrant tang of lemon grass) and yam mamuang, a tangy salad of green mango, chicken and prawns. Both were delicious, but the yam – meant to be the spiciest of all Thai dishes – had definitely been doctored to suit delicate Knightsbridge palates. Nua gheng pad phed was undeniably excellent with its tender slices of venison sautéed in a hot and sour sauce of green peppercorns, kaffir leaves and chillies, while plah goong (grilled tiger prawns in a zingy lemon grass and lime dressing) was also highly satisfactory. An excellent lunch was complemented by friendly and flawless service. Book in advance for the best seats in the house, next to the picture window.
Babies and chidren admitted. Booking advisable. No-smoking tables. Takeaway service. **Map 12/9F.**
For branches see index.

Thai Jen

Marylebone W1

Chaopraya
22 St Christopher's Place, W1 (020 7486 0777). Bond Street tube. **Lunch served** noon-3pm Mon-Fri. **Dinner served** 6.30-11pm Mon-Sat. **Main courses** £4.20-£15.50. **Set lunch** £9.95 two courses. **Set dinner** £19 two courses. **Service** 12½%. **Credit** AmEx, MC, V.
Located underground in what looks to be a recycled wine cellar, Chaopraya is a series of rooms connected by low wide archways. The cream walls, with their taupe trim and white-on-white table settings, help create a calm, classic atmosphere that is only broken by the noisy groups of suits tucking into their business lunches. The menu offers three set dinners and over 100 dishes, including a sprinkling from other parts of Asia. There are over 20 starters and soups, some of which are only offered for two or four people. From this list we tried gai hor bai toey (fried chicken in pandan leaves) with accompanying 'special brown sauce', which was suitably moist and tasty, and pla muek thod (very disappointing fried squid with thick oily batter and vinegary tasting dip). From the main dishes we chose a beef tamarind curry that was wonderfully rich and creamy, but the star dish of the day was ped makham. The slices of crispy fried duck melted in the mouth and were surrounded by a rich tamarind sauce with crispy garlic, cloud ear fungus, red capsicum and shallots. At these kinds of prices, all the food should be this good.
Babies and children admitted. Takeaway service. **Map 2/6G.**

Thai West
10-12 Crawford Street, W1 (020 7224 1367). Baker Street tube. **Lunch served** noon-3pm Mon-Fri; 11am-3pm Sun. **Dinner served** 6-11.30pm daily. **Main courses** £5.50-£13.50. **Set lunch** £9 two courses. **Service** 12½%. **Credit** AmEx, DC, MC, V.
Plenty of thought has obviously gone into creating a genteel Thai ambience downstairs at Thai West, with tasteful statues, carvings and paintings and a wooden long boat as a centrepiece. Along one wall there are private little cubby holes for parties of four to six. As for the food, marinated prawns in rice paper were a disappointment; their heavy deep-fried cases and plain contents were far from the light rice paper-wrapped delights we were expecting. The platter of mixed starters for two contained a redeeming selection of tasty (if rather oily)

Blue Lagoon

appetisers, including deliciously marinated satay, but the chicken wings were mysteriously missing. Green chicken curry was rich, creamy and exactly as it should be, while the mixed seafood stir-fried with fresh chilli and basil leaves exceeded our expectations and had us squabbling over the last crab claw. We finished with three good-sized scoops of mango sorbet, and ice-cream with banana fritters, which were actually more like banana spring rolls. With these beautiful surroundings and the generally good food, it's a pity Thai West has such stroppy serving staff.
Babies and children admitted (lunch and early evening). Booking advisable Thur-Sat. Takeaway service. **Map 2/5F.**

Soho W1

Soho Thai
27-28 St Anne's Court, W1 (020 7287 2000). Leicester Square, Piccadilly Circus or Tottenham Court Road tube. **Lunch served** noon-3pm, **dinner served** 6-11.30pm Mon-Sat. **Main courses** £5.75-£14.95. **Set lunch** £9.95 three courses. **Credit** AmEx, MC, V.
A heavenly aroma greeted us as we stepped inside this busy Soho lunch spot. The low-key tan and beige rag-rolled walls and marble and metal furniture may be very early '90s, but Soho Thai retains a slick café vibe that is obviously popular with those who work and play in the area. The menu offers some interesting departures from tradition and has a good selection of vegetarian dishes. For those short of time, there is also the practical but tasty set lunch, which comprises a starter, a soup, a main dish and rice served simultaneously on a round tray in five interlocking dishes. As we weren't in a rush, we started with some moist and mild Thai dumplings, which were set off a treat by a topping of crunchy fried garlic slivers, and some Thai fish cakes. Deciding to try our luck with duck, we ordered gang phed, a deliciously creamy and rich roast duck curry with coconut

milk and lychees, and phed makham, a memorable dish of char-grilled duck breast with a sublime tamarind sauce, surprisingly accompanied by crispy seaweed. The food was all attractively presented and served by charming but efficient staff.
Babies and children admitted. Book dinner Fri, Sat. No-smoking tables. Takeaway service. **Map 13/6K.**

Thai Pavilion
42 Rupert Street, W1 (020 7287 6333). Leicester Square, Piccadilly Circus or Tottenham Court Road tube. **Lunch served** noon-2.30pm Mon-Sat; 12.30-4.30pm Sun. **Dinner served** 6-11.30pm Mon-Thur; 5.30-11.30pm Fri, Sat; 6-10.30pm Sun. **Main courses** £5.95-£16.75. **Set buffet lunch** (Sun) £9.95, £4.95 children **Set meals** £10.95-£26. **Service** 12%. **Credit** AmEx, DC, MC, V.
Although Thai Pavilion has three floors, supple diners should head straight for the top one, as it offers the chance to lounge on the floor on traditional Thai cushions with triangular back rests and eat from a low table Khantoke style. The tables may be a little too close together for this to be true lounging but it's still a novel experience. The decor is pleasantly minimal, with bamboo panelling on matt green walls and beautifully carved statues illuminated by spotlights. The menu is extensive (47 vegetarian dishes are available on request, as are organic wines) and includes several surprises such as lobster pineapple curry. Miang Thai (from the hors d'oeuvres selection), was a sublime collection of roasted coconut, lime, shallots, ginger and prawn that we wrapped and ate in bai chapou leaves. Barbecued chicken in pandan leaves was also very tasty, although a little oily, while the squid soup, described as 'delicately herbed', was a bit on the bland and watery side. From a selection of highly tempting main courses, the fried rainbow trout with tamarind sauce was cooked to delicate perfection, while the kang phed pet yang, a

delicious duck and lychee curry, was a perfect accompaniment to the Buddha rice and the three-colour fried rice that we were unable to resist sampling. The service was warm and attentive, making this an enjoyable evening all round.
Babies and children admitted (dinner). Booking advisable. Separate room for parties, seats 35. Takeaway service. **Map 13/7K.**

Trafalgar Square SW1

Thai Square
21-23 Cockspur Street, SW1 (020 7839 4000). Charing Cross tube/rail.
Bar **Open** 5pm-3am Mon-Sat; 5-11.30pm Sun.
Restaurant **Lunch served** noon-3pm, **dinner served** 5pm-midnight daily. **Main courses** £7-£15. **Set meals** £20 four courses, £25 five courses. **Credit** AmEx, MC, TC, V.
Thai Square's imposing entrance is inherited from its former life as the Norwegian Embassy. The restaurant itself is divided into two large sections; the front is ornately decorated with an abundance of gold leaf and Thai artefacts, while the back has a more spartan, function-room feel to it. The Thai Square selection (£12) was an excellent choice of starter; as well as the usual sampling of satay and deep-fried delicacies, it also included a traditional spicy Thai salad. The kai ho bai toey, tender marinated chicken pieces wrapped in spinach leaves and deep fried, made an enjoyably edible change from the pandan leaf version. From the 'special dish' section of the menu, we chose succulent phed makham (slices of duck char-grilled then smothered in a rich tamarind sauce) and homok talay, a seafood curry soufflé presented in banana leaves that was a melt-in-the-mouth sensation. Although the food and service were both of a high standard (as you would expect in this price range), our dinner was slightly marred by a couple of heavy smokers who were seated right next to us, in spite of the abundance of vacant tables further away.
Babies and children admitted. Disabled: toilet.

Entertainment: Thai music 6-11pm Mon-Sat. Takeaway service. **Map 14/7K.**
For branch (Thai Pot on The Strand) see index.

Victoria SW1

Blue Jade
44 Hugh Street, SW1 (020 7828 0321). Victoria tube/rail. **Lunch served** noon-2.30pm Mon-Fri. **Dinner served** 6-11pm Mon-Sat. **Main courses** £6.95-£8.50. **Set lunch** £10 two courses. **Set dinner** £18 per person (minimum two), three courses, incl coffee. **Credit** AmEx, DC, JCB, MC, £TC, V.
Tucked away on a small street behind Victoria Station, the Blue Jade probably gets few impulse eaters, but the local nine-to-fivers seem happy to while away their afternoons in the spacious cream dining room beneath the hanging plants. In the evening the basement offers more intimate dining at its cosy alcove tables. Although we arrived seconds before the kitchen closed at 2.30pm and the staff served us somewhat swiftly, they retained their charm and good humour. We tucked into complimentary prawn crackers as we surveyed the hundred or so dishes on the menu. The starters held no surprises; chicken satay and crispy fried corn cakes were tasty but unremarkable. tom yam poh tag (seafood steam boat), on the other hand, was a rich, aromatic tapestry of smooth textures and tangy flavours, underscored by the bite of the prik khii nuu, known as 'mouse dropping' chillies by the Thais and 'bird's eye' chillies by the rest of us. Pla mueg gra tiam was a generous pile of tender squid steeped in garlic, pepper and coriander, which rendered the pad Thai quite bland in comparison. While Blue Jade may not wow Thai food aficionados, it continues to offer reliably good meals and smiley, efficient service.
Babies and children admitted. Takeaway service. Vegetarian menu. **Map 6/11H.**

West

Bayswater W2

Nipa
Royal Lancaster Hotel, Lancaster Terrace, W2 (020 7262 6737). Lancaster Gate tube/ 12, 94 bus.
Bar **Open** 11am-11pm Mon-Sat; 11am-10.30pm Sun.
Restaurant **Lunch served** noon-2pm Mon-Fri. **Dinner served** 6.30-10.30pm Mon-Sat. **Main courses** £9-£14. **Set meals** £23-£26 three courses. **Credit** AmEx, DC, JCB, MC, £TC, V.
Not exactly located in the hippest of hotels, or about to be recognised as cool or stylish, the Nipa has instead put its energy into providing good authentic Thai food in a formal setting. This objective must be paying off, as the large wood-panelled dining room was full by 8pm on the evening we visited; the prime tables are by the window overlooking Hyde Park and have to be booked well in advance. The waitresses wear traditional two-piece silk outfits and exude an air of efficiency, but although we ordered our drinks on arrival, we waited 15 minutes for them to arrive and only slightly less long to receive our menus. In fact service was slow throughout the meal, and dogged by mishap every step of the way. Our waitress even managed to knock over a glass of bubbly, but luckily we were appeased by the maitre d' instantly offering us a complimentary half-bottle of champagne. From a lengthy menu we chose the Nipa platter for two (£16) consisting of four standard starters, all of which were nicely moist on the inside and crisp on the outside, accompanied by four sauces. To follow we ordered phad ped po tack (stir-fried mixed seafood with chillies and basil leaves), yam woon sen (glass noodles with shrimp and chillies), plus khanom chin kaeng kai rue nuea (Thai noodles topped with chicken curry). The food was uniformly delicious, exceptionally well executed, pleasingly hot and faithful to authentic Thai ingredients.
Babies and children welcome; high chairs. Book dinner Fri, Sat. Vegetarian menu. **Map 1/6D.**

Chiswick W4

Bedlington Café ★
24 Fauconberg Road, W4 (020 8994 1965). Chiswick Park or Turnham Green tube then E3, E4 bus/Chiswick rail. **Open** 8am-2pm Mon-Sat. **Dinner served** 6.30-10pm Mon-Sat; 6-9.30pm Sun. **Main courses** £3.75-£5.50. **Unlicensed. Corkage** 60p per person. **No credit cards or cheques.**
This greasy spoon turned Thai restaurant in the middle of leafy Chiswick looks tired. The interior sports tightly packed Formica tables and off-white walls covered in Thai tourist board posters and an impressive number of faded clippings praising the Bedlington's food a decade ago. On the warm Sunday evening of our (early) visit, however, the only other customers were a couple who appeared briefly to collect their takeaway. The menu has around 70 dishes, including a selection from Laos. Chicken satay and chicken with coconut soup were exemplary, as was a very good chicken liver dish from the 'specials' section. We also opted for Thai Muslim curry, which was a rich tasty chicken mussaman, with whole potatoes to provide welcome relief from the heat of the chillies. Thai fried noodles were above average and contrasted pleasantly with the curry. In general, the Bedlington offers good food at very reasonable prices, but not one to cross town for.
Babies and children admitted. Booking essential. No smoking indoors. Tables outdoors (5, pavement). Takeaway service.
For branch see index.

Thai Bistro
99 Chiswick High Road, W4 (020 8995 5774). Turnham Green tube/27, 237, 267 bus.
Lunch served noon-3pm Mon, Wed, Fri-Sun. **Dinner served** 6-11pm Mon-Sat; 6-10.30pm Sun. **Main courses** £4.95-£7.95 **Service** 12½% for parties of five or more. **Credit** MC, V.
Bright and breezy, with a huge window facing onto the street, Thai Bistro is another trendy Wagamama-esque canteen-style eaterie, with five long shared tables. Although chef Vatcharin Bhumichitr has moved to the newer Maida Vale branch (**Southeast W9**, *see p148* **Oriental**), the food is still excellent, with a good vegetarian menu in addition to the main and regional menus. To whet our appetites we had po pea hat yai, light crispy spring rolls containing a juicy prawn and lychee combo (not cheap at £5.50 for four), and yum woon sen, a vermicelli salad with ground pork and shrimps tossed in coriander, lime juice and chilli to create a clever blend of hot and sour. After this promising start, both main courses seemed a little lacklustre; pad kimow gung at least was hot and tangy, with a generous helping of prawns, but gang pa had overly large chunks of vegetables and only the merest hint of beef. The meal was redeemed by pla lad prik, which contained generous slices of light, flaky fish in a crisp, delicate batter with a rich tamarind and chilli sauce. On the whole, the meal was very good, but prices seem steep considering the casual surroundings.
Babies and children admitted. Book dinner. No smoking. Tables outdoors (4, garden). Takeaway service. Vegetarian menu.

Kensington W8

Blue Lagoon
284 Kensington High Street, W8 (020 7603 1231). High Street Kensington tube. **Meals served** noon-11.30pm daily. **Main courses** £6.95-£11.95. **Set lunch** £7.50 three courses. **Set dinner** £13.95-£17.95. **Credit** AmEx, DC, JCB, MC, V, £TC.
Standards are high at this owner-operated restaurant. Fresh ingredients are flown in from Thailand and all the food is prepared on the premises daily by the executive chef, who worked for the Thai royal family for four years. The dining room is pleasant and airy, with generously spaced tables and large picture windows overlooking High Street Ken. A pair of statues stand by the door greeting guests as they arrive and a vase of blue orchids picks out the colour of the carpet, ceiling and tablecloths, while the miniature orchids on the table repeat the buttery golden tones of the rag-rolled walls. The centre-piece, however, is a large rockery complete with greenery, tinkling waterfall and pond with chubby goldfish. The extensive menu has plenty to tempt the tastebuds. Six jumbo prawns were served with a tasty chilli, garlic and coriander dip. These juicy char-grilled big boys were a stark contrast to the measly three prawns in the mee grob. However, the fried vermicelli that made up the dish was deliciously crispy, with a pleasantly sweet flavour that avoided sickliness. Deep-fried squid were as soft and succulent as one would hope, and were served in an exceptional sauce of garlic, chilli and basil leaves. Our final choice was larb, a north-eastern Thai salad of freshly minced pork in a delicious mix of hot and tangy chilli, mint, garlic and lime juice. Fine food and good service at reasonable prices make this an attractive dinner venue.
Babies and children welcome; high chairs. Separate room for parties, seats 50. Vegetarian menu. **Map 5/9A.**

Maida Vale W9

Ben's Thai ★
above the Warrington, 93 Warrington Crescent, W9 (020 7266 3134). Maida Vale or Warwick Avenue tube. **Lunch served** noon-2.30pm, **dinner served** 6-10pm daily. **Main courses** £5. **Credit** MC, V.
Upstairs at the Warrington and sharing the same elaborately moulded grandiose decor, Ben's was packed even on a Monday evening. Service was fast, friendly and efficient but the food was definitely pub-style Thai grub. The prices reflect that, with starters at £2.95 and mains for around £5, and judging by the general buzz in the place, no-one seems to mind. We started with moo yang (marinated pork strips on skewers with chilli dip), and homok talay (a seafood curry in a scallop shell that looked seriously nuked) accompanied by two thick slices of white bread (Sainsbury's economy?). Despite being slightly mollified by an alright tom kha gai, our expectations weren't too high for the next course. We shared a tasty kaeng ped phied yang (roast duck curry with basil), and an average pad prik khing (chicken stir-fried with PK curry paste and Thai long beans). True Thai food fans might feel let down here, as corners are obviously being cut and all the meat was over-cooked, suggesting a microwave at work, but for big groups out on the booze it's probably perfect.
Babies and children admitted. Booking advisable, essential dinner. No-smoking tables. Separate room for parties, seats 25. Takeaway service.
For branches see index.

Notting Hill W8, W11

Churchill Arms ★
119 Kensington Church Street, W8 (020 7792 1246). High Street Kensington or Notting Hill Gate tube. **Open** 11am-11pm Mon-Sat; noon-10.30pm Sun. **Lunch served** noon-2.30pm daily. **Dinner served** 6-9.30pm Mon-Sat. **Main courses** £5.20-£5.50. **Credit** DC, LV, MC, £TC, V.
The first pub in London to combine pulling a pint with pad Thai, the Churchill is still packing 'em in. Beyond the pub's dark panelled walls and clutter of potties, baskets and other collectibles, is the low-ceilinged leafy dining annexe. Food is ordered and paid for at the counter, then eaten wherever you can find a space. The menu is divided into noodles, curry, rice and stir-fried dishes, which come with pork, beef, chicken or prawn. The portions are generous and the inclusion of rice in the price of a dish makes this great value for money. We sampled the chicken green curry, listed as hot in the menu and definitely lip-numbing. Mixed vegetables were not on the menu but a delicious plate of baby corn, straw mushrooms, red and green capsicum, cabbage, carrots, beans and bean sprouts was cheerfully whipped up at our request. Surprisingly good food for such bargain-priced pub grub.
Babies and children welcome; high chairs. Book dinner. Takeaway service. **Map 11/8B.**

Market Thai
First floor, The Market Bar, 240 Portobello Road, W11 (020 7460 8320). Ladbroke Grove or Notting Hill Gate tube/7, 23, 52 bus. **Lunch served** noon-3pm, **dinner served** 6-10pm Mon-Fri, Sun. **Meals served** noon-10.30pm Sat. **Main courses** £4.50-£7.25. **Set meal** £13.95 per person (minimum two). **Service** 10%. **Credit** AmEx, JCB, MC, V.
Situated above the Market Bar on Portobello Road, the Market Thai has a light, minimalist ethnic look (did the proprietors shop at David Wainwright's across the road?), with stone walls, antique wooden fittings and wrought-iron furniture. The menu is more manageable than most, with 27 dishes ranging from £3.50 to £6.50, plus a one-plate express menu (£4.50 to £5.50) and a set meal (£13.95 per person), which we ordered. The starter was a platter of two chicken satay sticks, two Thai dim sum, four mini spring rolls and crispy seaweed, plus accompanying sauces. The satay sauce was particularly tasty and rendered the chicken soft and succulent. Next came two chicken soups: tom yam gai had the tang of lemon grass and the buzz of chilli, while kang jead was a somewhat bland clear soup with minced chicken and cucumber. From a selection of four main courses we chose the choo chee goong – wok fried prawns in rich curry with coconut milk and lashings of lemon grass), which was gorgeous, and an equally delicious dish of kai ma muang (stir-fried chicken with cashew nuts, chilli and sping onion), plus mixed vegetables and steamed fragrant rice. A tasty Thai meal at a good price in buzzy surroundings.
Babies and children admitted. Booking advisable Thu-Sat. Takeaway service.
Map 11/5Az.

Shepherd's Bush W12

Esarn Kheaw
314 Uxbridge Road, W12 (020 8743 8930). Shepherd's Bush tube/207, 260, 283 bus.
Lunch served noon-3pm Mon-Fri. **Dinner served** 6-11pm daily. **Main courses** £5.95-£8.95. **Credit** AmEx, DC, MC, V.
It's quite difficult to see beyond the mint green decor, pink velvet chairs, Thai tourism posters and prominent black gloss woodwork at Esarn Kheaw, but it's worth the effort since this restaurant is well known for authentic Thai cooking, particularly north-eastern (Esarn) cuisine. The menu is lengthy, with almost 100 dishes on offer, and makes a departure from the common practice of offering standard curries that can be chosen with either pork, beef, chicken or prawn. The flavouring here is robust and spicy; those used to more diluted western versions of Thai might find it pretty zingy, while those familiar with the region will find themselves transported back to some nighttime food stall in a small town market. Succulent and spicy marinated pork spare ribs were a welcome change from the usual deep-fried starters, but kai bay tauy (marinated chicken wrapped in pandan leaves and deep fried) was bland and dry, rescued only by the chilli sauce. From the wide selection of main courses we chose spiced duck north-east style (a satisfying collage of salty, sweet, sour and very hot flavours) and pla muk pad prik (wonderfully tender squid with a blend of sweet basil, chilli and oyster sauce). These dishes were accompanied by a woven basket of sticky rice, a staple of the north-eastern diet that is eaten with the fingers or used to pinch up other dishes or soak up sauces. Although the food is well above average, the high prices at Esarn Kheaw are at odds with the dodgy decor.
Babies and children admitted. Book dinner. Takeaway service.

Ingredients

Bal horapa: holy basil or Thai basil; darker than European basil with a sharper aniseed flavour.
Galangal, **Siamese ginger** or **kha**: used fresh; roughly similar to common ginger.
Kecap: a sweeter and thicker version of soy sauce. Used particularly in sauces and noodle dishes.
Kratiem: garlic, used for frying and in sauces.
Ma-grood: kaffir lime. Shards of these tough citrus leaves give a lemon/lime flavour; in Thailand, the zest of the knobbly green fruit is also used.
Makua paw or **ma-khue puang**: 'baby green' aubergine – a golf ball sized aubergine that, like the pea aubergine, is often substituted in recipes.
Maprao: coconut, usually used as reconstituted coconut 'milk', which can be bought tinned or in packets.
Nam pla: fish sauce, used in a similar manner to soy sauce, as a condiment and as a salt substitute. There are several types made from different varieties of fermented seafood; they all have distinctive tastes, but all are salty.
Nam prik: a very hot sauce of red chillies and fermented shrimp paste (gapi). A pungent and salty flavouring, essential to many Thai dishes.
Pak chee: coriander; fresh leaf (bai pak chee) and root (raak pak chee) are both used.
Pandan leaf: Malaysian screwpine leaf (aka Pandanus), used to flavour savoury and sweet dishes.
Papaya: 'green' papaya isn't fully ripened.
Pea aubergines: expensive, tough and very slightly bitter. English peas are sometimes used as a substitute.
Peppercorns: fresh green peppercorns are used in the top London restaurants, as they are in Thailand.
Prik: chillies; prik size *is* important; the small ones (bird's-eye chilli peppers) are often the hottest. In this country, sliced capsicums are sometimes used as a substitute for the real thing as a garnish.
Ta-krai: lemongrass or citronella – woody stalks that look like small leeks. Tough and inedible, they give Thai food that distinctive lemony aroma.
Turmeric: fresh root turmeric is widely used in the south of Thailand. Its strong yellow dye is distinctive.
Zerumbet or **krachai**: lesser ginger, smaller than galangal (qv) and with a milder taste.

Westbourne Grove W2

Tawana ★
3 Westbourne Grove, W2 (020 7229 3785). Bayswater, Queensway or Royal Oak tube.
Lunch served noon-3pm, **dinner served** 6-11pm daily. **Main courses** £4.95-£17.95. **Set meal** £15.95. **Service** 10%. **Credit** AmEx, DC, MC, V.
Tawana's fresh green and white decor with its rattan chairs, potted palms and sprays of orchids conjure up visions of colonial Asia à la Somerset Maugham. Charmed by the menu's silver-plated cover, we were further delighted to find Mekong and other Thai drinks listed inside. The food here is of an impressively high standard. All the dishes were well executed and beautifully presented, from the marinated pork wrapped in yellow noodles and the piquant tom ka gai to the rich chicken and coconut curry and the spicy larb moo salad. Of particular note was the steamed baby squid, cooked to perfection and feistily flavoured with chilli, garlic and lime. In spite of the intriguing range of elegant Thai desserts, which were unfortunately brought cling film-covered to the table, we chose the palette-cleansing mango sorbet to cool us down after the chilli-laden larb. On a busy Saturday night, with the restaurant packed to capacity, the service was definitely on the slow side. The overcrowding left us feeling a tad cramped and detracted from the otherwise languid ambience of the dining room. Nevertheless, this is still one of London's best Thai restaurants.
Babies and children admitted. Booking advisable. Separate room for parties, seats 50. Takeaway service. Vegetarian menu.
Map 11/6B.

South West

Chelsea SW10

Busabong Tree ★
112 Cheyne Walk, SW10 (020 7352 7534).
Bus 11, 22, 31, 49, 319. **Lunch served**
noon-3pm daily. **Dinner served** 6-11.15pm
Mon-Sat. **Main courses** £7.95-£16. **Set
lunch** £9.95 three courses incl coffee. **Set
dinner** £22.25, £27.25, three courses incl
coffee. **Credit** AmEx, JCB, MC, £TC, V.
The decor here is light and airy; the cream walls
are adorned with various Thai photos, hangings,
statues and scenes of Thai life, and surround a
rockery with a tinkly waterfall cascading into a
pond full of fat carp and (faux) water lilies. The
fresh roses on the table were an immediate
indication of the restaurant's careful attention to
detail. Our drinks arrived quickly, followed by hot
towels and complimentary prawn crackers with
peanut sauce. From an enormous menu featuring
160 dishes, including 37 vegetarian options, we
ordered the set menu for two (£27.50). It kicked off
with the deliciously light Busabong royal platter of
prawn satay, stuffed chicken wings, Thai fish cakes
and crab claws. Next we enjoyed penang red curry
with seafood and a beautifully tender drunken
lamb with peppercorns and sake, accompanied by
fragrant jasmine rice. Chicken with ginger and
mushrooms seemed rather Chinese in style and
flavour, but was no less scrumptious for that. The
food was lavishly presented by efficient staff,
smartly attired in traditional Thai uniforms, and
the quality was all as you would expect in this
location and price range.
*Babies and children welcome; high chairs. Book
dinner Thur-Sat. Separate rooms for parties,
seating 15, 40 and 50. Tables outdoors (10,
garden). Takeaway service. Vegetarian menu.*
Map 5/13D.
For branch see index.

Thai on the River
*Chelsea Wharf, 15 Lots Road, SW10 (020
7351 1151). Bus 11, 19, 22, 31.* **Lunch
served** 12.30-3pm Tue-Fri; 1-4pm Sun.
Dinner served 6.30-11pm Mon-Thur, Sun;
6.30-11.30pm Fri, Sat. **Main courses**
£7-£26.95. **Set lunch** £7.95 two courses. **Set
dinners** £30-£48. **Service** 12½%. **Credit**
AmEx, DC, JCB, MC, V.
There's an elegant tropical palm court vibe about
this place. Comfortable cushioned rattan chairs

overlook the river through large picture windows,
while the riverside patio promises balmy al fresco
dining during London's keenly anticipated
annual week of sunshine. The menu is extensive
with over 100 dishes on offer. The dishes we
chose were all well executed and tasty, although those
who enjoy a good chilli buzz might have found
them a little on the mild side. Frogs' legs were
tender and juicy on the inside and encrusted with
garlic, chilli and coriander on the outside; crispy
chicken wings stuffed with pork and shrimp were
similarly succulent, while mieng gai kung was a
tasty treat of minced chicken and other goodies
wrapped in leaves and eaten as little parcels.
From the salad selection, yum neau, a warm beef
salad with lashings of garlic, coriander, lime and
chilli, was a suitably zingy accompaniment to
melt-in-the-mouth duck in tamarind sauce,
sublimely married with crunchy cashews.
Although the service was warm and attentive
(hot towels were provided between courses), on
our visit the hyperactive air-con gave the
restaurant a distinctly chilly atmosphere. In fact,
both the food and the dining room would have
benefited from some extra heat.
*Babies and children welcome; high chairs;
Booking advisable. Tables outdoors (25,
riverside terrace). Takeaway service.*
Map 5/13D.

Fulham SW6

Blue Elephant
*4-6 Fulham Broadway, SW6 (020 7385 6595).
Fulham Broadway tube.* **Lunch served** noon-
2.30pm Mon-Fri; noon-3pm Sun. **Dinner
served** 7pm-12.30am Mon-Sat; 7-10.30pm Sun.
Set meals £29 three courses, £34 four
courses. **Set buffet lunch** (Sun) £16.75
adults, £4-£8 children. **Credit** AmEx, DC, MC,
£TC, V.
Long established as one of London's most
spectacular Thai restaurants, the Blue Elephant is
an undeniably impressive choice for a romantic
(and pricey) dinner à deux. Dining amid the
luscious tropical plants, or on wooden walkways
overlooking the ornamental ponds brimming with
'lucky' carp, it is easy to imagine you are relaxing
in the tropical paradise of one of Thailand's
famous resorts. Sprays of hot pink miniature
orchids decorate the tables, which are set with
signature blue and white crockery and bamboo-
style cutlery (available for sale alongside Blue
Elephant cookery books and other merchandise).
The evening menu offers both à la carte choices and

three set meals; we opted for the royal Thai banquet
menu (£29 per head, minimum two people), which
includes six starters and six main courses, plus pad
Thai, mixed vegetables and steamed rice, topped
off with fresh fruit and ice-cream. The starters were
the usual combination of satay, fish cakes, spring
rolls, vermicelli salad, paper stuffed prawns and
dim sum, served on one large, attractively
garnished platter and all flawlessly executed. Main
dishes of fish, prawns, lamb, beef, chicken and
vegetables were presented on a high brass serving
dish in matching blue bowls and had been
prepared in a variety of ways to offer a rep-
resentative (if safe) sampling of flavours. On the
whole, the food was very good, with occasional
bursts of excellence, so it was a shame that the
service was rather more uneven; attentiveness
bordered on overzealous hovering, and a string of
mistakes included an over-charged bill.
*Babies and children welcome; high chairs
(Sun). Booking essential. Dress: smart casual;
no shorts. Takeaway service. Vegetarian menu.*
Map 5/13B.

Putney SW15

Talad Thai ★ ★
*320 Upper Richmond Road, SW15 (020 8789
8084). East Putney tube.* **Lunch served**
11.30am-3pm, **dinner served** 5.30-10pm
Mon-Sat. **Meals served** 12.30-8pm Sun.
Main courses £3.50. **Unlicensed. Corkage**
£1. **No credit cards.**
This café-style eaterie is reminiscent of Bangkok.
Rows of tables covered in red and white
chequered cloths and typical condiment sets fill
the front of the room, while a gleaming stainless
steel kitchen takes up the back half. Drinks are
selected from a large fridge and include Thai
beers (Elephant and Siam) and an exotic range of
fruit juices, while a huge chill cabinet is packed
with large containers of sliced and diced raw
vegetables. The menu is clearly set out and simple
to understand; everything costs £3.95 or £4.40
with rice. Tod man, described as 'spicy seafood
savoury', was a generous serving of five very
tasty fish cakes. Equally good were the tender
and delicately flavoured chicken pieces wrapped
in pandan leaves. Next, tom yam soup was ideally
hot, sour and fragrant. Stir-fried squid came soft
and succulent in its coriander, garlic and pepper
sauce and was accompanied by special fried rice
with prawns, squid and egg. All of these dishes
were produced with rapid expertise by the
laughing and joking kitchen crew, and served by

efficient staff in uniform white shirts, aprons and
peaked caps. Feeling inspired after our excellent
meal, we popped into the Talad shop to stock up
on a few chilli pastes.
*Babies and children admitted. Cookery classes
(11am-noon Sun, £3; phone for details). No
smoking. Takeaway service.*

South Kensington SW7

Bangkok
*9 Bute Street, SW7 (020 7584 8529).
South Kensington tube.* **Lunch served**
12.15-2.30pm, **dinner served** 6.45-11pm Mon-
Sat. **Main courses** £6.80-£12.50. **Credit** MC,
£TC, V.
Bangkok was positively heaving on a Sunday
night as we arrived. A quick glance around
confirmed that people were here for the food not
the decor, which consisted of inoffensive but
uninspired wooden furniture in rather bland
cream surroundings, brightened only by an
interesting selection of high school-style artwork.
Despite the crowds, slick service insured we were
immediately given menus and our drinks quickly
followed. Bangkok has done away with Thai
names on its menu and gives a descriptive English
one instead. To get the ball rolling we ordered
chicken soup piquant, a delicious blend of hot and
spicy flavours in creamy coconut milk. The
savoury Thai toast was surprisingly pleasant
minced pork on bread, deep fried with only a
touch of spice. Penang prawns proved
unexpectedly hot, while the beef with crispy Thai
basil and chilli was a rich and spicy but delicately
balanced medley of Thai flavours. Thai rice-
noodle was the only disappointment: a pale,
prawn-less immitation of pad Thai. On the whole,
despite its departure from 'authentic' ingredients
and recipes, the food here is tasty, well prepared
and obviously very popular with the locals.
*Babies and children admitted. Booking
essential.* **Map 12/10D**.

Exhibition
*19 Exhibition Road, SW7 (020 7584 8359).
South Kensington tube.* **Lunch served** noon-
2.30pm, **dinner served** 6.30-11pm daily.
Main courses £10.95-£16.95. **Service**
12½%. **Credit** AmEx, DC, JCB, MC, V.
It's so pleasant to visit a Thai restaurant with
stylish, understated Eastern decor rather than the
usual Thai travel agency school of design.
Instead of tourist board posters and Burmese
wall hangings, Exhibition gives us matt taupe

Charuwan. *See page 169.*

walls, salmon silk roman blinds, Lana Thai sculptures and large arrangements of orchids. Thick white plates, rattan placemats, hand-beaten steel cutlery and wooden chopstick sets are all imported from Thailand but are the type of tableware usually found in the Conran Shop rather than a Thai restaurant. Unfortunately, the food did not live up to its stylish setting. The lunch menu has a choice of nine mains ranging in price from £5.95 (yellow noodles topped with stir-fried vegetables) to £10.95 (seared scallops with Thai herb salad), each served Western-style as a complete dish. We tried noodle soup with seared duck breast, which was blander than a pack of instant noodles and bore no relation to the feisty dish served in stalls all over Thailand. The pan-fried fish on banana leaves, which translated as three sardines and a salad, was also disappointing, while the rice was only brought on request and was cold. The service was friendly but slow and haphazard and the food was missing the crucial zing of the Thai awesome foursome: hot, salty, sweet and sour.
Book dinner Thur-Sat. **Map 12/10D**.

South

Clapham SW4

Pepper Tree ★
19 Clapham Common Southside, SW4 (020 7622 1758). Clapham Common tube/35, 37, 88, 137, 345 bus. **Lunch served** noon-3pm Mon-Sat. **Dinner served** 6-10.30pm Mon; 6-11pm Tue-Sat. **Meals served** noon-10.30pm Sun. **Main courses** £4.50-£6. **Service** 10% for parties of eight or more. **Credit** JCB, MC, £TC, V.
Another highly successful suburban canteen-style joint with long shared tables and bench seating. The elbow-to-elbow proximity and low prices ensure a noisy, casual camaraderie, while the cream walls and pale wooden furniture give the place a light contemporary feel. The menu is brief and refreshingly to the point, although the omission of proper Thai names is perhaps indicative of the kitchen's departure from a rigorously traditional approach. For starters we sampled sweetcorn cakes, which came with a typical sweet and sour sauce, and Thai dim sum, tasty little pockets of pork, prawn and water chestnuts with a soy and ginger sauce. Red curry trout, chosen from the specials board and the most expensive dish at £5.50, was perfectly cooked and flaked off the bone in tender morsels, while green chicken curry was suitably rich and flavoursome but lacking aubergine. For dessert the yellow bean cake and home-made vanilla ice-cream were delicious, while the mango sorbet was enjoyably refreshing. Impressively good food for such bargain prices, served in an attractive, buzzy environment.
Babies and children welcome; high chairs. Bookings not accepted dinner. No-smoking tables. Takeaway service.

Tooting SW17

Oh Boy
843 Garratt Lane, SW17 (020 8947 9760). Tooting Broadway tube. **Dinner served** 6.30-11pm Tue-Sun. **Main courses** £5.25-£9.90. **Set meal** £22 four courses incl coffee. **Service** 10%. **Credit** AmEx, DC, JCB, MC, £TC, V.
Oh Boy is a veteran that was in business long before the 1990s boom in neighbourhood Thai restaurants. It's a small, local place that does a busy takeaway trade; the tiny, dated and slightly dingy interior doesn't really encourage lingering. The menu has a predictable roll-call of Thai dishes, but still offers the best Thai cooking for miles, infinitely preferable any of the other contenders on Garratt Lane. The som tam was made with proper green papaya (no carrot or cabbage substitution here) and the larb was correctly fiery, without blowing our heads off. Both these dishes suffered from an excess of decorative foliage, from frilly lettuce to orchid blooms, but this didn't detract from their delicious flavours. Beef massaman was the only slightly disappointing aspect of our meal; the beef was presented as fast-cooked thin strips instead of slow-cooked chunks. However, with such an extensive menu – 90 items – it's little wonder they're not all up to scratch.
Babies and children admitted. Booking advisable. Separate room for parties, seats 16. Takeaway service.

South East

Blackheath SE3

Laicram
1 Blackheath Grove, SE3 (020 8852 4710). Blackheath rail/53, 89, 108, 202 bus. **Lunch served** noon-2.30pm, **dinner served** 6-11pm Tue-Sun. **Main courses** £3-£8.50. **Credit** AmEx, MC, V.
A bright green neon sign announces the Laicram's presence on an otherwise fairly dark stretch of road. Inside the restaurant's bright and cheerful, although this could be attributed to a giggling hen-night group rather than the decor or staff. From the starters we sampled tom ka gai, an aromatic blend of galangal, lemon grass, lime leaves and coconut milk; straw mushrooms had been substituted with plain ones, but it was still a delicious soup. Chicken satay was less good: lacking in the marinade department and bizarrely accompanied by four triangles of white bread, instead of rice blocks. From the main menu, weeping tiger was tasty and came with a divine sauce, but was far from rare as we had requested. The green chicken curry, however, was a culinary masterpiece complete with both golf ball and pea aubergines. Aubergine in black bean sauce was also excellent: soft, succulent and infused with a delicious garlic and chilli flavour. The grand finale, though, was the sight of the bride-to-be standing on her chair to sing with a pair of pink knickers on her head and an inflatable groom handcuffed to her wrist. We were surprised not to be charged extra.
Babies and children admitted. Book dinner Fri, Sat. Takeaway service (10% discount).

Crystal Palace SE19

Tamnag Thai
50-52 Westow Hill, SE19 (020 8761 5959). Crystal Palace or Gipsy Hill rail/2, 3, 322 bus. **Lunch served** noon-3pm Mon-Fri, Sun. **Dinner served** 6-11pm daily. **Set dinners** £15-£22 per person (minimum two). **Credit** AmEx, DC, JCB, MC, £TC, V.
There's a lot to look at at Tamnag Thai: a kaleidoscope of Thai parasols is suspended from the ceiling, while beneath them various objets d'art ranging from gold leaved statues to carved Lana stone reliefs vie for attention. Out the back, a small enclosed patio area, wreathed in greenery and protected by large garden umbrellas and a couple of Buddha statues, provides an alfresco option. On a Monday evening we found the restaurant half full and were glad to have pre-booked a window seat. After munching through the complimentary prawn crackers we tested the staff's patience by ordering a course at a time, but they remained cheerfully attentive and were happy to substitute vegetable tempura for spring rolls in the Tamnag platter. Chicken satay was marinated magic on a stick, but unfortunately the rest of the platter was strictly average. Tamarind duck came on a mini brazier and was also only adequate; once it had cooled, the meat toughened considerably. The sizzling seafood was a tasty medley of prawns, mussels, a scallop and plenty of crab, flavoured with garlic, chilli and basil, but it was the fiery tang of the green papaya salad that was the highlight of the meal. Tamnag Thai is an attractive local, but the food is clearly geared towards British tastes.
Babies and children welcome (before 8.30pm Fri, Sat); high chairs. Booking advisable dinner Thur-Sat. Dress: smart casual. No-smoking tables. Separate room for parties (conservatory, seats 20). Tables outdoors (5, patio). Takeaway service. Vegetarian dishes.

London Bridge SE1

Kwan Thai
The Riverfront, Hay's Galleria, Tooley Street, SE1 (020 7403 7373). London Bridge tube/rail. **Lunch served** 11.30am-3pm Mon-Fri. **Dinner served** 6-10pm Mon-Sat. **Main courses** £7.95-£12. **Set lunches** £7.95-£15. **Set dinners** £20, £25. **Service** 12½% for groups of seven or more. **Credit** AmEx, DC, MC, V.
Kwan Thai was lacking in ambience on the night of our visit; bad acoustics in the downstairs section almost sabotaged the pleasure of a river view, while the green and cream colour scheme and hall-marked silver was redolent of '80s hotel dining. On the plus side, we were pleased to see Mekong whisky and three Thai beers on the drinks menu. To start us off we ordered the Kwan Thai platter of succulent chicken satay, spicy corn cakes and spring rolls, fried golden bags and vegetables in pastry cups, which were all perfectly executed with light flavoursome fillings and crisp, delicate deep-fried pastry. From a tempting menu we eventually opted for hoi prig pao (eight medium-sized mussels in a roasted chilli paste) – a good choice, although a tad light on the chilli – and gaeng massaman, a rich peanuty curry with hearty chunks of juicy beef. These were accompanied by fragrant Thai rice and pad Thai goong, an above-average version of the fried noodle dish that sadly contained only four prawns and no shrimps. Kwan Thai is a competent restaurant, but in this price range we would expect more. It certainly wouldn't hurt the smartly dressed, over-efficient staff to squeeze out an occasional smile.
Babies and children welcome; high chairs. Booking advisable. No-smoking tables. Separate room for parties, seats 20. Tables outdoors (10, riverside terrace). Takeaway service. Vegetarian menu. **Map 8/8Q**.

New Cross SE14

Thailand ★
15 Lewisham Way, SE14 (020 8691 4040). New Cross or New Cross Gate tube/rail. **Dinner served** 6-11pm Tue-Sun. **Main courses** £4.75-£8.95. **Credit** MC, V.
It's a relief to find that this award-winning, quirky restaurant has survived recent changes of both ownership and chef and continues to delight diners from all over London. The menu offers many outstanding options but contrary to the restaurant's name, its best dishes are probably from the Lao section. Aided by the colour photos in the menu, we chose chicken satay, bo'la lope (beef with onion wrapped in wild pepper leaves, charcoal grilled on satay sticks) and ka lampee yatsai (steamed parcels of spiced crab and pork covered in vermicelli and wrapped in cabbage leaves). All were culinary triumphs that were let down by below par chilli sauce. From the Lao menu we chose two dishes: a rather mild but very tasty larb (sour minced beef) wrapped in lettuce leaves and accompanied by spicy fried rice balls, plus heavenly steamed whole poussin stuffed with a mixture of lemon grass, bergamot, galangal, coriander roots and vermicelli, also wrapped in lettuce leaves. While the food was sublime, the service was uneven and the decor can only be described as dodgy, with DIY stained glass featuring prominently on the doors and ceiling. Somehow, though, these details merely reinforce the fact that you're here for the exceptional food, not the tricks of the trade. Not to be missed.
Booking essential. Takeaway service.

Menu

Thai food is usually eaten with a fork and spoon, but fingers are also acceptable if the food is best handled that way.

Useful terms

Khantoke: originally a north-eastern banquet conducted around a low table while seated on triangular cushions; some restaurants have khantoke seating.
Khing: with ginger.
Op or **ob**: baked.
Pad or **pat**: stir-fried.
Pet or **ped**: hot (spicy).
Prik: chilli.
Tom: boiled.
Tod, **tort**, **tord** or **taud**: deep-fried.

Starters

Khanom jeep or **ka nom geeb**, etc: dim sum. Little dumplings of minced pork, bamboo shoots and water chestnuts, wrapped in an egg and rice (wun tun) pastry, then steamed.
Khanom pang na koong: prawn sesame toast.
Kratong thong: tiny crispy batter cups ('top hats') filled with mixed vegetables and/or minced meat.
Popia or **porpia**: spring rolls.
Tod mun pla or **tauk manpla**, etc: small fried fish cakes, rubbery in consistency, with virtually no 'fishy' smell or taste.

Soups

Poh tak or **tom yam potag**, etc: hot and sour mixed seafood soup, sometimes kept simmering in a Chinese 'steamboat' dish.
Tom kha gai or **gai tom kar**, etc: hot and sour chicken soup with coconut milk.
Tom yam: a watery hot and sour soup, smelling of lemongrass, often with chicken or prawn pieces. Tom yam koong is with prawns; tom yam gai is with chicken; tom yam hed is with mushrooms.

Rice

Khao, **kow**, **khow**, etc: rice.
Khao nao: sticky rice, from the north-east. **Khao pat**: fried rice.
Khao suay: steamed rice.
Pat khai: egg-fried rice.

Salads

Larb or **laab**: minced and cooked meat with lime juice and other ingredients such as ground rice and herbs.
Som tam: a popular cold salad of grated green papaya.
Yam or **yum**: refers to any tossed salad, hot or cold, but it is often hot and sour, flavoured with lemon and chilli. This type of yam is originally from the north-east of Thailand, where the Laotian influence is greatest.
Yam nua: hot/sour beef salad.
Yam talay: hot and sour seafood salad (served cold).

Noodles

Eaten in greater quantities in the north of Thailand. There are many types of **kwaitiew** or **guey teow** noodles. Common ones include **sen mee**: rice vermicelli; **sen yai** (river rice noodles): a broad, flat, rice noodle; **sen lek**: a medium flat noodle, used to make pad Thai; **ba mee**: egg noodles; and **woon sen** (cellophane noodle): transparent vermicelli made from soy beans or other pulses. These are often prepared as stir-fries. The names of the numerous noodle dishes depend on the combination of other ingredients. Common dishes include:
Khao soi: chicken curry soup with egg noodles; a Burmese/Thai dish, sometimes referred to as the national dish of Burma. Not to be confused with khao suay (steamed rice).
Mee krob or **mee grob**: sweet crispy fried vermicelli.
Pad si-ewe or **cee eaw**, etc: noodles fried with mixed meat in soy sauce.
Pad Thai: stir-fried noodles with shrimps (or chicken and pork), beansprouts, salted turnips and garnished with ground peanuts.

Curries

Thai curries differ quite markedly from the Indian variety. Thais cook them for a shorter time, and use thinner sauces. Flavours and ingredients are different, too. There are several common types of curry paste; these are used to name the curry, with the principal ingredients listed thereafter.
Gaeng, **kaeng** or **gang**, etc: the generic name for curry. Yellow curry is the mildest; green curry (gaeng keaw wan/kiew warn) is medium hot and uses green chillies; red curry (gaeng pet) is similar, but uses red chillies.
Jungle curry: often the hottest of the curries, made with red curry paste, bamboo shoots and just about anything else that comes to hand.
Massaman or **mussamun**, etc: also known as Muslim curry, as it originates from the area along the border with Malaysia where many Thais are Muslims. For this reason, pork is never used. It's rich but mild, with coconut, potato and some peanuts.
Penang, **panaeng** or **panang**: a dry, aromatic curry made with 'Penang' curry paste, coconut cream and holy basil.

Fish & seafood

Hoi: shellfish.
Hor mok talay or **haw mog talay**: steamed egg mousse with seafood.
Koong, **goong** or **kung**: prawns.
Maw: dried fish belly.
Pla meuk: squid.

Nid Ting

South Norwood SE25

Mantanah ★
*2 Orton Building, Portland Road, SE25 (020
8771 1148). Norwood Junction rail.* **Dinner
served** 6.30-10.45pm Tue-Sat; 6.30-10.30pm
Sun. **Main courses** £5.75-£8.50. **Set dinners**
£16 three courses, £20 four courses, per person
(minimum two). **Credit** AmEx, MC, £TC, V.
Located inconspicuously on a busy road, this
highly acclaimed restaurant offers few external
clues to its culinary genius. The interior is small
and fairly plain, while the welcome is warm and
solicitous. Curious phrases such as 'sideways', 'on
diet' and 'buddies' dot the extensive menu, which
includes a sprinkling of exceptional regional
dishes and a matching vegetarian section. The
pork satay immediately transported us back to the
nocturnal street stalls of Bangkok, while the
plump and succulent goong pao (charcoal-grilled
butterfly king prawns with a tamarind sauce) were
probably the best we had ever tasted. Larb ped was
tender juicy slices of roast duck in a harmoniously
piquant blending of mint, coriander, chilli, lemon
grass and lime. From the main menu we sampled
the enigmatically named midnight curry, a smooth
rich chicken and pumpkin curry, flavoured with
coconut milk. This provided an excellent contrast
to neua yang (melt-in-the-mouth slices of rare beef)
accompanied by an excellent chilli sauce that
contained plenty of garlic and coriander. Pay
Mantanah a visit.
*Babies and children welcome. Book dinner Fri,
Sat. Takeaway service. Vegetarian menu.*

Bethnal Green E2

Thai Garden
*249 Globe Road, E2 (020 8981 5748).
Bethnal Green tube/rail/8 bus.* **Lunch served**
noon-2.45pm Mon-Fri. **Dinner served**
6-10.45pm daily. **Main courses** £4-£6.95.
Set meal (noon-2.45pm, 6-7.30pm) £7.50 two
courses. **Set dinners** £16-£21 four courses.
Service 10%. **Credit** MC, £TC, V.
The small and cosy Thai Garden serves
vegetarian and fish dishes, and has a clutch of
awards that are testament to the superb menu of
meatless cuisine created by the Thai chef and her
husband (Mr and Mrs Hufton). The menu is
divided into separate vegetarian and seafood
sections with roughly 40 dishes in each. From the
appetisers we chose som tum poo ud, a version
of spicy green papaya salad with shredded
crabsticks. This was well executed and had the
required hot zing to it, but came inexplicably
without any crab. Yum pla foo, described as
'crispy tuna fish marinated with hot and sour
spicy sauce and dressed with red onion, chillies,
spring onion and coriander', was disappointing.
We had imagined tender and juicy chunks of
fresh tuna, but were presented with deep fried
flakes of what looked to be the tinned variety. For
a main course we sampled mee grob, a superb
rendition of sweetish tamarind-flavoured crispy
noodles, plus goong pad med mamuang,

succulent king prawns stir-fried with tasty oyster-flavoured sauce together with a variety of deliciously al dente vegetables. These dishes were all way beyond the 'substitute tofu for meat' school of vegetarian cooking, but we've had much better meals here. Perhaps the culinary standards depend on the presence of Mrs Hufton in the kitchen.
Babies and children welcome; high chairs. Book Thur-Sat. No-smoking tables. Separate room for parties, seats 14. Takeaway service. Vegetarian menu.

Whitechapel E1

Sweet Chilli ★
63-67 Mile End Road, E1 (020 7702 7977). Whitechapel tube. **Dinner served** 6-11pm daily. **Main courses** £5-£8. **Set meals** £15-£20. **Service** 10%. **Credit** AmEx, JCB, MC, V.
Occupying a large corner site, Sweet Chilli is a spacious canteen-style eaterie, although the sweeping curve of the retro bar and the large picture windows hint at a previous incarnation as a pub. From a choice of ten appetisers, we chose the chicken satay, which was moist, tender and deliciously marinated. Tom ka gai, although tasty, looked like mushroom soup; in the absence of straw mushrooms, the entire surface was bobbing with diced plain ones, while other essentials such as galangal, lime leaves and lemon grass were just tiny slivers at the bottom of the bowl. However, all was forgiven with the arrival of a deliciously tender and juicy weeping tiger. The sliced char-grilled beef was nicely crispy on the outside, rare on the inside and arrived on a sizzling platter with a wonderful chilli dipping sauce. Ped ma kham was thin medallions of duck on an unusual bed of snow peas, with a rich thick tamarind sauce: flavoursome, but nowhere near as moist and succulent as duck should be. All in all the standard of the dishes was inconsistent, which is a pity considering the high quality this place can achieve when it puts its mind to it.
Babies and children admitted. Separate rooms for parties (2), both seating 40. Takeaway service.

North East

Stoke Newington N16

Yum Yum
30 Stoke Newington Church Street, N16 (020 7254 6751). Stoke Newington rail/73 bus. **Lunch served** noon-2.30pm daily. **Dinner served** 6-10.45pm Mon-Thur, Sun; 6-11.15pm Fri, Sat. **Minimum** £10 (dinner). **Credit** AmEx, MC, V.
The exterior of Yum Yum is easy to spot on Stoke Newington High Street by way of its high-gloss black and red exterior. Inside, however, it has a sunny colourful decor with lemon yellow walls, blue table cloths, green serviettes, bunches of orange lilies and a scattering of Thai artefacts. The restaurant is large with several adjoining rooms, but although it was only partially full on our Tuesday evening visit, we felt too close to the neighbouring tables for comfort. The staff were chatty and helpful as we waded through the sizeable menu, from which we eventually chose the yum platter (£5.50 per head, minimum two people). As expected this was a selection of six goodies from the appetiser list. The chicken satay was exemplary – tender, moist morsels coated in a tasty marinade with a pleasing peanut sauce; the stuffed purses, fish cakes and spring rolls were all crisp and tasty; but the inclusion of two miniature oily chicken drumsticks was a mistake. Next up we had steamed rice and a very tasty chicken pad Thai. The star dish, however, was undoubtedly murk pad grappa, a delicious, hot creamy pile of squid with chilli and basil leaves. Yum Yum by name, yum yum by nature.
Babies and children welcome; high chairs. Booking advisable. Entertainment: face painting, balloon modelling and raffle (Sat, Sun). Separate rooms for parties, seating 20 and 24. Takeaway service. Vegetarian menu.
For branch see index.

North

Archway N19

Charuwan ★ ★
110 Junction Road, N19 (020 7263 1410). Tufnell Park tube. **Lunch served** noon-3pm Mon-Fri. **Dinner served** 6-11.30pm daily. **Main courses** £4.95-£7.95. **Set meals** £16, £18 (minimum two). **Service** 10%. **Credit** AmEx, MC, V.
Definitely one of North London's best kept secrets, Charawan is run by a friendly family and is a winner in every way. We were delighted to see both Thai beers and Thai whiskey (Mekong) on the drinks menu and further charmed by the complimentary bowl of prawn crackers that appeared immediately on our arrival. To start we had a delicious mixed platter of appetisers, followed by an exceptional tom kah gai, with tender chunks of chicken and a very generous sprinkling of authentic straw mushrooms. The main dishes were also impressive: a rich creamy massaman gai and pla nueng ma naow – a divine light flaky fish with chopped ginger, chilli, garlic and coriander in zesty lime sauce. To accompany this we were served flavoursome coconut rice and som tam – a hot and spicy green papaya salad often excluded from menus. Charuwan's decor is typical Thai, with a roofed bar (sala) at the back and Burmese embroidered wall hangings and statues dotted around. The food, however, is really something special and painstakingly prepared down to the intricately carved vegetable garnishes. Great value for money and a lovely local.
Takeaway service.

Nid Ting ★
533 Holloway Road, N19 (020 7263 0506/ 020 7561 1249). Archway or Holloway Road tube/271 bus. **Dinner served** 6-11.15pm Mon-Sat; 6-10.15pm Sun. **Main courses** £4.95-£5.50. **Set dinner** £15. **Credit** AmEx, DC, JCB, MC, V.
Amid the dinge of upper Holloway Road, this little gem was almost full by 7.30pm on a Tuesday night. Tucking into our complimentary prawn crackers, we ordered Singha beer (the only Thai offering in the drinks department) and pored over the lengthy menu. We chose the golden basket – five disappointingly dry little cases with mince and corn – and the tom ka kai, which was very good but unusually sweet. For our next instalment we had two salads. Som tam was a hot, zingy salad consisting of grated green papaya, long beans and tomato with lashings of chilli, garlic and lime juice, while yum woon sen was another delicious combination of hot and sour, this time using minced pork, prawns and mushroom with vermicelli. Accompaniment was provided by koong kratiem (fried prawns with garlic and pepper) and pla muk kaprow (stir-fried squid with garlic, chilli and basil leaves), both of which superbly exceeded our expectations. For the grand finale we ordered rumbutan stuffed with pineapple and deep-fried ice-cream, which made a pleasant end. Although the restaurant was filled to capacity soon after 8pm, the traditionally clad waitresses kept up their smiley fast service.
Babies and children welcome; high chairs. Booking advisable; essential Fri, Sat. Separate room for parties, seats 25. Takeaway service. Vegetarian menu.

Crouch End N8

O's Thai Café
10 Topsfield Parade, N8 (020 8348 6898). Finsbury Park tube/rail then W2, W7 bus. **Lunch served** noon-3pm Tue-Sun. **Dinner served** 6.30-11pm daily. **Main courses** £5.50-£12.95. **Set meal** £13.95 three courses. **Service** 10% for parties of six or more. **Credit** MC, £TC, V.
This long, narrow, buzzing canteen is decorated in minimalist cream with blond wood furniture and a single spotty, coloured wall for that oh-so Soho vibe. The menu is short and sweet: an assortment of starters and two soups, eleven mains divided into beef, chicken, pork, bean curd or king prawn versions, followed by eight specials. Feeling more hungry than inspired, we chose O's special starters – a sampling of each starter on the menu, plus stuffed chicken wings, with sweet chilli and spicy peanut dipping sauces – followed by gaeng kiew wan and then kratien prik tai talay from the blackboard menu. The special starter, attractively decorated with a pink carnation on a parsley bed, was crisp, tasty and fresh, but also amounted to a lot of deep-frying. Gaeng kiew wan was rich and flavoursome and consisted of good chunks of chicken and vegetables with lime and basil in green curry and coconut cream, but the dish of the day was definitely the kratien prik tai talay, a generous, succulent garlicky combination of seafood in coriander paste and oyster sauce. As a bonus, it was a pleasant change to have the rice included in the price of the dish, making O's Thai Café excellent value for money.
Babies and children welcome; high chairs. Booking advisable; essential dinner Fri, Sat. Takeaway service (020 8348 3231).

Turkish

At its best Turkish food is delicious, wildly imaginative and astonishingly cheap. For vegetarians the options are endless – which other world cuisine can compete with meze for sheer range and breadth of flavour? For meat lovers, few things are more irresistible than a feast of freshly assembled kebabs charcoal-grilled to tender perfection.

Among this year's stars are **Tas**, a stylish, innovative Turkish restaurant just a short walk from the South Bank. We were also impressed by the buzzy **Gallipoli** duo in Islington and by the quirky and riotously colourful **Iznik** in Highbury.

If you're looking for the real thing, you'll find it in the Turkish heartland of Dalston in north-east London. Here, the likes of **Mangal** and **Istanbul Iskembecisi** offer some of the best kebabs in town. Often it's the tiny, family-run eateries, such as fish specialist **Sariyer Balik Lokantasi** on Green Lanes, that serve the best food. For a gentler introduction to Turkish cuisine, sample one of the **Sofra** branches in the West End. Or you could splash out on the Sofra chain's latest creation, Ottoman-inspired **Ozer** near Regent Street.

Central

Covent Garden WC2

Sofra
36 Tavistock Street, WC2 (020 7240 3773). Covent Garden tube. **Meals served** noon-midnight daily. **Main courses** £6.95-£14.95. **Set lunch** £5.75; £8.95 mixed meze. **Set dinner** £6.50; £9.95 mixed meze. **Service** 12½%. **Credit** AmEx, DC, MC, TC, V.
The Tavistock Street branch of Sofra, with its creamy yellow walls, potted palms and air of efficiency, is a fine, stress-free place to escape the crowds of Covent Garden. At lunchtime, it was filled with office workers and quiet, unshowy groups of tourists, many of them Japanese. We also spotted a few people dining alone. Our waitress was eager to please despite her faltering English, and the long, admirably clear menu made ordering a straightforward affair. The hot and cold meze or 'healthy lunch' was slow to arrive, but worth the wait. Presented in dinky, individual bowls decorated with fresh sprigs of mint, it looked appealing and most of it was. We liked the parsley salad and the kisir with hazelnuts, which we mopped up with delicious pide bread. We were less impressed by the oily lamb chunks swimming in houmous; the effect of combining the two produced ugly, orange stains in the bowl, and the flavours didn't quite work. All in all, though, the food is streets ahead of the average lunchtime fare and we were well-fed enough to forego main courses (char-grills such as shish, kofta, and chicken breast with wings and garlic) and puddings. Our waitress had incorrectly billed us for two coffees, but the mistake was quickly and apologetically amended.
Separate room for parties, seats 90.
Map 14/7L.
For branches see index.

Fitzrovia W1

Efes I
80-82 Great Titchfield Street, W1 (020 7636 1953). Great Portland Street tube. **Meals served** noon-11.30pm Mon-Sat. **Main courses** £6.30-£11. **Set meal** £17 per person (minimum two) three courses incl coffee. **Credit** AmEx, DC, JCB, MC, £TC, V.
Deep disappointment characterised our visit to Efes in elegant, unhurried Marylebone. We found the restaurant's serried ranks of lugubrious male waiters provided an unhappy mix of obsequious and offhand service. Our assigned waiter was surly when we asked for help with the long menu of mainly chicken and lamb dishes. There was amusement at least in the surroundings: a profusion of folkloric kitsch and nostalgia. We were surrounded by beaming, signed photos of 1970s DJs. Most of our middle-aged fellow diners – in bright, tight-fitting outfits – seemed to be tourists and out-of-towners. The Abigail's Party-style mixed meze consisted of fussy twirls of piped, toothpaste-textured dips on a metal platter bearing a wine glass adorned with a ludicrous tomato rose. It looked and was unappetising. The wine, an unpalatable white Italian, was a spectacular rip-off at £5 a glass. Mains, by contrast, were lacking in presentation. Lamb kebabs consisted of hunks of good meat on pitta bread, with a wodge of iceberg. Spotting desserts whizzing past (orange sorbet in a scooped out orange), we ordered Turkish coffee which was strong, potent and grainy. We left soon after, cowardly tipping our undeserving waiter, who hovered menacingly when cheque books appeared.
Babies and children welcome; high chairs. Booking advisable. Separate room for parties, seats 45. Tables outdoors (8, pavement).
Map 2/5J.
For branch see index.

Ozer
4-5 Langham Place, W1 (020 7323 0505). Oxford Circus tube.
Bar **Open** noon-11pm daily.
Restaurant **Lunch served** noon-2.30pm Mon-Fri; noon-3pm Sat, Sun. **Dinner served** 6-11pm Mon-Sat; 6-10.30pm Sun. **Main courses** £14-£18. **Set meals** (before 7.30pm) £14.95 two courses, £17.95 three courses. **Service** 12½%.
Both **Credit** AmEx, DC, MC, V.
We had hoped Ozer would have an exotic, harem-like atmosphere. Instead, this new 'modern Ottoman' restaurant just north of Regent Street, has a brash, 1980s gloss that makes it anything but sensual. Modern and shiny, with red walls and lots of marble, the room reminded us of an upmarket airline terminal. Although the service, from goateed waiters in black, was smooth and confident, the food was variable. Seared tuna was enjoyable and exquisitely presented, but artichoke hearts with dill and poppy seeds was dull. Shoulder of lamb with a marmalade of kumquats and limequats was succulent, tender and infused with rich, deep flavours – a shame there was no rice or vegetables to accompany it. Grilled seabream was a disaster. It came with tiny, very dry chickpea cakes, and the fish was undercooked to the point of being inedible. The maitre d' immediately offered to replace it (we refused) and then removed the item from the bill. He also insisted that we have desserts on the house. We didn't feel adventurous enough to try basil sorbet or aubergine pannacotta, but the apple purée with yoghurt was delicate and delicious. Ozer's outstanding wine list is an added attraction: an unsnobbish, gutsy compilation packed with treasures from around the world. The restaurant is owned by Husseyin Ozer, founder of the Sofra group.
Babies and children admitted. **Map 2/5H.**

Mayfair W1

Sofra Bistro
18 Shepherd Market, W1 (020 7493 3320). Green Park tube. **Meals served** noon-midnight daily. **Main courses** £7.45-£9.45. **Service** 12½%. **Credit** AmEx, MC, £TC, V.
Thanks to its popularity with well-heeled tourists and local office workers, this Mayfair branch of Sofra was almost full on a Tuesday night, despite the extra tables outside. Standards are generally high and we arrived with high hopes. Our youthful waiter was accommodating and didn't attempt to hurry us, even though the restaurant was full. Our starters – which included broad beans and yoghurt, kisir, and squid with walnut sauce – were all tasty, nicely textured and pretty to look at, but the rest of the meal was hit and miss. The vivid, beautifully presented halibut

Tas

courses were also unmemorable. We chose the 'chef's speciality' of charcoal-cooked lamb and chicken fillets, and the skewered chicken and pepper Pilot izgara. Service was courteous, if a little eccentric – the waiter informed us the sea bass wasn't fresh, but 'I froze it myself'. We were running late for our film and the waiter insisted on wrapping up our delicious, dense, treacly baklava to eat on the way. There were also complimentary slices of fruit. In spite of this, the food wasn't really good enough to justify spending time in the gloomy venue. Perhaps you'd be better off ordering a kebab from the front of house takeaway. As a takeaway, Marmaris seems popular, judging by the small queue of Pimlico kebab lovers in crumpled cords and lawn-coloured jumpers.
Babies and children welcome; high chairs. Booking advisable. Takeaway service. **Map 6/8H.**

South

Battersea SW11

Beyoglu
50 Battersea Park Road, SW11 (020 7627 2052). Battersea Park or Queenstown Road rail. **Dinner served** 6pm-midnight daily. **Main courses** £5-£10. **Set dinner** £10.50 per person (minimum two) two courses incl coffee. **Credit** MC, £TC, V.
Something of a maverick in an area where ethnic restaurants are few and far between, Beyoglu was packed with the opulent denizens of Battersea on the evening we visited. This is a place with a strong local following and it's easy to see why. Fairy lights twinkle from its windows, and the room – with its blue walls, pretty tiles and pot-plants – has a reassuring, homespun look. The atmosphere is low-key, the service pleasant and unobtrusive, the background music folksy and subdued. If you're new to Turkish food, Beyoglu is a good place to start, but if you've already tasted punchier versions in north London, you'll probably find the cooking a little bland and underspiced. All the meze (a varied choice of 19) were well-executed, but lacked the kick we'd come to expect. The beyti (lamb) kebabs were lean and well-flavoured, but the char-grilled swordfish had been spoiled by overcooking. And the baklava was soggy. Throughout the meal we drank a rough, young Turkish Buzbag red and Efes beer. Beyoglu isn't worth a detour for its food, but we were charmed, nonetheless, by the restaurant's friendly, easygoing atmosphere and lack of pretence.
Babies and children admitted. Booking advisable weekends. Separate room for parties, seats 35. Takeaway service (10% discount).

Waterloo SE1

Tas
33 The Cut, SE1 (020 7928 2111). Waterloo tube/rail. **Meals served** noon-11.30pm Mon-Sat; noon-10.30pm Sun. **Main courses** £4.50-£14.20. **Set meals** £6.45-£17.95. **Service** 10%. **Credit** AmEx, MC, V.
This light, airy, glass-fronted restaurant, a short walk from the South Bank, is a welcome new addition to the Turkish restaurant circuit. It's beautifully run, thoroughly professional and an inventive, modern Turkish food (no rough edges or offal) is delicious, imaginative and keenly priced. The chefs in black and yellow can be spotted cooking in the narrow, stainless-steel kitchen, behind the counter. There's a friendly buzz to the place, both in the evening and at lunchtime; it's not unusual to see a working lunch taking place next to a family outing, complete with baby in carry-cot. The food is extremely fresh and handsomely presented on cobalt blue plates. The own-made pide is exemplary and there's a wonderful range of hot and cold starters, including a fabulous fried aubergine. Mains include a good choice of vegetarian dishes, grills, casseroles and fish. Foil-wrapped halibut was a triumph – crisp, perfectly cooked and beautiful to behold. Swordfish was also enjoyable although the potatoes were slightly underdone. Our only quibbles are with a tendency to overseason and an over-lavish use of dill. Desserts also need work: on one visit we ate a powdery, cloyingly sweet chocolate cake, a disappointing finale considering the restaurant's otherwise high standards. Our bill was extremely fair, but the credit card slip was left open, despite the fact we'd already had 10% added. Our overall impression, though, was a happy one.
Entertainment: guitarist nightly. Separate room for parties, seats 40. Tables outdoors (2, pavement). **Map 7/8N.**

with peppers cooked in foil smelt delicious, but the fish was dry and overcooked. We loved the caramelised, herby peppers that accompanied it, though, and the mystery addition of grapefruit. Moving on to puddings, sütlac, with its trio of apricots, pistachios and whipped cream, was crunchy and well-judged. Less appealing was kayisi or rice pudding which was cold, bland and milky, low on rice, and had no perceptible trace of the rosewater that had tempted us to order it. We drank a very ordinary Mâcon-Villages white and wondered if we would have fared better with the Australian chardonnay. The toilet downstairs was in a sorry state.
Babies and children admitted. Booking advisable. Dress: smart casual. Separate room for parties, seats 25. Tables outdoors (14, pavement). **Map 6/8H.**
For branches see index.

Pimlico SW1

Marmaris
45 Warwick Way, SW1 (020 7828 5940). Pimlico tube/Victoria tube/rail/24 bus. **Meals served** noon-midnight Mon-Sat. **Main courses** £5.75-£8.80. **Set meals** £14, £17.50 incl coffee. **Credit** AmEx, MC, £TC, V.
Arriving at Marmaris, we were instantly put off by its stuffy smell, shabby, crumbling appearance and the small TV tuned into Turkish gameshows. The restaurant is in a backroom decked out with tatty maps of Turkey and posters of deer in sun-dappled glades. Our only fellow diner was a lone man reading a Turkish newspaper. We kicked off with tabouleh, patlican salad, houmous and cacik – all under £3, all acceptable, but unexceptional. Main

South East

Sydenham SE26

Lokal
107 Sydenham Road, SE26 (020 8659 4361). Sydenham rail. **Dinner served** 6pm-midnight Mon-Sat. **Main courses** £8.50-£12.95. **Set meal** £13.95 per person (minimum two). **Credit** MC, £TC, V.
Unless you happen to live locally, you'd probably never think of making the pilgrimage out to Lokal, but this is a decent little place all the same. It's a quiet and thoroughly unpretentious restaurant, with spring yellow walls, understated Turkish ornaments and an atmosphere that's easy and relaxed, if a little unexciting. Only a few tables were occupied when we visited. The menu majors in meze; you'll find all the old favourites (tarama, dolma and so on), plus a selection of unglamorous-sounding 'bites' from the charcoal grill, most under £3. Spotting interlopers such as entrecôte steak and prawn cocktail, we expected dull, suburban cooking, but our fears were quickly dispelled when the food arrived. The falafel and imam bayildi were both spot-on, as was the white bean stew. The lavish chunks of swordfish that followed were delicious, and we were equally impressed by the quality of the kleftiko. Desserts were less successful. We quickly gave up on our 'lady's belly button dessert', an intensely sweet filo and cream affair, topped by a glacé cherry. The baklava though nicely nutty, lacked freshness. Service is good.
Babies and children welcome. Booking essential dinner Fri, Sat. Entertainment: belly dancer 9.30-10pm Sat. Takeaway service.

North East

Dalston E8, N16

Anadolu Lokantasi ★
117 Kingsland High Street, E8 (020 7275 0403). Dalston Kingsland rail/67, 76, 149, 243 bus. **Open** 24 hours, **meals served** noon-7pm daily. **Main courses** £1.25-£8. **Unlicensed. Corkage** no charge. **No credit cards.**
A few Turkish men were slouched over hot bean casseroles when we arrived at this modest, unlicensed eatery in the Turkish heartland of Dalston (close to the Rio cinema). There's the usual display of raw meat in the window and the token Turkish touches inside (in this case straw hats hanging from the walls, with strange, blond plaits attached), but fripperies are few: this is where to go for the spartan, canteen experience at which Dalston excels. Very little English is spoken although there's a short English menu. Service was unorthodox, but agreeable. Simple, home-cooking such as bean and lamb stew comes with no frills or surprises. Kusbasi pide arrived topped with herbs, tomatoes, peppers and lamb – it was a little overspiced and underseasoned for our liking, but at £4 we weren't complaining. Almost nothing on the menu costs over £5; drinks are all 50p including ayran and Turkish coffee. The staggeringly low bill arrived with toothpicks and a paper napkin. A great pitstop if you're in the area.
Babies and children admitted. No-smoking tables. Takeaway service.

Gazi Antep Lahmacun Salonu ★
115 Stoke Newington Road, N16 (020 7275 7924/www.londraturk.com). Dalston Kingsland rail. **Meals served** 8am-11pm daily (Turkish breakfast until 5pm). **Main courses** £1.25-£4.50. **Unlicensed. Corkage** no charge. **No credit cards.**
Firmly in the canteen mould, Gazi Antep produces cooking that's a notch above many of its competitors. Staff have negligible command of English, the décor's dire (pink walls and palm-fringed beaches at sunset) and there's little atmosphere, beyond mournful Turkish music playing on the stereo. We were alone save for a hunched male diner and an eccentric, hippy couple. The meze were almost non-existent, apart from a very decent tarama. Our opinions were divided over the buttery, elusively flavoured lentil soup, but we agreed that the pide bread was superlative. Main courses included an attractively presented shish kebab that was a little too dry. We made the mistake, too, of tackling a fiery green chilli, nestling innocently in a pile of soft rice. Karisik pide was the best we'd tasted – crisp, tasty and far superior to the average pizza. No desserts were available on the night we visited, but the cook insisted on going out and buying us some baklava (delicious). Six beers came to an astonishingly cheap £9. The entire bill, for four, was just £39 without service.
Babies and children welcome. Takeaway service; delivery service.

Istanbul Iskembecisi ★
9 Stoke Newington Road, N16 (020 7254 7291). Dalston Kingsland rail. **Meals served** noon-5am daily. **Main courses** £5-£8.50. **No credit cards.**
Tripe soup, a concoction so extraordinary that the bemused waiter advised us not to order it, has become something of a cult dish at Istanbul Iskembecisi – it supposedly has the power to cure hangovers. The slimy grey tripe comes swimming in warm milk with chilli flakes, vinegar and a garlic sauce. It was the only low point in an otherwise perfect evening. The 25-strong meze selection is fabulous; imam bayildi, kisir and muska börek were all faultless. Mains – an appetising, well-seasoned iskender kebab and a meltingly delicious vegetarian turlu – didn't disappoint either, although we could have done without the accompanying mounds of shredded salad. It was sheer greediness that prompted us to order cakes for pudding: dinky baklava squares, which arrived with whipped cream. They were fresh and delicious, as was the thick, grainy coffee. Service is old-fashioned and elegant, but friendly. Turkish families, hip Stoke Newington couples, American bohemians – all can be found eating here. The room, with its upholstered chairs and sombre fittings, is reminiscent of a refurbished provincial hotel. Chocolate-box prints of Istanbul hang on the walls. Istanbul Iskembecisi is tremendous value and definitely worth seeking out, even if you don't live locally.
Babies and children welcome; high chairs. Book Fri, Sat. Takeaway service.

Mangal ★
10 Arcola Street, E8 (020 7275 8981). Dalston Kingsland rail. **Meals served** noon-midnight daily. **Main courses** £6-£8.50. **Unlicensed. Corkage** no charge. **No credit cards.**
This tiny branch of Mangal, on a rubbish-strewn side street in Dalston, is little more than a takeaway with a few tables and chairs inside. The smell of barbecued meat wafts out tantalisingly to the street and it's not unusual to see a queue of hungry people at the window, waiting for a free table. You'll have to rough it once you're inside, but the food is cheap and delicious, and you'll find yourself sitting cheek by jowl with a fun, eclectic mix of ages and nationalities. There's no menu, so it's worth investigating the contents of the fridge before ordering, or pointing to a kebab roasting over the open charcoal grill. When we arrived, Mangal was full to bursting (despite it being Sunday evening), but the waiter offered to come and fetch us from the pub when a table was free. He duly appeared, as promised, some 15 minutes later. Our orders – a mixed grill that came with a lemony, red cabbage salad; and grilled quails – were succulent. The melting, tasty aubergine was also superlative. Mangal doesn't have a drinks licence, but there are plenty of shops round the corner selling wine or beer. The chewy pide bread was delicious, too.
Babies and children admitted. Takeaway service.
For branches see index.

Mangal II
4 Stoke Newington Road, N16 (020 7254 7888). Dalston Kingsland rail. **Meals served** noon-1am daily. **Main courses** £5.50-£11. **Set meals** £11, £13.50, per person (minimum two) incl coffee. **No credit cards.**
The upmarket version of Mangal is a better option if you fancy a quiet, low-key evening, or a more extensive choice of food. The décor here avoids the Turkish sweetshop approach and is refreshingly sober, with prints and lithographs of European capitals on otherwise sparse cream walls. The grill's at the back, making for a more relaxing atmosphere. Staff are unfailingly discreet, efficient and congenial. Though the wine list isn't a strong point (it includes Liebfraumilch, Piat d'Or and Mateus Rosé), we went native and enjoyed a very drinkable white Cankaya (£7.50). Meze were good, particularly the houmous, although portions were a little small. Both our main courses – a lavish plate of lightly smoked mackerel, and a lean, lightly spiced dish of grilled lamb with yoghurt and pide bread (yoghurtlu beyti) – were a success. We devoured a delectable milk pudding with cinnamon and an equally moreish vanilla-flavoured rice pudding, both of which were presented on unappealing M&S-style foil trays. At just under £30 for two, excluding service, Mangal is extremely good value. The restaurant has a strong local following, judging by the beaming couples and families walking in throughout the evening.
Babies and children welcome; high chairs. Booking advisable. Takeaway service.
For branches see index.

Newington Green N16

Sariyer Balik Lokantasi ★ ★
56 Green Lanes, N16 (020 7275 7681). Bus 141, 341. **Meals served** 5-11.30pm daily. **Main courses** £6.50-£10. **Unlicensed. Corkage** no charge. **No credit cards.**
At Sariyer Balik Lokantasi you'll find some of the most intimate and delightful Turkish cooking in London. Recently taken over by the Cubuk family (mum and dad cook, while the three kids wait on tables), it's a little gem of a place festooned with a serendipitous mix of fishing nets, shells and rocks. The emphasis is on fish. There's a glass-cased cabinet by the tiny, bustling kitchen at the back, full of delicious-looking meze, many of which hail from the sea. Starters (all £3 or under) included octopus with sweet peppers, spiced prawns, and tomato with aubergine. All were wonderfully seasoned and positively singing with flavour. For mains we chose sea bream on the advice of the owner's son (he'd bought the fish himself that morning). The bream, when it arrived, was flawless and very fresh. It also came with a salady accompaniment. No desserts were to be had, but, after settling the bill (admirably low) we were lured into the restaurant's dim, dusky basement where an eccentric band of Turkish musicians quickly transported us to the pavilions and palaces of Istanbul.
Babies and children welcome. Booking advisable. Entertainment: Turkish musicians, from 9pm Fri, Sat. Takeaway service.

North

Finchley N3

Izgara ★ ★
11 Hendon Lane, N3 (020 8371 8282). Finchley Central tube. **Meals served** noon-midnight daily. **Main courses** £6.95-£11. **Set meal** £14.95 three courses. **Credit** JCB, MC, V.
This basic canteen serves some of the best Turkish food in London. It's a no-frills diner/takeaway that attracts a loyal local crowd. Meze all cost under £3. We were bowled over by the zip and zing of cracked wheat kisir, served with warm, delectable pide bread. Stuffed vine leaves were bland and over-chilled, but this was the only blip of the evening. From the range of main courses under £10, we were particularly impressed by the patlican salata, a rich, smoky-tasting mix of diced aubergines, peppers and tomatoes. Grilled kebab and salad was also well-judged. We drank a youthful, slightly spicy Turkish red by the glass from a short wine list, which includes a stylish Argentinian Malbec for £10.95. Desserts, from a choice of six, were also a treat. We demolished the cinnamony milk pudding; the rich, nutty sobiyet was a resounding success, too. Potent, grainy coffee rounded off the meal. Service was impeccable.
Babies and children admitted; high chairs. Disabled: toilet. No-smoking tables.

Harringay N4

Erenler ★
64 Grand Parade, Green Lanes, N4 (020 8802 3263). Harringay rail/29, 141, 341 bus. **Meals served** noon-1am daily. **Main courses** £5.50-£8. **Credit** MC, V.
It's worth tracking down this above-average Turkish eatery on the bustling section of Green Lanes known as Grand Parade. At first glance it seems nothing special, with its skewered raw meat on display in the window, its charcoal grill throwing out tiny sparks, and its warm orangey-pink walls adorned with kilims. There's a fine selection of meze, kebabs and casseroles on the menu, while the wine list contains the inevitable quartet of Turkish labels (Buzbag, Villa Doluca, Cankaya and Yakut), plus a short list of western European wines displayed by region, without vintage or producer. Instead we ordered a marvellously sour, yoghurty ayran. From a mouthwatering list of 27 starters, light, flaky, cigar-shaped börek, with its savoury cheese filling, and crisp, toasty mücver (vegetable balls) were impressive. We also loved the chewy, seeded pide bread. Next, we ordered patlican kebab from the grill and were a little let down by the meat's blandness. The kebab came with a miserly portion of rice and a fiery duo of chilli and onion rings. A better choice was the meat with spicy sauce, which was tender and packed with flavour. We also enjoyed the strong, grainy, Turkish coffee. Service came from a courteous and accommodating waitress.
Babies and children welcome; high chairs. Book weekends. Takeaway service.

Highbury N5

Iznik
19 Highbury Park, N5 (020 7354 5697). Highbury & Islington tube/rail/19 bus. **Meals served** 10am-3.30pm Mon-Fri; 9am-3.30pm Sat, Sun. **Dinner served** 6.30-11pm daily. **Main courses** £7.50-£9.50. **Service** 10%. **Credit** MC, £TC, V.
You could be forgiven for mistaking Iznik for a Turkish bazaar or souk. The place positively heaves with mirrors, tiles and antique pottery, and there are so many lamps hanging from the ceiling, you wonder how staff manage to cross the room without incident. Customers are similarly exotic; our fellow guests on a Sunday included a boho Islington couple in chunky jumpers, and two girl-punks with fluorescent, dreadlocked hair. Each dish is clearly defined on the menu – fortunately, as the charming waitress has shaky English. We settled for an excellent kisir, falafel and patlican salata, from the list of 19 starters. Main courses lacked the vivacity of the meze, but marinated lamb Beykoz kebabi, and aubergine- and chicken-based tavuklu karniyarik were both well-executed. Desserts are uncommonly imaginative; many are fruit-based. We enjoyed 'bramble mousse' and poached pears with pistachios and dark chocolate sauce. Turkish beer and wine is available, but we sipped salep, a hot, milky drink flavoured with nutmeg and cinnamon. We were regaled throughout with a blend of Enya, Edith Piaf and Ella Fitzgerald. Prices are very fair, helping make Iznik a lovely place to while away an afternoon or evening.
Babies and children admitted. Booking advisable. Takeaway service.

Islington N1

Angel Mangal
139 Upper Street, N1 (020 7359 7777). Angel tube. **Meals served** noon-midnight daily. **Main courses** £6-£11. **Set meals** £4 mixed meze, £8.50 mixed kebabs; £22.50 set meal (minimum two). **Credit** MC, V.
A kebab shop may not be the biggest crowd-puller these days, but then again Angel Mangal Ocakbasi isn't your average kebab shop. OK, décor is sparse (just a few perfunctory Turkish touches, and photobooth-style lighting), and kebabs are the mainstay, but these are beautiful chunks of meat cooked to order over a charcoal grill. Main courses are huge, so you'd do well to share a starter. Karisik meze (mixed hors d'oeuvres) included a wonderfully garlicky but not overpowering houmous, and a light and fluffy tarama. Yet on another occasion, we were disappointed by an aubergine starter that was swamped with yoghurt. Mains of pilic sis (breast of chicken seasoned and grilled on skewers) and a cop sis (marinated cubes of lamb grilled on skewers) were perfectly cooked and came with mounds of fresh salad and charcoal-grilled peppers and wedges of tomato. Overcooking isn't unknown, though, as we discovered from a rather dry quail. Desserts include baklava that oozes syrup and firin sütlac (rice pudding). Atmosphere

Menu

Meze dishes

Arnavut cigeri: thinly sliced or cubed liver, fried then baked in an oven.
Börek or boregi: savoury pastries, small, flat, fried or baked. These filo-pastry parcels are filled with cheese, spinach, meat, or a mixture of cheese and egg. The most common are muska or peynirli böreks (cheese). Sigara börek are roll-shaped.
Cacik (pronounced 'ja-jik'): diced cucumber with garlic in yoghurt.
Dolma: stuffed vegetables.
Hellim: Cypriot halloumi cheese, grilled.
Houmous: a creamy paste made from chickpeas, crushed sesame seeds, oil, garlic and lemon.
Fava: a broad-bean paste, similar to houmous.
Imam bayildi: aubergine stuffed with onions, tomatoes and garlic in olive oil.
Kisir: a mixture of chopped parsley, tomatoes, onions, crushed wheat, olive oil and lemon juice. Sometimes other ingredients are used, such as green peppers.
Köy ekmegi: literally 'village bread', paper-thin bread.
Lahmacun: a 'pizza' of minced lamb on pide (qv).
Manca: spinach and yoghurt with garlic.
Midye tava: mussels in batter dressed in a garlic sauce.
Mücver: courgette and feta fritters.
Patlican salad (pronounced 'pat-luh-jan'): a purée of aubergines (patlican) with garlic and olive oil; eaten with bread.
Pide: pitta bread.
Pilaki: beans in olive oil.
Piyaz: white bean salad with onions.
Sucuk: a spicy sausage from the east of Turkey.
Tabouleh: a salad of bulgur, parsley, mint, tomato and onion, dressed with olive oil and lemon.
Tarama: cod's roe paste.
Tarator: a bread, garlic and walnut mixture; **haruç tarator** comes with carrot; another variation is **ispanak tarator** (with spinach).
Yaprak dolmasi: stuffed vine leaves.

Main courses

Beyin salata: sheep's brain salad.
Çöp shish: little sticks of lamb kebab.
Güveç: a stew of meat (or fish) and vegetables, usually cooked in individual dishes.
Halep: a sauce of butter, onion, chilli and tomato.
Hünkar begendi: cubes of lamb braised with onions and tomatoes, served on an aubergine and cheese purée.
Incik: knuckle of lamb, slow-roasted in its own juices, with rosemary (very similar to the Greek dish kleftiko).
Iskembe: finely chopped tripe in a soup; also served as a starter.
Kebabs: Turkish restaurants serve several varieties. **Adana** (named after the Turkish town): spicy minced lamb. **Döner**: slices of marinated lamb packed tightly with pieces of fat on to a vertical rotisserie. **Iskender**: a combination of döner with tomato sauce, yoghurt and melted butter on bread. **Köfte**: minced lamb or beef mixed with spices, eggs and onions, and barbecued. **Shaslik**: lamb, rolled and skewered. **Shish**: cubes of marinated meat grilled on a skewer, often with tomatoes, onions and sweet peppers. **Yoghurtlu**: minced lamb on a bed of bread and yoghurt. Kebabs are served either in pide bread or accompanied by rice.
Mitite köfte: chilli meatballs.

Desserts

Armut tatlisi: baked pears (can be anglicised by smothering in cream and chocolate sauce).
Asure or **Noah's pudding**: a traditional dish served on holy days, comprising chickpeas and bulgur alongside dried fruits in a compote flavoured with rosewater.
Baklava: filo pastry interleaved with pistachio nuts, almonds or walnuts, and covered in syrup. A little goes a long way.
Kadayif: cake made from shredded pastry dough, filled with syrup and nuts, or sometimes cream.
Kazandibi: milk pudding with very finely chopped chicken breast (sounds vile, but is delicious).
Keskül: a milk pudding with almonds and coconut, topped with pistachios.
Revani: semolina cake.
Sütlac: rice pudding.

Drink

Ayran: a refreshing yoghurt drink.
Raki: a strong, aniseed-flavoured spirit, very similar to Pernod and ouzo.

here isn't always a forte – on a Friday night a buzz was decidedly lacking – but staff are good-natured and fast on their feet.
Babies and children admitted; high chairs. Disabled: toilet. No-smoking tables. Takeaway service. **Map 16/1O**.

Gallipoli
102 Upper Street, N1 (020 7359 0630). Angel tube/Highbury & Islington tube/rail. **Meals served** 10am-11.30pm Mon-Thur, Sun; 10am-midnight Fri, Sat. **Main courses** £5.95-£9.95. **Credit** MC, V.
The bijou branch of Gallipoli on Upper Street is probably one of the few restaurants in London where you won't regret being beguiled off the street by a waiter luring you inside. The restaurant (same menu as its other branch) attracts an older, quieter crowd than its larger, more boisterous sibling. At lunchtime on a Saturday, most tables were occupied by families, couples and Islington shoppers. In summer you can sit outside, but you'll find more atmosphere in the restaurant's charming, colourful Turkish interior. The meze are all bursting with taste and texture; we particularly enjoyed kisir and falafel. Mains – grilled king prawns and chicken kebabs – were full of flavour and generously portioned. Both came with rice and mounds of shredded, undressed salad and were greatly aided by Gallipoli's wonderfully piquant, chilli-fired sauce. Baklava were compact and nicely nutty, and the wickedly creamy apricots sprinkled with pistachios went down a treat. We drank a light, crisp Turkish Cankaya throughout. Service was a rare blend of friendliness and professionalism.
Babies and children welcome; high chairs. Book weekends. Tables outdoors (4, pavement). Takeaway service. **Map 16/1O**.

Gallipoli II
120 Upper Street, N1 (020 7359 1578). Angel tube. **Lunch served** 11am-6pm, **dinner served** 6-11pm, daily. **Main courses** £5.95-£9.95. **Set meal** £13.50 three courses incl coffee. **Credit** JCB, MC, V.
The newer, larger branch of Gallipoli is full to bursting every night of the week. It's popular with the dumb-haircuts, snowboarding and trainers crowd, but don't let that put you off. The food's delicious, the furnishings are delightful (in a baubly, rustic sort of way), and staff are friendly and amenable. Spatially it's a challenge – the tiny wooden tables are crammed so tight, it's almost impossible not to knock over your wine bottle, or your neighbour's, but amazingly our evening passed without mishap. The acoustics could be better, too: it's not the best place in London to have a conversation. But these are minor gripes with a well-run establishment that merits every ounce of its success. A riotously colourful meze arrived on one large plate and was stunningly fresh, tangy and well-textured. We especially liked the extra zip provided by the walnuts and hazelnuts. Main portions are lavish. Lamb incik was meltingly tender; a lighter option of marinated chicken was lemony and delicious. Both benefited by the oomph provided by an excellent chilli and tomato sauce. A dessert of apricots filled with cream was worth the calories, as was the rich, but not over-sweet baklava.
Babies and children admitted; high chairs. Tables outdoors (12, pavement). Takeaway service. Vegetarian menu. **Map 16/1O**).

Lezzet Lokanta
330 Essex Road, N1 (020 7226 7418/020 7354 1162). Essex Road rail/38, 56, 73, 341 bus. **Meals served** noon-12.30am Mon-Thur, Sun; noon-1.30am Fri, Sat. **Main courses** £5.50-£9. **Set meal** £14.50 four courses. **Cover** 50p. **Credit** MC, £TC, V.
Lezzet Lokanta, on a lacklustre stretch of the Essex Road, has a curiously dated appearance. Walls are salmon pink, there are tropical fish in a tank and the seating is of the button-backed banquette variety. Yet this Turkish local is the stuff of dreams. The restaurant was almost full on a Sunday evening. A mission statement menu tells diners that all dishes are made in-house, including pitta bread and desserts. Everything we ate was sublime. Meze, all of which cost under £3, were marvellously fresh, vibrant and authentic. We particularly enjoyed broad bean purée and filo pastry with soft cheese. Main courses were all nicely judged and well-presented. You can't go wrong with lamb here; the lamb with beans was superbly tender and tasty. Chicken was of a high standard, too, and came with a rich sauce. We had no room for desserts, but enjoyed the complimentary slices of watermelon. Service was faultless, and admirably unrapacious. When we requested water the waiter said 'tap?'
Babies and children welcome; high chairs. Book weekends. No-smoking tables. Separate room for parties, seats 15. Takeaway service.

Izgara.
See page 171.

Pasha
301 Upper Street, N1 (020 7226 1454). Angel tube. **Lunch served** noon-3pm Mon-Fri. **Dinner served** 6-11.30pm Mon-Thur; 6pm-midnight Fri. **Meals served** noon-midnight Sat; noon-11pm Sun. **Main courses** £6.95-£12.95 incl £1 cover. **Set meals** £10.95, £17.95. **Credit** AmEx, MC, V.
With its androgynous, black-suited Islingtonian clientele, Pasha is a smarter, slicker type of establishment than your average Turkish diner. The décor is more Modern European than Turkish, with few concessions to the motherland other than the odd sconce and picture. All our starters, selected from an entertainingly explanatory menu, hit the spot. Courgette fritters or mücver were crisp and moreish, if a little underseasoned; the aubergine classic, imam bayildi, was herby and deliciously caramelised. A main course of chicken wrapped in foil was overseasoned, but was otherwise delectable – it came in a rich tomato sauce, with peppers and mushrooms. Incik kleftiko lamb was meltingly succulent, but its accompanying vegetables were dull and uninspired. We enjoyed the tomato, red onion and thyme salad, though. Dessert took a long time to arrive, but the creamy rosewater rice pudding paired with a delectable Essencia Orange Muscat was a resounding success. Our scented fresh mint tea was replenished free of charge, yet service was otherwise brusque, offhand and very noisy: there was endless thumping and clattering of plates. With a little work on the front of house, though, Pasha would be one of the best Turkish restaurants in town.
Babies and children admitted. Booking advisable. Tables outdoors (3, pavement). Vegetarian menu. **Map 16/1O**.

Sedir
4 Theberton Street, N1 (020 7226 5489). Angel tube. **Meals served** noon-midnight daily. **Main courses** £4.95-£7.95. **Credit** AmEx, MC, V.
If you judged Sedir (formerly Sarcan) by its exterior, you'd probably never step inside. Yes, this place could do with a makeover, but the food is good all the same. The white ground-floor room was buzzing on a Saturday night, but we were directed to a room upstairs: a rustic, brown, poorly lit affair. There's a wide choice of hot and cold meze on a laminated orange menu. Börek was outstanding, kisir delectable and we were equally keen on the mücver. Only the vine leaves were overly oily and sweet, but consolation was easily found in the excellent pide bread. Other than the usual kebabs, there's a choice of fish (served with chips and salad), but we opted for lamb with fried aubergine, which was tender, succulent and of excellent quality. The wine list was unexpectedly cosmopolitan and included a Châteauneuf-du-Pape (no producer or vintage specified) at £15.95. We opted for a warm, fruity Argentinian malbec. The pear dessert came with vanilla ice-cream and a tart sauce – delicious. Service was good, too. Let's hope some effort is made to improve the surroundings, so the food can really shine. The lack of individual lights on tables (just a hideous central light) gave the room a gloomy aspect, which no amount of fine cooking could dispel. However, given that its name changed just before we went to press, it could be that improvements are in store.
Babies and children welcome; high chairs. Book weekends. Tables outdoors (4, pavement). Takeaway service. Vegetarian menu. **Map 16/1O**.

North West

Temple Fortune NW11

Baran
748 Finchley Road, NW11 (020 8458 0515). Golders Green tube. **Meals served** noon-midnight daily. **Main courses** £5-£8.50. **Set meals** £11 two courses, £12.50 three courses, incl coffee. **Credit** MC, V.
Sweaty men in white turn kebabs on an open grill as you walk into Baran. The split-level restaurant reminded us of a Tyrolean hut with its beams and rustic touches, but on closer inspection the emphasis is firmly Turkish. Colourful kilims are draped over the walls and there's the full whack of Turkish memorabilia to behold. The meze were all of a high standard. Börek came wrapped in a superlative, feather-light pastry. Kisir was also excellent, the only disappointment being the thin pitta bread accompaniment. The kebabs were top-notch in terms of flavour, but we couldn't get excited about the rabbit-food salad accompaniment. Presentation is attractive and service efficient. We finished – mightily impressed by the value and quality of the food – with baklava, sprinkled with pistachios.
Babies and children welcome. Takeaway service.

Vegetarian

Central

Barbican EC1

Carnevale
135 Whitecross Street, EC1 (020 7250 3452/www.carnevalerestaurant.co.uk). Barbican tube/Old Street tube/rail/55 bus. **Open** 10am-10.30pm Mon-Fri; 5.30-10.30pm Sat. **Lunch served** noon-3pm Mon-Fri. **Dinner served** 5.30-10.30pm Mon-Sat. **Main courses** £7-£8.50. **Minimum** £5.50 noon-2.30pm Mon-Fri. **Set meal** (noon-3pm, 5.30-7pm) £10.50 three courses. **Credit** LV, £TC.
Though last year saw a decline in standards at this former *Time Out* award-winner, this time around we were pleased to find that things were back on track. It's a tiny, simply decorated place with a charming courtyard at the back (note the magical unisex loo with pearly baubles and tiled mosaic sink) and a little deli counter at the front. The menu is short and prices are fair. A generous bowl of olives marinated in lemon and chilli was a nice appetiser: better still with a bottle of house red (Mundo Tempranillo 1998, from Spain). Imaginative, beautifully presented dishes included a starter of celeriac sushi on a bed of noodles, pak choy and pickled vegetables, flavoured with cardamom and a black bean sauce. Main course artichoke and Gorgonzola brioche pie, with red wine and mushroom sauce, was also a success, likewise the unusual but likeable combination of butternut squash spring rolls and a Thai-style green pea and coconut laksa with chilli, galangal and plentiful coriander. The pleasant surprises of coffee beans in the pavlova pudding, and half hazelnuts in the own-made chocolate mousse, were further proof that attention to detail and high standards have returned to Carnevale.
Babies and children welcome. Booking advisable. Tables outdoors (3, conservatory). Takeaway service. Vegan dishes. **Map 4/4P.**

The Quiet Revolution ★
49 Old Street, EC1 (020 7253 5556/www.quietrevolution.co.uk). Old Street tube/rail/55 bus. **Meals served** 8am-5pm Mon-Fri, 10am-2pm Sat, Sun. **Main courses** £3.95-£5.95. **Credit** MC, V.
It's not quite 100% vegetarian (there's usually a couple of fish and meat dishes), but the delicious food at this trendy minimalist café is 100% organic. Soup, arguably the forte (the QR range retails in organic delis across town), offers the best value for money: a bowl with two slices of bread costs £3.95; a mug with one slice of bread is £2.95. Other enticing options include salads like red rice with dill, feta, roast onion and beetroot; or a very peanutty noodle salad, served with wild rocket and alfalfa sprouts. Even the sandwich fillings are inspiring – Finn cheese (an English creamy cows-milk cheese) with tomato and black olive tapenade in own-made ciabatta, for example. To drink, there's an assortment of suitably fresh juices. It's all very flavourful but we couldn't help wondering whether the £1 eat-in surcharge was really worth it. The interior is bright and breezy (and there's abundant wheatgrass growing in the window) – but the staff were so slow and forgetful it took the edge off our enjoyment.
Babies and children welcome. No smoking. Tables outdoors (courtyard). Takeaway service. Vegan dishes. **Map 4/4P.**

City EC2

The Place Below
St Mary-le-Bow, Cheapside, EC2 (020 7329 0789). St Paul's tube/Bank tube/DLR. **Lunch served** 11.30am-2.30pm Mon-Fri. **Main courses** £5.80-£7. **Unlicensed. Corkage** no charge. **Credit** LV, MC, £TC, V.
Hordes of wholefood-happy City workers queue at this canteen-style café in the crypt of St Mary-le-Bow church. The menu changes daily and usually incorporates a soup, a hot dish, a quiche, a dairy-free salad (such as Chinese marinated vegetables) and a cheese salad. We enjoyed a crispy-cased quiche with a new potato, spring onion and Gruyère filling, and a ploughman's featuring Neal's Yard cheese and a fruity apple and currant chutney. The food was delicious, but we were frustrated by the consistently poor service. About half of the staff spoke so little English they didn't understand 'salad dressing', 'Stilton cheese' or 'no, we haven't finished yet' (we were still in full gastronomic flow when our plates were whipped away). This kind of *Fawlty Towers* service makes the £7-a-salad price tag seem steep. Nevertheless, the venue is a lovely cool and columned place with bare brick walls and a cavernous feel.
Babies and children welcome. Bookings not accepted. No smoking. Separate room for parties, seats 40. Tables outdoors (24, churchyard). Takeaway service. Vegan dishes. **Map 4/6P**.

Covent Garden WC2

Food for Thought ★
31 Neal Street, WC2 (020 7836 9072/0239). Covent Garden tube. **Breakfast served** 9.30-11.30am Mon-Sat. **Lunch served** noon-5pm daily. **Dinner served** 5-8.30pm Mon-Sat. **Main courses** £3.50-£5.30. **Minimum** £2.50 noon-3pm, 6-7.30pm. **Unlicensed. Corkage** no charge. **Credit** LV, £TC.
This intimate wholefoodie Covent Garden fixture is invariably super-busy at mealtimes – the answer, it seems, is to squeeze closer to the person sitting next to you. Small portions of well-loved classics such as vegetable stir-fry with rice, Mexican bake, or tofu and shiitake mushroom stew are served in earthenware plates and bowls, from behind a counter, by (generally) charming staff. We preferred a delicious fresh pea and rocket soup, served with oregano and onion bread, to a colourful, varied mixed salad incorporating pasta shells, french beans, mangetout, radiccio, rice, roasted peppers and beansprouts that was a little bland, for all its ingredients. The main eating area is in the basement; the takeaway counter is on the even more cramped ground floor.
Babies and children welcome. Bookings not accepted. Catering service. No smoking. Takeaway service. Vegan dishes. **Map 14/6L.**

Neal's Yard Bakery & Tearoom ★
6 Neal's Yard, WC2 (020 7836 5199). Covent Garden or Leicester Square tube. **Meals served** 10.30am-4.30pm Mon-Sat. **Main courses** £4.55-£6.55. **Minimum** £1.50 noon-2pm Mon-Fri; 10.30am-4.30pm Sat. **Unlicensed. Corkage** no charge. **Credit** LV.
Faded wooden fixtures and an assuredly alternative vibe tell you that this café was a forerunner to most others in the leafy retreat that is Neal's Yard. True to the Bakery's name, food is of the bready variety, with the famous Neal's Yard Bakery loaves, and the likes of quiches, sandwiches and bean burgers sold from the canteen-style counter downstairs. If you can, take the time to eat in the upstairs café with its hefty wooden tables and brightly coloured walls. It's a peaceful place and a lovely spot in which to sit alone with the company of a book and one of a range of herbal teas and ersatz coffees. A meal for two cost only £6.90 – pretty good value for the centre of town.
Babies and children welcome. Bookings not accepted. No smoking. Takeaway service (10.30am-5pm). Vegan dishes. **Map 14/6L.**

Neal's Yard Salad Bar ★
2 Neal's Yard, WC2 (020 7836 3233). Covent Garden tube. **Meals served** *summer* 11.30am-8pm Mon-Sat; 11.30am-6pm Sun; *winter* 11.30am-6pm Mon-Sat. **Main courses** £5.50-£6.50. **Minimum** £5. **Service** 10%. **Credit** LV, £TC.
When you have such excellent vegetarian choices as the **Neal's Yard Bakery** and **Food for Thought** so close, there is little reason to visit the Neal's Yard Salad Bar. For a start, it's expensive: lunch for two, consisting of three small dishes and two drinks, came to £20.90, compared to £6.90 at the Bakery. And the food doesn't live up to the price tag. From the so-called salad bar (where there is precious little variety to warrant the title), a small mixed salad was just a mish-mash of rice, vegetables and potato. There are more breads, cakes and puddings on the menu than anything else, but the Brazilian cheese bread that we tried was garishly yellow and too fluffy, while rice bread was overly salty. A very small plate of noodle stir-fry simply wasn't worth £5.50, while cauliflower and basil soup was just plain bland. Not a treat, in fact a disappointment in such a lovely corner of London.
Babies and children admitted. Tables outdoors (4, courtyard). Takeaway service. Vegan dishes. **Map 14/6L.**

World Food Café
Neal's Yard Dining Room, First floor, 14 Neal's Yard, WC2 (020 7379 0298). Covent Garden or Leicester Square tube. **Meals served** 11.30am-3.45pm Mon-Fri; noon-5pm Sat. **Main courses** £4.85-£7.85. **Minimum** £5 noon-2pm Mon-Fri; noon-5pm Sat. **Unlicensed. Corkage** 95p. **Credit** MC, V.
World Food Café continues to be a reliable source for fresh, adventurous and wholesome dishes. The interior is bright and clean, with seating either around the food-preparation area or at large tables overlooking the tree-shaded Neal's Yard. The menu is split into light meals and large meals, but both sides draw their influences from across the globe. Diners with small appetites could choose from Egyptian falafel, Mexican flour tortilla or Greek salad, while big eaters can tuck into the heartier options. We took great pleasure in demolishing a plate of west African stew, enjoying its flavoursome combination of banana, sweet potato and nut sauce, all served on a bed of steamed brown rice. Middle Eastern meze was a medley of surprises: plenty of fresh coriander, a wonderful mint and carrot salad, roasted aubergines, cabbage and tomato, houmous, tabouleh… Fruit lassi (usually banana- or mango-flavoured), served in ice-cold metal cylindrical glasses, is an essential accompaniment to all dishes.
Babies and children welcome; high chairs. Bookings not accepted. No smoking. Vegan dishes. **Map 14/6L.**

The Quiet Revolution

Fitzrovia W1

Cranks ★
9-11 Tottenham Street, W1 (020 7631 3912). Goodge Street tube. **Meals served** 9am-7pm Mon-Sat. **Main courses** £2-£4. **Credit** LV.
Long gone are the days when Cranks was an alternative health-conscious pit stop selling simple, wholesome food. Its current guise sits somewhere between that of Pret a Manger and McDonald's (without the meat of course). Like Pret, there are some interesting choices but, unlike Pret (and more like McDonald's), there is little evidence that what's on offer is particularly healthy. On our visit, the staff were unable to identify the contents of a salad box, let alone tell us if it was GM-free – God help any allergy-sufferers – and high prices seemed similarly out of touch (a tiny portion of sweet chilli stir-fry cost a disproportionate £3.55). A good plan, whether you eat-in or not, is to go for the takeaway boxed range (for instance, a mix of brown rice, beansprouts, lentils, tofu, basil and coriander), which is both cheaper (£2.95) and tastier. Smoothies are of a decent consistency, but any hint of fresh fruit is overpowered by sugar. Once beyond the canteen-style counter, the seating area is light and reasonably spacious, but discerning vegetarians will be dining elsewhere.
Babies and children welcome; high chairs. Bookings not accepted. No smoking. Tables outdoors (2, pavement). Takeaway service. Vegan dishes. **Map 2/5J.**
For branches see index.

Marylebone W1

Raw Deal
65 York Street, W1 (020 7262 4841). Baker Street or Edgware Road tube/16 bus. **Open** 8am-10pm, **breakfast served** 8am-noon, **meals served** noon-10pm, Mon-Sat. **Main courses** £5.50-£6.50. **Minimum** (lunch, after 6pm) £2. **Set lunch** £9.50 three courses incl coffee. **Credit** LV, £TC.
Looking newly painted and perky, this little Marylebone eatery was doing a roaring trade when we last visited. It was packed full of excitable women (local workers and a casual brand of lunching ladies, dressed in tracksuits), cooing across plates piled high with salads. Salads are a popular choice here, and very good – choose from Greek, carrot, egg and pea or

noodle varieties, to name a few. They're affordable too, with a large plate of eight salads costing £6 and a small plate of four at £3.50. There's also a choice of soups (gazpacho and mushroom, on our most recent visit) and two hot dishes. We ordered half a plate of filo with spinach, broad beans, red lentils and cottage cheese, plus two salads. What arrived, though, was a mushy, eggy mess, that, despite a fine amount of spinach, turned out to be rather dull and stodgy. The moral of the story is: stick to the salads or, if you have a sweet tooth, try one of the alluring cakes.
Babies and children admitted. No smoking. Tables outdoors (3, pavement). Takeaway service. Vegan dishes. **Map 2/5F.**

Soho W1

Beatroot ★

92 Berwick Street, W1 (020 7437 8591). Oxford Circus or Tottenham Court Road tube. **Meals served** 9am-6.30pm Mon-Sat. **Set meals** £2.50 small, £3.50 medium, £4.50 large. **Unlicensed. No credit cards.**
With the hubbub of Berwick Street market on its doorstep, this little haven is comparatively quiet. The paint job is bright (a mix of green, red and orange), the music is of the hippy skippy variety, and the staff make Cheech and Chong look like members of the wide-awake club. Cough loudly and you'll be served, if you smile they'll think you're just being friendly. The food, a fresh and appetising mix of hot dishes and salads, is served in classic New York takeaway cartons (choose between small, medium and large). We had a spicy tofu and vegetable stir-fry with rice and a selection of salads – grated carrot with pumpkin seeds, Greek salad with plenty of ripe tomatoes, and baby spinach. Another dish of cottage pie came with similarly diverse salad support. A medium carton is ample for one but, convenient as it is for takeaways, the packaging can be awkward if you're eating-in, especially as seats are in short supply. Take away a slice of cake as a memento when you re-engage Soho.
Babies and children admitted. No smoking. Tables outdoors (2, pavement). Takeaway service. **Map 13/6J.**

Mildred's

58 Greek Street, W1 (020 7494 1634). Leicester Square or Tottenham Court Road tube. **Meals served** noon-11pm Mon-Sat; noon-5pm Sun. **Main courses** £4-£7.50. **Credit** LV, TC.
A Soho institution, Mildred's is always busy, so arrive early to get a table. Jolly coloured formica furniture and a floral-motif bar give the place a 1950s feel. Staff are friendly and, though our waiter was new and not yet accustomed to the menu, efficient. Our meals may have lacked innovation but they were generously proportioned, tasty and wholesome. White bean falafel served with chilli sauce in a cone-shaped tortilla was a lighter option than the burger of the day (also white bean), which was a large, disappointingly tepid vegetarian patty in a wholemeal bun. Both dishes were satisfying, though, and the superb, crispy fries with the burger were a bonus. The drinks menu includes organic wines and, among the juices (of which there were surprisingly few) was a lurid green 'energiser' of soya, apple and orange juice and blue-green algae. There's a good showing of vegan dishes, marked on the menu with a V. If you don't fancy the peak-time crush, get a takeaway; the burger, or the choice of two hot dishes, costs £3.70.
Babies and children welcome. Bookings not accepted. No smoking. Tables outdoors (2, pavement). Takeaway service. Vegan dishes. **Map 13/6K.**

West

Hammersmith W6

The Gate ★

51 Queen Caroline Street, W6 (020 8748 6932). Hammersmith tube. **Lunch served** noon-3pm Mon-Fri. **Dinner served** 6-10.45pm Mon-Sat. **Main courses** £7.25-£9.75. **Credit** AmEx, MC, TC, V.
Stepping into the courtyard at the Gate, away from the chaos of Hammersmith roundabout, is like stumbling across a secret garden. The restaurant is situated in a former artist's studio, with a huge wall-to-ceiling window that, on a summer evening, bathes the room in warm sunlight. There's a disarmingly casual feel to the place, despite the starched white tablecloths and the stylish aproned staff. The clientele is a mix of boho artistic types and suits; service is attentive and friendly from the outset. We ordered a generous bowl of succulent marinated olives, bread and fruity olive oil before tucking into a series of stunning and well-flavoured dishes. Starters of Thai pancake, and sweetcorn fritters with a chilli jam were inventive and packed with fresh ingredients. A delicate, comforting pastry filled with baby vegetables came next. A second main course – stew of okra, spinach and tomato – was perked up by a zingy coriander and mint salad, and feta and couscous fritters. Only chocolate and star anise mousse was a letdown: too heavy and rich, with the bitter taste of powdered chocolate. On the whole, though, this level of fine vegetarian dining probably justifies the high prices.
Babies and children welcome; high chairs. Booking essential. Tables outdoors (10, courtyard). Takeaway service. Vegan dishes.

Shepherd's Bush W12

Blah Blah Blah

78 Goldhawk Road, W12 (020 8746 1337). Goldhawk Road tube/94 bus. **Lunch served** 12.30-2.30pm, **dinner served** 7-11pm Mon-Sat. **Main courses** £7.85-£8.95. **Unlicensed. Corkage** £1.25 per person. **No credit cards.**
Blah Blah Blah's rather neutral exterior melds well with the nondescript surroundings of Goldhawk Road. The venetian blinds conceal an equally unfussy interior of muted colours and sparse decoration that amounts to some handsome wreaths and mammoth stage spotlights looming above the rows of candlelit tables. The buzz here comes from the diners and, of course, the hum of creative activity emanating from the open-plan kitchen. Dishes are beautifully presented; they are also unfaltering in their tastiness and successful use of ingredients. Tomato and mozzarella torte, for example, was pungently flavoured with oregano, and had perfect flaky pastry. Another elegant starter of halloumi and superior salad leaves was accompanied by bruschetta and soft roasted peppers. A towering main course of meaty mushroom galette, in an equally rich sauce, had a powerful carnivore-pacifying effect, while pancakes wrapped like spring rolls around al dente asparagus and aubergine were a lighter kind of treat. Definitely up there with London's best places for vegetarian cooking.
Babies and children welcome. Booking advisable; essential weekends. Separate room for parties, seats 30. Vegan dishes.
For branch see index.

South

Brixton SW2

Bah Humbug

The Crypt, St Matthew's Church, Brixton Hill, SW2 (020 7738 3184/ www.bahhumbug.co.uk). Brixton tube/rail. **Brunch served** 11am-5pm Sat, Sun. **Dinner served** 5-11pm Mon-Thur; 5-11.30pm Fri, Sat. **Main courses** £7.50-£12.90. **Service** 10%. **Credit** MC, V.
In the cavernous basement of St Matthew's Church, Bah Humbug occupies a third of the über-hip complex of night-time indulgence that also includes the Bug Bar (next door) and Mass (above). At first glance, the restaurant seems rather grand: beyond the baroque entrance is a low-ceilinged, vaulted room with heavy wooden furniture, sumptuous red velvet seating, flowers and gold trimmings. But look more closely and you'll find paper napkins, canteen cutlery and, if you're really unlucky, a sticky table. The menu talks a good game, with well-phrased dishes (about 50/50 vegetarian/fish) but, cutting through the rhetoric, we found the bare essentials sadly lacking. Thyme tartlet and a nut and vegetable Wellington en croûte suffered either from soggy or chewy pastry, while an excellent chilli-hot fresh lime-leaf salad was let down by a cakey, cloying blini. A great crêpe would have provided some welcome relief, had it not been for its bland wild mushroom filling. Hardly a mecca for foodies, then, but Bah Humbug nevertheless remains a popular hangout for a lively twenty- to thirty-something crowd who come mainly for the atmosphere and for a bit of filling grub to accompany the drink and chat.
Babies and children admitted. Booking essential. Disabled: toilet. Tables outdoors (20, churchyard). Vegan dishes. **Map 18.**

Clapham SW4

Café on the Common ★

2 Rookery Road, SW4 (020 7498 0770). Clapham Common tube/35, 37, 88, 155, 345, 355 bus. **Meals served** 10am-6pm daily. **Main courses** £4-£4.50. **Unlicensed. Corkage** £1 per bottle. **No credit cards.**
Normally a festival atmosphere presides over this colourful ramshackle café, but we last visited on Glastonbury weekend, when the usual swarm of crust-encased traveller types had long-since fled to a muddy field. An altogether different breed of Cla'ham resident had temporarily replaced them. For best results, come here in warmer weather, as most seating is outside and – once you've got to grips with the fact your food is being cooked in a converted toilet – there's plenty of fresh air to sharpen the appetite. The superb vegetarian breakfast will set you up for the day with a large plate of own-made veggie sausage, baked beans, mushrooms, crispy potatoes and fried eggs, with a choice of tea or coffee. It's good value, too, at just £4.50, as is the doorstep veggie sausage sandwich for £2.60. The short menu also includes veggie burger, enchiladas and smaller dishes such as potato skins, soup and sandwiches, plus some great-looking cakes. Not the festival of the year, perhaps, but it's where the die-hards reside when on a break.
Babies and children welcome; high chairs. No smoking. Tables outdoors (15, courtyard; 4, patio). Takeaway service. Vegan dishes.

Vauxhall SW8

Bonnington Centre Café ★

11 Vauxhall Grove, SW8 (no phone). Vauxhall tube/rail. **Dinner served** 6.30-11pm daily. **Main courses** £4.50. **Unlicensed. Corkage** no charge. **No credit cards.**
This small café in quiet, leafy Bonnington Square used to have more of a community feel, with the majority of diners on first-name terms with staff. Not any more. The area is changing (much of what used to be squatted property is now housing association or privately owned) and the place was packed with a more affluent, middle-class crowd when we visited. The atmosphere is still very convivial, though, with punters chewing the cud, smoking and generally enjoying the laidback vibe, wholesome food and BYO alcohol policy. Two things haven't changed: the low prices (starters and desserts £2, mains £4.50); and the variable quality of the grub (still dependent on which night you visit and who's cooking). Our Monday night visit was a bit of a letdown, with a bland spinach and ricotta flan and falafels that were burnt on the outside and undercooked within. Despite patchy food, the place is more popular than ever (with resultingly slow service) and remains a great place for a relaxed and cheap dining experience.
Babies and children welcome. Vegan dishes. **Map7/12L.**

South East

Crystal Palace SE19

Domali

38 Westow Street, SE19 (020 8768 0096). Gypsy Hill rail/2, 3, 63, 322 bus. **Meals served** 9.30am-6pm Mon, Tue; 9.30am-11pm Wed-Sun. **Main courses** £4.70-£7.90. **Service** 10% for parties of six or more. **Credit** MC, V.
A fresh and funky establishment run by a sparky troupe of women, Domali has a light and comfortable feel, with bright walls and well-spaced tables. Vegetarian breakfast (served all day until 6pm) is popular: the menu lists endless variations, from a full brekkie or eggs benedict (weekends only) to a list of 'favourites' including scrambled egg with smoked salmon, and 'BCM' (baked beans, Marmite and cheese on toast). The full breakfast wasn't the best we've sampled (a burnt vegetarian sausage had a just-out-of-the-packet taste, and the scrambled egg was sloppy), but we liked the doorstep of bread drizzled with olive oil. Dinner specials feature the likes of vegetarian pasta carbonara, or bruschetta with char-grilled salmon and vegetables for fish-eaters. Prices are reasonable. There's also a long drinks list of wines, beers and spirits. Domali may not be worth a trip across London, but locals could do a lot worse.
Babies and children welcome; high chair. Book dinner Fri, Sat; bookings not accepted during day. Entertainment: DJs Wed, Sun. No-smoking tables. Tables outdoors (6, garden). Takeaway service. Vegan dishes.

Neal's Yard Bakery & Tearoom. *See page 173.*

Deptford SE8

Heather's
74 McMillan Street, SE8 (020 8691 6665/ www.heathers.dircon.co.uk). Deptford rail/47, 188, 199 bus. **Lunch served** 12.30-3.30pm Sun. **Dinner served** 7-10.30pm Tue-Sat; 6.30-9.30pm Sun. **Set buffet** £13. **Credit** AmEx, DC, MC, £TC, V.
Evening visitors will experience an almost dreamlike transition between the mean streets of Deptford and the warm candlelit glow of this innovative restaurant. It seems hard to believe that Heather's was once a pub; it now more closely resembles a large community centre or perhaps a venue for a wedding reception, with its eat-all-you-can buffet colonised by jolly, sociable hordes. The buffet allows you to mix and match some interesting home-style cooking. Certain things, like carrot and dill sauce, horseradish mash and various chutneys, were excellent, while other dishes weren't as memorable. Try to resist the temptation to overload your plate the first time round, as variety is the key here and it's worth saving room to try a bit of everything. Dessert was the high point of our visit, with a choice of pecan and orange flan, strawberry cake and an unprecedented oat, orange and chocolate slice that was moist and breathtakingly delicious. There's also a long list of organic wines, beer and ciders.
Babies and children welcome; high chairs; nappy changing facilities. Book weekends. Disabled: toilet. Entertainment: jazz 8pm first Tue of month. No smoking. Tables outdoors (8, garden; 10, roof terrace). Takeaway service. Vegan dishes.

West Norwood SE27

Hollyhocks ★
10 Knights Hill, SE27 (020 8766 8796). West Norwood rail. **Meals served** 6-10pm Wed, Thur; 11am-10pm Fri, Sat; 11am-5pm Sun. **Main courses** £4.30-£7.30 lunch; £7-£7.80 dinner. **Unlicensed. Corkage** 80p per person. **Credit** AmEx, MC, V.
The residents of West Norwood are lucky to have this fabulous little local. Think suburban tea shop with a New Age twist, set in an old tailor's shop with original glass panelling. Mismatched tea cups hang from the ceiling, freshly baked cakes are displayed against a wall, and the wonderful sound of Ella Fitzgerald soothes the senses. The daytime menu offers a mix of light meals such as pâté of the day, olive and tomato crostini, and vegetarian breakfast options (including American pancakes with butter and maple syrup). The evening menu is more ample, taking influences from across the globe. Rice paper pancakes filled with crunchy vegetables and served with a tasty plum sauce made a delicious, light starter; and no complaints could be made about an artichoke, red pepper and feta salad. A lovely medley of fresh food (tabouleh, vine leaves, own-made houmous, olives and spicy chickpeas) formed the Turkish meze. We were also impressed by mock duck with noodles and greens. What's more, staff are charming. An enjoyable experience.
Babies and children welcome; high chair; toys. Booking advisable. No smoking. Takeaway service. Vegan dishes.

East

Bethnal Green E2

The Gallery Café ★
21 Old Ford Road, E2 (020 8983 3624). Bethnal Green tube/8 bus. **Meals served** 10.30am-5pm Mon, Wed-Sat; noon-5pm Tue. **Main courses** £2.10-£3.80. **Unlicensed. Credit** MC, V.
While it's nothing special, this east London staple provides affordable, wholesome food. Set in the basement of a converted period building, The Gallery Café is run by men from the nearby Buddhist centre; women from the centre run Wild Cherry (241-245 Globe Road, E2/020 8980 6678 – it reopened at the beginning of September 2000). The best thing we sampled was a hearty but delicately spiced lentil soup. Pasta (Provençal with salad), on the other hand, was soggy and covered in grated Cheddar, as was a tortilla wrap with Mexican beans and salsa. A number of meze dishes were popular with other customers, but the aubergine we tried was over-chilled and had a fridgy taste. Visit on a sunny day when the light pouring in from the garden adds to the relaxed feel, or you can sit at tables on the patio area at the front.
Babies and children welcome; high chairs. No smoking indoors. Tables outdoors (10, garden). Takeaway service. Vegan dishes.

North

Camden Town & Chalk Farm NW3

Manna
4 Erskine Road, NW3 (020 7722 8028/www.manna-veg.com). Chalk Farm tube/31, 168 bus. **Brunch served** 12.30-3pm Sat, Sun. **Dinner served** 6.30-11pm daily. **Main courses** £8.25-£11.50. **Service** 12½% for parties of six or more. **Credit** MC, £TC, V.
Manna's calm, warm interior harks back to the Primrose Hill of old, when you didn't need a small fortune to call it home. It's almost like a smart yoga centre – cream walls, shiny pine, luscious plants – and staff are appropriately laidback (we had to ask to see the menu). Judging by the turn-out on the Saturday night of our visit, diners don't have to dress for dinner either. The modish fusion menu offers adventurous organic dishes, a huge choice for vegans and (almost) faultless execution. We enjoyed little fried balls of yam, served with a slightly spicy fresh tomato and parsley salsa, then paprika and peppercorn-stained baked ricotta on a bed of roasted onion and focaccia. Indonesian broccoli and tofu coconut curry was adequately spicy, but the 'chef salad' (choice of feta or tofu among a batch of fresh ingredients) lacked zing. For dessert, passion fruit cream and hazelnut roulade was strictly for cream-lovers. Despite us ordering before 7.30pm to benefit from a special offer of two courses for £11.50, staff failed to bill us accordingly, which rather took the shine off the excellent cooking.
Babies and children welcome; high chairs. Booking essential Thur-Sat. No smoking. Tables outdoors (2, pavement). Takeaway service. Vegan dishes.

Crouch End N8

Fiction
60 Crouch End Hill, N8 (020 8340 3403). Finsbury Park tube/rail then W7 bus. **Lunch served** 12.30-4.30pm Sun. **Dinner served** 6.30-11pm Wed-Sun. **Main courses** £8.50-£9.65 (dinner). **Service** 10%. **Credit** MC, V.
Sunday lunchtime isn't the best time to visit Fiction. Not only is the menu limited, but on our trip, there was only one waitress and so service was very slow. One benefit, however, is enjoying the bright daylight from the wall-to-wall windows at the front, or the lush green garden at the back. There's a choice of three starters (including soup of the day) and three mains. One of the main courses – roasted seeds, alfalfa and sprouted legume salad – was delicious, but would have worked best as an accompaniment, not the main contender. The most ample dish was roast butternut squash. A small mound of gnocchi with sun-dried tomato pesto was padded out considerably with salad leaves and didn't leave us satisfied. Prices are very reasonable, though (starters, £3.95; mains £5.95), and the food tasted fine. Next year we'll go in the evening, when the ample drinks list is complemented by a more extensive menu.
Babies and children welcome; high chairs. Booking advisable. Disabled: toilet. No-smoking tables. Separate room for parties, seats 12. Tables outdoors (8, garden).

Islington N1

St Paul's Steiner Café ★
1 St Paul's Road, N1 (020 7226 4454). Highbury & Islington tube/rail/Essex Road rail. **Open** 10am-4pm Tue-Sat. **Main courses** £1-£4.95. **Unlicensed. No credit cards.**
The café and gift shop occupies the front knave of the former St Paul's Church, a handsome Grade II listed gothic pile designed by Sir Charles Barry, of Palace of Westminster fame. There's a false ceiling with nifty modern lighting, but a cage at the back shows the work in progress converting the rest of the church into a school. All proceeds from the café and shop go towards the school project. The (all-organic) menu stretches from simple snacks such as roast vegetables on ciabatta to specials including pasta with olives and vegetables and lentil and vegetable bake. The enthusiasm put into the cooking is obvious and the earthy flavours aren't something you find in mass-produced food. The follow-up of apple and rhubarb crumble was a chunky pile of cooked fresh fruit, underneath a delicious topping of oats and sunflower seeds, and accompanied by a dollop of cold custard. Perfect.
Babies and children welcome.

Vietnamese

Central

Chinatown W1

Cam Phat
12 Macclesfield Street, W1 (020 7437 5598). Leicester Square tube. **Meals served** noon-1am daily. **Main courses** £3.90-£16. **Set meals** £8 three courses, £12 four courses, per person (minimum two). **Credit** AmEx, DC, JCB, MC, £TC, V.
With its plastic flowers, fake marble-chip walls and faux-gold gilded spiral staircase, you might be forgiven for thinking Cam Phat was the lobby of a business hotel rather than an oriental restaurant. The food didn't seem too sure of itself, either. An extensive menu features mostly Chinese food, but there are also a sprinkling of Vietnamese dishes, including frogs' legs. The starters – an alarmingly yellow Vietnamese pancake, and crispy chicken salad – were gratifying enough, but the main courses were mostly disappointing. Stir-fried chicken with lemongrass and green peppers was swamped by a heavy, glutinous sauce. Sweet and sour fish was similarly overwhelmed by its sauce, which drowned out all but the chilli seasoning. A dry, undistinguished vermicelli dish did little to improve things. Staff were polite and helpful, but the background Eurobeat and stream of tourist customers did little to dispel the impression that Soho, not Saigon, is the main influence here.
Babies and children admitted. Takeaway service. **Map 13/6K.**

Fitzrovia W1

Bam-Bou
1 Percy Street, W1 (020 7323 9130). Goodge Street or Tottenham Court Road tube.
Bar **Open** noon-1am Mon-Sat.
Restaurant **Lunch served** noon-3pm Mon-Sat. **Dinner served** 6-11.30pm Mon-Fri; 6pm-midnight Sat. **Main courses** £8.20-£11.90. **Set meals** £12.50 two courses (lunch, 6-7pm); £35 four courses (for parties of eight or more). **Credit** AmEx, DC, JCB, MC, TC, V.
Forget paddy fields and straw hats: Bam-Bou's version of Vietnam is full-on chi-chi colonial glamour. Launched in 1999, the restaurant is the brainchild of entrepreneur/restaurateur Mogens Tholstrup. His trademarks are on full display: a beautiful venue (four storeys of an elegant Georgian townhouse, with the two upper floors given over to the Lotus Room bars), beautiful decorations (antique chests and paintings) and beautiful people to match (enough strappy sandals and backless tops to fill *Vogue* twice over). The restaurant prides itself on serving traditional Vietnamese food with a modern twist, but we found the dishes pleasant though mostly uninspiring. Best are the starters: chicken brochette comes with a rich, nutty lemongrass and peanut sauce. The selection of salads – including a beetroot and basil mix, and tangy, sour green mango – was also refreshing and flavourful. Main courses disappointed by comparison: both the baked bream and the sesame lamb were slightly too dry; the sauté of beef was bland, and the accompanying stir-fried ginger noodles were clumpy. Luckily, desserts saved the day: melt-in-the-mouth mango millefeuille; delectable bitter chocolate and ginger mousse; and smooth, rich banana and coconut pudding. Not a bad dining experience, but more Hollywood than Hanoi.
Babies and children admitted (restaurant). Booking advisable. Separate rooms for parties, seating 14 and 50. Tables outdoors (3, patio). **Map 3/5K.**

Soho W1

Saigon
45 Frith Street, W1 (020 7437 7109). Leicester Square tube. **Meals served** noon-11.30pm Mon-Sat. **Main courses** £4.35-£7.35. **Set meals** £15.75 per person (minimum two) two courses, £19.35 per person (minimum two) three courses. **Service** 10%. **Credit** AmEx, DC, MC, V.
Picture-postcard Vietnam in the heart of Soho: serene waitresses in traditional ao gais (long shirts slit down the sides over baggy trousers) glide between the bamboo pillars, while candles, Vietnamese artefacts and music create an Eastern oasis of calm. The food is similarly restrained yet extremely flavourful. We began with light and crisp spring rolls (cha nem), a zesty green papaya salad, and chewy squid balls (eaten wrapped in fresh mint, coriander and lettuce leaves). A bottle of Tiger beer provided the lubrication. Spiced crab (dae huong cua) followed, steeped in garlic, lemongrass and herbs. It was tasty – once we'd managed to penetrate the shell (this is not a dish to order if you're in a hurry). Chicken hotpot, simmered in the pot with ginger and fish sauce, was a lovely, spicy, piquant dish that offset a bland vegetable pot. Divine desserts in the form of mango sorbet and banana fritters rounded off the meal. Although not as authentic as some East End Vietnamese restaurants, Saigon makes for a delightful evening out.
Babies and children admitted. Book dinner. Separate room for parties, seats 45.
Map 13/6K.

South West

Earlsfield SW18

Saigon Thuy ★
189 Garratt Lane, SW18 (020 8871 9464). Earlsfield or Wandsworth Town rail. **Dinner served** 6-10pm Mon-Thur; 6-11pm Fri, Sat. **Main courses** £4.50-£6.80. **Credit** MC, V.
Unless you live in the area, it's a bit of a trek to reach Saigon Thuy – but don't let that put you off. Simply but effectively decorated, with a palm tree, trailing ivy and a wooden lattice ceiling, the restaurant has a relaxing, homely atmosphere. A beaming waiter made us welcome, and took pains to explain the menu in detail. We began with an array of starters: an amazingly piquant crab salad (goi cua), papaya chicken salad with coriander and mint, gossamer-light crystal spring rolls (goi cuon bo), and a vegetarian spring roll served with a sweet and sour dip (cha gio chay). Flavours were fantastically fresh, each ingredient distinct yet combined to create a delicious whole. The main course continued the treat. We opted for a Vietnamese-style fondue (£24 for two, although there was easily enough for three). Two soups, one a rich buttery vegetarian broth, the other a spicy, meat stock were cooked at the table on a small burner. Noodles, prawns, scallops, chicken, vegetables and dumplings were then added and, after a few minutes, scooped out with a tiny fish-net spoon. The result – utterly fresh flavours and a healthy feast. Beautiful presentation and excellent service added to the charms of this south London gem.
Babies and children welcome; high chairs. Book dinner Fri, Sat. Takeaway service.

South Kensington SW3

Red River
1 Bray Place, SW3 (020 7584 0765). Sloane Square tube. **Lunch served** noon-2.30pm, **dinner served** 7-10.45pm daily. **Main courses** £8.50-£17.50. **Set lunch** £12.50 two courses. **Credit** AmEx, DC, JCB, MC, V.
Varying amounts of thought go into developing restaurant concepts but one basic premise should surely be that cuisines that have taken centuries to fine-tune *in situ* do not need to be meddled with. Red River encouragingly claims to cook 'authentic food from the region' (ie Vietnam) and the interior is equally enticing, with its lush colours and bright fabrics, Celadon plates and bamboo sprouting from cute table vases. The food isn't like you'll find in Hanoi, but it's as close as you'll get in the heart of Chelsea. First came the uniquely Vietnamese starter goi cuon, brittle rice paper wrapped around various fillings (in this case, prawn and vermicelli). Warm beef and garlic salad with watercress was not very typical – the beef was nicely cooked but thickly sliced in the European manner – and was slathered in mustardy dressing. Green mango salad was excellent, though, and spicy oxtail stew with coconut, carrots and bamboo shoots was superb. Finally, duck and noodle soup was full flavoured, with firm noodles, but it was so packed with ingredients that the broth was much thicker than in most Vietnamese soups. Red River is a likeable place, and we thought the dishes varied from okay to quite good; they just weren't very Vietnamese.
Babies and children admitted. Tables outdoors, 3 patio. Vegetarian menu. **Map 12/11F.**

Red River

East

Shoreditch E2

Hanoi Café ★ ★
98 Kingsland Road, E2 (020 7729 5610). Bus 26, 48, 55, 149, 242, 243. **Lunch served** 12.30-3pm, **dinner served** 6-11.30pm Mon-Fri. **Meals served** 3-11.30pm Sat, Sun. **Main courses** £2.30-£6.50. **Credit** MC, V.
This new establishment at the Shoreditch end of Hoxton has the feel of a clean, bright, upmarket café. The IKEA-style wooden seating, smattering of oriental prints and gentle Vietnamese music in the background contribute to a down-to-earth atmosphere. On our trip, the spacious dining area soon filled up with local Vietnamese. Polite and informative staff guided us through the menu. After downing a couple of zesty Ginseng lagers, we began the meal with a bland and spongy prawn mousse on sugar cane (cha tom mia), and slightly overdone grilled beef in piper leaves. The main courses proved more rewarding: tangy, succulent spicy duck in orange sauce (vit kho dua); a meaty and flavourful grilled fish in lemongrass (ca nuong sa ot); delicious, garlicky steamed-fried asparagus (mang tay sao tol); plus a moreish rice and peanut dish. Hanoi Café deserves to go from strength to strength.
Babies and children welcome. Booking advisable. **Map 17/3R.**

Loong Kee ★ ★
134G Kingsland Road, E2 (020 7729 8344). Bus 26, 48, 55, 67, 149, 242. **Meals served** noon-11pm Mon, Wed-Sun, 5-11pm Tue. **Main courses** £3.50-£6. **Unlicensed. Corkage** no charge. **Mineral water** £1 small bottle. **No credit cards.**
With its front door constantly open to the street, canteen-style seating and gingham oilcloth table coverings, Loong Kee has a no-nonsense approach that clearly goes down well with locals. On the Sunday afternoon of our visit, the place was bustling with Vietnamese families attracted by the homemade-style food and the informality. Our Vietnamese companion rates the pho here as London's best, so we ordered pho bo tai (steamed rice noodle soup with beef). It had been cooked in the northern Vietnamese manner (which is usually plainer than southern styles), and was delicately aromatic and delicious. The banh coun (rather gooey steamed spring rolls filled with pork), take a bit of getting used to, but the tom ot (chilli king prawns), served in their shells and dripping with ginger and garlic, were definite winners. The star of the evening, however, was the fresh and succulent ca chien (fried talapia fish), served with a rich concoction of chillies, ginger, spring onions and garlic. The genial atmosphere was enhanced by our lovely waitress, who gently pointed us in the right direction with the menu. It's the simplicity of the dishes and the superb, fresh flavours that put this unassuming café leagues ahead of more elaborate establishments.
Babies and children welcome. Takeaway service. **Map 17/3R.**

Viet Hoa ★
70-72 Kingsland Road, E2 (020 7729 8293). Bus 26, 48, 55, 67, 149, 242. **Lunch served** noon-3.30pm, **dinner served** 5.30-11pm daily. **Main courses** £4.15-£6.70. **Minimum** £3.50. **Credit** MC, V.
Combats and trainers share space with ties and pashminas at this popular East End venue. Originally a Vietnamese community canteen, Viet Hoa still manages to keep its prices low, while the quality of the food is consistently high. Upstairs, the check tablecloths and long tables give the place more of a café ambience. Downstairs is smarter. Both areas were packed on the weekday evening we visited, and the waiters (in bow ties and waistcoats) were a little aloof. We started with crispy spring rolls and salad, feather-light summer rolls, and rather chewy deep-fried mixed prawns and squid. Equally impressive main courses followed: fragrant beef pho, and drunken fish cooked to a perfect crispy finish. Although the steamed vegetables were nothing special, a punchy vermicelli dish with chicken (bun xa) rounded off an enjoyable meal. A good value, classy café.
Babies and children welcome; high chair. Booking advisable dinner. Takeaway service.
Map 17/3R.

North East

Dalston N1

Huong-Viet ★
An Viet House, 12-14 Englefield Road, N1 (020 7249 0877). Bus 67, 149, 236, 242, 243, 243A. **Lunch served** noon-3.30pm Mon-Fri; noon-4pm Sat. **Dinner served** 5.30-11.30pm Mon-Sat. **Main courses** £4.10-£6.80. **Unlicensed. Corkage** no charge. **Credit** JCB, MC, V.
Located in a characterful 19th-century building, An Viet House was started in 1986 as a support centre for Hackney's burgeoning Vietnamese community. Its restaurant, Huong Viet, has a good reputation. Recently, the whole place has been given a face-lift. Its newly painted red and white interior, white tablecloths and napkins and fresh flowers make an inviting and attractive space. At weekends, the place fills up quickly: it's difficult to get a table without a reservation (though these are treated in a somewhat cavalier fashion) and tables are very close together, so for a hassle-free experience, come early in the week. Spring rolls covered in wafer-thin pastry and packed with crisp herbs got our meal off to a good start, along with light spicy, fresh fried squid. The huge Saigon-style pancake was bursting with vegetables, and came with lettuce, mint and coriander leaves. We also tried fried pomfret; it was a little too sweet, but nevertheless made a delicious main course alongside crispy, garlicky greens. The meal was accompanied by glasses of sweet lemon squash, made on the premises. Friendly staff and a lively atmosphere contributed to a pleasant evening, but it's the freshness and individual flavours of the food that are the stars here.
Babies and children welcome; high chairs; toys. Book weekends. Takeaway service. Vegetarian menu.

Hackney E8

Green Papaya ★ ★
191 Mare Street, E8 (020 8985 5486). Bethnal Green tube/rail/D6, 253, 277 bus. **Open** 11am-midnight Mon-Sat, 11am-11.30pm Sun. **Main courses** £4.50-£6.95. **Credit** MC, V.
Green Papaya's quiet and spacious back garden, at night lit only by paraffin lamps and the moon, is the perfect place for an alfresco summer meal. For chillier evenings, the inside is similarly inviting; pine seating, pale yellow walls and mellow lighting infuse the space with a warm glow. The bar area, kitted out with potted plants and bamboo armchairs, contributes to the relaxing ambience. The menu, which includes a separate vegetarian selection, is a combination of dishes from North and South Vietnam and features some interesting offerings. The banana flower salad (bap chuoi nom) was moist, spicy and refreshing. More impressive was the exquisitely fluffy Vietnamese pancake (banh xeo), which elicited a plethora of contented 'oohs' and 'ahhs'. A huge bowl of fresh and flavourful noodle soup with fish cake (bun rieu ca) followed. Rice noodles with beef and ginger (bun bo xao) was similarly piquant and bursting with the tang of fresh herbs. Apart from the appetising food, our evening was enhanced by friendly staff who were positively brimming with good will.
Babies and children welcome; high chairs. Booking advisable weekends. No-smoking area. Tables outdoors, 30 garden. Vegetarian menu.

Hai-Ha ★
206 Mare Street, E8 (020 8985 5388). Hackney Central rail. **Lunch served** noon-3pm daily. **Dinner served** 5.30-11.30pm Mon-Fri, 5.30pm-midnight Sat, Sun. **Main courses** £3.80-£5.50. **Set meal** £7 two courses, £12 three courses. **Unlicensed. Corkage** no charge. **No credit cards.**
On a Saturday summer's evening this unassuming café was bursting with a loud, good-natured local crowd. Families were crammed around the narrow Formica-topped tables. Despite our booking, we were (a little cheekily) asked to move to make room for a larger group. We also missed out on the speciality ho fun noodle soup, which had run out by the time we arrived. However, the food we ordered, if not spectacular, definitely hit the spot. Smoked chicken fried in a sweet, delicious batter kicked off the meal, alongside spare ribs in a rich sauce, and crispy shredded lamb that came with a refreshing combination of lettuce leaves and plum sauce. Only the prawn satay was mediocre. Next, we couldn't resist a tongue-twister: bun thit de xao lan xa ot, a delicately flavoured dish of fried goat's meat with lemongrass, chilli, vermicelli and herbs. Grilled fish was crispy and

Hoa Phuong

packed with flavour. The only low point of the meal was the sliced duck with orange sauce: drowned in sauce, it had a charred, unpleasant-tasting skin. We drank beers bought from the shop next door; bringing your own drink is actively encouraged. Basic but good value, this is a cosy, lively local.
Babies and children admitted. Book weekends. Takeaway service.

Hoa Phuong ★
179 Mare Street, E8 (020 8533 6275). Bus D6, 106, 253, 277. **Open** noon-3pm, 5-11pm Mon-Thur, noon-11.30pm Fri-Sun. **Main courses** £3.25-£7.50. **Set meals** £9, £10.50 three courses. **No credit cards.**
With its rows of ducks hanging in the window, predominantly oriental customers, and distant strains of Vietnamese music wafting in the background, Hoa Phuong is one of the more atmospheric of the Vietnamese eateries in the area. As with the others, you can bring your own alcohol, though there is a wine list. Alternatively you could opt for a glass of the intensely sweet and creamy Vietnamese iced coffee with your meal. It's the contrast of distinct, delicate flavours that gives Vietnamese food its bite: zesty papaya and dried beef salad came combined with peanuts to add a warm, rich layer to the taste. Meat dishes, too, tend to be subtle rather than overwhelming; this was true of the fine-textured fried meat rolls with ravioli, and the lightly fried pork chops with rice and chillies. The litmus test of a Vietnamese restaurant is the pho, though. The Hoa Phuong special ho fun soup with beef passed with flying colours. A little more sophisticated than the neighbouring Vietnamese caffs, this is a worthy addition to the stable.
Babies and children welcome; high chairs. Entertainment: karaoke for groups. Separate room for parties, seats 30. Takeaway service. Vegetarian menu.

North

Highbury N5

Au Lac
82 Highbury Park, N5 (020 7704 9187). Arsenal tube. **Lunch served** noon-3pm Mon-Fri. **Dinner served** 5.30-11.30pm daily. **Main courses** £3-£8. **Set meals** £10-£16. **Credit** DC, JCB, MC, V.
It's surprising there are no plates flying at Au Lac, what with the North Vietnamese waiter and South Vietnamese manageress and their different

culinary backgrounds. In fact, the restaurant has succeeded in pooling together disparate dishes from all over Vietnam, as well as creating its own in-house specialities. The result is obviously a hit with the Highbury punters who packed the restaurant on a Saturday night. Decorated with a lovely tiled floor and a mural on one wall, the place is presided over by a pair of friendly-looking plastic Nha Trang Tourist lobsters tacked to the wall. The extensive menu comes with a handy introduction to the cuisine and to the story of the Au Lac dynasty, Vietnam's legendary first ruling family. There are seven set dinners, but we went à la carte, beginning with the mixed hors d'oeuvres consisting of crispy spring rolls, crunchy sesame triangles and spare ribs. There's also a wide choice of vegetarian dishes; stewed beancurd with tomato and coriander was incredibly fresh and piquant. Omnivores should try succulent lamb with lemongrass and onions. Only crispy pomfret fish was bland, although the fish sauce and ginger perked it up noticeably. Staff were extremely helpful, yet service was a little erratic. All in all, however, Au Lac provides a thoroughly enjoyable dining experience.
Babies and children welcome; high chairs. Book weekends. Separate room for parties (seats 50). Takeaway service. Vegetarian menu.

Islington N1

Nam Bistro
326 Upper Street, N1 (020 7354 0851). Angel tube. **Lunch served** noon-3pm, **dinner served** 6-11pm Tue-Sun. **Main courses** £3-£6.50. **Set meals** £12.50-£18 per person (minimum two). **Credit** AmEx, MC, V.
'User friendly' is the best way to describe the tiny Nam Bistro. Menus provide a sort of beginner's guide to Vietnamese food; recommended dishes are highlighted, and the list is divided into set meals, one-course meals (around £6), and à la carte. We opted for the main menu, beginning with spring rolls (goi coun) that were clad in delicate pastry and filled with refreshing fennel leaves, prawn or chicken, and vegetables. We also tried a spicy green salad with chicken (goi) and a rather soggy dish of deep-fried prawns (tom lan bot), made more palatable by a zesty lemon sauce. From the specials menu came tasty, but unspectacular, crispy duck pancakes. We also tried fried fish fillet with sweet-sour fish sauce (ca chien nuoc mam), but the dish might have been cooked at the local chippie, such was the amount of greasy batter that covered it. A more successful choice was the rich, nutty fried rice

noodles Vietnamese-style. With its bare, slightly down-at-heel interior, the restaurant has a perfunctory feel about it. Staff, although polite, were not particularly welcoming to us. The food's not bad, but Nam Bistro is probably best for a quick snack rather than a special meal.
Babies and children admitted. Book dinner. Separate room for parties, seats 24. Takeaway service. Map 16/2N.

Outer London

Walton-on-Thames, Surrey

Cuu Long ★
35 Bridge Street Walton-on-Thames, Surrey (01932 228579). Walton-on-Thames rail. **Open** 6.30-11.30pm Mon-Thur, Sun; 6pm-midnight Fri, Sat. **Main courses** £5-£8. **Set meals** £16, £17. **Service** 12%. **Credit** MC, V.
The Surrey countryside seems an unlikely place for an upmarket Vietnamese restaurant, but somehow Cuu Long seems to fit in well with the surrounding chic village boutiques and genteel country environs. This is a family-run restaurant, and despite the fancy napkins and sophisticated tableware, the atmosphere is relaxed, friendly and extremely welcoming. 'Elegant kitsch' best describes the furnishings, which include ornately-carved wooden seating, Vietnamese lacquer artwork and huge vases of flowers. The food certainly lives up to the refined surroundings. From the long list of starters, we chose lightly fried crispy spring rolls, smoothly textured Vietnamese steamed dumplings, and delectably sweet barbecued spare ribs with honey. For the main course we picked pancakes with crispy sole and lemongrass. The paper-thin pancakes were softened in hot water at the table, filled with fish and salad and then dipped into a tangy lemongrass sauce. The result was heavenly. Warm service and delicious food make Cuu Long a delightful alternative to the usual country pub.
Babies and children admitted. Entertainment: jugglers (Sun).

Eating on a Budget

Budget

If you aren't satisfied with a greasy burger or a sweaty hotdog – and who is? – eating in London on a tight budget can be a frustrating experience. All too often, apparently reasonable restaurants turn out to be big disappointments, plagued by limited menus, poor ingredients, and surly service. After scouring the capital, however, we've tracked down a number of prize venues offering decent food at bargain prices.

Central

Soho W1

Café Emm
17 Frith Street, W1 (020 7437 0723). Leicester Square, Piccadilly Circus or Tottenham Court Road tube. **Lunch served** noon-3pm Mon-Fri. **Dinner served** 5.30-10.30pm Mon-Thur; 5.30pm-12.30am Fri; 5pm-12.30am Sat; 5-10.30pm Sun. **Main courses** £5.50-£7.20. **Service** 10% for parties of six or more. **Credit** MC, £TC, V.
A simple, dark-wooden interior and low lighting combine to give Café Emm a cosy, intimate appearance that belies its lively, informal atmosphere. On a recent visit a predominantly young crowd's animated conversations gave this Soho favourite a buzz we'd not been expecting on a damp Tuesday evening. We plumped for a starter of deep-fried potato skins with sour cream, which seemed a touch expensive at £4.90 – until we saw the size of the portion, which was large enough for at least two to share. This proved a good indication of what to expect from the mains (divided into two menus priced £5.50 and £7.20) which come in gargantuan amounts. From the cheaper selection, spicy Cajun chicken, own-made salmon fish cakes, and superb half-pound burgers are worthy of special mention. From the pricier brasserie menu, blackened fillet of Cajun salmon was well worth the extra cash. Service was of a brisk, friendly nature, befitting the bustling feel of the place.
Babies and children welcome; high chairs. Table outdoors (1, pavement). **Map 13/6K.**

Centrale
16 Moor Street, W1 (020 7437 5513). Leicester Square or Tottenham Court Road tube. **Meals served** noon-9.30pm Mon-Sat. **Main courses** £3-£7. **Minimum** £3. **Service** 10%. **Unlicensed. Corkage** 50p. **Credit** LV, £TC.
Centrale likes to keep it very simple. It serves basic food in massive portions at rock-bottom prices – and in the heart of the West End, on a busy Friday night, there's every reason to be grateful. Rigatoni alfredo arrived with a heavy cream sauce spilling over the sides of the large white plate and proved a hearty, but bland meal. Risotto tonno was more sensibly proportioned, but was let down by some rather stodgy rice. The selection of starters was uninspiring, though the sheer size of the main courses renders such concerns superfluous. The largely inefficient service is successfully counterbalanced by the cheerful disposition of the staff. Tatty booths and an inviting ambience that's just the right side of seediness ensure Centrale's continued popularity with all walks of Soho life.
Babies and children admitted. Takeaway service. **Map 13/6K.**

Pierre Victoire ★
5 Dean Street, W1 (020 7287 4582). Leicester Square or Tottenham Court Road tube. **Meals served** noon-11pm Mon-Thur; noon-11.30pm Fri, Sat; noon-10.30pm Sun. **Main courses** £7-£13. **Set lunch** £5.90 two courses. **Set dinner** £7.90 two courses. **Credit** MC, V.
Anyone familiar with the now-defunct Pierre Victoire chain will recognise the distinctive style of this small Soho eatery, the last outpost of the once-extensive franchise. Dim-lighting, uncoordinated furniture, and candles propped up on wax-caked bottles create an intimate, relaxed atmosphere, while the menu offers a broad selection of traditional French cuisine. Victoire's two-course set menu is great value at £7.90, but choice is restricted and the portions are smaller than their à la carte equivalents. A starter of steamed mussels came in a cream sauce liberally flavoured with garlic and white wine, while main courses included supreme of chicken with mozzarella and Bayonne ham, and an intriguing Mediterranean vegetable cheesecake that was full of flavour but a little soggy. Desserts are excluded from the set menu, but tarte tatin and crème brûlée are recommended. If the haphazard tinklings of the pianist aren't accompaniment enough to a meal, an extensive and fairly priced wine list is also on hand.
Babies and children admitted. Tables outdoors (5, pavement). **Map 13/6K.**

Pollo
20 Old Compton Street, W1 (020 7734 5456). Leicester Square or Tottenham Court Road tube. **Meals served** noon-midnight daily. **Main courses** £3.90. **Credit** LV, £TC.
Entering Pollo, it's difficult to escape the notion that you've probably missed this celebrated caff's heyday by about 30 years. From the shady, decrepit booths to the muddy-brown mural of some Italian hillside on the wall, the interior reeks of the late 1960s. There's a distinct charm to the fading glamour, though, and the old place still embodies the quintessential Soho vibe. The food is variable, but stick to the basics and you won't go far wrong. Pasta and risotto came top of the class. Our choice (from a staggeringly huge selection), rigatoni amatriciana, wasn't exactly subtle, but spicy, palatable fare nonetheless. Risotto al funghi is also a good bet, enhanced by a fine consistency and plenty of chunky mushrooms. Sadly, most of the poultry dishes (including pollo supresa) are pedestrian, and you'd be well advised to steer clear of the soggy pizzas. Starters and desserts are cheap and cheerful. Drink beer, as the house wine tends to taste like vinegar. Gripes aside, Pollo is lively, friendly and perfect for a quick bite before a night out.
Babies and children admitted. Takeaway service. Vegetarian menu. **Map 13/6K.**

The Stockpot
18 Old Compton Street, W1 (020 7287 1066). Leicester Square tube. **Meals served** 11.30am-11.30pm Mon, Tue; 11.30am-11.45pm Wed-Sat; noon-11pm Sun. **Main courses** £2.95-£5.30. **Set meal** (11.30am-5.30pm) £3.80 two courses. **No credit cards.**
The cheapest of the cheap, the Stockpot – like Pollo next door – is something of a Soho institution. The interior is less remarkable than its neighbour's but is clean and comfortable. The tables near the open front are an ideal place at which to sit and watch Soho life drift by. Food is a bit hit-and-miss, but the pasta dishes (including spaghetti napolitana, and penne alfredo) are largely reliable. Omelettes served with chips and salad are another safe bet. The same cannot be said for the majority of the meat dishes, however. Pork chops were leathery and served with overcooked vegetables, while lamb cutlets were more bone than meat. Never mind: the fun, kids'-party-style puds, including jelly and ice-cream, cheered us up after the disappointing mains.
Babies and children welcome. Tables outdoors (2, pavement). Takeaway service. **Map 13/6K.**
For branches see index.

Trafalgar Square WC2

Café in the Crypt
Crypt of St Martin-in-the-Fields, Duncannon Street, WC2 (020 7839 4342/www. stmartinsinthefields.org). Embankment tube/Charing Cross tube/rail. **Lunch served** noon-3.15pm daily. **Dinner served** 5-7.30pm Mon-Wed; 8.30-10.30pm Thur-Sat. **Main courses** £3.75-£7. **Credit** £TC.
Situated in the dead-centre of town, underneath one of London's most famous churches, Café in the Crypt is an ideal meeting place, especially for those who aren't over-familiar with the capital. The café has to share the 18th-century crypt with the church's gift shop and brass rubbing centre, but thanks to the high vaulted ceilings and widely spaced tables, it never feels cramped. Service is obtained from a canteen-style counter that offers a selection of snacks, including pick-and-mix salads and soup, plus a variety of puddings. The main courses are renewed daily and on our last visit included a disappointing spicy vegetable casserole, which was overcooked and watery; and some roast mackerel that would have been delicious, had it not toughened up considerably under the heat lamps. Typical customers are weary looking tourists and chatty old ladies who seem to stick (perhaps wisely) to coffee and cakes.
Babies and children welcome; high chairs. No-smoking tables. Takeaway service. **Map 14/7L.**

Carlton Coffee House

West

Ladbroke Grove W10

Sausage & Mash Café
268 Portobello Road, W10 (020 8968 8898). Ladbroke Grove tube. **Meals served** 11am-10pm Tue-Sun. **Main courses** £2-£7. **Credit** MC, V.
Located in a dingy corner under the railway bridge on Portobello Road, the S&M Café has a somewhat claustrophobic setting that's compounded on Saturdays when hungry market crowds can make this trendy haunt uncomfortably busy. Turn up on a calmer weekday, however, and you'll find the subtly kitsch decor and relaxed, unpretentious atmosphere make this a perfect place in which to linger over good, old-fashioned comfort food. A splendid selection of sausages includes spicy Thai and Spanish, although you'd have a job to top the coarse, meaty Cumberlands. Vegetarians are also well catered for, with at least four types of meat-free sausages on the menu; the leek and blue cheese option appears to be a favourite. Two sausages with mash and gravy is plenty to satisfy most appetites, and good value at £5.75, although if you feel like showing off, you can order three for £7. Service can be slow, but the food compensates.
Babies and children welcome; high chairs; set children's meal £3.50. Takeaway service. **Map 11/5Az.**

South

Battersea SW11

Fish in a Tie ★
105 Falcon Road, SW11 (020 7924 1913). Clapham Junction rail. **Lunch served** noon-3pm, **dinner served** 6pm-midnight Mon-Sat. **Meals served** noon-11pm Sun. **Main courses** £4.95-£6.50. **Set meal** £5. **Credit** MC, £TC, V.
The name may sound like a suggestion as to the preferred mode of dress, but this excellent south London joint is in fact a very friendly, relaxed affair. A collection of nautical knick-knacks, including a string of fish-shaped lanterns, adorns the bare brick walls, while stripped floorboards and large wine racks give the interior a rustic, continental feel. Great-value fish dishes dominate the menu, but there's also plenty for vegetarians and meat-eaters. Several main courses – among them salmon stuffed with salmon mousse, duck in brandy sauce, and vegetarian filo pastry – cost just £4.95 each, but the daily specials are only marginally more expensive and often worth the extra. Grilled swordfish steak in pesto sauce was a great success, while chicken tricolore (stuffed with sun-dried tomatoes, mozzarella and basil) was tender and appetising. Starters included deep-fried Gouda, and parson's pastry (a crisp samosa filled with spiced, smoked chicken). The restaurant is hugely popular – it's best to book.
Babies and children welcome. Booking advisable. Separate room for parties, seats 40.

East

Docklands E14

Hubbub
269 Westferry Road, E14 (020 7515 5577). Mudchute DLR/D7 bus. **Meals served** 5-11pm Mon-Fri; 11am-11pm Sat, Sun. **Credit** MC, V.
Although the tranquil atmosphere of this east London establishment is in keeping with the building's previous incarnation as a church, it's somewhat at odds with the present name. No matter: this tatty stretch of Westferry Road could do with a few more calm retreats like Hubbub. The interior is attractive and the cooking equally so. A variety of modern art works decorates the walls, blending with the sturdy wooden furniture and some handsome original fixtures. The menu changes regularly and is chalked on a blackboard; a range of international dishes is offered. Linguine with roasted pepper, tomato and basil sauce was good value at £5.50, but we reckoned grilled snapper in lime and coriander crème fraîche (£7.90) was worth paying the extra. Lighter meals – including a delicious courgette and coriander soup, and a selection of inventive sandwiches – are available all day. Hubbub shares its premises with the local arts centre, so the well-stocked bar is usually populated with appropriately arty types.
Babies and children admitted. Disabled: lift, toilet. No-smoking tables. Tables outdoors (5, courtyard).

Shoreditch E2

Lennie's
6 Calvert Avenue, E2 (020 7739 3628). Bus 8, 48, 55, 242. **Meals served** 6.30am-4pm Mon-Fri. **Dinner served** 7.30-11pm Tue-Sat. **Main courses** £4.50-£8. **Unlicensed. Corkage** £1 for large parties. **No credit cards.**
With a plethora of tables stuffed into tiny premises, Lennie's lacks a bit of floor-space and is frequently cramped and stuffy. What it offers in abundance, however, is remarkably cheap, full-flavoured food – and that's what keeps the eager punters (from trendy Hoxtonites to scruffy builders) coming back. Daily specials are chalked on the blackboard above the small counter. On a recent visit, they included pasta with spinach and cream (passable, but overcooked), and generic chicken curry with basmati rice. The menu may not be outstanding, but at these prices complaining would be churlish, especially as each main course comes with a selection of salad and even vegetables. Decent fried breakfasts and jacket spuds are also served all day.
Babies and children admitted. Tables outdoors (3, pavement). Takeaway service. **Map 17/4R.**

North East

Hackney E8

Café Alba
183 Mare Street, E8 (020 8985 8349). Bethnal Green tube/rail/Hackney Central rail. **Meals served** 11am-11pm daily. **Main courses** £4.95-£7. **Unlicensed. Corkage** 50p per person. **Mineral water** 80p small bottle. **No credit cards.**
Wandering along a none too artful stretch of Hackney's Mare Street, we were drawn into Café

Alba by the spectacular Celtic design that fills the front window. Inside, though, the decor is pared down, with beige walls, mix-and-match furniture and contemporary parchment lampshades. The food adheres to the 'pile it high, sell it cheap' principle; each filling main course is served with new potatoes or mash, plus two vegetables. Indian-influenced dishes such as chickpea curry are on the menu, but more popular seem to be the 'continental' options, including minted lamb, and beef bourguignon. Tarragon chicken was a big hit, served in a creamy sauce with plenty of good chunks of tender meat. The vegetarian option, filo pastry filled with broccoli and Stilton was flavourful, albeit predictable. Café Alba doubles as a gallery space.
Babies and children welcome. Separate room for parties, seats 20. Takeaway service. Vegan dishes.

North

Archway N19

Paris-London Café

5 Junction Road, N19 (020 7561 0330). Archway tube. **Meals served** 9am-11pm Mon-Sat; 9am-10.30pm Sun. **Main courses** £5.95-£7. **Set meals** £5 (lunch) two courses, £9.95 three courses, £17.95 five courses. **No credit cards.**
Situated directly opposite Archway tube, the Paris-London Café boasts a convenient, though far from picturesque location. Inside, however, a lively mural depicting Parisian life runs the length of one wall and provides some welcome relief from the dreary urban north London surroundings. At lunchtime, a £5 two-course set menu offers good value (but limited choice), while the vast sandwich menu is what draws the takeaway customers. In the evening, the à la carte features a good selection of meat and fish dishes, but vegetarians have a rather slim choice: vegetable lasagne or goat's cheese and leek pastry. Sea bream came in a zesty sauce with Provençal herbs, but retained too many bones for our taste, while rich and tasty rabbit bourguignon was let down by limp vegetables. One of the more expensive of our budget restaurants, Paris-London scores highly on decor and atmosphere, but the jury's still out on the food.
Babies and children welcome. Booking advisable. Takeaway service.

Islington N1

Le Mercury

140A Upper Street, N1 (020 7354 4088). Angel tube/Highbury & Islington tube/rail/ 4, 19, 30, 43 bus. **Meals served** 11am-1am Mon-Sat; noon-11.30pm Sun. **Main courses** £5.85. **Set lunch** £5.95 three courses. **Credit** MC, V.
We weren't quite sure what to expect of Le Mercury. Its prestigious Upper Street address, and smart, intimate dining room suggest a pricey, upmarket establishment, and yet with all main courses costing just £5.85 and starters a mere £2.85, the food seems surprisingly cheap. So has quality been sacrificed in the name of economy? The starters were inconclusive; steamed mussels were a mite gritty and chewy, but the green salad with grilled goat's cheese proved to be a distinct improvement. Main courses impressed further, with the medallions of pork featuring tender meat and a peppery forestière sauce, and the fillet of mackerel nicely flavoured with Dijon mustard and white wine. Desserts included middling crème brûlée, and a slightly limp fruit salad, but our overall assessment was nevertheless a positive one. Situated within metres of the Almeida theatre (and not much further from the Screen on the Green), Le Mercury is perfect for a cost-controlled bite before the show.
Babies and children admitted. Booking advisable weekends. **Map 16.**

Holloway N7

Judy's

249 Holloway Road, N7 (no phone). Holloway Road tube/29, 43, 253, 271 bus. **Meals served** 11am-3pm, 5.30-9.30pm, Mon-Fri. **Main courses** £2-£5. **Unlicensed. No credit cards.**
Opposite an unsightly University of North London building on a busy stretch of Holloway Road, Judy's cannot lay claim to a very glamorous location. Nevertheless, keep your eyes away from the large window at the front of the restaurant and you'll find the interior quite pleasant. Dark tablecloths and two-tone beige and pink walls (plus the odd cactus and oriental print) provide clean, comfortable surroundings. The menu offers predominantly Chinese and Malaysian dishes at remarkably low prices. Fried chicken in satay sauce with rice and vegetables was sweet and spicy, although the meat lacked any real texture and the sauce was a little heavy. Noodles are a strong point, and prawn chow mein – subtly flavoured and loaded with prawns – was a particularly good choice. If you've had your fill of MSG, try something from the limited selection of 'continental' dishes, including steak and chips, and lamb chops. Reassuringly busy at lunchtimes, Judy's can feel a bit overcrowded in the evening as an endless stream of takeaway customers flows in and out.
Babies and children admitted. Takeaway service.

North West

Kilburn NW6

Small & Beautiful

351-353 Kilburn High Road, NW6 (020 7328 2637). Kilburn tube/Brondesbury rail/16, 32 bus. **Meals served** noon-midnight daily. **Main courses** £4.25-£5.95. **Set meal** (noon-7pm) £5.50 two courses. **Service** 10% for parties of seven or more. **Credit** AmEx, DC, MC, £TC, V.
We've never understood what brought on the name of this popular Kilburn restaurant. It's quite sizeable, and while the uncoordinated decor, with its baroque mirrors and cafeteria-style chairs, may have a certain charm, beautiful it is not. As for the food, small would be a highly inappropriate description; both starters – chicken wings in a honey marinade, and garlic 'Caesar' bread – could have easily fed two, and we were defeated in our main course by hefty portions of vegetables. Sadly, on our last visit, beautiful would be equally inaccurate. Pork schnitzel was tough and full of gristle, and we quickly tired of picking bones out of an overcooked salmon steak. Don't give up on Small & Beautiful completely, however; we've enjoyed a number of fine meals here in the past.
Babies and children welcome. Booking advisable. Takeaway service. Vegan dishes.

Daytime venues

The following places specialise in breakfast and lunch and are only open during the day.

Central

Clerkenwell & Farringdon EC1

Saints

1 Clerkenwell Road, EC1 (020 7490 4199/www.saintsphoto.co.uk). Barbican tube. **Open** 8am-6pm Mon-Fri. **Main courses** £4.75-£5.75. **Minimum** (noon-2pm) £4.75. **No credit cards.**
Located at the busy junction of Clerkenwell Road and Goswell Road, Saints has a well-ordered, dark-wooden interior that provides a welcome retreat from the din of traffic outside. The menu offers a number of old favourites, such as Cumberland sausage and mash, and impressive steak frites, but also encompasses more unusual dishes such as spicy Sri Lankan fish cakes with Thai dressed salad and mango chutney. Vegetarians are not forgotten; ratatouille and mozzarella pie benefited from firm vegetables and light puff pastry, while the delicately spiced cashew nut casserole was also a good bet. The daily specials are usually worth considering, too. And from the dessert menu, the bread and butter pudding is clearly the work of an expert. The friendly service and relaxed atmosphere also contributed to a highly enjoyable meal.
Babies and children welcome; high chairs. No-smoking tables. Takeaway service (cold food only). **Map 15/4O.**

Bloomsbury WC1

Goodfellas

50 Lamb's Conduit Street, WC1 (020 7405 7088). Holborn tube. **Main courses** £2.70-£4.25. **Open** 8am-7pm Mon-Fri; 10am-5pm Sat. **Main courses** £2.99-£4.25. **Unlicensed. No credit cards.**
Along with the usual selection of sandwiches and toasties, this bustling Bloomsbury café offers a good-value, hot buffet lunch. First decide upon a large (£4.25) or small (£3.50) plate, then pile it high with your choice of three main courses, vegetables and rice, and top it off with a trip to the salad bar. The menu changes daily and the quality of your meal depends largely on when you eat. Arrive much after 1pm and the choice of mains will be severely limited. All that remained when we last visited was a concoction of rolled-up slices of turkey breast in a cloying cheese sauce, topped with, of all things, glacé cherries. This disappointment was only partially made up for by the impressive cold rice and pasta salads. The dining room is in a comfortable pastel-coloured basement where some large Victorian bread ovens – survivors from Goodfella's previous life as a bakery – provide a striking centrepiece.
Babies and children admitted. Separate room for parties, seats 60. Tables outdoors (5, pavement). Takeaway service. **Map 3/5M.**

October Gallery Café

24 Old Gloucester Street, WC1 (020 7242 7367). Holborn tube. **Lunch served** 12.30-2.30pm Tue-Sat. **Main courses** £3.50-£5.50. **Unlicensed. Corkage** £1. **No credit cards.**
Located in a handsome Victorian school building, the October Gallery is a haven of tranquillity, a couple of minutes' walk from busy Southampton Row. Tables stand in the gallery space itself, so you may find yourself tempted to grab a coffee or a

Great caffs

The traditional greasy spoon might conjure up visions of a humid, grimy little cell serving chewy sausage, fatty bacon and limp fried eggs. It ain't necessarily so, though: London is awash with characterful caffs that will serve you a cracking fry-up, at a handsome price, with not a drip of grease in sight.

Alpino

8 Elizabeth Street, SW1 (020 7730 8400) Victoria tube/rail. **Open** 6am-4.30pm daily. **Main courses** £2-£5.95. **Unlicensed. No credit cards.**
Just opposite Victoria Coach Station, Alpino is never short of a customer or two. A steady flow of off-work coach drivers and hungry passengers passes through, so don't come here for a quiet bite. The atmosphere is lively and friendly, though, and the food a treat. A set breakfast of egg, bacon, sausage, beans, toast and tea costs a mere £3.70. The menu also offers a fine range of sarnies and some reasonable pasta dishes. Ideal for a swift, tasty snack. **Map 6/10H.**

Bern'e

470 Bethnal Green Road, E2 (020 7739 4407). Bethnal Green tube. **Meals served** 7am-4pm Mon-Fri; 8.30am-4pm Sat. **Main courses** £1.20-£3.10. **Unlicensed. No credit cards.**
Despite this caff's diminutive nature, the name painted in large letters in the front window makes Bern'e pretty easy to spot. Inside, there's just enough room for three tables. Much of the business comes from takeaway customers. If you're passing at a time when there's a table free, however, it's well worth sitting down to enjoy one of the great fry-ups. A top-notch set breakfast of egg, bacon, sausage, beans, toast and tea will set you back only £3.50. There's also a decent range of sandwiches and jacket spuds.

Borough Café

11 Park Street SE1 (020 7407 5048). London Bridge tube/rail. **Meals served** 4am-3pm Mon-Fri; 4am-1pm Sat. **Main courses** £2-£5. **Unlicensed. No credit cards.**
Film fans will probably recognise Park Street as home to some of the less than loveable cockneys in the Britflick *Lock Stock and Two Smoking Barrels*. Don't let that put you off, though: you're more likely to meet one of the chirpy local builders in here than any wannabe Krays. Maria Moruzzi and her 73-year-old mother serve up a selection of set breakfasts, starting at £1.60 for simple egg and bacon, and peaking at just £3 for egg, bacon, sausage, tomatoes and bubble. Alternatively, pick your own combo from a long list of fry-up staples, including black pudding and liver and bacon. Borough Café's bubble and squeak is second to none. **Map 8/8P.**

Gambardella

48 Vanbrugh Park, SE3 (020 8858 0327). 53 bus. **Meals served** 7am-6pm Mon-Sat. **Unlicensed. No credit cards.**
As soon as you spot the beautiful art deco façade of this friendly old caff, you know you're in for a treat. Entering Gambardella is a bit like walking on to the set of a period drama. The café opened in 1927 and has remained largely unchanged: all marbled formica panelling and huge bevelled mirrors. The food is mainly of the greasy spoon ilk (breakfast start at just £2.20 for egg, bacon and beans), but you can also get a basic pasta dish for £3 or so. It's a busy little place, despite the out-of-the-way location. Regulars are treated like family members.

Mario's Café

6 Kelly Street, NW1 (020 7284 2066). Camden Town tube/ Kentish Town tube/rail. **Meals served** 7.30am-5pm Mon-Sat. **Main courses** £2.40-£4.20. **Unlicensed. No credit cards.**
This charming caff, which has the unique distinction of featuring in a St Etienne song, is run by the genial Mario, who remembers your name after two visits and your preferences after just a few more. Sausage, egg, bacon and tomato with two slices of toast and a cup of tea is a very reasonable £3.80. You can top all that with various extras – including black pudding, bubble or beans – for just 50p each. We'd travel through several zones to have breakfast here; the superb chips are worth the journey on their own. **Map 10.**

Gambardella

Perdoni's

18-20 Kennington High Road, SE1 (020 7928 6846). Lambeth North tube. **Open** 7am-6.30pm Mon-Fri; 7am-2.30pm Sat. **Main courses** £3-£6.95. **Unlicensed. No credit cards.**
All right, so Perdoni's is a little too sophisticated food-wise to be called a greasy spoon (the menu lists a couple of fine pasta dishes and a tasty chicken with asparagus and white wine sauce), but most customers still come for the huge English breakfasts. It's not the cheapest café around – egg, bacon, mushrooms, beans and fried bread costs £4.50 – but the line of cabs regularly parked outside shows that those in the know think Perdoni's is worth it. The decor is very 1970s, with a long partition down the centre of the room, flip-down seats and bevelled edges to the Formica table-tops. Worth crossing the river for. **Map 7/9M.**

bite to eat even if you only went in for a look at the latest exhibition. The menu typically consists of two main courses each day, and a selection of cakes and pastries for dessert. We sampled both of the mains: a peppery beef casserole served with near-perfect basmati rice; and pasta tossed in olive oil with crisp Mediterranean vegetables. Both came with generous helpings of salad and were worth their respective prices (£5.50 and £4.50). To the rear is a spacious paved garden (with a number of attractive plants and sculptures), which offers a charming alternative to the gallery on sunny days. Whatever the weather, arrive early as the food has a tendency to run out remarkably quickly.
Babies and children admitted. No smoking. Tables outdoors (7, courtyard). **Map 3/5L.**

Soho W1

Carlton Coffee House ★

41 Broadwick Street, W1 (020 7437 3807). Oxford Circus tube. **Meals served** 7am-5.30pm Mon-Fri; 7am-6pm Sat. **Main courses** £4-£4.50. **Unlicensed. Corkage** £2. **Credit** LV.
With queues stretching out on to the pavement most lunchtimes, the Carlton is extremely popular for takeaways. Its impressive panini and focaccia rolls stuffed with classic Italian fillings have a deservedly high reputation with the local work-force. Those who can spare the time to take a seat, though, will be rewarded with some of the best-value lunchtime pasta in London, in mammoth portions. From a fine selection, penne fiorentina (with smoked salmon and spinach in cream) stands out. It's always worth checking the specials menu for more unusual sauces, including, on our last visit, a Cajun seafood concoction. The decor is agreeable, with a spotless tiled floor and white walls hung with photos of Italian landscapes. Service can be brisk and efficient or brusque and unfriendly, depending on the mood of the staff.
Babies and children welcome. Book lunch. Tables outdoors (4, pavement). Takeaway service. **Map 13/6J.**

Star Café

22 Great Chapel Street, W1 (020 7437 8778). Tottenham Court Road tube. **Meals served** 7am-4pm Mon-Fri. **Main courses** £4.95-£6.95. **Minimum** £3.50. **Credit** LV.
Despite being hugely popular with local media types, the Star remains pretty secret. It's a bright, lively venue, with colourful old signs on the walls, and a selection of basic Italian dishes, inventive sarnies and all-day breakfasts on the menu. Pasta with meatballs is highly recommended: the meatballs coarse, spicy and covered in a rich tomato sauce. The large omelettes, served with salad and potatoes, are a reliable alternative. Daily specials typically include supreme of chicken, grilled salmon and a stir-fry, but occasionally the odd surprise leaps forth, such as roast ostrich or kangaroo. Specials are generous and good value at around £6. Service is friendly and efficient.
Babies and children admitted. Booking advisable. No-smoking tables. Takeaway service. **Map 13/6K.**

Thanks for Franks

26 Foubert's Place, W1 (020 7494 2434). Oxford Circus tube. **Open** 7am-6pm Mon-Sat. **Minimum** £2.95 noon-2pm. **Main courses** £3.95-£5.50. **Unlicensed. Credit** LV, £TC.
Best for breakfasts, Thanks for Franks is a bright and lively little caff, with a cheerful blue and white interior and equally jolly staff. 'The works', a large plate loaded with sausage, bacon, egg, toast and chips, comes with a cup of tea for an excellent £3.25. If greasy breakfasts aren't your thing, try a jacket spud (there's the usual range of fillings), an omelette or one of the fine selection of sarnies. The char-grilled variety – a toasted cholla roll filled with a hot chicken fillet, crisp salad and a tangy tomato and chilli salsa – is especially flavour-packed. Squeezed up to the rear of the café, the seating often feels a bit cramped; weather permitting, it's much better to grab a table outside where you can also eye the trendy Soho bods as they parade up and down Newburgh Street.
Babies and children welcome. Tables outdoors (6, pavement). Takeaway service. **Map 13/6J.**
For branches see index.

South

Clapham SW4

Abbevilles

88 Clapham Park Road, SW4 (020 7498 2185). Clapham Common tube/35, 37 bus. **Meals served** 9.30am-4pm Mon-Fri. **Main courses** £2-£5. **Set meal** £4.95 two courses. **No credit cards.**
Established by a charitable trust to provide work experience for people with learning difficulties, Abbevilles offers high-quality cooking at unfeasibly low prices. The interior is spotlessly clean and pleasantly decorated. The menu features a selection of Mediterranean-style dishes, including fresh spaghetti with sun-dried tomatoes and olives, along with old favourites such as fillet steak, and scampi and chips. Breakfasts, starting at just £1, are also available all day. The only real drawback with Abbevilles is that, despite being

Pie & mash

Who pays the pie-man? It's a question London's pie and mash vendors must have asked themselves dozens of times over the past 20 years. With the unstoppable growth of fast food chains, coupled with the gentrification of working class districts, the purveyors of the food with best claim to be 'London's own cuisine' have seen their numbers shrinking.
Pies have been peddled on London's streets for hundreds of years, sold by hawkers at roving street markets and meeting places. Eels caught in the Thames Estuary were often used as the filling, though as their price rose minced beef took their place. By the mid-19th century, pie-sellers began to trade from permanent premises, mostly sited on street markets; pie and mash became the traditional food of the London coster.
Pie and mash is a family affair; a handful of clans still dominate the trade, running shops founded by their forefathers three or four generations ago. The Manzes, the Cookes and the Kellys are the most prominent of these dynasties, between them owning about a dozen shops, mostly in east and south-east London.
Half the thrill of eating at a pie and mash shop is the chance to admire the furnishings: wooden benches, bolted-down tables, beautiful patterned tiles. The best example is London's oldest pie shop, Manze's on Tower Bridge Road, SE1, founded in 1892, though for classic simplicity and a long history, Cooke's of Broadway Market, the Kellys' shops and Gooding's take some beating.
But an equal amount of pleasure comes from devouring freshly made minced-beef pie, mashed potato, liquor (an unfathomable green sauce involving parsley) and eels (stewed or jellied), followed (sometimes) by cherry pie and custard – and still having change from a fiver.
Pie-eaters tend to be remarkably monocultural. You might think tourists would be attracted to the older shops, or that they would become suddenly fashionable. Not yet. Pie and mash shops remain the preserve of working-class locals whose families have lived in the borough for decades. That is why gentrification often sounds the death knell to these establishments. Manze's in Chapel Market, Islington (1897-1998) was just the latest in a line of such victims.
Periodically, fashion has flirted with pie and mash, with relatively posh restaurants offering a version of the dish. The latest is Pie2Mash in Camden (9-11 Jamestown Road, NW1; 020 7482 2770), where pies with puffed up tops might have a chicken filling; mash could be mixed with mustard or parsley; and roast beef and fish and chips share the menu. So far these neophytes haven't had the staying power of the originals.
For novices to the cuisine, it's worth making a note on pie shop etiquette. Nearly always you'll have to queue for your helping at the counter. Then grab cutlery; a fork and spoon are customary (you'll need the spoon for the liquor). Once at a bench, you're likely to encounter an array of condiments, often including own-made chilli vinegar. Squirt it on the liquor to temper the saltiness. None of these establishments serves alcohol; all do takeaways.

Central

Clerkenwell & Farringdon EC1

Clark & Sons
46 Exmouth Market, EC1 (020 7837 1974). Farringdon tube/rail. **Open** 10.30am-4pm Mon-Thur; 10.30am-5.30pm Fri; 10.30am-5pm Sat. **Main courses** 60p-£3. **No credit cards. Map 15/4N.**

West

Ladbroke Grove W11

Cockneys Pie & Mash
314 Portobello Road, W11 (020 8960 9409). Ladbroke Grove tube. **Open** 11.30am-5.30pm Tue-Thur, Sat; 11.30am-6pm Fri. **Main courses** 75p-£2. **No cheques or credit cards. Map 11/4Az.**

South

Stockwell SW8

Harrington's
361 Wandsworth Road, SW8 (020 8672 1877). Bus 77, 77A. **Open** 11am-8pm Tue-Sat. **Main courses** £1.75-£2.30. **No cheques or credit cards.**

Tooting SW17

Harrington's
3 Selkirk Road, SW17 (020 8672 1877). Tooting Broadway tube. **Open** 11am-9pm Tue, Thur, Fri; 11am-2pm Wed; 11am-7.30pm Sat. **Main courses** £1.55-£2.50. **No cheques or credit cards.**

Walworth SE17

W J Arment
7 & 9 Westmoreland Road, SE17 (020 7703 4974). Bus 12, 35, 40, 45, 68A, 171, 176, 468. **Open** 10.30am-5pm Tue, Wed; 10.30am-4pm Thur; 10.30am-6.15pm Fri; 10.30am-6pm Sat. **Main courses** £1.38-£2.34. **Credit** LV.

Waterloo SE1

R Cooke
84 The Cut, SE1 (020 7928 5931). Southwark and Waterloo tube/rail. **Open** 10am-2.30pm Tue-Sat. **Main courses** £1.60-£3.60. **Credit** LV; no cheques. **Map 7/8N.**

South East

Deptford SE8

Goddard's
203 Deptford High Street, SE8 (020 8692 3601). Deptford rail/1, 47 bus. **Open** 9am-4pm Mon-Fri; 9am-4.30pm Sat. **Main courses** 70p-80p. **No cheques or credit cards.**

Manze's
204 Deptford High Street, SE8 (020 8692 2375). Deptford rail or Deptford Bridge Street DLR/1, 47 bus. **Open** 9.30am-4pm Tue-Sat. **Main courses** £1.70-£2.75. **No credit cards.**

London Bridge SE1

Manze's
87 Tower Bridge Road, SE1 (020 7407 2985). Bus 1, 42, 188. **Open** 11am-2pm Mon; 10.30am-2pm Tue-Thur; 10am-2.15pm Fri; 10am-2.45pm Sat. **Main courses** £1.95-£3. **Credit** LV. **Map 8/10Q.**

Peckham SE15

Bert's
3 Peckham Park Road, SE15 (020 7639 4598). Bus 21, 53, 63, 78, 172, 177, 351. **Open** 11.30am-1.30pm, 4.30-6.30pm Tue, Thur-Sat; 11.30am-1.30pm Wed. **Main courses** £1.20-£2.20. **No cheques or credit cards.**

East

Bethnal Green E2

G Kelly
414 Bethnal Green Road, E2 (020 7739 3603). Bethnal Green tube/rail/8 bus. **Open** 10am-3pm Mon-Thur; 10am-6.30pm Fri; 10am-4.30pm Sat. **Main courses** £1.55. **No cheques or credit cards.**

S & R Kelly
284 Bethnal Green Road, E2 (020 7739 8676). Bus 8. **Open** 10am-2.30pm Mon-Thur; 10am-6.30pm Fri; 10am-3.30pm Sat. **Main courses** £1.40-£2. **No cheques or credit cards. Map 4/4S.**

Bow E3

G Kelly
526 Roman Road, E3 (020 8980 3165). Bus 8. **Open** 10am-2pm Mon, Wed; 10am-3pm Tue, Thur; 10am-6.30pm Fri; 10am-5.30pm Sat. **Main courses** £1.40-£1.60. **No credit cards**; cheques accepted over £5 only.
For branch see index.

Shoreditch N1

F Cooke
150 Hoxton Street, N1 (020 7729 7718). Bus 48, 55, 149, 242, 243. **Open** 10am-7pm Mon-Thur; 9.30am-8pm Fri, Sat. **Main courses** £1-£1.80. **No credit cards. Map 4/2R.**

North East

Hackney E8, E9

F Cooke
9 Broadway Market, E8 (020 7254 6458). Bus 55, 106, 236. **Open** 10am-7pm Mon-Thur; 10am-8pm Fri, Sat. **Main courses** £1.50. **Credit** LV.

J Gooding
257 Well Street, E9 (020 8985 4900). Bus 26, 30, 277. **Open** 10am-3pm Mon-Thur; 10am-6.30pm Fri; 10am-6pm Sat. **Main courses** £1.85. **No credit cards.**

Walthamstow E17

L Manze
76 Walthamstow High Street, E17 (020 8520 2855). Walthamstow Central tube/rail. **Open** 10am-4pm Mon-Wed; 10am-5pm Thur-Sat. **Main courses** £2.35. **No cheques or credit cards.**

North

Camden Town & Chalk Farm NW1

Castle's
229 Royal College Street, NW1 (020 7485 2196). Camden Town tube/Camden Road rail. **Open** 10.30am-3.30pm Tue-Fri; 10.30am-4pm Sat. **Main courses** £1.75. **Credit** LV. **Map 10.**

Fish & Chips

Ask folk about the best fish and chips they've tasted and they may make a passing reference to the crispness of the batter, but what makes everyone go misty eyed are memories of walking into the cold night air with piles of steaming chips encased in vinegar-soaked newspaper. It seems our national dish is like our national game – best sampled standing up.

So if you're after the full deep-fried experience, why go to a restaurant? Well, fish and chips is simple food, yet easy to get wrong. When cooked with care, however, as it is at most of the establishments listed here, it's quite simply a revelation. So adopting a seated position and ensuring a strong cup of sweet tea is to hand isn't just a consumer choice, it's a vital safety procedure. When the fish is fresh, the batter crisp, and the chips golden brown, fish and chips is more than fast food. It deserves time and space and even the accompaniment of a bottle of light ale.

London's fish and chip lovers will lament the demise of the **Upper Street Fish Shop**, an Islington landmark that's regarded by many as the best fish and chip shop in town.

Central

Barbican EC1

Fish Central
149-151 Central Street, EC1 (020 7253 4970). Angel tube/Barbican or Old Street tube/rail/55 bus. **Lunch served** 11am-2.30pm, **dinner served** 4.45-10.30pm Mon-Sat. **Main courses** £4.35-£8. **Credit** LV, MC, £TC, V.
Fish Central certainly packs in the eclectic crowd it attracts. Luckily a tough-looking geezer didn't seem to mind that a tourist was almost rubbing shoulders with his lady wife, while a bifocal-wearing academic appeared happy to listen to a group of City brokers rap. So what kept everyone smiling? Certainly not the intrusive piped muzak or the maître d' who surveyed the dining area like a hovering hawk, swooping down to collect empty plates at the first sign of resting cutlery.

Nor was it the blond wood and royal blue décor (reminiscent of a mid-range commercial hotel). What everyone comes for is the food. Fish soup had a predominantly crab flavour and had been thickened with potato and cream. Crisp see-through batter surrounded a steaming haddock fillet, whose brilliant white flesh contrasted with the bright green of the creamy, tangy mushy peas. Surprisingly, the cabbies overlooked the crunchy, brown chips in favour of grilled fish, salad and jacket potatoes.
Babies and children welcome; high chairs. Booking advisable. Tables outdoors (4, pavement). Takeaway service (until 11.30pm). **Map 4/3P.**

Bloomsbury WC1

North Sea Fish Restaurant ★
7-8 Leigh Street, WC1 (020 7387 5892). Russell Square tube/King's Cross tube/rail/68, 168 bus. **Lunch served** noon-2.30pm, **dinner served** 5.30-10.30pm Mon-Sat. **Main courses** £6.50-£15.95. **Credit** AmEx, DC, MC, £TC, V.
No wonder families flock to North Sea – there are chips for junior, the cooking is good enough to satisfy mum and dad, and there's no garlic to scare grandma. The kind waitress dealt tactfully with a moody Italian teenager and even lent out own newspaper to a lonely American. Unfortunately, prawn cocktail was only ordinary; perhaps fish cakes or cod's roe would have been better. Our main course, however, was superb. As we cracked open the thin batter, the brilliant white flakes of haddock were momentarily obscured by great wafts of steam. The chips arrived crisp, brown and almost greaseless. Trifle and tiramisu were a temptation, but we had no regrets in choosing the crumble: a layer of tart, cinnamon-seasoned apple bubbling through a buttery topping. The wall lights, and the pink velour upholstery may be reminiscent of the worst of 1970s décor, but fish is the focus here.
Babies and children welcome. Book dinner. Separate room for parties, seats 36. Takeaway service (until 11.30pm). **Map 3/4K.**

Covent Garden WC2

Rock & Sole Plaice
47 Endell Street, WC2 (020 7836 3785). Covent Garden tube. **Meals served** 11.30am-10pm Mon-Sat; noon-9pm Sun. **Main courses** £3-£13. **Credit** MC, £TC, V.
The compact, but surprisingly light and airy, white-tiled interior of this chippy is invariably crammed with a varied mix of businessmen, tourists and luvvies on a budget. The owners' roots seemed more authentically represented by the Efes beer than the generous portion of taramasalata and microwaved pitta bread. For a chip shop that delicately quarters its pickled onions, Rock & Sole thankfully takes a more robust attitude to potatoes, believing in a low chip-to-spud ratio, and double frying the thick wedges in hot oil until crisp and brown – delicious. The fish was less successful. Both the haddock and the cod weren't as fresh as they might have been, and were covered in thick, if crunchy, batter. Specials included tuna, mackerel and trout, but not dolphin or whale, which feature strongly in the impressive basement mural. Office workers, no doubt wary of sleeping in afternoon meetings, seemed to ignore the pudding menu (which includes apple pie, banana fritters and cheesecake), preferring a high-octane espresso.
Babies and children welcome; high chairs. Book dinner. Separate room for parties, seats 28. Tables outdoors (10, pavement). Takeaway service (11.30am-11.30pm Mon-Sat; 11.30am-10pm Sun). **Map 14/6L.**

Holborn WC1

Fryer's Delight ★
19 Theobald's Road, WC1 (020 7405 4114). Chancery Lane or Holborn tube/19, 38, 55, 505 bus. **Meals served** noon-10pm Mon-Sat. **Main courses** £1.30-£4.95. **Minimum** £1.30. **Unlicensed. Corkage** no charge. **Credit** LV; cheques not accepted.
Situated on the busy Theobald's Road, Fryer's Delight has long been a cabbies' favourite. Its interior – a formica fetishist's fantasy – is decked out in wipe-clean surfaces, with the occasional Eames coat hook to please the art and design crowd. You can order a pie, pasty or saveloy, or choose from the usual selection of fried fish. The plaice was none too fresh, the haddock was either overcooked or had been kept in the warmer too long, and even the batter on the large fresh piece of cod was floury and chewy. The chips looked pale but were surprisingly crisp and there was plenty of them. If you require additional carbohydrates – there being no sweets or starters – the best option is to try the family-sized slice of bread and butter. Despite food quality that's only a touch above average, Fryer's Delight remains popular. People come here for the great atmosphere and to solve the mystery of how cabbies get the energy to rant all the way from Wimbledon to Wembley.
Takeaway service (until 11pm). **Map 3/5M.**

Marylebone W1, NW1

Golden Hind
73 Marylebone Lane, W1 (020 7486 3644). Baker Street or Bond Street tube. **Lunch served** noon-3pm Mon-Fri. **Dinner served** 6-10pm Mon-Sat. **Main courses** £4.70-£10.70. **Minimum** £4 (lunch), £5 (dinner). **Unlicensed. Corkage** no charge. **Credit** AmEx, DC, LV, MC, £TC, V.
Sitting in this beautifully preserved, art deco fish restaurant and watching the rain fall on to the early evening streets, we had the somewhat romantic notion of being in an Edward Hopper picture. Friendly, verging on the flirtatious, waiters serve in front of an impressive backdrop formed by a gleaming stainless-steel and Bakelite deep-fat fryer, complete with matching sun-burst wall panel. Preserved chillies gave the Hellenic mixed pickles a kick that was matched by the tabasco in the prawn cocktail sauce. A fantastic fish cake made with chunks of white fish mixed with parsley and smooth mash was covered in parchment-thin batter and fried until golden. The same crisp coating sealed in the juices of the expertly filleted haddock, which hid a generous portion of thick-cut chips. Though the filling in the square of treacle tart was too solid for perfection, it came with custard that was sweet, creamy and very yellow.
Babies and children welcome. Booking advisable. Separate room for parties, seats 24. Takeaway service. **Map 2/5G.**

Seashell
49-51 Lisson Grove, NW1 (020 7224 9000). Marylebone tube/rail. **Lunch served** noon-2.30pm, **dinner served** 5-10.30pm Mon-Fri. **Meals served** noon-10.30pm Sat. **Main courses** £9-£16. **Set meal** (noon-2.30pm, 5-7pm Mon-Fri; noon-7pm Sat) £10, £11, three courses. **Credit** AmEx, LV, MC, £TC, V.
On the evidence of the impeccable plastering and the etched monogram on the glass partitions, we were just dismissing this place as soulless and corporate when Frankie Valli's *Grease is the Word* came over the sound system. Such self-effacing humour was markedly absent from the stony-faced maître d', but the rest of the waiting staff were friendly. Being a more upmarket establishment, Seashell has a creditably long wine list, with a number of labels being sold by the glass. The fish cake was a ball of herby mash and fish covered in breadcrumbs, fried until crisp and brown. It came with a large and varied salad garnish, but didn't taste fishy enough. Mains include scampi and trout, but we chose haddock. A large, juicy, boneless fillet fried in peanut oil came with crunchy thick chips and seemed perfect until the fat end of the fish was reached. Here, under a wodge of uncooked batter, lurked a clutch of green and black chips. There wasn't enough room for a sponge pudding, but the apple pie was disappointing: a bland apple filling in pastry lacking sugar and butter.
Babies and children welcome; children's menu; high chairs. Bookings accepted for parties of six or more. No-smoking tables. Takeaway service. **Map 2/4F.**

Victoria SW1

Seafresh Fish Restaurant
80-81 Wilton Road, SW1 (020 7828 0747). Victoria tube/rail/24 bus. **Meals served** noon-10.30pm Mon-Sat. **Main courses** £3.95-£14.65. **Credit** AmEx, DC, LV, MC, £TC, V.
Model boats, ships' wheels and fishermen's lamps may all be chip shop clichés, but the addition of tapestry-upholstered pews complete with brass fittings give Seafresh the much more interesting air of a Methodist chapel that has been cast to the deep. Luckily the fishing nets strung from the ceiling beams have been strategically placed, thus

Golden Hind

preventing shoals of plastic fish from falling into your pint of Tetley's. The fish soup, justifiably trumpeted on the menu, arrived as a thin but tasty broth containing chunky bits of prawn, white fish and winter vegetables. Though the fish kebabs and fisherman's pie looked tempting, we plumped for an 11in haddock – perfectly filleted and fried in batter thin enough to see the juices from the large, white flakes of fish turn to steam. The thin square fingers of spud were tasty but the mushy peas had a thick and dry consistency more in keeping with a DIY material than a vegetable. In a list of classic sweets, the lemon sorbet brûlée was both different and delicious.
Babies and children welcome; high chairs. Book dinner. No-smoking tables. Takeaway service. **Map 6/11J**.

West

Notting Hill W8

Costas Fish Restaurant ★
18 Hillgate Street, W8 (020 7727 4310). Notting Hill Gate tube/28, 31, 94 bus. **Lunch served** noon-2.30pm, **dinner served** 5.30-10.30pm Tue-Sat. **Main courses** £3.90-£6.90. **Credit** £TC.
Expectations were riding high as we sat down in Costas's cosy, Cypriot-style dining room. To get there we'd walked through the kitchen, a route that suggests the chef has great confidence in his cooking. Evidence that the welcome would be warm and relaxed faced us in the furry form of a fellow customer's lap dog, sitting in its owner's shopping bag munching on sausage scraps. Costas didn't disappoint. Service was efficient and came with a smile, and the food was of a high standard. Five rings of calamares, encased in thin, golden batter, arrived piping hot. Alternative appetisers include king prawns in filo pastry and an authentic looking houmous. The main course also arrived straight from the fryer. Tasty chips had an unusual, slightly rough surface, which gave them extra crunch. Haddock fillet was quite small, but very fresh and at £6.90 was good value for money. For afters, baklava and fruit fritters were overlooked in favour of a trip back to childhood via a stainless-steel cup of jelly and ice-cream.
Babies and children welcome. Book dinner. Takeaway service. **Map 11/7A**.

Geales
2 Farmer Street, W8 (020 7727 7528). Notting Hill Gate tube. **Lunch served** noon-3pm Mon-Sat. **Dinner served** 6-11pm Mon-Sat; 6-10.30pm Sun. **Main courses** £6.95-£11.95. **Credit** AmEx, JCB, MC, £TC, V.
The new owners of this Notting Hill institution have successfully created a modern fish restaurant without completely obliterating the original family-run atmosphere. Renovations to the interior include a blond wood floor, but 1930s details such as the wrought-iron ornament shelves have been kept. This mixture of traditional and new is also reflected in the clientele. Two Pooterish gentlemen, too squiffy to check the cost of the claret they'd consumed, sat next to a couple of female execs discussing David Beckham's crossing skills. There were plenty of fish chunks in the soup, swimming around in a rich peppery broth. Even better was a salad, with great wheels of toasted goat's cheese nestling in a bed of mixed leaves. After that, a bland salmon fish cake and a slightly dry haddock fillet were disappointing. But there were no complaints about piping hot chips, buttery new potatoes or minty mushy peas. For afters, a thick slab of apple crumble was much lighter than it looked, and the treacle tart had a hint of citrus to complement the sweet molasses. Best of all, both dishes arrived with a large dollop of thick, artery-clogging cream.
Babies and children welcome; high chairs. Bookings accepted for parties of six or more. Separate room for parties, seats 30. Tables outdoors (5, pavement). Takeaway service. **Map 11/7A**.

South West

Wimbledon SW19

Broadway Place ★
8-10 Hartfield Road, SW19 (020 8947 5333). Wimbledon tube/rail/57, 93, 155 bus. **Lunch served** 11.30am-2.45pm Tue-Sat. **Dinner served** 5-10pm Tue-Fri; 5-9pm Sat. **Main courses** £2.20-£5.20. **Unlicensed. No credit cards.**
Fast service, cheap prices and large portions keep this unpretentious caff full of regulars. They are served by two energetic waiting staff, who flit between tables ensuring the place is spotless, while keeping the banter flowing as fast as the orders coming out of the open-plan kitchen. Plate-glass windows give a track-side view of the Wimbledon one-way system, while photos adorning the walls recall a time when the only traffic-calming measures were kerb-side bales of hay. The smoked fish in a salmon and trout starter may have been a little coarse in texture and taste, but for £2 it more than satisfied two, with enough left over to fill a doggy bag for the cat. Next, the dark brown crunchy batter was thick, so it held some grease, but the white flesh inside was firm and retained that strong fishy taste unique to fresh plaice. The only duff note was the small amount of water standing on the dark green surface of the mushy peas, making them reminiscent of the centre court covers during a Wimbledon downpour. Puds are uninspired but cost just £2.20 apiece.
Disabled: toilet. Takeaway service.

South

Wandsworth SW18

Brady's ★
513 Old York Road, SW18 (020 8877 9599). Wandsworth Town rail/28, 44 bus. **Dinner served** 6.30-10.30pm Mon-Wed, Sat; 6.30-10.45pm Thur, Fri. **Main courses** £5.65-£6.75. **Service** 10%. **No credit cards.**
We were just sitting down when a formidable, Home Counties lady loudly pronounced 'I only eat fried food when I'm at Brady's'. By the end of a great meal we could understand why. The interior bears some resemblance to a nursery; a naively drawn frieze of sea creatures runs above lemon-coloured wooden panelling. With smoked salmon, whole prawns and grilled bream on the menu, however, the food may be comforting, but it's most definitely adult. Salmon fish cake, a disc of crisply fried breadcrumbs containing enough flesh to tinge the smooth mash pink, had a pleasantly spicy aftertaste. We were mistakenly brought a side salad, which was fresh and varied but went back untouched – who wants rabbit food when you can have chips? Unfortunately, said chips were slightly undercooked, but the fillet of cod, curled by the heat of the oil, seemed very fresh even though it was a Monday. Mushy peas in a bowl were sweet and creamy. A tart with a treacle and coconut filling oozing over a triangle of thin buttery pastry made a near-perfect ending to the evening. This is a fast-paced joint, so service is to the point. Be prepared to queue for a table on a busy night. There's a possibility that Brady's may open for weekend lunches in the autumn – phone to check.
Bookings not accepted. Takeaway service.

Waterloo SE1

Masters Super Fish
191 Waterloo Road, SE1 (020 7928 6924). Waterloo tube/rail. **Lunch served** noon-3pm Tue-Sat. **Dinner served** 5.30-10.30pm Mon; 4.30-10pm Tue-Thur, Sat; 4.30-11pm Fri. **Main courses** £5.10-£13.50. **Credit** MC, £TC, V.
With its exposed brick walls and mahogany tables and chairs, Masters Super Fish looks like the set of the sitcom *Cheers*. The owners were certainly having a laugh when they classified the haddock supper as a meal for one. The fish's head flopped over the edge of the plate, and its tail wasn't far from tickling our neighbour's ribs – it's no fisherman's tale to say that this expertly fried fillet was over a foot long. A covering of the same golden, almost translucent batter ensured the generous portion of melt-in-the-mouth calamares ran the haddock a close second. Sadly, the addition of fortified wine tipped an already rich tomato and seafood broth into the sickly category, so we used the free pickled onion as an unorthodox palate cleanser. Other freebies included bread and butter and a three-prawn appetiser. Chips were limp and pallid, but because they'd been fried in peanut oil, also very tasty. We were considering whether to have crème caramel or apple pie when we heard the sound of shutters falling and decided that the calling of last orders had saved us from our greed.
Babies and children welcome; high chairs. Book weekends. Tables outdoors (3, pavement). Takeaway service. **Map 7/9N**.

South East

Herne Hill SE24

Olley's
67-69 Norwood Road, SE24 (020 8671 8259). Herne Hill rail/3, 68 bus. **Lunch served** noon-3pm Tue-Sat. **Dinner served** 5-11pm daily. **Main courses** £6.80-£9.90. **Credit** AmEx, JCB, MC, £TC, V.
In an attempt to create a 'Dickensian atmosphere', the designer of Olley's inexplicably plumped for pink plasterwork, rustic beams and exposed bricks and mortar. The result is more Torremolinos theme pub than Ye Olde Coaching Inn. This, coupled with the jokey menu, meant that the seriousness and quality of the food came as a pleasant surprise. Fish soup was rich, creamy and satisfying; seafood platter contained melt-in-the-mouth calamares and a juicy king prawn. The halibut was so dense and meaty the chef must have struggled to land it out of the deep-fat fryer. It came in the same light, crisp batter that perfectly complemented the juicy, brilliant-white haddock fillet. Chips were thick, crunchy and brown, but also much too dry. In contrast, the mushy peas were very creamy and, as they lacked luminosity, looked gratifyingly like a vegetable. Treacle pudding was light but short on that vital ingredient, treacle. However, the lemon tart had plenty of zest and was obviously freshly baked. The food was brought by polite waiting staff who really couldn't do enough for us.
Babies and children welcome; children's menu; high chairs. Tables outdoors (6, pavement). Takeaway service.

Lewisham SE13

Something Fishy ★
117-119 Lewisham High Street, SE13 (020 8852 7075/020 8318 9577). Lewisham rail/DLR/54, 136, 208 bus.
Café **Open** 9am-6pm Mon-Sat. **Main courses** £1.80-£5.
Blighty's **Lunch served** 11am-3pm Tue-Sat. **Main courses** £2.40-£5.
Both **Credit** LV, MC, £TC, V.
Pie and mash shares star billing with the usual deep-fried fare here, making Something Fishy a veritable centre for cockney cuisine. You can join the fryers downstairs in the simple blue and white caff or climb the stairs and take your seat to experience the unique atmosphere of Blighty's restaurant – there aren't many places you can eat mushy peas sitting under a mirror ball. The cheery rose-tinted hues of the tablecloths and wallpaper matched the vivid pink of the prawn cocktail sauce, chosen from a list of starters including soups, salads and jellied eels. While the watery-tasting prawns didn't match their colourful presentation, there could be no faulting the crisp, dark brown batter surrounding the cod fillet. This sometimes thick, but virtually greaseless casing contained a fish that was white and juicy but also a little chewy. The limpness of the chips was disappointing, but the meal ended on a high, with a knockout knickerbocker glory.
Babies and children welcome; high chairs. Tables outdoors (5, pavement). Takeaway service.
For branch see index.

North East

Dalston E8

Faulkner's
424-426 Kingsland Road, E8 (020 7254 6152). Dalston Kingsland rail/55, 67, 76, 149, 242, 243 bus. **Lunch served** noon-2pm Mon-Fri. **Dinner served** 5-10pm Mon-Thur; 4.15-10pm Fri. **Meals served** 11.30am-10pm Sat; noon-9.30pm Sun. **Main courses** £6.30-£12.50. **Minimum** £3. **Credit** LV.
Tiled floors, elaborate glass lamp fittings and frosted glass partitions give Faulkner's something of a Mediterranean feel, which on a rainy Tuesday night made a welcome contrast to the grey streets of Hackney outside. Diners – a large crowd, composed mainly of an older generation of locals – invariably kicked off by munching on pickled gherkins while deciding whether to have the usual fried fish or opt for one of the sole or halibut specials. We decided to try a fish cake starter – a ball of pleasantly herby mash mixed with cod and covered in crisp breadcrumbs, on a bed of semi-shredded iceberg. Next came a bowl of scalding hot chips, just out of the peanut oil, all glistening and brown. The haddock, a well-filleted, 10in specimen in paper-thin batter, was fresh and white but not quite as juicy as the thick, half-moon shaped piece of steaming battered cod that was our other choice. From a selection that included trifle, apple pie, and ice-cream, a perfectly circular sticky toffee pudding was artfully presented in a sea of bright yellow custard; it was, however, just a little stingy on the sticky stuff.
Babies and children welcome; children's menu; high chairs. Bookings not accepted. No-smoking tables. Takeaway service.

North

Finchley N3

Two Brothers Fish Restaurant
297-303 Regent's Park Road, N3 (020 8346 0469). Finchley Central tube. **Lunch served** noon-2.30pm, **dinner served** 5.30-10.15pm, Tue-Sat. **Main courses** £7.30-£17.50 (lunch); £8.65-£17.50 (dinner). **Credit** AmEx, MC, £TC, V.
Stained panelling and salmon-pink walls lend this north London restaurant a little of the swank of a Californian bar. The two brothers in their dress-down Friday togs set a relaxed tone enjoyed by a large, smart but casual, Finchley crowd. 'Athena ahoy' may sum up the artistic merit of the numerous seascape reproductions, but the LED digital display used to keep the orders flowing slickly would grace any white cube gallery. Fish soup arrived looking more like the alternative rice and tomato broth, but lurking in the depths of the bowl was a thick layer of white fish pieces. Many customers opt for grilled sole or one of the excellent-looking specials such as tuna with salsa verde. But the real speciality here is fresh fish fillets fried in oil hot enough to make the thick batter turn crunchy and brown. The chips came straight from the fryer, piping hot and glistening under the spotlights. Layers of Mr Whippy raspberry sauce, tinned peaches, strawberry ice and squirty cream may have sent us into nostalgic reveries, but the Two Brothers' peach melba is hardly the sophisticated sundae Dame Nelly first sampled.
Babies and children welcome. Bookings accepted lunch only. No-smoking tables. Takeaway service (until 10pm).

Muswell Hill N10

Toff's
38 Muswell Hill Broadway, N10 (020 8883 8656). Highgate tube then 134 bus. **Meals served** 11.30am-10pm Tue-Sat. **Main courses** £5-£16.50. **Minimum** £5. **Set meal** £8.95 three courses; £7.50 two courses. **Credit** AmEx, DC, LV, MC, £$TC, V.
Given its silver-ball track lighting, brown tiled floor and false wooden ceiling, the small restaurant at the back of this famous take-away resembles a 1970s bachelor pad. Except no self-respecting 1970s bachelor would have kept it either as clean or as tidy as does the energetic waiter at Toff's. The fish soup was more of a fish stew, with medium-sized chunks of crab and salmon jostling with an array of cubed vegetables in a herb-flecked broth. The plaice had been cooked to perfection, so plenty of juice flowed between the firm flakes of flesh. Sadly the dark brown batter was too thick and turned stiff and greasy as it cooled, but a large portion of chips along with a bowl of big juicy, spherical peas in a creamy sauce more than made up for this. Treacle pud in a sea of yellow custard was so light it was easy to tuck away. After that we sat back to finish a glass of drinkable house wine and eavesdrop on the confessions of a jovial crowd, including an astonishing admission of illicit lust for Nick Berry.
Babies and children welcome. Bookings not accepted. No-smoking tables. Takeaway service (until 10.30pm).

North West

West Hampstead NW6

Nautilus
27-29 Fortune Green Road, NW6 (020 7435 2532). West Hampstead tube/rail then 28 bus. **Lunch served** 11.30am-2.30pm, **dinner served** 4.30-10.15pm Mon-Sat. **Main courses** £7.50-£17. **Credit** LV, £TC.
First impressions of Nautilus can be disconcerting. Behind a blue and white utilitarian frontage lies a riot of pot plants, knick-knacks and marble. We recovered by parking ourselves on a red leatherette bench seat and sampling an excellent Cypriot lager, Keo. From a list of starters including soup, fruit and smoked salmon, prawn cocktail came with a round of sliced brown bread and butter. Resting on a bed of iceberg, a long line of juicy prawns in a tangy sauce stretched along the length of a banana-split bowl. Nautilus fries all its fish in matzo meal, which guarantees a crisp coating but perhaps doesn't seal in the fish juices as well as batter. Still, the flesh from sole fillet fell on to the fork and was delicately flavoured. Chips were piping hot and plentiful enough to banish any thoughts of trying one of the bought-in ice-creams or sorbets.
Babies and children welcome; high chairs. Bookings not accepted. Takeaway service.

Pizza & Pasta

For more restaurants serving pizzas and pastas *see page 21* **The Americas** and *page 99* **Italian**.

Central

City EC2

Pizza Express
125 London Wall, EC2 (020 7600 8880/ www.pizzaexpress.co.uk). Barbican or Moorgate tube/rail. **Meals served** 11.30am-11pm Mon-Fri; 11.30am-9pm Sat; 11.30am-8pm Sun. **Main courses** £4.75-£7.55. **Credit** AmEx, DC, MC, V.
You spot the distinctive blue neon of the sign before you see this branch, which is discreetly set on the raised Barbican walkway in two sections: a lunchtime bar-café and the evening restaurant. It's a split-level, chrome and glass affair, with the tables for smokers given the view out over the City. On a midweek visit, the place was populated by City folk trying to unwind. We stuck to tried and tested choices on the familiar menu. The packed vegetarian pizza veneziana was fine, however; its price (£5.05) includes a donation to keep Venice above water. And pasta Parmigiana came in a great tomato sauce; only a mixed leaf salad lacking variety failed to please. We finished with a solid traditional cheesecake, and rich chocolate ice-cream. Service was friendly, as it usually is at this chain. Pizza Express serves its niche market well and can always be relied upon – those seeking culinary excitement should try elsewhere. *Babies and children welcome; high chairs. No-smoking tables.* **Map 4/5P.**
For branches see index.

Clerkenwell & Farringdon EC1

Strada ★
8-10 Exmouth Market, EC1 (020 7278 0800). Farringdon tube/rail. **Meals served** noon-11pm Mon-Sat; noon-10.30pm Sun. **Main courses** £5.95-£12.50. **Credit** AmEx, MC, V.
Let's get this straight from the off: Strada is a smashing place. Perfectly situated on the corner of Exmouth Market, with a swathe of outdoor tables setting the continental vibe, the restaurant sets about its job with genuine style. Deep reds and lime greens colour the airy split-level dining

area, with paper light boxes mellowing the mood (aided by dance beats then Latin rhythms). Staff are easy-going (going on not-quite-with-it sometimes). We're in wood-burning oven territory here, with olive oil bread baked in-house. Caprese con mozzarella had wonderful creamy buffalo-milk cheese, along with sliced plum tomatoes and basil. Pizza Caprino came with goat's cheese, basil and wood-roasted vegetables, perfectly crisp and delicately flavoured. Risotto con funghi was wild with mushrooms, all in a slightly soupy brew that infused the rice with flavour. Only a trio of meat dishes break the £10 barrier. Finally, lemon sorbet was full of zest, with a real kick of liqueur, and profiteroles were light and arrived in a rich sauce. Special perks: a pager so you can wait for a table elsewhere; proper cloth napkins; and, for Clerkenwell, reasonable prices (three courses for two with wine and service: £49). *Babies and children welcome; high chairs. No bookings accepted. Tables outdoors (10, patio).* **Map 15/4N.**
For branches see index.

Covent Garden WC2

Café Pasta
184 Shaftesbury Avenue, WC2 (020 7379 0198). Leicester Square or Tottenham Court Road tube. **Meals served** 11.30am-11.30pm Mon-Sat; 11.30am-11pm Sun. **Main courses** £4.95-£11.95. **Credit** AmEx, DC, MC, V.
The pasta wing of Pizza Express, Café Pasta seems to work well as a quiet chain just getting on with business in a relaxed, unfussy way. This Covent Garden branch, tiny at street level (a large dining floor fills the basement), was quiet on a weekend mid-afternoon drop-in, so we sat upstairs and enjoyed the very polite and efficient service. Cool jazz hummed in the background, and even with all five tables occupied, there was no sense of crowding. Soup of the day (broccoli and pea) was wholesome and filling. To follow, spaghetti puttanesca offered a tangy tomato and anchovy mix, while linguine al pesto delivered a clean, fresh taste. Only the mozzarella and tomato salad smacked of mass-production. Lemon tart with ice-cream was almost too much by this stage, but good nonetheless. All told, the chain seems successfully to have adopted its mother company's qualities of reliable cooking presented in pleasant surroundings. *Babies and children welcome; high chairs;*

Tables outdoors (4, pavement). Takeaway service. **Map 13/6K.**
For branches see index.

Palms Pasta on the Piazza
39 King Street, WC2 (020 7240 2939). Covent Garden or Embankment tube/Charing Cross tube/rail. **Meals served** noon-11.30pm daily. **Main courses** £5.50-£9.95. **Set lunch** £8.95 two courses. **Service** 12½%. **Credit** JCB, MC, £TC, V.
Our hopes were not high for this tourist-focused operation. Its mural-coated premises, stretching way back, seemed perfect for the coach-feed. But such cynical thoughts were dashed as some rather decent food came our way. A shared calamares opener was soft if a little bland, but mains excelled. Well-flavoured penne arrabbiata had a strong punch of chilli. Risotto of the day – tuna and tomato – was smooth and flavoursome, and priced at a scarcely greedy £6.25. Later, raspberry sorbet and strawberry ice-cream delivered genuine fruit flavour. There was a problem with the credit card machine at the end, but otherwise the service was fine. A decent example of what can be done with high-turnover venues if a little effort is made. *Babies and children welcome; high chairs. Bookings advisable.* **Map 14/7L.**
For branch see index.

Pasta Browns
31-32 Bedford Street, WC2 (020 7836 7486). Covent Garden or Embankment tube/ Charing Cross tube/rail. **Open** 8am-midnight Mon-Fri; 10am-midnight Sat; 12.30-6.30pm Sun. **Breakfast served** 8-11.30am Mon-Fri; 10-11.30am Sat. **Meals served** noon-11pm Mon-Fri; noon-midnight Sat; 12.30-6.30pm Sun. **Main courses** £6.95-£12.95. **Service** 12½%. **Credit** AmEx, MC, V.
Perhaps we were silly to have many expectations of this clearly tourist-oriented Covent Garden venue. Prices here are completely over the top for food of mundane quality. House wine costs £12.45, and starters are priced at around £5 plus (though are sizeable enough to work as mains). That's not to say Pasta Browns is an unpleasant set-up. Its large floorplan includes corporate canvases (the brand secreted in the picture: a shame) and 3D metal sculptures, alongside an old black and white photo that the waitress assured us was of her grandmother. Take that with a pinch of salt perhaps, but not the mussels marinière, which had a coastal tang palpable through the white wine and garlic sauce. Linguine con langoustine proved that size matters, particularly when the shellfish are this small. Pollo al limone had stringy chicken, and vegetables that smacked of reheating. By far the best of four main courses we sampled was rigatoni alla siciliana – a gorgeous blend of grilled aubergine, Parmesan and mozzarella. We passed on desserts (the usual bunch) and left notably underwhelmed by Pasta Browns. *Babies and children admitted. Bookings not accepted. Tables outdoors (5, pavement). Takeaway service.* **Map 14/7L.**

ASK
48 Grafton Way, W1 (020 7388 8108). Euston Square or Warren Street tube/Euston tube/rail. **Meals served** noon-11.30pm daily. **Main courses** £4.10-£6.75. **Service** 10% for parties of seven or more. **Credit** AmEx, DC, MC, £TC, V.
On a not particularly busy weekday lunchtime we waited ten minutes before a waiter came to take our order. By this stage, we had already listened to more than enough of the excessively loud piped music (Pet Shop Boys, Sting, Tina Turner – you get the picture), and so ordered swiftly. The menu is long, but not especially original or interesting. Antipasti includes baked mushrooms stuffed with Parmesan; pizzas range from margheritas to del figones (with peperone, mushrooms and Gorgonzola); penne al pollo della casa (chicken, mushrooms and Parmesan in a cream sauce) is among the pasta choices; and salads include a niçoise and a tricolore. Pizza Emilia – featuring bolognese sauce, green chilli peppers, tomato and mozzarella – had a base that was too evocative of ill-advised supermarket pizza experiences. The topping was OK, but by that stage it needed to be exceptional to turn the meal around. Once we'd paid, it took a surprisingly long time to get our change. *Babies and children welcome; high chairs. Booking advisable lunch; bookings not accepted after 7.30pm. Separate room for parties, seats 60. Tables outdoors (6, pavement). Takeaway service.* **Map 2/4J.**
For branches see index.

Pasta Plus
62 Eversholt Street, NW1 (020 7383 4943). Euston Square tube/Euston tube/rail. **Lunch served** noon-3pm Mon-Fri. **Dinner served** 5.30-11pm Mon-Sat. **Main courses** £6.50-£14.50. **Set meals** £12 three courses. **Credit** AmEx, DC, MC, £TC, V.
Tucked down a fairly shabby side street next to Euston Station, Pasta Plus is an unassuming but pleasant restaurant – more than simply a refuelling stop before hitting the track. The place makes very effective use of its small premises, being light and airy (skylights doing the business towards the back). Friendly staff set the scene nicely. Mozzarella and tomato salad, alongside strecciatela romana, got us started well. To follow, risotto con funghi was creamy and flavoursome, and cannelloni with a simple tomato and herb sauce equally effective. Worthy of note is the immaculate dressings dispenser: a moulded glass contraption holding both oil and vinegar, one suspended globe within the other. Tiramisu and sorbet were fine examples of their respective genres, and the always-excellent Illy coffee came in beautiful Mitterteich cups. A meal for two, all in, at this easy-going, relaxing venue came to just over £40. We'll be back, and not just before catching the 11.45pm. *Babies and children welcome; high chairs. Booking advisable. No-smoking tables. Tables outdoors (27, conservatory).* **Map 3/3K.**

Fitzrovia W1

Pizza Paradiso
35 Store Street, WC1 (020 7255 2554). Goodge Street or Tottenham Court Road tube. **Meals served** noon-midnight Mon-Sat. **Main courses** £4.55-£7.50. **Credit** AmEx, DC, MC, V.
Paradise? Well, hardly, but we'll come on to that later. First, though, the good points. Pizza Paradiso benefits from a tidy little two-floor location in Bloomsbury. The service, too, was nigh on impeccable: a dish of delicious olives on arrival, while one of our party's request for a pasta dish not on the menu – tagliatelle arabiatta – was greeted with nary a blink. The beer (Nastro Azzurro, £2.60) was properly chilled, and the desserts were both more than adequate: a fine chocolate fudge cake and a slightly too heavy panna cotta. Indeed, the only thing at which the place really fails is the thing at which they're supposed to excel. From a pretty standard list of 20 pizzas, a Mediterranea was a peculiar affair. The base was fine, and the toppings – grilled courgettes, aubergine, red and yellow peppers – about all we expected, but the consistency of the tomato sauce was thin and the pizza as a whole was oily enough to drown a seagull. The aforementioned pasta was a little better, but glowed an alarming orange. Paradise? No, but a useful pit-stop as long as you don't set your sights too high. *Babies and children welcome; high chairs. Separate room for parties, seats 30.* **Map 3/5K.**

Pizza Express

Strada. *See page 185.*

Knightsbridge SW1

Pizza on the Park

11 Knightsbridge, SW1 (020 7235 5273). Hyde Park Corner tube. **Meals served** 8.15am-midnight Mon-Sat; 9.15am-midnight Sun. **Main courses** £6.50-£10.15. **Credit** AmEx, DC, JCB, LV, MC, £TC, V.

Peter Boizot's flagship has all the trappings of a chic restaurant, but an almost palpable air of complacency and inconsistent food. Reading the menu gives you a sense of déjà vu: the Pizza Express standards are all there, with few exceptions or additions. You can add extra ingredients to a pizza – but at a whopping £1.20 each. A single order of extra jalapeños was so large it smothered the vegetarian giardiniera from crust to core, overpowering the taste of other ingredients. In contrast, the dismal portion of leeks on the Prinz Conti had sunk without trace into the mozzarella and tomato base. A greasy pizza-crust garlic bread was ridiculously short of garlic. Frustrating hints of the quality this joint can attain were provided by a generous plate of excellent smoked salmon simply served with lemon and delicately sliced brown bread; and a zippily fresh fruit salad. Despite the powerful and lingering smell of bleach that wafted suddenly and inexplicably over the eating area, it was a pleasure to eat in the large high-ceilinged, open-plan dining room. Efficient, if rushed, service also counts in POTP's favour. But laurels are being rested upon, and food comes a poor second to jazz here.

Babies and children welcome; high chairs. Bookings not accepted. Disabled: toilet. Entertainment: jazz musicians (basement) 9.15-11.15pm nightly, cover charge variable; cabaret nightly £10-£18 admission; string quartet lunch Sun. No-smoking tables. Tables outdoors (5, patio). Takeaway service. **Map 6/8G.**

Marylebone W1

ITS

60 Wigmore Street, W1 (020 7224 3484). Bond Street tube. **Meals served** noon-11.30pm daily. **Main courses** £4-£9.45. **Credit** AmEx, DC, MC, V.

An excellent pasta provider, the small chain that is ITS deserves to be much better known – and the Wigmore Street branch is a great place to start the acquaintance. Its large, open floor and the effective use of glass and steel lend it a clean, unobtrusive air that encourages a relaxed meal. The smooth house red was particularly good at setting the scene, too. Baked mushrooms al forno with Parmesan, garlic, breadcrumbs and sherry was not only well priced at £3.70, but would have made a splendid main course. However, the enjoyable penne della casa with ricotta, basil and tomato soon took our attention, as did the tagliatelle al funghi. A wedge of cassata was too large to finish, but cappuccinos slipped down swimmingly. Precise, attentive service and no sense of being hurried contributed to an evening worth repeating. This branch is well placed on a quiet central stretch, making it a useful escape route from Oxford Street's culinary desert.

Babies and children welcome; high chairs. Bookings not accepted. Disabled: toilet. No-smoking tables. Tables outdoors (4, pavement). Takeaway service (evenings only). **Map 2/6H.**

For branches see index.

Purple Sage

90-92 Wigmore Street, W1 (020 7486 1912). Bond Street tube. **Lunch served** noon-2.30pm Mon-Fri. **Dinner served** 6-10.30pm Mon-Sat. **Main courses** £9.50-£14.50. **Credit** AmEx, MC, £TC, V.

Despite receiving complaints about lax service and 'garlic bread and pizza tougher than old leather', we've kept our favourable impression of this sibling to **Red Pepper** *(see p189)*. Our recommendation isn't unqualified, though: the dishes are pricey (especially when you're expected to pay extra for bread) and the food isn't without the odd glitch. However, the menu offers interesting choices – not just among the pasta and pizza. The surroundings are hard-edged, with an open kitchen, warm colours and a few potted palms offsetting bare boards and brick. Service is generally efficient, especially at lunchtime, which is a business-like affair enabling the local suits to hurry back to their Harley Street offices. Pizzas, cooked in a wood-fired oven, are only served in the evening. The rest of the monthly changing menu offers various antipasti, pasta dishes, and meat or fish mains. 'Contorni' (including some soggy zucchini fritti) cost extra. Mozzarella with rocket and fennel, squid salad with new potatoes, and chilled tomato soup with marinated king prawns all feature among the antipasti, together with a curiously bland pepper and green bean salad. Pasta (we tried a big plateful of orecchiette with peas and prosciutto) costs around £9.50 and mains (char-grilled slices of veal wrapped around spears of asparagus, or sea bass served with roasted aubergines and rocket, for instance) average £14. A cut above the chain norm.

Babies and children admitted. Booking advisable. Separate room for parties, seats 35. **Map 2/6G.**

La Spighetta ★

43 Blandford Street, W1 (020 7486 7340). Baker Street tube. **Lunch served** noon-2.30pm Mon-Sat. **Dinner served** 6.30-10.30pm Mon-Thur, Sun; 6.30-11pm Fri, Sat. **Main courses** £6.50-£11. **Credit** AmEx, MC, £TC, V.

Located near bustling Marylebone High Street, La Spighetta was doing a roaring lunchtime trade on our visit. It's not just the location, though, that has the punters flooding in. You'll find excellent, good-value Italian food here, and pizza that beats the crust off the competition. Our meal had a flying start with some finely carved carpaccio of wild boar with rocket, but this was trumped by another starter of perfectly gooey grilled goat's cheese served with garlicky french beans. A few sips of good house white later we got stuck into the pizzas. The kitchen turns out the kind of awesomely crispy pizza bases that make you wonder what other so-called pizzerias are playing at. Quattro stagione was laden with fresh ingredients bursting with their own flavours; a liberal portion of artichoke hearts and some delicate prosciutto were especially tasty. The vegetariana, too, was stacked with a variety of veg, though perhaps too much aubergine. The airy basement dining area combines the best of trattoria style – warm terracotta floor tiles, wood and wicker furniture – with modern clean decor and on the ball service. This place is a gem.

Babies and children welcome; high chairs. Booking advisable. No-smoking tables. Tables outdoors (4, pavement). Takeaway service (pizzas only). **Map 2/5G.**

Mayfair W1

Condotti

4 Mill Street, W1 (020 7499 1308). Oxford Circus or Piccadilly Circus tube. **Meals served** 11.30am-midnight Mon-Sat. **Main courses** £6.60-£8.10. **Service** 12½% for parties of seven or more. **Credit** AmEx, DC, JCB, MC, £TC, V.

Hidden in the backstreets of Mayfair, Condotti is a subdued eaterie that turns out reliable pizza and pasta dishes to the jaded palates of the opulent locality. It is the least flamboyant of Peter Boizot's triumvirate of restaurants (**Kettners** and **Pizza on the Park**), but the food shares many characteristics: the quality is consistent, the ingredients are good, but the result is hardly inspiring. On our visit the service was a little world-weary, too. We had to wait for our food, and though the waiter was friendly and apologetic, he seemed to have his mind on other things. Tricolore salad was abundant and beautifully fresh, with delicious mozzarella. The pizzas, when they arrived, were of modest size, appetising and well put together, though the bases were a touch too thick. The kitchen had been rather heavy-handed with the mozzarella on an otherwise flavourful la reina, while the tasty but oily fiorentina sported plentiful spinach and an appealingly sunny egg. We refused to be tempted by desserts – the likes of chocolate fudge cake and cheesecake – and opted instead for (excellent) coffees.

Babies and children welcome; high chairs. Book lunch Mon-Fri. Separate room for parties (dinner and weekends), seats 50. Takeaway service. **Map 13/6J.**

Soho W1

Kettners ★

29 Romilly Street, W1 (020 7734 6112). Leicester Square, Piccadilly Circus or Tottenham Court Road tube.
Bar **Open** 11am-11pm Mon-Sat.
Restaurant **Meals served** noon-midnight daily. **Main courses** £5.85-£15.10.
Both **Credit** AmEx, DC, JCB, MC, £TC, V.

Kettners is like Pizza Express with carpet. Pretty grubby carpet, too. But that's part of the relaxed – some would say shabby – charm of the place. The menu is similar to that of Pizza Express, unsurprisingly since Peter Boizot (who owns Kettners, as well as pizza restaurants **Pizza on the Park** and **Condotti**) was a founder of the now separately owned chain. We had a couple of Peroni beers, a mixed salad, an 'American hot' pizza (peperoni, sausage, mozzarella, peppers and tomatoes) and a capricciosa pizza (ham, peperonata, anchovies, egg, capers, tomatoes, olives and mozzarella), all meeting the high standards set – and always maintained – here. What sets Kettners well apart from the chains is neither the subtle piano-playing, nor the jocular affability of the staff, but the apple pie: with cream and a hint of cinnamon, it's outstanding. Sir Peter Boizot? It has a ring to it.

Babies and children welcome; high chairs. Bookings not accepted. Entertainment: pianist lunch Wed-Sun; 6.30pm-midnight nightly. No-smoking tables. Separate rooms for parties, seating 15, 30, 60 and 80. Takeaway service. **Map 13/6K.**

Pulcinella

37 Old Compton Street, W1 (020 7287 3920). Leicester Square, Piccadilly Circus or Tottenham Court Road tube. **Meals served** noon-midnight Mon-Wed, Sun; noon-1am Thur-Sat. **Main courses** £6.05-£10.95. **Minimum** £6. **Credit** AmEx, MC, V.

When the pizzas are the size of stealth bombers and the tables so tightly packed together, it would be better if staff kept their eye on the ball, so to speak. Our waiter made the mistake of looking away while one of our pizzas was preparing to land and it was almost very messy. No joke: the pizzas here are stupendously, fantastically big. Too big, you have to say, given their moderate quality (the base and crust are somehow too crispy and too chewy at the same time). As an alternative, there's a fair choice of pastas, including own-made ricotta and spinach gnocchi in tomato and basil sauce. The most popular pizza choice is the Pulcinella, with a vast collection of ingredients including mushrooms, artichokes, ham, sausages, fried egg and olives. We managed to finish our choices – a marinara (with prawns and clams) and an arrabbiata (with anchovies, capers, tomatoes, garlic and chilli) – mainly out of a sense of duty. A couple of beers were not really enough, given how much cheese, tomato and dough there was to get through, but £3 a time for Peroni seems a bit steep. If your main pizza requirement is diameter, then come to Pulcinella; if it's top quality, look elsewhere.

Babies and children admitted. Bookings not accepted. Tables outdoors (2, pavement). Takeaway service. **Map 13/6K.**

Soho Pizzeria

16-18 Beak Street, W1 (020 7434 2480). Oxford Circus or Piccadilly Circus tube. **Meals served** noon-midnight Mon-Sat; 1.30-10pm Sun. **Main courses** £4.25-£6.20. **Service** 10% for parties of seven or more. **Credit** AmEx, DC, JCB, LV, MC, £TC, V.

On a weekday lunchtime here you can get a very pleasant, reasonably priced pizza – and a lot more besides. Go for an African Neptune and you'll contribute 30p to Third World charities, try an Ortolana and you'll be tucking into ingredients not normally found on a rolled piece of dough: marinated aubergine, courgette, parsley and garlic. We enjoyed a quattro formaggi and a Hawaiian (ham and pineapple); both were faultless, of fair size and decent crispiness, but pineapple chunks, of course, wouldn't get through the door at certain pizza restaurants. Puddings include profiteroles, tiramisu, chocolate fudge cake and ice-cream. There's a limited choice of red and white wines, plus Peroni beer and a range of soft drinks. The inferior peperone sausage used in the pizzas is a drawback, but that doesn't stop Soho Pizzeria mounting a spirited challenge to local rivals.

Babies and children welcome; high chairs. Booking advisable. Entertainment: jazz musicians 7pm-midnight Mon-Sat. No-smoking tables. Takeaway service. **Map 13/7J.**

West

Ladbroke Grove W10

Cascabel

Canalot Studios, 222 Kensal Road, W10 (020 8960 2732). Ladbroke Grove tube. **Open** 11am-11pm Mon-Thur; 11am-midnight Fri, Sat; 11am-6pm Sun. **Main courses** £5.25-£9.95. **Credit** AmEx, MC, V.

This canteen in a former chocolate factory used to be called the Canal Brasserie. It has the same owners, the same customers who work in the Canalot Studios (mostly music biz and fashion types), and the same lousy acoustics: 'Cacophony' would have been a more apt name, with the open kitchen and cranked-up Rough Trade soundtrack. However, the interior has been given a stunning makeover, and the cooking has improved dramatically. A wood-fired oven is at Cascabel's core. Pizzas are the mainstay, and ours were good: wild mushroom, truffle and olive oil was pungent with earthy aromas. The pizza base was exactly the right consistency: thin, elastic, but not too chewy. A pasta dish of tagliarini incorporated sautéed squid, green beans and basil. Most dishes are kept simple; an organic green salad wasn't much of an improvement on a supermarket salad bag. Best was dessert: a cascabel (chilli) and orange ice-cream, which had just the right amount of chilli kick to match the citrus tang, served with biscotti. In contrast, the wine list is a bog-standard selection of Italian bottles with nothing interesting costing less than £15. And the cappuccino was poor. In all, an archetypal Notting Hill restaurant.

Babies and children admitted.

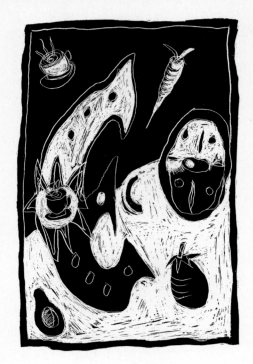

table. A useful pit-stop while shopping, rather than a destination restaurant.
Babies and children welcome. Book Fri, Sat. Tables outdoors (2, pavement). Takeaway service.

Maida Vale W9

Red Pepper
8 Formosa Street, W9 (020 7266 2708). Warwick Avenue tube. **Lunch served** 12.30-2.30pm Sat; 12.30-3.40pm Sun. **Dinner served** 6.30-10.45pm Mon-Sat; 6.30-10.30pm Sun. **Main courses** £7-£15.50. **Service** 12½% for parties of five or more. **Credit** MC, £TC, V.
Welcome to the contortionists' pizza restaurant! Having booked (for 8.30pm and been told a table would be ours until 10pm), we turned down the first table we were offered on the grounds that it was a throughway. 'I know. What can I do?' pleaded the waitress. We accepted a table in the basement – it was just as cramped but, because it was in the corner, would experience less passing traffic. We squeezed in and ordered pizza parmigiana (mozzarella, aubergine, goat's cheese, fresh tomato) and pizza peperoni rossi (tomato, mozzarella, roasted red peppers, chilli oil). The parmigiana came first, by about five minutes, and while we were impressed by the way the goat's cheese appeared to have been dribbled across the large disc of dough, the pizza was rather dry. Peperoni rossi was OK: there was nothing wrong with it but it wasn't exciting. A half-bottle of pinot grigio Attems (£9) had an unpleasant aftertaste. In addition to the menu, there are specials (grilled tuna with samphire, pizza with ham and asparagus, on our visit). This popular restaurant has pretensions to be more than just a pizza parlour, but the policy of cramming as many tables in as possible means we couldn't wait to leave.
Babies and children welcome. Booking advisable. Separate room for parties, seats 25. Tables outdoors (5, pavement). Takeaway service. **Map 1/4C.**

South

Battersea SW11

Basilico ★
175 Lavender Hill, SW11 (020 7924 4070). Clapham Junction rail. **Meals served** 11am-11pm Mon-Thur; 11am-midnight Fri-Sun. **Main courses** £5.95-£15.75. **Unlicensed. Corkage** no charge. **Credit** MC, V.
The emphasis here is on quality – the pizzas are baked in wood-fired ovens and the toppings include smoked chicken, Dolcelatte, fresh salmon and even truffle oil with wild mushrooms. With prices ranging from £7.95 for a 13in margherita to a hefty £15.75 for an 18in Palermo (wilted spinach, smoked haddock and Gruyère), you expect quality. How you rate the place partly depends on your definition of the perfect pizza: some prefer a more substantial and less dry base than that which Basilico serves, but we rate them. Side lines include soup, salads (rocket and Parmesan) and antipasti. Lemon tart and bitter-sweet chocolate tart are among the desserts. Large smoothies complete the picture. Basilico is chiefly a takeaway and delivery joint, but it is possible to eat on the premises: either on high stools looking out on to Lavender Hill, or at the little tables lining one wall. On our visit, staff were still helpful at the end of a long night and gave us our garlic bread for free (having missed it on the bill).
Babies and children admitted. Takeaway service; delivery service (within 2-mile radius). **For branch see index.**

C Notarianni & Sons
142 Battersea High Street, SW11 (020 7228 7133). Clapham Junction rail/45, 249, 319 bus. **Lunch served** noon-2.45pm Mon-Fri. **Dinner served** 6.15-11pm Mon-Sat. **Main courses** £4.90-£6.50. **Minimum** £5 after 8pm. **Service** 10% for parties of five or more. **Credit** MC, V.
A confusing place – Notarianni's is an art deco Italian restaurant that feels like an American diner. There's a classic Coke fridge, a working Rock-ola jukebox and neon cigarette signs offset by large, tacky art deco mirrors. On our midweek visit it was quiet; only two other tables had diners. The high street location may bring plenty of daytime trade, but this doesn't seem to continue into the evening. We were excited by the prospect of linguine with wild clams (on the board as the daily special) but disappointed to find there was no more. The same applied to a starter of mussels (from the main menu). Excellent garlic bread with anchovies, a decent antipasto, and slurps of the house red (from Puglia) revived our spirits. However, a spaghetti polpette (with meatballs), and a spaghetti funghi sustained rather than inspired. We rounded off the meal with a better-than-average tiramisu, while the chef wound down with a game of patience on an adjacent

Brixton SW9

Pangaea
15 Atlantic Road, SW9 (020 7737 6777). Brixton tube/rail. **Meals served** noon-11pm Mon-Fri, Sun; noon-11pm Sat. **Main courses** £4.95-£9.25. **Service** 10%. **Credit** AmEx, DC, JCB, MC, TC, V.
Tucked into one of the railway arches along Atlantic Road, Pangaea is a perfect place to soak up the buzzy Brixton vibe. *Playschool*-style coloured furniture, *Magic Roundabout* mushroom lights and unquenchably chirpy staff ensure a fun evening. Even the grumble of the odd train overhead adds to the relaxed atmosphere. The menu offers various pasta, meat and fish dishes, plus an interesting choice of pizzas. Tricolore salad to start was plentiful, attractive yet under-seasoned. Slightly soapy-tasting calamares and zucchini in batter with garlic mayonnaise was also found wanting. Luckily the garlic 'bread' – a crispy pizza base coated in tomato, garlic and herbs – was a winner. To follow, salmon and shrimp linguine had a pleasantly delicate flavour, but the lurid pink sauce gave away the tinned origins of the fish. The contadina pizza promised a palette of aubergine, courgettes, peppers and sun-dried tomatoes, so we were surprised to receive a quattro stagione. The error was quickly rectified and the contadina proved a good choice. Tangy lemon tart was an excellent way to finish a meal that came to just over £50 for two including wine, coffee and service. A lively and enjoyable place.
Babies and children welcome; high chairs. Separate rooms for parties, both seating 60. Takeaway service. Vegetarian dishes. **Map 18.**

Clapham SW4

Eco
162 Clapham High Street, SW4 (020 7978 1108). Clapham Common tube. **Lunch served** noon-4pm Mon-Fri; noon-5pm Sat, Sun. **Dinner served** 6.30-11pm Mon-Thur; 6.30-11.30pm Fri, Sat; 6-11pm Sun. **Main courses** £4.95-£7.90. **Service** 10% for parties of five or more. **Credit** AmEx, JCB, LV, MC, £TC, V.
Lingering over a coffee is not on the menu at Eco. The hordes of Claphamites pouring into this popular pizzeria mean that customers are under pressure to order, gobble it down and then get the hell out. We ate early – at 7pm – and by the time we left (barely 45 minutes later) there was a queue of hungry punters. A long, thin layout with all the tables lined close together intensifies the sensation of conveyor-belt dining. That said, the food isn't bad and includes plenty of salads (chicken pesto, for instance), calzone, oven-baked dishes (baked avocado crab) and pastas (green-lip mussels with spaghetti) as well as a variety of interesting-sounding pizzas. The open-plan kitchen means you can watch the flamboyant pizza chefs in action. We enjoyed pungent garlic bread and a generous green salad before tucking into mains. Pizza tonno (tuna with capers, red pepper, olives and mozzarella on a tomato sauce base) was nothing out of the ordinary, but tasty and dauntingly large, while a calzone, generously filled with goat's cheese, courgettes and peppers, avoided sogginess. Just to ensure we rolled all the way home, we finished with a mound of profiteroles. Loud music and vaguely stressed-out staff mean that eating at Eco is not a relaxing experience. The food is satisfactory, but you'd do far better heading down the road to **Verso 84** *(see below)*.
Babies and children welcome; high chairs. Booking essential. No-smoking tables. Takeaway service.
For branch see index.

Cascabel.
See page 187.

Verso 84
84 Clapham Park Road, SW4 (020 7720 1515). Clapham Common tube/35, 37, 137A bus. **Dinner served** 6-11pm Tue-Sun. **Main courses** £4.80-£8.50. **Credit** AmEx, JCB, LV, MC, TC, V.
Previously known as La Vineria, Verso is still run by the same cheerful Italian family. It's just far enough from the High Street to avoid the brash Clapham crowds, and serves winning food in a supremely relaxed, totally un-British atmosphere. Local Italians strolled in throughout the evening to pick up takeaways or enjoy a family meal; the waitress chatted amiably with us in appalling English; and the unfinished redecoration lent the restaurant an air of take-it-or-leave-it casualness. In these surroundings the prices were a bit of a shock; not expensive, but a clear indication this is no run-of-the-mill pizza joint. Garlic bread was a masterpiece of crispness and flavour and rendered our other generous starters – carpaccio di bresaola (with fresh Parmesan and olives on a bed of rocket) and insalata di avocado – completely gratuitous. Main courses include one daily pasta dish, but we kept to the pizzas. Crucca pizza with Parma ham matched a perfect base with tasty toppings that retained their identities against a background of mozzarella and tomato. Calzone with ricotta, spinach, tomatoes and mozzarella came dripping with sublime creamy mushroom sauce. Desserts were out of the question after all this, but we found room for excellent Italian coffee and complimentary own-made lemon liqueurs.
Babies and children welcome; high chairs. Disabled: toilet. Tables outdoors (4, pavement). Takeaway service.

Elephant & Castle SE1

Pizzeria Castello
20 Walworth Road, SE1 (020 7703 2556). Elephant & Castle tube/rail. **Meals served** noon-11pm Mon-Thur; noon-11.30pm Fri; 5-11.30pm Sat. **Main courses** £4.30-£9.80. **Credit** AmEx, MC, £TC, V.
Pizzeria Castello lurks on a corner opposite the hulking red mass of the Elephant & Castle shopping centre. It's a friendly, no-frills joint with an open-plan kitchen and a narrow dining area that's always packed to the rafters with contented-looking locals. To get ourselves in the mood, we ordered a couple of glasses of house red and a tricolore salad that was saved from blandness by a deliciously ripe avocado. Pizzas are prepared with a medium crust, unless you specify otherwise. We had a medium-crust fiorentina, lavishly smothered with tasty spinach and a well-cooked egg. We also sampled a thin-crust Vesuvio – a combination of mildly spicy chicken and artichoke hearts that was so restrained in flavour we hardly noticed eating it. After careful consideration we decided the thin crust was the better choice, although the medium crust proved perfect for the non-greasy garlic bread. The menu contains all the usual pizza choices, plus a seafood-infested pizza del pescatore (clams, prawns, baby octopus, cuttlefish, mussels and kings prawns), a couple of calzone and some simple pasta dishes. The food may be nothing out of the ordinary, but the smiley, bustling staff and buzzy, relaxed atmosphere make this a very pleasant place for a good-value meal in an area sorely in need of decent eateries.
Babies and children welcome; high chairs. Booking advisable; essential dinner and weekends. Takeaway service. **Map 8/11O.**

Walworth SE17

La Luna
380 Walworth Road, SE17 (020 7277 1991). Bus 12, 35, 40, 45, 68, 68A, 171, 176. **Lunch served** noon-3pm, **dinner served** 6-11pm Tue-Sat. **Meals served** 12.30-10.45pm Sun. **Main courses** £4.50-£13.90. **Service** 10% for parties of five or more. **Credit** AmEx, DC, JCB, MC, V.
Hurrah for progress! Our main – and, in some years, only – complaint about La Luna has been the uncovered dessert trolley, which can hardly improve either the taste or the hygiene of its contents. This year, though, the trolley has been banished, and the range of sweets, such as the delicious crème caramels and huge servings of moreish tiramisu, are brought out of the kitchen to order. Before we got on to them, though, we sampled some savoury delights at this terrific and cosy local. Garlic bread*f* with cheese was served in double-quick time as a starter, before the pizzas arrived with a flourish from the Italian waiters. The quattro stagioni hit all the right spots, though the rustica proved even better: crisp of base and rich of flavour, with toppings – peperoni,

mushrooms, olives and onions – that almost edged off the plate. Service was prompt and pally, the house white was drinkable, and an entirely lovely time was had by all at what is one of the unsung highlights on London's pizza circuit. Extra points, too, for the Paolo Conte album that acted as a pleasingly raffish soundtrack throughout.
Babies and children welcome; high chairs. Book weekends. Entertainment: Italian musicians 7.30-11pm Tue, Thur. Takeaway service. **Map 8/12P.**

Waterloo SE1

Gourmet Pizza Company

Gabriel's Wharf, 56 Upper Ground, SE1 (020 7928 3188). Waterloo tube/rail. **Lunch served** noon-3.15pm Mon-Sat; 12.15-3.15pm Sun. **Dinner served** 5.30-11pm daily. **Main courses** £5.20-£9.25. **Minimum** main course. **Service** 10% for parties of seven or more. **Credit** AmEx, DC, MC, £TC, V.
You have to feel sorry for the chefs at the Gourmet Pizza Company; not only are they forced to adulterate pizzas with the likes of Chinese-style duck and black pudding, but they have to wear red and white checked headscarves while they do it. The management, on the other hand, must be ecstatic, since the punters keep flooding in. A near-perfect location on the South Bank, combined with a no-bookings policy means there's always a substantial queue of diners at the door. To start, we shared a disappointing salad of watery beef tomatoes, bland mozzarella and poor-quality olives; and a canary-yellow, suspiciously smooth garlic pizza crust. As for the pizzas, we avoided Mexican lime chicken and chose instead a grilled aubergine pizza generously laden with roasted vegetables (aubergine, red onion and peppers), goat's cheese and dollops of pesto. This was a flavoursome if rather oily option that was marred by the return of the yellow pizza base. We also tried a tasty Camembert calzone, stuffed with a circumspect portion of cheese and an excess of undercooked spinach. Service was friendly if slightly hurried, and there were still people queuing at the door as we left.
Babies and children welcome; children's menu; high chairs. Bookings accepted for parties of seven or more only. Tables outdoors (20, riverside terrace). **Map 3/7N.**
For branches see index.

East

Walthamstow E17

Franco's (Uffizzi)

753-755 Lea Bridge Road, E17 (020 8509 2259). Walthamstow Central tube/rail/Wood Street rail. **Dinner served** 5.30-11pm Tue-Thur, Sun; 5.30pm-2am Fri, Sat. **Main courses** £4.20-£12. **Credit** AmEx, MC, V.
Impossible to miss, this one. The only culinary stop on this stretch of busy through road, Franco's (aka Uffizzi) is almost opposite the huge Italian trade warehouse. Outside, there's a life-sized Elvis figure standing next to the single pavement table. Mr Presley is presumably advertising the musicians who supposedly play, but at 8.30pm on a Saturday it was canned Abba all the way – until one of the bar staff took control of the small stage to kick off the karaoke with a fully-lit version of *Stuck in the Middle With You*. The three assembled party tables lapped it up. We probably left at the wrong moment, because unfortunately the meal itself was nothing to sing about. Funghi firenze had mushrooms, ricotta and spinach in an off-putting soupy brew, while the avocado/Gorgonzola combo came similarly equipped. Seafood spaghetti was cheap but not so cheerful. Tagliatelle salmone, while better, sacrificed the spinach to the fish. Tiramisu, anarchic but solid, was the only option when all the other (frozen) desserts were plainly visible in a large cabinet located just down from the Renaissance murals (draped with plastic bunting declaring: 'sorry to see you go'). There's no denying the cheeky energy of this place, but it's a shame the kitsch collisions extend to the plate.
Babies and children welcome; children's menu; high chairs. Entertainment: karaoke, band from 10pm Fri; Italian soloist from 10pm Sat. Tables outdoors (3, patio). Takeaway service.

Wapping E1

Il Bordello

75-81 Wapping High Street, E1 (020 7481 9950). Wapping tube/100 bus. **Lunch served** noon-3pm Mon-Fri. **Dinner served** 6-11pm Mon-Sat. **Meals served** 1-10.30pm Sun. **Main courses** £6.75-£16.95. **Credit** AmEx, MC, V.
An oasis in the desert of new Thameside housing, this dining room for the Docklands dormitories is well worth a trip east. Absolutely packed on a Tuesday night (mostly with local City types), its tables gather around a central square bar, mounted with beaten copper. The menu has an extensive list of hors d'oeuvres and main courses, with a healthy crop of mainly fish and meat dishes (monkfish with mushrooms, tomatoes and white wine; and veal chop grilled with sage, butter and wine, for instance). Prices soar well into double figures; only pizzas and pasta cost under a tenner. Rocket salad with grilled prawns combined spicy leaves with very soft shellfish, while garlic mushrooms came swimming in olive oil and chilli yet were surprisingly bland. Pizza Ricardo delivered the expected topping of aubergine (a little thickly sliced) and Parmesan; and a large helping of seafood risotto was well-presented and tasty. A huge tomato salad defeated us. A tip-off from regulars at the next table steered us away from sorbet, but we were happy with crème brûlée and profiteroles. All in all, Il Bordello makes for a pleasant dining experience, and is clearly vital for the area.
Babies and children welcome; high chairs. Booking advisable. Disabled: toilet. Takeaway service.

North East

Stoke Newington N16

Il Bacio

61 Stoke Newington Church Street, N16 (020 7249 3833). Stoke Newington rail/73 bus. **Dinner served** 6-11.15pm Mon-Fri. **Meals served** 12.30-11.15pm Sat, Sun. **Main courses** £6- £14.95. **Credit** AmEx, DC, MC, V.
Il Bacio works, no doubt about that. Regardless of its siting on this restaurant-packed axis of Stoke Newington, it's always full by mid-evening. Service has a family feel to it. Decorations are informal and somewhat mixed, including a large number of assorted pictures. However, it's the pizzas that are at are the heart of the operation. Sporting supremely delicate bases, they're among the best, and certainly the biggest we've come across. Don't get sidetracked by starters; asparagus heads with goat's cheese and mushroom, and calamares, were both well presented, but bland, dishes. In contrast, pizza segreta – topped with olives, rocket and the thinnest slices of aubergine – had a stunning simplicity and sensational flavours. Against this, risotto funghi had no chance; a little on the small side, it was creamy but lacked depth of flavour. For dessert, however, zabaglione had the authentic kick of liquor, and a pancake with ice-cream and Amaretto was equally distinctive. Il Bacio has recently opened a delicatessen, just opposite the restaurant.
Babies and children welcome; high chairs. Takeaway service.

North

Finchley N3

Zucchero

202-208 Regent's Park Road, N3 (020 8371 0833). Finchley Central tube/82, 260 bus. **Lunch served** noon-2.30pm Tue-Fri. **Dinner served** 6-11.30pm Tue-Sat. **Meals served** noon-11.30pm Sun. **Main courses** £8.50-£16.90. **Service** 10%. **Credit** AmEx, MC, V.
The wide frontage and light, spacious interior of this Finchley favourite boded well for our first visit, a late-evening midweek sortie. We arrived at 9.45pm, and it soon became clear most customers eat here significantly earlier. By 10.15pm the reasonably busy floor had emptied, and service noticeably sped up to push us the same way. Maybe we hit a bad night, but this certainly put a damper on events. Pizza focaccia (the now standard garlic and tomato bread entrée) was fair enough, and went well with a quaffable red wine while we waited for the pasta mains. A special, spaghetti rospo, with its monkfish and herb zest, outperformed its admittedly cheaper seafood counterpart. The offered salad dressing (a thick creamy white sauce) was swiftly declined, but the tiramisu, though poorly presented, was the real McCoy. Rushed but decent coffees finished off a patchy excursion. Zucchero may not be worth a long trip, but is a useful local watering-hole if you eat before the stars come out.
Babies and children welcome. Booking advisable dinner. Tables outdoors (2, pavement). Takeaway service.

Pangaea.
See page 189.

Islington N1

Calzone

35 Upper Street, N1 (020 7359 9191). Angel tube. **Meals served** noon-11pm Mon-Thur, Sun; noon-11.30pm Fri, Sat. **Main courses** £4.95-£7.85. **Credit** AmEx, MC, V.
Green is the colour at this lively branch of the chain specialising in folded pizzas. A warm night meant the windows and doors were wide open, bringing the Upper Street bustle into an already high-volume mix of chatting patrons and soft-rock/Europop soundtrack. Once you clock that the venue calls itself a pizza bar (the key word being 'bar'), all the attendant stuff falls into place: fast turnover, small tables, a long bench seat down one wall. Peroni is among the beers; a small glass of house white wine costs £2.75. To eat, rocket salad with Parmesan was our first port of call: fresh and welcome. Tagliatelle carpigliana was surprisingly fine, too; its mix of spinach, pine nuts, Gorgonzola and mascarpone was as appetising as it sounds. The seafood calzone (in open-plan format) brimmed with prawns, mussels, salmon and anchovies. Desserts continued the generous trend: house speciality, chocolate goloso, was creamy but colossal, while tiramisu acquitted itself well. In short, the menu worked, the bill was fine, but the place doesn't make you want to linger – a shame after such a decent meal.
Babies and children welcome; children's menu; high chairs. Tables outdoors (4, pavement). Takeaway service. **Map 16/2N.**
For branches see index.

La Porchetta

141 Upper Street, N1 (020 7288 2488). Angel tube/Highbury & Islington tube/rail. **Meals served** noon-midnight daily. **Main courses** £4-£6.10. **Credit** MC, V.
The new branch of La Porchetta may look very different to the original in Stroud Green, being minimal rather than cosy, but scratch beneath the surface and they're pretty much the same. So if you liked the noise (pop music played too loudly for easy conversation), the crush (tables too close together, a constant queue at the door), the pizzas (pretty good efforts that overhang large white plates) and the staff (friendly, dippy, rushed) at the original, you'll like them here. Minuses include the drinks list ('rosé' is as much description as you get) and the salads – unless specified, they come drenched in an unpleasant goo-like dressing. There's also a huge list of pastas, including paglia with broccoli, chillies and garlic; and spaghetti al nero di seppia (cuttlefish in their own ink). Stinco di porco (shin of pork in a garlic, mushroom and white wine sauce) is one of four meat dishes. We, however, chose pizzas and had no complaints about the Porchetta's romano (tomato, mozzarella, ricotta and spinach) and rucola (tomato, rocket and Parma ham). Nevertheless, we couldn't wait to drink up the not-quite-cold-enough Italian lager and head for the relative peace and quiet of Islington's streets.
Babies and children welcome; high chairs. Takeaway service. **Map 16/1O.**
For branch see index.

Scu-zi

360 St John Street, EC1 (020 7833 4393). Angel tube. **Meals served** 11am-11pm daily. **Main courses** £6.95-£8.95. **Credit** AmEx, MC, V.
A large, new and confused operation. Scu-zi is positioned presumably to catch the Upper Street and Clerkenwell overspills, yet there's an identity dilemma about the place. On one hand you have the theme-bar influences all over the place: multiple levels, primary-coloured walls, faux-primitivist paintings and laminated menus (plus an admittedly great wall of glass giving views on to the Islington house backs). Then you have the desire for Italian authenticity mixed with a decidedly Yankee accent to both menu and presentation. All this adds up to a lack of distinctive character only partly alleviated by service that's almost too eager to please. We kicked off with two choices from the varied list of bruschettas – artichoke pâté was creamy but bland; the field mushroom variety, however, was excellent. A shared tomato and onion salad was ruined by a cheap-tasting dressing. On to the mains: pizza Mediterranean carried a clutch of vegetarian toppings, but was heavy in both portion-size and crust. Black linguine with tiger prawns was interesting in an inky sort of way, but the tomato sauce swamped the dish, leaving the shellfish barely visible. We finished the meal with a firm, filling, enjoyable traditional cheesecake. A lot of money has gone into this venture; whether it was well-spent is questionable.
Babies and children welcome; high chairs. Disabled: toilet. Entertainment: musicians Sat evenings (phone for details). Separate room for parties, seats 50. Tables outdoors (7, pavement). Takeaway service. **Map 15/3O.**

North West

West Hampstead NW6

La Brocca

273 West End Lane, NW6 (020 7433 1989). West Hampstead tube/rail/139, C11 bus.
Bar **Open** noon-11pm daily.
Restaurant **Dinner served** 6.30-10.30pm Mon, Sun; 6.30-11pm Tue-Thur; 6.30-11.30pm Fri, Sat. **Main courses** £4.95-£8.45.
Both **Credit** AmEx, JCB, MC, £TC, V.
With La Brocca buzzing on a Tuesday night, we searched in vain for our booked table before realising we were in the (ground floor) bar area. You can get snacks here but the restaurant proper is down some stairs to the left. The room is as hot as a pizza oven when full, yet on balance it's probably worth enduring the heat to sample what is clearly highly popular local cuisine. There was an ever-changing line-up of waiters during our meal, one per course it seemed, but all were friendly and attentive. First off, a special of bruschetta with aubergine paste was fresh, with a tang of rosemary. A slightly amended four seasons pizza switched Parma ham for goat's cheese, but worked well, despite some over-large toppings. Fettuccine con funghi was exactly as described, and did the job. Mixed salad came packed in a small, deep bowl and was too heavy to be a welcome contrast. To conclude a satisfying meal, strong coffees made more of an impact than the standard desserts. A decent local pizza parlour.
Babies and children welcome. Booking advisable. Entertainment: jazz duo (in the bar) 8.30-11pm Thur. Tables outdoors (4, garden).

"I must have died and gone to heaven... The Elbow Room
is like New York... only better" - - The Independent

"A wonderful pool bar / restaurant / nightclub...
No wonder they call it the rebirth of pool" - - Time Out

"An ingenious combination of nightclub & pool hall" - - GQ

"The coolest place to play pool" - - Elle

FREE LUNCH
pay for an hour of pool (£6) from
12 noon til 3pm & get 1 meal FREE

tel> 020 7278 3244 / fax> 020 7278 3266
website: www.elbow-room.co.uk
e-mail: islington@elbow-room.co.uk
89-91 chapel market, islington, london N1

The Elbow Room
POOL LOUNGE AND BAR

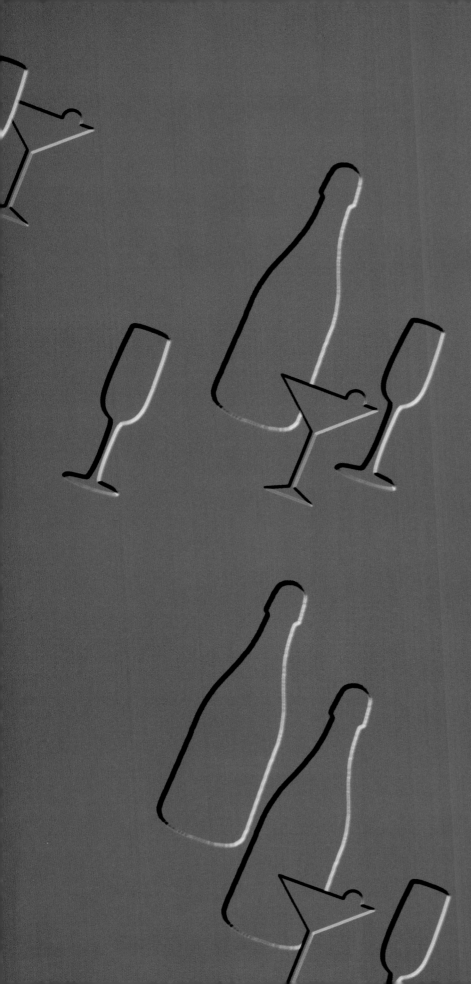

On the Town

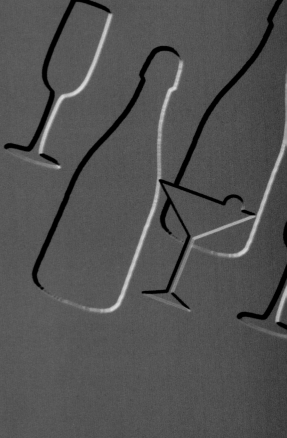

Brasseries

Central

City EC4

The Bridge
*1 Paul's Walk, off High Timber Street, EC4
(020 7236 0000). Blackfriars tube/rail.* **Open**
11am-11pm Mon-Fri; 11am-6pm Sat, Sun.
Lunch served noon-3pm daily. **Dinner
served** 6-10pm Mon-Fri. **Main courses** £11-
£13. **Service** 12½%. **Credit** AmEx, MC, V.
This new venture has suffered from the great
wobbly bridge fiasco, having opened at the
beginning of May 2000 to coincide with it. Despite
a great view over Tate Modern, the Bridge has a
total lack of ambience. Blue lights and a tiled floor
make it feel like a hotel lobby. The food has an
Eastern bent: all-day dim sum (including crispy
duck spring rolls and vegetable won ton) was
expensive at £8, and the seaweed needed to be
crispier. Tiger prawn and baby squid salad came
doused in a curry-flavoured sauce (not mentioned
on the menu) that obscured the flavour of the
mango and water chestnuts. The same curry
sauce appeared with the (too salty) crab and
ginger fish cakes, which were meant to come with
coconut cream dressing. A daily special of lamb
and aubergine curry arrived in a creamy sauce.
Desserts include lemon and elderflower tart with
raspberry sauce and crème fraîche. Each dish
would have been better if simplified – all the extra
flavours just created confusion. A redeeming
feature was the impressive service. Though the
Bridge should pick up when the bridge reopens,
it has wobbles of its own, and appears to be aimed
at City wallets.
*Babies and children admitted. Disabled: toilet.
Tables outdoors (9, terrace).* **Map 4/7O.**

Clerkenwell & Farringdon EC1

Al's Bar Café
*11-13 Exmouth Market, EC1 (020 7837
4821). Angel tube/19, 38, 55, 341 bus.* **Open**
8am-1am Mon, Tue; 8am-2am Wed-Sat; 10am-
11pm Sun. **Meals served** 8am-11pm Mon-
Sat; 10am-11pm Sun. **Main courses**
£5.50-£8.50. **Set lunch** (noon-4pm Mon-Fri)
£6. **Service** 12½% for parties of five or more.
Credit AmEx, MC, V.
Al's was ensconced in Exmouth Market several
years ago, and continues to draw people for its
whopping breakfasts and chirpy, lively feel. If you
can't cope with the bustle or the smoke (from
frying food and fags), try the heated outside area.
There's a choice of mini, English, Builder's, Rather
Big and Super Veggie breakfasts, with prices from
£3.50 to £6.50. We sampled the breaded Brie to
start – it was a bit miserly and burnt. The English
breakfast comprised a Cumberland sausage, egg,
tomato, mushrooms, two slices of toast and two
rashers of bacon. Though not bad for the price, it
wasn't great – all a bit black around the edges.
Chunky chips are the thing here, or daily specials
like sausages, beans and mash (which was going
down a storm with gangs of local journos and
wide boys). There are posher dishes such as fish
cakes, chicken fajitas and lamb skewers, too. To
drink, try a cocktail: the absinthe and Red Bull
should sort the men from the boys. Al's is down
to earth, busy and unpretentious, yet not always
as friendly as you'd expect.
*Babies and children welcome (until 8pm).
Booking advisable. Entertainment: basement
clubs and parties every fortnight (phone for
details). Tables outdoors (10, pavement).
Takeaway service.* **Map 3/4N.**

Covent Garden WC2

Café des Amis du Vin
*11-14 Hanover Place, WC2 (020 7379 3444).
Covent Garden tube.* **Meals served** 11.30am-
11.30pm Mon-Sat. **Main courses** £9.95-
£16.95. **Set lunch** £12.50 two courses,
£15 three courses. **Pre- & post-theatre
menu** (5.30-7pm, 10.30-11.30pm) £10.50 two
courses. **Service** 12½%. **Credit** AmEx, DC,
JCB, MC, £TC, V.

This spick and span venue offers unexpectedly
good food in a setting that's better suited to
business lunches than cosy evening meals. The
room is smart and determinedly modern, with
plenty of pale wood furnishings. In summer,
glass doors open on to a colourful mural in an
unprepossessing little alleyway. Starters range
from £5.75 to £7.95 and include Thai red fish and
calamares cakes with sweet chilli dressing. The
priciest main course is a Scotch fillet steak at
£16.95. A black buttery risotto with four big
prawns was deliciously creamy and light, and
looked handsome on the plate, as did the
beautifully cooked duck with sweet potato
fondant and baby pak choi, served with vivid
pink berries. The dessert menu is enticing too; it
includes summer pudding with clotted cream,
and strawberry crème brûlée with jus de fraise.
Service is bright and brisk. Nowhere in Covent
Garden is cheap, but here you get something
worth paying for.
*Booking advisable. Separate room for parties,
seats 65. Tables outdoors (10, pavement).*
Map 14/6L.

Tuttons
*11-12 Russell Street, WC2 (020 7836 4141).
Covent Garden tube.* **Meals served** 9.30am-
11.30pm Mon-Sat; 9.30am-11pm Sun. **Main
courses** £9.70-£14.50. **Service** 12½%.
Credit AmEx, DC, JCB, TC, V.
The ultimate tourist-trap brasserie, bang in the
heart of Covent Garden, this one's really cruising
on its location. On a blistering hot day, it was
pleasant to sit in the conservatory and look out
over the bustle – but don't come here for the food.
For starters, spicy, lifeless spicy crab cakes were
paired with a pleasant sweet tamarind sauce, while
some tiny grilled tiger prawns lay on a soggy bed
of pak choi, lemongrass and ginger. Penne with
sun-dried tomatoes in a rather heavy cream and
pesto sauce was a generous plateful, but didn't
merit its £9.80 price tag. Oriental duck and fine
noodle salad consisted of six small slices of rather
limp duck swamped in a tangle of anaemic
noodles, bedded in a mass of lettuce leaves.
Wines range from £11.90 to £28.50 and there are
a dozen available by the glass. Most of the staff
look suicidally miserable and are very reluctant to
accommodate the endless stream of tourists and
tables of office workers. A basic lunch for two
without wine came to over £40. Blame the location.
*Babies and children welcome. Separate rooms
for parties, seating 20 and 30. No-smoking
tables. Tables outdoors (8, pavement).*
Map 14/6L.

Knightsbridge SW1, SW3

The Fifth Floor Café
*Harvey Nichols, Knightsbridge, SW1 (020 7823
1839). Knightsbridge tube.* **Meals served**
10am-11pm Mon-Sat; noon-6pm Sun. **Tea
served** 3.30-6pm daily. **Main courses** £8.95-
£14.50. **Set tea** £12.50. **Set dinners** £17.50
two courses, £20 three courses. **Service** 12½%.
Credit AmEx, DC, JCB, MC, TC, V.
Sunglasses and, of course, mobiles are *de rigueur*
at this haven for ladies (and lads) who lunch. The
Fifth Floor is a light, bustling space, with brightly
coloured chairs, and tables that are too close
together. Aproned, white-shirted staff are brisk
and clued-up, though a bit grim-faced. There's a
terrace with heaters and a view over the rooftops.
From the set menu, which changes daily, we
sampled a warm salad of chicken livers, bacon
and Madeira; it was deliciously moist and very
moreish. Risotto primavera was a fresh, creamy
concoction with plenty of broccoli and Parmesan.
There's also an à la carte menu; expect dishes like
an impeccable Caesar salad, wun tun wrapped
prawns with sweet chilli jam, and gorgeous
sun-dried tomato and olive tortelloni with tomato
and basil sauce. We finished with a generous
slice of subtle, creamy, chocolate mocha cheesecake to share. The menu suggests wines to pair
with each dish. There are plenty of bottles to
choose from, starting at £12.50 and rising to
£2,500 for a 1982 Chateau Pétrus. All the food's
very fresh, comes in good portions and is nicely
presented. The perfect spot for a lunchtime
indulgence, or to treat your mum.

*Babies and children welcome; high chairs.
No-smoking tables. Tables outdoors (18, roof
terrace).* **Map 12/9F.**

Leicester Square WC2

Browns
*82-84 St Martin's Lane, WC2 (020 7497
5050). Leicester Square tube.* **Meals served**
noon-midnight Mon-Sat; noon-11pm Sun.
Main courses £5.95-£16.95. **Set meals**
(noon-3pm, 4-6.30pm, from 10pm, daily) £9.95
two courses. **Service** 12½% for parties of five
or more. **Credit** AmEx, DC, MC, £TC, V.
With this spruce chain, you always know what
you're getting. Occupying a large light space with
a profusion of plants and overhead fans, Browns
gets very busy – on our visit mainly with big
groups of women on office outings. It's also very
noisy: not the place for a quiet tête-à-tête. If you
don't book, you might have to wait a while in
the very cramped bar. The food's as reliable
as the setting. We liked a well-balanced Caesar
salad starter and a generous portion of king
prawns in garlic. The pies are always good;
fisherman's pie was a hearty dish packed with
fresh fish. Confit of duck was beautifully cooked
and not too dry. Chips are great, too. Daily
specials include dishes such as tuna niçoise, and
Chinese-style pork chops with stir-fried veg. The
sickly-sweet stem ginger ice-cream was a bit of a
let-down, but otherwise this was a satisfying
meal, with impressively on-the-ball, friendly
service. A tad predictable, then, but a safe bet for
a group night out.
*Babies and children welcome; high chairs;
under-12s eat for free (when accompanied by
an adult eating from the carte). Booking
advisable. Disabled: toilet. Separate rooms for
parties (4), seating 10-100.* **Map 14/7L.**
For branches see index.

Marylebone W1

Café Bagatelle
*The Wallace Collection, Manchester Square,
W1 (020 7563 9505). Bond Street tube.*
Meals served 10am-4.15pm daily. **Main
courses** £10-£12. **Credit** AmEx, MC, V.

Part of the revamp at the Wallace Collection,
Café Bagatelle is housed in a glassed-over courtyard. There's a café and brunch menu, but we
couldn't resist the weightier brasserie menu
(especially after queueing for a while). Lighter
dishes include mixed leaves with walnuts and
sweet peppers (a decent enough starter), iced raw
tomato soup with basil mayonnaise and duck
rillettes on toasted onion bread. But the main
courses were the real stars: plaice fillets with
fennel salad and a white sauce with a hint of
vanilla sounded odd but was surprisingly good;
lemon-roasted poussin, dusted with paprika
and served with brown lentils in an earthy, rich
stock was another winner. Stephen Bull (*see p131*
Modern European) is overseeing the Café and
it shows – an impressive debut.
*Babies and children admitted. Disabled: toilet.
No smoking.* **Map 2/5G.**

Piccadilly SW1

Café Flo
*11-12 Haymarket, SW1 (020 7976 1313).
Piccadilly Circus tube.* **Open** 10am-11.30pm
Mon-Sat; 10am-11pm Sun. **Breakfast served**
10am-noon daily. **Meals served** noon-
11.30pm Mon-Sat; noon-11pm Sun. **Main
courses** £6.70-£14.80. **Set meal** £8.50 two
courses incl coffee. **Service** 12½%. **Credit**
AmEx, JCB, MC, £TC, V.
This branch of the well-worn chain is typically
pleasant but oddly characterless, with palm trees
and bleached-wood panels (covering what was
originally a beautiful room). The main space is
way too bright, with weird lights resembling
paper bags. There's a smart second room with
softer lighting and close-together tables. Flo
mainly caters for business lunches, tourists and
Bridget Jones types downing the chardonnay.
Wine costs £9.85-£21.30 a bottle. Deep-fried
king prawns, and chicken liver salad were both
fine starters. Irritatingly, mains were brought
within a minute of the starters being cleared.
Salmon fish cake with salad and garlic aïoli
was pretty good. The steak, however, was
awful – chewy, dry and in a tasteless pepper
sauce – it tasted nothing like sirloin. The service
was generally keen, if somewhat dippy. Yet our

overall impression was of blandness, and for these prices the food should really be much better. Flo is fine for a coffee, or snacks such as olives and potato skins, but we'd prefer taking a five-minute stroll into Soho to sample something less ordinary.
Babies and children welcome; children's menu. No-smoking tables. Separate room for parties, seats 70. **Map 13/7K.**
For branches see index.

Zinc Bar & Grill
21 Heddon Street, W1 (020 7255 8899). Piccadilly Circus tube. **Open** noon-midnight Mon-Sat. **Meals served** noon-11pm Mon-Wed; noon-11.30pm Thur-Sat. **Main courses** £8.95-£14. **Set meal** (noon-7pm Mon-Sat) £11.50 two courses, £14 three courses. **Credit** AmEx, DC, JCB, MC, £TC, V.
To be honest we didn't expect much of the Zinc Bar, so the quality of both the food and service came as a pleasant surprise – it's certainly not resting on the Conran laurels. Everything is very shiny and sleek, as you'd expect, and gets pretty loud – the place works best as a handy after-work spot, and has plenty of bar space should you just fancy a drink. Smoked fish soup was heartily fishy, while a fish cake was packed full of fresh salmon and served on a light buttery sauce that was the perfect complement. We were tempted by the crustacea, too: crab or lobster mayonnaise, or half a dozen Irish rock oysters. Confit duck leg was beautifully crisp, served with creamy herb mash and a lip-smackingly rich sauce. The leg of lamb was similarly successful, with unusual minted hollandaise and crunchy golden chips. Fairly standard brasserie desserts like lemon tart, crème brûlée with berry compote, and vanilla bavarois with poached plums, were prettily presented. The thud of music can be an irritant here, as can the fog of cigar smoke. We'd have liked a cooler for the wine, but staff were otherwise amenable and keen (particularly the maitre d').
Babies and children welcome; children's menu; high chairs. Separate room for parties, seats 40. Tables outside (9, pavement). **Map 13/7J.**

St James's SW1

ICA Café ★
The Mall, SW1 (020 7930 8619). Piccadilly Circus tube/Charing Cross tube/rail. **Membership** £1.50 (day). **Open** noon-11pm Mon; noon-1am Tue-Sat; noon-10.30pm Sun. **Lunch served** noon-4pm daily. **Dinner served** 6-11pm Mon-Fri. **Main courses** £8.80-£11.80. **Credit** AmEx, LV, MC, V.
Food is served in a dark cavernous room with shared tables, as well as in the bar (which is full of louche arty types, all smoking avidly, who treat it like their club). It was totally chaotic on our visit – not enough staff – and our intensely fashionable waiter was seriously stressed. The food is pretty good, and imaginative too. Brunch is served at weekends, and an 'Italianate Kitchen' is available on weekdays from noon to 4pm. The ICA 'street foods' served in the evening include Japanese and Brazilian dishes (£2.75 per dish, £10.50 four dishes). Yakitori (skewers of organic chicken with peppers and dipping sauce) was beautifully served on a Japanese-style wood and tiled platter. Perfectly cooked, it came with a great lime and coriander dressing. Brazilian salt-cod croquettes with chilli salsa are also worth trying. Bar snacks range from Caesar salad to pad Thai, and okonomiyaki (Japanese pancake, with shiitake mushrooms and nori flakes; it tastes like a dull omelette). Safer bets are the organic burgers and falafels. Drinks take up most of the menu, with a stonking list of cocktails (from £5.25), a choice of around 16 wines (£11.50-£29), and even absinthe. Well worth forking out £1.50 day membership for.
Babies and children admitted. Disabled: toilet. Entertainment: DJs and club nights (phone for details). No-smoking tables. Separate rooms for parties, seating 60 and 80. **Map 7/8K.**

Soho W1

Bar du Marché
19 Berwick Street, W1 (020 7734 4606). Piccadilly Circus or Tottenham Court Road tube. **Meals served** noon-11pm Mon-Sat. **Main courses** £6.95-£10.95. **Set meals** £8.95 two courses, £10.95 three courses. **Credit** MC, £TC, V.
This old favourite exudes charm and character amid the chaos of Berwick Street market; you feel almost as if you've walked into the Marais. It's usually busy with regulars, locals and general easy-lifers. Smoking is undertaken with a vengeance. Staff are French, charming and easy-going. There's a set menu of light meals, with entrées such as smoked duck salad, plus baguettes, steak frites, chicken, lamb, sausages and salmon. The slightly more expensive main menu is still pretty good value, featuring wild mushroom vol au vent, own-made fish soup, and ravioli of goat's cheese (a chunky pastry parcel packed with goodies). Main courses of rack of lamb with rosemary and gratin dauphinoise, and breast of duck in (delicious) honey sauce with sautéed potatoes, were both top-notch – beautifully cooked meat, generous portions, piquant flavours. Puds include the flamboyant crêpe à l'orange et Grand Marnier, and tarte au citron. The crisp house white costs £9.50. A wonderfully laidback spot, with better than average food.
Babies and children admitted. Book Thur-Sat. No-smoking tables. Tables outdoors (2, pavement). Takeaway service. **Map 13/6K.**

Café Bohème
13 Old Compton Street, W1 (020 7734 0623). Leicester Square tube. **Meals served** 8am-3am Mon-Thur; 24 hours Fri, Sat; 9am-11pm Sun. **Main courses** £9.75-£12.95. **Cover** £3 before 11pm, £4 after 11pm Wed-Sat. **Credit** AmEx, DC, MC, £TC, V.
This highly successful venture has expanded, and now includes the Bohème Kitchen next door for less formal dining. The bar has been redecorated, and ruined in the process, making it bland and All Bar One-like, with wicker chairs; it used to be darkly atmospheric. The place is still crushingly busy every night of the week, however, largely due in part to its late licence. Thankfully, the restaurant's furnishings have been left alone and the room is still charmingly cosy. The menu features breakfast, sandwiches and salads plus light mains, fish and meat. A starter of grilled goat's cheese and fennel tartlet with roast pepper pesto was pleasingly chunky, on a light pastry; kiln-smoked salmon with pickled gherkins and baby fennel on sautéed new potatoes was another enjoyable starter. Warm chicken, bacon and mushroom salad with tarragon vinaigrette was fine, but better was fillet of sea bass, warm salad of wild rocket, crushed new potatoes and artichokes with roast pepper infused balsamic. A bottle of house white came beautifully chilled. Bohème isn't cheap, but it's not as astro as it could be in this prime position on Soho's main thoroughfare, and service is friendly and unpushy, unlike the often snotty, chaotic dealings in the bar.
Babies and children admitted. Book dinner Wed-Sun. Entertainment: jazz 3-5pm Tue-Thur, Sun. Tables outdoors (7, pavement). **Map 13/6K.**

Dôme
57-59 Old Compton Street, WC2 (020 7287 0770). Piccadilly Circus or Leicester Square tube. **Meals served** 9.30am-1am Mon-Wed, Sun; 10am-midnight Thur-Sat. **Main courses** £4.95-£8.95. **Set meal** (noon-8pm) £8.95 two courses. **Service** 10% for parties of eight or more. **Credit** AmEx, LV, MC, V.
The original brasserie chain, with its familiar green and gold decor, long bars and bargain fixed-price menu, the Dôme has always made a useful stop-off point for a coffee or wine. We've been used to lacklustre service at this branch, but on this visit it was exemplary. Poor quality food quickly dampened our enthusiasm. A spiced crab fritter starter was nasty, having a texture like dry pâté, and came with tomato hamburger relish (rather than the advertised tomato and chilli jam dip). The burger was OK, and came with comfortingly chunky chips and, yes, that same old tomato relish. Black penne with chilli, tomato and basil sauce looked striking and tasted fine, but wasn't a show-stopper: it could have done with spicing up a little. Hot Belgian waffles with vanilla ice-cream and hot chocolate sauce was dire; the waffle (singular) didn't taste fresh and was filled with some kind of sickly sweet almond paste. Our advice, then – stick to liquid refreshment.
Babies and children welcome. **Map 13/6K.**
For branches see index.

Hujo's
11 Berwick Street, W1 (020 7734 5144). Oxford Circus or Piccadilly Circus tube. **Meals served** noon-midnight Mon-Sat. **Main courses** £7.25-£9.95. **Set meal** (3-7.30pm) £7.45 two courses. **Credit** AmEx, DC, MC, £TC, V.
A handy spot on this bustling, atmospheric market street, Hujo's is more like a posh café than a restaurant. It's a colourful place, with yellow and green tables and cheery yellow walls, but the food is no more than average. Spinach and ricotta cheese filo pastry parcel was very ordinary, while escalibada (grilled red pepper, onion and aubergine with olive oil) was not as tasty as it sounds, consisting of strips of cold vegetables. Not tempted by the scary special of grilled conger eel with plantain, we tried grilled squid salad. Generous rolls of squid were served with new potatoes and came with an oily garlic and lemon dressing. Salmon fish cakes, though, were mundane. Aberdeen Angus rump steak and lyonnaise potatoes might have been a better bet. Hujo's is fine for a relaxed glass of wine in the heart of town: everyone smokes and tables are close together so it's all very cosy. Service is cheerful and the place has a lively vibe on a weekday lunchtime. One for convenience rather than great culinary delights.
Babies and children welcome; high chairs. Takeaway service. **Map 13/6K.**

Randall & Aubin
16 Brewer Street, W1 (020 7287 4447). Piccadilly Circus tube. **Meals served** 11am-midnight Mon-Sat; 4-10.30pm Sun. **Main courses** £6.70-£25. **Credit** AmEx, DC, JCB, MC, V.
This chi-chi little joint was once a butcher's, and retains the white tiled walls and marble-topped counters. Posers, City types and Soho decadents pull up a stool and tuck into enticing fresh seafood – at a price. The menu is divided into hors d'oeuvres, such as Japanese 'fish cakes'; entrées like Caesar salad; baguettes; and rotisserie, with spit-roast chicken and a side order of chips, potatoes, vegetables or salad costing £8.50. Fish-wise, go for a whole lobster and chips with garlic butter, or treat yourself to the platter of fruits de mer (£21.50 per head), a sumptuous display of crab, oysters, prawns, lobster and more; a more modest version can be had for £15.50. Bread and olives were a nice touch – until we discovered they incur a £3 cover charge. Crostini with crab, scallops and more make a good shared starter. Chicken baguette is served with thin, crunchy chips, but avocado, bacon salad with blue cheese dressing was boring – mainly lettuce – and a mean portion for £7.75. The wine list complements the fish, with prices from £11.50 for a 'fruity, quaffable' house wine.
Babies and children admitted. Bookings not accepted. Takeaway service. **Map 13/6K.**

Soho Soho (Rôtisserie)
11-13 Frith Street, W1 (020 7494 3491). Leicester Square tube.
Bar **Open** noon-11pm Mon-Sat; noon-10.30pm Sun.
Rôtisserie **Meals served** noon-12.30am Mon-Sat; noon-10.30pm Sun. **Main courses** £6.80-£23.50.
Both **Service** 12½%. **Credit** AmEx, DC, JCB, MC, V.
Despite being in the heart of Soho, this place is completely devoid of atmosphere: it's neither intimate nor lively, cosy nor buzzy. Whether this lack of character is caused by the cheery painted chairs, the bland tiled floor or the wall-to-wall media types droning on about themselves, we can't be sure. The food's not bad, but pricey. Wines (£9.95-£25.50) are divided into sections such as 'light and crisp', or 'soft and round' (but we hate it when staff give you the large glass of house wine without asking). Goat's cheese gratin on french bread with salad was appetising, but squid in batter (with a dull, vinegary 'Calypso' sauce) was greasy. For mains, choose from omelettes and pasta, or rotisserie and grills. A sirloin steak with béarnaise sauce was a little dry, as was fish cake with tartare sauce and fries. Attentive and on-the-ball service was the highlight – oh, and coffee came with hot milk, always a nice touch. Lunch for two with a glass of wine was nearly £50: steep for food so ordinary.
Babies and children welcome; high chairs. Book dinner. Entertainment: pianist 9.30pm-12.30am Mon-Sat; 8.30-10.30pm Sun. No-smoking tables (until 5.30pm). Separate room for parties, seats 60. Tables outdoors (10, pavement). **Map 13/6K.**

Brasserie Metz.
See page 197.

West

Acton W3

Lehane's

100-102 Churchfield Road, W3 (020 8992 6299). Acton Town tube/Acton Central rail. **Meals served** 10.30am-3.30pm Mon-Fri; 9.30am-4pm Sat. **Dinner served** 7-10pm Tue-Sat. **Main courses** lunch £6.25-£7.50, dinner £8.50-£14.50. **Credit** AmEx, MC, V.

On a rainy night in Acton, Lehane's long, spacious wooden-floored front room and cosy caramel walls made a pleasant first impression, though lower lighting would add more atmosphere. Smokers are relegated to a less salubrious corridor and back room. There's also a mini patio at the rear, with heaters for cooler evenings. Daily specials might include grilled sea bream with warm coriander and tomato dressing, or calf's liver with olive and mustard mash and shallot gravy. A chilled bottle of chardonnay (£10.95) went down well, but starters were unimpressive: field mushrooms with leeks and cheese was merely OK; boring potato skins only just merited the plural – a single potato cut in half. Mains were better: crispy, potatoey salmon fish cakes with good chips; and a tender roast rump of lamb with creamy gratin dauphinoise, red wine and slightly watery mushroom jus. Efficient black-clad staff help make this a more than decent local.

Babies and children welcome (lunch); high chairs. No-smoking tables. Separate room for parties, seats 14. Tables outdoors (5, patio; 2, pavement). Takeaway service.

Ladbroke Grove W10

Brasserie du Marché

349 Portobello Road, W10 (020 8968 5828). Ladbroke Grove tube/15, 52, 295 bus. **Open** noon-midnight daily. **Lunch served** noon-4pm, **dinner served** 7-11pm daily. **Main courses** £8.95-£13.95. **Set lunch** £10.95 two courses Mon-Fri; £12.50 three courses Sun. **Service** 12½% dinner. **Credit** AmEx, DC, JCB, MC, £$FTC, V.

This chirpy little blue place off shabbily hip Golborne Road is laid back and welcoming, particularly at night when fairy lights and candles come into play. There are plenty of seats outside for warmer days; sit and sip decent house white (£9.95) or one of a feisty selection of cocktails. Smoked salmon, marinated anchovies, potato salad with crème fraîche was handsomely presented, though the anchovy was way too salty. Seared scallops, served with lardons, mixed leaves and a sweet chilli sauce, were beautifully tender. Mains were similarly successful. The asparagus risotto had just the right amount of pea and spring onion to prevent it being bland, while grilled duck magret came with broccoli and gorgeously creamy celeriac dauphinoise potatoes, though the honey and lemon coulis was cloyingly lemony. Puddings include the usual brûlées. Unpretentious and easygoing, this is a quirky, quality local.

Babies and children welcome; high chairs. Booking advisable Wed-Sat. Separate room for parties, seats 40. Tables outdoors (12, pavement). **Map 11/Az.**

Notting Hill W11

Portobello Gold

95-97 Portobello Road, W11 (020 7460 4918/4913). Notting Hill Gate tube.
Bar **Open** 11am-11pm Mon-Sat; noon-10.30pm Sun. **Meals served** noon-11pm Mon-Sat; noon-10.30pm Sun.
Café **Open** 10am-midnight daily.
Restaurant **Lunch served** noon-5pm Mon-Sat; 1-5pm Sun. **Dinner served** 7-11.15pm Mon-Sat; 7-9.30pm Sun. **Main courses** £7.50-£11.75. **Service** 10%. **Credit** DC, MC, V.

Portobello Gold looks rather ordinary and backpackerish from the street, but once inside you'll find a hidden oasis past the bar serving decent food in chilled surroundings. The glass-roofed conservatory restaurant bursts with greenery and birdsong. There's a mixture of wicker chairs and a naff/kitsch mural, but get there early and you can nab the hippyish little cushioned platform with low table. Staff are friendly and accommodating. Starters include Irish rock oysters, salads and gazpacho. Our choices – sashimi of salmon and Cajun prawns – were both fresh and zesty. Mains are just as good, with plenty of fish (swordfish steak with potatoes and salad for instance) plus hearty staples such as lasagne and chilli con carne. Coffee's good and the terrine of white and dark chocolate is worth pigging out on. A peaceful hangout for escaping the market's chaos.

Babies and children welcome. Book dinner, lunch Sun; bookings not accepted lunch Sat. No-smoking tables. Tables outdoors (2, balcony; 6, pavement; 14, conservatory). Takeaway service. **Map 11/6A.**

South West

Chelsea SW3

The Market Place

Chelsea Farmers' Market, 125 Sydney Street, SW3 (020 7352 5600). Bus 11, 19, 22, 31, 49. **Meals served** *winter* 9.30am-5pm, *summer* 9.30am-6pm daily. **Main courses** £7.50-£12.95. **Service** 12½% for bills over £10. **Credit** MC, V.

In a golden position just off King's Road, this venue has been subdued by a council ban on evening opening. Poor summer weather hasn't helped its barbecue business, either. On a weekday lunchtime it was dead, though at weekends it still piles punters on to its terrace, which is complete with hanging baskets, parasols and heaters. Locals in shades make up the majority of the clientele. The menu is not the most imaginative, but the food is pretty good on a quiet day, as is the service. Starters include chilli and garlic prawns, antipasti and bruschetta, while mains range from steak to Thai fish cakes, pasta, lamb and burgers (meat and vegetarian). Salad niçoise sounded a bit pricey at £9, but came with a tender tuna steak and a creamy anchovy dressing. For lunch try open focaccia sandwiches with smoked salmon, chicken or steak. There are four red and four white wines (£11-£18.80), plus smoothies or jugs of rum summer punch and Pimm's.

Babies and children welcome. No-smoking tables. Tables outdoors (40, patio). **Map 6/12E.**

Oriel

50-51 Sloane Square, SW3 (020 7730 2804). Sloane Square tube. **Meals served** 8.30am-10.45pm Mon-Sat; 9am-10pm Sun. **Main courses** £6.95-£12.25. **Service** 10% for parties of six or more. **Credit** AmEx, DC, MC, £TC, V.

In the past we've found this Sloane-zone a tad snooty, but it seems to have mellowed with age. In the evening there's a cosy atmosphere, with warm yellow walls, chandeliers and dimmed wall lights. Service was pleasant, we weren't rushed, although there is a constant demand for tables. Non-smokers are rewarded with a window seat in the front room; the main room is smoky. It's loud – often too loud – as well-groomed girls and suity, chain-smoking boys talk at full volume while admiring themselves in the numerous mirrors. We loved the prawn and crab spring rolls with chilli jam; and the seared king scallops with grilled radicchio and balsamic dressing were beautifully cooked and attractively displayed. From a choice of salads and pasta, fish, meats and grills, free-range chicken with Sichuan vegetables and noodles had a pleasant sesame oil flavour, but the chicken was a little on the dry side and overcooked, as was the confit of guinea fowl, served with a rich turnip and potato dauphinoise and Armagnac prune cream sauce. We couldn't manage a pudding, but the list was enticing: raspberry and clotted cream brûlée and steamed sticky pudding with toffee sauce. The wine list starts at £12.50 and includes, of course, plenty of champers (£25.95-£57.80). A low-lit lounge bar with sofas is downstairs.

Disabled: toilet. No bookings accepted. Separate room for parties, seats 80. Tables outdoors (10, pavement). **Map 6/10G.**

Putney SW15

Frère Jacques

136 Upper Richmond Road, SW15 (020 8780 9000/www.frerejacques.co.uk). East Putney tube/Putney rail. **Meals served** noon-11pm daily. **Main courses** £6.90-£13.50. **Set lunch** £7.90 two courses. **Set dinner** £15.90 three courses. **Credit** AmEx, DC, MC, £TC, V.

Sister to the popular Kingston restaurant of the same name, FJ is blond, navy and a little bland, though clean and bright. The food isn't bad. Deep-fried Camembert could have been hotter, but came in a sweet cranberry and red wine coulis, while the special of mushroom tartlette with asparagus sauce was nicely creamy. Crab and prawn salad was pretty unexciting; we didn't expect so much crab mousse. Lamb steak was cooked well, but came in a dull rosemary, red wine and garlic jus. A giant crème brûlée rounded things off swimmingly. Good-value set menus (with a fine choice of dishes), a decent selection of wines (house at £11.90) and pleasant service also count in Frère Jacques' favour. Our main complaint concerns the 'music of the world' tape, which ran the gamut from bagpipe rock to Irish jigs – all a bit much for a Sunday lunchtime.

Babies and children welcome; children's menu; high chairs. No-smoking tables. Separate rooms for parties, seating 14 and 35.
For branch see index.

South Kensington SW3

La Brasserie

272 Brompton Road, SW3 (020 7581 3089). South Kensington tube. **Meals served** 8am-11.30pm Mon-Sat; 9am-11.30pm Sun. **Main courses** £4.60-£19.90. **Set meals** £14 two courses. **Service** 12½%. **Credit** AmEx, DC, JCB, MC, £TC, V.

The scruffy awning doesn't do justice to the grand interior, with its Parisian brasserie-style lamps, gleaming fish bar and penguin-suited waiters. Customers range from the inordinately well-heeled (including a braying crowd wearing jodhpurs), to chain-smoking regulars – all willing to pay premium prices. Deep-fried mushrooms with tartare sauce, and thick, warming fish soup, were both spot-on. To follow, minute steak came with good crispy chips and was utterly French. A burger, served with an egg and anchovy on top, was rough-hewn and flavoursome. Yet La Brasserie is not without drawbacks. We resented being jammed in so close to the next table. And though we were chuffed when our request for two filter coffees yielded a huge cafetière, we were shocked to be charged £5.30 for it. An oddly hefty bill left a sour taste after an otherwise decent meal in lively surroundings.

Babies and children admitted. Book dinner; bookings not accepted lunch Sat, Sun. Disabled: toilet. Tables outdoors (4, pavement). **Map 12/10E.**

Francofill

1 Old Brompton Road, SW7 (020 7584 0087). South Kensington tube/14, 49, 74, 345, C1 bus. **Meals served** 11am-11pm daily. **Main courses** £7.95-£11.95. **Credit** AmEx, LV, MC, £TC, V.

This bright blue venue opposite South Ken tube station deals in French fast food. Inside it's all pale wood and paper tablecloths, with a red, white and blue colour scheme. The bar area has TVs and sofas. The pukka clientele is generally made up of smart office workers after a quick steak and chips. Starters include snails in garlic butter, and asparagus with béarnaise sauce. Then choose lamb, chicken, beef or salmon (£7.50-£8.25) and select a sauce (mustard, herb or Provençal); this comes with chips or salad. There are also heavier mains such as stews, ratatouille, duck breast or sausage and mash with beans, plus salads (£8-£9). An onion and cheese tart was a bit soggy – steak and chips is the best bet. Puds are the usual tartes, brûlées and mousses. A bar snack menu is served from 11am-5pm. There's a range of cocktails and over a dozen wines by the glass. It's all perky enough, but feels more like somewhere for a quick bite rather than a leisurely lunch: a kind of upmarket French McDonald's.

Babies and children welcome; crayons; high chairs. No-smoking tables. Tables outdoors (4, pavement). Takeaway service. **Map 12/10D.**

The Oratory

232 Brompton Road, SW3 (020 7584 3493). South Kensington tube. **Meals served** noon-10.30pm daily. **Main courses** £7-£13.50. **Service** 12½%. **Credit** AmEx, MC, £TC, V.

This good-value venue, mere steps from the South Ken museums, is worth knowing about. Its decor is a cross between shabby and grand, with wrought-iron chairs and burgundy velvet banquette seating, walls painted with gold foliage, coloured-glass chandeliers, and rather lurid light fittings. Giant terracotta pots of ferns add to its slightly eccentric air. Staff are hugely accommodating and smiley. Food is fairly priced for the area, but it's the wine that comes as the best surprise, with a perfectly decent bottle of house white at just a fiver, or a chardonnay for £7.50. We plumped for a veritable mountain of crispy deep-fried potato skins with sour cream and chives, and good spring rolls with sweet chilli sauce. Mains include Thai chicken curry with lemon and poppy-seed rice, and own-made fish cakes with spinach and sorrel béchamel. Stir-fried vegetables with ginger, coriander and noodles didn't look too exciting but was packed with flavour, if a little on the salty side; a generous pile of tagliatelle with sun-dried tomatoes, basil and toasted pine nuts was also appetising. As the evening wears on, the Oratory starts to swing – not surprisingly with wine at these prices.

Babies and children welcome. Booking advisable. Tables outdoors (5, pavement). **Map 12/10E.**

Sheen SW14

The Depot

Tideway Yard, Mortlake High Street, SW14 (020 8878 9462). Barnes Bridge or Mortlake rail/209 bus. **Open** 10am-11pm Mon-Sat; 10am-10.30pm Sun. **Lunch served** noon-3pm, **dinner served** 6-11pm, Mon-Sat. **Meals served** noon-10.30pm Sun. **Main courses** £8.50-£13.50. **Set lunch** (Mon-Fri) £9.95 two courses. **Set dinner** (Mon-Thur) £13.50 three courses. **Service** 12½%. **Credit** AmEx, DC, MC, £TC, V.

It's clear from the nose-to-tail BMWs in the car park that the Depot has Barnes sewn up. With its airy, light interior, bold paintings and conservatory with river view, the restaurant makes a bright first impression. Sadly, having a rich and ready market on the doorstep has made the staff a little lazy. Service was vague and lacklustre. White wine was served tepid, and there wasn't an ice cube in sight. Starters cheered us up: Jerusalem artichoke soup with saffron mascarpone was pleasingly subtle, while a Caesar salad was well presented. Next, though, fish cakes had an overpoweringly haddocky flavour and came with avocado salad drenched in lime juice. Char-grilled vegetables with spring onion polenta and goat's cheese salad made a fine (though only) vegetarian option. Desserts included vanilla cheesecake with exotic fruits, and apple and almond tart with its own ice and apple balsamic. The decent wine list starts at £10.50 a bottle. The Depot is certainly a room with a view (but only if you book early and ask for a window seat) but appears to be on cruise control, despite a new chef.

Babies and children welcome; children's menu; crayons and books; high chairs. Booking advisable. No-smoking tables. Tables outdoors (10, patio).

South

Balham SW12

Café Méliès

104 Bedford Hill, SW12 (020 8673 9656). Balham tube/rail. **Meals served** 9am-7pm Mon-Wed; 9am-10.30pm Thur-Sat; 9am-3pm Sun. **Main courses** £6.50-£11. **Unlicensed. Corkage** No charge. **No credit cards.**

In essence a deli with some tables, Méliès is smartly decorated with ice-blue walls and those trendy spotlights that hang down on a wire. It's curiously lacking in atmosphere though, and on a Thursday evening was completely empty, save for the chefs sitting smoking (they shuffled off reluctantly when we arrived). There's a small menu featuring sandwiches, Toulouse sausages, lasagne, poached salmon, salad niçoise, and lamb casserole, plus a daily special (on our visit, roast chicken and chips). Apple juice arrived freshly squeezed, but stale french bread wasn't a good start. Friendly service couldn't compensate for the little plate of lacklustre lasagne – for £6.50 you'd expect at least a garnish, and it needed to be reheated. Chips were crispy and pretty decent. Another main course, chicken in cream sauce, was lacklustre (though not bad). Desserts like crème brûlée are good value. We weren't charged for the lasagne, but when only two people are eating, you'd think the kitchen would pay more attention to getting it right. We've had better luck during the day, so maybe this was an off-night.

Babies and children welcomed. No-smoking tables. Tables outdoors (4, pavement).

Battersea SW11

Brasserie Metz

30 Battersea Rise, SW11 (020 7228 0611). Clapham Junction rail/44, 344 bus. **Meals served** 6-11pm Mon-Wed; 10.30am-11pm Thur; 10.30am-11.30pm Fri, Sat; 10.30am-11pm Sun. **Main courses** £6.20-£13.20. **Set meal** £12.50 two courses. **Credit** AmEx, MC, V.

A warm welcome and charming service are part of the attraction at this small, big-hearted, French-run restaurant. The decor's pleasant but nothing special, with a bog-standard tiled floor, pale walls and too-bright yellow lamps. In summer the front opens on to busy Battersea Rise. There's also a long light side room. After good warm bread with complimentary dips, starters were a big disappointment: asparagus with smoked salmon and hollandaise was bland and seemed microwaved; the tomato sauce in the calamares provençale lacked much taste, too. Salad niçoise and deep-fried Camembert both looked better choices. Mains – lamb with rosemary sauce and green beans; and rib-eye steak with béarnaise sauce and chips – came

as a relief: beautifully cooked, and with great flavour. For puddings, standard brûlées and tartes cost around £3.60, while wines go from £10 to £18.
Babies and children admitted; half-price children's portions (lunch); high chairs. Book weekends. No-smoking tables. Tables outdoors (8, pavement).

The Lavender ★

171 Lavender Hill, SW11 (020 7978 5242). Clapham Junction rail. **Open** noon-11.30pm Mon-Sat; noon-10.30pm Sun. **Lunch served** noon-3.30pm Mon-Fri; noon-4pm Sat, Sun. **Dinner served** 7-10.30pm Mon-Thur, Sun; 7-11.30pm Fri, Sat. **Main courses** £6.80-£10.50. **Credit** AmEx, MC, V.
This place is always cheerful, friendly and buzzy – and we've yet to have a bad meal here. The brick walls and wooden floors are set off by warm lighting and fresh flowers. There are imaginative combinations on the menu. Warm smoked chicken, Cumberland sausage and black pudding salad with spring onions and spiced plum and cashew nut chutney had too many competing flavours, but roast fennel, tomato and coriander tart with mozzarella glaze, salad and balsamic dressing was light and succulent. Yam ratatouille and goat's cheese filo pie with ginger wild rice, cherry tomato salad and sweet red cabbage oil, and pan-seared calf's liver with olive oil, mashed potato, buttered green cabbage and mustard seed jus both went down well. The only weak link in an otherwise spot-on meal was the chicken breast with bland, watery red wine pearl barley risotto, grilled leeks and tomato salsa. A white chocolate and raspberry cheesecake with chocolate sauce was sickly sweet. Wines range from £8.50 to £19.50, or there are vodka shots, and pitchers of Sea Breeze, Lavender Tea and Pimm's. Rare for a local, this popular, good-value venue is actually worth travelling to.
Babies and children welcome. Booking advisable. Tables outdoors (15, patio).
For branches see index.

Clapham SW4

The Abbeville

67-69 Abbeville Road, SW4 (020 8675 2201). Clapham South tube. **Open** 11am-11pm Mon-Fri; 10am-11pm Sat; 10am-10.30pm Sun. **Lunch served** 11am-5pm, Mon-Sat; 11am-4pm Sun. **Dinner served** 7-11pm Mon-Sat. **Main courses** £8.50-£14.50. **Service** 12½%. **Credit** AmEx, MC, V.
This used to be the very average, dank-green Flumbs. After a bright-blue and yellow refit, it's now the very average Abbeville, despite having loftier aims. The menu, which changes daily, is badly printed on flimsy paper. A Caesar salad was a travesty – just a few leaves of little gem with flakes of Parmesan and an onion-flavoured dressing – not a croûton or anchovy in sight. Mussels in a bland cream, white wine and herb sauce was unimaginative. A passable main course of goat's cheese in pastry came with one slice of sun-dried tomato and rested on top of half an onion. Baked salmon with tian of aubergine, basil mash and gazpacho sauce didn't even pass muster, looking like a school dinner and tasting far worse. Perhaps the kitchen should have stuck to burger and chips. It bugged us to be given the more expensive-sized glass of house wine without getting a choice; in general prices seem high. Though the back rooms by the fire are cosy, and staff are friendly, The Abbeville is just another indifferent, Fulham-esque money-spinner.
Babies and children welcome; high chairs. Booking advisable. No-smoking tables. Tables outdoors (5, pavement).

Gastro

67 Venn Street, SW4 (020 7627 0222). Clapham Common tube. **Open** 8am-midnight daily. **Breakfast served** 8am-5pm, **meals served** noon-midnight, daily. **Main courses** £7.25-£29.95. **No credit cards.**
Smoky, quirky and bohemian, Gastro continues to ooze a slightly chaotic, authentically Gallic charm. It now has an attractive new dining room with smart bottle-green banquette seating and pretty coloured glass windows. Fairy lights and candles add to the atmosphere (though we still prefer the smoky old original room). We were a bit miffed to be shoe-horned into a tiny table, packed in together at the back; if you can, sit round the huge table in the main room and enjoy the company. Gastro is always fun and bustling, with bubbly French waitresses. Food has not always been a high point, so we were delighted with six immense langoustines, served with prawn cocktail sauce, and a delicate goat's cheese salad. Even better were the mains: roast

Café Méliès

vegetables in a pancake topped with béchamel sauce was delicious; while the special, fish brochette, consisted of wonderfully meaty chunks of white fish and salmon in a piquant sauce with green beans. The house wine, served in tumblers, is more than drinkable. As ever, Gastro isn't flawless, but for atmosphere and joie de vivre it's hard to beat.
Babies and children admitted. Bookings accepted. No-smoking tables.

Newtons

33-35 Abbeville Road, SW4 (020 8673 0977). Clapham South tube. **Open** noon-11.30pm Mon-Sat; noon-10.30pm Sun. **Main courses** £7.95-£18. **Set lunch** Mon-Sat £6 two courses. **Set dinner** £12.95 two courses. **Service** 12½%. **Credit** AmEx, MC, £TC, V.
This good-hearted local looks fairly nondescript on the outside, with white plastic seating on a patio. Inside, it's pleasant enough, with bare-brick walls and colourful prints. Dark-blue tablecloths and bright-yellow napkins give the place a 1980s look, but in cold weather a fire makes it cosier. Staff are extremely attentive and eager to please. There's a wide variety of menus; from the main summer menu, we chose deep-fried calamares with sweet plum sauce, which was attractively displayed and came with a pleasantly tangy sauce. Crab and lobster salad with balsamic and olive oil dressing was tasty and light. However, asparagus tips and spring onion risotto with bold yellow saffron cream was disappointingly bland, and the burger didn't taste own-made and came with overcooked dark soggy chips. Yet prices are low in a generally overpriced area, and Newtons is both friendly and unpretentious.
Babies and children welcome; children's menu; crayons; high chairs. Booking advisable. No-smoking tables (Mon-Thur). Separate room for parties, seats 30. Tables outdoors (8, patio).

South East

Bankside SE1

Tate Modern

7th floor, Tate Modern, Sumner Street, SE1 (020 7401 5020). London Bridge tube/rail. **Breakfast served** 10.15am-noon, **lunch served** noon-3pm daily. **Dinner served** 6.30-9.30pm Fri, Sat. **Main courses** lunch £5.50-£9.50; dinner £6.75-£15.75. **Service** 12½%. **Credit** DC, MC, V.
With its dramatic views – St Paul's on one side, the Eye on the other – this is your poor man's Oxo Tower. It's a bit canteen-like if you sit in the middle; try waiting for a window seat. Bookings aren't taken, so get there early or late for lunch. There has been some criticism of the food, but we found it pretty good. True, sandwiches didn't look too impressive, and a burger was lukewarm on arrival, but a new one was brought with great efficiency and it was well-flavoured and came with a tasty tomato relish and a huge hunk of gherkin. Chips were square, chunky and golden. A generous portion of fish and chips with tartare sauce was a tad greasy, but arrived with delicious fresh garden pea purée, and was good value at £7.95. Ciabatta with mozzarella and tomato looked a good option for a light lunch. Otherwise you could simply indulge in apple and blackberry crumble with clotted cream, or delicious baked dark chocolate tart. Wines start at £9.95 a bottle; beers, spirits, teas and coffees are also served. Prices aren't hiked up as high as they could be, and the menu changes regularly. A pretty pukka lunch spot – and not to be confused with the café on the second floor.
Babies and children welcome; crayons; high chairs. Disabled: toilets in gallery. No-smoking. **Map 4/7O.**

Crystal Palace SE19

Joanna's

56 Westow Hill, SE19 (020 8670 4052). Crystal Palace or Gipsy Hill rail. **Open** 10am-11.15pm Mon-Thur; 10am-11.30pm Fri, Sat; 10am-10.30pm Sun. **Brunch served** 10am-7pm daily. **Meals served** noon-11.15pm Mon-Thur; noon-11.30pm Fri, Sat; noon-10.30pm Sun. **Main courses** £6.80-£18. **Credit** AmEx, DC, JCB, MC, £TC, V.
This local does a roaring trade in well-presented, good value food in an area not famed for great cuisine. It's all dark wood and lamps, and feels a bit like a theme pub, but is smart and comfortable. Best is the cosy little snug room that seats six. The menu is huge. 'Small Plates' include a delicious crab and cardamom tart with red onion marmalade; and (rather watery) chicken, shiitake mushrooms and pak choi in an oriental broth. In addition there's a variety of pastas, salads, seafood, roasts and grills. Char-grilled fillet steak with chilli-roasted onions, deep-fried cabbage and thick chips was in great demand on our visit. A superlative own-made hamburger came with one of those relish trays you always relished as a kid. Great egg noodles with pak choi was paired with huge marinated king prawns. Desserts such as apple tarte tartin with cinnamon and honey ice-cream, or pineapple and raspberry sorbet, round off a meal well. Staff are hard-working and efficient. There's a good selection of wines starting at £10, with nearly all under £20. Brunch is served until 6pm daily, and a roast is available at weekends (noon-6pm). A high-class, high-quality local.
Babies and children welcome; children's menu; crayons; high chairs. Booking advisable. Tables outdoors (5, patio).

London Bridge SE1

Café Rouge

Hays Galleria, 3 Tooley Street, SE1 (020 7378 0097). London Bridge tube/rail. **Meals served** noon-10pm Mon-Fri; noon-6pm Sat, Sun. **Main courses** £6.95-£13.95. **Service** 12½%. **Credit** AmEx, DC, JCB, LV, MC, £TC, V.
The most reliable of the French brasserie chains, Café Rouge is a safe, affordable bet for a coffee stop or light lunch, with its familiar cosy decor, newspapers, and seats outside. A prix fixe menu is offered from noon to 7pm on weekdays; the main menu includes sandwiches, and specialities such as grilled salmon with potatoes, or mussels in white wine. Starters like crab, avocado, lime and coriander salad, and deep-fried Camembert, are nicely done, but brasserie staples are generally the wisest choice. Caesar salad with chicken was excellent, with large, char-grilled strips of meat and a tasty dressing. We've found the service unfailingly attentive, polite and unpushy, and there are always fresh flowers on the tables. A good selection of fairly priced wines includes over a dozen by the glass. Puds are fine too; try the creamy tarte tartin.
Babies and children welcome; children's menu; high chairs. No-smoking tables. Tables outdoors (100, terrace). **Map 8/8Q.**
For branches see index.

East

Bethnal Green E2

291

291 Hackney Road, E2 (020 7613 5675). Bus 26, 48, 55. **Meals served** 6pm-midnight Tue-Sat; noon-8pm Sun. **Main courses** £5.95-£9.95. **Set meal** £17.50 three courses. **Service** 12½% for parties of six or more. **Credit** MC, V.
Part of a gallery space and bar, this small eaterie is a bit of a find. The cool white walls are lined with African sculptures, topped by black beams and set off by spotlights. The à la carte menu is petite but appealing, and reasonably priced. Delicious warm ciabatta and oil to start, and a fruity, chilled house white made a great first impression. After about half an hour, the waiter admitted he'd forgotten to place our order, but was so charming (plying us with more wine), it didn't seem to matter. Starters were faultless: seared squid salad was dressed with a chilli and lime oil; Turkish aubergine salad with yoghurt. Mains could only be a let-down, especially as we had to wait another hour for them. Both dishes seemed as if they'd been chucked together: huge lumps of rock salt punctuated the rather lumpy broccoli mash that nestled beneath a nicely cooked sea bass; and steak arrived too rare and with a bland red wine sauce. We'd return to try other dishes though, and the coffee's great. Music is eclectic, from Turkish tunes to *Diamonds are Forever*. The comments book (nice touch) is full of compliments, and it's true: 291 is a good-value, atmospheric spot. Just don't come if you're in a hurry; bring your arty friends and chill out.
Babies and children welcome; high chairs. Booking advisable. Disabled: toilet. Entertainment: bands or DJs weekends. Separate rooms for parties, seating 150 and 250. Tables outdoors (6, garden). **Map 4/3S.**

North East

Stoke Newington N16

The Fox Reformed

176 Stoke Newington Church Street, N16 (020 7254 5975). Stoke Newington rail/73 bus. **Meals served** 5pm-midnight Mon-Fri; noon-midnight Sat, Sun. **Main courses** £8.25-£10.75. **Service** 10% for parties of six or more. **Credit** AmEx, DC, MC, V.
This timewarp wine bar has a cosy, appealingly eccentric air. On a warm evening we sat in the small back yard (which could do with a lick of paint), with a mixed clientele that included a birthday party, a mother and young baby, and a scattering of snogging couples. The brief menu consists of a few meaty dishes like steak and chips, and the intriguing 'variation of bangers and mash'. The wine list features mainly non-European labels, with half a dozen available by the glass. On the blackboard there's a wider range of starters, from (surprisingly small) tiger prawns in filo, to duck breast with plum sauce (slightly fatty meat but tasty enough). Roast poussin with sage jus was OK, but not especially exciting. Gigot of lamb with redcurrant sauce and sautéed potatoes was better. Of particular note was the own-baked bread, and the fresh, crisp veg. To finish, the choc pot, a creamy coffee/chocolate concoction served with a top layer of single cream, was fine, but the crème brûlée was truly horrible, with an oily, greasy flavour. Generally, though, the Fox is a quirky, charismatic bar serving decent food; locals seem to have a soft spot for it.
Babies and children welcome; high chairs. Book weekends; dinner. Tables outdoors (5, garden).

North

Camden Town & Chalk Farm NW1

Café Delancey

3 Delancey Street, NW1 (020 7387 1985). Camden Town tube. **Meals served** 9am-11.30pm Mon-Sat; 9am-10pm Sun. **Main courses** £7.70-£14.60. **Service** 12½%. **Credit** MC, £TC, V.
Café Delancey offers respite from the burger

bars and kebab houses of Camden. Rooms are pale, with wooden floors and elegant art works. There's also a pretty little enclosed patio that's a real suntrap. Mini deep-fried Camembert was a teeny, pretty portion served with flavourless Calvados jelly and apple slices, while feuilleté de champignons – a giant mushroom vol au vent – was OK but a little heavy for a summer starter. Fresh salmon fish cake served on a bed of spinach with lemon butter sauce made a light, appetising main course, apart from a rather stodgy rösti. The vegetarian dish of the day, spinach and cream cheese roulade in a vivid yellow pepper sauce, looked gorgeous, but tasted slightly bland. Lighter mains include club and toasted sandwiches, salads and rösti with fried eggs. A full or vegetarian breakfast is also served. Desserts include crème brûlée and the notable les trois mousses Delancey. Wines, a small but select group, cost from £10 a bottle, with four available by the glass. An attractive spot.
Babies and children admitted. Book dinner. Tables outdoors (6, pavement).

Sauce Organic Diner ★
214 Camden High Street, NW1 (020 7482 0777). Camden Town tube. **Meals served** noon-11pm Mon-Sat; noon-5pm Sun. **Main courses** £6.50-£11.80. **Set meal** (noon-7.30pm Mon-Fri) £7.50 two courses. **Service** 12½%. **Credit** JCB, MC, V.
Though it's in a basement, Sauce still manages to be cheery, with its mini light-wood tables, yellow walls, brightly coloured paintings and fairy lights. Everything is organic (even the ketchup) and GM-free, but this isn't a prissy venue – smoking is allowed and there is an impressive list of cocktails, including 100% Organic with organic vodka, carrot and orange juices and fresh ginger. Brunch includes American-style pancakes with poached egg, spinach and hollandaise. For lunch, make up your own salad, starting with a base (£3) and adding whatever ingredients you fancy, from chickpeas to herb tofu. There are also burgers, wraps and sandwiches. From the great-value two-course menu, we tried light and crispy tortillas with cheese and garlic. Fat chips and sweet chilli sauce complemented a beautifully fat, fresh fish cake made with creamy mash; lamb wrap with green pepper and minted yoghurt was also full of flavour. Puds include a rich chocolate nut tarte with crème fraîche. The only thing to steer clear of is the organic coffee – watery and lacking flavour. Once you've sampled this place, you'll wish for a bit of Sauce every lunchtime.
Babies and children welcome; children's menu; high chairs; toys. Takeaway service.
Map 10.

Crouch End N8

Banners
21 Park Road, N8 (020 8348 2930). Finsbury Park tube/rail then W7 bus. **Meals served** 9am-11.30pm Mon-Thur; 9am-midnight Fri; 10am-midnight Sat; 10am-11pm Sun. **Main courses** £7.95-£10.35. **Credit** MC, £TC, V.
Banners is a Crouch End institution. With its laidback, beatnik vibe and hearty portions, it's a local that feels a bit like a beach bar. Pull up a stool at the bar, grab a wooden table or get cosy in the dark snug at the back. The menu's as big as a book, but breakfast's the meal to order – vast servings of tomatoes, bacon, toast, fried eggs, sausages or black pudding, mushrooms and beans for a very reasonable £5.75. Accompany it with a top-notch Virgin Mary or a smoothie of the day. Or plump for comfort food such as kedgeree, or ham and cheese omelette with potato cakes. Main dishes range from standard fare of fish cakes, burgers and sandwiches to more exotic jerk snapper with fried plantain, or pan-fried calamares. Banners is famously child friendly, offering an extensive children's menu for under-tens. It gets furiously busy at weekends; kids will love the popcorn machine and the jelly beans that come with the bill. There are plenty of grown-up drinks too, including flavoured vodka and a whole host of cocktails.
Babies and children welcome; children's menu (until 7pm); crayons; high chairs; toys. Book weekends; dinner.

Finsbury Park N4

The Meeting Place
17 Blackstock Road, N4 (020 7354 1411). Finsbury Park tube/rail. **Meals served** 10am-11pm Mon-Sat; 10am-10.30pm Sun. **Main courses** £6.50-£9.95. **Service** 10% for parties of four or more. **Credit** MC, V.
This inexpensive local seems to have let itself go a bit since last year. Inside is caff-like, with unexceptional decor: peachy pink walls, Impressionist prints and dated light fittings. Out back is a walled garden filled with plastic furniture, and not a flower pot in sight. There's an all-day breakfast (until 5pm) for £4.50 (meat or vegetarian), light meals and sandwiches for lunch, and a choice of pasta, salads and more substantial mains in the evening. Greasy potato skins with bacon, mushrooms and cheese was served with sour cream, but still tasted like a fry-up. However, a hearty slab of caramelised onion and Swiss cheese tart was appetising. Own-made cheeseburger and chips with tomato chutney was well cooked and very chunky. Grilled goat's cheese with roasted vegetables was less of a hit; though a generous portion, it was oily, soggy and looked far from appealing. Puds include white chocolate, rice and almond flan with crème anglaise. Cheap and cheerful it may be, but the Meeting Place could do with sharpening up its act.
Babies and children welcome; high chairs. Booking advisable. No-smoking tables. Tables outdoors (11, garden).

The Triangle
1 Ferme Park Road, N4 (020 8292 0516). Finsbury Park tube/rail then W3, W7 bus. **Open** noon-midnight Tue-Fri; 10am-midnight Sat, Sun. **Lunch served** noon-3pm, **dinner served** 7pm-midnight Tue-Sat. **Main courses** £7.95-£12.50. **Service** 10%. **Credit** V.
From its red, white and blue exterior to the brightly coloured inside, the Triangle (formerly WXD) looks like a student gaff. Inept paintings, an orange fireplace and lots of plants increase the similarity. A lean-to overlooks a pretty, tiny garden. Cooking is described as 'fusion food' – in other words, a hotchpotch. Breakfast might be coconut halloumi cheese with rocket, poached egg and sweet chilli oil, for instance. After warm bread and great starters – squid with chilli sauce and rocket; a parcel of pak choi, roasted pepper, goat's cheese and pistachio with mustard dressing – main courses were a huge disappointment. Mediterranean fish cake, made with whitebait and salmon, came with tsatsiki, rocket and fries, but fish flavours were drowned by the same chilli sauce as the starter. Moroccan chicken with plantain was awful – dry fowl with chunks of tasteless vegetables. The waitress was too busy to notice our half-eaten meal. We weren't inspired to try the Baileys and caramel cheesecake for pudding. Stick to a couple of starters or cocktails; you get free tapas with your drink. A pleasant spot, with an over-ambitious kitchen.
Babies and children welcome; high chairs; toys. Booking advisable. Disabled: toilet. Separate room for parties, seats 15. Tables outdoors (8, garden; 30, pavement).

Tate Modern.
See page 197.

Islington EC1

Candid Café ★
3 Torrens Street, EC1 (020 7278 9368/ www.candidarts.com). Angel tube. **Meals served** noon-10pm Mon-Sat; noon-5pm Sun. **Main courses** £2.50-£7. **Unlicensed. Corkage** £1. **Mineral water** £1 small bottle. **No credit cards.**
Piles of rubbish at the door, courtesy of the council, aren't much of a welcome to the Candid. This bohemian hangout is looking a bit shabby. It occupies a warm, oblong room with a long table down the middle. Sun pours through windows, there are gold chairs and comfy velvet sofas – it's lovely and light by day. Food isn't a strong point, with choice limited: soup (not available on our visit), spinach rice with cashew nuts, Greek salad, or chicken with honey sauce. There are sandwiches and salads containing avocado, mozzarella cheese, tuna and so on. Spinach rice was lukewarm if tasty; Greek salad was a nice fresh plateful and came with French bread. Service is lackadaisical, but, hey, everything's very laid-back. You could nurse a huge cup of coffee for hours on end without being hassled. Student heaven.
Babies and children admitted. Separate room for parties, capacity 180. Tables outdoors (7, courtyard). **Map 16/2O.**

Muswell Hill N10

Café on the Hill
46 Fortis Green Road, N10 (020 8444 4957). Highgate tube then 43, 134 bus. **Open** 8am-10.30pm Mon-Sat; 9am-10pm Sun. **Lunch served** noon-4pm, **dinner served** 6-10.30pm daily. **Main courses** £4-£13. **Service** 12½% for parties of 6 or more. **Credit** MC, V.
Being packed on a rainy Tuesday evening is a sign of a good local. This one has a cosy, pleasant atmosphere with soft lighting, bare-brick walls, fans, and a double-bass and guitar duo (there are popular jazz evenings twice a week). Traditional English breakfast is served until 4pm at the weekend; alternatively, try the baguettes, wraps or salads for lunch. The dinner menu changes regularly. Our meal kicked off well, with seafood beignet (white fish in a light batter) served with pak choi and a sweet chilli sauce. Brasserie staples were no great shakes, though: Cumberland sausages were burnt, and came with lumpy, tired mash and very boring gravy (sorry, 'jus'). Steak, requested medium, arrived rare and rather dry and chewy, with piping-hot, pale chips. A special of roasted cod with sun-dried tomatoes looked better. The Café's a cheery, friendly place though; maybe a shorter menu would be more manageable.
Babies and children welcome; books; highchairs; toys. Entertainment: jazz Wed evenings. Tables outdoors (4, pavement). Takeaway service.

North West

Hampstead NW3

Giraffe ★
46 Rosslyn Hill, NW3 (020 7435 0343). Hampstead tube. **Open** 8am-midnight Mon-Fri; 9am-midnight Sat; 9am-12pm Sun. **Brunch served** 8-11.45am Mon-Fri; 9am-4pm Sat, Sun. **Lunch served** noon-5pm daily. **Dinner served** 5-11.15pm Mon-Sat; 5-10.45pm Sun. **Main courses** £6.95-£10. **Credit** MC, V.
This cheery, bright-orange little joint serves a great range of well-priced grub. Drop in for stacked pancakes with blueberry and banana for breakfast, sweet chilli chicken skewers for lunch, or grilled bluefin tuna for supper. The choice is almost bewildering. Sashimi salad with smoked salmon was fresh and light, with a great tangy chilli flavour. The meze plate featured excellent houmous, falafels and aubergine salad. Mains were just as good: a generous bowl of barbecued duck salad with kai lam, shiitakes and chilli plum jam was delicious, as was roast stuffed peppers with goat's cheese and ratatouille risotto. There's a smashing range of teas and coffees (including Tazo and Moroccan tea and frozen vanilla mocha latte), plus some mouthwatering desserts: try vanilla bean cheesecake with berry compote, or the Toblerone and mascarpone trifle. Service is brisk but not rushed. Customers must cosy up together on benches (unless they go outside). Giraffe can get pretty noisy, but with food so good, who cares?
Babies and children welcome; high chairs. No smoking. Tables outdoors, (3, pavement). Takeaway service.
For branches see index.

St John's Wood NW8

The Salt House ★
63 Abbey Road, NW8 (020 7328 6626). St John's Wood tube. **Open** noon-11pm daily. **Lunch served** 12.30-3pm Mon-Fri; 12.30-4pm Sat, Sun. **Dinner served** 6.30-10.30pm Mon-Fri; 7-10.30pm Sat, Sun. **Main courses** £7-£12.50. **Set lunch** (Mon-Fri) £9.75 three courses. **Credit** AmEx, JCB, MC, £TC, V.
This former pub, just up from the famous zebra crossing, changed hands in 1999 and has had a full refurb; the troughs of lavender, heaters and smart paint job make a good first impression. The comfortable bar filled with blue sofas has more character than the mauve-coloured back-room restaurant, which is pleasant but could do with lower lighting. The food here's so good, though, you'd sit anywhere. Roast beetroot and balsamic vinegar soup was a bit over-sweet and pungent, but the sesame prawn rolls with pak choi and black beans were excellent – tasty, fresh and melt-in-your-mouth tender. All the mains looked good, but we went for the rib of beef with chips and Montpellier butter, at £25 for two. It was superb: a beautifully cooked piece of meat with herby butter and chunky chips. We had no room left for puds such as roast figs with yoghurt ice-cream, or raspberry ripple ice-cream. Service was faultless, too. We left vowing to return, and wishing the Salt House was our local.
Babies and children welcome; games room with video; high chairs. Tables outdoors (10, pavement).

Cafés

De Gustibus.
See page 200.

Cafés, pâtisseries & tearooms

Central

Bloomsbury WC1

Coffee Gallery ★
*23 Museum Street, WC1 (020 7436 0455).
Holborn or Tottenham Court Road tube.*
Open 8.30am-5.30pm Mon-Fri; 10am-5.30pm
Sat; 12.30-5.30pm Sun. **Afternoon tea
served** 3-5.30pm Mon-Sat. **Set tea** £3.40.
Unlicensed. Credit MC, £TC, V.
Run by the same team as that behind the Habitat
cafés (*see* **Table Café** *p100* **Italian**) and the new
café at the Courtauld Gallery, the Coffee Gallery
is a charming Italian-biased place that serves
cakes (mango cheesecake, perhaps, or pear tart),
Sally Clarke pastries, sandwiches (great
doorstopper ciabattas, filled with mozzarella,
tomato and basil, or smoked salmon, avocado and
mayonnaise) and light lunches. Dishes change
daily, but usually include a couple of salads, a
vegetable dish (grilled marinated vegetables, for
example) and a more substantial dish, such as
pasta with seafood and tomato sauce, or frittata.
The coffee is good, service comes with a smile
and, outside of busy times, this is a calm place to
peruse the newspapers.
*Babies and children welcome. No smoking.
Tables outdoors (4, pavement). Takeaway
service.* **Map 14/5L.**

Clerkenwell & Farringdon EC1

The Deli Bar
*117 Charterhouse Street, EC1 (020 7253
2070).* Barbican tube/Farringdon tube/rail.
Open 9am-11pm Mon-Fri; 9am-6pm Sat.
Licensed. Credit AmEx, MC, V.
To all intents and purposes, the Deli Bar looks like
a smart edge-of-City restaurant, with modern,
bright interior and smart waiting staff – but it is
really a café in the guise of a restaurant, serving
a successful mix of Mediterranean-style salads,
sandwiches in focaccia (such as mozzarella,
Parma ham, tomatoes and rocket with olive oil),
pasta dishes, and platefuls such as 'beef and oil'
– bresaola, olive oil, Parmigiano flakes and sun-
dried tomatoes. An insalate de mare (£6.95) was
a generous portion of squid, mussels, octopus and
crab on a big bed of undressed rocket (oil and
balsamic vinegar are provided in bottles). With a
glass of pinot grigio, it made a simple but
pleasant lunch. Downstairs in the basement is a
delicatessen that also sells ready-prepared salads.
*Babies and children admitted. No-smoking
tables. Tables outdoors (3, pavement).
Takeaway service.* **Map 15/5O.**

feast
86 St John Street, EC1 (020 7253 7007).
Farringdon tube/rail/55, 505 bus. **Open**
7.30am-4pm Mon-Fri. **Licensed. Credit**
MC, V (on bills of £10 or more).
A state-of-the-art establishment producing wraps
(along with soups, salads and jacket potatoes) for
the workers of Clerkenwell. Wraps are made to
order at the counter and ingredients are eclectic;
choices range from the likes of 'greek goddess'
(baba ganoush, feta cheese, olives, lettuce and
tomato) to 'texas red' (a hot wrap with chilli con
carne, grated Cheddar and crème fraîche). There
is also a good selection of own-made smoothies,
teas (including herbal) and coffee. A lot of trade
is in takeaways, but there are some pleasant
tables if you want to eat in.
*Babies and children admitted. No smoking.
Takeaway service.* **Map 15/5O.**

Lunch
*60 Exmouth Market, EC1 (020 7278 2420/
www.lunch.uk.com). Farringdon tube/rail/
19, 38, 55, 341 bus.* **Open** 8.30am-4pm
Mon-Fri; 10am-4pm Sat. **Licensed. Credit**
LV, £TC.

A sparsely decorated room, mostly taken up with
a display and service counter, leads through to a
small but pleasant decked garden. Food is served
in New York Chinese takeaway-style cartons, and
dishes change daily. There's not much left if you
arrive after about 1.30pm, but early birds might
catch a variety of salads (new potato, pea and
mint; Moroccan carrot; or tabouleh), a soup
(potato and watercress or chicken noodle) and a
special (costing about £5) such as falafel and
houmous (a good version, and plenty of it) or
chorizo and couscous. Desserts don't run to much
more than flapjacks or fruit; drinks include
organic ginger beer and various smoothies.
*Babies and children admitted. No-smoking
tables. Tables outdoors (2, pavement; 25,
garden). Takeaway service; delivery service.*
Map 15/4N.
For branch see index.

Covent Garden WC2

The Cinnamon Bar
*One Aldwych, WC2 (020 7300 0800). Covent
Garden tube/Charing Cross tube/rail.* **Open**
7am-9pm Mon-Fri; 9am-9pm Sat. **Licensed.
Credit** AmEx, DC, MC, V.
Centrally located at the thin end of the wedge that
is One Aldwych hotel, the Cinnamon Bar is trying
hard to keep the hip hotel flag flying. High
chrome tables, matching scoop chairs and photo-
printed pebble lino make an apt setting for the
equally lifestyle-conscious menu. Drinks are
predominantly the healthy variety – freshly
squeezed melon and rosemary juice was one –
with attendant captions to remind you why you
might be doing this (perhaps to obtain 'a calming
effect on the digestive system' or even 'a mild
stimulating action on the kidneys'). Our own
errant ways were punished with an insipid-
coloured Bloody Mary and a lacklustre Sea
Breeze. Foodwise, with couscous salad and
Parma ham salad both sold out, third choices of
prawn salad and roasted vegetables with penne
were not enhanced by coming straight from the
chiller cabinet, nor by being served in plastic
containers. Were it not for the hi-tech furniture
and faux-kitsch lino this could be the Sainsbury's
salad bar. A prime example of form over content.
*Babies and children admitted. Takeaway
service.* **Map 14/7M.**

M J Bradley's
*9 King Street, WC2 (020 7240 5178).
Covent Garden tube.* **Open** 8am-11pm daily.
Licensed. No credit cards.
There's a quieter seating area in the basement,
but Bradley's clean, breezy ground-floor café has
a lively buzz to it. A glass-fronted bar displays a
handsome choice of enticing salads and
sandwich fillings that can be encased in a variety
of breads. Cooked breakfast is served all day, as
is a selection of pastries, fruits and yoghurts. For
dinner, main courses take on a Mediterranean
flavour, with falafels, kebabs, salads, and more
substantial options such as kleftiko up for grabs.
Portions are ample and food is light, well-
presented and very fresh. To drink, there's wine
from France, Australia and Italy, as well as beer,
fruit juices, soft drinks, coffees and teas. Quick,
friendly service also counts in Bradley's favour.
*Babies and children admitted. Tables outdoors
(2, pavement). Takeaway service.* **Map 14/7L.**

Mode
*57 Endell Street, WC2 (020 7240 8085).
Covent Garden tube.* **Open** 8am-11pm
Mon-Fri; 9am-9pm Sat. **Minimum** £1.60.
Licensed. Credit MC, V.
Slightly off the main tourist track, this cosy little
café is popular with an unpretentious younger
crowd looking for good-value meals without too
many frills. Downstairs is a prime spot for a lazy
coffee and a browse through the wide choice of
newspapers and magazines offered, while the
more airy, well-lit backroom upstairs (behind the
bar) is better suited to a quick bite. Main courses
include pasta dishes, hot specials such as chicken
breast stuffed with spinach and mozzarella, and
some good-sized salads, as well as sandwiches
made to order. There's a small but delicious
selection of desserts such as apple pie or

chocolate fudge cake. The Chilean house wines
were fine; look at the specials menu for a couple
of slightly more expensive choices. Beers, fruit
juices and smoothies can also be ordered.
Otherwise, try one of the Italian-style coffees.
*Babies and children admitted. No-smoking
tables. Tables outdoors (5, pavement).
Takeaway service.* **Map 14/6L.**

Neal's Yard Café Society
*13 Neal's Yard, WC2 (020 7240 1168).
Covent Garden tube.* **Open** 10.30am-8pm daily.
Licensed. Credit DC, JCB, MC, V.
A specials board decorated with waves is the only
reminder that this place used to be the garish Beach
Café. That's not to say it has gone posh exactly; Ant
chairs and Asian lettering on the walls give it a
distinctly boho feel, although the pumping techno
and generally stressed atmosphere during our
lunchtime visit didn't really ease us into 'café
society' either. Location-wise, it's a bit too far up the
alley to be a part of the real wheatgrass and soya-
burger scrum of cafés that feed into the Yard itself.
The food also reflects this, with a predominance of
pizza and pasta options to choose from. Service is
slow and portions aren't much cop either – the
'salad on the side' of the ciabatta sarnies is a snip
of iceberg lettuce. In fact, the main reason to come
here is to sample one of the delicious smoothies (the
'energizer', for instance, has a fantastic melon zing),
which, ironically, are a hangover from the Beach
Café days.
*Babies and children welcome. Tables outdoors
(4, courtyard). Takeaway service.* **Map 14/6L.**

Fitzrovia W1

Carluccio's Caffè ★
*8 Market Place, W1 (020 7636 2228).
Oxford Circus tube.* **Open** 8am-11pm Mon-Fri;
10am-11pm Sat; 11am-1pm Sun. **Licensed.
Credit** MC, V.
Carluccio's is somewhere between a café and an
Italian restaurant, and moves more towards the
latter during the evening. The big open area
beyond the deli gets noisy when full, but the food
is so good that the crowds keep coming back.
Savoury dishes run from antipasti and salads
through pastas (own-made ravioli stuffed with
spinach and ricotta) and mains (vegetable
calzone, grilled swordfish in Parmesan and

parsley breadcrumbs) to panna cotta, chocolate
truffle pudding or ice-creams. Cakes and pastries
and fine coffee every which-way keep shoppers
fuelled through the day. An unexpected treat so
close to Oxford Circus.
*Babies and children welcome. Book dinner.
Takeaway service.* **Map 13/6J.**

Leicester Square WC2

Portrait Café
*National Portrait Gallery, 2 St Martin's Place,
WC2 (020 7312 2465). Embankment or
Leicester Square tube/Charing Cross tube/rail.*
Open 10am-5.30pm Mon-Wed, Sat, Sun;
10am-8.30pm Thur, Fri. **Licensed. Credit**
MC, £TC, V.
This small basement café is saved from gloominess
by a deft stroke of architectural inventiveness – it
has a glass ceiling. There's also an assortment of
black and white photos to keep the arty theme
going. The food, however, is no-nonsense,
nourishing fare, with a refreshing drinks list to
match: half-bottles of chardonnay or chenin blanc,
best bitters, organic carrot and apple juices and
yoghurt drinks abound. Our coffees were strong
and generous (latte is reasonably priced at £1.40
for a large mug), while a hearty snack of Caesar
salad was also a respectable size and not too chilled.
Otherwise, there's a fine range of organic ice-
creams, wholesome baps and nutritious-looking
cakes to choose from. Staff are understandably
proud of their surroundings and seem genuinely
enthusiastic about their task of watering and
feeding ailing culture-vultures and West End-
bound tourists.
*Babies and children admitted. Disabled: toilets.
Takeaway service.* **Map 14/7K.**

Photographers' Gallery Café
*5 Great Newport Street, WC2 (020 7831
1772). Covent Garden or Leicester Square
tube.* **Open** 11am-5.30pm Mon-Sat; noon-
5.30pm Sun. **Unlicensed. No credit cards.**
Don't expect lattes in paper cups, chrome seats
or chiller cabinets – this watering hole of the
modern, white-washed Photographers' Gallery
feels more like an upmarket student union with
its large beech tables and benches. The self-
service kitchen in the corner is run by the
sweetest of staff and the set-up is distinctly

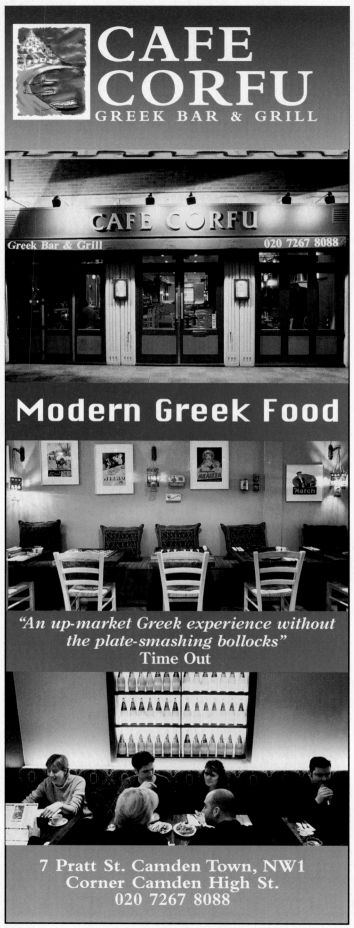

homely: top up your drink with a big jug of fresh milk, or dip into the jar of honey and take a lemon slice from the bowl. There are cold drinks, too; a large glass of cranberry or grapefruit weighs in at a very reasonable 85p. Food includes a comforting selection of sweet stuff (coffee cake, flapjacks and the like) and savoury snacks such as freshly made poppy-seed bagels with prawn mayonnaise or egg salad. Despite its rather utilitarian decor (there are no windows, either), this remains a fair-priced oasis in central London. *Babies and children welcome; high chairs; nappy-changing facilities. Disabled: toilet. No smoking. Takeaway service.* **Map 14/6K.**

Marylebone W1

De Gustibus
53 Blandford Street, W1 (020 7486 6608). Bond Street tube. **Open** 7am-4.30pm Mon-Fri; 9am-3pm Sat. **Unlicensed. No credit cards.**
Although it functions primarily as a superior sandwich bar – sandwiches come with Mediterranean fillings such as feta with olive oil and wild oregano, or marinated mozzarella, and are encased in hunks of De Gustibus's robust, own-made bread – this is also a delicatessen and a calm and pleasant place to stop for lunch. Daily specials supplement the sandwiches; they included, on our last visit, stuffed pepper, tortino (double-filled focaccia with Provençal vegetables, mozzarella and olives) and Thai fish cake. The latter was stuffed with plenty of tuna and served with a punchy salsa and sizeable portions of carrot and courgette, green, and beansprout salads. You can accompany your coffee with brownies, raisin crunches or coconut and apple slices.
Babies and children admitted. No smoking. **Map 2/5G.**

Pâtisserie Valerie at Sagne
105 Marylebone High Street, W1 (020 7935 6240). Baker Street or Bond Street tube. **Open** 7.30am-7pm Mon-Sat; 9am-6pm Sun. **Licensed. Credit** AmEx, DC, LV, MC, £TC, V.
This old-timer is holding up nicely against the coffee chain competition on Marylebone High Street. It is popular with all ages for the superior pastries and light meals; much of its character comes from genteel locals of a certain age. Top choices include smoked salmon and scrambled eggs on granary, croques monsieur or madame, and various types of millefeuille, éclair and fruit tarts. For total indulgence, try a slice of gateaux and a Belgium hot chocolate, gaze at the mural of Lake Geneva and forget you're in W1.
Babies and children admitted. No-smoking tables. Tables outdoors (4, pavement). Takeaway service. **Map 2/5G.**
For branches see index.

Mayfair W1

Victory Café
Basement, Gray's Antiques Market, South Molton Lane, W1 (020 8960 0086). Bond Street tube. **Open** 10am-5.30pm Mon-Fri. **Unlicensed. Credit** £TC.
The theme here is 1950s retro. Poster-sized renditions of period ads and headline events cover the walls, while a solid old juke box provides the finishing touches with the Everley Brothers et al crooning away in the background. The menu's decidedly modern, though, with plenty of goat's cheese and feta cropping up in the salads, and fancy French interlopers like croque monsieur rubbing shoulders with the more trad chicken and mushroom pie or the bargain Victory brunch (eggs, Cumberland sausage, tomatoes, mushrooms, beans and toast for £3.95). We were surprised to discover that an ostensibly vegetarian option of warm couscous with grilled peppers and halloumi also contained some unadvertised chunks of spicy chicken. Thankfully, the relaxed, friendly staff soon rectified this – but vegetarians, be vigilant.
Babies and children admitted. Takeaway service. **Map 2/6H.**

Piccadilly W1

La Madeleine
5 Vigo Street, W1 (020 7734 8353). Green Park or Piccadilly Circus tube. **Open** 8am-8pm Mon-Sat; 11am-7pm Sun. **Licensed. Credit** DC, MC, £TC, V.
As French as its name suggests, La Madeleine is a friendly café with some limited outdoor seating on a relatively quiet strip of pavement just off Regent Street. There's something here to suit every moment in a busy London day: buttery croissants can kick-start your morning, salads or croque monsieurs will get you through lunch, while a large array of pastries, millefeuilles, éclairs and tarts will satiate that mid-afternoon

sugar craving. Meanwhile, the sumptuous window display of delicately sculpted marzipan figures, chocolates and cheesecakes should take care of any stragglers and random passers-by. There's even the offer of a free drink (non-alcoholic) during the lunch hour, which the like-able staff call noon-1pm (targeting early-start shoppers as opposed to the late-rising workers indigenous to this part of town).
Babies and children welcome; high chairs. Book lunch. No-smoking tables. Tables outdoors (4, pavement). Takeaway service. **Map 13/7J.**
For branch see index.

Soho W1

Amato ★
14 Old Compton Street, W1 (020 7734 5733/ www.amato.co.uk). Leicester Square or Tottenham Court Road tube. **Open** 8am-10pm Mon-Sat; 10am-8pm Sun. **Licensed. Credit** AmEx, DC, MC, V
Beyond the sumptuous pâtisserie counter at Amato is a long art deco-style room that's usually packed with happy customers tucking into excellent cream cakes and coffee, splendid doorstep toasted sandwiches, or light lunches such as omelette of the day or quiche of the day. Come in the morning for croissants and brioche, or in the afternoon when the pace slackens and time slows down over pots of tea (there's a decent range, with some speciality blends such as elderflower and lemon) and newspapers. The chirpy staff provide a warm welcome, whatever the time of day. If you're having a meal, you can also order wine (there's a couple of simple bottles to choose from).
Babies and children admitted. Takeaway service. **Map 13/6K.**

Bar Italia ★
22 Frith Street, W1 (020 7437 4520). Leicester Square, Piccadilly Circus or Tottenham Court Road tube. **Open** 24 hours Mon-Sat; 7am-4am Sun. **Unlicensed. No credit cards.**
One of a trio of Italian cafés along a small stretch of Frith Street, Bar Italia remains the godfather of them all. Punters spill out on to the pavement seats from the long thin room, or perch on the bar stools and admire themselves in the huge mirror opposite the bar. With a pumping soundtrack, a large video screen, fruit machines crammed in at the end, and countless photos of popular Italian exports (De Niro, Rocky Marciano, Brando and, of course, the beloved Juventus), Bar Italia has been London's answer to Little Italy all on its own for several years now. While the young and beautiful are happy just to be seen here, especially around the midnight hour, they are also drawn by the quick service, frothing cappuccinos and creamy lattes. There's a fine assortment of hefty ciabatta or focaccia sandwiches, too, plus quiches, salads, bagels, and, of course, soft and melting cakes. The hot panini specials (melted Brie and cranberry sauce is particularly enticing) are the latest addition to the roster. Come, see and conquer.
Babies and children admitted. Tables outdoors (7, pavement). Takeaway service. **Map 13/6K.**

EAT ★
16A Soho Square, W1 (020 7222 7200/ www.eatcafe.co.uk). Tottenham Court Road tube. **Open** 7am-5pm Mon-Fri; 10am-6pm Sat. **Unlicensed. No credit cards.**
Winner of the British Sandwich Association's 'UK sandwich bar of the year', this successful branch of an equally successful chain offers a broad selection of speedy lunches. The emphasis is on fresh, natural food, from soups and sandwiches to salads and sushi. Bag a takeaway or grab a seat in the quiet mezzanine area. Comfortable wooden seats and tables match the geometric angles used throughout. There's an interesting choice of Italian coffees as well as a range of health drinks and some delicious own-made smoothies. The fairly priced sandwiches are constructed from a wide variety of breads and have many different fillings. Soups are deliciously fresh and flavoursome. Health-conscious folk might want to try one of the yoghurts or berry compôtes for pudding; otherwise there's a great choice of biscuits, muffins and tarts. Service is fast and friendly. A great little lunch venue.
Babies and children admitted. No smoking. Takeaway service. **Map 13/6K.**
For branches see index.

The Garden Café
4 Newburgh Street, W1 (020 7494 0044). Oxford Circus or Piccadilly Circus tube. **Open** 8am-7pm Mon-Fri; 9am-7pm Sat; 11am-6pm Sun. **Minimum** £5 12.30-2.20pm. **Unlicensed. Credit** AmEx, DC, LV, MC, TC, V.

Unsurprisingly, this place's greatest attribute is its garden (actually it's more of an enclosed courtyard, painted pink and yellow with vines growing up lattices along every wall). Inside, the decor is suitably bright and cheerful, and the staff are friendly. A popular takeaway place during the lunchtime rush, it caters to the hungry masses with a quick and easy array of sarnies. For something more substantial you could try vegetable lasagne, veggie burger and chips, or scampi and chips. There's a brief choice of desserts – Mississippi mud pie and Alabama soft rock pie both figured on our last visit. We rounded things off with an iced coffee (which, on our request, staff agreed to make), but the £2.50 price tag did leave a bitter aftertaste.
Babies and children welcome; high chairs. Tables outdoors (8, garden). Takeaway service. **Map 13/6J.**

Maison Bertaux ★
28 Greek Street, W1 (020 7437 6007). Leicester Square tube. **Open** 9am-8pm daily. **Unlicensed. Credit** £TC.
French in every way, this buzzy, unpretentious little café is popular with tourists, media types and some lively locals. It serves an enviably varied choice of delicious pastries, along with some savouries – all cooked on the premises and the equal of anything you'd find in Paris. Order at the counter and your food may or may not appear sometime later (service is a bit erratic, especially when things get busy). The decor is basic but authentic: the small downstairs seating area around the counter feels homely and welcoming, while the yellowing smoking room upstairs, crammed full of plastic-covered tables, smacks of a French railway café. Freshly baked cakes are carried from the upstairs kitchen to the shop window. The savoury croissants and quiches would have been better hot, but were palatable all the same. There's a limited range of teas, coffees and soft drinks, but the trip is made worthwhile by the mouth-watering cakes.
Babies and children admitted. No-smoking tables (ground floor). Tables outdoors (3, pavement). Takeaway service. Vegetarian savouries. **Map 13/6J.**

Pâtisserie Valerie ★
44 Old Compton Street, W1 (020 7437 3466). Leicester Square tube. **Open** 7.30am-10pm Mon-Fri; 8am-10pm Sat; 9.30am-6pm Sun. **Licensed. Credit** AmEx, LV, MC, £TC, V.
This well-established French pâtisserie needs little introduction. Its coveted pavement tables still rank among the prime spots for enjoying the vibrant street life of Soho. The house citron pressé is what sunny days were invented for, and the coffees are still good and strong, although it now costs £1.60 for a cappuccino and £1.70 for a pot of loose-leaf tea (worth it for the great selection). All manner of breakfasts are served (until 11.30am), from full English to toasted brioche, via pancakes with crème fraîche and strawberries, to simple croissants and pains au chocolat. Lunches include club and house sandwiches, soup and quiche of the day and a dish of the day (aubergine stuffed with risotto on a mixed leaf salad, say). The specialities, though, are the multicoloured rows of cakes and heavenly confections that mesmerise passers-by through the big shopfront windows.
Babies and children admitted. No-smoking tables. Takeaway service. **Map 13/6K.**
For branches see index.

Pronto
26 Rupert Street, W1 (020 7734 5821). Piccadilly Circus tube. **Open** 7.30am-10.30pm Mon-Fri; 10.30am-11pm Sat; 11am-10.30pm Sun. **Unlicensed. No credit cards.**
You know you're in the heart of Theatreland when you step through the doors of this exuberant Italian café – the bright red and yellow walls are plastered with old posters. A shelf of obscure Sri Lankan teas adds a touch of exoticism to the decor. Unlike the ostentatious surroundings, however, the bill of fare is pretty much bog standard, offering a fine selection of cakes and delicious biscuit bars, and the usual sandwiches of egg, tuna or prawn mayo, chicken tikka, and cottage cheese with slices of cucumber on white or granary. It's not exactly unique but the staff are friendly and the atmosphere is warm and welcoming.
Babies and children admitted. No-smoking tables. Tables outdoors (2, pavement). Takeaway service. **Map 13/6K.**
For branch see index.

West

Chiswick W4

Grove Park Deli ★
22 Fauconberg Road, W4 (020 8995 8219). Chiswick rail. **Open** 8am-6.30pm Mon-Fri; 8am-4pm Sat. **Unlicensed. Credit** LV, MC, V.

Grove Park Deli

Situated between the Great West Road and Chiswick riverside, this small but richly stocked, mauve-fronted delicatessen is a haven for local gourmets. There's an excellent assortment of pastas, fresh olives, olive oils, own-made breads, soups and cakes, as well as an interesting selection of cheeses including a smooth Manchego sheep's milk cheese (delicious with quince paste). Although there are only two tables (situated on the forecourt), the varied and appealing eat-in or takeaway menu includes whole corn-fed chicken with lemon and thyme, lamb with cumin and mint, and Greek salad with pickled chillies. We chose a fragrant couscous salad and a deliciously fresh focaccia sandwich with ham, cheese and sun-dried tomato paste. Among the desserts were chocolate and butter pudding, orange and almond cake and cabernet sauvignon or chardonnay sorbets. We settled on mouth-watering Portuguese tarts and delectably moist jallousies with blackberries and vanilla sugar. Service is knowledgeable, efficient and friendly. It's also worth noting that fresh flowers are sold here from Thursday to Saturday.
Babies and children admitted. Takeaway service.

Ladbroke Grove W11

Coins Bar & Grill
105-107 Talbot Road, W11 (020 7221 8099). Ladbroke Grove, Notting Hill Gate or Westbourne Park tube. **Open** 9am-11pm Tue-Sat; 10am-10.30pm Sun. **Licensed. Credit** MC, £TC, V.
Coins is an unusual cocktail of styles: one part Mediterranean-style bistro, one part pseudo working-class caff. It's light and airy with well-spaced tables both inside and out and was very busy on the Saturday morning of our first visit. This might explain the flippant attitude of the maitre d', who made us wait and wait for a table – after 20 minutes we got bored and left. We came back, this time on a Tuesday morning, and things were quite different: the service was charming and the food was above average. Coins' breakfast consisted of two perfectly cooked eggs, grilled bacon, tomato, herb sausage and mushrooms (plus caff-style pre-buttered toast). Drinks were a mixed success; latte was delicious, but a mug of tea arrived with a teabag stewing in it and no obvious place to put the used bag. Other brunch options (between 9am and noon) include fresh fruit salad with natural yoghurt, honey and walnuts, or french toast with banana, walnut and maple syrup. Coins serves a good, albeit pricey breakfast in pleasant surroundings, but avoid weekends.
Tables outdoors (6, pavement). Takeaway service. **Map 11/3A.**

Nectar ★
The Tabernacle Arts Centre, Powis Square, W11 (020 7565 7808). Ladbroke Grove, Notting Hill Gate or Westbourne Park tube. **Open** 8.30am-11pm Mon-Fri; 9.30am-11pm Sat; 10am-5pm Sun. **Licensed. Credit** MC, £TC, V.
This charming café in (and outside) the Tabernacle Arts Centre offers a quiet, reasonably priced oasis of calm amid the chaos of Portobello market. Local chef, Maggie Mitchell, produces a winning menu of Caribbean and Mediterranean cuisine and serves a mean veggie breakfast (£4) of scrambled egg, tomatoes, potatoes, fried peppers in olive oil with thyme, and toast. Typical main courses include Caribbean stewed chicken with peas and rice; king fish steak served with callaloo and sweet potato; and tomato, red onion, feta and basil salad. During the day, order at the bar and your meal will be brought to your table, but in the evening you can expect waiter service. The relaxed and friendly vibe of Nectar makes a pleasant change from the grouchy attitude of certain other local establishments. A further plus: on Sundays, breakfast is served all day, alongside the regular menu.
Babies and children welcome. Tables outdoors. **Map 11/5A.**

Maida Vale W9

Raoul's
13 Clifton Road, W9 (020 7289 7313). Warwick Avenue tube/6 bus. **Open** 8.30am-10.30pm Mon-Sat; 9am-10.30pm Sun. **Minimum** (12.30-2.30pm) £3.75. **Licensed. Credit** AmEx, DC, MC, £TC, V.
Amid the villagey atmosphere of Clifton Gardens, Raoul's is more than just your average caff – it also has a thriving restaurant operation. The interior is simply but tastefully decorated, with Jazz Age photos scattered across the white walls. For snacks, baguette fillings include char-grilled chicken, tuna melt and classic club; otherwise, opt for one of the ciabatta rolls. Naturally, there's also a selection of cakes (of the cream and chocolate type) and teas and coffees. More serious eaters might like to try dishes such as lamb kofta – we did and found it deliciously spicy and complemented by a generous serving of fresh, own-made tsatsiki. Other options might include lamb cutlets served with mint couscous, or healthy options such as mozzarella or spinach salads. The wine list contains some good bottles, many of which are served by the glass.
Babies and children welcome; high chairs. No-smoking tables. Tables outdoors (15, pavement). Takeaway service (until 6pm). **Map 1/4D.**

Westbourne Grove W11

Tom's Delicatessen
226 Westbourne Grove, W11 (020 7221 8818). Notting Hill Gate tube. **Open** 8am-10pm Mon-Fri; 8am-6pm Sat; 10am-4pm Sun. **Licensed. Corkage** £1.50. **Credit** AmEx, MC, V.
This corner of London may have more celebs per square inch than most others, but our visit to Tom's unearthed nothing more glam than locals popping in for a fill of brunch. Some were lucky enough to find a table in the pretty, cosily cramped garden out back. From the extensive, rather bitty menu we assembled two versions of a proper English breakfast, one meaty and one vegetarian. Both were good but, considering the grand total came to twenty quid for two fry-ups, we were irritated by a litany of minor faults – most significantly, rubbery veggie sausages and over-fried eggs. On the plus side, hash browns were enjoyably soft and squidgy, and black pudding was nice and light – though there wasn't enough of it. Tom's is not a big place and queues do build up, so be prepared for a wait. There are also delicious own-made cakes, breads, sandwiches and delicacies to be sampled, plus a range of meals in the evening (duck breast, pasta dishes and the like).
Babies and children welcome; high chairs. No smoking. Takeaway service (daytime); delivery service. **Map 11/6A.**

South West

Earl's Court SW5

Troubadour
265 Old Brompton Road, SW5 (020 7370 1434). Earl's Court tube. **Open** 9am-midnight daily. **Licensed. Credit** MC, £TC, V.
This charming café on Old Brompton Road has a relaxed and friendly atmosphere, with dark-wood benches and tables blending seamlessly with the clutter of old musical instruments and motley pots and pans suspended from the ceiling. There's also a small patio garden out back that provides further seating. Friendly staff are very accommodating, offering a range of coffees and teas, fruit juices and soft drinks to accompany nibbles (perhaps a bowl of fries), sandwiches and pastries. On our visit, daily specials included soup of the day and main courses of steak frites and a spaghetti dish with garlic, prawns and herbs, as well as a couple of vegetarian options. Evening entertainment comes in the form of comedy (every Tuesday), regular poetry readings and jazz musicians.
Babies and children welcome; high chairs. Entertainment: various (phone for details). No-smoking tables. Tables outdoors (2, pavement; 5, garden). **Map 5/11B.**

South Kensington SW3

Gloriette Pâtisserie
128 Brompton Road, SW3 (020 7589 4750). Knightsbridge tube. **Open** 7am-8.30pm Mon-Fri; 7am-7pm Sat; 9am-6pm Sun. **Licensed. Credit** AmEx, MC, V.
Gloriette has been around since 1956 offering respite to Knightsbridge shoppers within its cosy interior. At the front is a stunning display of cakes and chocolates. There's a handful of outside tables, too, for those hardy enough to brave the Brompton Road traffic. It's worth checking the specials before ordering food. Our uninspiring tuna sweetcorn sandwich, and an equally bland deli-style order of bagel and lox, were both expensive options at £6.50, whereas the daily pasta dish cost £6.75 and a two-course menu comprising a starter (soup or sautéed chicken livers) and a main course (pan-fried salmon or cold roast beef) was available for just £7.90. We also tried seared tuna on bruschetta, which was substantial, but rather soggy (caused by the salsa being below, rather than above, the tuna). Latte and hot chocolate were both delicious. Service was a little slow.
Babies and children welcome. Tables outdoors (10, pavement). Takeaway service. **Map 12/9F.**

Troubadour. See page 201.

South

Battersea SW11

Boiled Egg & Soldiers ★
*63 Northcote Road, SW11 (020 7223 4894).
Clapham Junction rail/45, 219, 319 bus.* **Open**
9am-6pm Mon-Sat; 10am-5pm Sun. **Licensed.
No credit cards.**
A popular hangout for local families, Boiled Egg
& Soldiers presents a sunny exterior to the bustle
of Northcote Road. There's a convivial huddle of
outdoor tables, but most customers are tightly
packed (with their sometimes noisy kids) into the
cosy little interior. Gentrified caff food is the
order of the day, freshly prepared and daintily
presented. The muffin with egg, ham and cheese
looked and tasted delicious. It being the signature
dish, we decided to order boiled eggs and soldiers
(two for adults, one for children) and were glad
we did – they arrived perfectly cooked and sitting
in individually crafted egg cups. Tea is served in
brightly coloured pots (none of that nasty stainless steel greasy-spoon gear here). Bruschetta
with various fillings and all-day breakfasts (with
veggie and meat options) all look appetising, and
an extensive specials board fills in the gaps. The
place is small and can feel a little cramped when
busy, but this didn't seem to bother the customers
or the staff.
*Babies and children welcome; children's menu;
high chairs; toys. Tables outdoors (24, garden).
Takeaway service.*

Brixton SW9

lounge
*88 Atlantic Road, SW9 (020 7733 5229).
Brixton tube/rail.* **Open** 8am-midnight
Mon-Sat; 10am-10pm Sun. **Unlicensed.
Corkage** £1 wine, 30p beer. **No credit
cards.**
A great place to do as the name suggests, lounge.
This relaxed venue offers welcome respite from
the Brixton street life, but it's as bright and
diverse as the other buildings on Atlantic Road.
The decor here combines colour and industrial

furnishings to good effect and is complemented
by the hip staff and clientele, and a sassy
modern menu. You don't have to wait long for
your order to be taken and processed, so use the
time to choose between a wide variety of
sandwiches, bagels and ciabattas, as well as
salads, soups and quiches. Prices range from
£2.50 to £4.50; we sampled such delights as
goat's cheese, roast peppers, aubergine and fresh
basil (this comes either as a salad or a sarnie),
and a crunchy peanut butter, bramble jelly and
banana sandwich. For the price of a drink and a
slice of one of the tempting, calorific cakes you
can use either of the two Internet terminals.
Original artwork (for sale) adds further interest.
*Babies and children admitted. Tables
outdoors (6, patio). Takeaway service.*
Map 18.

Clapham SW4

The Pavement
*21 The Pavement, SW4 (020 7622 4944).
Clapham Common tube.* **Open** 7am-7pm daily.
Unlicensed. Credit LV.
Far from the madding crowds of Clapham High
Street, the Pavement has decent views over
Clapham Common. If you happen to be facing
inward, however, all that meets the eye is a dimly
lit, cappuccino-coloured interior that can seem a
bit depressing. During our lunchtime visit the
place was packed; teas and toasted paninis
flowed freely out of the kitchen. Annoyingly,
though, the diminutive size of the place meant
that noisy locals talking about their previous
night's drunken antics and scraping the Ikea
chairs on the floor drowned out any chances of a
relaxing chat or a read of one of the newspapers
provided. Service was a bit of a shambles on our
visit, even surly at times, and tables were left
uncleared for ages. Food looked more enticing
than it was: the banana cake was OK, if dry and
sickly sweet. You can also get the usual range of
sandwiches, baguettes and paninis to eat-in or
take away.
*Babies and children welcome; high chairs.
No-smoking tables. Takeaway service.
Vegetarian dishes.*

Borough SE1

Konditor & Cook ★
10 Stoney Street, SE1 (020 7407 5100). London Bridge tube/rail. **Open** 7.30am-6.30pm Mon-Fri; 8.30am-2.30pm Sat. **Unlicensed. Credit** AmEx, MC, V.
An excellent bakery forms the backbone of this snappy modern-looking operation around the corner from Borough Market. Cakes, pastries and breads are conjured from a variety of regional recipes, from carrot cake and pecan pie to Greek orange and almond pudding. Free-range eggs, organic butter, even wheat- and yeast-free breads, show a commitment to quality and, as they describe it, 'bespoke' catering. Our own ricotta and roasted vegetable walnut-bread sandwich was superb, likewise the mozzarella, pesto and tomato variety on herb bread. Salads are tasty, too, and reasonably priced – pasta, roasted vegetables and feta with pine kernels cost £3.95. There's also the bonus of a decent selection of wines and beers. Go on Saturday, when a farmers' market take place at Borough Market.
Babies and children admitted. **Map 8/8P.**
For branch see index.

East

Bethnal Green E2

Blue Orange
65 Columbia Road, E2 (020 7366 9272). Bus 26, 48, 55. **Open** 10am-4.30pm Thur, Fri; 9.30am-5pm Sat; 7.30am-4pm Sun. **Unlicensed. No credit cards.**
A little slice of rustic bohemia in the East End, the Blue Orange is a real favourite on Sundays. Normally the tables and chairs are all confined to the courtyard out back, but during the glorious Columbia Road flower market, customers at the café are allowed to sit in among it all. We chose a tasty panini filled with avocado, mozzarella, pesto and sun-dried tomatoes (the house favourite). There's a range of other fillings, plus slices of pizza and a list of savoury croissants stuffed with the likes of tomato, cheese and mushroom, spinach and cheese, or ham and cheese. Good coffee comes in all its many guises and there's also a particularly enticing array of Portuguese cakes and tarts, and a selection of cakes made on the premises.
Babies and children welcome; high chairs. Tables outdoors (2, courtyard). Takeaway service. **Map 4/3S.**

Jones Dairy Café ★
23 Ezra Street, E2 (020 7739 5372). Bus 26, 48, 55. **Open** 9am-3pm Thur-Sat; 8am-2pm Sun. **Unlicensed. No credit cards.**
On Sunday, when Columbia Road market is in full swing, Jones limits itself to producing a fast turnover of coffee, fresh orange juice, filled bagels, cakes (a wonderful lemon cheesecake) and buns. There's always a queue, but staff remain calm and polite. It's a treat to go at less frenetic times, though, when there's also a short menu listing the likes of smoked haddock, scrambled eggs, goat's cheese salad, ham and eggs, and a very fresh fruit salad. All are prepared with care and attention, in an unruffled fashion. A great little place.
Babies and children admitted. Seats outdoors (12, courtyard). Takeaway service. **Map 4/3S.**

North East

Stoke Newington N16

Blue Legume
101 Stoke Newington Church Street, N16 (020 7923 1303). Stoke Newington rail/73 bus. **Open** 9.30am-6.30pm daily. **Licensed. No credit cards.**
An independent venture serving simply divine, and predominantly vegetarian, food to the lucky locals of Stokey. It's child-friendly and cosy, in a kind of baroque hippy-chic way. A giant sun smiles down from the ceiling, as does a rather more ominous wire mosquito. Mosaic tables, imitation Cézannes and flowers complete the look. The food is definitely worth a punt. Asparagus and Gorgonzola quiche; vegetable tortilla; carrot, nut and ginger burgers; and nut roasts – all come with a selection of salads (around £5). Everything looked appetising and the dishes we tried were delicious. And that's before you get to the desserts: organic honey waffles with maple syrup, natural yoghurt and fresh fruit, sticky date pudding, key lime pie, and mango cheesecake, to name but a few.
Babies and children welcome; high chairs. Tables outdoors (4, pavement). Takeaway service. Vegetarian dishes.

North

Camden Town & Chalk Farm NW1

Primrose Pâtisserie
136 Regent's Park Road, NW1 (020 7722 7848). Chalk Farm tube/31, 168 bus. **Open** *winter* 8am-9pm, *summer* 8am-10pm, daily. **Unlicensed. No credit cards.**
Unlike some of its more chi-chi competitors on affluent Regent's Park Road, this pretty, well-established café continues to offer excellent value for money. We last visited on a warm summer evening when the few outdoor tables had already been snapped up, so we settled instead for the slightly cramped interior. The food has a definite Eastern European slant – rye bread features prominently. There are even loaves to take home. Our smoked salmon and cream cheese sandwiches on rye were freshly made and delicious. Cakes are a forte, from the rich, vanilla-tinged baked cheesecake to the tangy apple and peach crumble cake. Pleasant service completes the picture, making this a great place to come for a decent snack and a chat.
Babies and children admitted. No smoking. Tables outdoors (6, pavement). Takeaway service. **Map 10.**

Crouch End N8

World Café
130 Crouch Hill, N8 (020 8340 5635/ www.worldcafe.smallplanet.co.uk). Finsbury Park tube/rail then W3, W7 bus/41, 91 bus. **Open** 9.30am-11pm Mon-Sat; 9.30am-10.30pm Sun. **Licensed. Credit** MC, V.
World Café continues to pull in the punters. On our lunchtime visit the place was buzzing with an eclectic mix of trendy loafers and mums with toddlers in tow, all spilling out on to the pavement tables, to the accompaniment of blaring funky music. As its name suggests, this café draws inspiration from around the globe, offering an extensive menu of breakfast, lunch and supper options, ranging from coco de natas cakes to steak and chips. 'Freshly squeezed orange juice' tasted as if it had been freshly poured from a plastic bottle, but the falafel with salad and pitta, and toasted goat's cheese with avocado and bacon were tasty and gratifyingly generous. Desserts include waffles, tarts, flans and an array of ice-creams.
Babies and children welcome; high chairs. Book dinner. Tables outdoors (7, pavement). Takeaway service. Vegetarian dishes.

Highgate N6

Café Mozart
17 Swains Lane, N6 (020 8348 1384). Highgate tube/Gospel Oak rail/214, C2, C11, C12 bus. **Open** 9am-10pm daily. **Licensed. Credit** MC, V.
We can't necessarily tell you how they all translate into English, but if you try any of the pastries at this Viennese café, whether it's kipfel, apfelfleck, basler brinski or zwetschenkenfleck, you're in for a treat. Nestled between the Heath and Highgate Cemetery, Café Mozart is all wood-panelling and portraits of the maestro inside, while outside a handful of tables make good use of the wide Highgate pavement. The menu boasts one of the best tuna niçoise salads in town (plus other great salad options), along with some interesting sandwiches, rolls and bagels (pancetta and dill cucumber, for instance). There are more substantial options too, such as schnitzel and goulash. Of course, there's also decent coffee (this is a Viennese café after all), and a limited but well-chosen wine list.
Babies and children admitted. Book dinner. No smoking. Tables outdoors (8, pavement). Takeaway service.

Islington N1

Caffè Mobile
By south bound bus stops near Angel tube, Islington High Street, N1 (020 7704 6363). Angel tube. **Open** 7am-12.30pm Mon-Fri; 8am-4.30pm Sat.
The Royal Oak, Columbia Road Market, E1 (no phone). Bus 8, 26, 48, 55. **Open** 8am-2pm Sun.
Highbury & Islington tube/rail, N1 (no phone). **Open** 7am-noon Mon-Fri.
Belsize Park tube. **Open** 7am-1pm Mon-Fri.
Spitalfields Market **Open** 10am-5pm Sun.
All **Unlicensed. No credit cards.**
These Italian vans with espresso machines in the back are parked at strategic locations around London. Choose between espresso, macchiato, cappuccino or latte, for around a pound. A few pastries are sold, too.
Map 16/2N.

Maison Blanc.
See page 203.

Viva
236 St Paul's Road, N1 (020 7704 8227). Highbury & Islington tube/rail/4, 19, 30, 277 bus. **Open** 9am-6pm Mon-Fri; 10am-6pm Sat, Sun. **Unlicensed. Credit** MC, V.
Colombia has never been at the centre of Britain's love affair with South America – most of the attention goes to its scene-stealing neighbour, Brazil. But Viva packs a friendly, exotic latino punch and is well worth a visit. Hammocks and woven baskets hang from the ceiling, and samba and bossa nova play quietly in the background: this is a cosy family place (there's even garden seating in the sun-drenched Islington back yard). Colombian-style eggs (huevos pericos) come with toast and coffee and make a refreshing change from the Sunday fry-up. Bocatas (focaccia sandwiches with a range of fillings from basil and mozzarella to smoked salmon and cream cheese), quiches, baguettes, soups and an array of cakes are there to fill you up if you don't feel like indulging in the pasta of the day. By the way, the toilet's outside.
Babies and children welcome; high chairs; toys (in garden). Tables outdoors (6, garden). Takeaway service. Vegetarian dishes.

North West

Belsize Park NW3

Chamomile
45 England's Lane, NW3 (020 7586 4580). Belsize Park or Chalk Farm tube/C11 bus. **Open** 7am-6.30pm daily. **Licensed. No credit cards.**
A fine place in which to relax over a leisurely breakfast or lunch, Chamomile has welcoming service and a calming effect. Plenty of room between tables, high ceilings, bright walls and simple decor give a welcome impression of space. A pinboard by the counter offers a wealth of local information on groups and activities. Add to this a location slightly off the beaten track, and you have a café with a strong following of locals ready to pay slightly over the odds for a pretty extensive menu. There's a wide choice of breakfasts (including healthy options) costing £3.50-£4.50. You'll also find a variety of well-filled sandwiches, toasted sandwiches, baked potatoes, an own-made soup of the day, and omelettes. For dessert, try one of the delicious pastries or exotic ice-creams. Coffees come in various guises at fair prices, and there's also a decent range of health drinks, and great smoothies made in-house in several flavours.
Babies and children welcome; high chairs. No-smoking tables. Tables outdoors (8, pavement). Takeaway service.

Hampstead NW3

Louis Pâtisserie
32 Heath Street, NW3 (020 7435 9908). Hampstead tube/46, 268 bus. **Open** 9am-6pm daily. **Unlicensed. No credit cards.**
Despite its French name, Louis is a steadfastly traditional Viennese-style tearoom where Hampstead's older residents come for quiet afternoon tea and to relax in leather sofas, surrounded by coats of arms and paintings depicting the old English country life. The window is adorned with a beautiful display of reasonably priced cakes and gateaux. As soon as we were seated, a tray of tempting cakes was brought over. There is no menu, so everything feels a little like pot luck. We decided to start with the sausage roll, but it was disappointingly dry, and little attention had been paid to presentation. A hazelnut gateaux and a strawberry cheesecake were a let down, too, tasting stale, bland and heavy. Louis is certainly a unique slice of history, but it isn't everyone's cup of tea.
Babies and children admitted. No-smoking tables. Takeaway service. **Map 9.**
For branch see index.

St John's Wood NW8

Maison Blanc
37 St John's Wood High Street, NW8 (020 7586 1982). St John's Wood tube. **Open** 8.30am-6.30pm Mon-Sat; 9am-6pm Sun. **Unlicensed. Credit** MC, V.
After a leisurely stroll down St John's Wood High Street, this traditional French pâtisserie makes for a good pit stop. Everything gives off an authentic vibe: from the delicious spread of pastries and chocolates, to the slightly inattentive service offered by the friendly French staff. A long, subtly-lit glass bar tempts you with alluring

cakes and pâtisseries. It leads on to a bright, sunny dining area at the back (a popular retreat for well-heeled locals). Try the millefeuilles or the pain au chocolat aux amandes – both were exceptional. Continental breakfast is served until 11.30am, and tasty quiches, croissants, salads and sandwiches are also to be had, though prices are quite high. There's a selection of reasonably priced teas, too, along with coffees and soft drinks. On your way out, ogle and perhaps buy some of the French goodies on show, such as biscuits or coffees.
Babies and children admitted. No smoking. Tables outdoors (3, pavement).
For branches see index.

Outer London

Kew, Surrey

Hothouse Café
9 Station Approach, Kew, Surrey (020 8332 1923). Kew Gardens tube. **Open** 10am-6.30pm daily. **Licensed. Credit** £TC.
Snappily decked out in bright blue and white, with a few scattered pot plants and a mellow jazz soundtrack, the Hothouse has a pleasantly laid-back atmosphere. Customers can choose from a large selection of teas and coffees, including the particularly fine Jamaican Blue Mountain blend, while breakfast options range from the likes of a warm croissant with Bonne Maman jam to a full-scale English breakfast. The menu gets a bit more substantial at lunchtime, with a host of upmarket sandwiches, filled jacket potatoes and salads. Service is pleasant and food is delivered to the table with admirable promptness.
Babies and children admitted. No-smoking tables. Takeaway service.

The Kew Greenhouse
1 Station Parade, Kew, Surrey (020 8940 0183). Kew Gardens tube. **Open** 9am-dusk daily. **Licensed. No credit cards.**
On a prime corner site just a short walk from Kew Gardens tube, this sedate, friendly café, with an extensive pavement dining area, appeals to locals and visitors alike. The greenhouse theme is driven home by the decor: pale green walls, floral prints, cane chairs and a pretty conservatory filled with ferns, geraniums and hibiscus plants. The menu offers simple, traditional pleasures, from an English breakfast to weightier dishes such as organic pork roulade. But it's the tempting display of own-made pastries and cakes that takes pride of place. Our cherry flapjack was a huge, wonderfully sticky concoction. The clientele is an accurate reflection of the Kew demographic – families with small children messily demolishing bowls of pasta, and old ladies sipping coffee and chatting cheerfully in the conservatory.
Babies and children welcome; high chairs. No-smoking tables. Tables outdoors (14, pavement). Takeaway service.

Internet cafés

Note that Internet cafés put terminals before food, so don't expect any great culinary fireworks from the places listed below.

Buzz Bar
95 Portobello Road, W11 (020 7460 4906/ www.buzzbar.co.uk). Ladbroke Grove or Notting Hill Gate tube. **Open** 10am-9pm Mon-Fri; 10am-7pm Sat; noon-7pm Sun. **Licensed. Credit** DC, MC, £TC, V.
Internet access: £5 per hour.
Babies and children admitted. **Map 11/6A.**

Café Internet
22-24 Buckingham Palace Road, SW1 (020 7233 5786/www.cafeinternet.co.uk). Victoria tube/rail. **Open** 8am-10pm Mon-Fri; 10am-8pm Sat; 10am-6pm Sun. **Licensed. Credit** AmEx, LV, MC, £TC, V.
Internet access: 99p for 10 mins, £1.20 per half hour, £1.50-£2.50 per hour.
Internet training: from £15 per half hour.
Babies and children admitted. No-smoking tables. Tables outdoors (4, pavement). Takeaway service. **Map 6/9H.**

Cyberia Internet Café
39 Whitfield Street, W1 (020 7681 4200/www.cyberiacafe.net). Goodge Street or Tottenham Court Road tube. **Open** 9am-9pm Mon-Fri; 11am-7pm Sat; 11am-6pm Sun. **Licensed. Credit** MC, £TC, V.
Internet access: no charge.
Babies and children admitted. Tables outdoors (3, pavement).
For branch see index.

easyEverything
9-13 Wilton Road, opposite Victoria Station, SW1 (020 7233 8456/ www.easyEverything.com). Victoria tube/rail. **Open** 24 hours daily. **Unlicensed. No credit cards.**
Internet access: the busier it is, the more it costs.
Babies and children admitted. No-smoking tables.
For branches see index.

Fulham.ebar
42-48 New King's Road, SW6 (020 7384 9746). Fulham Broadway tube. **Open** 9am-10.30pm Mon-Fri; 9am-11.30pm Sat; 10am-11pm Sun.
Computers shut down at 7pm on Saturdays.
Internet access: 10p per minute (no minimum).

Global Café
15 Golden Square, W1 (020 7287 2242/ www.globalcafe.net). Oxford Circus or Piccadilly Circus tube. **Open** 9am-11pm Mon-Sat; noon-10.30pm Sun. **Licensed. Credit** MC, V.
Internet access: 50p for 5 mins, £5 per hour.
Babies and children welcome. Entertainment: DJ Fri, Sat nights; occasional multimedia events and art exhibitions. Tables outdoors (4, pavement). Takeaway service. **Map 13/7J.**

Intercafé
25 Great Portland Street, W1 (020 7631 0063/www.intercafe.co.uk). Oxford Circus tube. **Open** 7.30am-7pm Mon-Fri; 9.30am-5pm Sat. **Licensed. Credit** MC, £TC, V.
Internet access: £1.50 per 15 mins, £3 per half hour, £5 per hour.
No smoking. Tables outdoors (3, pavement). Takeaway service.

Sunshine Catering @ The Vibe Bar
The Truman Brewery, 91 Brick Lane, E1 (020 7247 1685/www.vibe-bar.co.uk). Aldgate East tube. **Open** noon-3pm Mon-Fri; 10am-6pm Sun. **Licensed. Credit** AmEx, MC, V.
Internet access: no charge.
Tables outdoors (6, courtyard). Takeaway service. **Map 4/5S.**

Surf.Net.Café
13 Deptford Church Street, SE8 (020 8488 1200/www.surfnet.co.uk). Deptford rail/47, 53, 177 bus. **Open** noon-9pm Mon-Fri; noon-7pm Sat. **Unlicensed. Corkage** 50p beer, £1 wine. **No credit cards.**
Internet access: £1 per 15 mins.
Babies and children admitted. Takeaway service. Vegetarian dishes.

Webshack
15 Dean Street, W1 (020 7439 8000/ www.webshack-cafe.com). Oxford Circus, Piccadilly Circus or Tottenham Court Road tube. **Open** 9.30am-11pm Mon-Sat; 1-8pm Sun. **Licensed. Credit** DC, MC, V.
Internet access: £1 per half hour, £2 per hour.
Babies and children admitted. **Map 13/6K.**

Juice bars

More fresh juices can be had at the organic food outlets **Planet Organic** (42 Westbourne Grove, W2/020 7221 7171 and 18-22 Torrington Place, W1/020 7436 1929) and **Fresh & Wild** (49 Parkway, NW1/020 7428 7575), as well as at **Ranoush Juice** (*see page 127* **Middle Eastern**).

Central

City EC3

Crussh
48 Cornhill, EC3 (020 7626 2175). Bank tube/DLR. **Open** 7am-4pm Mon-Fri. **Unlicensed. Credit** MC, V.
With its curved wooden benches and perching stools, and its purple and red colour scheme, Crussh provides some welcome relief from the grey City landscape that surrounds it. This isn't exactly your typical pin-striped hangout, but the formula seems to work – the place was frantically busy during our lunchtime visit. All available space is given over to seating (squidgy sofas as well as the stools), so orders have to be passed down to the kitchen via a baby walky-talky. As its name suggests, this place specialises in freshly squeezed juices and smoothies. We tried the 'clean & lean' Crussh classic, a refreshing blend of melon, apple and cranberry. The health-conscious menu is a medley of salads, sushi and the like, but our nicely presented tuna salad turned out to be a dry disappointment. Staff were very chipper and helpful and didn't seem to be too harassed after what had obviously been a very busy day's trading, having to bark orders through a plastic baby-monitor and run up and down stairs without spilling a drop of juice.
Babies and children admitted. No smoking. Takeaway service. **Map 4/6Q.**
For branches see index.

Covent Garden WC2

Farmacia
169 Drury Lane, WC2 (020 7831 0830). Covent Garden, Holborn or Tottenham Court Road tube. **Open** 8.30am-7pm Mon-Fri; 9am-6pm Sat. **Unlicensed. Credit** MC, £TC, V.
If you're running a bit low on *chi*, or city life has drained you of your *chakra*, then Farmacia claims to have exactly the brand of 'urban healing' that you're needin'. This is not a typical juice bar; a variety of tonics and teas strongly reminiscent of Chinese herbal remedies is sold to punters wishing to realign their oneness and tweak their general wellness. While the mischievously named 'chi devil' sounded tempting (apparently it enhances a woman's sensuality) we decided to try something far more ambitious with the 'mind over muddle', a concoction using ginseng to get the brain back into full working order. All drinks are available hot or cold. Staff seem knowledgeable and eager to help. It's a little disconcerting having drinks made up for you by somebody who looks more ready to drill your teeth, but, for all its pretensions, Farmacia is really quite fun. For the ultimate health-kick, try the freshly prepared wheatgrass shots – they may not look or taste very appetising, but they certainly make you feel good. There's no food but, hey, who needs it? Eating's a waste of energy, man.
Babies and children admitted. Takeaway service. **Map 14/6L.**
For branch see index.

West

Kensington W8

Squeeze
27 Kensington High Street, W8 (020 7376 9786). High Street Kensington tube. **Open** 8am-7pm Mon-Fri; 9am-7pm Sat; 10am-7pm Sun. **No credit cards.**
A Bob Marley soundtrack, over-sized fruit painted on to citrus-coloured walls, and comfy-looking sofas – all help give this colourful little juice bar a student living-room kind of vibe that seems at odds with well-to-do High Street Ken. Once you're inside, there are some tough decisions to be made between delicious-sounding selections of smoothies and juices. 'Peach passion' (peach, strawberry, banana and orange) was our particular favourite, while the 'female boost' (iron, folic acid, calcium, pineapple juice, honeydew, banana and low-fat yoghurt) in the right-on 'girl power' smoothie was a little too much to take in one go. Food looked tasty and inviting; it includes a range of freshly-made salads, wraps and soups providing the ideal complement for the virtuous juices. Health freaks will also be delighted with the information displayed around the service area regarding the nutritional values of all the ingredients. Staff are relaxed and amiable.
Babies and children admitted. **Map 5/9C.**

South West

Fulham SW10

Fluid
208 Fulham Road, SW10 (020 7352 4372). South Kensington tube/14 bus. **Open** 7.30am-7pm Mon-Fri; 9am-7pm Sat; 10am-7pm Sun. **Unlicensed. No credit cards.**
The smell of freshly squeezed oranges lures you into the yellow minimalism of this bright and trendy juice bar. Having placed your order, step back and watch scrumptious-looking fruit being prepared and blended into large or extra-large

Hotel teas

There's something comforting and self-indulgent about a three-course tea in a posh hotel. When everything is as it should be – fresh and interesting sandwiches, hot crumpets dripping with melted butter, refreshing teas constantly replenished, and a stand loaded with extravagant cakes (not to mention tip-top service and elegant surroundings) – this is a great way of spending an afternoon. Just don't expect to want any supper, and do book well in advance.

Central

Belgravia SW1

The Lanesborough Hotel
Hyde Park Corner, SW1 (020 7259 5599). Hyde Park Corner tube. **Tea served** 3.30-6pm daily. **Set teas** £20.50-£26.50. **Minimum** £7.50. **Credit** AmEx, DC, JCB, MC, TC, V.
Map 6/8G.

Covent Garden WC2

Waldorf Meridien
Aldwych, WC2 (020 7836 2400). Covent Garden or Temple tube. **Tea served** 3-5.30pm Mon-Fri. **Tea dance** 2.30-5pm Sat; 4-6.30pm Sun. **Set teas** £21, £28 incl glass of champagne. *Tea dance* £25, £28 incl champagne. **Licensed. Credit** AmEx, DC, MC, TC, V. **Map 14/6M.**

Knightsbridge SW3

Basil Street Hotel
Basil Street, SW3 (020 7581 3311/www.thebasil.com). Knightsbridge tube. **Tea served** 3.30-6pm daily. **Set tea** £7.75, £11.50. **Licensed. Credit** AmEx, DC, TC, MC, V. **Map 12/9F.**

Mayfair W1

Brown's Hotel
33-34 Albemarle Street, W1 (020 7518 4108). Green Park tube. **Tea served** two sittings: 3pm and 4.45pm Mon-Fri; 2.30-5.45pm Sat, Sun (first-come first-served). **Set tea** £18.95. **Licensed. Credit** AmEx, DC, JCB, MC, V. **Map 13/7J.**

Claridge's
Brook Street, W1 (020 7629 8860). Bond Street tube. **Tea served** 3-5.30pm daily. **Set tea** (Mon-Fri) £22; (Sat, Sun) £28.50 incl champagne. **Licensed. Credit** AmEx, DC, MC, TC, V. **Map 2/6H.**

The Dorchester (The Promenade)
54 Park Lane, W1 (020 7629 8888). Hyde Park Corner tube. **Tea served** 2.30-6pm, *high tea* 5-8pm daily. **Set teas** £19.50, £25.50 incl champagne; *high tea* £29.50. **Licensed. Credit** AmEx, DC, JCB, MC, TC, V. **Map 6/8G.**

Piccadilly W1

The Ritz
Piccadilly, W1 (020 7493 8181). Green Park tube. **Tea served** 2-6pm daily; reserved sittings 3.30pm, 5pm. **Set tea** £27. **Licensed. Credit** AmEx, DC, JCB, MC, £TC, V. **Map 13/7J.**

St James, Fortnum & Mason
181 Piccadilly, W1 (020 7734 8040). Green Park or Piccadilly Circus tube. **Lunch served** noon-2.30pm, **tea served** 3-5.45pm Mon-Sat. **Set teas** from £11.95; *high tea* £16.50, £18.95 incl champagne. **Minimum** £6.95. **Licensed. Credit** AmEx, DC, JCB, MC, £TC, V. **Map 13/7J.**

Strand WC2

Savoy
Strand, WC2 (020 7836 4343). Covent Garden or Embankment tube/Charing Cross tube/rail. **Tea served** 3-5.30pm daily. **Set tea** (Mon-Fri) £21, (Sat) £23, adults; £14 under-10s. **Tea dance** (Sun) £26.50 with four-piece band. **Licensed. Credit** AmEx, DC, JCB, MC, TC, V. **Map 14/7L.**

smoothies and small and medium-sized combination juices. Staff are relaxed and friendly. Every inch of the premises seems to be littered with piles of fine fruit and veg (including organic carrots fresh from Highgrove, no less). Our smoothie, a delicious, thick blend of orange, strawberry, banana and frozen yoghurt, was generous to the point where we grudgingly had to leave some. This and other combinations exist on the menu as preset options, but customers are free to create any combination of their choosing. There was never a shortage of people queuing during our visit; we even caught sight of some of the more health-conscious clientele knocking back fresh wheatgrass, which boasts an abundance of vitamins and minerals but looks like something your mother might have made you drink under protest. Juices are also available to take away in one-litre cartons.
Babies and children welcome. No smoking.
Map 5/12C.
For branch see index.

Park cafés

West

Kensington W8

The Orangery

Kensington Palace, Kensington Gardens, W8 (020 7376 0239). High Street Kensington or Queensway tube. **Open** *Oct-Easter* 10am-5pm, *Easter-Sept* 10am-6pm, daily. **Set teas** £7.25-£12.95. **Licensed. Credit** MC, £TC, V.
This café lives up to its truly elegant setting in an 18th-century orangery in the grounds of Kensington Palace. Surrounded by vases of flowers and huge Grecian urns, you can choose from a dangerously tempting array of cakes. We sampled a delicious berry tart – tangy blackcurrants contrasting wonderfully with a butter-rich filling – and chic chocolate and vanilla sablés. A fine choice of teas includes some classy options (the leaf tea is particularly good). The lunchtime menu was equally well conceived, ranging from soup to smoked trout salad, with the handy addition of a reasonably priced children's menu (£3.95). Teatime, as one might guess, is a forte; those with especially royal tastes can indulge in the 'grand tea', which includes a glass of bubbly.
Babies and children welcome; high chairs. No smoking. **Map 11/8C.**

North

Highgate N10

Oshobasho Café

Highgate Wood, Muswell Hill Road, N10 (020 8444 1505). Highgate tube/43, 134 bus. **Open** 9am-one hour before dusk Tue-Sun. **Licensed. No credit cards.**
Tucked discreetly away in a hedge-lined pavilion in Highgate Wood, this established café has an ample outdoor eating area. Largely due to the proximity of a popular playground, it is awash with parents and their toddlers; there's a seemingly perpetual queue. Food is brought out to diners by faintly harassed but friendly waiters. The menu is vegetarian, offering simple, freshly made food that ranges from own-made soups to tasty focaccia sandwiches. Portions are generous, though £6.20 for a simple tomato and ricotta pasta bake seemed ridiculously expensive. There's a wide selection of herbal teas, but less healthy options are also available: lots of cakes, pastries, coffee, and ice-creams ranging from Mini Milks to Loseley.
Babies and children welcome; high chairs. Disabled: toilet. Entertainment: jazz Wed, harpist Fri, electric cello Sat, on summer evenings. No smoking (indoors). Tables outdoors (30, patio). Takeaway service.

North West

Golders Green NW3

Golders Hill Park Refreshment House

North End Road, NW3 (020 8455 8010). Golders Green tube. **Open** *Feb-Nov* 10am-sunset Mon-Sat. **Licensed. No credit cards.**
Housed in light, modern, slightly utilitarian surroundings looking out over a green and pleasant park, this 'continental cafeteria' is vaguely reminiscent of an Italian autostrada caff. The food is simple and unpretentious, again with a strong Italian influence: pasta, Parma ham with melon, buffalo mozzarella with avocado and salad, slices of watermelon and packets of grissini. The relaxed and down-to-earth vibe here seems to hold a universal appeal – the clientele bridges all the age gaps from OAPs to toddlers. The star attraction is the delightful ice-cream kiosk at the side of the café, offering excellent own-made Italian-style gelati starting at £1, with a myriad tempting choices such as fresh peach sorbet, pistachio and coffee.
Babies and children welcome; high chairs. Disabled: toilet. No smoking (indoors). Tables outdoors (35, patio). Takeaway service.

Hampstead NW3

Brew House

Kenwood, Hampstead Lane, NW3 (020 8341 5384). Bus 210, 214. **Open** *Oct-Mar* 9am-4pm daily; *Apr-Sept* 9am-6pm (7.30pm on concert nights) daily. **Licensed. Credit** £TC.
Located in the spacious former laundry at the side of Kenwood House, this pleasant café has also made good use of its extensive garden area with plenty of smart sun-shaded tables providing a peaceful spot for al fresco munching. The menu places a commendable emphasis on the quality of the ingredients used, from free-range eggs to coffee from Martyns in Muswell Hill. We sampled the full breakfast, a tasty combo of excellent field mushrooms, a meaty free-range pork sausage, tomatoes and scrambled egg served with toast. Lunch dishes range from soup to more substantial options of corn-fed chicken, along with a generous range of high-quality sandwiches, soft drinks and pastries. Staff work hard to keep the tables clean and neat and even dogs are thoughtfully catered for with a bowl of drinking water near the outside tables.
Babies and children welcome; high chairs. Disabled: toilets. No smoking. Tables outdoors (44, garden; 24, patio). Takeaway service.

Regent's Park NW1

Park Café The Broadwalk

Regent's Park, off Chester Road, NW1 (020 7224 3872). Regent's Park tube. **Open** *summer* 8am-7pm daily; *winter* 9am-4pm daily. **Unlicensed. Credit** MC, £TC, V.
Despite its prime position in Regent's Park, this café is a example of unimaginative catering. Tourists, who form the majority of its clientele, are faced with a dispiriting choice of very basic pre-packed sandwiches, crisps, chocolate bars and muffins. The closest thing to freshly prepared food was a cone from the ice-cream counter, trailed as 'real Italian ice-cream made from natural ingredients'. Tutti-frutti, however, was horribly sweet and cloying. Fine if you're just after crisps and a Coke, but a guaranteed let down for those in search of something a little more appetising.
Babies and children welcome; high chairs. No smoking. Tables outdoors (23, patio). Takeaway service.

Ice-cream parlours

Our favourite London ice-cream parlour remains **Marine Ices**, for its distinctive Italian atmosphere and ices. For a more full-on American-style ice-cream with all the trimmings, try a **Häagen-Dazs** outlet or **Wintons Soda Fountain**.

Häagen-Dazs on the Square

14 Leicester Square, WC2 (020 7287 9577). Leicester Square tube. **Open** *winter* 10am-midnight Mon-Thur, Sun; 10am-1am Fri, Sat; *summer* 9am-1am Mon-Sat; 10am-1am Sun. **Licensed. Credit** AmEx, MC, £TC, V.
Map 14/7K.
For branches see index.

Harrods Ice-cream Parlour & Crêperie

Fourth floor, Harrods, Knightsbridge, SW1 (020 7225 6628). Knightsbridge tube. **Open** 10am-6.45pm Mon-Sat. **Licensed. Credit** AmEx, DC, JCB, MC, V. **Map 12/9F.**

Marine Ices

8 Haverstock Hill, NW3 (020 7482 9003). Chalk Farm tube. **Open** 10.30am-11pm Mon-Sat; 11am-10pm Sun. **Licensed. Credit** MC, £TC, V. **Map 10.**

Regent Milk Bar

362 Edgware Road, W2 (020 7723 8669). Edgware Road tube. **Open** 7.30am-5.30pm Mon-Sat. **Unlicensed. No credit cards.**
Map 1/4E.

Wintons Soda Fountain

Second floor, Whiteley's, Queensway, W2 (020 7229 8489). Bayswater or Queensway tube. **Open** *winter* noon-10pm Mon-Thur, Sun; noon-11pm Fri, Sat; *summer* noon-11pm Mon-Sat; noon-10pm Sun. **Unlicensed. No credit cards. Map 11/6C.**

Bars

What makes a good bar? There's little doubt that you should expect a distinctive range and quality of drinks, particularly wines and cocktails; you expect good service; and you might expect a certain flamboyance and style alien to most pubs.

London has a decent stock of good bars, from the fashionable (**Shoreditch Electricity Showrooms, The Social**) to the fastidious (**Claridge's, American Bar** at the Savoy), the stylish (**Clipper Bar**), the trash-glamorous (**Saint**), the idiosyncratic (**Café Kick, Dragon Bar**) and the specialist (**Dovetail**). Most of the best are concentrated in Soho, Shoreditch and Hoxton, and Clerkenwell, all of which have thriving bar scenes, although there are others of flair and distinction to be found in less obvious locations (**25 Canonbury Lane** in Islington, and **Boisdale** in Victoria).

The ubiquitous chain bars, dotted all around the capital, are unlikely to have escaped your notice. The sign spotted over a Soho All Bar One – 'An exceedingly good place' – would seem to confirm that the chains are indeed the Mr Kipling's cakes of bar culture. Ubiquity often can breed corporate blandness. It will be interesting to see if the stylish **Match** can maintain its reputation as it becomes a mini-chain, with outlets in Oxford Circus, Clerkenwell, and Shoreditch.

Other bars (Saint, for example) operate in the grey area between bar and night club, which when it works well can provide a seamlessly enjoyable evening out. It's worth noting that some venues operate extortionate entry charges (often levied as early as 9pm), queues and 'guest lists'. Keep an eye out also for non-discretionary service charges. **Trader Vic's** is the worst offender, with a huge 15 per cent 'tip' built in. 'If you have a problem with the service you can dispute it with the manager, but basically it's standard,' a staffer explained. Almost worth a boycott.

For many more drinking haunts, see the *Time Out Pubs & Bars Guide* (£6).

Central

Belgravia SW1

The Library

Lanesborough Hotel, Hyde Park Corner, SW1 (020 7259 5599). Hyde Park Corner tube. **Drinks and food served** 11am-11pm Mon-Sat; noon-10.30pm Sun. **Credit** AmEx, DC, JCB, MC, £TC, V.
Not a library at all, we're afraid; the 'books' lining the wall are fake – a design detail that exemplifies the Library's none-too-subtle decorative take on the English gentlemen's club. The bar is nevertheless elegant, with heavy dark wood panelling, deep leather armchairs, and a background pianist. There's also an amusing array of cigar-toting American businessmen and trashy-rich tourists to survey. Naturally, drinks don't come cheap, but they are exceptional. Head bartender Salvatore Calabrese mixes what are reputedly London's finest vodka Martinis (£9.50), and the champagne cocktails (Bellini, £12) are delicious. Bar food (Scotch smoked salmon, £8.50) is of similar calibre. The service is effortless and stylish, carried out with grace and humour. If you can handle the prices, it all makes for a very special treat.
Disabled: toilet. Dress: smart casual; no jeans or trainers. Entertainment: pianist 6-11pm daily.
Map 6/8G.

Clerkenwell & Farringdon EC1

Café Kick ★

43 Exmouth Market, EC1 (020 7837 8077). Farringdon tube/rail. **Drinks and food served** 11.30am-11pm Mon-Sat. **Credit** £TC.
Don't be put off by the shambolic appearance; this is a gem of a bar, slightly frayed round the edges but well-loved and charming. It's a football bar, true, but you won't find tacky souvenirs, giant Sky sports screens, or replica-shirt-wearing beer monsters here. There are three table-football games (which can be reserved in advance), and the walls are adorned with offbeat vintage football memorabilia. The punters are predominantly (but not exclusively) male, but there's a relaxed vibe. There's a choice of off-the-beaten-track continental beers (French Jenlain, £3.95), an exotic coffee menu, cocktail standards (£5.50-£6.50) and lunchtime sandwiches (£2.95-£3.50). One of a kind.
Tables outdoors (4, pavement). **Map 15/4N.**

Clerkenwell House

23-27 Hatton Wall, EC1 (020 7404 1113). Chancery Lane tube/Farringdon tube/rail.
Drinks served noon-11pm Mon-Fri; 5-11pm Sat; 1-6pm Sun. **Food served** noon-3pm, 6-10pm Mon-Fri; 6-10pm Sat; 1-10pm Sun. **Credit** MC, V.
Dramatic neon lighting provides an unmissable blue glow around the entrance to this roomy, open-plan bar. The interior is decked out with brown leather sofas and chairs, polished wood floors, free-standing ashtrays and uncluttered, creamy-white walls. A spiral staircase leads to a dive-like basement with another bar and five pool tables (hired by the hour). Busy but laidback, the venue attracts the young, trendy, Clerkenwell set and slightly addled, loquacious office workers alike. Beers include draught Hoegaarden at £1.90 a half-pint; wines cost £9.90-£13.50 a bottle. Nicely presented food (house salad, 'devilishly good and demoniacally healthy', £6.66) is served until 9.45pm.
Map 15/5N.

Dovetail

9 Jerusalem Passage, EC1 (020 7490 7321). Farringdon tube/rail. **Drinks and food served** noon-11pm Mon-Fri; 6-11pm Sat; noon-6pm Sun. **Credit** LV, MC, £TC, V.
This friendly shrine to Belgian beer works hard to overcome its rather dingy, light-starved setting. The list of around 100 beers includes exotica such as the 8.8% proof McChouffe brown ale (£9 for 75cl) and Mort Subite Gueze, the so-called 'champagne of beers' (£3 for a 25cl glass). There are fruit beers, spicy beers, wheat beers, chocolate beers and Trappist beers, as well as more familiar brands (Stella Artois) on draught. Fears that such fare would magnetically draw boisterous stag parties appear to have been unfounded; women make up a fair proportion of the pleasingly eclectic clientele (who keep themselves to themselves). Sadly, the food (venison sausage and mash in Leffe Brun gravy, £7.50) was, on our visit, flaccid and uninspiring.
Map 15/4O.
For branches see index.

Covent Garden WC2

Detroit

35 Earlham Street, WC2 (020 7240 2662). Covent Garden tube. **Drinks and food served** 5pm-midnight Mon-Sat. **Credit** AmEx, DC, MC, £TC, V.
A low-ceilinged, cave-like, deceptively small basement bar – with mud-brown walls, interconnecting pod-like rooms, and bizarre stained-glass art works – may not appeal to the claustrophobic, but this funk-soundtracked journey into the bowels of Covent Garden is clearly a hit with Detroit's groovy young punters.

" the cocktails rank alongside those from the best cocktail bars in town."

Edward Sullivan – The Evening Standard

"Very mellow and drop-dead gorgeous surroundings."

GQ Guide to London's Coolest Bars and Clubs

Want somewhere private for 8-10 people? Check into the intimate and exclusive cocoon room complete with your own bartender to attend to your every need.

Want a private venue for a party? Zeta has a state-of-the-art sound system, DJ booth, DVD player and some of the best bar-bites and cocktails in town.

Open for lunch, from Monday to Friday, 12 noon onwards. Open for drinks 11am-1am Monday to Tuesday, 11am to 3am Wednesday to Friday and from 5pm-3am on Saturdays.

Zeta Bar, 35 Hertford Street, W1
Telephone: +44 (0) 20 7208 4067 Facsimile: +44 (0) 20 7208 4068
Web: www.zeta-bar.com

The cheerful staff make cocktails to order from a long list (£4.90-£7.60) comprising all the classics plus some over-proof cocktails (if you've an iron constitution, try a Cherry Aide: absinthe, cherry vodka, sloe gin, lemon juice and Perrier). Snacks are also available (Serrano ham with bread and oil, £4.50).
Entertainment: DJs from 7pm Thur-Sat.
Map 14/6L.

Freedom Brewing Company
41 Earlham Street, WC2 (020 7240 0606). Covent Garden tube. **Drinks served** 11am-11pm Mon-Sat; noon-10.30pm Sun. **Food served** noon-3pm, 5.30-10pm Mon-Sat; noon-6pm Sun. **Credit** AmEx, MC, £TC, V.
Beer is the raison d'être of this large basement bar and micro brewery. The firm's Freedom Pilsner (brewed in Fulham to exacting German purity standards, £3.10 a pint) and Soho Red (a tasty American-style ale, £2.95), are rather good. There are also own-brewed versions of India Pale Ale and German wheat beer, huge brass brewing vats of which are displayed in a glass cabinet running the length of one wall. The decor – exposed brick and air ducts, IKEA-style furniture and trendy toilets – of this huge, busy bar will strike some as a bit chilly. Sterling but unexciting food includes lamb steak with grilled vegetables (£8.50).
Map 14/6L.
For branches see index.

Freuds
198 Shaftesbury Avenue, WC2 (020 7240 9933). Covent Garden tube. **Drinks served** 11am-11pm Mon-Sat; noon-10.30pm Sun. **Food served** 11.30am-4.30pm Mon-Sat; noon-4.30pm Sun. **No credit cards.**
A mercifully unspoilt old stager among the capital's bars, Freuds is a tiny basement venue with granite walls and slate table tops that help it retain an air of faintly Gothic romantic gloom. By day there's a cool, languorous air to the place; in the evening the bar heats up, playing host to a mixed, youthful and arty set. It serves bottled beer, cocktails, and simple bar food of the salad, sandwiches, and cake variety. There's also an impressive choice of around 30 decently priced coffees (double latte, £1.75), around half of which feature liqueurs.
Map 14/6L.

The Langley
5 Langley Street, WC2 (020 7836 5005). Covent Garden tube. **Drinks and food served** 4.30pm-1am Mon-Sat. **Admission** £3 Mon-Thur (after 10pm); £5 Fri, Sat (after 10pm). **Credit** AmEx, MC, V.
The Langley's discreet, 'blink and you'll miss it' entrance may suggest exclusivity; what you get is a huge low-ceilinged cellar with lots of exposed brick and breeze-blocks. Someone has struggled bravely to carve pockets of intimacy out of the vast spaces. The bar is popular, nonetheless, with young drinkers who are slightly too hip for All Bar One. There's a short cocktail menu (moderns and classics, £4.25), and decent beers (Kirin, £3.25). A startlingly white restaurant area is screened-off at one end of the room; bar food is also served (cod, chips and mushy peas, £5.25). Drinks are half-price during happy hour (5-7pm), making a champagne cocktail a very fair £3.50; or you can have a tenner off your £80 bottle of Bolly.
Entertainment: DJs from 9pm Thur-Sat.
Map 14/6L.

Fitzrovia W1

Jerusalem
33-34 Rathbone Place, W1 (020 7255 1120). Tottenham Court Road tube. **Drinks and food served** noon-2am Mon-Thur; noon-3am Fri; 7pm-3am Sat. **Admission** £3 after 10.30pm Mon-Thur; £5 after 10.30pm Fri, Sat. **Credit** AmEx, MC, V.
By day, Jerusalem is surprisingly light and airy, by night the thick red velvet curtains are drawn across the basement windows and this spacious dive becomes a dark, groovy club space. There's a chunky simplicity to the decor: slab-like battered wooden tables lit by candles in metal globe-shaped cages encourage group drinking; more intimate seating is available in the raised eating area. Punters range from clubbers to office blokes, with a few foreign language students blown in off the street. Bar snacks include prawn cocktail open sandwich with chips (£5.50), while there's more elaborate fare in the restaurant.
Map 13/5K.

Mash
19-21 Great Portland Street, W1 (020 7637 5555). Oxford Circus tube. **Open** 11am-1am Mon, Tue; 11am-2am Wed-Sat. **Drinks served** 11am-11pm daily. **Food served** 8am-3pm, 6-11pm Mon-Fri; 11am-4.30pm, 6-11pm Sat, Sun. **Credit** AmEx, DC, JCB, MC, V.
The shine has yet to come off this bold, witty bar. With decor best described as sculpted space-age retro given a modern twist, Mash combines novelty and idiosyncratic flair with chain-bar corporate efficiency, to pleasurable effect. Its 'home brew' beer – mash, wheat, strawberry cream, and peach, from the gleaming on-site micro brewery – is an acquired taste; order a four-glass sampler set to see if you'll acquire it. Furnishings are sparse, although there's a cosy sunken lounge area with massively enlarged, backlit (and sneakily subverted) 1970s travel brochure pics on the walls. Decent grub (smoked salmon, rocket and fromage frais pizza, £9.90) helps attract a mixed, happy, young clientele; the place seems to be avoided by the glacially hip.
Disabled: toilet. **Map 13/6J.**

The Social

Match
37-38 Margaret Street, W1 (020 7499 3443). Oxford Circus tube. **Drinks served** 11.30am-midnight, **food served** noon-11.30pm Mon-Sat%. **Service** 12½% (for diners). **Credit** AmEx, MC, V.
Much-lauded, and deservedly so, this is a cool, smart (if not especially original) hangout for youthful West Enders. The colour scheme is coffee and chocolate; the bar staff are knowledgeable and obliging (happy to mix cocktails to your own recipe, or improvise a tall, delicious non-alcoholic tipple); and the waitresses are friendly and efficient. Match has a large selection of cocktails, some unfathomably named after film stars ('Steve McQueen'), as well as some in-house creations (Match originals, £5.75). The bar food has a Far Eastern/Latino feel (Match Platter – sirloin medallions, chicken skewer, grilled chorizo and broccoli, with dips – £6.95); it's competent, but unlikely to satisfy more demanding taste buds.
Entertainment: DJs from 7pm Thur, Fri; 8pm Sat. **Map 2/6H.**
For branches see index.

The Social ★
5 Little Portland Street, W1 (020 7636 4992). Oxford Circus tube. **Drinks and food served** noon-midnight Mon-Sat; 5-10.30pm Sun. **Credit** AmEx, MC, V.
A groovy crowd (even the after-work suit wearers sport tell-tale goatee beards) hang out at this trendy but relaxed offshoot of the hip Heavenly Organisation. Upstairs there's a small, narrow galley bar (where movement is impossible when it's packed) decked out with sauna-style wood panelling. The choice of beer is small but stalwart (draught Red Stripe, £2.70), while the cocktail list is small and safe (Bloody Mary, £4.80). Grub is functional (perversely hip?) bedsit fare – baked beans on toast, for instance. But the music rocks: there's a wonderful, eclectic jukebox upstairs; in the larger basement bar a heaving, buzzing, clubby mix of punters enjoys pounding dance music.
Entertainment: acoustic music from 7pm Wed (£3, basement); DJs daily. **Map 13/5J.**

Leicester Square WC2

Saint
8 Great Newport Street, WC2 (020 7240 1551). Leicester Square tube. **Drinks served** 5pm-1am Mon-Thur; 5pm-3am Fri; 7.30pm-3am Sat. **Food served** 5.30-11pm Mon-Sat. **Admission** (after 9pm) £3 Wed; £5 Thur; £9 Fri, Sat. **Credit** AmEx, DC, JCB, MC, £TC, V.
A cheesy, dramatic entrance – you descend down a wide staircase bathed in purple neon – sets the tone for this brash, voluptuously sculpted hangout for wannabe-glamorous monied youth. There's more perma-tans, sparkly jewellery, blond highlights and Gucci gear than you can shake a stick at. Early (Essex) birds will get the curvaceous sofas lining one wall, otherwise it's mainly standing room only. A restaurant is at the rear and there's a Far East-flavoured bar menu (Tiger prawn balls with banana relish, £4.50). The bar serves the usual cocktails (£6.50-£7.50) and for the truly flash, Grande Martinis (£12.50). Saint is heaving at weekends, when it becomes a quasi-club; even during the week the management operates a guest list and charges an outrageous £7 for entry after 9pm. Come here for preening, posing, and 'avin' a larf; if you feel old, or fancy a quiet chat, give it a miss.
Entertainment: DJs from 8pm Wed-Sat.
Map 14/6K.

Mayfair W1

Claridge's ★
Brook Street, W1 (020 7629 8860). Bond Street tube. **Drinks and food served** 11am-11pm Mon-Sat; noon-10.30pm Sun. **Credit** AmEx, DC, MC, TC, V.
Revamped three years ago, this famous watering-hole retains the classic deco spirit of the hotel in which it resides, producing an immaculate modern bar of rare style, character, and sophistication. The elegant chairs, the layered marble-topped bar, the extravagantly cushioned bar stools, the fabulous wedding-cake ceiling… we could go on. All this doesn't come cheap: you could blow £750 on a bottle of Louis Roederer Cristal 1985. For the merely well-off, £8.50 will get you a cocktail, £7.75 a glass of jolly good house champagne. The bar menu offers overpriced 'savouries' (mushroom risotto and Parmesan crisp costs £11) in tiny portions. If you can handle (or avoid) the Sloanes ordering 'shampoo' in loud voices, and the unfortunate piped soft rock (Christopher Cross anyone?), come here for a treat, and enjoy the furnishings.
Disabled: toilets. Dress: smart; no jeans or trainers. **Map 2/6H.**

Trader Vic's
Hilton Hotel, Park Lane, W1 (020 7493 8000 ext 420). Green Park or Hyde Park Corner tube. **Drinks and food served** 5pm-12.30am Mon-Sat; 5-10.45pm Sun. **Credit** AmEx, DC, MC, £TC, V
A kitsch Hilton Hotel basement bar done out in mock-Polynesian beach-hut style, this is corporate high-camp of a disconcertingly agreeable kind. There are Trader Vic's from Abu Dhabi to Vancouver, and one suspects they are little different to this one. It offers a huge list of efficiently mixed rum-based cocktails (reputedly the best Mai Tai in town, £6.50) served by waitresses in the requisite flowery-print dresses to an unpretentious, ethnically varied (if hardly fashionable) clientele. Bar food is pretty good (Tahitian crab sandwich, £11.50), and the service is hyper-efficient. This bubbly throwback to the 1970s is best experienced as a fun night out, or as a light-hearted bar crawl refuelling stop. Your sense of humour will be severely tested by the 15% service charge.
Entertainment: Latin music 10.30pm-12.30am Mon-Sat. **Map 6/8G.**

Zeta
Hilton Hotel, Park Lane, W1 (020 7208 4067). Green Park or Hyde Park Corner tube. **Drinks and food served** Mon, Tue 11am-1am; 11am-3am Wed-Fri; 5pm-3am Sat. **Admission** £5 after 11pm. **Credit** AmEx, DC, MC, £TC, V.
Zeta's pretentious, new-agey manifesto (a seemingly non-ironic 'philosophy of drinking') promises a 'healthier approach to alcohol'. Thus you can sink that silky-smooth Polish Martini (vodka, fresh apples and organic honey, £6.50) safe in the knowledge that 'apples are rich in pectin and vitamin C which makes them great detoxifiers'. So that's all right then. This is a plush, overwhelmingly tasteful, and beautifully lit place. And the (possibly unintentionally) camp staff in their skin-tight grey shirts make fabulous cocktails into the early hours. The door policy appears to favour ostentatious spending power, which makes for an eclectic, expensively dressed (if not particularly stylish) clientele. Zeta tries hard to hide its Hilton parentage, but ultimately fails: you can take the bar out of the international hotel, but you can't take the international hotel out of the bar.
Entertainment: musicians Mon; DJs from 9pm Tue-Sat. **Map 6/8G.**

Piccadilly W1

Atlantic Bar & Grill ★
20 Glasshouse Street, W1 (020 7734 4888). Piccadilly Circus tube. **Drinks and food served** noon-3am Mon-Sat; 6pm-10.30pm Sun. **Credit** AmEx, DC, MC, £TC, V.
For some time a byword for metropolitan swank, this stylish, grand-but-not-posh establishment represents a fabulous experience for all but the most jaded barflies. Punters are vetted on the door; once past the cordon you have a choice of the main bar with its high ceilings and elegant furnishings, or the more intimate Dick's Bar, a plush lounge-lizard's hangout serving critically acclaimed Martinis. The music can be uncomfortably loud, the service sometimes irritatingly slow, and – naturally – prices are high (crisp dry house champagne, £36 a bottle). The cognoscenti may recoil from the hordes of Essex-girl hen parties that invade the place at weekends, but rumours of the Atlantic's decline are surely exaggerated.
Map 13/7J.

Clipper Bar at China House
160 Piccadilly, W1 (020 7499 6996). Green Park tube. **Drinks served** noon-3.30pm, 5.30-11pm Mon-Sat. **Service** 12½%. **Credit** AmEx, MC, V.
A tiny two-person lift whisks you up to this intimate galley bar overlooking Piccadilly. The Clipper was a seaplane that plied the Hong Kong-USA route in days gone by, and the bar – with its low, curved ceiling and scattered leather seats – clearly draws on the aircraft design for inspiration. No turbulence here, however. Friendly bar staff serve excellent cocktails and expensive wines (glass of Pouilly Fumé, £7.50) from the 'inflight menu'. The bar food is superb: exquisite Cantonese snacks from the kitchens of the Orient restaurant next door. Try the seasoned prawns wrapped in crisp honeyed breadcrumbs

TSAR'S
"Vodka Chill"

'The bar has an unarguable mood of class and indulgence. It's a place for people who are serious about their vodka and can afford to sample the best.'

Katie O'Neill, London's Top Bars, Wine & Spirit International.

Chilled, spiced, mild & fruity or strong enough to knock more than your socks off, with over 100 vodkas to choose from, Tsar's Bar at The Langham is for the dedicated vodka lover.

And for the vodka hedonist, try a little indulgence on the side. Sevruga, Oscietra and Beluga caviars served by the gram, complete with blinis and condiments, make the Cold War seem almost churlish.

Tsar's Bar at The Langham Hilton. A mood altering experience.

The Langham Hilton

The Langham Hilton, 1c Portland Place, Regent Street, London W1B 1JA, United Kingdom
T. +44 (0) 20 7636 1000   F. +44 (0) 20 7323 2340
Web: www.langham.hilton.com

(£5.80). Not a cheap night out by a long way, but classy – and there's a 'two for the price of one' deal on drinks every day during the 5.30-8pm 'happy hour'.
No-smoking. **Map 13/7J.**

Soho W1

Alphabet
61-63 Beak Street, W1 (020 7439 2190). Leicester Square, Oxford Circus or Piccadilly Circus tube. **Drinks and food served** 11am-11pm Mon-Fri; 4-11pm Sat. **Credit** MC, £TC, V.
Smart, arty and popular (you may have to queue for entry on some evenings), this glass-fronted hangout is beloved of thirty-something Soho advertising and media types in elegant lounge suits. There's a lengthy cocktail menu (£3.50-£6), fresh juices, wine, a small but well-chosen beer collection (Mexican Negra Modelo, £2.85), and bar food (calamares with aïoli and sweet soy, £4.50). Downstairs, the average age of the clientele drops, there's a second bar, a DJ, some interesting furniture, and an old-school Space Invader machine. And they've still got the giant A-Z map of Soho painted on the floor, too.
Entertainment: DJs & singers 7-11pm Fri.
Map 13/6J.

The Dog House
187 Wardour Street, W1 (020 7434 2116/ 2118). Leicester Square, Piccadilly Circus or Tottenham Court Road tube. **Drinks served** 5-11pm Mon-Fri; 6-11pm Sat. **Credit** AmEx, MC, £TC, V.
Eclectic, cartoonish, deliberately idiosyncratic, the Dog House is a long way from being stylish or fashionable. It's an odd place that's unlikely to draw much custom from Soho's trendier set, but is not without a certain awkward charm. Stairs deliver you down to a horseshoe-shaped basement bar, to each side of which lie a series of smoky, cave-like rooms, packed with groups of unpretentious, fun-loving punters. Blues, soul and jazz play on the sound system; on the menu is beer (Red Stripe, £2.70 a bottle), cocktails (£4.50-£5), and basic bar food (potato wedges, nachos and the like, £2.50-£5).
Map 13/6J.

Freedom
60-66 Wardour Street, W1 (020 7734 0071). Leicester Square or Piccadilly Circus tube. **Drinks served** 11am-3am Mon-Sat; noon-midnight Sun. **Admission** £3 after 10.30pm Mon-Wed; £5 after 10.30pm Thur-Sat. **Credit** MC, V.
A smart, chic bar that's one of the few to manage a complete mix of sexual orientations. Freedom blends challenging contemporary art with plush red sofas and pale wood tables. The bar promises to take 'very seriously' its range of 'award-winning' cocktails (which award is not specified); the excellent Freedom Spring punch (champagne, vodka and Midori melon liqueur, £8.50) was seriously smooth and peppery. Bottled beers cost around £3.30, and you can nibble on a blue cheese, celery and walnut salad for £5.50. There's also an oddly poignant slide show projecting black and white images of Freedom punters carousing happily – an endearing remembrance of drinks past.
Entertainment: DJs from 10pm Wed-Sat.
Map 13/6K.

Lab
12 Old Compton Street, W1 (020 7437 7820). Piccadilly Circus or Tottenham Court Road tube. **Drinks served** noon-midnight Mon-Sat; 5-11pm Sun. **Food served** 5pm-midnight daily. **Credit** AmEx, DC, MC, V.
A bar for predominantly straight mid-twentysomethings (in what is largely a gay bar area), Lab exploits its lucrative niche with vibrant gusto. It has two bars, ground floor and basement; each room is narrow, low-ceilinged and relatively short on seating. Add to this the gold-painted walls, the 'space age bachelor pad' furniture, and the thumping house music (courtesy of the DJ), and you get a loud, sweaty, crush. The overstretched bar staff serve excellent cocktails (Apple Breeze, £5.60) from a long list; bottled beer is available, too. There's a lively bar menu: breakfast might be black pudding with poached eggs and caviar; mixed meze platter could be for dinner. Winner of Best Bar in the *Time Out* Eating & Drinking Awards 2000 because, as the judges said 'Lab may not be as polished as some bars, but it makes up for its lack of panache with plenty of guts'.
Entertainment: DJs from 9pm Mon-Sat.
Map 13/6K.

Rupert Street
50 Rupert Street, W1 (020 7292 7141). Leicester Square tube. **Drinks served** noon-11pm Mon-Sat; noon-10.30pm Sun. **Food served** noon-5pm Mon-Fri; noon-6pm Sat, Sun. **Credit** MC, V.
This simple, modern, smartly designed place (exposed air ducts, polished wood floor, big glass windows to watch and be watched through) may be small but it has a big reputation as London's trendiest gay bar. Rupert Street is patronised by crowds of fashionable, handsome and impeccably groomed gay men; the atmosphere is loud, cruisey, posey and almost exclusively male. It's an extremely popular venue, especially at weekends. Sadly, the staff clearly feel rudeness and arrogance is all part of the service. Spirits come in double measures; unless the barman remembers to alert you, or you specifically ask for a single, this means a vodka tonic will set you back £4.45. Mainstream beers are also in stock (Beck's, £2.95 a bottle).
Disabled: toilet. **Map 13/7K.**

Strand WC2

The American Bar
The Savoy, Strand, WC2 (020 7836 4343). Embankment tube/Charing Cross tube/rail. **Drinks served** 11am-11pm Mon-Sat; noon-3pm Sun. **Lunch served** noon-2.30pm Mon-Sat. **Credit** AmEx, DC, JCB, MC, £$TC, V.
A twist of deco, a warm, calm atmosphere, and a raft of exquisite cocktails makes this luxurious bar the perfect venue for an intimate romantic rendezvous. The decor may seem a bit dated, and despite the Hollywood prints on the wall, the clientele are more Discreet Old Money than International Jet Set (though you might spot the odd celebrity). Nonetheless, the service is as excellent as you would expect, and the drinks (sipped to lounge-bar piano accompaniment) superb. The vodka Martini, served in a frosted glass (£9.90), was heavenly, the cocktails (Washington Eagles: Jack Daniels, Southern Comfort, lime juice, cranberry juice, £9.10) equally top notch. Adventurous tipplers take note: this bar is reputed to mix the finest absinthe cocktails in town.
Dress: smart casual. Entertainment: pianist 7.30-11pm Mon-Sat. **Map 14/7L.**

The Lobby Bar at One Aldwych
1 Aldwych, WC2 (020 7300 1070). Temple tube. **Drinks served** 9.30am-11pm Mon-Fri; 10.30am-11pm Sat; 10.30am-10.30pm Sun. **Food served** 5.30-10pm Mon-Sat. **Credit** AmEx, MC, £TC, V.
It struggles valiantly to convince you otherwise, but at the end of the day this highly polished, well-scrubbed bar is as its name implies, located in a hotel lobby, with all the attendant impersonality. The vast, ceiling-high arched windows, high-backed chairs and ostentatious objets d'art strain heroically to create atmosphere, but it doesn't quite work. The City boys, theatre-goers and tourists seem perfectly at home in such over-styled circumstances, however. What's more, the efficient staff serve up delicious, if expensive (£7.75-£9), cocktails from the extensive formal menu – there are 18 Martinis alone to choose from. They were happy to improvise a superb non-alcoholic cocktail (£3.50) on request.
Map 14/7M.

Victoria SW1

Boisdale ★
15 Eccleston Street, SW1 (020 7730 6922). Victoria tube/rail. **Drinks served** noon-1am Mon-Sat; noon-11pm Sun. **Food served** noon-2.30pm, 7-11.30pm Mon-Sat; 7-11pm Sun. **Brunch served** noon-5pm Sat, Sun. **Admission** £10 after 10pm. **Credit** AmEx, DC, MC, £TC, V.
This charming, slightly fogey-ish, whisky bar brings a taste of Scotland – a rather posh Scotland of tartan, grouse-shooting, and languid malt-sipping, mind – to Belgravia. It offers a choice of over 200 whiskies, which glow invitingly on their perch behind the bar. Helpful, good-humoured staff do the pouring. A jazz trio provides a lively speakeasy feel, merrily appreciated by the well-to-do, older punters. There are two bars; food is available in the restaurant (*see p35* **British**) or over the bar (Roast McSween's haggis with mash and neeps, from the two-course haggis menu, for example). A short of smooth, smoky 16-year old Laphroiag will set you back £4.70, a shot of an exquisite older malt upwards of a tenner. Beware: non-members are charged £10 entry after 10pm.
Entertainment: jazz from 10.30pm Mon-Sat.
Map 6/10H.

South

Brixton SW2

The Bug Bar
The Crypt, St Matthew's, Brixton Hill, SW2 (020 7738 3184). Brixton tube/rail. **Drinks and food served** 7pm-1am Mon-Thur; 7pm-3am Fri, Sat; 7pm-2am Sun. **Admission** £3 9-11pm, £5 after 11pm Fri, Sat. **No credit cards.**
Situated in the crypt of St Matthew's Church, the Bug Bar offers 'Luscious Lounging' to the Brixton set. With old sofas and heavy velvet drapes, angelic frescoes and ecclesiastical knick-knacks – offset against the original church architecture – the result is a location that any set dresser would kill to achieve. Drinks are reasonably priced; there's a selection of imported beers and lagers to enjoy, as well as a range of cocktails (£4.50-£7). Popular with professionals and students, Bug Bar is exciting, buzzy and well worth a visit. Regular DJs play a heady and varied choice of music, and there are club nights as well as a monthly roster of entertainments (check handouts or website for updates).
Entertainment: music Wed; DJs Thur-Sun.
Map 18.

South East

Tower Bridge SE1

Circle Bar
13-15 Queen Elizabeth Street, SE1 (020 7407 1122). Tower Bridge tube/London Bridge tube/ rail/Tower Gateway DLR. **Drinks and food served** noon-11pm Mon-Sat; noon-10.30pm Sun. **Service** 12½%. **Credit** AmEx, MC, V.
This lively modern bar and brasserie in the heart of Shad Thames provides friendly and efficient dining and drinking to the Thames-side set. A converted street-level wharf, the entire space is bright and airy, painted in bold colours, and with artwork on the wall. The brasserie menu includes meat and vegetarian dishes, pastas and fish, a wide choice of bar snacks, and a tempting tapas selection. Meals are well-presented and arrive speedily. Our choices – lamb cutlets with seasonal veg, and traditional sausage and mash – were equally delicious. There's an extensive wine list (£10-£35 per bottle; champagne from £30 to £135 for Dom Perignon). A bass and sax duo complemented proceedings; there's live entertainment throughout the week.
Entertainment: musicians Sun. Tables outdoors (4, pavement). **Map 8/9R.**

East

Shoreditch EC1, EC2, N1

Cantaloupe
35-42 Charlotte Road, EC2 (020 7613 4411). Old Street tube/rail. **Drinks and food served** 11am-midnight Mon-Fri; 2pm-midnight Sat; noon-11.30pm Sun. **Credit** AmEx, MC, £TC, V.

Bar chains

In the past, the big chains blazed a trail. They blurred the boundary between pub and bar, setting new quality standards with their light, spacious design and high-quality, efficiently served food and drink. These virtues, however, are no longer so rare in the bar world. Yes, the big chains can offer a comforting brand reliability, and are a firmly established part of the London drinking scene. But could their very ubiquity and corporate blandness prove their undoing in a world where consumers seek not merely competence, but individuality, idiosyncrasy, and local flavour?

All Bar One
Liverpool Road, N1 (020 7843 0021). **Drinks served** noon-11pm Mon-Sat; noon-10.30pm Sun. **Food served** noon-10pm Mon-Sat; noon-9pm Sun. **Credit** AmEx, MC, V.
One of the smaller branches of the mega-chain, this Islington bar is nonetheless stamped with all the ABO hallmarks: well-spaced pine furniture, tolerable beers, enticing racks of decent – if pricey – wines (£11-£15.50), tasty food in big servings (steamed halibut steak on fennel with sun-roasted tomato and chive butter) and friendly, efficient bar staff. A mixed clientele (from students to grannies) enjoys the warm, pleasant, café-style ambience during the day; things become sweatier and smokier after 5pm when local office staff descend for a post-work snifter and gossip.
Map 16/2N.

The Fine Line
33-37 Northcote Road, SW11 (020 7924 7387). Clapham Junction rail. **Drinks served** noon-11pm Mon-Sat, noon-10.30pm Sun. **Food served** noon-10pm Mon-Thur; noon-9pm Fri; 11am-9pm Sat; 11am-9.30pm Sun. **Credit** AmEx, DC, JCB, MC, V.
This former bank has been nicely refurbished to provide an airy atmosphere by day and a lively vibe at night. Popular among twenty- and thirty-somethings, it is well-lit, with blond-wood furniture, sofas, and polished floors presided over by an impressive chrome and glass bar. A moderately modish menu lists the likes of couscous and pasta. The wine list is impressive (£10.50-£21). There are also cocktails (£4.50-£6) and a selection of imported beers. The music complements rather than overpowers – as long as you like Balearic beats with your bagels. A DJ leads the entertainment in the evenings from Thursday through to Sunday.
Disabled: toilet. Entertainment: DJs Thur-Sun. Tables outdoors (7, patio).

Pitcher & Piano
40-42 William IV Street, WC2 (020 7240 6180). Covent Garden or Leicester Square tube. **Drinks served** noon-11pm Mon-Sat; noon-10.30pm Sun. **Food served** noon-10pm Mon-Thur; noon-9pm Fri-Sun. **Credit** AmEx, JCB, MC, V.
A bar on a big scale, incorporating a split-level ground floor, and an upstairs space clustered round an atrium, both with bars. The decor might be described as ageing Habitat: well-spaced light-wood furniture and the occasional sofa. The wine (house white £10 a bottle) isn't bad, ditto the limited food menu (tuna loin, with lime and coriander butter on stir-fry veg, for instance). There's the usual range of bottled and draught beers. So far, so predictable. On the minus side: the sound system (Robbie Williams, REM) is painfully loud, and the place reeks of tobacco – there's no separate smokers' section. Not that the boisterous, happily-carousing young office-workers care one jot.
Disabled: toilet. Entertainment: musicians Sun. **Map 14/7L.**

Slug & Lettuce
14 Upper St Martin's Lane, WC2 (020 7379 4880). Covent Garden or Leicester Square tube/Charing Cross tube/rail. **Drinks served** 11am-11pm Mon-Sat; 11am-10.30pm Sun. **Food served** noon-9pm daily. **Credit** AmEx, LV, MC, V.
The Slug & Lettuce's reputation as a slightly artier place than its rivals seems misplaced, despite this branch's fashionable location in the heart of Covent Garden. The chain tends to be dubbed the 'yuppie bar' in the press, which seems more apposite a description given its bland demeanour and loud, besuited clientele. There's a more interesting and intimate bar space in the basement, furnished with sofas. No surprises drinks-wise, although the food (linguine carbonara, £6) – normally thoroughly decent – was, when we visited, rather lame.
Tables outdoors 3. **Map 14/6L.**

One of the first of the new generation of Shoreditch bars, Cantaloupe has aged perhaps a little inelegantly. A sweaty pub-style bar at the entrance connects to a small lounge area with sofas, which in turn connects to the rear space where there's a restaurant (*see p126* **Mediterranean**), and a tiny, slightly less frantic bar. It's loud, crowded and low-ceilinged – more student bar than fashionable hangout, as the presence of the youthful, garrulous but decidedly non-glamorous hordes who drink here attests. From an impressive drinks list, Cantaloupe serves beer (Pilsner Urquell on draught, £2.60 a pint), wine (house wines £9.25-£21) and cocktails (jugs of Sangria or Sea Breeze for the very thirsty, £15). On the food side, tapas cost £1.50-£4.
Entertainment: DJs from 8pm Fri, Sat. **Map 17/4R.**

Dragon Bar

5 Leonard Street, EC2 (020 7490 7110). Old Street tube/rail. **Drinks served** 11am-11pm Mon-Sat; noon-10.30pm Sun. **Credit** AmEx, MC.
The unobtrusive entrance at the City Road end of Leonard Street (watch out for the tiny metal 'Dragon Bar' legend fitted to the entrance step) gives a suitably discreet clue to the intimate bar within. Inside, there's a muscular, rough-hewn New York loft-feel, with exposed brick, rough wooden floor, salvaged windows and radiators, and deep sofas, softened by a couple of tall house plants. A DJ deck is on the bar, and one or two Brit-art pieces (which may include the bespectacled moose head) adorn the walls. The dingy basement room is disconcertingly windowless and smoky. Punters are invariably young and smart, a good number of them from the harder, edgier nose-ringed end of Shoreditch fashion. Slightly sullen, a bit dark, and idiosyncratic, Dragon is a bar that feels like it's at one with itself.
Entertaiment: DJs from 8pm. **Map 4/4Q.**

Home

100-106 Leonard Street, EC1 (020 7684 8618). Old Street tube/rail. **Drinks served** 5pm-midnight Mon-Sat. **Food served** 12.30-3pm, 7-10pm Mon-Fri; 7-10pm Sat. **Credit** MC, £TC, V.
One of the first bars to emerge from the revolution that transformed Shoreditch into the hippest area of the capital, Home's legendary basement bar is still the dark, buzzing, well-worn dive of old, beloved by art students and after-work drinkers alike. Upstairs, however, it has commandeered extra space and opened a bright , open-plan bar-restaurant area, which is deservedly popular with fashionable well-to-do thirty-somethings. There's a range of wines and a mix of cocktail classics and 'Home specials' such as Tulip: brandy, apricot, cherry and lemon, £5.25). The food (hake encrusted with pistachio, for instance) is superb, great value, and served with finesse.
Map 17/4R.

Hoxton Square Bar & Kitchen

2 Hoxton Square, N1 (020 7613 0709). Old Street tube/rail. **Drinks served** 11am-midnight Mon-Sat; 11am-10.30pm Sun. **Lunch served** 11.30am-2.30pm Mon-Fri; noon-3.30pm Sat, Sun. **Dinner served** 6.30-10.30pm Mon-Fri; 6-10pm Sat, Sun. **Credit** MC, V.
The reputation of this somewhat austere (think Bulgarian underground car park) basement bar next to the Lux Cinema is still sky-high, and the fashionably-cropped, flipflop-shod, skateboard-carrying habitués of smart Hoxton continue to come in droves, spilling irrepressibly out on to the square in the evenings. Long and narrow, with sofas, easy chairs and tables up against the concrete walls, the bar has an impressive street-level window at the far end, which gives a cinematic view of passing cars. Naturally, there's art on the walls. Beer (Kirin, £2.50 a bottle), wine (including an undrinkable glass of house white) and food (dishes range from gazpacho to marinated lamb chops) are served, but you may be put off trying to eat when the bar is at its most noisy and sweaty, with punters packed in like sardines.
Disabled: toilet. Tables outdoors (5, patio). **Map 17/3R.**

The Light

233 Shoreditch High Street, E1 (020 7247 8989). Liverpool Street tube/rail. **Drinks and food served** noon-11pm Mon-Fri; 6-11pm Sat; noon-10.30pm Sun. **Credit** AmEx, MC, V.
On the southern reaches of the Shoreditch bar zone, the Light is an elegantly understated converted industrial building, with lovely high ceilings, exposed brickwork, nicely spaced wooden tables and a few black leather sofas. There's also an upstairs cocktail bar, and a beer garden, which, while not quiet – the railway is on one side, the main road the other – is spacious. Loud, but a little short on atmosphere, the bar attracts crowds of City guys 'n' gals, although there seemed little sign of champagne-popping excesses on our visit. No surprises on the drinks front (Guinness £1.30 a half pint, house white £3.25 a glass, cocktails), but the bar food is excellent: tangy fresh smoked salmon; luscious mozzarella with marinated vegetables; and, for oyster-lovers, £7.50 will get you six of the little treats.
Entertainment: DJs from 7.30pm Thur-Sat (upstairs, members only). **Map 17/5R.**

The Pool

104 Curtain Road, EC2 (020 7739 9608). Old Street tube/rail. **Drinks served** noon-11pm Mon-Fri; 5-11pm Sat; noon-10.30pm Sun. **Food served** noon-4pm, 5-10pm daily. **Credit** MC, V.
There are pool tables, big glass windows, clean lines and large, sexy beanbags strewn about the Pool, but at first glance nothing to suggest this seemingly bland bar offers anything to distinguish it from any number of wannabe-stylish drinking holes. The basement is a different matter; on the night we visited, a DJ was orchestrating a booming hip-hop party, enjoyed by young, fashionable black punters perched on vinyl corner seats or shuffling sinuously at the edge of the dancefloor. The classic cocktails (Margarita, £4.50) are fresh-tasting and enthusiastically mixed.
Entertainment: DJs from 7pm Tue-Sun. **Map 17/4R.**

Shoreditch Electricity Showrooms ★

39A Hoxton Square, N1 (020 7739 6934). Old Street tube/rail. **Drinks served** noon-11pm Tue, Wed; noon-midnight Thur; noon-1am Fri, Sat; noon-10.30pm Sun. **Food served** 1-3pm, 7-10.15pm Tue-Sun. **Credit** MC, V.
Possibly less glacially hip than in its glory days a couple of years ago (when it was the fresh, unofficial house bar to Hoxton's thriving Brit-Art scene), Shoreditch Electricity Showrooms has still got what it takes. Upstairs the decor is simple: huge glass windows, scattered chairs and tables, a few battered brown leather sofas, and dining area (where Modern European food is served). Down the stairs is a spartan white basement gallery space with DJ console for weekend club sorties. Staff are friendly, and cheerfully mixed up a couple of off-menu cocktails for us (Polish Vodka, £5.50). There's a decent list of beers on tap, too (Red Stripe, Kirin).
Map 17/3R.

North

Camden Town & Chalk Farm NW1

WKD

18 Kentish Town Road, NW1 (020 7267 1869). Camden Town tube/Camden Road rail/29 bus. **Drinks served** noon-2am Mon-Thur; noon-3am Fri, Sat; noon-1am Sun. **Food served** noon-8pm daily. **Admission** £3-£6 Mon-Thur; £5-£7 Fri, Sat; £3 before 10pm, £5 after 10pm Sun. **Credit** AmEx, MC, V.
A cool oasis nestling alongside the stark glass and steel of Sainsbury's next door, WKD ('Wisdom, Knowledge, Destiny') is colourful, characterful and warm. There's a balmy lightness to the place by day, and a pleasantly lazy feel underscored by a gently chugging soul-jazz-hip-hop soundtrack. All of which is quietly enjoyed by the laidback, racially mixed punters. By night the joint hots up, and there's a mini stage for jams, plus a range of club nights. Cocktails are fairly priced (£4.95 or £12.50 for a jug), and the usual beers are sold (Kirin 330ml, £1.50). Food ranges from Thai cuisine to Cajun chicken with rice and peas. Happy hour runs from 4pm to 8pm daily.
Entertainment: DJs and musicians (phone for details). **Map 10.**

25 Canonbury Lane

Islington N1

25 Canonbury Lane

25 Canonbury Lane, N1 (020 7226 0955). Highbury & Islington tube/rail. **Drinks and food served** 5-11.30pm Mon-Thur; noon-midnight Fri, Sat; noon-11pm Sun. **Credit** MC, V.
The cocktail menu promises a 'fresh new direction', but thankfully the charm of this, tiny, unflashy bar just off busy Upper Street lies in its straightforward exposition of the simple pleasures of social drinking. It is elegantly decked out with dark-wood floor, duck-egg blue walls, antique fittings and a high, gold-painted ceiling bedecked with a pair of chandeliers. There's a cosy little garden out back. Punters range from work-weary pin-striped City types to wedged-up Islington geezers quietly cracking open a bottle of champers. A range of cocktails is offered (Deluxe Margarita, £6) and wines (£10.95-£15.95), plus lunch specials (meat lasagne, say) and evening tapas (chicken kebab in lime juice).
Tables outdoors (5 garden).

Elbow Room

89-91 Chapel Market, N1 (020 7278 3244). Angel tube. **Drinks and food served** noon-2am Mon-Thur; noon-3am Fri, Sat; noon-11pm Sun. **Admission** £3 after 10pm Sun-Thur; £4 after 10pm Fri, Sat. **Credit** MC, V.
Off the chaotic raggle-taggle of Chapel Market lies this huge, purple-fronted, neon-signed aircraft hangar of a pool hall, with bar attached. Despite its size, it retains the panache and attention to detail of its smaller sister branch in west London, wrapping a faint hint of sleazy 1960s pool hall glamour around modern, efficient and comfortable surroundings. The purple baize pool tables are hired out by the hour (up to £9 depending on the time of day/week). A gender-balanced mix of students, office workers, and hipsters hangs out here; the mood is bustling, rather than hustling. The bar has the usual draught and bottled beers, and serves fast food – sandwiches, burgers and so on (£3.95-£6.95).
Entertainment: DJs from 10pm nightly.
Map 3/2N.
For branch see index.

Medicine Bar

181 Upper Street, N1 (020 7704 9536/020 7704 1070). Angel tube/Highbury & Islington tube/rail. **Drinks served** 5pm-midnight Mon-Thur; 5pm-1am Fri; noon-1am Sat; noon-10.30pm Sun. **Food served** noon-5pm Sat, Sun. **Credit** MC, V.
A long-established, spacious, and dressed-down stylish venue, the Medicine Bar oozes relaxed trendiness, from the daylight-bathed tables by the shop-front window to its cosy, shadowy recesses. The punters are similarly fashionable, in a studiously casual way, having clearly spent long hours immersed in the teachings of *i-D* and *Dazed & Confused*. In case you don't get it, a sign makes it clear – in so many words – that the wearers of cheap office suits are not welcome. To a global musical soundtrack (the cool tunes might come from India, Detroit, or Ibiza) you can sup beer (Beamish, Guinness and Fosters on draught), and cocktails (Sea Breeze, £4.50), but there's no food to be had (to eat, try the Allotment, the bar's weekend daytime incarnation – comfort food forms the basis of the menu). DJs hold court later in the week, when the bar becomes members-only.
Entertainment: DJs from 9pm Thur-Sun.

Tufnell Park NW5

Grand Banks

156-158 Fortress Road, NW5 (020 7419 9499). Tufnell Park tube. **Drinks and food served** 5-11pm Mon-Wed; 5pm-midnight Thur-Sat; noon-11pm Sun. **Credit** MC, V.
A converted bank now packed with sofas, the Grand Banks has light and simple decor. It's a cool, laid-back watering hole for twenty-something north Londoners, though its pleasures are provincial rather than cutting edge. The service is a bit slow, and the cocktail mixing (a sloppy Vodka Martini was £4.50) is unlikely to win awards, unless wooden spoons are involved. A range of beers is offered (including draught Leffe at £4.30 a pint); wines go for £10-£25 a bottle. You can eat at the attached restaurant (fillet steak with brandy and peppercorn sauce, for instance). DJs or musicians perform most nights. Overall, Grand Banks represents a welcome attempt to export bar culture out of central London.
Entertainment: jazz from 8pm Sun-Tue; DJs from 8pm Wed-Sat.

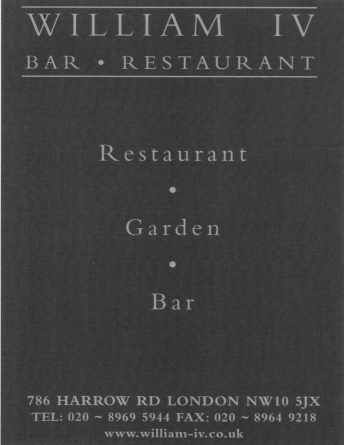
Pubs

Gastropubs

Central

Bloomsbury WC1

Duke of York
7 Roger Street, WC1 (020 7242 7230). Russell Square tube. **Open** noon-11pm Mon-Fri; 6-11pm Sat. **Lunch served** noon-3pm Mon-Fri. **Dinner served** 6-10pm Mon-Sat. **Main courses** £6.50-£10. **Credit** MC, V.
These uncluttered premises are split into two rooms: the somewhat dingy dining room and the larger, brighter, airier main room. Staff are perfectly happy for you to dine in either. The menu, chalked on a blackboard, offered lots of choice in starters and mains, but only two desserts. We tried the soups: leek broth had a peppery kick to it while being a tad thin, but carrot and coconut soup was rich and flavoursome. Roast salmon fillet, caramelised red cabbage and herb sauce was rich, too; the salmon was lovely, the cabbage if anything slightly too sweet. A robust dish of red snapper, melted leeks and Bombay potatoes was filling and, again, very rich. To finish, we managed to get past the crust of the coffee crème brûlée – of truly manhole-lid strength – but the gloopy interior varied in temperature in a slightly unsettling way. Choice of coffee was filter or nothing: go Gaggia, we say. Service was entirely pleasant and the ambience, aided by lively acid jazz, perfect. We'll go again and hope to strike luckier, food-wise.
Free House: Old Speckled Hen £2.
Tables outdoors (3, pavement). **Map 3/4M.**

Clerkenwell & Farringdon EC1

The Eagle
159 Farringdon Road, EC1 (020 7837 1353). Farringdon tube/rail/19, 38, 63, 341 bus. **Open** noon-11pm Mon-Sat; noon-5pm Sun. **Lunch served** 12.30-2.30pm Mon-Fri; 12.30-3.30pm Sat, Sun. **Dinner served** 6.30-10.30pm Mon-Sat. **Main courses** £7-£12. **Credit** £TC.
The moment staff start serving food (12.30pm) there's a queue at the bar. You're lucky if you've got a table. If so, don't leave it unoccupied even for a second; the place is full of table-vultures. It's for this reason – the overcrowding – that you never relax at the Eagle as much as you might at other gastropubs, despite the fact this was the first. You can't run a tab, nor pay by credit card. And yet the place is packed all the time. How do they do it? Is it because there's Leffe on draught and a good selection of wines? Whatever the reason, it's probably not the food, not if our most recent experience is anything to go by. We ordered a couple of fish-based main courses and both disappointed: grilled wild sea trout with fennel, rocket, lemon, mangetout salad and a strong, distinctive tapenade was fine apart from the trout, which was a lot drier than the sea from whence it came; the grilled barracuda was not so much char-grilled as carbonised, its accompanying patatas bravas extremely bland. The pudding choice was ewe's cheese or pastel de nata. We went for the Portuguese custard tart dusted with cinnamon (too liberally for our taste). The Eagle seems to have taken its eye off the ball, not that the regulars appear unduly bothered.
Free House: Gambrinus £2.50; Guinness £2.50; Stella Artois £2.40.
Children admitted. Tables outdoors (4, pavement). **Map 15/4N.**

Peasant ★
240 St John Street, EC1 (020 7336 7726). Angel tube/55 bus. **Open** noon-11pm Mon-Fri; 6-11pm Sat. **Lunch served** 12.30-3pm Mon-Fri. **Dinner served** 6.30-11pm Mon-Sat. **Main courses** £7.50-£11. **Service** 12½%. **Credit** AmEx, DC, MC, £TC, V.
A short hop from the ever-packed **Eagle** (*see above*), the Peasant is calm and relaxed in comparison, although it deserves to be every bit as successful. One half of the dark-wood bar room

is given over to drinkers, who can enjoy a roaring gas-fed 'real' fire; diners occupy the laid-out tables on the other side of the room. Portions are of a magnitude most rural workers can only dream of. Spring minestrone soup was thick, hearty and copious. There were great helpings of spicy sausage and green veg in the sautéed chorizo, spinach and oyster mushroom. Next, the prawn, salmon, monkfish and calamares kebab melted off the skewer and benefited from the moist support of a subtly flavoured tabouleh. Baked sea bass with roasted courgettes was cooked to perfection and, again, extremely generously proportioned. Side orders of chips were superb: firm, fat and non-greasy. Desserts-wise, the panna cotta and Amaretto caramel was wicked, its texture that of a sturdy blancmange, while the chocolate cake with chantilly cream was so smooth it was mousse-like. Draught beers include the excellent Bavarian Schneide Weisse wheat beer, which comes in a glass as long as your forearm.
Free House: Boddingtons £2; Murphy's £2.40; Stella Artois £2.40.
Children admitted. Tables outdoors (4, terrace). **Map 15/4O.**

Marylebone NW1

The Chapel
48 Chapel Street, NW1 (020 7402 9220). Edgware Road tube. **Open** noon-11pm Mon-Sat; noon-3.30pm, 7-10.30pm Sun. **Lunch served** noon-2.30pm, **dinner served** 7-10pm daily. **Main courses** £8-£12.50. **Credit** AmEx, DC, MC, V.
With its bare look and All Bar One acoustics, the Chapel needs some help from the food. Fortunately it gets it. Our starters – sautéed calamares, smoked salmon and mixed baby leaves salad; and warm smoked chicken with salami and dandelion – were excellent. The former benefited from good use of capers and non-rubbery calamares, while the latter was packed with alarmingly pink (but reassuringly succulent) chicken and slightly too hard salami. A complimentary basket of very moreish date and walnut bread helped pass the time between courses. More sauce would have been nice with the grilled chicken breast, crispy courgettes and dill, but only because the sauce was so good. Fish cakes and fennel gratin, sautéed potatoes and bisque sauce was spot on, the fish cakes surprisingly light and fluffy. Of the two chardonnays on the wine list, the one that came by the glass was so good that £2.80 didn't seem excessive. Only in the tea/coffee department did the Chapel disappoint: there's no decaf coffee, and lemon tea turned out to be a cup of not-much-hotter-than-warm water containing half a slice of lemon and an Earl Grey teabag. Good job the food was better.
Leased from Bass: Fuller's London Pride £2.30; Grolsch £2.50; Guinness £2.50; Scrumpy Supreme £2.30.
Children admitted. Tables outdoors (15, garden). Separate room for parties, seats 35. **Map 2/5E.**

West

Brook Green W14

Havelock Tavern
57 Masbro Road, W14 (020 7603 5374). Shepherd's Bush tube. **Open** 11am-11pm Mon-Sat; noon-10.30pm Sun. **Lunch served** 12.30-2.30pm Mon-Sat; 12.30-3pm Sun. **Dinner served** 7-10pm Mon-Sat; 7-9.30pm Sun. **Main courses** £6.50-£11. **Credit** £TC.
You don't get many goujons in your deep-fried goujons of cod with tartare sauce and lemon at the Havelock Tavern, but it is only a starter and the main courses are generously proportioned. The large warm salad of duck confit, green beans, pancetta, shallots, beetroot, crème fraîche and horseradish wins the award for longest and most specific dish name, but it deserves to win other awards as well because it is superb, like most things here. The osso bucco with Spanish butter beans and spinach was hearty and full of flavour. Whole roast loin of pork, mash, peas, Calvados and mustard sauce was rich and perfectly cooked

(although we were surprised to find it on the bone). Of puddings, the most irresistible were apple and rhubarb crème brûlée, and prune, Armagnac and gingerbread pudding with vanilla ice-cream and toffee sauce; both were extremely moreish.
Whitbread: Boddingtons £2.40; Guinness £2.50; Heineken £2.30; Strongbow £2.30.
Children admitted. Tables outdoors (6, garden; 2, pavement).

Hammersmith W6

The Stonemason's Arms

54 Cambridge Grove, W6 (020 8748 1397). Hammersmith tube. **Open** noon-11pm Mon-Sat; noon-10.30pm Sun. **Lunch served** noon-4pm daily. **Dinner served** 6.30-10pm Mon-Sat; 6.30-9.30pm Sun. **Main courses** £7-£10.70. **Credit** AmEx, MC, V.

If we get a couple of gripes out of the way at the start – the tomato and mozzarella salad was very generous but the mozzarella was not the very best; the big chips were just a bit too big and slightly undercooked, and the fries a mite soggy – we can concentrate on the positive. The atmosphere here is excellent, ultra relaxed and inclusive (our party was drawn from three generations and each was made very welcome). The service was friendly and efficient. There's plenty of room; tables are not squeezed up against each other. There's not only Hoegaarden on tap but Leffe Blonde as well. The own-made game pie with roast parsnips and game jus came with perfect pastry – thin and crisp – and the various flavours within remained strong and distinct. Risotto of butternut squash, pine nuts, spinach and mascarpone was very creamy and made with the right kind of rice (always a good start). Apple pie had generous amounts of cinnamon, and was beautifully presented.
Babies and children admitted. Disabled: toilet.
Free House: Stella Artois £2.55; Wadsworth 6X £2.20.

Kensal Green W10, NW10

Paradise by Way of Kensal Green

19 Kilburn Lane, W10 (020 8969 0098). Kensal Green tube/Kensal Rise rail/52, 302 bus. **Open** noon-11pm Mon-Sat; noon-10.30pm Sun. **Lunch served** noon-4pm daily. **Dinner served** 7.30-11pm Mon-Sat; 7.30-10.30pm Sun. **Main courses** £6.50-£13.50. **Credit** MC, £TC, V.

We must have been unlucky: the service here can't always be this bad. Can it? With things taking an inordinately long time to materialise, our extremely pleasant waitress offered us more bread (failing to mention we would later be charged £1.50 a basket), and when even that took an age to arrive, she suggested some drinks on the house. So, later and well fed, we ordered a bottle of Muscat. A bottle of rosé wine and two bottles of Muscadet arrived in sequence (all uncorked), before we finally took delivery of *two* bottles of dessert wine (not Muscat, which turned out to be unavailable). But what about the food? Deep-fried mozzarella sticks with spicy mango compote was rather ordinary, but spicy salad of char-grilled beef, Thai-style was zesty and appetite-whetting. Fillet of Scotch beef, béarnaise sauce, big chips was very good, the meat lean and cooked exactly as requested, the chips also cooked right through. Monkfish and tiger prawns in old-style Creole sauce, rice 'n' peas didn't put a fin wrong either. Paradise boasts an excellent space, much of the food can't be faulted, but staff training leaves something to be desired and the music's far too loud. Maybe that's the problem: you can't hear yourself think, never mind listen to what customers are ordering.
Scottish Courage: Holsten £2.40; Kronenbourg £2.40; Miller £2.30.
Children admitted. Entertainment: jazz 8.30pm Sun. Separate room for parties, seats 100. Tables outdoors (7, patio).

William IV

786 Harrow Road, NW10 (020 8969 5944). Kensal Green tube. **Open** noon-11pm Mon-Thur; noon-midnight Fri, Sat; noon-10.30pm Sun. **Lunch served** noon-3pm Mon-Fri; noon-4pm Sat, Sun. **Dinner served** 6-10.30pm Mon-Thur; 6-11pm Fri; 7-11pm Sat; 7-10pm Sun. **Main courses** £7-£12.90. **Set lunch** (Mon-Fri) £7.50. **Credit** MC, £TC, V.

The door staff eye the passing traffic on the Harrow Road, separated from Kensal Green Cemetery by a high wall. It's difficult to know from where they perceive the greater threat – from the streets of Victorian terraces behind, or the Victorian boneyard across the street – but there's little sense of history inside this big, bright, beautiful boozer, which has a sort of indoor/outdoor area that's nice on a summer evening. A starter of merguez sausages proved spicy but not overwhelming. Seared swordfish

Havelock Tavern

was surprisingly cold, but a friendly waitress was quick to offer to warm it up. Other mains included sirloin steak with mash and red onion gravy, and smoked haddock fish cakes, which make a change from the ubiquitous salmon variety. A pavlova had concrete-hard meringue and our request for cream, which was mysteriously absent, met with a jug of single cream rather than whipped. Still, the William IV has a good feeling about it.
Free house: Fuller's London Pride £2.40; Guinness £2.60; Stella Artois £2.60.
Children admitted. Entertainment: DJ 9.30pm Fri, Sat. Separate rooms for parties, seating 20 and 100. Tables outdoors (13, garden; 4, pavement).

Ladbroke Grove W10

Golborne House

36 Golborne Road, W10 (020 8960 6260). Westbourne Park tube. **Open** noon-11pm, **lunch served** 12.30-4pm daily. **Dinner served** 6.30-10.15pm Mon-Sat; 6.30-9.45pm Sun. **Main courses** £4-£11.50. **Service** 10%. **Credit** MC, V.

Wooden tables, blackboard menu and a young, mobile-toting clientele mark out this former corner boozer as a gastropub along the lines of the nearby Westbourne and Prince Bonaparte. Our starters were delicious. We shared a bowl of tiny steamed mussels served with a tasty aïoli and a slice of bruschetta, and a plate of serrano ham with quince jam and rocket. Mains – cumin-rubbed chump of lamb with rosemary mash and caramelised onions, and a whole baked sea bream topped with sweet chilli and basil served with a crusty buttered taro root – were a bit pricey for a pub at £10.50, but were both top-notch. For dessert, a small slice of near-perfect banana cheesecake cost a hefty £4.50. The most glaringly obvious difference from other pubs in the area was the fantastic service: bar staff couldn't do enough to help.
Leased from Enterprise Inns: Beck's £2.80; Fuller's London Pride £2.40; Guinness £2.60; Staropramen £2.90; Stella £2.80.
Babies and children admitted. Entertainment: DJ Fri, Sat. Separate room for parties, seats 40. Tables outdoors (4, pavement).
Map 11/4Az.

North Pole

13-15 North Pole Road, W10 (020 8964 9384). Latimer Road or White City tube. **Open** 11.30am-11pm Mon-Sat; noon-10.30pm Sun. **Lunch served** 12.30-3pm Mon-Sat; 12.30-4pm Sun. **Dinner served** 6.30-10pm Mon-Sat; 6.30-9.30pm Sun. **Main courses** £7.95-£13.95. **Credit** AmEx, MC, £TC, V.

It didn't come in the fantastically tall glasses you get at the Peasant (*see above*), but the Schneide Weisse wheat beer goes down a treat whatever vessel it's served in. Also good was the brown soda bread, for which there was happily no cover charge. A starter of razor clams with garlic butter and rocket was lukewarm and unpalatable, but blackened chicken Caesar was hot and spicy and lipsmackingly good. Five pence shy of 14 quid might seem a lot to pay for char-grilled rib-eye steak with caramelised shallots, truffle mash and red wine jus, but the meat was tender and cooked to perfection, the onions deliciously sweet and the mash plentiful. A shared sticky toffee pudding with vanilla ice-cream was a fine way to finish the meal, but the real climax to the evening was provided by a game of table football in the bar area, with its many friendly regulars and comfortable chairs.
Free House: Carling £2.30; Freedom £2.60; Fuller's London Pride £2.30; Guinness £2.40; Stella Artois £2.50.
Children admitted. Tables outdoors (5, pavement).

Shepherd's Bush W6

Anglesea Arms

35 Wingate Road, W6 (020 8749 1291). Goldhawk Road or Ravenscourt Park tube. **Open** 11am-11pm Mon-Sat; noon-10.30pm Sun. **Lunch served** 12.30-2.45pm Mon-Sat; 1-3.30pm Sun. **Dinner served** 7.30-10.45pm Mon-Sat; 7.30-9.45pm Sun. **Main courses** £7.25-£9.95. **Credit** MC, V.

Best get to this popular eaterie early to bag your table, as staff don't take bookings. The menu, which changes daily, is chalked on a blackboard. Red onion and cottage goat curd tart with bitter leaves, plum tomatoes and basil was creamy and very tasty; the gravadlax with pickled cucumber seemed flavourless in comparison. Moving on to mains, we went for char-grilled chump of lamb with chips, and breast of Gascony duck with broad beans and sweet-and-sour cherries. Both meats were succulent and cooked to perfection, filling us up to the point where we had to resist the strong temptation of poached peach and raspberry knickerbocker glory with pecan nut brittle. There's a decent selection of wines and the coffee is palatable. We felt able to forgive the indifferent service, won over by the generally pleasant ambience and the attractive Brackenbury Village setting, not forgetting the food.
Leased from Courage: Courage Best £2.10; Directors £2.30; Kronenbourg £2.40.
Children admitted. Tables outdoors (4, pavement).

Westbourne Park W2

The Chepstow

39 Chepstow Place, W2 (020 7229 0323). Bayswater, Notting Hill Gate or Westbourne Park tube. **Open** noon-11pm Mon-Sat; noon-10.30pm Sun. **Meals served** noon-3pm, 7-10.30pm daily. **Main courses** £9-£15. **Credit** MC, £TC, V.

Watch out for the sauces at The Chepstow. A Bloody Mary was too heavy on the Worcester sauce (to remedy matters, the waiter decanted it into a pint glass and added more tomato juice, lemon and ice). The pleasure we took in a crab, guacamole and rocket salad starter was compromised somewhat by an unidentified brownish sauce that encircled the leaves like an electric fence. Roast pork chop came with a sauce that was preposterously garlicky, and the rack of lamb slid around the plate rather too easily, thanks to a sauce that was a little too oily. Rib-eye steak was excellent (if served medium rare and not medium, as requested), arriving with faultless pepper sauce, fries and side salad. To be fair, garlicky sauce notwithstanding, the pork chop was also very good. As was a rhubarb tart with vanilla cream. We weren't charged for the bread (which came with a dipping bowl of olive oil and balsamic vinegar), but there's a hefty service charge. The dining area of this friendly, attractive pub is decorated with plain canvases painted bright colours.
Courage: Budweiser £2.60; Guinness £2.60; Stella Artois £2.60.
Children admitted. **Map 11/6B.**

The Cow

89 Westbourne Park Road, W2 (020 7221 5400). Royal Oak or Westbourne Park tube. **Open** noon-midnight Mon-Sat; noon-10.30pm Sun. **Lunch served** 12.30-3pm Mon-Fri; 12.30-4pm Sat, Sun. **Dinner served** 7-11pm Mon-Sat; 7.30-10.30pm Sun. **Main courses** £10.50-£20. **Credit** AmEx, MC, V.

'It's a *bloody* good wine list,' brayed the suited advertising type at the next table the minute we sat down. It is a good wine list, but if there's one thing wrong with the Cow it's the people you have to share it with. Preeners, hasslers, shouters, waitress fondlers – they're all here. Or they were on our last visit to the Cow's dining room (on the first floor above the bar). Still, the service and food are excellent. When it's available, the entrecôte steak between two with mayonnaise and crisp, honey-hued fries is worth trying. On this occasion we sampled a starter of leek and lobster vinaigrette, a winning combination, followed by sea bass and parsley salad, and roast chicken, girolles, rocket and summer truffle salad. The fish and chicken were highly enjoyable, but the parsley salad proved a challenge. Portions weren't so large that we couldn't find room for two superb desserts: crème brûlée and wild strawberries, and raspberry and passion fruit sorbets. Luckily we'd just finished by the time the guy at the next table started his cigar, which the waitress was happy to provide despite the house request that cigar smokers consider other diners. Considering others is an alien concept to a certain kind of diner.
Free House: Budvar £2.50; Fuller's London Pride £2.20; Hoegaarden £2 (½ pint); Red Stripe £2.50.
Tables outdoors (2, pavement). **Map 11/5A.**

Prince Bonaparte

80 Chepstow Road, W2 (020 7313 9491). Notting Hill Gate or Westbourne Park tube. **Open** noon-11pm Mon, Wed-Sat; 5-11pm Tue; noon-10.30pm Sun. **Lunch served** 12.30-3pm Mon, Wed-Sun. **Dinner served** 6.30-10.30pm Mon-Sat; 6.30-10pm Sun. **Main courses** £7.50-£10.50. **Credit** JCB, MC, V.

The Prince Bonaparte sports the stripped-down, bare-boards look, which goes towards creating a relaxed ambience. The sun streaming in through the west-facing picture windows and the seductive melodies of a Dot Allison CD floating out of the loudspeakers helped, too. The menu,

which changes from day to day, is written on a blackboard. You order from the bar, where the range of beers extends beyond the norm to include Staropramen (although not the dark version, sadly) and Hoegaarden on tap, and Tiger in bottled form. Owing to the presence of a large party and there being only one cook in the open-to-view kitchen, we were told we'd have to wait five to ten minutes before we could order. Ten minutes later the message was the same. Finally, from a menu that included Cumberland sausages, red onion, mash and gravy; and tuna steak with couscous and fresh tomato sauce, we chose bruschetta of roasted salmon, rocket and lemon mayonnaise. The salmon was cold as the ocean, limp and slippery; but the bread and rocket were excellent, both fresh, almost a sustaining dish in themselves. Desserts are of the sticky toffee pudding/ice-cream/plate of Dolcelatte variety. The corner setting is a bonus, light reflecting off the white stucco that's one of many lovely features of the area.
Bass: Fuller's London Pride £2.30; Grolsch £2.60; Guinness £2.60.
Children admitted. **Map 11/5B.**

The Westbourne ★
101 Westbourne Park Villas, W2 (020 7221 1332). Royal Oak or Westbourne Park tube. **Open** 5-11pm Mon; noon-11pm Tue-Fri; 11am-11pm Sat; noon-10.30pm Sun. **Lunch served** 12.30-3pm Tue-Fri; 12.30-3.30pm Sat, Sun. **Dinner served** 7-10pm daily. **Main courses** £7.25-£11.25. **Credit** AmEx, MC, V.
Heaving in the evening, both inside and out, whatever the weather, the Westbourne is much more relaxed at lunchtime. It scores highly in all departments: the wine list is interesting; there's a fine range of beers, including bottled Tiger and Chimay, with Leffe and Hoegaarden on tap; the food is excellent; and the service (order at the bar and it's brought to you) was friendly and professional (although we've had reports of rude service, too). We enjoyed smoked mackerel with beetroot, watercress and horseradish cream; and char-grilled quail with white beans and artichokes, saffron shallots and sherry sauce. So the mackerel had a few bones and the quail likewise: that's vertebrates for you. Both were perfectly cooked and presented with care. We tried two puddings (chocolate terrine with crème fraîche, and crème caramel with berries and tuile biscuit) and declared both a success. The crème caramel was particularly good, not too rich, the fruit fresh and sweet, and the biscuit worked well in place of the more usual rock-hard crust. There's bacon on the menu, too – on the wall, in fact. Francis Bacon. An original.
Free House: Dortmunder Union £2.60; Guinness £2.60; Leffe £2.20 (½ pint); Old Speckled Hen £2.30; Stella Artois £2.60.
Children admitted. Tables outdoors (22, terrace). **Map 11/5B**

South West

Chelsea SW3

Builders Arms
13 Britten Street, SW3 (020 7349 9040). South Kensington tube/14 bus. **Open** 11am-11pm Mon-Sat; noon-10.30pm Sun. **Lunch served** noon-2.30pm, **dinner served** 7-10pm daily. **Main courses** £6.95-£10.95. **Credit** DC, MC, V.
To enjoy lunch or dinner at the Builders Arms unreservedly, it helps to like the sort of people who live, work or shop around the King's Road. That self-satisfied air, that way of holding a cigarette – there's no getting away from it. Luckily, the service remains unaffected by the local manners; it's jaunty and friendly, if a tiny bit unreliable. There are several beers on tap and a decent wine list. The key word in the warm crispy duck salad is 'crispy': the fatty meat is cut into small crunchy discs. Char-grilled vegetables with goat's cheese sprang no surprises and was generous with the fennel. The main courses were more successful: Cumberland sausages with mash was distinguished by good, strong-tasting sausages, while the chicken and leek pie with rocket pesto mash was extremely flavoursome and so rich it couldn't be finished if pudding was to be contemplated. We tried two of the own-made ice-creams – mascarpone and lemon, and raspberry. While the latter was watery and bland, the former couldn't be faulted. With a couple of halves of Hoegaarden the bill came to just under £40 for two.
Geronimo Inns: Caffreys £2.50; Guinness £2.50; Heineken £2.25; Heineken Export £2.60; Hoegaarden £3.15; Stella Artois £2.60.
Disabled: toilet. Tables outdoors (3, patio). **Map 6/11E.**

Fulham SW6

The Atlas ★
16 Seagrave Road, SW6 (020 7385 9129/ 020 7386 9113). West Brompton tube. **Open** noon-11pm Mon-Sat; noon-10.30pm Sun. **Lunch served** 12.30-3pm daily. **Dinner served** 7-10.30pm Mon-Sat; 7-10pm Sun. **Main courses** £6.50-£11. **Credit** MC, £TC, V.
The moment you step through the door you know you've made the right decision. The place just feels right. The quality of the wood lining the bar, the worn footrest, the old tiles, the atmospheric black and white photographs on the wall, the bebop playing at just the right volume (loud enough if you want to listen to it but quiet enough to ignore), and the friendly welcome extended by the staff – all the details are in place. Fortunately, the food is not a let-down. The menu has a Moorish slant, but not overwhelmingly so. We enjoyed grilled chicken breast 'alla Diavolo' with chilli and black-pepper rice and cucumber, yoghurt and mint salsa. The pan-roast salmon steak was another winner. Other dishes included grilled Tuscan sausages with puy lentils, and roast leg of lamb salad with rosemary. The only reason we couldn't finish the lemon tart with cream was because it was so big and so rich. As we left we were already looking forward to coming back.
Free House: Charles Wells Bombardier £2.20; Theakston XB £2.20.
Separate room for parties, seats 36. Tables outdoors (10, garden). **Map 5/12B.**

Salisbury Tavern
21 Sherbrooke Road, SW6 (020 7381 4005). Fulham Broadway tube. **Open** 11.30am-11pm Mon-Sat; noon-10.30pm Sun. **Lunch served** noon-2.30pm Mon-Fri; noon-3.30pm Sat, Sun. **Dinner served** 7-11pm Mon-Sat; 7-10.30pm Sun. **Main courses** £8.25-£12.75. **Service** 12½%. **Credit** AmEx, MC, V.
Small wonder that the Salisbury Tavern's refurb reflects the Fulham locale, with its assured, affluent, almost Home Counties taste. There are distinct dining and drinking areas. The pub part is subdued but appealing: clean wooden floors, sturdy banquettes, well-mannered bar staff and a couple of good real ales. Food is served in the atrium-ceilinged dining area. The brief menu offers smart pub food at restaurant prices; decent bottles on the wine list start at £20. Starters were excellent: tarte tatin of onion and goat's cheese had light pastry encasing onion layers caramelised into sweetness, balanced by the salty sourness of the goat's cheese; risotto of asparagus and wild mushroom had a perfect texture. A main course of sautéed calf's liver, however, had a texture more akin to that of pig's liver. There was no mistaking the provenance of smoked haddock, though, served with bubble and squeak, a poached egg and a béarnaise sauce with a tarragon tang. Simple but good cooking, in a pleasant atmosphere.
Leased from Punch Taverns: Charles Wells Bombardier £2.30; Fuller's London Pride £2.30; Guinness £2.70; Heineken £2.50; Staropramen £2.70; Stella £2.80.
Babies and children admitted; high chairs. Dress: smart casual.

Putney SW15

Coat & Badge
8 Lacy Road, SW15 (020 8788 4900). East Putney tube. **Open** 11am-11pm Mon-Sat; noon-10.30pm Sun. **Lunch served** noon-2.30pm Mon-Fri; noon-3pm Sat; noon-4pm Sun. **Dinner served** 7-9.30pm daily. **Meals served** noon-9.30pm Sun. **Main courses** £7.95-£10.95. **Credit** MC, V.
First the staff tell us they don't take bookings, so when we arrive and find no tables free and one table with a reserved sign on it, we wonder what's afoot. At first, no one knows. It turns out they had reserved it for us anyway. How nice, even if they haven't got a clue what's going on. Our waitress looked a bit unhappy most of the time, but who wouldn't, surrounded by stuffed pink shirts and rowing club types? This is Putney – what do you expect? What we didn't expect was a starter of grilled king prawns with salsa. The prawns were OK, but the salsa was weird. Californian sausages and mash was a more successful combination, although there was nothing exciting about it. Smoked chicken Caesar salad was better all round, with just one tiny complaint: the croûtons could have been crispier. The best was definitely saved till last. Among the puddings menu lurked two of the loveliest concoctions we've tasted at any of London's gastrobars: a chocolate cake that was well on the way to being chocolate pudding (or was it vice versa?). Whichever, it occupied the middle ground superbly; and bread and butter pudding that melted in the mouth.

Geronimo Inns: Bass £2.15; Boddingtons £2.05; Guinness £2.60; Kronenbourg £2.60; Stella Artois £2.65; Young's Bitter £2.15.
Entertainment: jazz singer 1-5pm Sun. Separate room for parties, seats 20. Tables outdoors (10, courtyard).

Wandsworth SW18

Alma Tavern
499 Old York Road, SW18 (020 8870 2537). Wandsworth Town rail. **Open** 11am-11pm Mon-Sat; noon-10.30pm Sun. **Meals served** noon-10.30pm Mon-Sat; noon-4pm Sun. **Main courses** £6.60-£10.25. **Credit** AmEx, LV, MC, £TC, V.
The Alma continues to draw them in as they spill out of Wandsworth Town station. The motley crew of City workers, locals and the young 'south Chelsea' crowd ensures that this simple pub remains as popular as ever. The large room you first enter holds a central bar surrounded by wooden tables and chairs and the occasional sofa. Beyond lies the dining room, with its plaster frieze above the picture rail, and a deep green and yellow either side of a dado rail. Apart from a few front covers of *Voilà* magazine, the dining room feels a touch barren, especially midweek when there are fewer diners. The menu continues to offer a good mix of pub staples (with a twist), and some more ambitious dishes such as moules au cidre or stuffed boneless quail. The char-grilled leg of lamb steak was beautifully tender, but needed a sauce of some sort to accompany the dry deep-fried potatoes and rocket salad. Similarly, banoffi pie, from the short puddings list, was fine, but would have benefited from some cream. A reliable if unspectacular dining room.
Young's: Guinness £2.50; Young's Bitter £2.05; Young's Export £2.55.
Children admitted (restaurant only). Separate room for parties, seats 75.

Ship
41 Jew's Row, SW18 (020 8870 9667). Wandsworth Town rail/28, 295 bus. **Open** 11am-11pm Mon-Sat; noon-10.30pm Sun. **Meals served** noon-10.30pm daily. **Main courses** £6.75-£11. **Credit** AmEx, MC, V.
Heaving at weekends, this riverside boozer by Wandsworth Bridge has a relaxed, laid-back feel on a weekday lunchtime. You can sit in the pub's main room, where natural light floods the space and makes it seem huge, or in the smaller dining room, where extractor fans in the open kitchen add a background hum. If the Gruyère and farmhouse cheese soufflé was slightly too subtle, the eggs on a bed of spinach with pink peppercorn sauce on a toasted brioche was a delicate delight. Mains include hearty-sounding fare such as fish stew, roasted cod and pork chop, but we opted for own-made and reared sausages with mash, which, sadly, was nothing special, and breast of duck blackened with balsamic vinegar, served with Chinese leaves, dauphinoise potatoes and a sharp raspberry jus, which was superb. Puddings are worth investigating: treacle tart was excellent, apple and rhubarb crumble just like your mum used to make. The bottled beer selection was extremely limited (Beck's), but staff can rustle up a good Bloody Mary. After a couple of drinks, you'll need a compass to find the railway station, as the Ship is moored in a depressing no-man's land of roundabouts, fast-food joints, petrol stations and DIY superstores.
Young's: Young's Bitter £2.15; Young's Pilsner £2.55; Young's Special £2.25.
Children admitted (restaurant and garden). Separate room for parties, seats 10; marquee for parties. Tables outdoors (20, beer garden; 24, restaurant garden). **For branches see index.**

South

Battersea SW11

Duke of Cambridge
228 Battersea Bridge Road, SW11 (020 7223 5662). Clapham Junction rail. **Open** 11am-11pm Mon-Sat; noon-10.30pm Sun. **Lunch served** noon-2.30pm Mon-Sat; noon-2.45pm Sun. **Dinner served** 7-9.45pm Mon-Sat; 7-9.30pm Sun. **Main courses** £6.95-£10.95. **Credit** MC, V.
If the Duke of Cambridge looks familiar, it may be because it's run by Geronimo Inns, which also operates the **Queens**, the **Coat & Badge** and the **Builders Arms**. There are shelves of old books, a few shelves of fake books, a large painting of the pub, tables out front that are reasonably well shaded from the busy road, and quiet corners inside in which to relax. Main courses are pretty standard gastropub fare (swordfish steak, rib-eye steak, chump of lamb).

We enjoyed breast of chicken tandoori-style with cumin potatoes and yoghurt, but it couldn't be described as outstanding (and why does chicken breast come with a bone attached?). Fizzy mineral water was flat and a Virgin Mary lacked bite. Still, the service was friendly and fun, and the summer pudding looked like a winner. The wine list draws from the New World as much as France and Italy (plus a sparkling wine from Kent).
Young's: Guinness £2.65; Heineken £2.25; Hoegaarden £3.70; Strongbow £2.50; Young's Bitter £2.05; Young's Special £2.25.
Disabled: toilet. Separate room for parties, seats 20. Tables outdoors (10, patio).

Camberwell SE5

Sun & Doves
61-63 Coldharbour Lane, SE5 (020 7733 1525). Oval tube then 185 bus/Brixton tube/rail then 35, 45 bus. **Open** 11am-11pm Mon-Fri; noon-11pm Sat; noon-10.30pm Sun. **Lunch served** noon-3pm Mon-Sat; noon-5pm Sun. **Dinner served** 7-11pm Mon-Sat. **Main courses** £4.75-£9.95. **Credit** AmEx, DC, MC, £TC, V.
The Sun & Doves is the perfect setting on a sunny day. Its rear garden offers unsheltered areas as well as tables with parasols, while the interior is roomy and cool. The menu is less adventurous than many, but has innovative touches, such as numerous skewer options. So numerous are they, in fact, and not all that easy to understand, that we sought clarification from a somewhat impatient member of bar staff. Suitably chastened, and only a little illumined, we tried two skewers mixing haloumi and vegetables (nicely charred) with juicy, succulent swordfish. The combination arrived – by the hands of a much pleasanter waiter – on a bed of couscous full of fresh mint. Rib-eye steak was on the small side and rather fatty, but the accompanying fries and salad were enjoyable. A good local, then, but perhaps not worth going out of your way for.
Courage: Directors £2.20; Guinness £2.30; Kronenbourg £2.30.
Children admitted. Tables outdoors (10, restaurant garden; 10, beer garden).
For branch see index.

Clapham SW4

Belle Vue
1 Clapham Common Southside, SW4 (020 7498 9473). Clapham Common tube. **Open** 5-11pm Mon-Fri; 12.30-11pm Sat; 12.30-10.30pm Sun. **Lunch served** noon-4pm daily. **Dinner served** 6.30-10.30pm Mon-Sat; 6.30-10pm Sun. **Main courses** £8.50-£9.50. **Credit** £TC.
The Belle Vue has grown in hipdom as Clapham has. Set on the corner by the tube, its triangular shape is largely lost in the collection of tables and chairs, sofas and open-plan kitchen, overlooked by orange-brown walls displaying the latest set of paintings for sale. The young and beautiful meet here, a sizeable number of them to sample the menu. This contains a fair range of gastropub classics such as salad niçoise, Toulouse sausages, or smoked haddock and cod fritters with Dijon mustard and dill mayonnaise. The rib-eye steak with blue cheese butter was good, although the accompanying chips were limp and soggy, while the salad simply loitered on the edge of the plate, glistening from a recent shower. Warm duck salad was better – a generous mix of lettuce, peppers and beans tossed together with plenty of duck. A fine lemon brûlée and chocolate-chip pudding, along with a chirpy house chardonnay, gave a final lift to the meal. This is a lively venue, but there's the sense that the kitchen is resting on its laurels a tad.
Leased from Courage: Beamish £2.20; John Smith's Extra Smooth £2.20; Kronenbourg £2.30.

South East

Greenwich SE10

North Pole
131 Greenwich High Road, SE10 (020 8853 3020). Greenwich rail/DLR. **Open** 5-11pm Mon; noon-11pm Tue-Sat; noon-10.30pm Sun. **Meals served** 6.30-10.30pm Mon-Sat; noon-10pm Sun. **Main courses** £8-£16. **Credit** AmEx, DC, MC, V.
Maybe Monday nights are always slow in this quiet corner of Greenwich, but by 9.30pm the North Pole wasn't much busier than its arctic namesake. Passing through the groovy, zebra-upholstered ground-floor bar, we made our way upstairs to the sumptuous, country-style restaurant. The half-bottle of Sancerre could have been chilled for longer, but went well with an adequate starter of crab and avocado salad with sweet potato crisps that amounted to no

more than the sum of its parts. Roast lamb chump served with red peppers stuffed with anchovy, plum tomato and basil was better, the meat cooked to perfection and cut into slices that combined tenderness with crispiness. Spatchcock chicken marinated in sour cream and lime served with red lentil and sweet potato mash was fine too, but prices in general are high given that dishes aren't spectacular. The dark chocolate tart with white chocolate ice-cream was small but very rich, sweet and slightly heavy. Ordering tea with lemon, we were disappointed (if not surprised) when it came without the requested two slices of lemon, but one slice cut into halves.
Free House: Boddingtons £2.30; Hoegaarden £1.80 (½ pint); Murphy's £2.50. *Children admitted. Separate room for parties, seats 50. Tables outdoors (10, pavement).*

North

Camden Town & Chalk Farm NW1

The Engineer
65 Gloucester Avenue, NW1 (020 7722 0950). Chalk Farm tube/31, 168 bus. **Open** 9am-11pm Mon-Sat; 9am-10.30pm Sun. **Breakfast served** 9-11.30am Mon-Fri; 9am-noon Sat, Sun. **Lunch served** noon-3pm Mon-Fri; 12.30-3.30pm Sat, Sun. **Dinner served** 7-11pm Mon-Sat; 7-10.30pm Sun. **Main courses** £9-£15.50. **Credit** MC, V.
The Engineer is definitely at the posher, more refined end of London's range of gastropubs, but service remains pleasantly informal. Due to a choice location, it has no trouble filling its tables, so do book. We shared a fine starter of baby squid pan-fried and served with red onion and lime salsa and crème fraîche, then got straight into free-range chicken breast marinated in yoghurt and spices served with plantain poached in coconut milk and lemongrass and basmati rice; and duck leg glazed with Sichuan pepper and honey, served with tossed salad of apple, mooli, cucumber, mint, coriander, rocket, mung beans and hoi sin sauce. Both were excellent, the chicken in particular, and so generously proportioned that pudding – the selection was enticing – was out of the question. Two glasses of dessert wine would have to do instead, which they did, very well indeed.
Leased from Bass: Fuller's London Pride £2.20; Grolsch £2.50; Guinness £2.50. *Children admitted. Separate rooms for parties, seating 16 and 30. Tables outdoors (15, garden).* **Map 10.**

Lansdowne
90 Gloucester Avenue, NW1 (020 7483 0409). Chalk Farm tube/31, 168 bus. **Open** 6-11pm Mon; noon-11pm Tue-Sat; 12.30-3pm, 7-10.30pm, Sun. **Lunch served** 12.30-2.30pm Tue-Sat; 1-3pm Sun. **Dinner served** 7-10pm daily. **Main courses** £8.50-£14. **Credit** MC, V.
The thing about Primrose Hill is that not only does everyone around you look famous, but some of them actually are. But there's no rubbernecking, because *everyone's* famous. Except you. So what about the food? Is the chef famous? He ought to be, for serving the largest roasted plaice we'd ever seen on a dinner plate, complete with bulging egg-sacs and a huge blob of extremely garlicky aïoli. The fish was expertly cooked but, due to its size, the salad got lost and became soggy. The chips were excellent – thin, crackly little numbers. Courgette, lemon and basil risotto was very good, if a little over-salty and low on basil; the presence of lemon zest was a nice touch and the quantity was just right. Puddings didn't sound too tempting (peach and almond tart, egg custard) but mint ice-cream with chocolate sauce was delicious. There's a relaxed feel to the Lansdowne, along with decent cappuccino (and first-rate lemon tea) and the vague allure of vicarious glamour. Note that there's also another dining room on the first floor.
Bass: Caffreys £2.50; Carling £2.50; Fuller's London Pride £2.20; Staropramen £2.75. *Children admitted. Tables outdoors (6, pavement).* **Map 10.**

Lord Stanley
51 Camden Park Road, NW1 (020 7428 9488). Camden Town tube/Camden Road rail then 29, 253 bus. **Open** 6-11pm Mon; noon-11pm Tue-Sat; noon-10.30pm Sun. **Lunch served** 12.30-3pm Tue-Sun. **Dinner served** 7-10pm daily. **Main courses** £6-£9. **Credit** AmEx, MC, £TC, V.
A friendly and easy-going local, with its mixed clientele matched only by its variety of chairs, the Lord Stanley seems to have decided that the heart

of the operation lies in a small menu well prepared. We're inclined to agree. We tried both starters, pumpkin and gazpacho soups, the former very filling and the gazpacho with a real tang to offset the ice. A vegetarian thali tasted unlike any we'd had at an Indian restaurant: a case of 'inspired by' rather than carbon copy, and mild, but a decent version, all the same. Swordfish steak with vegetables was fresh and easy on the knife, a pleasure to consume. The fact the pub occupies an interstice between neighbourhoods seems not to have affected its popularity at all. Appealingly ramshackle and relaxing all round, it is definitely a place to drop in on if you're passing.
Allied Domecq: Guinness £2.30; Lowenbrau £2.40; Marston's Pedigree £2.20. *Children admitted. Entertainment: pianist 1pm Sun. Tables outdoors (3, pavement; 5, garden).*

The Warrington Hotel.
See page 216.

The Queens
49 Regent's Park Road, NW1 (020 7586 0408). Chalk Farm tube/31, 168 bus. **Open** 11am-11pm Mon-Sat; noon-10.30pm Sun. **Lunch served** noon-2.30pm Mon-Sat; noon-5pm Sun. **Dinner served** 7-10pm Mon-Sat; 6-8pm Sun. **Main courses** £6.95-£10.95. **Credit** MC, V.
The best spot in this lovely location has to be the balcony overlooking, on one side, Primrose Hill itself and, on the other, a house where Friedrich Engels once lived. We can only imagine what Engels would have thought of the concept of the gastropub – the middle classes elbowing the working class out of their own playground – but at least the lunch menu here is relatively unpretentious, if you ignore the starter of sweet carrot and rosemary soup. We thoroughly enjoyed Cumberland sausages and mash with

roast shallots, garlic and red wine jus, and the battered cod with chunky chips. The fish was perfectly cooked, the sausages were sausages and the mash was wonderfully fluffy and buttery. We could have sat inside on the first floor or down in the main bar. Service was helpful and friendly; nothing was too much trouble. You haven't got far to go afterwards if you want to walk off any excess. Cross the road and climb the hill for what is surely the best of all views of London.
Young's: Guinness £2.60; Young's Bitter £2.10; Young's Export £2.50. *Children admitted. Tables outdoors (5, balcony; 4, pavement).*

Islington N1

Centuria
100 St Paul's Road, N1 (020 7704 2345). Highbury & Islington tube/rail/30, 277 bus. **Open** 5-11pm Mon-Fri; 12.30-11pm Sat; noon-10.30pm Sun. **Dinner served** 6-11pm Mon-Fri. **Meals served** 12.30-11pm Sat; 12.30-10.30pm Sun. **Main courses** £9.50-£13. **Credit** MC, £TC, V.
The dining room, which is open evenings-only during the week, is large and beautifully lit. Tables are well-spaced and the kitchen is open for all to see. We shared an insalata tricolore, which was enjoyable if rather small. However, meagreness wasn't a feature of the main courses, which were huge and extremely good. Spinach and ricotta ravioli with leeks, mascarpone and Dolcelatte, from the specials board, was excellent – filling but not too rich. Brochette of grilled tiger prawns with chilli and coriander and egg-fried rice was fresh-tasting and exquisitely presented: a triumph. Over large glasses of deliciously syrupy dessert wine, we realised that for once in a gastropub we hadn't had to shout to make ourselves heard: the absence of piped music (at least on a weekday evening) is a bonus. The only criticism one could make would be that the waitresses, although friendly, were few in number: best not be in a hurry. Note that on Friday and Saturday evenings, the atmosphere becomes much more frenetic.
Allied Domecq: Guinness £2.40; Lowenbrau £2.40; Marston's Pedigree £2.40. *Children admitted. Tables outdoors (9, pavement).*

The Crown ★
116 Cloudesley Road, N1 (020 7837 7107). Angel tube. **Open** noon-11pm Mon-Sat; noon-10.30pm Sun. **Lunch served** noon-3pm Mon-Sat; noon-4pm Sun. **Dinner served** 6-10pm Mon-Sat. **Main courses** £7-£9.75. **Main courses** £7.25-£9. **Credit** AmEx, MC, V.
Even at 1.30pm on a Friday lunchtime we could pick and choose where to sit at The Crown, either in the wooden Victorian bar room, with some fantastically low-slung armchairs, or in the smaller area reserved for diners, which benefits from a skylight. You order from the bar, where you may run a tab (provided you hand over a credit card). The tomato, spring onion and haloumi salad starter was plenty for two and it worked surprisingly well with a pint of draught Hoegaarden (£3.60). Main courses – gnocchi di patate with red pesto and Parmesan; and pan-fried chicken breast stuffed with banana, wrapped in bacon, served with papaya sauce and courgette batons – were remarkably good. Attention was lavished on presentation, and everything was cooked to perfection. A shared lemon tart rounded the meal off nicely. Service was painstaking and friendly, the atmosphere convivial and ultra-relaxed.
Fuller's: London Pride £1.90; Guinness £2.20; Stella Artois £2.30. *Children admitted. No-smoking tables. Tables outdoors (6, patio).*

Duke of Cambridge
30 St Peter's Street, N1 (020 7359 3066). Angel tube. **Open** noon-11pm Tue-Sat; noon-10.30pm Sun. **Lunch served** 12.30-3pm Tue-Sat. **Dinner served** 6.30-10.30pm Mon-Sat; 6.30-10pm Sun. **Main courses** £8-£12. **Credit** MC, TC, V.
This award-winning organic gastroboozer is bound to get even busier, so come early on a weekday lunchtime if you want to appreciate the airiness of the space. In fact there are three spaces – the main bar room, the smaller dining area and a small yard – and you can eat in any of them. Staff are friendly, keen and attentive without being overbearing. Food and drink is, for the most part, organic. The wine list is excellent if you're prepared to pay. We opted for pints of Pitfield Eco Warrior, brewed down the road in Hoxton, and shared an excellent starter of rich, creamy courgette and potato soup. Our only slight niggles came with the main courses. Roast leg of lamb stuffed with apricots, pistachio, sweet potato mash and red wine jus could have had more tender meat, and the sweet potato dominated the other ingredients. As for the

grilled tuna with aubergine, houmous, cucumber and mint yoghurt, the individual elements couldn't be faulted, but there was too much going on. The Duke's stock climbed again with puddings: both tiramisu, and strawberry ice-cream were unbelievably good. Also worth visiting is the new branch in Victoria Park – it has a separate dining room on the first floor and a more spacious drinking area downstairs.
Free House: Freedom Lager £2.80; Pitfield Eco Warrior Bitter £3; Golden Promise £3.35; St Peter's Ale £2.80.
Booking advisable. Children welcome; high chairs; toys. No-smoking tables. Tables outdoors (6, garden; 4, pavement).
For branch (The Crown) see index.

The Hanbury
33 Linton Street, N1 (020 7226 3628). Essex Road rail. **Open** noon-11pm Mon-Sat; noon-10.30pm Sun. **Lunch served** noon-4pm, **dinner served** 6.30-10.30pm daily. **Main courses** £7.25-£13.65. **Set meal** £9.85 two courses, £12.95. **Credit** AmEx, DC, V.
Tucked away in one of London's interstitial locations – neither Hoxton nor Islington, not quite De Beauvoir Town and a good walk from Canonbury – the Hanbury is pleasantly quiet on a week-night. The evening of our last visit there were even armchairs to be had in the bar. We headed for the dining area and it wasn't too long before we were tucking into a couple of sizeable main courses (having bypassed the alluring array of starters only to save room for pudding). Baked duck breast came on a *Close Encounters*-style mountain of spicy sweet potato mash, while lemon sole was accompanied by courgette mousse and boiled potatoes. Both dishes were excellent, once you accept that sole has bones, and duck fat. The meringue in the strawberry pavlova was chewy, but worth the effort. The unfussy decor and informal service work well. Maybe the range of beers could do with being wider. A decent choice, though; certainly worth a visit.
Charles Wells: Bombardier £2.20; Fosters £2.30; Red Stripe £2.50.
Separate room for parties, seats 80. Tables outdoors (3, pavement).

Kentish Town NW5

Bull & Last
168 Highgate Road, NW5 (020 7267 3641). Kentish Town tube/rail. **Open** 11am-11pm Mon-Sat; noon-10.30pm Sun. **Lunch served** noon-3pm Mon-Sat; noon-4pm Sun. **Dinner served** 6.30-10.30pm Mon-Sat; 6-9.30pm Sun. **Main courses** £6.25-£12. **Credit** MC, V.
There's a first-floor dining room, but you may also eat in the large, somewhat clattery bar, which has tables and chairs for the purpose as well as comfy armchairs. The menu is short, but the specials blackboard comes to the rescue: risotto with baby scallops, red mullet and baby spinach was superb, yet so voluminous we couldn't finish it. Macaroni with prosciutto and cheese came from the regular menu and was very good too. We had been brought a basket of bread and a dish of olive oil, for which no charge was made; service was pleasant and unfussy throughout. The only complaint we had of this long-established gastropub – and it's a small, picky one – was that an order for Diet Coke produced a can of Diet Pepsi. Still, the Bloody Mary (always a good test) had real bite. The place was packed with a young, exuberant crowd, but we realised our visit had coincided with the publication of A-level results, so the sight of dozens of 18-year-olds engaging in group hugs isn't what you'd normally expect at the Bull & Last.
Leased from Bass: IPA £2; Stella Artois £2.50.

The Vine
86 Highgate Road, NW5 (020 7209 0038). Tufnell Park tube/Kentish Town tube/rail. **Open** noon-midnight Mon-Sat; noon-11.30pm Sun. **Lunch served** noon-2.30pm Mon-Fri; noon-3.30pm Sat, Sun. **Dinner served** 7-10pm daily. **Main courses** £7.95-£14.50. **Credit** AmEx, MC, £TC, V.
Truly a top-end outfit, the Vine is out in front but not sitting back. It has the space (large, airy halls, front courtyard and back covered garden) needed to amplify the attention to detail that is paid at all stages of dining. A late lunchtime visit found it quiet but pleasant, and immaculate service soon had us settled. There's a clear split between daytime and evening offerings, with lunches on the whole light and yet filling. Haloumi and spinach tart was surprisingly sweet, with a fine, crisp pastry and a palpable immediacy that can't be faked. Tagliatelle in mushroom sauce had a richness and variety in the fungi that lifted the dish way beyond the average pasta. Capping it all with a wedge of chocolate marquise – nouvelle and well done – we were more than replete, and in no mood to hurry off. Don't be put off by the road numbering, it's very confusing on this stretch. Persevere and you shall be rewarded: this is the genuine article.
Bass: Guinness £2.60; Staropramen £3.
Tables outdoors (18, garden; 10, patio).

Tufnell Park NW5

The Dartmouth Arms ★
35 York Rise, NW5 (020 7485 3267). Tufnell Park tube. **Open** 11am-11pm Mon-Fri; 10am-11pm Sat; 10am-10.30pm Sun. **Meals served** 11am-10pm Mon-Fri; 10am-10pm Sat, Sun. **Main courses** £5.95-£8.95. **Credit** MC, V.
A recent addition to the fold in – or just up the road from – Tufnell Park, the Dartmouth Arms revels in its oddness and is all the more likeable for it. There are two menus: a round-the-world all-day brunch menu, including, 'from North London Polytechnic', baked beans and cheese on toast; and the more usual gastro-type list, but with a couple of big differences. For a start, some of the dishes are not ones you come across in other gastrobars: lamb and mint sausages with rosemary gravy, chicken with vermouth tarragon and cream, pork chops with juniper butter. The other major difference is that they all cost around five or six quid. Even the puddings are cheap; a sustaining strawberry sundae was only £2.50, and very good coffee a reasonable £1. There are sofas, newspapers, tables and chairs outside, and an airy back room. There's even a bookshelf full of second-hand books for sale: pay at the bar, read at your leisure.
Leased from Punch Taverns: Adnams Bitter £2; Stella Artois £2.60.
Tables outdoors.

Lord Palmerston
33 Dartmouth Park Hill, NW5 (020 7485 1578). Tufnell Park tube. **Open** noon-11pm Mon-Sat; noon-10.30pm Sun. **Lunch served** 12.30-3pm Mon-Sat; 1-4pm Sun. **Dinner served** 7-10pm Mon-Sat; 7-9pm Sun. **Main courses** £4-£12. **Credit** MC, V.
Thursday lunchtime, Tufnell Park, two grizzled regulars propping up the bar – you wonder if you should rethink your order for fizzy mineral water and grilled sardines with tomato and green salad, but before you can, it's slipped out. No eyebrows are raised, no pint glass smashed against the edge of the bar. You're all right, the Lord Palmerston *is* a gastropub, after all, although it looks a little less like one than many of its brethren. The place has the stripped-down look to the power of ten, but it slowly starts to fill with a nicely democratic mix of different types. The grilled sardines, sadly, were too small to offer much apart from heads, bones and skin, and the salad had already drowned in its too-rich dressing. The blackboard menu offered several gastro staples such as rib-eye steak and chips, grilled liver and bacon with mash and onion jus, and smoked salmon, avocado and rocket salad; prices are pretty standard. Worth investigating in the evening.
Supply Line: Directors £2.20; Marston's Pedigree £2.10.

North West

Queens Park NW6

The Salusbury
50-52 Salusbury Road, NW6 (020 7328 3286). Queens Park tube. **Open** 5-11pm Mon; noon-11pm Tue-Sat; noon-10.30pm Sun. **Lunch served** 12.30-3.30pm Tue-Sun. **Dinner served** 7-10.30pm Mon-Sat; 7-10pm Sun. **Set Sunday lunch** £15 three courses. **Main courses** £9-£12. **Minimum** £10. **Service** 12½% for parties of seven or more. **Credit** MC, V.
Make sure you book a table here because the Salusbury never seems to let up. Tables are of a size that sharing doesn't force you into undesired intimacy. The service, right from the off, is friendly, informal and pretty quick. On our last visit, we tried the starter of pan-fried squid with chilli and rocket. The squid was just right – not too rubbery – and there was so much of it we were glad we'd only ordered one to share. From a marine-flavoured menu we chose taglioline with lobster and tomato and basil, which was superb, and grilled sea bass with samphire, which also came with green beans and sautéed potatoes, but since vegetable activity hadn't been signalled on the menu we also got a side order of mash, which was so good we made room for it, somehow. The promising wine list includes 250ml glasses for £5. The whole place – the drinking side, the eating side and the tables outside – has a lively, noisy, excitable vibe.
Free House: Bass £2.30; Caffreys £2.40; Carling £2.20; Grolsch £2.40; Guinness £2.50; Scrumpy Jack £2.30.
Babies and children admitted (lunch only); high chairs. Tables outdoors (4, pavement).

Drinking Pubs

Central

Clerkenwell & Farringdon EC1

Jerusalem Tavern
55 Britton Street, EC1 (020 7490 4281). Farringdon tube/rail. **Open** 9am-11pm, **lunch served** noon-3pm Mon-Fri. **Credit** MC, V.
The sole London outpost for Suffolk's pioneering St Peter's Brewery – whose beers sit so prettily in green flask-like bottles on the supermarket shelf – the Jerusalem borrows its name from a famous Tavern of the area. Although the building was built 300 years ago, up to recently it was a Turkish coffee house. The exterior isn't the most flamboyant and it's possible to miss the place altogether on a dark, foggy night. But inside, the look is of a small Georgian parlour, with rough bare boards and dark wood settles. There are usually five beers on draught, including Best Bitter and Suffolk Gold, as well as 15 of the dinky green bottles.
St Peter's Brewery: Best £2.20; Fruit Beer £2.25; Wheat Beer £2.25.
Tables outdoors (2, pavement). **Map 15/4O.**

O'Hanlon
8 Tysoe Street, EC1 (020 7837 4112). Angel tube/19, 38, 341 bus. **Open** noon-11pm Mon-Sat; noon-10.30pm Sun. **Lunch served** 12.30-2.30pm Mon-Sat; *Sept-Apr* 1-4pm Sun. **Dinner served** 6-9pm Mon-Thur. **Credit** LV, MC, V.
You'll find the former Three Crowns just up from Mount Pleasant sorting office. Inside is a small square bar with bare floorboards, a cramped servery to the right, opposite some hefty wooden furniture, and an elongated drinking area at the back. O'Hanlon is bigger on atmosphere than on light and can seem quite dark, especially when it's busy – which it often is. Most beers are brewed at John O'Hanlon's brewery, tucked away in a railway arch near the MI5 building. The kegged Dry Stout is to Guinness what home-baked bread is to Mother's Pride, but not as good as the Port Stout, which is creamy and served from a hand-pump. We also relish the malty Blakeley's Best. Food often has a hearty Irish accent.
Free House: Blakeley's Best No.1 £1.90; O'Hanlon's Dry Stout £1.90; O'Hanlon's Red Ale £2.
Separate room for parties, seats 30. Tables outdoors (5, conservatory). **Map 15/3N.**

Holborn WC1

The Lamb
94 Lamb's Conduit Street, WC1 (020 7405 0713). Holborn tube. **Open** 11am-11pm Mon-Sat; noon-4pm, 7-10.30pm Sun. **Lunch served** noon-2.30pm daily. **Dinner served** 6.30-9pm Mon-Fri. **Credit** MC, V.
One of London's more graceful pubs, the Lamb has been done-over more times than a bad boxer, but miraculously retains its etched-glass Victorian snob screens around the bar and is now Grade II listed. The comfortable vintage feel is enhanced by sturdy wooden tables with their own brass balustrades and dark green leather upholstery, all of which suits the customers – typically besuited solicitors and their staff – no end. There's a small no-smoking area and out back is what the landlord calls a 'beer garden', but what we term a 'beer yard'. The beer is Young's and very well kept.
Young's: Bitter £1.94; Guinness £2.37; Stella Artois £2.50.
Tables outdoors (3, patio; 3, pavement).
Map 3/4M.

Princess Louise
208 High Holborn, WC1 (020 7405 8816). Holborn tube. **Open** 11am-11pm Mon-Fri; noon-11pm Sat. **Meals served** noon-9pm Mon-Sat. **Credit** AmEx, DC, MC, V.
Aficionados of Victorian pub interiors are in for a treat at the Princess Louise, a glorious palace of a pub within easy spitting distance of the British Museum. Ranks of original engraved mirrors reach practically to the beautiful red and gold moulded ceiling, with the island bar (a riot of carved dark wood) sitting regally in the centre. This used to be a free house, but now it's Samuel Smith who calls the shots; his cask Old Brewery Bitter is something of a snip.
Samuel Smith: Old Brewery Bitter £1.64.
Map 14/5L.

Seven Stars
53-54 Carey Street, WC2 (020 7242 8521). Chancery Lane tube. **Open/meals served** 11am-11pm Mon-Fri. **Credit** AmEx, DC, MC, V.
This plain-looking boozer behind the Royal Courts of Justice has hardly been tampered with since its conception as the Leg and Seven Stars in 1602. The rough cream plaster, puny dark wood beams and thin creaking red velvet settles that line the walls suggest that the last major refit celebrated the repeal of the corn laws. You enter the bar through a door marked 'general counter', with the 'private counter' entrance leading into a lilliputian room to your right. Beers are good, with up to six real ales – including, when we visited, a near-perfect pint of Charles Wells Bombardier. No TV, no music, no fruit machines and the landlord is liable to close early if it's quiet.
Free House: Charles Wells Bombardier £2.10; Slaters £2.10.
Map 15/6M.

West

Ealing W5

Red Lion
13 St Mary's Road, W5 (020 8567 2541). South Ealing tube/Ealing Broadway tube/rail. **Open** 11am-11pm Mon-Sat; noon-10.30pm Sun. **Lunch served** noon-3pm, **dinner served** 6-9pm daily. **No credit cards.**
Its nickname 'Stage Six' (there were five sound stages at the nearby Ealing Studios) derives from when the likes of Jack Warner, Dennis Price and latterly Little & Large inhabited the Red Lion between takes. It hasn't changed much over the years: a small L-shaped single room arranged around a chunky wooden serving area, polished timber floor, green upholstered banquettes, sand-coloured walls studded with pictures of famous (and forgotten) Ealing protagonists. There are no fruit machines, no canned music, but being a Fuller's pub, there are no complaints about the beer, either. The semi-enclosed garden out back has won awards and is well worth a gander.
Fuller's: Carling £2.10; Chiswick £1.55; ESB £2.70; Heineken £1.90; London Pride £1.95; Stella Artois £2.35; Tennant's Extra £2.25.
Tables outdoors (15, garden; 3, pavement).

Hammersmith W6

Dove
19 Upper Mall, W6 (020 8748 5405). Hammersmith or Ravenscourt Park tube. **Open** 11am-11pm Mon-Sat; noon-10.30pm Sun. **Lunch served** noon-2.30pm Mon-Fri; noon-3pm Sat, Sun. **Dinner served** 6.30-9pm daily. **Credit** AmEx, MC, V.
Think historic riverside pubs with decent beer and Hammersmith's Dove (with its full range of Fuller's ales) will no doubt be high up a pretty short list. It's 300 years old, steeped in local history, and can count the likes of Graham Greene, Charles II and William Morris (who lived across the way) among its regulars. James Thomson wrote the words to *Rule Britannia* in an upstairs room. The Dove is reached via a small alleyway that runs beside Hammersmith Bridge. It contains what the *Guinness Book of Records* has decreed is the smallest bar in the UK, measuring just 3.12 square metres. Apart from that, the Dove is all authentic dark oak and has a rather pleasing veranda shaded by a thriving vine.
Fuller's: ESB £2.20; London Pride £2.15.
Tables outdoors (riverside terrace).

Maida Vale W9

The Warrington Hotel
93 Warrington Crescent, W9 (020 7286 2929). Maida Vale tube. **Open** 11am-11pm Mon-Sat; noon-10.30pm Sun. **Lunch served** noon-2.30pm, **dinner served** 6-10pm daily. **Credit** (restaurant only) MC, V.
Once owned by the Church of England and frequented by Victorian music-hall stars including Marie Lloyd, the Warrington is an imposing pub presiding over a four-road roundabout. A pair of magisterial pillars, wrought-iron lamps and mosaic flooring at the entrance hint at the opulence of the interior. There are three bars here – one huge – with ornate high ceilings, marble pillars, art nouveau glasswork framed in carved mahogany, and a staircase that would give Dame Edna a run for her money, plus a couple of animated friezes. Nowadays it's a haunt of down-at-heel roadies and musicians, as well as a centre of activities for well-heeled twenty- and thirtysomething locals. Beers are plentiful and tasty. Upstairs is the Thai restaurant, **Ben's Thai** *(see p163)*.
Free House: Fuller's London Pride £2.15; Brakspear's Special £2.30.
Tables outdoors (courtyard, pavement).

Pineapple

Notting Hill W8

Windsor Castle
114 Campden Hill Road, W8 (020 7243 9551). High Street Kensington or Notting Hill Gate tube. **Open** noon-11pm Mon-Sat; noon-10.30pm Sun. **Meals served** noon-10.30pm daily. **Credit** AmEx, MC, V.
They say that before the high-rises arrived in west London, it was possible to spy the eponymous royal Berkshire residence from an upstairs window here, hence the name. These days you'll be lucky to catch a glimpse of nearby Portobello Road market. The ivy-covered walled garden is one of the best in London – all flagstones, wooden seats and (at the right time) blooming flowers. The inside isn't too bad either, especially if dark wood panelling, etched glass, settles and bare boards are your thing. The draught beer usually includes draught Bass and Fuller's London Pride, which suits the male end of the largely Sloaney crowd that meets here.
Bass: Fuller's London Pride £2.25; Grolsch £2.70; Guinness £2.80.
No-smoking area (until 3.30pm). Tables outdoors (garden). **Map 11/8A**.

South West

Barnes SW13

Ye White Hart
The Terrace, Riverside, SW13 (020 8876 5177). Barnes Bridge rail/209, N9, R69 bus. **Open** 11am-3pm, 5.30-11pm, Mon-Thur; 11am-11pm Fri, Sat; noon-10.30pm Sun. **Lunch served** 12.15-2pm Mon-Sat; 12.30-2.30pm Sun. **Credit** MC, V.
Back in 1676 it was the plain old King's Arms, but following the occasional makeover and a couple of changes of ownership, this pub was rebuilt in 1899 as a grand Victorian pile under its new name. What was once four bars is now a vast open-plan expanse of sturdy dark wood and painted plaster walls around an imposing central island bar, with a layered terrace offering superb views of the river. The beer is Young's – so no complaints there – and the clientele is about as mixed as Barnes can offer.
Young's: Carling £2.40; Stella Artois £2.60; Young's Bitter £2; Young's Export £2.50; Young's Pilsner £2.25; Young's Special £2.10.
Separate room for parties, seats 80. Tables outdoors (10, patio; 5, riverside terrace).

Parsons Green SW6

White Horse ★
1 Parsons Green, SW6 (020 7736 2115). Parsons Green tube. **Open** 11am-11pm Mon-Fri; 10.30am-11pm Sat; 11am-10.30pm Sun. **Lunch served** noon-3pm Mon-Fri. **Dinner served** 6-10pm Mon-Fri. **Credit** AmEx, DC, JCB, MC, £TC, V.
Beer is the name of the game here, which for a hangout of the younger end of the Chelsea/Fulham upper crust, is unusual. Aside from the regular beer festivals, which see as many as 300 different draught beers offered up, regulars include Harvey's Sussex Bitter, Bass and something from Adnams. Add on 57 types of bottled beers (including a host of Belgian and Trappist specialities), over 100 wines and Carling Black Label for the taste-impaired, and you'll see why this place gets so full. Inside is modern pub retaining traditional features, all very smart. Outside is a huge patio where half of Parsons Green congregates in summer.
Bass: Adnams £2.10; Bass £2.20; Grolsch £2.60; Staropramen £2.65.
Separate rooms for parties, seating 30 and 80. Tables outdoors (40, patio). .

South

Clapham SW4

Bread & Roses
68 Clapham Manor Street, SW4 (020 7498 1779). Clapham North tube. **Open** 11am-11pm Mon-Sat; noon-10.30pm Sun. **Lunch served** noon-3pm Mon-Fri; noon-4pm Sat; 1-4pm Sun. **Dinner served** 7-9.30pm Mon-Fri; 6-9.30pm Sat, Sun. **Credit** MC, V.
The Workers' Beer Company are the people who run bars at music festivals, and Bread & Roses is their first London pub. A song written during a strike by American women garment workers in 1912 provides the name: 'Hearts starve as well as bodies/Give us bread but give us roses'. Expect enough chilled lager and wine to keep the bosses happy, but for the proletariat there's Workers' Ale (brewed by Bristol-based Smiles Brewing Company) and a couple of guest ales – often from Adnams of Suffolk. Beneath the striking minimalist decor (bare floorboards and pastel-coloured walls) there's a traditional pub trying to break out. A conservatory with toys and games, plus regular community-conscious events and weekly African-themed Sunday afternoons make B&R a local legend.
Free House: Adnams Bitter £2.20; Budvar £2.60; Carlsberg £2.25; Guinness £2.40; Workers Ale £2.
Babies and children welcome; play area. Entertainment: musicians, workshops, comedy (phone for details). Separate room for parties, seats 60. Tables outdoors (8, patio).

South East

Borough SE1

Royal Oak ★
44 Tabard Street, SE1 (020 7357 7173). Borough tube. **Open** 11am-11pm Mon-Fri. **Lunch served** noon-2.30pm, **dinner served** 6-9.30pm Mon-Fri. **Credit** MC, V.
The only pub in London that sells the full range of superb beers from Harvey's of Lewes – and it's only sensible to try them all. The trip (from the copper-brown Sussex Mild, through light and smooth Pale, and the rich and hoppy Sussex Best, to the prevailing seasonal brew) is the beer lover's equivalent of a gourmet dinner. The pub has recently been refurbished to Victorian splendour with plenty of well-carved mahogany and sparkling glass throughout the two bars, straddling a large serving area. The clientele is an easy-going mix of CAMRA buffs reaching for nirvana, office workers relaxing after a hard day's usury, and locals.
Harveys of Lewes: Sussex Best Bitter £2.10; Sussex Mild £1.80.
Disabled: toilet. Separate room for parties, seats 20. **Map 8/9P**.

Deptford SE8

Dog & Bell ★
116 Prince Street, SE8 (020 8692 5664). Deptford rail. **Open** noon-11pm Mon-Sat; noon-10.30pm Sun. **Lunch served** noon-2.30pm Mon-Fri. **Dinner served** 6-9pm Mon-Fri. **No credit cards**.
Hidden away in a part of Deptford that would give the Bronx run for its money, this local boozer attracts a wide range of customers, including the odd TV personality, lecturers and students from the nearby Greenwich University, musicians, actors, writers, builders, pensioners and market traders. It's a genuine free house, with Fuller's London Pride and ESB always available, together with a trio of guest beers. The pub is divided into three small rooms, with walls painted a pleasant shade of peach and plenty of rustic wooden furniture. At the back there's a bar billiards table and shove ha'penny board.
Free House: Fuller's ESB £2.20; Fuller's London Pride £1.85.
Tables outdoors (8, garden).

East

Brick Lane E1

Pride of Spitalfields
3 Heneage Street, E1 (020 7247 8933). Aldgate East or Shoreditch tube. **Open** 11am-11pm Mon-Sat; noon-10.30pm Sun. **Lunch served** noon-2.30pm Mon-Fri. **No credit cards**.
A small and genial two-room boozer on the edge of Brick Lane. Arty types from the studios next door rub shoulders with Asian businessmen, medical students, builders and grey-haired pensioners. The beer's good and cheap: Crouch Vale Woodham IPA, Fuller's London Pride, plus a couple of guest ales, all for well under £2. The customary lagers, cider and stout also make an appearance. The Pride of Spitalfields' decor is typically East End pub: plenty of red velvet, dark wood tables and stools, a carpet that's suitably psychedelic, and any wall or ceiling space that's not covered with old photographs of Victorian enterprise is painted in a coquettish tint of nicotine-cream.
Free House: Crouch Vale Woodham IPA £1.65; ESB £1.85; London Pride £1.75.
Tables outdoors (2, pavement). **Map 4/5S**.

Shoreditch N1

Wenlock Arms ★
26 Wenlock Road, N1 (020 7608 3406). Old Street tube/rail. **Open** noon-11pm Mon-Sat; noon-10.30pm Sun. **No credit cards**.
Just a short stroll from City Road, the Wenlock is to pubs what the Taj Mahal is to mausoleums, only with less marble. The array of hand-pumps is impressive; there's always a mild available (we enjoyed a sweet and nutty pint of Greene King for £1.60), as well as a cask cider, an impressive selection of ever-changing real ales and a clutch of Belgian beers. The bar is horseshoe-shaped, the decor traditional going-on scruffy, with semi-partitioned seating areas around the walls and a smattering of stools hogging the bar.
Free House: Carlsberg £2; Guinness £2.20.
Entertainment: jazz musicians 9pm Fri, Sat; jazz pianist 2.30pm Sun. **Map 4/3P**.

Wapping E1

Prospect of Whitby
57 Wapping Wall, E1 (020 7481 1095). Wapping tube. **Open** 11.30am-3pm, 5.30-11pm Mon-Fri; 11.30am-11pm Sat; noon-10.30pm Sun. **Lunch served** noon-2.30pm Mon-Sat; noon-3pm Sun. **Dinner served** 6-9pm daily. **Credit** AmEx, DC, MC, V.
The Prospect of Whitby was built in 1520 and remodelled in 1777 – what was the Devil's Tavern has been a feature of Wapping life since Henry VIII was a prince. Judge Jeffreys used to pop in for a quickie before sentencing and Charles Dickens, Dr Johnson and Samuel Pepys have all blotted their copybooks here. Inside, little has changed over the years: the pewter-topped counter rests on wooden casks and the stone-flagged floors, low ceilings, giant timbers and pebbled windows hark back to a time before tourists crammed the settle seats and prices hit the authentically plastered ceiling. Beers usually include Courage Directors and Young's Special.
Scottish & Newcastle: Courage Directors £2.29; Old Speckled Hen £2.50.
Babies and children admitted (separate area). No-smoking area. Tables outdoors (riverside terrace).

North

Camden NW1

Spread Eagle
141 Albert Street, NW1 (020 7267 1410). Camden Town tube/Camden Road rail. **Open** 11am-11pmMon-Sat; noon-10.30pm Sun. **Meals served** noon-7.30pm Mon-Sat; noon-5pm Sun. **Credit** MC, V.
Camden's most cosmopolitan pub has a clientele that mixes besuited estate agents with scantily-clad representatives of the indie music scene (who monopolise the outside bench tables). If the Spread Eagle (a Roman sign signifying nobility) looks like several houses knocked into one, that's because it is. The core of the boozer was built in 1858 when Albert Street was Gloucester Street and Parkway was Park Street. The Parkway entrance arrived in 1963. The decor gives a nod to the pub's Victorian roots, with cream-painted walls, wood panelling, framed prints, and picture windows that look out on to a Camden that's gentrified but trying desperately to appear street-wise.
Young's: Bitter £1.99; Special £2.16.
Tables outdoors (pavement).

Kentish Town NW5

Pineapple
51 Leverton Street, NW5 (020 7485 6422). Kentish Town tube/rail. **Open** 12.30-11pm Mon-Fri; noon-11pm Sat; noon-10.30pm Sun. **No credit cards**.
A friendly, locals' local featuring a dark wood Edwardian-style serving area, with drinking areas wrapped around it in an elongated horseshoe shape. Dark red velvet is a theme, with opulent curtains framing the windows (there are even curtains for the toilet windows) and thickly piled banquettes lining the walls. The wallpaper is vintage Laura Ashley dotted with various qualities of original art, plus roaring fires and vases of lavish fresh flowers. The beer includes Brakspear's Special and a particularly toothsome drop of Marston's Pedigree at £2.10. The customer base of the Pineapple is wide: a mixture of TV actors and personalities (TV architect Maxwell Hutchinson used to play piano here), postmen, musicians, designers and stained-glass engineers.
Free House: Boddingtons £2.10; Brakspear Bitter £2.10; Marston's Pedigree £2.10.
Tables outdoors.

North West

Hampstead NW3

Flask
14 Flask Walk, NW3 (020 7435 4580). Hampstead tube. **Open** 11am-11pm Mon-Sat; noon-10.30pm Sun. **Lunch served** noon-3pm Mon-Fri; noon-4pm Sat, Sun. **Dinner served** 6-9pm Tue-Sat. **Credit** MC, V.
Not to be confused with a similarly named boozer across the Heath, this high-ceilinged Young's pub is a prime haunt for Hampstead's arty crowd. It is one of the few boozers in London to retain a public bar. If you can nudge aside the Oscar-winning actors and Booker-nominated authors who tend to congregate here, there are games of darts and cribbage to be played. Between the Public and the Saloon is a noteworthy Victorian screen and, at the rear, a separate restaurant and a conservatory where occasional 'events' take place. The pub is named after a container for local spring water.
Young's: Bitter £1.95; AAA £2.08.
Babies and children admitted (conservatory). Tables outdoors (pavement, terrace).
Map 9.

Wine Bars

Somewhat eclipsed in recent years by the rise of cocktail bars and polenta pubs, the wine bar has shown new signs of life of late. Specialisation is in the air, with recent openings including **Osteria d'Isola**, (which boasts an exclusively Italian wine list) and **Cellar Gascon** (exclusively French), while **Shiraz** majors in… shiraz.

Central

Bloomsbury WC1

Truckles of Pied Bull Yard

off Bury Place, WC1 (020 7404 5338).
Holborn or Tottenham Court Road tube. **Open** 11.30am-10pm Mon-Fri; 11.30am-3.30pm Sat. **Main courses** £3.50-£11.95. **House wine** £10.95 bottle, £2.75 glass. **Credit** AmEx, DC, JCB, MC, £TC, V.
Despite the name and setting – a cloistered yard – this place is not remotely olde worlde. If there was ever any sawdust on the floor it has been swept away, and there isn't a serving wench in sight. Part of the Davy's wine bar chain, Truckles has scrubbed up nicely to become a bright, uncluttered, very yellow venue with a compact wine list and a tempting range of posh rolls and salads. The wine list is bijou, comprising mainly a selection of Davy's own labels, such as Davy's Chilean chardonnay (£3.60 a glass) and Davy's Australian shiraz/cabernet sauvignon (£3.75). Regionally, it's very well balanced and most wines are available by the glass. Truckles has the obligatory open-view kitchen, but the construction of salads and rolls is hardly high drama. However, a glass of blackcurranty Davy's claret (£4.95) did its supple, brambly best to wash down a smoked ham, sun-blush tomato and Parmesan roll. The basement restaurant is a more traditional affair with a few more clarets offered, but essentially the wine list is the same as upstairs. There's also Bishop's Finger Kentish ale for the bearded and chunky jumpered (£3.35 a bottle).
Babies and children admitted. Book lunch. No-smoking tables. Separate room for parties, seats 100. Tables outdoors (50, courtyard). **Map 3/5L.**
For branches of Davy's see index.

City E1, EC2, EC4

City Limits

16-18 Brushfield Street, E1 (020 7377 9877).
Liverpool Street tube/rail.
Wine bar **Open** 11.30am-3pm, 5-11pm Mon-Fri. **Main courses** £3.50-£6.95 . **House wine** £10.50 bottle, £2.60 glass.
Restaurant **Lunch served** 11.30am-3pm, **dinner served** 5.30-9.30pm Mon-Fri. **Main courses** £10.95-£18.95. **Service** 12½%.
House wine £11.50 bottle, £2.75 glass.
Both **Credit** AmEx, DC, MC, £TC, V.
Previously a banana wholesaler's within spitting distance of Old Spitalfields market, City Limits is one of the very few City wine bars that is still independently owned – in this case, by ex-shipbroker and oenophile extraordinaire, David Hughes. Despite its belle epoque windows emblazoned with the Perrier-Jouët logo, the small wooden bar and raised perching-stools give the impression of a pub selling wine (which is no bad thing). The food is solid, satisfying and unashamedly old school. Here, avocados still come with the prawns inside. Own-made chilli with sour cream, Cheddar and bread costs £5.50, while hot roast beef in a baguette will set you back a fiver. For further options there's an informal downstairs bistro. The wine list is large and lovingly assembled, with a slight leaning towards the French and more than its fair share of cult bottles. Celebrity listings include New Zealand's Cloudy Bay sauvignon blanc 1999 (£26.95), the super-Tuscan Tignanello 1996 from Marchesi Antinori (£48.50), and the legendary Lebanese Chateau Musar 1994 from Gaston Hochar (£20.95). Six daily specials (three red and three white) are served by the glass.
Babies and children admitted. Booking advisable (restaurant). Tables outdoors (8, pavement). **Map 4/5R.**

La Grande Marque

47 Ludgate Hill, EC4 (020 7329 6709). St Paul's tube/Blackfriars tube/rail. **Open** 11.30am-9.30pm, **lunch served** 11.30am-2.30pm Mon-Fri. **Main courses** £4-£6.50. **House wine** £11.95 bottle, £2.50 glass. **Credit** AmEx, DC, JCB, MC, £TC, V.
Grande marque is an obsolete French term for any of the major champagne brands, but can also be applied to anything a bit upmarket. La Grande Marque wine bar in the old City Bank building lives up to its name with a swanky banky posture and some excellent wines. Large gold Ferrero Rocher-style letters above the marble bar inform imbibers that the bottles are selected by Lay & Wheeler, a highly respected wine merchant. The resulting wine list is extremely broad ranging and well chosen, with fine wines conveniently segregated from the rest. White burgundy Mâcon-Villages Blanc 1997 (£16.95), for example, is not allowed to sit next to its well-heeled sibling, the Meursault les Tillets 1997 (£37), both from the esteemed Olivier Leflaive. We sipped on a light, crisp, gooseberry-scented Pouilly-Fumé (£4 a glass) and eyed the superb champagne selection, which ranged from Lay & Wheeler Extra Quality Brut (£30.50 a bottle) all the way up to Louis Roederer Cristal 1993 (£117). Food revolves around posh sandwiches such as Thai-style tuna or crab and lemon mayonnaise.
Map 3/6O.
For branch see index.

The Pavilion

Finsbury Circus Gardens, EC2 (020 7628 8224). Liverpool Street or Moorgate tube/rail.
Wine bar **Open** 11.30am-10pm Mon-Fri. **Main courses** £6.
Restaurant **Lunch served** noon-2.30pm Mon-Fri. **Main courses** £6.95-£12.50.
Both **House wine** £12.50 bottle, £3.25 glass. **Credit** AmEx, DC, MC, V.
In the middle of a summer's afternoon, when the Pavilion is not exactly bustling, drinking here is rather like sitting in a giant rabbit hutch, watching strange white figures padding silently across unfeasibly bouncy lawns. Don't blame the wine for this surreal experience; the wine bar doubles as the clubhouse for the City of London Bowling Club and you're witnessing its members in action. At such times of day, this music-free zone offers unexpected tranquillity in the heart of the City. Turn up at office chucking-out time, on the other hand, and the place is smoky and cosy. We sampled the house white, Crystal Brook colombard/chardonnay 1999 from the Beresford Estate in South Australia (£12.50) – a greenish-tinged Granny Smith in a glass that was as refreshing as a cold shower after a frenetic game of bowls. The wine list has been cunningly divided into bite-size pieces, each dutifully representing a region or country, with a small selection in each. Wines by the glass are plentiful, and there's a good choice of champagnes, with Taittinger (£35) also available by the half-bottle and the glass. Food includes club sandwiches (try the Hurst Farm rare roast beef, spinach and horseradish at £5.75) or a plate of Neal's Yard incomparable English and Irish farmhouse cheeses.
Book lunch (restaurant). **Map 4/5Q.**

El Vino

47 Fleet Street, EC4 (020 7353 6786/www.elvino.co.uk). Chancery Lane or Temple tube/City Thameslink rail.
Wine bar **Open** 11am-8.30pm Mon-Wed; 11am-9pm Thur, Fri.
Restaurant **Lunch served** noon-3pm Mon-Fri. **Main courses** £8.45-£12.95. **Service** 12½%.
Both **House wine** £10.95 bottle, £2.80 glass. **Credit** AmEx, MC, V.
El Vino provides incontrovertible evidence (as its largely legal clientele would say) of how a mere wine bar can become 'an establishment'. Regimented stacks of wine racks line the walls and there's a small partitioned dining area towards the back of the premises, with leather upholstered seating and a fireplace. Here you can see portly pinstriped men in their natural environment, leaning against a wooden bar actually smoking real pipes – quite remarkable, in a Dickensian kind of way. As a practising wine merchant El Vino has a vast and impressive wine list that really goes to town on the claret section. We tried the ripe Chateau de Terrefort-Quancard 1995 (£14.80), leaving the limited stocks of Chateau Latour 1985 (£151) to the hard working legal profession. Food, as you might expect, is mainly traditional English with some excellent fish thrown in for good measure. Try pigeon

Shiraz

supreme over wild rice with vermouth and white grape sauce, or steak and kidney pie made from prime Aberdeen Angus. Small carafes of water are provided on each table for diluting El Vino's very own Connoisseur's Blend 12-year-old Scotch whisky (£3 a double). Upman and Partagas Havana cigars can be bought at the bar.
Booking advisable. Dress: smart. **Map 3/6N.**
For branches see index.

Clerkenwell & Farringdon EC1

Bleeding Heart ★

Bleeding Heart Yard, off Greville Street, EC1 (020 7242 8238). Chancery Lane tube/ Farringdon tube/rail.
Bar **Open** noon-11pm Mon-Fri. **Main courses** £6.95-£10.95. **House red** £10.50 bottle, £2.50 glass. **House white** £10.75 bottle, £2.75 glass.
Bistro **Lunch served** noon-3pm, **dinner served** 6-10.30pm Mon-Fri. **Main courses** £7.50-£11.50. **Wine** from £15.95 bottle.
Restaurant **Lunch served** noon-2.30pm, **dinner served** 6-10.30pm Mon-Fri. **Main courses** £11.50-£15.95. **Wine** from £15.95 bottle.
All **Service** 12½% for parties of six or more. **Credit** AmEx, DC, JCB, MC, £TC, V.
If you don't get lost searching for the Bleeding Heart Bistro (it's bleeding hard to find), you can easily get lost in its enormous wine list. With more pages than most bars have wines, it could be quite intimidating for anyone who is not a complete wine anorak. This friendly, cluttered bistro is a Bordeaux-spotter's paradise with the selection lovingly dissected into the individual sub-appellations (Médoc, St-Estéphe, Pauillac, St-Julian, and so on). The Rhône, Burgundy and Champagne regions are also well covered. Of the New World producers, New Zealand features most prominently; the wine buyer admits that he has fallen in love with the place following four visits there. Pride of place, however, has to go to the magnum of Chateau Calon-Segur from 1945, the vintage of the century (a snip at £995). The menu is far, far shorter than the wine list and includes such hearty delights as duck and apricot terrine with a sweet mustard dressing; and sautéed lamb's sweetbreads, kidneys and black pudding in a brioche crust – for real animal lovers. The superb selection of cask-strength and malt whisky, cognac, Armagnac, calvados and specialist eaux de vie is not to be sniffed at, or rather they should be… sniffed at, that is.
Babies and children admitted. Booking essential (restaurant). Separate rooms for parties, seating 44, 50 and 120. No pipes (bistro). Tables outdoors (15, terrace).
Map 3/5N.

Cellar Gascon ★

59 West Smithfield, EC1 (020 7253 5853). St Paul's tube/Barbican or Farringdon tube/rail.
Open noon-midnight Mon-Sat. **Tapas** £2-£12. **House wine** £10.50 bottle, £2.70 glass. **Credit** MC, V.
Next door to the Priory Church of St Bartholomew the Great (London's oldest church, built in 1123) and facing Smithfield meat market, Cellar Gascon fits in well with this part of London, with its surprising juxtaposition of old and new. The décor is lilac and the overall design is modern, but there are battered old rugby balls set among the gleaming wine racks, and the bar stools are upholstered in leather. The all-male, all-French staff, with their cropped hair and black uniforms, contribute to the atmosphere by being as pleasant as pie to the customers while barking terse orders at each other. The wine list is entirely French and leans heavily towards feral, farmyardy wines from the far-flung corners of the south-west, with evocative names like Irouléguy, Cahors and Jurançon; many are available by the glass. The macho food features boudin noir, farmhouse ham from Béarn and lashings of foie gras. We nibbled charcuterie to a funky soundtrack, drinking gutsy Domaine Berthoumieu 1996 from Madiran at £4 a glass. There's a great range of Armagnac, cognac and calvados, and a good choice of Havana cigars to savour, too. For **Club Gascon**, *see p59* **French.**
Map 15/5O.

Covent Garden WC2

Shiraz

12 Saint Martin's Lane, WC2 (020 7379 7811). Leicester Square tube. **Open** 11am-11pm Mon-Fri; 5-11pm Sat. **Main courses** £9.50-£14. **Set meals** £15 two courses; £17.50 three courses. **House wine** £14 bottle, £3.50 glass. **Service** 12½%. **Credit** AmEx, DC, MC, V.
It's hard to believe that the contemporary Shiraz, with its clean lines and restful blues and lilacs, is owned by the same proprietor (Don Hewitson) as the cluttered 1970s-style Cork & Bottle (see p219). Maybe they are the yin and yang of wine bar philosophy. The wine list at Shiraz lingers on the shiraz/syrah grape variety, with 11 examples from the New World, six from the Rhône and two 'Rhône Ranger' classic blends. If the feral delights of shiraz are not for you, look elsewhere on the list, which is as varied as that of the Cork & Bottle, though it has been condensed into a more manageable size. In addition to sampling the wine, people seem to come to Shiraz to talk, while mellow jazz tinkles away quietly in the background. The bar area leads through to the dining section at the back, where choices include seared kangaroo loin with rocket and smoked paprika potatoes; and pan-fried tuna with lemongrass and coconut risotto. Bar snacks might be Caesar salad with chorizo sausages and Parmesan wafers, or Thai beef salad with wasabi dressing.
Babies and children admitted. No-smoking tables. **Map 14/7L.**

Fitzrovia W1

Jamies

74 Charlotte Street, W1 (020 7636 7556/www.jamiesbars.co.uk). Goodge Street tube. **Open** 11am-11pm, **lunch served** noon-2.45pm Mon-Fri. **Main courses** £8.95-£12.95. **Service** 12½%. **House wine** £12.50 bottle, £3.25 glass. **Credit** AmEx, DC, MC, £TC, V.
With its long, curved wooden bar and bold blocks of sunshine-yellow, reds and purples on the walls, Jamies feels like a laidback gastropub that just happens to major in wines. On our visit many punters were drinking bottled beer, and beach football was being shown on a real telly. Despite Jamies ostensibly relaxed approach to the occasionally fraught subject of wine, the list reveals, on closer inspection, the involvement of a true wine nerd. Doffing its cap to the major wine-producing countries of the world, it offers a small but perfectly formed selection of three or four wines from each. There's a good choice of champagne, with Taittinger non-vintage and Brut Prestige rosé both served by the glass (£7 and £8.40). Someone has even unearthed a soft, peachy wine from just north of Naples made from the unheard-of falanghina grape variety grown on 'non-grafted phylloxera-free vines'. More information than you needed? It's exclusive to Jamies. The unpretentious menu includes a meze selection featuring houmous, olives, feta, stuffed vine leaves and pitta bread; there's also an oriental plate for two laden with chicken satay, spring rolls, wun tuns, sesame prawn toast, samosas and prawn crackers. The friendly staff, who frequently came to our table unbidden, get Brownie points for attentiveness.
Booking advisable. Dress: smart casual. Separate rooms for parties, both seating 55. Tables outdoors (5, patio). **Map 2/5J.**
For branches see index.

Leicester Square WC2

Cork & Bottle ★

44-46 Cranbourn Street, WC2 (020 7734 7807/www.donhewitsonlondonwinebars.com). Leicester Square tube. **Open** 11am-midnight Mon-Sat; noon-10.30pm Sun. **Meals served** noon-11.30pm Mon-Sat; noon-10pm Sun. **Main courses** £3.95-£11.95. **House wine** £10.95 bottle, £3 glass. **Credit** AmEx, DC, JCB, MC, £TC, V.
The years drop away as you descend each step of the spiral staircase until you reach the bottom and find yourself in a wine bar straight out of the 1970s. The Cork & Bottle is a subterranean time-capsule with acres of densely scripted blackboards, old wine adverts and mirrors covering every inch of wall space. Couples sit in alcoves listening to Edith Piaf and Ella Fitzgerald. Bottles of vinaigrette (made in-house) are placed on each table to dress the plats du jour. Opened by Don Hewitson back in 1972, this is the original wine bar blueprint from that cheesiest of decades. It remains a great place to enjoy wine. The enormous, idiosyncratic wine list fizzes with Don's enthusiasm and sparkles with his knowledge. There's a great choice of champagne escalating from Don Hewitson's very own Premier Cru (£25) to the dizzying heights of Vintage Krug 1988 (£150). It's obvious that affordability is high on the list of priorities, though. For a self-styled simple bistro the food is surprisingly adventurous, featuring broad bean and lemongrass vichyssoise, and tartare de loup (chopped sea bass with tartare sauce and parsley wrapped in smoked salmon). Hewitson also owns the **Hanover Square Wine Bar & Grill** and **Shiraz** (for both, *see p219*).
Babies and children admitted. **Map 14/7K.**

Corney & Barrow ★

116 St Martin's Lane, WC2 (020 7655 9800). Leicester Square tube/Charing Cross tube/rail.
Bar **Open** noon-midnight Mon-Wed; noon-2am Thur-Sat. **Main courses** £4.75-£7.95.
Brasserie **Lunch served** noon-3pm, **dinner served** 5-11pm, Mon-Sat. **Main courses** £8.95-£16.95. **Set meals** (noon-3pm, 5.30-7pm) £10.95 two courses, £12.95 three courses.
Both **House wine** £10.95 bottle, £2.80 glass. **Credit** AmEx, DC, JCB, MC, £TC, V.
Think of Corney & Barrow's first West End wine bar as a very stylish sandwich. The upstairs restaurant and basement champagne bar act as the bread, and the ground-floor wine bar is the tempting filling. In an impossibly prime location, C&B does extremely well from the pre- and post-theatre crowd. The staff are as friendly as they are knowledgeable, and 38 wines are available by the glass. The excellent wine list, despite featuring some very posh labels, is presented under grape variety headings, so that even a lager drinker can order a Chablis Domaine Servin 1997 (£19.95) and confidently expect a chardonnay. Not content to major in champagne – the house champagne is the lemony, aromatic Delamotte at £5.60 for a large glass – C&B also offers a great selection of champagne cocktails (all £6.29). If that's not enough, how about a glass of flavoured champagne (£5.95) with perhaps a hint of Pisang Ambon (green banana) or Goldschlager (cinnamon)? Wine bar fare includes haddock and chips with tartare sauce, and ciabatta with grilled vegetables and goat's cheese. Cuban cigars complete the glitzy picture.
Babies and children welcome (brasserie); high chairs. **Map 14/7L.**

Knightsbridge SW3

Le Metro

28 Basil Street, SW3 (020 7591 1213). Knightsbridge tube. **Open** 7.30am-10.30pm Mon-Sat; 8.30-10.30am Sun. **Breakfast served** 7.30-10.30am Mon-Sat; 8.30-10.30am Sun. **Meals served** noon-10.30pm Mon-Sat. **Main courses** £8.50-£10.50. **Service** 10%. **House wine** £10.95 bottle, £2.85 glass. **Credit** AmEx, DC, MC, £TC, V.
Le Metro, which is in fact the basement bar of L'Hotel just behind Harrods, should win an award for its clever use of limited underground space. It's a chic place that was chilling to the trancey beats of Morcheeba when we called in for an afternoon sharpener. Settling back in the grey banquette seating we sipped a suitably chilled, gooseberry-infused Trinity Hills sauvignon blanc 1999 from Hawkes Bay, New Zealand (£15.80), admired the bucket of pink fuchsias on top of the bar, and hoped the staff were smirking with us not at us. The mainly French wine list is of a manageable size, with a page for whites and a page for reds. The good news is that virtually all wines are served by the glass. Pudding wines include the legendary Museum Show Reserve Rutherglen Muscat from Yalumba in Victoria, Australia – pure indulgence at £6.25 a glass. The food is sensible European, meaning it's well-made but doesn't suffer from too much imagination. You could start with chilled gazpacho or baked goat's cheese salad, followed by fillet of lemon sole with capers and beurre noisette, or merguez sausage with tabouleh.
Babies and children admitted. Book dinner.
Map 12/9F.

Osteria d'Isola

145 Knightsbridge, SW1 (020 7838 1044/1099). Knightsbridge tube. **Meals served** noon-10.30pm Mon-Sat; noon-9.30pm Sun. **Bar snacks** £10 eight antipasti. **Service** 12½%. **House wine** £13.50 bottle, £4.50 glass. **Credit** AmEx, DC, MC, V.
If you like posing amid chrome and leather and enjoy Italian wines, you'll just love Osteria d'Isola, the ever-so-slightly more relaxed basement area of Oliver Peyton's award-winning Isola restaurant (*see p103* **Italian**). However, we've had some reports of appalling service here, so watch out for the coolly indifferent staff. Osteria d'Isola sells only Italian wines, with the merciful exception of Taittinger Brut non-vintage champagne (£7.50 a glass). We counted 64 wines available by the glass (excluding sparklers), and because they looked so damned expensive we got our calculator out and did a few sums. We concluded that although you can have a glass of Vigna Palazzi Falerio dei Colli Ascolani 1998 for £4.50 (the cheapest), the average price per glass at this place is a whopping £9.79. If you're undecided how to part with your hard-earned cash, try one of the taster options, such as 'Native Italian Varieties' (£13.50) or 'Super-Tuscans' (£34.20), comprising five (7.5cl) shots. There's also a great, typically Peyton range of cocktails. Top marks for value and taste, however, go to the eight dishes of antipasti for £10 available from noon until 7pm Monday to Saturday. The delicious selection includes prosciutto di Parma, bruschetta with pickled artichokes, and crostini with salt cod and ink-braised baby squid.
Babies and children welcome; high chairs. Booking essential. Disabled: toilet. Dress: smart casual. **Map 6/9F.**

Mayfair W1

Hanover Square Wine Bar & Grill

25 Hanover Square, W1 (020 7408 0935/www.donhewitsonlondonwinebars.com). Leicester Square tube. **Meals served** 11am-11pm Mon-Fri. **Main courses** £8.95-£14.95. **Set meal** (8-11pm) £20 three courses incl. wine. **House wine** £10.95 bottle, £3 glass. **Credit** AmEx, DC, MC, V.
This large basement bar is owned by Don Hewitson, the same affable Kiwi behind Leicester Square's legendary **Cork & Bottle** (*see p219*) and **Shiraz** wine bar in Covent Garden (*see above*). The wine list is the same as the Cork & Bottle's, which considering the quality and range on offer, is hardly cause for disappointment. Not surprisingly, Don gives New Zealand wines equal billing with those from Australia rather than treating them as the poor, possibly in-bred, relations. This makes for a great Kiwi collection including the gooseberry-tastic Cloudy Bay sauvignon blanc 1999 (only £21.50) and the creamy, bubbly Pelorus Vintage 1995 (£26.50). Like the Cork & Bottle, Hanover Square has an unreconstructed 1970s feel, which is alarming considering it only opened in 1993. It attracts loads of office workers, who are drawn like moths towards the tinkly jazz and candlelight. Don's latest ruse is his Grape Dinners menu where for only £20 a head you can have a three-course dinner with unlimited wine (yes, unlimited wine) after 8pm. The deal is limited to one white, one red and one rosé wine from southern France: Les Pierres Blanches chardonnay 1998; Abbay Saint Hilaire rouge 1998; and Domaine de Jarras rosé Gris de Gris. Crazy guy, crazy deal.
Babies and children admitted (lunch). Booking advisable. Dress: smart casual. **Map 2/6H.**

Soho W1

Shampers

4 Kingly Street, W1 (020 7439 9910). Oxford Circus or Piccadilly Circus tube. **Open** 11am-11pm Mon-Sat. **Main courses** £6.50-£12. **Service** 10% for parties of six or more. **House wine** £10.75 bottle, £2.95 glass. **Credit** AmEx, DC, JCB, MC, £TC, V.
Relaxed, cosy and slightly cluttered, with acres of blackboards and wine racks, Shampers is an unreconstructed 1980s wine bar that attracts a loyal following (a considerable achievement in the West End). Save for the vintage, its house wines – the light, unoaked Cune dry white Rioja 1999 (£10.75) and the juicy Ochoa Tempranillo garnacha 1999 from Navarra (£10.75) – haven't changed since 1991, but the large wine list is excellently selected with ample choice by the glass. The extensive French section covers just about every base – it's refreshing to see more space devoted to Burgundy (reasonably priced) than Bordeaux – and the Spanish wine choice is particularly well developed. A glass of vaguely salty, tangy Manzanilla La Gitana sherry makes the perfect aperitif at £7.75 for a half-bottle or £2.75 by the glass. The list even has a few German wines such as the off-dry, beautifully honeyed Graacher Himmelreich riesling kabinett 1997 from Dr Loosen in the Mosel (£16.75). Shampers has a classic bistro menu, but seems particularly good at fish; we were tempted by grilled fresh sardines, char-grilled dark tuna steak with lentils and green vegetables, and half a dozen Rossmore oysters.
Babies and children welcome (restaurant). Booking advisable. Separate room for parties, seats 50. **Map 13/6J.**

Strand WC2

Gordon's

47 Villiers Street, WC2 (020 7930 1408). Embankment tube/Charing Cross tube/rail.
Open 11am-11pm, **meals served** noon-9pm Mon-Sat. **Main courses** £6. **House wine** £9.25 bottle, £2.70 glass. **Credit** MC, £TC, V.
If El Vino (*see above*) on Fleet Street is an establishment, then Gordon's is an institution. Forget the tourist trap in Tooley Street, this is the real London dungeon, and the only wine bar out of all those we visited that had real dust on the bottles. Allegedly, wine has been sold on this site since 1364, so it seems appropriate that Gordon's has a selection of sherries, ports and Madeiras that it serves straight from the barrel in schooners or beakers. The manageable wine list dips in and out of most wine-producing countries and offers

Painting the town Rhône.

The night is young, and you're out to enjoy yourself. This is not a moment for doing things by halves. And you don't have to, because you'll find Côtes du Rhône wines in all the best and brightest bars and restaurants. Generous, fruity, great tasting wines from the warmest valley in France, Côtes du Rhône offers tremendous choice and dependable quality. Enjoy!

CÔTES DU
RHÔNE

Think red.
Think Côtes du Rhône.

good value for money with many bottles selling for around £12. Ten reds, ten whites and one sparkler are available by the glass. The food includes simple cold platters like rare roast beef salad or poached salmon salad, and a fantastically maintained cheeseboard. Gordon's Gothic surroundings are presided over by manageress Bernadette Giacomazzo, who is seldom without a fag. The bar gets packed in the evenings, but once the crowds have gone home you wouldn't want to spend the night here alone. *Bookings not accepted. Tables outdoors (10, terrace).* **Map 14/7L.**

Victoria SW1

Tiles

36 Buckingham Palace Road, SW1 (020 7834 7761). **lunch served** noon-2.30pm, **dinner served** 6-10pm Mon-Fri. **Main courses** £4.95-£11.95. **Service** 12½%. **House wine** £9.95 bottle, £2.50 glass. **Credit** AmEx, MC, £TC, V.

Tiles is small, informal, unpretentious and a little shabby round the edges. On weekday lunchtimes it's buzzing with activity, acting as a staff canteen for the people lucky enough to be working nearby. Fewer folk come back in the evenings, making for a more leisurely atmosphere. The place is run by friendly, welcoming staff who take their extensive wine list very seriously, endeavouring to find a suitable alternative if a particular vintage or producer is unavailable. We counted 16 wines by the glass, including two champagnes. The balance dips in favour of French wines here, but filed away under 'Bits and Bobs' we found the elusive and delicious English sparkling wine Nyetimber 1993 (£23.95). We also discovered fine examples of Argentina's two must-have grape varieties in the light, fresh and aromatic Medrano torrontes 1999 and the plummy, spicy Medrano malbec 1999 (both £13.95). A good place to come for a light lunch of own-made leek tart, or perhaps moules marinière with French bread and butter. Puddings on the blackboard include chocolate fudge cake, banoffi pie and black cherry cheesecake (all £3.50). *Booking advisable. Separate rooms for parties, seating 20 and 60. Tables outdoors (4, pavement).* **Map 6/10H.**

Waterloo SE1

The Archduke

Concert Hall Approach, SE1 (020 7928 9370) Waterloo tube/rail. **Meals served** 8.30am-11pm Mon-Fri; 11am-11pm Sun. **Main courses** £3.50-£8.50. **House wine** £10.25 bottle, £2.60 glass. **Credit** AmEx, DC, MC, V.

Such has been the regeneration of the South Bank that the Victorian railway arches housing this wine bar have become a mega-prime site, while the Archduke itself has become a popular fuelling point for tourists flooding towards the new attractions. Its 'new look' conservatory with terracotta floor-tiles, wooden venetian blinds, rattan chairs, potted palms, fig trees and hanging ferns, is a lovely place to sit and listen to the trains clunking overhead. The thoughtful yet manageable wine list features five wines available by the half-bottle, including the excellent Le Brun de Neuville Brut non-vintage champagne (£13). Most geographical bases are covered and all the table wines cost less than £20. The Archduke specialises in affordable pre- and post-theatre eating and drinking, offering two-course dinners for £10.95 in its upstairs restaurant. The bar's founder, the late Liz Philip MBE, also launched the Save Our Sausage campaign, so handmade sausages with red onion relish and mash or chips are a speciality (£8.50). Jazz musicians play every evening except Sunday, and San Miguel beer is sold on draught. *Babies and children admitted. Dress: smart casual. Entertainment: jazz 8.30-11pm Mon-Sat. Tables outdoors (15, conservatory; 6, garden; 8, terrace). Separate room for parties, seats 35.* **Map 7/9M.**

West

Holland Park W11

Julie's

135-137 Portland Road, W11 (020 7229 8331/www.juliesrestaurant.demon.co.uk). Holland Park tube.
Wine bar **Open** 9am-11pm Mon-Sat; 9am-10pm Sun. **Lunch served** 12.30-2.45pm Mon-Sat; 12.30-3.30pm Sun. **Afternoon tea** served 3-7.30pm daily. **Dinner served** 7.30-11pm Mon-Sat; 7.30-10pm Sun. **Main courses** £8.95-£19.95. **House wine** £11.95 bottle, £2.95 glass.

Restaurant **Lunch served** 12.30-2.45pm Mon-Sat; 12.30-3pm Sun. **Dinner served** 7-11.30pm Mon-Sat; 7-10.30pm Sun. **Main courses** £12.95-£19.95. **House wine** £13.95 bottle, £3.25 glass.
Both **Service** 12½%. **Credit** AmEx, DC, JCB, MC, £TC, V.

Well-heeled west Londoners have been getting well-chilled at Julie's for three decades now. It's a labyrinthine affair, crammed with ornate artefacts and hanging baskets of ivy. Small rooms are sub-divided further by Arabic wooden screens. The overall effect (compounded by soporific, ambient music) could be described as posh hippy. The sensibly sized wine list (only two pages) is a good balance of Old World and New World with, surprisingly, only three bottles and the champagnes (of course) costing more than £20. It's short on surprises but features a good number of crowd-pleasers such as Penfolds Private Bin chardonnay 1999 (£15.50) and Woodbridge Estate sauvignon blanc 1997 (£16.95) among the whites, and Torres Gran Sangre de Toro 1996 (£14.95) and Coldstream Hills cabernet-merlot 1996 (£16.95) among the reds. Eight wines are offered by the glass. In addition, there's a decent selection of competently made cocktails, comprising all the regulars, for about £5 a throw. An à la carte menu is served in Julie's restaurant next door; food in the bar ranges from sausages with onions and olive mash to the wonderfully preposterous smoked salmon with Sauternes-scented shallot glaze. *Babies and children welcome; children's set meal (£9) Sun; crèche (1-4pm Sun); high chairs. Book dinner. Separate rooms for parties, seating 14-42. Tables outdoors (11, pavement).* **Map 11/7Az.**

Shepherd's Bush W12

Albertine

1 Wood Lane, W12 (020 8743 9593). Shepherd's Bush tube/49, 72, 94, 207, 285 bus. **Open** 11am-11pm Mon-Fri; 6.30-11pm Sat. **Main courses** £4.90-£6.10. **House red** £9.50 bottle, £2.50 glass. **House white** £9.30 bottle, £2.40 glass. **Credit** MC, £TC, V.

Within ambling distance of the BBC, this small, unpretentious wine bar on a corner of Shepherd's Bush Green could be the Corporation's best kept secret. Mismatching wooden chairs and pews give Albertine a laidback, almost studenty feel, yet the terrific wine list is clearly compiled by folk who know their Barsac from their Elba. We counted an astonishing 58 wines by the glass, including a selection of ports, sherries and dessert wines. It's rare to find bottles of wine in wine bars for under a tenner, but here you can choose from Mas Montel grenache-syrah (£9.50) and Domaine de Haubet (£9.30) vin de pays wines, or RH Phillips Night Harvest Mistura (£9.50) from California. If money's not too tight, take a look at the separate fine wine list offering the likes of Château Léoville-Barton 1985 (£40) and Jean Grivot's Clos Vougeot 1990 (£45). The only dampener on our evening was a couple of Beeboids discussing, in unnaturally loud voices, what it means to be a celebrity in 2000. Disappointingly, they didn't choke on their roasted pepper and feta tart or chorizo and chickpea casserole.
Separate room for parties, seats 30.

South West

Earlsfield SW18

Willie Gunn

422 Garratt Lane, SW18 (020 8946 7773). Earlsfield rail/44, 77, 270 bus. **Open** 11am-11pm Mon-Sat; 11am-10pm Sun. **Main courses** £7.50-£12. **Service** 12½%. **House wine** £10 bottle, £2.50 glass. **Credit** JCB, MC, V.

Willie Gunn takes its name from a type of fishing fly. Opened in 1996, it's a light, airy wine bar recently decorated in a restful pale green. Primarily it's a local bar, though some regulars travel from Battersea, Fulham and Tooting and one particularly dedicated set of fans drives here from Kent. They come because the thoughtfully chosen wine list and the substantial gastropub-style food offer great value. We opted for the juicy Angus beefburger with fries, accompanied by two stonkingly delicious wines, and were transported to carnivore heaven. The Monte Verde cabernet sauvignon 1998 from Maipo in Chile (£14.50) was pure blackcurrants and came with a sprig of mint on top, while L'Ancien Courrier Corbières 1999 (£13.50) had a tarry, chocolatey nose, a palate of ripe blackberries and was as soft in the mouth as a silkworm's

dressing gown. Both wines are available by the glass and feature among the helpfully recommended wines on the list. Some 14 wines are available by the glass, including the house champagne, Canard-Duchêne non-vintage (£6 a glass, £27.50 a bottle). *Babies and children welcome; high chairs. Booking essential. Entertainment: 6ft screen for rugby matches.*

Fulham SW10

Wine Gallery

49 Hollywood Road, SW10 (020 7352 7572). Earl's Court tube/14, 31 bus. **Lunch served** noon-4pm, **dinner served** 7pm-midnight daily. **Main courses** £6-£12. **Service** 12½%. **House wine** £5 bottle, £2.25 glass. **Credit** MC, £TC, V.

Your pound's worth more at the Wine Gallery. Bottles of house red and white (French table wines) are yours for only a fiver, a truly remarkable price for a wine bar. How's it done? A chap called John Brinkley had the brainwave of opening a restaurant, a wine shop and a wine bar all next to each other in a sleepy Fulham backroad. Although the wine list only has two house wines by the glass, the great news is that the list is merely a selection of what's offered in the adjacent wine shop. Just nip next door for a choice of some 200 wines at high-street retail prices, then drink your selection here. Etienne Guigal's Côtes-du-Rhône 1997 and Etienne Guigal or Wolf Blass barrel-fermented chardonnay 1999 are £9.50, and even the super-Tuscan Tignanello 1996/7 from Antinori is only £38. The Wine Gallery is wood-panelled and intimate, with a small walled garden at the back. A plentiful supply of young local gals attracts a large number of not-so-young local chaps. Watch their hilarious courtship rituals played out to a soft-rock soundtrack of INXS and Bryan Adams. Food includes spring rolls with a sweet chilli sauce, own-made fish cakes with prawns and tomato and basil salad, and sirloin steak with béarnaise sauce and chips. *Babies and children welcome. Booking advisable. Tables outdoors (3, pavement; 12, garden).* **Map 5/12C.** **For branch see index.**

Vinopolis Wine Wharf

South Kensington SW3

The Crescent

99 Fulham Road, SW3 (020 7225 2244). South Kensington tube. **Open** 11am-11pm Mon; 10am-11pm Tue-Sat; 11am-10.30pm Sun. **Brunch served** 11am-6pm Sun. **Main courses** £6.25-£10.95. **Set lunch** (11.30am-4pm Mon-Fri) £6.99 two courses. **Service** 10%. **House wine** £9.95 bottle, £2.75 glass. **Credit** AmEx, DC, MC, £TC, V.

The Crescent is a bit like an iceberg; it's pretty cool and only a small part is visible at street level. The ground-floor bar looks dauntingly cramped when you enter, but there's a much larger area downstairs where you can enjoy some fabulous wines. When the venue opened in 1996, its simple, clean lines and minimalist interior were hailed as the antidote to the cluttered look of the 1970s wine bar. This is a place where thirty- and fortysomething locals rub shoulders with weary shoppers taking a break from retail exertions in Knightsbridge. At weekends they chill out in the basement, reading the papers to a background of jazzy funk. The wine list, featuring some 200 labels, visits all four corners of the globe, but remains seriously and devoutly Francophile. There are some smartly selected, excellent wines to choose from. Most of the list weighs in at less than £30; try the Chateau Bellegarde, Fûts de Chêne 1997 (£22.50) or the sauvignon de Saint-Bris, Domaine Jean-Hugues Goisot 1998 (£18.50). Non-French stars include St Hallett Old Block shiraz 1996 from South Australia's Barossa Valley (£29.50) and Cloudy Bay sauvignon blanc 1999 from Marlborough in New Zealand (£26.50). Each wine has succinct, useful notes to help with the tough job of selecting your tipple.

Bookings not accepted. Separate room for parties, seats 40. **Map 12/10E.**

South East

London Bridge SE1

Balls Brothers

Hay's Galleria, Tooley Street, SE1 (020 7407 4301/www.ballsbrothers.co.uk). London Bridge tube/rail.

Bar **Open** 11.30am-9.30pm, **meals served** 11.30am-9pm Mon-Fri. **Main courses** £5.95-£16.50.

Restaurant **Lunch served** 11.45am-2.45pm, **dinner served** 6-9pm Mon-Fri. **Main courses** £8.95-£16.95.

Both **House wine** £13 bottle, £3.30 wine. **Credit** AmEx, DC, JCB, MC, £TC, V.

Balls Brothers has been plying wines to the City of London for five generations, since the partnership was kick-started by Austin and Harry Balls. There are now 16 Balls Brothers restaurants and wine bars; the Hay's Galleria outlet is one of the latest. It's a well-appointed, brightly lit cellar. There are only five red and five white wines served by the glass and these are marked on the blackboard. A ripe, golden, slightly toasty, nutty Australian semillon 1999 was utterly delicious at £4 a glass. More than half the wine list is French, with Burgundy particularly well covered. There's a good selection of wines by the half-bottle, for today's more abstemious lunchtimes – try the Domaine des Valanges Saint-Veran 1998 (£10.30) or the Chateau Moulin de Launay 1998 (£6.80) – and the excellent champagne selection includes Krug, Bollinger and Louis Roederer. The food has a distinctly fishy slant; specials included half a dozen Strangford Lough rock oysters, dressed crab salad, and half a fresh lobster salad. In the summer months Balls Brothers opens its outdoor Terrace Bar, where local office workers gather to play pétanque. What better way to unwind after a hard day than throwing balls at one another?

Dress: smart casual. Separate rooms for parties, both seating 10. Tables outdoors (20, terrace). **Map 8/8Q.**

For branches see index.

Borough SE1

Vinopolis Wine Wharf ★

Stoney Street, SE1 (020 7940 8335). London Bridge tube/rail. **Open** 11am-11pm Mon-Fri; 11am-9pm Sat, Sun. **Meals served** noon-10pm Mon-Fri; noon-6pm Sat, Sun. **Bar snacks** £2.25-£7.50. **Service** 10% for parties of 12 or more. **Credit** AmEx, MC, V.

London's only wine tourist attraction has at last opened its own wine bar. Not to be confused with Cantina Vinopolis (*see p131* **Modern European**), the Vinopolis Wine Wharf is a stylish place, with a mildly utilitarian design that incorporates chunky galvanised steel and timber. As you might expect, the wine list is so enormous you'll need a glass of wine just to get through it. Or maybe a 'quartino' – an Italian measure that equates to two glasses – would be more satisfying. A quartino of Aglianico del Vulture Basilicum 1997, for example, costs £5. There's a very impressive range of 20 champagnes served by the glass, including Bruno Paillard (£8.10) and Bollinger Special Cuvée (£9), both non-vintage. The adventurous might want to try a Wine Flight, a themed set of five wines assembled by various wine merchants; choose from 'In a Bordeaux Mood' (£6.75), 'Thirst Quenchers' (£8) and 'Gentlemen of Verona' (£10.50). Like the décor, the food is bold, simple and very appealing. Go for octopus salad, imam bayildi (a Turkish aubergine dish) or a selection of Spanish charcuterie.

Babies and children admitted (lunch). Bookings accepted for parties of 12 or more. Disabled: toilet. Separate room for parties. **Map 8/8P.**

North

Camden Town & Chalk Farm NW1

Odette's Wine Bar

130 Regent's Park Road, NW1 (020 7722 5388). Chalk Farm tube. **Lunch served** 12.30-2.30pm Mon-Sat; 12.30-3pm Sun. **Dinner served** 5.30-10.30pm Mon-Sat. **Main courses** £7.50-£11. **House wine** £10.95 bottle, £3.15 glass. **Credit** AmEx, DC, MC, TC, V.

Opened at the tail-end of the 1970s by local Primrose Hill resident, Simone Green, this is an epoch-defining wine bar. It has the archetypal candle-lit alcoves, and every available inch of wall-space is covered by pictures that reveal a penchant for art deco. The wine list is superlative. Most wines are presented under style headings such as 'light, crisp, dry whites' or 'full-bodied reds' and are accompanied by concise, knowledgeable notes. About 30 wines are served by the glass, but what really stands out is the selection of 27 wines available by the half-bottle, including three champagnes. Regionally, the list leaves no stone unturned – even Mexico gets a look-in – and it is littered with stellar names that read like a wine *Who's Who*. There's Alto Adige pinot grigio 1998 by Alois Lageder (£12), Alsace gewurztraminer 1995 by Rolly Gassmann (£17.95) and a magnum of the cultish Le Cigar Volant 1997 by Californian maverick, Randall Grahm (£77) – you get the picture. The food is comforting wine bar fare: cauliflower and Gruyère quiche; marinated char-grilled neck of lamb with white beans, capers and lamb jus; and baked trout with new potatoes and herbs. *See p131* **Modern European** for Odette's restaurant.

Babies and children admitted. Booking advisable Fri-Sun. **Map 10.**

North West

West Hampstead NW6

No.77 Wine Bar

77 Mill Lane, NW6 (020 7435 7787). West Hampstead tube/rail. **Open** noon-11pm Mon, Tue; noon-midnight Wed-Fri; noon-midnight Sat; noon-10.30pm Sun. **Main courses** £8.95-£14. **Set Sunday lunch** £10.95 two courses, £13.95 three courses. **Service** 12½%. **House wine** £9.95 bottle, £2.50 glass. **Credit** JCB, MC, V.

On a late, lazy Sunday lunchtime the punters at No.77 resemble the casts of dramas like *This Life* and *Hearts and Bones* – vaguely bohemian, slightly hung over and postponing Monday for as long as possible. Jazz plays quietly in the background; as a concession to 'the lads', soccer is on the telly with the sound turned down. Children dart between the potted palms, pews and pine furniture. The stylish and well-sourced wine list has comprehensive notes and offers 20 wines by the glass. We took full advantage of this to match a selection of wines with the Sunday lunch. Since our visit last year, the food (Modern European) has improved beyond recognition. A crisp, nettley Chilean Santa Rita sauvignon blanc 1998 (£3.25 a glass) worked wonders with wild rocket salad in balsamic vinaigrette, as did a fresh, raspberryish Côtes de Duras Grand Mayne rosé (£2.95) with duck confit salad and raspberry jus. The soft, luscious Bodega Berberana Rioja (£3.45) lifted poached smoked haddock (with poached egg and bubble and squeak) to new heights, while a brambly Norton Estate Barbera 1997 from Argentina (£3.35) kicked ass with a flavoursome and well-cooked braised lamb shank, carrot and swede purée with rosemary jus.

Babies and children admitted. Booking advisable. Entertainment: jazz and blues musicians 2-4pm Sun. Separate room for parties, seats 40. Tables outdoors (7, pavement).

Eating & Entertainment

Bach to Brunch

The New Restaurant at the V&A

Victoria & Albert Museum, Cromwell Road, SW7 (020 7581 2159). South Kensington tube. **Open** 10am-5.30pm daily. **Brunch served** 10am-3pm Sun. **Credit** AmEx, LV, MC, £TC, V.

The serene sound of classical piano music emanates from the V&A's conservatory-style restaurant on Sunday, as customers enjoy a buffet brunch of salads, fish, pasta and veggie dishes. For a proper Sunday lunch, there's traditional roast beef and Yorkshire pudding.

Map 12/10E.

Palm Court

Waldorf Meridien, Aldwych, WC2 (020 7836 2400). Covent Garden or Temple tube. **Brunch served** noon-2.30pm Sun. **Credit** AmEx, DC, MC, £TC, V.

A swanky way to spend your Sunday. For £40 you can eat as much as you like from the buffet and enjoy unlimited top-ups of champagne, while jazz musicians provide background entertainment.

Map 14/6M.

Cabaret

10

10 Air Street, W1 (020 7734 9990). Piccadilly Circus tube. **Open** 6pm-3am Mon-Sat. **Jazz** 7pm-midnight Tue-Thur. **Credit** AmEx, MC, V.

A hip and happening spot with vivid purple and plum decor. On Monday it plays host to American musician Patrick Allen, who regularly brings the house down with his giant jazz-funk jams. Food comes in the form of snacks like canapés, wun tun and chicken satay, rather than substantial mains – dishes start at £5.75. At weekends the place is packed and the dance floor is pumping as resident DJs and musicians present a mix of jazz and funk.

Map 13/7J.

Globe

100 Avenue Road, NW3 (020 7722 7200). Swiss Cottage tube/13, 31 bus. **Lunch served** noon-3pm Tue-Fri; Sun. **Dinner served** 7-11pm Mon-Sat; 6-10pm Sun. **Credit** AmEx, MC, £TC, V.

The 'Globe girls' – consisting of manager Neil and his chef, offer the likes of a camped-up version of *Absolutely Fabulous* (as if the original wasn't camp enough). Their 15-minute send-up, which began as a Christmas one-off, now occupies a regular Thursday evening slot. The Globe is a restaurant first, cabaret second – *see p99* **International.**

Comedy

Aztec Comedy

First floor, The Borderland, 47-49 Westow Hill, SE19 (020 8771 0885). Crystal Palace or Gypsy Hill rail. **Open** 6.30-11.30pm Mon-Sat; 12.30-10.30pm Sun. **Shows** 9-11.15pm Fri, doors open 8pm (*Dec only* show moves to Sun). **Admission** £4-£5. **Credit** AmEx, DC, MC, £TC, V.

The cosy upstairs Aztec Room of this cantina-style bar and restaurant is home to comedy on Friday. Food is a secondary factor, with basic Mexican dishes such as enchiladas and burritos starting at £5. Comedy is the thing, and luckily it's top-notch. Newcomers regularly join old circuit hands, but the standard is constant and the atmosphere friendly. It's popular with locals, hen nights and couples, so it's best to book ahead.

Canal Café Theatre

First floor, The Bridge House, corner of Westbourne Terrace Road and Delamere Terrace, W2 (020 7289 6056). Warwick Avenue tube. **Meals served** 6-10pm Tue-Sun. **Shows** 7.30pm, 9.30pm Mon-Sat; 7pm, 9pm Sun. *Newsrevue* 9-10.30pm Thur-Sat; 9-10pm Sun. **Admission** £7; £5 concs plus £1 annual membership. **Credit** MC, V.

The immensely popular Newsrevue company performs a series of satirical sketches and songs, all based on current news stories. Food is basic pub grub: the likes of pie and chips, roasts and jacket potatoes start at around £4.

Booking advisable Fri, Sat.

Map 1/5C.

Comedy Café

66-68 Rivington Street, EC2 (020 7739 5706). Old Street tube/rail. **Open** 7pm-midnight Wed-Thur; 7pm-2am Fri, Sat. **Meals served** 7-10.30pm Wed-Sat. **Shows** 9-11.30pm Wed-Sat. **Admission** free Wed; £3 Thur; £10 Fri; £12 Sat. **Credit** MC, V.

A Shoreditch venue that showcases some of the most talented unknown comedians on the circuit. Weekends are reserved for more famous faces and ends with a disco at 2am. A three-course meal costs around £20 per head. A good choice for large parties.

Booking essential Fri, Sat. **Map 17/4R.**

Comedy Store

1A Oxendon Street, SW1 (info 020 7344 0234/ bookings: Ticketmaster 020 7344 4444). Piccadilly Circus tube. **Open** occasional Mon, phone for details; 6.30-11pm Tue-Thur, Sun; 6.30pm-3am Fri, Sat. **Meals served** 6.30-10.15pm Tue-Thur, Sun; 6.30pm-2.15am Fri, Sat. **Shows** 8-10.15pm Tue-Thur, Sun; 8-10.15pm, midnight-2.15am Fri, Sat. **Admission** £11 Tue, Wed; £12 Thur, Fri, Sun; £15 Sat (£8 concs Tue-Thur, midnight Fri). **Credit** £TC.

The likes of Josie Lawrence and Greg Proops perform on a regular basis at this world-renowned venue. Book well in advance if you can. Food is along the lines of substantial snacks (burgers, chips and so on) rather than large-scale meals.

Booking advisable. Disabled: toilet. **Map 13/7K.**

Jesters

682 High Road, E11 (020 8556 6821). Leytonstone tube. **Open** noon-3pm, 6pm-12.30am Mon-Sat; noon-10pm Sun. **Credit** MC, £TC, V.

With jesters, jugglers and musicians entertaining every Saturday night, this venue certainly lives up to its name. Food is a simple selection of pastas, burgers, steaks and fajitas, with main courses priced between £5.80 and £16.50. Book early for Saturday nights.

Jongleurs Camden Lock

Middle Yard, Camden Lock, Chalk Farm Road, NW1 (020 7564 2500/www.jongleurs.com). Camden Town or Chalk Farm tube/N5, N31 bus. **Open** 7.15pm-2am Fri; 6-10pm, 10.30pm-3am Sat. **Meals served** 7.15-8.15pm Fri; 6-7.15pm, 10.30-11.15pm Sat. **Shows** 8.15-11pm Fri; 7.15-9.45pm, 11.15pm-1.45am Sat. **Admission** £12-£14. **Membership** £5. **Credit** MC, V.

Part of an ever-expanding chain of comedy clubs (there are now eight venues nationwide), Jongleurs in Camden has a reputation for attracting some of Britain's leading comedians – Mark Hurst and Sean Meo are regular performers here. Basket food can be ordered before the start of the show; dishes cost £4.50-£7.50.

Booking advisable. Disabled: toilet. **Map 10.**

For branches see index.

Up the Creek

302 Creek Road, SE10 (020 8858 4581/ www.up-the-creek.com). Greenwich rail/DLR. **Open** 8pm-2am Fri; 7.30pm-2am Sat; 8pm-midnight Sun. **Shows** 9-11.15pm Fri, Sun; 8.30-11pm Sat. **Admission** £4-£14. **Credit** AmEx, DC, MC, V.

Since it opened in 1991, this comedy club has attracted some of the biggest names in the business. Performers of the stature of Jo Brand, Steve Coogan and Vic and Bob have all graced the stage and still return for one-off performances. A surprisingly cheap Thai menu is served (mains start at around £3); you can eat in the upstairs restaurant and watch the show from a TV screen, or enjoy the performance downstairs while balancing a plate on your lap. The evening ends with a post-performance disco. Note that the venue is closed on Sundays in July and August.

Map 19.

Shoeless Joe's.
See page 226.

Dining afloat

See also **El Barco Latino** *(page 225).*

The Elizabethan
The Signal Box, 119-123 Sandycombe Road, Richmond, Surrey (020 8940 6688/ www.thamesluxurycharters.co.uk). **Hourly hire rate** £350-£380 day, from £420 evening. **No credit cards.**
With a silver-service capacity of 220, the *Elizabethan* is the largest of this company's three boats, which are all available for private hire. The entertainment for your party aboard this replica 1890s paddle steamer can include caricaturists, a casino and a jazz or rock 'n' roll band; staff can even put on special nights with themes ranging from Mardi Gras to the Wild West.

The Floating Boater
Prince Regent *corner of Warwick Crescent and Westbourne Terrace Road Bridge, W2 (020 7266 1066). Warwick Avenue tube.* **Hourly hire rate** £190 per hour. **Minimum** 12-48 (formal dining). **Maximum** 80 (buffet). **Lapwing** *Pool of Little Venice, W2 (020 7266 1066). Warwick Avenue tube.* **Hourly hire rate** £120 per hour. **Minimum** 12-22 (formal dining). **Maximum** 30 (buffet). *Both* **Credit** AmEx, MC, V.
A family-run business with two attractive boats for hire, both moored at Little Venice. The *Prince Regent* is Edwardian, with a mahogany and ash interior and oak floor; the *Lapwing* was one of the first diesel-powered narrowboats, now restored to its former glory with the addition of a couple of modern extras – smoked glass windows and central heating for winter cruising. Both offer hot and cold buffets and three-course meals. The three-hour trip takes cruisers through St John's Wood, Primrose Hill and Camden, past sights like the Central London Mosque, Regent's Park and London Zoo. Entertainment can include a disco, magicians, musicians and a casino.
Map 1/5C.

RS Hispaniola
Victoria Embankment, WC2 (020 7839 3011). Embankment tube. **Lunch served** noon-2.30pm daily. **Dinner served** 6.30-11pm Mon-Thur; 6.30-11.30pm Fri, Sat. **Credit** AmEx, DC, JCB, MC, £TC, V.
Moored at the Victoria Embankment, the *Hispaniola* has an à la carte menu of international dishes, while the resident pianist plays jazz while you dine at weekends. A private booking means a choice of entertainment in the form of belly dancers, magicians and musicians. Meals cost from £19 to £36 per head and there's a Cuban bar with a tapas menu on the upper deck.
Map 14/7L.

Leven is Strijd
West India Quay, Hertsmere Road, West India Docks, E14 (020 7987 4002). West India Quay DLR. **Credit** £TC.
This 1920s barge is much in demand for hen nights, birthday parties and corporate functions. There's a minimum booking of ten and maximum of 20 for dinner; the boat has a maximum capacity of 50 for drinks-only events. A set price of £35 per head buys a four-course menu which begins with a small buffet followed by starters and mains (choices include Thai prawns sautéed in ginger and garlic on tagliatelle), followed by desserts, coffee and chocolates.

Dinner & dance

For a truly glamorous night out, visit one of London's grand hotels for a dinner and dance. The **Savoy**'s (*see page 35* **British**) River Restaurant has a dinner dance (£39.50 Mon-Thur, Sun; £44.50 Fri, Sat); the **Ritz** (*page 76* **Hotels & Haute Cuisine**) and **Claridge's** (*page 204* **Cafés**) host similar events (**Ritz** £59 Fri, Sat; **Claridge's** £48, Sat), as does the Conservatory restaurant in the **Lanesborough** (£44, Fri, Sat/020 7259 5599). The **Waldorf Meridien** (*page 204* **Cafés**) offers a weekend afternoon tea dance (£25). *See also page 226* **Windows.**

DIY

Blue Hawaii
2 Richmond Road, Kingston-upon-Thames, Surrey (020 8549 6989). Kingston-upon-Thames rail. **Meals served** 7pm-1am Mon-Sat; noon-1am Sun. **Credit** AmEx, DC, JCB, MC, £TC, V.
Hawaiian shirts and garlands of flowers are the order of the day at this heavily themed barbecue restaurant. For £6.95 before 8.45pm and £10.95 afterwards, diners can choose from a range of fish, meat and vegetables. There are different discounts throughout the week. On Monday, diners get a 20% discount on tickets at the cinema next door; spend over £50 on Tuesday and you'll get free holiday vouchers. Wednesday is couples night, when loved-up lads and lasses get a free bottle of wine. Bring your reward card in on Thursday and you'll get a 15% discount off your bill. And weekends are the time for crazy hula dancing. Oh, and on Sundays, kids eat free if they're with an adult. Musicans play every night and a resident magician performs card tricks at the tables.

East One
175-179 St John Street, EC1 (020 7566 0088). Farringdon tube/rail/55 bus. **Open** noon-midnight Mon-Fri; 5pm-midnight Sat; **Lunch served** noon-5pm Mon-Fri. **Dinner served** 5-11.30pm Mon-Sat. **Credit** AmEx, JCB, MC, £TC, V.
East One is now split into two sections. One serves an expanded à la carte menu; in the other, the buffet still offers a choice of some 30 oriental raw ingredients and an 'eat as much as you like' deal for £11 (lunch) and £14.50 (dinner).
Map 15/4O.

Mongolian Barbecue
12 Maiden Lane, WC2 (020 7379 7722). Charing Cross tube/rail/Covent Garden tube. **Meals served** noon-3pm, 6-11pm Mon-Fri; noon-midnight Sat; 6-11pm Sun. **Credit** AmEx, MC, V.
For £10.95 you can select the ingredients of your meal from an array of meats and seafood, including beef, prawns, fish and chicken (and 'dodo wings'!). Add some sauces, herbs and spices (of 'Mongolian' origin, of course) and watch it being stir-fried before your eyes.
Map 14/7L.
For branches see index.

Tiger Lil's
270 Upper Street, N1 (020 7226 1118). Highbury & Islington tube/rail. **Lunch served** noon-3pm Mon-Fri. **Dinner served** 6-11.30pm Mon-Thur; 6pm-midnight Fri. **Meals served** noon-midnight Sat; noon-11pm Sun. **Credit** AmEx, MC, V.
The emphasis is on performance here, as overheated chefs put on a brave show of stir-frying customers' ingredients in woks at great speed. For £11.50 you can select a variety of chopped food from the selection of vegetables, seafood and meats on display. Present this to the chefs, who will ask for your choice of sauce, then sit back and watch your ingredients sizzle into a meal. Eat as much as you like, but don't expect authenticity.
For branches see index.

Dogs' dinners

Walthamstow Stadium
Chingford Road, E4 (020 8531 4255). Blackhorse Road tube then 58A, 158 bus/ Walthamstow Central tube/rail then 97, 97A, 215, 257 bus. **Admission** £2.50 (Tue free) popular enclosure, £5 main stand. **Race times** *first* 7.30pm Tue, Thur, Sat; *last* 10.15pm Tue, Thur; 10.30pm Sat; also Mon lunchtime and occasional Fri evening races, phone for details. **Meals served** 6.30-10pm Tue, Thur, Sat. **Credit** MC, V.
Walthamstow Stadium's Stowaway and Paddock restaurants have recently been refurbished. Both serve extensive à la carte menus, but while the Paddock has the advantages of a tote betting service at your table and seats overlooking the track, the Stowaway counters with an expensive wine list. If you're more in the mood for a snack in informal surroundings, the Classic diner has comfy seating, TV monitors at the bar and a basic menu of burgers, flame-grilled chicken, and veggie burgers (from £4).

Wimbledon Stadium
Plough Lane, SW17 (020 8946 8000/ www.wimbledondogs.co.uk). Tooting Broadway tube/Earlsfield rail/44, 156, 270, 272 bus. **Admission** £3 popular enclosure, £5 grandstand. **Race times** *first* 7.30pm, *last* 10.30pm, Tue, Fri, Sat (Wed in Dec). **Meals served** 7-9.30pm Tue, Fri, Sat. **Credit** AmEx, MC, TC, V.
There are two restaurants at this dog track. The Broadway has a three-course menu for £17; individual table monitors are provided to watch the action on the track while you dine. The Star Attraction's three-course, silver-service menu costs £21. This restaurant's close proximity to the finishing line is an added advantage, with great views of the races through the huge picture windows. Food in both is a selection of standard dishes such as grilled dover sole, lamb chops, or

spicy vegetable-filled crêpes. Friendly staff and a lively, raucous atmosphere make this stadium – and its restaurants – a popular bet.
Booking advisable. Disabled: toilet.

Gimmicks

Elvis Gracelands Palace
881-883 Old Kent Road, SE15 (020 7639 3961). Elephant & Castle tube/rail then 53, 172, 21 bus. **Open** 6pm-midnight Mon-Thur, Sun; noon-2pm, 6pm-midnight Fri, Sat. **Shows** 10pm, 11pm Fri, Sat; 10pm-late (on request) Mon-Thur, Sun. **Set menus** £15-£17.50; £10-£14 vegetarian. **Credit** AmEx, DC, MC, £TC, V.
A bit of an institution on the Old Kent Road, Gracelands attracts visitors from all over London, not to mention quite a few tourists in search of an offbeat experience. Paul Chan (the Chinese Elvis) does his renditions of the King's classics, while customers dine on Chinese food. Staff are friendly and conscientious (the waitress kindly called us after we'd booked a table for 7.30pm to warn us that 'Elvis' wouldn't be performing until 11pm – would we like to come later?). Popular with large parties.
Booking essential Fri, Sat.

Garlic & Shots
14 Frith Street, W1 (020 7734 9505/www.garlicandshots.com). Leicester Square or Tottenham Court Road tube. **Meals served** 5pm-midnight Mon-Wed; 6pm-1am Thur-Sat; 5-11.30pm Sun. **Credit** MC, £TC, V.
Garlic is incorporated into almost everything here, including the beers. The tapas menu has a choice of three different garlic dips (chicken, veggie and seafood), served with toast or tortilla chips. Main courses include the likes of siskgryta (garlic fish casserole, £9.25) and garlic chicken supreme (£10.95). There are 101 different shots to choose from – only half are garlic flavoured.
Map 13/6K.

Just Around the Corner
446 Finchley Road, NW2 (020 7431 3300). Finchley Road or Golders Green tube. **Meals served** 6pm-midnight Mon-Sat; noon-midnight Sun. **Credit** AmEx, DC, MC, £TC, V.

This restaurant's novelty value has led to numerous TV appearances since its establishment 14 years ago. Diners choose from a menu of traditional French and English dishes such as lamb Wellington with leeks and mushrooms or chicken breast stuffed with avocado. There are no prices on the menu and at the end of the meal, staff present a list of what you've eaten rather than a bill. You decide what the food was worth and pay accordingly. The owners maintain that they've never disagreed with a payment.
Booking essential.

La Pergola
66 Streatham High Road, SW16 (020 8769 2646). Streatham Hill rail. **Lunch served** noon-3pm Mon-Sat. **Dinner served** 6-11pm Mon-Thur; 6pm-2am Fri, Sat. **Set dinners** £15.50 Fri, £18.50 Sat, three courses. **Shows** 9pm-2am Fri, Sat; also by arrangement. **Credit** AmEx, MC, £TC, V.
La Pergola is for partying. It packs in a raucous crowd of hen parties and large groups, serenaded by Kim Bridges – who has been doing his Elvis act here for the past 30 years. Food is Italian, with mains starting at £5.50: the DiMarcos from Eastenders have been spotted tucking in.
Booking essential.

Capital Radio Café
Leicester Square, WC2 (020 7484 8888). Leicester Square tube. **Open** 11.45am-midnight Mon-Sat; noon-11pm Sun. **Credit** AmEx, MC, V.
Primarily a hangout for teens and their parents, the café shows pop videos and has a resident DJ to give the place that 'radio' feel. Food is a selection of meat and Quorn burgers, pizzas, salads and stir-fries. Prices reflect the touristy location (£9 for a burger) but the lunch menu has a small number of dishes for £5. Cocktails, shooters and champagne are available; happy hour is 5-7pm.
Map 14/7K

Sound
Leicester Square, W1 (020 7287 1010). Leicester Square tube. **Open** noon-1am Mon-Thur; noon-3am Fri; noon-4am Sat; noon-midnight Sun. **Credit** AmEx, MC, V.
Teens, tourists and music video fans watch their pop idols gyrate on screen while they masticate; the fries, burgers, salads and main courses are surprisingly palatable for such a highly themed West End venue. The bar offers a wide choice of alcoholic and non-alcoholic cocktails. At the weekends the tables are moved to accommodate the many club nights held here.
Map 13/7K.

Jazz & soul

See also **Pizza on the Park** and **Soho Pizzeria** *(page 185* **Pizza & Pasta***) and the* **Tenth** *(page 226).*

606 Club
90 Lots Road, SW10 (020 7352 5953). Earl's Court or Fulham Broadway tube/14, 22 bus. **Open** 7.30pm-1am Mon-Wed; 8.15pm-1.30am Thur; 8.15am-2am Fri, Sat; 8.15-11.30pm Sun. **Music** 8pm-1am Mon-Wed; 9.30pm-1.30am Thur; 10pm-2am Fri, Sat; 9-11.30pm Sun. **Credit** MC, £TC, V.
This small club makes an effort with its food as well as its music. A daily-changing menu includes dishes such as grilled marlin on cannelloni beans (£14.95) or filo pastry filled with a julienne of vegetables, served with crème fraîche, new potatoes and salad (£6.75). Music is a mixture of jazz and R&B, with an emphasis on jazz trios and quartets. At weekends, non-members must have dinner to gain admission. A meal (including the entrance fee, which is added to your bill at the end of the evening) costs around £30 per head.
Map 5/13C.

Dorchester Bar
54 Park Lane, W1 (020 7629 8888). Hyde Park Corner tube. **Open** 11am-12.30am Mon-Sat; noon-11.30pm Sun. **Music** 7pm-midnight Mon-Sat. **Credit** AmEx, DC, MC, £TC, V.
Three resident pianists take it in turns to play jazz and blues in the Dorchester's bar for the first half the week. Then, from Wednesday to Saturday evening, it's the turn of a five piece jazz band. An Italian menu offers pastas (£12.50-£15) and fish, chicken and meat dishes (£16.50-£27.50). The cocktail list has over 50 combinations, including more than 10 champagne cocktails.
Map 2/7G.

Jazz Café
5 Parkway, NW1 (020 7916 6060). Camden Town tube. **Open** 7pm-1am Mon-Thur, Sun; 7pm-2am Fri, Sat. **Meals served** 7-11pm daily. **Bar food served** 11pm-midnight Mon-Thur, Sun; 11pm-1am Fri, Sat. **Music** 9/9.30-11/11.30pm daily; *club nights* 11/11.30pm-2am Fri, Sat. **Admission** £12-£15. **Credit** MC, V.
A popular stop for jazz and soul acts – the Jazz Café pulls in a crowd of thirty-something aficionados. The coveted balcony seats overlooking the stage are reserved for diners, who must also have a ticket for the show and who must spend a minimum of £14.50 per person (the cost of a main course). Food is modern and fairly mediocre, considering the price. An entrance fee (often £15 for a well-known act) is required before you enter the restaurant.
Booking advisable.
Map 10/.

Mezzo
100 Wardour Street, W1 (020 7314 4000). Tottenham Court Road tube. **Dinner served** 6pm-1am Mon-Thur; 6pm-3am Fri, Sat. **Entertainment charge** £5 Mon-Thur; *festivals* £10. **Credit** AmEx, DC, MC, £TC, V.
Terence Conran's large Soho restaurant features jazz and funk musicians alongside the food. For full listings and menu details *see p137* **Modern European**.
Map 13/6K.

Jazz After Dark
9 Greek Street, W1 (020 7734 0545/www.jazzafterdark.co.uk). Leicester Square tube. **Open** noon-2am Mon-Thur; noon-3am Fri, Sat. **Music** 9pm-1.30am Mon-Thur; 10pm-2.30am Fri, Sat. **Admission** (free to diners Mon-Thur) £3 Mon-Thur, Sun; £5 Fri, Sat. **Credit** AmEx, DC, LV, JCB, MC, £TC, V.
Jazz after Dark is a peculiar mixture of tourist attraction and late night drinking den for post-pub punters. Crowds don't start arriving until at least 9pm; music – easy-listening jazz and blues – begins much later. Food is rather basic, with dishes such as moussaka (£5.50), grilled tuna steak (£9.50) and Cajun chicken (£9.50). There's also a three-course set menu for £12.95. The late licence and Soho location make this a popular venue for large parties, but it nevertheless remains rather bland.
Map 13/6K.

Vertigo 42. *See page 226.*

Pizza Express

10 Dean Street, W1 (020 7439 8722). Oxford Circus or Tottenham Court Road tube. **Meals served** noon-midnight daily. **Music** 9pm-midnight Mon-Thur, Sun; 9pm-11.30pm Fri, Sat. **Admission** £8-£20. **Credit** AmEx, DC, LV, MC, £TC, V.
Dean Street's Pizza Express still packs in the crowds for jazz sessions. Music is performed downstairs; there are no surprises on the menu for Pizza Express fans.
Map 13/6K.

Ronnie Scott's

47 Frith Street, W1 (020 7439 0747/ www.ronniescotts.co.uk). Leicester Square, Piccadilly Circus or Tottenham Court Road tube. **Open** 8.30pm-3am Mon-Sat. **Music** 9.30pm-2am Mon-Sat. **Admission** *non-members* £15 Mon-Thur; £20 Fri, Sat; *members* £5 Mon-Thur, £9 Fri, Sat; £9 students (Mon-Wed). **Membership** £50 per year. **Credit** AmEx, DC, MC, £$TC, V.
The late Ronnie Scott was just 32 when he opened this world-famous venue back in 1959. Since then, every jazz and blues great from Miles Davis to Tom Waits has played here. The menu includes the likes of club sandwiches, spring rolls, spicy potato wedges and chilli. Don't expect the quality of the food to match the music, though. The jazz is the thing.
Map 13/6K.

Smollensky's on the Strand

105 The Strand, WC2 (020 7497 2101/ www.smollenskys.co.uk). Embankment tube/ Charing Cross tube/rail. **Meals served** noon-midnight Mon-Thur; noon-12.30am Fri, Sat; noon-10.30pm Sun. **Music** *pianist* 7pm-midnight Mon-Sat; *jazz bands* 8-10.30pm Sun; *DJ* 10pm-midnight Thur-Sat. **Admission** free Mon-Sat; £4.50 cover Sun. **Credit** AmEx, DC, MC, £TC, V.
Regular adverts on Jazz FM and a Sunday spot for the station ensure that Smollensky's is a name that's synonymous with jazz, soul and blues, and it succeeds in pulling in healthy crowds of tourists and jazz lovers for the nightly music sessions. Try to get one of the tables overlooking the stage for the best dining experience. Food is a mixture of regional American-style cuisine; two courses cost around £15.
Map 14/7L.

Vortex

139-141 Stoke Newington Church Street, N16 (020 7254 6516). Stoke Newington rail/73 bus. **Open** 10am-11.30pm Mon-Thur; 10am-midnight Fri, Sat; 11am-midnight Sun. **Meals served** 10am-6pm, 8-10pm, daily. **Music** 9-11pm Mon-Thur, Sun; 9-11.30pm Fri, Sat. **Admission** (for music only) £3-£10. **Credit** MC, V.
A hotch-potch mix of bright, hippy colours and jumble sale-style furniture dominate this small north London venue, popular with locals for weekend brunches and with music lovers in the evenings. Food consists of a selection of pastas, salads, quiches, home-made soups and specials (from £5); it's adequate but unremarkable. As well as bands throughout the week there's a DJ every Sunday.

Kids Out

Babe Ruth's

172-176 The Highway, E1 (020 7481 8181/ www.baberuths.com). Shadwell DLR/D1, 100 bus. **Meals served** noon-11pm Mon-Thur; noon-midnight Fri, Sat; noon-10.30pm Sun. **Credit** AmEx, MC, £TC, V.
A mini-basketball court, pool tables and arcade games are just a few of the entertainments that keep kids well and truly engrossed, and give parents a well-earned break. A main course, dessert and soda costs £7.99. Order a cake for your child's birthday (£15) and see his or her face appear on screen courtesy of an in-house video camera. *See also p27* **The Americas.**

Rainforest Café

20 Shaftesbury Avenue, W1 (020 7434 3111/ www.rainforest.co.uk). Piccadilly Circus tube. **Meals served** noon-10pm Mon-Fri; noon-8pm Sat; 11.30am-10pm Sun. **Credit** AmEx, MC, V.
Dim lighting, thunder and lightning, cascading waterfalls, animated creatures, a cacophony of wild animal noises and lush synthetic greenery recreate the rainforest in the basement of the Rainforest Café premises (there's a souvenir shop upstairs). The food continues the exotic theme, with dishes such as Seychelles seafood pasta and deep forest dip. Treats for kid's parties include balloons, colouring sheets and crayons and unlimited sodas.
Map 13/7K.

TGI Fridays

6 Bedford Street, WC2 (020 7379 0585). Covent Garden or Embankment tube/Charing Cross tube/rail. **Open** noon-11.30pm Mon-Sat; noon-11pm Sun. **Entertainment** noon-5pm Sat, Sun. **Credit** AmEx, MC, £TC, V.
The *Sesame Street* menu gives kids the chance to colour in their favourite TV characters before they tuck into child-friendly food along the lines of cheese and ham wigwams (£3.25), fish 'n' chips (£3.70) and hot dogs (£3.45). The Clubhouse menu is for kids with adult appetites and there's a free gift with the set menu (main course, dessert and soft drink, £7.25). Staff entertain by making balloon animals and there are free jars of Organix baby food. *See p23* **Americas.**
Map 4/7L.

Latin

Many Latino restaurants have professional dancers to entertain. And to meet with the demands of London's Latin craze, Spanish restaurants **Bar Lorca** (*page 159*) and **Finca** (*page 160*) even offer salsa classes.

Cuba

11-13 Kensington High Street, W8 (020 7938 4137). High Street Kensington tube. **Open** *restaurant and bar* noon-2am Mon-Sat; 1-10.30pm Sun; *classes* 7.30-9.30pm Mon, Wed; 8-9.30pm Tue; 7-8.30pm Sat; *club* 9.30pm-2am Mon-Sat; 2-10.30pm Sun. **Admission** £2-£6. **Credit** AmEx, DC, MC, £TC, V.
Cuba boasts an impressive selection of Latin American tapas (£4.45), unusual main dishes such as spicy marinated shark pieces (£11.95) and traditional ones such as paella. Musicians, DJ sessions and dance classes take place in the basement nightclub, and a visit during happy hour (noon-8.30pm daily) is an opportunity to sample the extensive list of rum-based cocktails.
Map 11/8C.

El Barco Latino

Temple Pier, Victoria Embankment, WC2 (020 7379 5496). Temple tube. **Open** noon-3am daily. **Admission** £6 after 9pm Fri, Sat for non-diners, incl free drink. **Credit** AmEx, MC, V.
'Don't worry about taking lessons,' said the waiter when we phoned to ask about Latin dancing aboard *El Barco Latino*. 'I'll teach you.' Expect more flirting and non-stop salsa, lambada and rhumba from 9.30pm to midnight on Friday and Saturday, when the lights go down to make way for a disco on this Latin-crazed vessel. The restaurant serves tapas and Colombian dishes.
Map 3/7M.

Salsa!

96 Charing Cross Road, WC2 (020 7379 3277). Tottenham Court Road tube.
Bar **Open** 5.30pm-2am Mon-Sat.
Restaurant **Meals served** 6-11pm Mon-Sat; Bar snacks 5.30pm-1.30am Mon-Sat.
Both **Admission** *after 9pm* £4 Mon-Thur; £2 after 7pm; £4 after 8pm; £8 after 9pm Fri, Sat. **Music** *Dance classes* from 7-9pm daily. **Credit** AmEx, MC, £$TC, V.
Hugely popular with office and birthday parties, Salsa! is the place to go to learn how to samba, lambada or rhumba. The emphasis is on fun, with dance instructors shimmying on the dance floor along with the packed and sweaty crowd. Bands from around the world play a mixture of Latin and world beats. Monday is salsa night, Tuesday is Brazilian music, and Wednesday offers an introduction to salsa dancing. Thursday is for lambada and salsa fans. At weekends, there are salsa club nights with two sessions of salsa dance classes followed by music from a salsa band so you can practise what you've learned. A set menu of Tex-Mex food (£15) is available.
Map 13/6K.

Music & dancing

Break for the Border

5 Goslett Yard, WC2 (020 7437 8595/ www.bftb.com). Tottenham Court Road tube. **Open** 5pm-1am Mon-Wed; 5pm-3am Thur-Sat. **Music** *bands* 8.30pm-midnight Mon-Sat; *DJs* midnight-3am Wed-Sat. **Meals served** 5-11pm Mon-Wed; 5pm-2am Thur-Sat. **Admission** (refunded against food) £3 after 11pm Wed, £5 after 9.30pm Thur-Sat. **Credit** AmEx, MC, V.
Tex-Mex food and retro theme nights are the order of the day at this Western-styled bar and restaurant. Music comes from the '50s through to the '90s, depending on the theme for the night. Popular with office parties and birthdays, the place pulls a motley crew of tourists, students and suits.
Map 13/6K.

Dover Street

8-10 Dover Street, W1 (020 7629 9813/ www.doverst.co.uk). Green Park or Piccadilly Circus tube. **Open** noon-3.30pm, 5.30pm-3am Mon-Thur, noon-3.30pm, 7pm-3am Fri; 7pm-3am Sat. **Music** *bands* 9.30pm Mon, 10.30pm Tue-Sat; *DJs* until 3am Mon-Sat. **Admission** £5-£10 (free before 9.30pm Mon; before 10pm Tue-Sat). **Credit** AmEx, DC, LV, MC, £TC, V.
Leave your scruffy garments at home when you come to Dover Street. This upmarket premises has three bars, all with a good view of the stage, where you'll find musicians playing jazz, soul, Latin and R&B. The French/Mediterranean menu features dishes such as pot roast duck (£15.85). *Dress: smart casual; no jeans or trainers.*
Map 13/7J.
For branch see index.

Roadhouse

Jubilee Hall, 35 The Piazza, WC2 (020 7240 6001/www.roadhouse.co.uk). Covent Garden tube. **Open** 5.30pm-2.30am Mon; 5.30pm-3am Tue-Sat. **Happy hour** 5.30-10.30pm Mon-Thur; 5.30-7.30pm Fri; 5.30-8.30pm Sat. **Admission** £3-£10. **Credit** AmEx, MC, V.
A theme bar and diner that's popular with tourists and a raucous West End crowd. Live bands play six nights a week; food is a mixture of American-style burgers, pizzas, fajitas and ribs. Kickstart your week with happy hour (3.30-8.30pm Monday-Wednesday) where food and drinks are sold at discount prices. Tuesday is ladies' night – women get in free and receive a complimentary glass of champagne.
Map 14/7L.

Music hall

Brick Lane Music Hall

134-146 Curtain Road, EC2 (020 7739 9997/ www.brick/lane/music/hall.co.uk). Old Street tube/rail. **Open** 6.30pm-midnight, **dinner served** 7.30-9pm, **shows** 9-11.15pm daily. **Admission** £30-£35 incl three-course set dinner and show. **Credit** MC, V.
Recreate the spirit of the Victorian music hall in this beautifully reconstructed theatre. Enjoy a traditional British dinner by candlelight before settling down for an evening with Danny La Rue or an audacious panto. Audience participation is encouraged and the bar is open throughout the evening. The whole venue is available for private hire and can cater for anything from fashion shows to barmitzvahs.
Booking essential.
Map 17/4R.

Opera

The **Organic Café** (*see page 99* **International**) has occasional opera nights (phone for details).

Café Baroque

33 Southampton Street, WC2 (020 7379 7585 www.cafebaroque.co.uk). Covent Garden tube.
Brasserie **Open** noon-midnight Mon-Sat.
Restaurant **Lunch served** noon-3pm, **dinner served** 5.45-11.30pm Mon-Sat.
Both **Credit** AmEx, DC, MC, V.
Opera is performed on the last Tuesday of every month at this intimate venue. The singers are all professionals; they perform with a piano accompaniment for 15 minutes at a time. Get there before 8pm for the first session and the £13.95 set menu. After 8pm, the set meal price increases to £17.95. There is also an à la carte globally inspired menu.
Map 14/7L.

Mama Amalfi's

45 The Mall, Ealing, W5 (020 8840 5888). Ealing Broadway tube/rail. **Open** 10am-11pm Mon-Sat; 10am-10.30pm Sun. **Credit** AmEx, MC, V.
A wooden interior, plenty of plants and a glass front which opens out on to the street in summer give Mama Amalfi's a distinctively Mediterranean feel. Pizzas are cooked in traditional wood-burning ovens; there are also pasta dishes and a range of trad-style Italian mains. Opera is performed on Sundays after 8pm. The singers are not announced but tend to wander out from the kitchens in full flow to serenade diners.

Sarastro

126 Drury Lane, WC2 (020 7836 0101). Covent Garden tube. **Meals served** noon-11.30pm Mon-Sat; noon-10.30pm Sun. **Credit** AmEx, DC, MC, £TC, V.
The Big Night Out lives on here. A doorman greets guests at the door; they proceed into an interior adorned with plush red velvet, gilt

statues, mosaics and frescoes. Every Sunday and Monday, dining takes place to a background of melodic arias delivered by performers from the Royal Opera House. On these evenings a three-course set menu (£19.50) is served. Book early to make sure of a table; the cosy opera boxes elevated above the restaurant floor are especially popular for intimate parties. Food is a varied mix of Turkish starters and European main courses.
Map 14/6M.

Spaghetti Opera at Trat Est
109 Fleet Street, EC4 (020 7353 2680). Blackfriars tube/rail/City Thameslink rail. **Lunch served** noon-3pm, **dinner served** 6.30-11pm Mon-Fri. **Music** 7.30-11pm Mon-Fri. **Credit** AmEx, DC, MC, £TC, V.
Renditions of great moments from opera come in 15-20-minute slots at the Spaghetti Opera. The owners try to ensure that at least two of the singers are professionals, but if you fancy a warble, there's no need to feel intimidated. Anyone with guts and sheet music can have a go. Food is traditional Italian, with a three-course set meal costing £13.50. A disco can be arranged for party bookings.
Map 3/6N.

Scoff & shop

See also the **Fifth Floor** and **Nicole's** (both **Modern European**, *page 131*) and **Table Café** and **Emporio Armani Express** (*page 99* **Italian**).

Bluewater
Greenhithe, Kent (08456 021021/ www.bluewater.co.uk). Greenhithe rail, then 3min shuttle bus ride. **Open** 10am-9pm Mon-Fri; 9am-8pm Sat; 11am-5pm Sun.
The wide range of eateries at this mega-shopping complex runs from the likes of Coffee Republic, Starbucks and Costas, through Yo! Sushi and Ed's Easy Diner, to Hediard (a branch of a Parisian outlet).

The Café, Heal's
First floor, Heal's, 196 Tottenham Court Road, W1 (020 7636 1666). **Map 3/5K.**

Joe's Restaurant Bar
Fenwick, 63 Bond Street, W1 (020 7495 5402). **Map 2/6H.**

Premier at Selfridges
Third floor, Selfridges, Oxford Street, W1 (020 7318 3155). **Map 2/6G.**

Sports bars

See also **Babe Ruth's** (*page 225*).

Shoeless Joe's
555 King's Road, SW6 (020 7610 9346/ www.shoelessjoes.co.uk). Fulham Broadway tube/11, 14, 22 bus. **Open** 10am-11pm Mon-Wed; 10am-1am Thur-Sat; 11am-5pm Sun. **Credit** AmEx, DC, MC, V.
SJ's is aimed at a lively twenty- to thirty-something crowd. Rugby player Victor Obugu's bar has replaced its downstairs booths with leather sofas, and now concentrates on mainstream sports matches and tournaments, but its reputation as the best sports bar in London means it still attracts sports-crazy fans who come to watch matches on the bar-length video screens. A three-course meal (with dishes such as wild mushroom tagliatelle and grilled tuna) costs around £20 per head. Drinks include signature cocktail Shoeless Ziggy.
Map 5/13C.
For branches see index.

The Sports Café
80 Haymarket, SW1 (020 7839 8300/ www.sportscafe.com). Piccadilly Circus tube. **Open** noon-2am Mon-Thur; noon-3am Fri, Sat; noon-10.30pm Sun. **Admission** £3 Mon-Thur after 11pm; £5 Fri, Sat after 11pm. **Credit** AmEx, MC, £$TC, V.
An enormous venue covering two floors, with 140 video screens showing all the major sports tournaments and matches. The restaurant area has an American menu (main courses from £8); other attractions include a pool table, arcade games and a dance floor. Happy hour is 3-7pm daily.
Map 13/7K.

Terry Neill's Sports Bar & Brasserie
Bath House, 53 Holborn Viaduct, EC1 (020 7329 6653/6579). Chancery Lane tube. **Open** 11am-11pm, **meals served** noon-3pm Mon-Fri. **Credit** AmEx, DC, LV, MC, £TC, V.

Terry Neill was the original importer of the sports bar concept to the UK, and his bar is still going strong. Major tournaments and matches are shown on 16 screens that are visible from anywhere inside the bar. Food is a selection of burgers, sandwiches, pastas and steaks; mains average around £8. The venue is also available for private hire.
Map 15/5O.

Views & victuals

See also **Where to...** (*page 10*).

The Tenth
Royal Garden Hotel, Kensington High Street, W8 (020 7361 1910). High Street Kensington tube. **Lunch served** noon-2.30pm Mon-Fri. **Dinner served** 5.30-11pm Mon-Sat. **Credit** AmEx, DC, MC, £TC, V.
For views over Kensington, the Tenth is the place. A jazz trio plays every Saturday evening and on occasional 'Manhattan Nights' guests dine to the sounds of a big band jazz orchestra. The menu has an eclectic mix of influences. As you'd expect, it's not cheap to eat here – reckon on £40 per head.
Map 11/8B.

Vertigo 42
Tower 42, Old Broad Street, EC2 (020 7877 7842). Bank tube/DLR. **Lunch served** 11.45am-3pm, **dinner served** 5-9pm Mon-Fri. **Credit** AmEx, MC, V.
The best views over the City of London and beyond, from the top of the former NatWest building. Getting in discourages spontaneity – you need to ring in advance for a reservation, then on arrival someone chaperones you up to the right floor. Although primarily a cocktail bar with most of the chairs facing out towards the plate glass, you can also eat (expensive) seafood.
Map 4/6Q.

Windows
London Hilton, 22 Park Lane, W1 (020 7208 4021). Hyde Park Corner tube. **Brunch served** 12.30-2.30pm Sun. **Lunch served** 12.30-2.30pm Mon-Fri. **Dinner served** 7-10.30pm Mon-Thur; 7-11.30pm Fri, Sat. **Credit** AmEx, DC, JCB, MC, TC, V.
Windows is on the 28th floor of the Hilton. Dinner here costs serious money (*see p76* **Hotels & Haute Cuisine**), but there's a Sunday buffet brunch menu at £29.50. Music comes courtesy of the resident jazz band during the evening.
Map 6/8G.

24-hour eats

See also **Where to...** (*page 10*).

Old Compton Café
34 Old Compton Street, W1 (020 7439 3309). Leicester Square tube. **Meals served** 24 hours daily (closed for an hour around 5-6am for cleaning). **No credit cards.**
A busy and popular café that serves a seemingly endless choice of sandwiches (including some moreish toasted ciabatta ones), plus salads and hot food. Service can be a touch curt and slap-dash when things get busy, but portions are large and prices are reasonable (sandwiches range from £2.50 to £5). It gets packed in the evenings.
Map 13/6K.

Tinseltown
44-46 St John Street, EC1 (020 7689 2424). Farringdon tube/rail. **Meals served** 24 hours daily. **Credit** AmEx, DC, MC, V.
A screen shows Sky films and walls are littered with stills of the stars in this Hollywood-themed basement diner. Food is pretty average – fries, burgers, omelettes, garlic mushrooms, chicken wings and so on – with prices starting at £3 for starters and £6 for mains. The place is dead during the day, but its close proximity to the pubs and clubs of Clerkenwell makes it a regular hangout for clubbers and nocturnal snackers. You can even sit in the Edward Hopper-style booths and imagine you're in the Big Apple.
Map 15/5O.

Vingt-Quatre
325 Fulham Road, SW10 (020 7376 7224). Bus 14, N14. **Meals served** 24 hours daily. **Credit** AmEx, MC, V.
A refurbishment is currently bringing more comfortable seating, along with healthier food options, to Vingt-Quatre. For six years, this 24-hour café has served English breakfasts, salads, pastas, burgers and desserts to hordes of hungry clubbers and party animals. Beers, wines and cocktails are served until midnight and there is a £1 cover charge from 10.30pm until 7am.
Map 5/12D.

Out of Town

The Vineyard

For more pubs and restaurants outside London, see the *Time Out Book of Weekend Breaks* (£12.99) – it's full of suggestions for where to eat, with food ranging from great ploughman's lunches to innovative cooking by top chefs.

Berkshire

The Vineyard

Stockcross, Newbury, Berks (01635 528770). **Lunch served** noon-2pm, **dinner served** 7-10pm daily. **Main courses** £19.75-£24. **Set lunch** £16 two courses, £22 three courses. **Set dinner** £42 three courses, £75 or £100 five courses incl wine. **Credit** AmEx, DC, MC, V.
What to do Walk the Ridgeway, visit stately homes Highclere Castle or Stratfield Saye, or have a day at the races.
Imagine a wedding cake hitching a lift on a country road and you have the Vineyard. A young man assumes control of your car in the driveway and announces you to a hovering welcoming committee who deliver bar menu, canapés, drinks, food menu and wine lists. The restaurant showcases the Californian wines of owner Sir Peter Michael and has become, without doubt, a glamour-pusses' convention. The place is all tiers of creamy stone, wrought-iron 'vines' and bold modern paintings. Food is familiar, as a dish of Goosenargh duck with roasted carrots, fondant potato and port jus might suggest. The 'fusion' menu – five courses with preselected wines – is a tempting, but vastly expensive tasting menu. The wine lists are huge, one international, the other listing over 500 wines just from California. Sommeliers and waiters are bright and non-threatening. From the carte, Crottin goat's cheese had a smooth chalky centre and came with red and yellow peppers, aubergine and courgette – all carefully grilled. Beef carpaccio was perfectly correct but its sweet flavour was sapped by the strength of a Parmesan wafer. A main course of guinea fowl breasts, stuffed with orange-scented prunes and an airy mousseline, was unquestionably successful. Dover sole was also beautifully presented with vibrant green vegetables and vermouth cream sauce, yet a bit tough. Desserts were excellent (as were canapés and petits fours). The decor is a matter of taste, as is the zealous service, but the food is splendid and the wine list certainly begs exploration.
Booking advisable.

East Sussex

Black Chapati

12 Circus Parade, New England Road, Brighton, East Sussex (01273 699 011). **Dinner served** 7-10pm Tue-Fri; 6.30-10pm Sat. **Main courses** £10.50-£13.50. **Service** 10%. **Credit** AmEx, MC, £TC, V; no cheques accepted.
What to do Essential sights are the Lanes, the Museum, the Royal Pavilion and other examples of Regency architecture, not to mention the Pier – and, of course, the beach. The shopping's good, too, particularly around the Lanes.
The Black Chapati may have become an institution – an icon, even – but it certainly hasn't become dull. Its near-seedy shopping-parade location, inadvertently retro decor, characterful staff and inspired menu (eclectic, not Indian as the name might suggest) see to that. It's a simple one-roomer decked out with photos of Asia's spice markets, fresh flowers and black 1980s-esque tables – tightly packed, especially for smokers, who, the menu suggests, should consult their neighbours before lighting up (which can make things tense). There's a tiny bar and a hatch on to the kitchen, from which emanates a short, changing menu that delivers contemporary world classics transformed by exquisite spicing (usually Asian, just occasionally overdone) and high-quality raw materials. Starters might include plumptious scallops with fish sauce-flavoured glass noodles and a carrot and mustard seed side salad; and plain but expert Sri Lankan lamb patties with revelatory chutneys. Pork belly with caramelised garlic and pak choi is a favourite main; in winter there were several other rib-stickers (such as an intelligently flavoured rack of lamb with couscous and spiced pumpkin broth), plus lighter choices: grilled chicken with lemongrass and Malaysian pickles, for example. Wines are a secondary attraction, but well priced and chosen, as are desserts, though the cardamom crème brûlée – its shallow dish facilitating a high caramel-cream ration – is developing a reputation for itself. One warning: on our visit service was charming, but we've had reports this isn't always the case.
Babies and children admitted. Booking advisable. Vegetarian dishes.

Gingerman

21A Norfolk Square, Brighton, East Sussex (01273 326688). **Lunch served** 12.30-2pm, **dinner served** 7.30-10pm Tue-Sat. **Set lunch** £12.95 two courses, £14.95 three courses, incl coffee. **Set meal** £18.95 two courses, £21.50 three courses. **Credit** AmEx, DC, MC, V.
What to do *As above* **Black Chapati**.
It's pretty much impossible to get a booking later than a week ahead at the Gingerman. Once you've been you'll want to go back, and with the limited capacity, that means a bookings war. The draws are an intimate space (it's basically the ground floor of an ordinary townhouse, plain, tasteful and suffused with candlelight); personal but unaffected service; and a fixed-price, very fairly priced menu. The food is seasonal and contemporary, with a slant towards the special occasion. On our summer visit, starters included butternut squash and crab soup, potato and Pecorino ravioli with summer truffles; main courses had rabbit with pressed potatoes, and grilled venison with red cabbage among their number; and desserts (a strong suit) were pears poached in Marsala, and a plate of mini raspberry desserts (crème brûlée, raspberry tart and chocolate raspberry soufflé). Our starters were excellent, the mains OK and the raspberry dessert sensational. With a good wine list (lots at the low end) and unannounced extras to boot, the Gingerman is a little gem.
Babies and children admitted; high chairs. No-smoking tables. Vegetarian dishes.

Terre à Terre

71 East Street, Brighton, East Sussex (01273 729051). **Dinner served** 6-10.30pm Mon. **Meals served** noon-11pm Tue-Sun. **Main courses** £9.50-£10.50. **Service** 10% for parties of six or more. **Credit** AmEx, MC, £TC, V.
What to do *As above* **Black Chapati**.
Hugely and justifiably popular, Terre à Terre is the kind of vegetarian restaurant that makes meat-eaters wonder why they bother. The set-up – generously spaced tables among lots of wood, flowers and ochre-reds, and prompt, friendly staff (though they could have told us about the specials) – is professional and relaxing. The globally inspired menu rings with contemporary buzz-ingredients and styles (in somewhat overdone menu-ese); it delivers dishes that are diverse, complex and thoroughly of the moment. Typical among the starters (£3.75-£5.50) and salads (£4.95-£9.50) are fried corncakes with chipotle and tamarillo salsa (a piquant mix of tang and texture); soba salad infused with a catalogue of Japanese flavours; and zhuganoush, a Middle Eastern confection of aubergine, peppers and halloumi 'finished' with a poached egg. Mains are equally elaborate but more formal. On our visit, they included a Camembert soufflé, an asparagus fava millefeuille, some dosa-encased vegetables, and – our choice – a sweet potato laksa with udon noodles, aubergine brochette and 'spice dust plantain horns'. Delicious, but rich, as is the whole menu – a shame, especially since the only lighter dish, porcini and thyme bavarois on wild leeks and Jerusalem artichoke rösti, was exquisite. Even the sorbet came only in chocolate.
Babies and children welcome; high chairs; nappy-changing facilities. Bookings accepted for dinner only. Disabled: toilet. No-smoking tables. Vegan dishes.

Kent

The Dove Inn

Plum Pudding Lane, Dargate, Kent (01227 751360). **Lunch served** noon-2pm Tue-Sun. **Dinner served** 7-9pm Wed-Sat. **Main courses** £9.99-£16. **Credit** DC, MC, V.
What to do Dargate lies between the coast at Whitstable (*see below*) and Canterbury, where the attractions include the cathedral and various museums.
Plum Pudding Lane couldn't be a more appropriate address for The Dove Inn. It's a pub with an outstanding reputation for food, but doesn't pretend to be a restaurant. Much of the little brick inn is given over to dining, though not at the expense of the atmosphere, which remains that of a well-scrubbed, well-loved local. There are notices about quiz nights, sepia photographs of previous landlords, the current chef's plaques and awards, and garlands of hop flowers. Although the cooking owes much to the other side of the Channel, ingredients are palpably local. This is the Garden of England at its most riotously productive, as the Dove's lovely garden with trees that droop with fruit in summer and autumn testify. Fish comes from the coast nearby, game is bagged locally, vegetables are grown almost on the doorstep. There are rustic bar snacks such as croque monsieur, and rillettes with toasted brioche, to go with the Shepherd Neame ales, but the main menu lists cholesterol-rich classics such as langoustines in gingery butter, Dover sole with herb butter, and mackerel with tarragon and shallot sauce. Rack of lamb was cooked to perfection. Underlying the deceptive simplicity of dishes is a professional precision. Puddings such as an apple and almond tart make skilful use of local fruit, there's a plate of peerless French and British cheeses, and if passion fruit crème brûlée sounds inappropriately exotic, take a look at the climber outside the dining room window – a passion flower.
Babies and children admitted. Booking advisable. Tables outdoors (15, garden).

Hotel du Vin

Crescent Road, Tunbridge Wells, Kent (01892 526455). **Lunch served** noon-1.30pm, **dinner served** 7-9.30pm daily. **Main courses** £11-£13.95. **Set Sunday lunch** £22.50 three courses incl coffee. **Credit** AmEx, DC, MC, V.
What to do Explore Tunbridge Wells, where the main attraction is the Pantiles, a colonnaded late-17th-century street. .
Tunbridge Wells makes an excellent base for exploring the many wonders of the Kent Weald – and what better way to start than eating and possibly staying at this exceptionally tasteful and well-run hotel? Inside the atmospheric Grade II listed building, the bistro is intimate and candlelit but not in any way stuffy. The menu is French with New World influences. Skate roulade with lemon-grass dressing was well-balanced, with the Thai herb complementing the delicate fish flavour. Pan-fried foie gras with poached pear was delicious. Next, we enjoyed a mouth-watering roasted halibut with sweet potato fondant and lime coriander butter, while pork and duck cassoulet was judged to be traditional, hearty French fare with excellent flavours all round. Loin of lamb and celeriac mash was among the most succulent and flavourful pieces of meat we've eaten in ages. A delightful apricot cobbler came with clotted cream; the only duff note was a rather dry plum torte with balsamic syrup. The wine list is exemplary, with many wines by the glass and enough choice to please serious oenophiles. A knowledgeable wine waitress steered us away from sauvignon blanc and chardonnay to an intense Vacqueyras Rhône white that slipped down with ease. Fab food, with great beds too.
Babies and children admitted; high chairs; nappy-changing facilities. Disabled: toilet. Tables outdoors (9, patio). Vegetarian dishes.

Whitstable Oyster Fishery Company

Royal Native Oyster Stores, The Horsebridge, Whitstable, Kent (01227 276856). **Lunch served** noon-1.45pm Tue-Fri; noon-2.15pm Sat; noon-3.15pm Sun. **Dinner served** 7-8.45pm Tue-Fri; 6.30-9.45pm Sat. **Main courses** £9.50-£24. **Service** 10%. **Credit** AmEx, DC, MC, £TC, V.
What to do Enjoy the beach – it (and the restaurant) are an easy walk from Whitstable railway station.
Richard and James Green's impact upon the small north Kent town of Whitstable can be compared (on a smaller scale, perhaps) to Rick Stein's upon Padstow. The Whitstable Oyster Fishery Company – and their Hotel Continental – has provided scores of local jobs and drawn in hordes of high-living out-of-towners, revitalising the sleepy town (or destroying its unique atmosphere, depending on your point of view). What isn't a matter of opinion is the excellence of the restaurant, an informal place where anyone will feel comfortable. It serves simply prepared, high-quality seafood. A black-board menu hangs from the bare brick walls, beneath beamed ceilings and above cosily-packed bistro-like tables and wooden-boarded floor. Local dressed crab was packed with sea-fresh brown and white meat, while langoustine salad (more like crayfish with garnish) featured six equally fine crustacea. Mains are equally straightforward, but when you've got Dover sole or half a local lobster

Quod Bar & Grill

(with potato salad) of this calibre, it'd be a crime to do more than the culinary minimum. The heavenly stem ginger or honeycomb ice-cream is worth the journey on its own.
Babies and children welcome; high chairs. Booking essential. Tables outdoors (10, boardwalk).

Oxfordshire

Crazy Bear
Bear Lane, Stadhampton, Oxford (01865 890 714). **Lunch served** noon-3pm, **dinner served** 7-10.30pm Mon-Sat. **Main courses** £9.95-£14.95. **Credit** AmEx, MC, V.
What to do Didcot Rail Centre is a must for steam buffs; otherwise the Ridgeway is close.
The Crazy Bear – hotel, bar, restaurant, smokehouse and Thai brasserie – is a one-off. Here, 16th-century brick-and-flint meet art deco, tournedos Rossini meet pho tack (hot and sour soup), and stuffed bears and zebra skins meet marshmallow-flavoured vodka. The restaurant is a few steps up from the bar, giving a nice feeling of belonging, without the crush. Food is sensibly brief and Frenchified with desirable sidelines such as oysters, nut nibbles and caviar. A heavily caramelised, chewy-rimmed tarte tatin of shallots came with either foie gras or goat's cheese (both £9), green peppercorn sauce and roasted pear. Neatly boned quail had likewise spent long in a hot pan, was fruitily stuffed and lay supine on buttered cabbage. Potato rösti was unappetisingly over-cooked. The day's special, roast turbot, was excellent, but the accompanying asparagus and wild mushrooms were limp, and pomme purée dissolved into a creamy herb sauce. Braised lamb shank fared better; it was tender, with a perky panache of beans and rosemary jus. For dessert, a crème brûlée tasting plate featured a thick, vanilla-packed classic, a second overloaded with chocolate, and a disastrous strawberry version. Service was appallingly slow, wine by the glass is served in tiny quantities (and one glass went back for being warm and long-opened). Yet, for its nutty ambience, superb bar snacks, Thai brasserie and huge collection of cigars and alcohol, this is an unforgettable venue for a lazy Sunday afternoon.
Booking advisable.

The Goose
Britwell Salome, near Watlington, Oxon (01491 612304). **Lunch served** noon-2.30pm Tue-Sat; noon-3pm Sun. **Dinner served** 6.30-10pm Tue-Sat. **Set lunch** (Tue-Sat) £10 three courses. **Set meal** (dinner, Sunday lunch) £25 three courses. **Credit** MC, £TC, V.
What to do Henley and the Thames are close.
Unlike most country pubs, which rely on the view and forget the provenance, scenery is a mere casual aside at the Goose. Relaxing-with-drinks space is surprisingly neglected in both garden and bar areas, so enjoy the superb view before arriving. Much of the food is sourced locally. On the summer evening of our visit tables were laden with vivid fans of asparagus, plump English veal and extravagantly scented wine from a brief, delectable list of moderate mark-ups. Pork terrine made a robust beginning, served with pear chutney and hunks of good bread. Grilled halibut from a main course list of four was tempting, but curiosity and hunger drove us to beef and more pork. Ballottine of suckling pig was truly top notch – meltingly innocent with a superb farce of seasoned shredded pork and truffle. Simple jus and spring cabbage completed a mosaic of depth, earthiness yet delicacy. No less satisfying was fillet of Orkney beef. Ceps, broccoli and new potatoes came alongside, but the meat was a stand-alone piece of nearly forgotten flavour and à point tenderness. We nipped in a cheese plate – a conservative but ambiently served and well cared for bunch – before evening finally fell to the sound of crunching brûlée toppings and 'oohs' over the 5in-high hot chocolate soufflés. Let's hope the Goose keeps flying on course.
Babies and children welcome. Booking advisable; essential weekends. No-smoking tables. Tables outdoors (6, garden).

The Lemon Tree
268 Woodstock Road, Oxford (01865 311936). **Meals served** noon-11pm Mon-Sat; noon-11pm Sun. **Main courses** £11.95-£17.50. **Service** 10% for parties of five or more. **Credit** AmEx, MC, £TC, V.
What to do Explore Oxford – as well as looking at the colleges, visit the Covered Market. Woodstock Road is also handily placed for Blenheim Palace, 6 miles away.
The Lemon Tree has made a decent fist of becoming a Mediterranean villa. Past the gravelled courtyard garden is an airy high-ceilinged bar, and behind that an equally spacious dining room. Here, arched windows, large palms, distressed yellow walls, rattan chairs and lino flooring (faking elderly tiles) complete the conceit. Yet crisply attired tables and smart, breezy staff show a seriousness way beyond that of a thrown-together theme joint. As does the food. Confidence suffuses Shaun Mitchell's menu, which offers mostly Med-influenced dishes (roast spatchcock of poussin marinated in lemon and yoghurt with couscous, say) plus a few more daring daily specials. Off the latter, grilled salmon fillet on mixed leaves with a (rogue) pork and leek sausage and warm tapenade simply didn't hang together, despite excellent ingredients. Vegetables (savoury mash in our case) cost extra. We preceded this with mushroom bruschetta: chunks of lightly cooked fungi well-paired with a sharp balsamic dressing, creamy ricotta and barely discernible truffle oil. Talent, ingredients and taste all came together for dessert, however: a bravely citric lemon tart with a perfect brûléed top. Few use the Lemon Tree mid-afternoon – on our visit, just some spectacularly upholstered ladies-who-lunch. Come evening, tourists and north Oxford gentlefolk populate the tables. Our bill (including a bottle of gooseberryish Cape Charlotte dry muscat from a New World accented wine list) was high, but so was the skill on display. No lemon, this.
Babies and children welcome. Booking advisable. Disabled: toilet. Tables outdoors (10, garden).

Le Petit Blanc
71-72 Walton Street, Oxford (01865 510999). **Lunch served** noon-3pm Mon-Fri; noon-3.30pm Sat, Sun. **Tea served** 3.30-6pm Mon-Fri; 4-6pm Sat, Sun. **Dinner served** 6-11pm Mon-Sat; 6.30-10pm Sun. **Main courses** £8-£13.50. **Credit** AmEx, DC, MC, £TC, V.
What to do *As above* **The Lemon Tree**.
Raymond Blanc's popular brasserie has large picture windows, blue walls and a mural showing a quirky artist's impression of Oxford. The light, bright surroundings cannot fail to put you in a good mood. 'Blanc Vite' dishes – 'fresh fast food on a plate' – are served throughout the day, but we recommend lingering over a long lunch, enjoying the French regional specialities. We began in style: (barely) pan-fried red mullet had retained its startling scarlet and silver hue and wonderfully fresh flavour; it came with soused aubergine and summer vegetables. Melt-in-the-mouth foie gras and chicken liver parfait was offset by tangy red onion marmalade. To follow, coq au vin 'Maman Blanc' was two portions of succulent chicken cooked in a deep but liquid dark wine sauce. It rested on golden tagliatelle, with delicately cooked french beans. Roast sea bass and crab ravioli with teriyaki butter and spinach sauce wasn't as successful; the potency of the crab paste in the single raviolo overpowering the fish's delicate flavours. As a finale, floating island 'Maman Blanc' was a fluffy cloud of vanilla: the perfect prelude to a strong cup of coffee. It's difficult to fault the attentive but unobtrusive service or the exquisite presentation of the food here. Tables are perhaps too close together, yet this is a small gripe given the relaxed ambience. Families are well catered for, but romantic couples won't be disappointed either.
Babies and children welcome; children's menu; high chairs. Booking essential. Disabled: toilet.

Quod Bar & Grill
92-94 High Street, Oxford (01865 202505). **Breakfast served** 8-11am, **meals served** 11am-11pm daily. **Main courses** £6.55-£10.65. **Credit** AmEx, MC, V.
What to do *As above* **The Lemon Tree**.
On a Saturday night soon after opening, the noise and crush were testimony to Quod's hit with the discerning Oxford set. This sleek, stone-floored, zinc and leather animal is caged in a Georgian Grade II-listed hotel smack in the centre of the city. Herb bread arrived soft, warm and pliant with a bowl of olive oil on a 'Q' shaped bread-board. From a sunny, vaguely Italian menu, starters of the 'charred veg, cured meat and country cheese' type all cheerfully carry over from lunch to dinner; then pasta and risotto are offered in two sizes before a meatier section. First courses arrived quickly. Saffron risotto was rich, plump and golden, topped by perfectly pink and peppery chicken livers. Fresh sardine salad was the one letdown; a single skinny fish lay stricken on a heap of grated root vegetables with an acidic dressing. We had a fairly long wait for main courses, but staff couldn't be faulted for their smiling efficiency. A nice tuna steak was presented with unconvincing accompaniments of grapefruit and rhubarb. Classic rib-eye steak with sage butter was superbly supple and rested, although the chips with it weren't sparkling. To finish, helium-light tiramisu was balanced by gorgeous Amaretto ice-cream. Coffee was good and the bill a mere £40 (for two, without wine).
Booking advisable.

Suffolk

The Trinity
The Crown & Castle, Orford, near Woodbridge, Suffolk (01394 450205). **Open** 11am-11pm Mon-Sat; noon-10.30pm Sun. **Lunch served** noon-2.30pm daily. **Dinner served** 7-9.30pm Mon-Fri, Sun; 7-10pm Sat. **Main courses** £9-£15. **Credit** MC, V.
What to do The Suffolk coast provides miles of scenic walks; Orford Ness, a ten-mile long expanse of shingle, is a desolate but fascinating place.
As a hotel, The Crown & Castle is no great shakes; we stayed there and thought it disappointing and overpriced. But the Trinity restaurant is sensational – easily one of the best in Sussex. Chef Brendan Ansbro has great talent, and excellent ingredients have been sourced by the owners, Ruth and David Watson. The menu is a deeply appealing read. Plump, succulent Burford-Orford oysters were served with hot sausage patties in the Breton style; the dish was a huge success both in terms of flavour and texture. A seasonal risotto with broad beans, dill and Gorgonzola was light yet intensely flavoured. Main courses were even better. Vietnamese belly of pork with pak choi, shiitake and oyster mushrooms was outstanding, as good as any pork belly we've eaten in Chinatown, with the skin crisp and the fat full flavoured. Crab cake was packed with firm crab meat and contrasted beautifully with crushed avocado, lime and coriander mayonnaise. We didn't have room for puds but they looked good – the woman at an adjacent table nearly did a *When Harry Met Sally* when hers arrived. The wine list is notable too, with a diverse range of styles. One of the best meals we've had all year, no question.
Babies and children admitted; high chairs. Booking advisable; essential weekends. Tables outdoors (20, bar terrace; 9, restaurant terrace).

Surrey

Bel & the Dragon
Bridge Street, Godalming, Surrey (01483 527333). **Open** 11am-11pm daily. **Lunch served** noon-2.30pm Mon-Sat; noon-3pm Sun. **Dinner served** 7-10pm Mon-Sat; 7-9.30pm Sun. **Main courses** £9.95-£19.95. **Credit** AmEx, MC, V.
What to do Loseley Park, Winkworth Arboretum and family-orientated Birdworld.
The name is from the Old Testament and also belongs to a pub in Cookham converted to a restaurant. The same owners have since bestowed it on a second restaurant in Windsor, and this, their third, forming a mini-chain around the commuter belt. Godalming's Bel is in a converted chapel, decorated in Gothic style and staffed by friendly young people. With a bar in the nave and a galleried eating area above, it's designed to attract a broad church: most tastes and all ages are accommodated. The food is robust, middle of the road, modern: no airs and graces, but fresh, chunky, boldly flavoured, and served in generous quantities. The menu isn't divided into starters and mains; dishes are graded from £3.95 for 'a bowl of rustic country breads with roast garlic, olive oil and olives' to £17.95 for a 12oz rib-eye steak. Starter-equivalents – fish cakes with lemon butter sauce, baby spinach and watercress salad; and Middle Eastern-style meat balls nicely spiked with cumin, with a Greek-like salad – are big enough to make a main course a struggle. Half a roast chicken and chips with bread sauce had a slightly institutional pre-cooked feel to it, yet the gravy was classy; smoked haddock with cheesy sauce (perked up with paprika, a poached egg and parsley-speckled mash) was a well-made plateful. Puds of the sticky toffee, and ice-cream variety lack subtlety but are fancily presented. Satisfying family dining without undue reverence, but at Surrey prices.
Booking advisable.

West Sussex

Lickfold Inn
Lickfold, nr Lodsworth, Petworth, West Sussex (01798 861285). **Lunch served** 11am-3.15pm Mon-Sat; noon-3.15pm Sun. **Dinner served** 6-10.45pm Mon-Sat; 7-10.15pm Sun. **Main courses** £8.50-£15.50. **Credit** AmEx, MC, V.
What to do The magnificent Petworth House and Park is a few miles away.
This ancient pub with its voguish interior decor and modern fusion cuisine must surely be most urbanites' idea of heaven. It stands on its own beside a babbling brook, surrounded by stunning countryside. The restaurant is above the pub: bare brick walls are hung with unpulled curtains resembling medieval colours. Elegant tables with white damask cloths enhance the understated luxury. The wine list isn't bad, either: you could opt for a glass of house champagne, or even the local Gospel Green cider champagne. The menu is a wonderful mix of taste and colour. Char-grilled scallops and cuttlefish with sweet chilli butter was fresh and succulent, but even more exciting was the highly spiced tuna Moroccan-style with yoghurt and tomato concassé. Next came seared salmon with stir-fried vegetables and noodles in teriyaki sauce; and roast lamb rump with mint couscous and redcurrant jus. Both were superb and came with seasonal vegetables (the only parochial, but charming, touch of the evening). Char-grilled peaches with mascarpone and lavender syrup; and delectable raspberry crème brûlée made a fitting finale to a first-rate meal.
Booking essential.

Lickfold Inn

Subject index

Area index

El Vino
30 New Bridge Street, EC4
(020 7236 4534)

El Vino
6 Martin Lane, off Cannon
Street, EC4 (020 7626
6876)

El Vino
3 Bastion High Walk, 125
London Wall, EC2 (020 7600
6377)

Espres
101 Fleet Street, E4 (020
7583 6669)

The Fine Line
1 Bow Churchyard, EC4 (020
7248 3262)

The Fine Line
124-127 The Minories, EC3
(020 481 8195)

The Fine Line
Equitable House, 1
Monument Street, EC3 (020
623 5446)

Foxtrot Oscar
16 Byward Street, EC3 (020
7481 2700)

Gaucho Grill
12 Gracechurch Street, EC3
(020 7626 5180)

La Grande Marque
55 Leadenhall Market, EC3
(020 7929 3536)

Habit (branch of Davys)
65 Crutched Friars, Friary
Court, EC3 (020 7481 1131)

Jamies
13 Philpot lane, EC3 (020
7621 9577)

Jamies
Bankside House, 107-112
Leadenhall Street, EC3 (020
7626 7226)

Jamies
119-121 The Minories, EC3
(020 7709 9900)

Jamies
5 Groveland Court, EC4 (020
7248 5551)

Jamies
54 Gresham Street, EC2
(020 7606 1755)

Jamies
155 Bishopsgate, EC2 (020
7256 7279)

Jamies,
64-66 West Smithfield, EC1
(020 7600 0700)

Lococo
9A Cullum Street, EC3 (020
7220 7722)

Lunch
7 Old Street, EC1 (020 7490
7557)

Moshi Moshi Sushi
Liverpool Street Station, 24
Upper Level, Broadgate, EC2
(020 7375 3571)

Moshi Moshi Sushi
7-8 Limeburner Lane, EC4
(020 7248 1808)

Noto
2-3 Bassishaw Highwalk,
London Wall, EC2 (020 7256
9433)

Number 25
(branch of Jamies)
25 Birchin Lane, EC3 (020
7623 2505)

The Orangery
Cutlers Gardens, 10
Devonshire Square, EC2
(020 7623 1377)

Pacific Spice (branch of
Silks & Spice)
42 Northampton Road, EC1
(020 7278 9983)

The Pavilion (branch of
Jamies)
Finsbury Circus Gardens,
EC3 (020 7628 8224)

Pitcher and Piano
28-31 Cornhill, EC3 (020
7929 3989)

Pitcher and Piano
200 Bishopsgate, EC2 (020
7929 5914)

Pitcher and Piano
The Arches, 9 Crutched
Friars, EC3 (020 7480 6818)

Pizza Express
7-9 St Brides Street, EC4
(020 7583 5126)

Pizza Express
125 Alban Gate, London
Wall, EC2 (020 7600 8880)

Pulpit (branch of Davys)
63 Worship Street, EC2 (020
7377 1574)

Ravi Shankar (branch of
Chutneys)
422 St John Street, EC1
(020 7833 5849)

Scu-zi
2 Creechurch Lane, EC3
(020 7623 3444)

Shotberries
(branch of Davys)
167 Queen Victoria Street,
EC4 (020 7329 4759)

Silks & Spice City
(branch of Silks and
Spice)
11 Queen Victoria Street,
EC4 (020 7236 7222)

Silks and Spice
9-10 Liverpool Street, EC2
(020 7626 1155)

Singapura
78-79 Leadenhall Street,
EC3 (020 7929 0089)

The Slug and Lettuce
9 Stoney Lane, E1 (020
7626 4994)

Sri Siam City
85 London Wall, EC2 (020
7628 5772)

British

City Rhodes   p33
1 New Street Square, EC4
(020 7583 1313)

Cafés

Crussh   p204
48 Cornhill, EC3 (020 7626
2175)

Chinese

Imperial City   p45
Royal Exchange, Cornhill,
EC3 (020 7626 3437)

Poons in the City   p45
2 Minster Pavement, Minster
Court, Mincing Lane, EC3
(020 7626 0126)

Eating & Entertainment

Spaghetti Opera
at Trat Est   p226
109 Fleet Street, EC4 (020
7353 2680)

Vertigo 42   p226
Tower 42, Old Broad Street,
EC2 (020 7877 7842)

Fish

Fishmarket   p54
Great Eastern Hotel, 40
Liverpool Street, EC2 (020
7618 7200/www.fish-
market.co.uk)

Sweetings   p54
39 Queen Victoria Street,
EC4 (020 7248 3062)

French

1 Lombard Street   p59
1 Lombard Street, EC3 (020
7929 6611/
www.1lombardstreet.com)

Le Coq d'Argent   p59
No.1 Poultry, EC2 (020
7395 5000/5050/
www.conran.com)

Indian

Shimla Pinks   p77
7 Bishopsgate Churchyard,
EC2 (020 7628 7888)

International

Bar Bourse   p94
67 Queens Street, EC4 (020
7248 2200/2211)

Italian

Caravaggio   p99
107 Leadenhall Street, EC3
(020 7626 6206)

Japanese

City Miyama   p111
17 Godliman Street, EC4
(020 7489 1937)

Aykoku-Kaku   p111
Bucklersbury House,
9 Walbrook, EC4
(020 7236 9020/
www.japanweb.co.uk/ak)

K-10   p111
20 Copthall Avenue, EC2
(020 7562
8510/www.k10.net)

Miyabi   p111
Great Eastern Hotel,
Liverpool Street, EC2 (020
7618 7100)

Moshi Moshi Sushi   p113
Unit 24, Liverpool Street
Station, EC2 (020 7427
3227/www.moshimoshi.co.uk)

Noto Ramen House   p113
Bow Bells House, 7 Bread
Street, EC4 (020 7329
8056)

Korean

Arana   p120
116 Newgate Street, EC1
(020 7600 1134/020 7606
2320)

Malaysian, Indonesian
& Singaporean

Singapura   p122
1-2 Limeburner Lane, EC4
(020 7329 1133)

Singapura EC2   p122
31 Broadgate Circle, EC2
(020 7256 5044)

Modern European

1 Blossom Street   p131
1 Blossom Street, E1 (020
7247 6530)

Prism   p131
147 Leadenhall Street, EC3
(020 7256 3888)

Terminus Bar
& Grill   p131
40 Liverpool Street, EC2
(020 7618 7400)

Oriental

Pacific Oriental   p146
1 Bishopsgate, EC2 (020
7621 9988)

Tao   p146
11-11A Bow Lane, EC4 (020
7248 5833)

Pizza & Pasta

Pizza Express   p185
125 London Wall, EC2 (020
7600 8880/
www.pizzaexpress.co.uk)

Spanish

Barcelona Tapas
Bar y Restaurante   p152
15 St Botolph Street –
entrance in Middlesex Street,
EC3 (020 7377 5111)

Leadenhall
Wine Bar   p152
27 Leadenhall Market, EC3
(020 7623 1818)

Mesón Los
Barriles   p152
8A Lamb Street, E1 (020
7375 3136)

Thai

Sri Thai   p160
Bucklersbury House, 3
Queen Victoria Street,
EC4 (020 7827 0202)

Vegetarian

The Place Below   p173
St Mary-le-Bow, Cheapside,
EC2 (020 7329 0789)

Wine Bars

City Limits   p218
16-18 Brushfield Street, E1
(020 7377 9877)

El Vino   p218
47 Fleet Street, EC4 (020
7353
6786/www.elvino.co.uk)

La Grande Marque   p218
47 Ludgate Hill, EC4 (020
7329 6709)

The Pavilion   p218
Finsbury Circus Gardens,
EC2 (020 7628 8224)

Clapham SW4, SW9, SW11

The Americas

Café Sol   p32
56 Clapham High Street,
SW4 (020 7498 9319)

Branches

All Bar One
32-38 Northcote Road,
SW11 (020 7801 9951)

Arancia BAC
Battersea Arts Centre,
Lavender Hill, SW11 (020
7228 2286)

Bierodrome
(branch of Belgo)
44-48 Clapham High Street,
SW4 (020 7720 1118)

Cafe Rouge
40 Abbeville Road, SW4
(0208 673 3399)

The Fine Line
182-184 Clapham High
Street, SW4 (020 7622
4436)

Jongleurs Battersea
49 Lavender Gardens, SW11
(020 7564 2500)

The Lavender
24 Clapham Road, SW9 (020
7793 0770)

Nando's Chicken
59-63 Clapham High Street,
SW4 (020 7622 1475)

Pitcher and Piano
94 Northcote Road, SW11
(020 7738 9781)

Pizza Express
43 Abbeville Road, SW4
(020 8673 8878)

Pizza Express
230-236 Lavender Hill,
SW11 (020 7223 5677)

La Rueda
66-68 Clapham High Street,
SW4 (020 7627 2173)

Tiger Lil's
16A Clapham Common, SW4
(020 7720 5433)

Wok Wok
51-53 Northcote Road,
SW11 (020 7978 7181)

Brasseries

The Abbeville   p197
67-69 Abbeville Road, SW4
(020 8675 2201)

Gastro   p197
67 Venn Street, SW4 (020
7627 0222)

Newtons   p197
33-35 Abbeville Road, SW4
(020 8673 0977)

Budget

Abbevilles   p182
88 Clapham Park Road, SW4
(020 7498 2185)

Cafés

The Pavement   p202
21 The Pavement, SW4 (020
7622 4944)

Central & East
European

Café Wanda   p39
153 Clapham High Street,
SW4 (020 7738 8760)

Fish

Moxon's   p57
14 Clapham Park Road, SW4
(020 7627 2468)

International

The Rapscallion   p98
75 Venn Street, SW4 (020
7787 6555)

Italian

Tuba   p108
4 Clapham Common
Southside, SW4 (020 7978
3333/www.tuba.co.uk)

Modern European

Polygon   p140
4 The Polygon, SW4 (020
7622 1199)

The Sequel   p140
75 Venn Street, SW4 (020
7622 4222)

North African

Kasbah   p145
73 Venn Street, SW4 (020
7498 3622)

Pizza & Pasta

Eco   p189
162 Clapham High Street,
SW4 (020 7978 1108)

Verso 84   p189
84 Clapham Park Road, SW4
(020 7720 1515)

Pubs

Belle Vue   p214
1 Clapham Common
Southside, SW4 (020 7498
9473)

Bread & Roses   p217
68 Clapham Manor Street,
SW4 (020 7498 1779)

Spanish

Carmen   p157
6 Clapham Common
Southside, SW4 (020 7622
6848)

El Rincón Latino   p157
148 Clapham Manor Street,
SW4 (020 7622 0599)

Thai

Pepper Tree   p167
19 Clapham Common
Southside, SW4 (020 7622
1758)

Vegetarian

Café on the
Common   p175
2 Rookery Road, SW4 (020
7498 0770)

Clerkenwell &
Farringdon EC1

Bars

Café Kick   p205
43 Exmouth Market, EC1
(020 7837 8077)

Clerkenwell House   p205
23-27 Hatton Wall, EC1 (020
7404 1113)

Dovetail   p205
9 Jerusalem Passage, EC1
(020 7490 7321)

Branches

Balls Brothers
158 Bishopsgate, EC2 (020
7426 0567)

The Bean
70 Compton Street, EC1
(020 7253 5972)

Burgundy Ben's
(branch of Davys)
102-108 Clerkenwell Road,
EC1 (020 7251 3783)

Cafe Lazeez
88 St. John Street, EC1 (020
7253 2224)

Chez Gérard
64 Bishopsgate, EC2 (020
7588 1200)

Colonel Jaspers
(branch of Davys)
City House, 190-196 City
Road, EC1 (020 7608 0925)

Match EC1
45-47 Clerkenwell Road,
EC1(020 7250 4002)

Silks and Spice
42 Northampton Road, EC1
(020 7278 9983)

Yum Yum
245 Old Street, EC1 (020
7553 3027)

Brasseries

Al's Bar Café   p194
11-13 Exmouth Market, EC1
(020 7837 4821)

British

Quality Chop
House   p33
94 Farringdon Road, EC1
(020 7837 5093/020 7833
3748)

St John   p33
26 St John Street, EC1 (020
7251 0848/4998/
www.stjohnrestaurant.co.uk)

Top Floor
at Smiths   p34
Smiths of Smithfield, 67-77
Charterhouse Street, EC1
(020 7236 6666)

Budget

Saints   p181
1 Clerkenwell Road, EC1 (020
7490 4199/
www.saintsphoto.co.uk)

Cafés

The Deli Bar   p199
117 Charterhouse Street,
EC1 (020 7253 2070)

feast   p199
86 St John Street, EC1 (020
7253 7007)

Lunch   p199
60 Exmouth Market, EC1
(020 7278 2420/
www.lunch.uk.com)

Central & East
European

Potemkin   p41
144 Clerkenwell Road, EC1
(020 7278 6661)

Eating & Entertainment

East One   p223
175-179 St John Street, EC1
(020 7566 0088)

Tinseltown   p226
44-46 St John Street, EC1
(020 7689 2424)

Fish

Rudland & Stubbs   p54
35-37 Greenhill Rents,
Cowcross Street, EC1 (020
7253 0148)

Stream Bubble
& Shell   p54
50-52 Long Lane, Smithfield,
EC1 (020 7796 0070)

French

Café du Marché   p60
22 Charterhouse Square,
Charterhouse Mews, EC1
(020 7608 1609)

Chez Gérard   p60
84-86 Rosebery Avenue, EC1
(020 7833 1515/
www.santeonline.co.uk)

Club Gascon   p60
57 West Smithfield, EC1
(020 7796 0600)

Dibbens   p60
2-3 Cowcross Street, EC1
(020 7250 0035)

Vegetarian

Heather's p176
74 McMillan Street, SE8
(020 8691 6665/
www.heathers.dircon.co.uk)

Docklands E14, E19

Branches

All Bar One
42 Mackenzie Walk, South
Colonnade, Canary Wharf,
E14 (020 7513 0911)

Browns
Hartsmere Road, E14 (020
7987 9777)

Café Rouge
20 Cabot Square, E14 (020
7537 9696)

Cafe Rouge
29-35 Mackenzie Walk, E1
(02074280998)

Corney & Barrow
9 Cabot Square, E14 (020
7512 0397)

Cranks
Unit RP 380-385 Concourse
Level, 15 Cabot Place,
Canary Wharf, E14 (020
7513 0678)

Crussh
Tower Concourse, Level 1, 1
Canada Square, Canary
Wharf, E14 (020 7513
0076)

Davys
31-35 Fisherman's Walk,
Canary Wharf, E14 (020
7363 6633)

EAT
Unit 1 Canada Place, E14.

The Fine Line
29-30 Fishman's Wharf,
Cabot Square, Canary Wharf,
E14 (020 7513 0255.

**Gourmet Pizza
Company**
18-20 Mackenzie Walk,
Canary Wharf, E14 (020
7345 9192)

fish!
Hanover House, 33
Westferry Circus, E14 (020
7234 3333)

**Gourmet Pizza
Company**
18-20 Mackenzie Walk,
Canary Wharf, E14 (020
7345 9192)

Scu-zi
37 Westferry Circus, Canary
Riverside, E14 (020 7519
6007)

The Slug and Lettuce
30 South Colonnade,
E14(020 7519 1612)

Budget

Hubbub p180
269 Westferry Road, E14
(020 7515 5577)

Chinese

**Lotus Chinese
Floating Restaurant** p51
38 Limeharbour, Inner
Millwall Dock, E14 (020
7515 6445)

Eating & Entertainment

Leven is Strijd p223
West India Quay, Hertsmere
Road, West India Docks, E14
(020 7987 4002)

Indian

**Mem Saheb
on Thames** p85
65 Amsterdam Road, E14
(020 7538 3008/
www.memsaheb.
demon.co.uk)

Tabla p85
West India Dock Gate,
Hertsmere Road, E14 (020
7345 0345/
www.tablarestaurant.com)

Spanish

Baradero p157
Turnberry Quay, off Pepper
Street, E14 (020 7537
1666)

Dulwich SE21

Branches

Café Rouge
84 Park Hall Road, SE21
(020 8766 0070)

Pizza Express
94 The Village, SE21 (020
8693 9333)

Modern European

Belair House p141
Gallery Road, SE21 (020
8299 9788)

Ealing W3, W5, W13

African & Caribbean

BB's p19
3 Chignell Place, off Uxbridge
Road, W13 (020 8840
8322)

Branches

All Bar One
64-65 The Mall, Ealing
Broadway, W5 (020 8280
9611)

Ben's Thai
King's Arms, The Vale, W3
(020 8740 4210)

Café Rouge
17 The Green, W5 (020
8579 2788)

Cyberia Cyber Café
73 New Broadway, W5 (020
8840 3131)

Monty's
1 The Mall, Ealing
Broadway, W5 (020 8567
5802/8122)

Nando's Chicken
1-2 Station Buildings,
Uxbridge Road, W5 (020
8992 2290)

Pizza Express
23 Bond Street, W5 (020
8567 7690)

The Slug and Lettuce
96-98 Uxbridge Road, W12
(020 8749 1987)

Tootsies
35 Haven Green, W5 (020
8566 8200)

**Central & East
European**

Café Grove p39
65 The Grove, W5 (020
8810 0364)

Chinese

North China p49
305 Uxbridge Road, W3 (020
8992 9183)

Eating & Entertainment

Mama Amalfi's p225
45 The Mall, Ealing, W5
(020 8840 5888)

Indian

Sigiri p93
161 Northfield Avenue, W13
(020 8579 8000)

Japanese

Momo p117
14 Queen's Parade, W5 (020
8997 0206)

Sushi-Hiro p117
1 Station Parade, Uxbridge
Road, W5 (020 8896 3175)

Modern European

Gilbey's p138
77 The Grove, W5 (020
8840 7568)

Parade p138
18-19 The Mall, W5 (020
8810 0202)

Pubs

Red Lion p216
13 St Mary's Road, W5 (020
8567 2541)

Earl's Court SW5

Branches

Dome
194-916 Earls Court Road,
SW5 (020 7835 2200)

Nando's Chicken
204 Earls Court Road, SW5
(020 7259 2544)

Cafés

Troubadour p201
265 Old Brompton Road,
SW5 (020 7370 1434)

Fish

Lou Pescadou p56
241 Old Brompton Road,
SW5 (020 7370 1057)

Indian

Loofs p81
234 Old Brompton Road,
SW5 (020 7370 1188/1199)

Earlsfield SW18

Branches

Café Rouge
573 Garratt Lane, SW18
(020 8947 9616)

Vietnamese

Saigon Thuy p177
189 Garratt Lane, SW18
(020 8871 9464)

Wine Bars

Willie Gunn p221
422 Garratt Lane, SW18
(020 8946 7773)

East Dulwich SE22

Branches

**Barcelona Tapas
Bar y Restaurate**
481 Lordship Lane, SE22
(020 8693 5111)

French

Le Chardon p67
65 Lordship Lane, SE22
(020 8299 1921)

East Finchley N2

**Central & East
European**

The Old Europeans p38
106 High Road, N2 (020
8883 3964)

East Sheen SW15

African & Caribbean

The Melting Pot p19
180 Upper Richmond Road,
SW15 (020 8408 4833)

Edgware, Middlesex

Branches

Chai
236 Station Road, Edgware,
Middx (020 8905 3033)

**Mangal Barbeque
Restaurant**
165-167 Station Road,
Edgware, Middx (020 8951
4460)

Nando's
137-139 Station Road,
Edgware, Middx (020 8952
3400)

Sakonis
116 Station Road, Edgware,
Middx (020 8951 0058)

Jewish

Aviv p119
87 High Street, Edgware,
Middx (020 8952 2484)

**B&K Salt
Beef Bar** p119
11 Lanson House,
Whitchurch Lane, Edgware,
Middx (020 8952 8204)

Edgware Road W2

Branches

Beirut Express
112-114 Edgeware Road W2
(020 7724 2700)

Café Flo
14 Thayer Street, W1 (020
7935 5023)

Caffè Uno
11 Edgeware Road, W2 (020
7723 4898)

ITS
17-20 Kendal Street, W2
(020 7724 4637)

Maroush IV
68 Edgeware Road, W2 (020
7224 9339)

San Miguel's
256 Edgeware Road, W2 (020
7262 1709/020 7706
2063)

Tarboush
143 Edgeware Road, W2 (020
7287 1220)

Cafés

Regent Milk Bar p205
362 Edgeware Road, W2 (020
7723 8669)

Global

Mandalay p69
444 Edgeware Road, W2 (020
7258 3696)

**Malaysian, Indonesian
& Singaporean**

Bali p122
101 Edgeware Road, W2 (020
7262 9100/020 7723
3303)

Mawar p122
175A Edgeware Road, W2
(020 7262 1663)

Middle Eastern

Al-Dar p126
61-63 Edgeware Road, W2
(020 7402 2541)

**Iran the
Restaurant** p126
59 Edgeware Road, W2 (020
7723 1344)

Kandoo p126
458 Edgeware Road, W2 (020
7724 2428)

**Lebanese
Restaurant** p126
60 Edgeware Road, W2 (020
7723 9130)

Maroush p127
21 Edgeware Road, W2 (020
7723 0773)

Patogh p127
8 Crawford Place, W1 (020
7262 4015)

**Ranoush
Juice Bar** p127
43 Edgeware Road, W2 (020
7723 5929)

Safa p127
22-23 Nutford Place, W1
(020 7723 8331)

Edmonton, E4

Branches

Pizza Express
45-47 Old Church Road, E4
(020 8523 5551)

Elephant & Castle
SE1

Pizza & Pasta

Pizzeria Castello p189
20 Walworth Road, SE1 (020
7703 2556)

Embankment WC2

Eating & Entertainment

El Barco Latino p225
Temple Pier, Victoria
Embankment, WC2 (020
7379 5496)

RS Hispaniola p223
Victoria Embankment, WC2
(020 7839 3011)

Enfield, Middlesex

Branches

Caffè Uno
15 Silver Street, Enfield,
Middx (020 8367 0337)

Nando's
2 The Town, Enfield, Middx
(020 8366 2904)

Pizza Express
2 Silver Street, Enfield,
Middx (020 8367 3311)

Euston NW1

The Americas

Terra Brasil p29
36-38 Chalton Street, NW1
(020 7388 6554)

Indian

Chutneys p90
124 Drummond Street, NW1
(020 7388 0604)

**Diwana Bhel
Poori House** p90
121 Drummond Street, NW1
(020 7387 5556)

Great Nepalese p78
48 Eversholt Street, NW1
(020 7388 6737)

Pizza & Pasta

ASK p185
48 Grafton Way, W1 (020
7388 8108)

Pasta Plus p185
62 Eversholt Street, NW1
(020 7383 4943)

Ewell, Surrey

Branches

Jim Thompson's
65 London Road, Ewell,
Surrey (020 8393 2242)

Finchley N3

Branches

**Ben's Elephant (branch
Ben's Thai)**
283 Ballards Lane, N12
(020 8492 0201)

Café Rouge
Leisure Way, High Road, N12
(020 8446 4777)

Fish & Chips

**Two Brothers Fish
Restaurant** p184
297-303 Regent's
Park Road, N3 (020 8346
0469)

Indian

Rani p90
7 Long Lane, N3 (020 8349
4386)

Korean

Yijo p121
1 Station Road, N3 (020
8343 3960)

Pizza & Pasta

Zucchero p191
202-208 Regent's
Park Road, N3 (020 8371
0833)

Turkish

Izgara p171
11 Hendon Lane, N3 (020
8371 8282)

Finsbury Park N4

The Americas

Exquisite p32
167 Blackstock Road, N4
(020 7359 9529)

Branches

Nando's Chicken
106 Stroud Green Road, N4
(020 7263 7447)

La Porchetta
147 Stroud Green Road, N4
(020 7281 2892).

Brasseries

The Meeting Place p198
17 Blackstock Road, N4
(020 7354 1411)

The Triangle p198
1 Ferme Park Road, N4 (020
8292 0516)

Indian

Jai Krishna p91
161 Stroud Green Road, N4
(020 7272 1680)

Mediterranean

La Ventura p126
28 Crouch Hill, N4 (020
7281 5811)

North African

Yamina p146
192 Stroud Green Road, N4
(020 7263 6161)

Fitzrovia W1

Bars

Jerusalem p207
33-34 Rathbone Place, W1
(020 7255 1120)

Mash p207
19-21 Great Portland Street,
W1 (020 7637 5555)

Match p207
37-38 Margaret Street, W1
(020 7499 3443)

The Social p207
5 Little Portland Street, W1
(020 7636 4992)

Branches

All Bar One
108 New Oxford Street, W1
(020 7323 7980)

Caffè Uno
64 Tottenham Court Road,
W1 (020 7636 3587)

Chez Gérard
8 Charlotte Street, W1 (020
7636 4975)

Cranks
9-11 Tottenham Street, W1
(020 7631 3912)

Efes II
175-177 Great Portland
Street, W1 (020 7436 0600)

Espres
13 New Oxford Street (020
7242 8326)

**The Great American
Bagel Factory**
20 Charlotte Street, W1 (020
7631 0790)

ITS
98 Tottenham Court Road,
WIP (020 7436 5355)

**Lees Bag (branch of
Davys)**
4 Great Portland Street, W1
(020 7636 5287)

Pizza Express
7 Charlotte Street, W1 (020
7580 1110)

**Punkum (branch of Sabai
Sabai)**
31 Windmill Street, W1 (020
7636 0610)

**Rasa Express (branch of
Rasa Samundra)**
5 Rathbone Street, W1 (020
7637 0222)

Bar Room Bar
48 Rosslyn Hill, NW3 (020 7431 8802)

Calzone
66 Heath Street, NW3 (020 7794 6775)

Dôme
58-62 Heath Street, NW3 (020 7431 0399)

Dome
58-62 Heath Street, NW3 (020 7431 0399)

The Gaucho Grill
64 Heath Street, NW3 (020 7431 8222)

Häagen-Dazs
75 Hampstead High Street, NW3 (020 7431 1430)

Hi Sushi
50 Hampstead High Street, NW3 (020 7794 2828)

Maxwell's
76 Heath Street, NW3 (020 7794 5450)

Pizza Express
70 Heath Street, NW3 (020 7433 1600)

Zen W3
83 Hampstead High Street, NW3 (020 7794 7863)

Brasseries

Giraffe p198
46 Rosslyn Hill, NW3 (020 7435 0343)

Cafés

Brew House p205
Kenwood, Hampstead Lane, NW3 (020 8341 5384)

Louis Pâtisserie p203
32 Heath Street, NW3 (020 7435 9908)

Japanese

Jin Kichi p118
73 Heath Street, NW3 (020 7794 6158)

Mediterranean

Base p126
71 Hampstead High Street, NW3 (020 7431 2224)

Modern European

Cucina p143
45A South End Road, NW3 (020 7435 7814)

Gresslin's p144
13 Heath Street, NW3 (020 7794 8386)

The New End p144
102 Heath Street, NW3 (020 7431 4423)

Oriental

dim T café p150
3 Heath Street, NW3 (020 7435 0024)

Pubs

Flask p217
14 Flask Walk, NW3 (020 7435 4580)

French

Monsieur Max p68
133 High Street, Hampton Hill, Middx (020 8979 5546)

Harringay N8

Spanish

La Viña p159
3 Wightman Road, N4 (020 8340 5400)

Turkish

Erenler p171
64 Grand Parade, Green Lanes, N4 (020 8802 3263)

Harrow, Middlesex

Branches

ITS
St George's Centre, Harrow, Middx (020 8427 0982)

Nando's
300 -302 Station Road, Harrow, Middx (020 8427 5581)

Pizza Express
2 College Road, Harrow, Middx (020 8427 9195)

Sakonis
6-8 Dominion Parade, Station Road, Harrow, Middx (020 8863 3399)

Chinese

Golden Palace p53
146-150 Station Road, Harrow, Middx (020 8863 2333)

Hayes, Middlesex

Branches

The Rotisserie (branch of Rotisserie Jules)
316 Uxbridge Road, Middlesex, MA5 (020 8421 2878)

Heathrow Airport

Branches

Chez Gerard
Terminal Three, Departures, Heathrow Airport, TW6 (020 8607)

Zen Oriental
Heathrow Hilton, Heathrow Airport Terminal 4 (020 8759 7755)

Hendon NW4

Chinese

Kaifeng p53
51 Church Road, NW4 (020 8203 7888)

Indian

Prince of Ceylon p93
39 Watford Way, NW4 (020 8202 5967)

Jewish

The White House p119
10 Bell Lane, NW4 (020 8203 2427)

Herne Hill SE24

Fish & Chips

Olley's p184
67-69 Norwood Road, SE24 (020 8671 8259)

Indian

3 Monkeys p83
136-140 Herne Hill, SE24 (020 7738 5500)

Oriental

Lombok p149
17 Half Moon Lane, SE24 (020 7733 7131)

Highbury N5

Italian

San Daniele de Friuli p108
72 Highbury Park, N5 (020 7226 1609)

Turkish

Iznik p171
19 Highbury Park, N5 (020 7354 5697)

Vietnamese

Au Lac p178
82 Highbury Park, N5 (020 7704 9187)

Highgate N6, N10

The Americas

Idaho p25
13 North Hill, N6 (020 8341 6633/ www.montana.plc.uk)

Branches

All Bar One
1-3 Hampstead Lane, N6 (020 8342 7661)

Café Rouge
6-7 South Grove, N6 (020 8342 9797)

Caffé Uno
4 South Grove, N6 (020 8342 8662)

Pizza Express
30 High Street, N6 (020 8341 3434)

Pizza Paradiso
109 Highgate West Hill, N6 (020 7221 0721)

Cafés

Café Mozart p203
17 Swains Lane, N6 (020 8348 1384)

Oshobasho Café p205
Highgate Wood, Muswell Hill Road, N10 (020 8444 1505)

French

Village Bistro p67
38 Highgate High Street, N6 (020 8340 0257/ www.villagebistro.com)

Holborn EC1

Branches

All Bar One
58 Kingsway, WC2 (020 7269 5171)

Bung Hole (branch of Davys)
Hand Court, 57 High Holborn, WC1 (020 7831 8365)

Chez Gérard
119 Chancery Lane, WC2 (020 7405 0290)

EAT
34-36 High Holborn, WC1.

Jamies
50-54 Kingsway, WC2 (020 7405 9749)

Lunch
Lincoln's Inn Fields, by the tennis courts, WC2 (020 7404 3110)

Pitcher and Piano
42 Kingsway, WC2 (071 404 8510)

Thanks for Franks
18 Gate Street. Holborn. WC2 (020 7405 0539)

Wagamama
4A Streatham Street, WC1 (020 7736 2333)

Central & East European

Na Zdrowie The Polish Bar p39
11 Little Turnstile, WC1 (020 7831 9679)

Eating & Entertainment

Terry Neill's Sports Bar & Brasserie p226
Bath House, 53 Holborn Viaduct, EC1 (020 7329 6653/6579)

-Fish & Chips

Fryer's Delight p183
19 Theobald's Road, WC1 (020 7405 4114)

French

High Holborn p62
95-96 High Holborn, WC1 (020 7404 3338/020 7404 3339)

International

115 at Hodgson's p94
115 Chancery Lane, WC2 (restaurant 020 7242 2836/ wine bar 020 7404 5027)

Pubs

The Lamb p216
94 Lamb's Conduit Street, WC1 (020 7405 0713)

Princess Louise p216
208 High Holborn, WC1 (020 7405 8816)

Seven Stars p216
53-54 Carey Street, WC2 (020 7242 8521)

Spanish

Centro p153
93 Gray's Inn Road, WC1 (020 7242 2252)

Holland Park W8, W11, W14

The Americas

Tootsies p24
120 Holland Park Avenue, W11 (020 7229 8567)

Branches

ITS
128 Holland Park Avenue, W11 (020 7243 1106)

Maison Blanc
102 Holland Park Avenue, W11 (020 7221 2494)

Fish

Offshore p56
148 Holland Park Avenue, W11 (020 7221 6090)

French

6 Clarendon Road p63
6 Clarendon Road, W11 (020 7727 3330)

Chez Moi p65
1 Addison Avenue, W11 (020 7603 8267)

Hotels & Haute Cuisine

The Room at the Halcyon p76
129 Holland Park Avenue, W11 (020 7221 5411/020 7727 7288)

International

Wiz p95
123A Clarendon Road, W11 (020 7229 1500)

Italian

Orsino p105
119 Portland Road, W11 (020 7221 3299)

Modern European

The Belvedere p138
Off Abbotsbury Road, Holland Park, W8 (020 7602 1238)

Wine Bars

Julie's p221
135-137 Portland Road, W11 (020 7229 8331/ www.juliesrestaurant.demon. co.uk)

Holloway N7

Budget

Judy's p181
249 Holloway Road, N7 (no phone)

Central & East European

Tbilisi p38
91 Holloway Road, N7 (020 7607 2536)

North African

Royal Cous-Cous House p146
316 Holloway Road, N7 (020 7700 2188)

Spanish

El Molino p160
379 Holloway Road, N7 (020 7700 4312)

Holloway Road N7

Korean

Busan p121
43 Holloway Road, N7 (020 7607 8264)

Hornsey N8

Branches

O's Bar (branch of O's Thai Cafe)
115 Park Road, N8 (020 8340 7845)

French

Le Cadre p68
10 Priory Road, N8 (020 8348 0606)

Hounslow, Middlesex

Branches

Nando's Chicken
1-1a Hounslow High Street, Middx(020 8570 5881)

Pizza Express
41-43 High Street, Hounslow, Middx (020 8577 8522)

Ilford, Essex

Branches

Mobeen
80 Ilford Lane, Ilford, Essex (020 8553 9733)

Pizza Express
410 Cranbrook Road, Gants Hill, Ilford, Essex (020 8554 3030)

Indian

Curry Special p87
2 Greengate Parade, Horns Road, Newbury Park, Ilford, Essex (020 8518 3005/ www.curryspecial.com)

Islington N1

African & Caribbean

Merkato p18
193A Caledonian Road, N1 (020 7837 1838)

The Americas

Cuba Libre p29
72 Upper Street, N1 (020 7354 9998)

La Piragua p32
176 Upper Street, N1 (020 7354 2843)

Santa Fe p27
75 Upper Street, N1 (020 7288 2288)

Bars

25 Canonbury Lane p211
25 Canonbury Lane, N1 (020 7226 0955)

Elbow Room p211
89-91 Chapel Market, N1 (020 7278 3244)

Medicine Bar p211
181 Upper Street, N1 (020 7704 9536/020 7704 1070)

Branches

Ask
Business Design Centre, 52 Upper Street, N1 (020 7226 8728)

Bar Latino
144 Upper Street, N1 (020 7704 6868)

Caffé Uno
62 Upper Street, N1 (020 7288 0954)

The Creative Cafe
212 Fortis Green Road, N1 (0208 4444 333)

Dome
341 Upper Street, N1 (020 7226 3414)

Giraffe
29-31 Essex Road, N1 (020 7359 5999)

Metrogusto Islington
14 Theberton Street, N1 (020 7226 9400)

Pitcher and Piano
68 Upper Street, N1 (020 7704 9974)

Pizza Express
335 Upper Street, N1 (020 7226 9542)

The Rotisserie
134 Upper Street, N1 (020 7226 0122)

Ruby in the Dust
70 Upper Street, N1 (020 7359 1710)

The Slug and Lettuce
1 Islington Green, N1 (020 7226 3864)

The Vine
190 North End Road, N1 (020 7388 0254)

Wok Wok
67 Upper Street, N1 (020 7288 0333)

Brasseries

Candid Café p198
3 Torrens Street, EC1 (020 7278 9368/ www.candidarts.com)

Budget

Le Mercury p181
140A Upper Street, N1 (020 7354 4088)

Cafés

Caffè Mobile p203
By south bound bus stops near Angel tube, Islington High Street, N1 (020 7704 6363)

Viva p203
236 St Paul's Road, N1 (020 7704 8227)

Central & East European

Luba's Place p41
164 Essex Road, N1 (020 7704 2775)

Chinese

New Culture Revolution p52
42 Duncan Street, N1 (020 7833 9083)

Eating & Entertainment

Tiger Lil's p223
270 Upper Street, N1 (020 7226 1118)

Global

Afghan Kitchen p68
35 Islington Green, N1 (020 7359 8019)

Bierodrome p69
173-174 Upper Street, N1 (020 7226 5835)

Tartuf p68
88 Upper Street, N1 (020 7288 0954)

International

Frederick's p99
Camden Passage, N1 (020 7359 2888)

Mediterranean

Café Med p126
370 St John Street, EC1 (020 7278 1199)

White Onion p126
297 Upper Street, N1 (020 7359 3533)

Modern European

Euphorium p143
203 Upper Street, N1 (020 7704 6909)

Granita p143
127 Upper Street, N1 (020 7226 3222)

Kavanagh's p143
26 Penton Street, N1 (020 7833 1380/ www.kavrestaurant.co.uk)

Lola's p143
The Mall Building, Camden Passage, 359 Upper Street, N1 (020 7359 1932)

North African
Maghreb p146
189 Upper Street, N1 (020 7226 2305)

Oriental
Yellow River Café p150
206 Upper Street, N1 (020 7354 8833)

Pizza & Pasta
Calzone p191
35 Upper Street, N1 (020 7359 9191)

La Porchetta p191
141 Upper Street, N1 (020 7288 2488)

Scu-zi p191
360 St John Street, EC1 (020 7833 4393)

Pubs
Centuria p215
100 St Paul's Road, N1 (020 7704 2345)

The Crown p215
116 Cloudesley Road, N1 (020 7837 7107)

Duke of Cambridge p215
30 St Peter's Street, N1 (020 7359 3066)

The Hanbury p216
33 Linton Street, N1 (020 7226 3628)

Spanish
The Finca p160
96-98 Pentonville Road, N1 (020 7837 5387)

Turkish
Angel Mangal p171
139 Upper Street, N1 (020 7359 7777)

Gallipoli p172
102 Upper Street, N1 (020 7359 0630)

Gallipoli II p172
120 Upper Street, N1 (020 7359 1578)

Lezzet Lokanta p172
330 Essex Road, N1 (020 7226 7418/020 7354 1162)

Pasha p172
301 Upper Street, N1 (020 7226 1454)

Sedir p172
4 Theberton Street, N1 (020 7226 5489)

Vegetarian
St Paul's Steiner Café p176
1 St Paul's Road, N1 (020 7226 4454)

Vietnamese
Nam Bistro p178
326 Upper Street, N1 (020 7354 0851)

Kennington SE11
Branches
The Finca
185 Kennington Lane, SE11 (020 7735 1061)

The Lavender Pub & Restaurant
112 Vauxhall Walk, SE11 (020 7735 4440)

Pizza Express
316 Kennington Road, SE11 (020 7820 3877)

Fish
The Lobster Pot p57
3 Kennington Lane, SE11 (020 7582 5556)

Modern European
Kennington Lane Restaurant & Bar p141
205-209 Kennington Lane, SE11 (020 7793 8313)

Kensal Green NW10
Japanese
Murasaki p118
43 Chamberlayne Road, NW10 (020 8964 3939)

Pubs
Paradise by Way of Kensal Green p213
19 Kilburn Lane, W10 (020 8969 0098)

William IV p213
786 Harrow Road, NW10 (020 8969 5944)

Kensington W8
The Americas
Sticky Fingers p24
1A Phillimore Gardens, W8 (020 7938 5338)

Branches
Ask
222 Kensington High Street, W8 (020 7937 5540)

Balans
187 Kensington High Street, W8 (020 7376 0115)

Café Flo
127 Kensington Church Street, W8 (020 7727 8142)

Café Pasta
229-231 Kensington High Street, W8 (020 7937 6314)

Cafe Pasta
373 Kensington High Street, W14 (020 7610 5552)

Caffè Uno
9 Kensington High Street, W8 (020 7937 8961)

Calzone
2A Kensington Park Road, W11 (020 7243 2003)

Dome
Kensington Court, 35A&B Kensington High Street, W8 (020 7937 6655)

Ken Lo's Memories of China
353 Kensington High Street, W8 (020 7603 6951)

Palms Kensington
3-5 Campden Hill Road, W8 (020 7938 1830)

Pizza Express
35 Earl's Court Road, W8 (020 7937 0761)

Stratford's (branch of Lou Pescadou)
7 Stratford Road, W8 (020 7937 6388)

Wagamama
26-40 Kensington High Street, W8 (0207 376 1717)

Wok Wok
7 Kensington High Street, W8 (020 7938 1221)

British
Maggie Jones's p35
6 Old Court Place, Kensington Church Street, W8 (020 7937 6462)

Cafés
The Orangery p205
Kensington Palace, Kensington Gardens, W8 (020 7376 0239)

Squeeze p204
27 Kensington High Street, W8 (020 7376 9786)

Central & East European
Wódka p39
12 St Alban's Grove, W8 (020 7937 6513/ www.wodka.co.uk)

Eating & Entertainment
Cuba p225
11-13 Kensington High Street, W8 (020 7938 4137)

The Tenth p226
Royal Garden Hotel, Kensington High Street, W8 (020 7361 1910)

International
The Abingdon p95
54 Abingdon Road, W8 (020 7937 3339)

Goolies p95
21 Abingdon Road, W8 (020 7938 1122)

Japanese
Koi p117
1E Palace Gate, W8 (020 7581 8778)

Middle Eastern
Phoenicia p129
11-13 Abingdon Road, W8 (020 7937 0120)

Modern European
Clarke's p138
124 Kensington Church Street, W8 (020 7221 9225)

Kensington Place p138
201 Kensington Church Street, W8 (020 7727 3184)

Launceston Place p138
1A Launceston Place, W8 (020 7937 6912)

The Terrace p138
33C Holland Street, W8 (020 7937 3224)

Thai
Blue Lagoon p163
284 Kensington High Street, W8 (020 7603 1231)

Kentish Town NW1, NW5
African & Caribbean
Lalibela p18
137 Fortress Road, NW5 (020 7284 0600)

The Americas
Zuni p32
134 Fortress Road, NW5 (020 7428 0803)

Branches
Nando's
227-229 Kentish Town Road, NW5 (020 7424 9363)

North African
Le Petit Prince p146
5 Holmes Road, NW5 (020 7267 3789)

Pubs
Bull & Last p216
168 Highgate Road, NW5 (020 7267 3641)

Pineapple p217
51 Leverton Street, NW5 (020 7485 6422)

The Vine p216
86 Highgate Road, NW5 (020 7209 0038)

Kew, Surrey
Branches
Browns
3-5 Kew Road, Kew Green (020 8948 4838)

Ceramics Café
1A Mortlake Terrace, Mortlake Road, Kew (0208 332 6661)

Cafés
Hothouse Café p204
9 Station Approach, Kew, Surrey (020 8332 1923)

The Kew Greenhouse p204
1 Station Parade, Kew, Surrey (020 8940 0183)

Modern European
The Glasshouse p144
14 Station Parade, Kew, Surrey (020 8940 6777)

Kilburn NW6
The Americas
Doña Olga p29
Latin American House, Kingsgate Place, NW6 (020 7624 3831)

Branches
Little Bay
228 Belsize Road, NW6 (020 7372 4699)

Nando's Chicken
308 Kilburn High Road, NW6 (020 7372 1507)

Budget
Small & Beautiful p181
351-353 Kilburn High Road, NW6 (020 7328 2637)

Indian
Geeta p91
57-59 Willesden Lane, NW6 (020 7624 1713)

Vijay p91
49 Willesden Lane, NW6 (020 7328 1087)

King's Cross NW1
The Americas
Sally's Diner p27
2 Pancras Road, NW1 (020 7713 8474/8462/ www.sallysdiner.co.uk)

Thai
Paolina Café & Thai Restaurant p161
181 King's Cross Road, WC1 (020 7278 8176)

Kingston-upon-Thames, Surrey
Branches
Café Rouge
4-8 Kingston Hill, Kingston-upon-Thames, Surrey (020 8547 3229)

Frère Jacques
10-12 Riverside Walk, Kingston-upon-Thames, Surrey (020 8546 1332)

Nando's Chicken
37-38 Kingston High Street, KT1 (020 8296 9540)

Pizza Express
41 High Street, Kingston, Surrey (020 8546 1447)

Eating & Entertainment
Blue Hawaii p223
2 Richmond Road, Kingston-upon-Thames, Surrey (020 8549 6989)

Knightsbridge SW1, SW3
Branches
Balans
239 Brompton Road, Knightsbridge, SW3 (020 7584 0070)

Café Rouge
27-31 Basil Street, SW3 (020 7584 2345)

Chez Gerard
3 Yeomans Road, SW3 (020 7581 8377)

Harrods Sushi Bar (branch of Noto)
Food Hall, Ground Floor, Harrods, Knightsbridge, SW1 (020 7730 1234 ext 2203)

Maroush II
38 Beauchamp Place, SW3 (020 7581 5434)

Pizza Express
7 Beauchamp Place, SW3 (020 7589 2355)

Searcy's
30 Pavilion Road, SW1 (020 7584 4921)

Spaghetti House
77 Knightsbridge, SW1 (020 7235 8141)

Stockpot
6 Basil Street, SW3 (020 7589 8627)

Wagamama
Lower ground Floor, Harvey Nichols, SW1 (020 7201 8000)

Yo! Sushi
Fifth Floor, Harvey Nichols, Brompton Road, SW1 (020 7235 5000 ext 2256)

Brasseries
The Fifth Floor Café p194
Harvey Nichols, Knightsbridge, SW1 (020 7823 1839)

Cafés
Harrods Ice-cream Parlour & Crêperie p205
Fourth floor, Harrods, Knightsbridge, SW1 (020 7225 6628)

Central & East European
Borshtch 'n' Tears p41
45-46 Beauchamp Place, SW3. (020 7589 5003)

Chinese
Mr Chow p45
151 Knightsbridge, SW1 (020 7589 7347)

Veg Veg p45
8 Egerton Garden Mews, SW3 (020 7584 7007)

French
Brasserie St Quentin p62
243 Brompton Road, SW3 (020 7589 8005)

Global
Lundum's p69
119 Old Brompton Road, SW7 (020 7373 7774)

Hotels & Haute Cuisine
The Capital p73
22-24 Basil Street, SW3 (020 7589 5171)

Foliage p74
Mandarin Oriental Hyde Park Hotel, 66 Knightsbridge, SW1 (020 7235 2000)

Restaurant One-O-one p74
101 William Street, SW1 (020 7290 7101)

La Tante Claire p74
The Berkeley, Wilton Place, SW1 (020 7823 2003)

Italian
Emporio Armani Caffè p100
191 Brompton Road, SW3 (020 7823 8818)

Floriana p100
15 Beauchamp Place, SW3 (020 7838 1500)

Grissini p103
Hyatt Carlton Tower Hotel, Cadogan Place, SW1 (020 7858 7171/ www.london.hyatt.com)

Isola p103
145 Knightsbridge, SW1 (020 7838 1044/1055)

Monte's p103
164 Sloane Street, SW1 (020 7235 0555)

Monza p103
6 Yeoman's Row, SW3 (020 7591 0210)

San Lorenzo p103
22 Beauchamp Place, SW3 (020 7584 1074)

Zafferano p103
15 Lowndes Street, SW1 (020 7235 5800)

Jewish
Harrods Famous Deli p118
Ground floor, Harrods, Knightsbridge, SW1 (020 7730 1234 ext 2997)

Middle Eastern
Al Bustan p127
27 Motcomb Street, SW1 (020 7235 8277)

Modern European
The Fifth Floor p132
Harvey Nichols, Knightsbridge, SW1 (020 7235 5250)

Oriental
Vong p147
The Berkeley, Wilton Place, SW1 (020 7235 1010)

Pizza & Pasta
Pizza on the Park p187
11 Knightsbridge, SW1 (020 7235 5273)

Portuguese
Caravela p150
39 Beauchamp Place, SW3 (020 7581 2366)

O Fado p151
49-50 Beauchamp Place, SW3 (020 7589 3002)

Thai
Patara p161
9 Beauchamp Place, SW3 (020 7581 8820)

Wine Bars
Le Metro p219
28 Basil Street, SW3 (020 7591 1213)

Osteria d'Isola p219
145 Knightsbridge, SW1 (020 7838 1044/1099)

Ladbroke Grove W10
Brasseries
Brasserie du Marché p196
349 Portobello Road, W10 (020 8968 5828)

Budget
Sausage & Mash Café p180
268 Portobello Road, W10 (020 8968 8898)

Cafés
Coins Bar & Grill p201
105-107 Talbot Road, W11 (020 7221 8099)

Nectar p201
The Tabernacle Arts Centre, Powis Square, W11 (020 7565 7808)

Eating & Entertainment
Canal Café Theatre p222
First floor, The Bridge House, corner of Westbourne Terrace Road and Delamere Terrace, W2 (020 7289 6056)

Global
Belgo Zuid p68
124 Ladbroke Grove, W10 (020 8982 8400)

Malaysian, Indonesian & Singaporean
Makan p123
270 Portobello Road, W10 (020 8960 5169)

Modern European

Alastair Little p138
136A Lancaster Road, W11
(020 7243 2220)

Pizza & Pasta

Cascabel p187
Canalot Studios, 222 Kensal
Road, W10 (020 8960
2732)

Portuguese

Café Algarve p151
129A Ladbroke Grove, W11
(020 7727 4604)

Casa Santana p151
44 Golborne Road, W10
(020 8968 8764)

Lisboa Patisserie p150
57 Golborne Road, W10
(020 8968 5242)

Oporto Patisserie p150
62A Golborne Road, W10
(020 8968 8839)

Pubs

Golborne House p213
36 Golborne Road, W10
(020 8960 6260)

North Pole p213
13-15 North Pole Road, W10
(020 8964 9384)

Spanish

Galicia p153
323 Portobello Road, W10
(020 8969 3539)

**Leicester Square W1,
SW1, WC2**

The Americas

Planet Hollywood p23
Trocadero, 13 Coventry
Street, W1 (020 7287 1000/
www.planethollywood.com)

Bars

Saint p207
8 Great Newport Street, WC2
(020 7240 1551)

Branches

All Bar One
48 Leicester Square, W2
(020 7747 9921)

Café Flo
51 St Martin's Lane, WC2
(020 7836 8289)

Caffè Uno
24 Charing Cross Road, WC2
(020 7240 2524)

Caffè Uno
37 St Martin's Lane, WC2
(020 7836 5837)

Cranks
17-19 Great Newport Street,
WC2 (020 7836 5226)

Espres
17 Charing Cross Road, W2
(020 7930 6090)

**Little Havana (branch of
Boardwalk)**
1 Leicester Place, WC2 (020
7287 0101)

Pizza Express
80-81 St Martin's Lane, WC2
(020 7836 8001)

Poons
4 Leicester Street, WC2 (020
7437 1528)

Spaghetti House
24 Cranbourn Street, WC2
(020 7836 8168)

Spaghetti House
30 St Martin's Lane, WC2
(020 7836 1626)

**Tappit Hen (branch of
Davys)**
15 William IV Street, WC2
(020 7836 9839)

Brasseries

Browns p194
82-84 St Martin's Lane, WC2
(020 7497 5050)

Cafés

**Häagen-Dazs on the
Square** p205
14 Leicester Square, WC2
(020 7287 9577)

**Photographers'
Gallery Café** p199
5 Great Newport Street, WC2
(020 7831 1772)

Portrait Café p199
National Portrait Gallery, 2 St
Martin's Place, WC2 (020
7312 2465)

Eating & Entertainment

**Capital
Radio Café** p224
Leicester Square, WC2 (020
7484 8888)

Sound p224
Leicester Square, W1 (020
7287 1010)

Comedy Store p222
1A Oxendon Street, SW1
(info 020 7344 0234/
bookings: Ticketmaster 020
7344 4444)

Fish

Café Fish p55
36-40 Rupert Street, W1
(020 7287 8989)

Manzi's p55
1-2 Leicester Street, WC2
(020 7734 0224)

J Sheekey p55
28-32 St Martin's Court,
WC2 (020 7240 2565)

Indian

Woodlands p90
37 Panton Street, SW1 (020
7839 7258)

International

Asia de Cuba p94
45 St Martin's Lane, WC2
(020 7300 5588)

Japanese

Seabar p113
St Martin's Lane, 45 St
Martin's Lane, WC2 (020
7300 5588)

Modern European

Seven p133
1 Leicester Square, WC2
(020 7909 1177)

North African

Souk p144
27 Litchfield Street, WC2
(020 7240 1796)

Wine Bars

Cork & Bottle p219
44-46 Cranbourn Street,
WC2 (020 7734
7807/www.donhewitsonlond
onwinebars.com)

Corney & Barrow p219
116 St Martin's Lane, WC2
(020 7655 9800)

Lewisham SE14

Fish & Chips

Something Fishy p184
117-119 Lewisham High
Street, SE13 (020 8852
7075/020 8318 9577)

Indian

Everest Curry King p93
24 Loampit Hill, SE13 (020
8691 2233)

Green Cabin p93
244 Lewisham High Street,
SE13 (020 8852 6666)

Leyton, E10

Branches

Mobeen
725 High Road Leyton, E10
(020 8556 0147)

Leytonstone E11

Branches

**Golden Orient
(branch of Indian
Connoisseurs)**
639 Leytonstone High Road,
E11 (020 8539 0747)

Eating & Entertainment

Jesters p222
682 High Road, E11 (020
8556 6821)

Spanish

Elche p159
567-569 Leytonstone High
Road, E11 (020 8558 0008)

Limehouse E14

Chinese

Old Friends p51
659 Commercial Road, E14
(020 7790 5027)

Tai Pan p51
665 Commercial Road, E14
(020 7791 0118)

Loughton, Essex

Branches

Caffè Uno
275-277 High Road,
Loughton, Essex (020 8508
5399)

Pizza Express
281 High Road, Loughton,
Essex (020 8508 3303)

**Maida Vale NW6,
NW8, W9**

Branches

Blah Blah Blah
28 Clifton Road, W9 (020
7289 6399)

**Café 100 (branch of
Greek Valley)**
100 Boundary Road, NW8
(020 7372 2042)

Café Rouge
30 Clifton Road, W9 (020
7286 2266)

Pizza Express
39 Abbey Road, NW8 (020
7624 5577)

Raoul's Express
10 Clifton Road, W9 (020
7289 6649)

Street Hawker
166 Randolph Avenue, W9
(020 7286 3869)

Cafés

Raoul's p201
13 Clifton Road, W9 (020
7289 7313)

Eating & Entertainment

**The Floating
Boater** p223
Prince Regent corner of
Warwick Crescent and
Westbourne Terrace Road
Bridge, W2 (020 7266 1066)

Fish

Jason's p56
Jason's Wharf, opposite 60
Blomfield Road, W9 (020
7286 6752)

Italian

Green Olive p105
5 Warwick Place, W9 (020
7289 2469)

Oriental

Southeast W9 p148
239 Elgin Avenue, W9 (020
7328 8883)

Pizza & Pasta

Red Pepper p189
8 Formosa Street, W9 (020
7266 2708)

Pubs

**The Warrington
Hotel** p216
93 Warrington Crescent, W9
(020 7286 2929)

Spanish

Don Pepe p153
99 Frampton Street, NW8
(020 7262 3834)

Mesón Bilbao p155
33 Malvern Road, NW6
(020 7328 1744)

Thai

Ben's Thai p163
above the Warrington, 93
Warrington Crescent, W9
(020 7266 3134)

Manor Park, E6

Branches

Mobeen
229 High Street North, E6
(020 8470 9365)

Marble Arch W1, W2

Branches

Ask
121-125 Park Street, W1
(020 7495 7760)

Maroush III
62 Seymour Street, W1 (020
7724 5024)

Hotels & Haute Cuisine

The Crescent p74
Montcalm Hotel, Great
Cumberland Place, W1 (020
7723 4440)

Indian

Porte des Indes p79
32 Bryanston Street, W1
(020 7224 0055/ www.la-
porte-des-indes.com)

Italian

Al San Vincenzo p103
30 Connaught Street, W2
(020 7262 9623)

Marylebone NW1, W1

Branches

All Bar One
7-9 Paddington Street, W1
(020 7487 0071)

Caffè Uno
100 Baker Street, W1 (020
7486 8606)

Davys at Basement 92
90-92 Wigmore Street, W1
(020 7224 0170)

**Dock Bilda (branch of
Davys)**
50-54 Blandford Street, W1
(020 7486 3590)

Espres
63 Wigmore Street, W1(020
7486 7788)

Giraffe
6-8 Blandford Street,
Marylebone, W1H (020
7935 2333)

Pâtisserie Valerie
RIBA, 66 Portland Place, W1
(020 7631 0467)

Pizza Express
133 Baker Street, W1 (020
7486 0888)

**Ragam (branch of
Malabar Junction)**
57 Cleveland Street, W1
(020 7636 9098)

Royal China
40 Baker Street, W1 (020
7487 4688)

La Rueda
102 Wigmore Street, W1
(020 7486 1718)

Souper Douper
Baker Street Station, NW1
(020 7486 3686)

Souper Douper
Marylebone Station (020
7723 1511)

Woodlands
77 Marylebone Lane, W1
(020 7486 3862)

Brasseries

Café Bagatelle p194
The Wallace Collection,
Manchester Square, W1
(020 7563 9505)

Cafés

De Gustibus p200
53 Blandford Street, W1
(020 7486 6608)

**Pâtisserie Valerie
at Sagne** p200
105 Marylebone High Street,
W1 (020 7935 6240)

**Central & East
European**

Tsar's Bar p42
Langham Hilton Hotel, 1C
Portland Place, W1 (020
7636 1000)

Chinese

Royal China p47
40 Baker Street, W1 (020
7487 4688)

Fish & Chips

Golden Hind p183
73 Marylebone Lane, W1
(020 7486 3644)

Seashell p183
49-51 Lisson Grove, NW1
(020 7224 9000)

French

Le Muscadet p62
25 Paddington Street, W1
(020 7935 2883)

Villandry p62
170 Great Portland Street,
W1 (020 7631 3131)

Global

Garbo's p71
42 Crawford Street, W1 (020
7262 6582)

The O'Conor Don p69
88 Marylebone Lane, W1
(020 7935 9311)

Hotels & Haute Cuisine

The Landmark p74
222 Marylebone Road, NW1
(020 7631 8000)

Italian

Ibla p103
89 Marylebone High Street,
W1 (020 7224 3799)

Japanese

Yumi p115
110 George Street, W1 (020
7935 8320)

Jewish

Reuben's p119
79 Baker Street, W1 (020
7486 0035)

**Malaysian, Indonesian
& Singaporean**

Selasih p122
114 Seymour Place, W1
(020 7724
4454/www.selasih.co.uk)

Middle Eastern

Al Fawar p127
50 Baker Street, W1 (020
7224 4777)

Ali Baba p127
32 Ivor Place, NW1 (020
7723 7474/5805)

Fairuz p127
3 Blandford Street, W1 (020
7486 8108/8182)

Levant p128
Jason Court, 76 Wigmore
Street, W1 (020 7224 1111)

Modern European

Orrery p133
55 Marylebone High Street,
W1 (020 7616
8000/www.orrery.co.uk)

Stephen Bull p133
5-7 Blandford Street, W1
(020 7486 9696)

North African

Ayoush p144
58 James Street & 77
Wigmore Street, W1 (020
7935 9839)

Original Tajines p144
7A Dorset Street, W1 (020
7935 1545)

Oriental

Wagamama p147
101A Wigmore Street, W1
(020 7409 0111)

Pizza & Pasta

ITS p187
60 Wigmore Street, W1 (020
7224 3484)

Purple Sage p187
90-92 Wigmore Street, W1
(020 7486 1912)

La Spighetta p187
43 Blandford Street, W1
(020 7486 7340)

Pubs

The Chapel p212
48 Chapel Street, NW1 (020
7402 9220)

Thai

Chaopraya p161
22 St Christopher's Place,
W1 (020 7486 0777)

Thai West p161
10-12 Crawford Street, W1
(020 7224 1367)

Vegetarian

Raw Deal p173
65 York Street, W1 (020
7262 4841)

Mayfair W1

African & Caribbean

Jamaica Blue p18
18 Maddox Street, W1 (020
7408 2272/
www.jamaicablue.co.uk)

The Americas

Hard Rock Café p23
150 Old Park Lane, W1 (020
7629
0382/www.hardrock.com)

Havana p23
17 Hanover Square, W1 (020
7629 2552)

Bars

Claridge's p207
Brook Street, W1 (020 7629
8860)

Trader Vic's p207
Hilton Hotel, Park Lane, W1
(020 7493 8000 ext 420)

Zeta p207
Hilton Hotel, Park Lane, W1
(020 7208 4067)

Branches

Balls Brothers
Mulligans of Mayfair, 13-14
Cork Street, W1 (020 7409
1370)

Balls Brothers
34 Brook Street, W1 (020
7499 4567)

Bar Exellence
33 Dover Street, W1 (020
7499 2689)

Chez Gérard
31 Dover Street, W1 (020
7499 8171)

Crussh
Lancashire Court, W1 (020
7409 7782)

Crussh
1 Curzon Street, W1 (020 7629 2554)

EAT
319 Regent Street, W1.

Miyama Mayfair
38 Clarges Street, W1 (020 7493 3807)

Pitcher and Piano
1 Dover Street, W1 (020 7495 8704)

Pizza Express
23 Bruton Place, W1 (020 7495 1411)

Sofra
18 Shepherd Street, W1 (020 7493 3320)

Zen Garden
15 Berkeley Street, W1 (020 7493 1381)

British

Dorchester Grill Room p34
The Dorchester, 53 Park Lane, W1 (020 7317 6336/www.dorchesterhotel.com)

The Guinea Grill p34
30 Bruton Place, W1 (020 7499 1210)

Cafés

Victory Café p200
Basement, Gray's Antiques Market, South Molton Lane, W1 (020 8960 0086)

Central & East European

L'Autre p39
5B Shepherd Street, W1 (020 7499 4680)

Firebird p41
23 Conduit Street, W1 (020 7493 7000/7088)

Chinese

Kai p47
65 South Audley Street, W1 (020 7493 8988/1456/www.kaimayfair.co.uk)

Oriental p47
The Dorchester Hotel, 55 Park Lane, W1 (020 7317 6328)

Zen Central p47
20-22 Queen Street, W1 (020 7629 8103)

Eating & Entertainment

Dorchester Bar p224
54 Park Lane, W1 (020 7629 8888)

Dover Street p225
8-10 Dover Street, W1 (020 7629 9813/ www.doverst.co.uk)

Windows p226
London Hilton, 22 Park Lane, W1 (020 7208 4021)

French

Mirabelle p62
56 Curzon Street, W1 (020 7499 4636/ www.whitestarline.org.uk)

Global

Mulligans of Mayfair p69
13-14 Cork Street, W1 (020 7409 1370)

Hotels & Haute Cuisine

1837 p74
Brown's Hotel, 33 Albemarle Street, W1 (020 7408 1837)

cheznico at Ninety Park Lane p75
90 Park Lane, W1 (020 7409 1290)

The Connaught p75
Carlos Place, W1 (020 7499 7070)

Le Gavroche p75
43 Upper Brook Street, W1 (020 7408 0881)

Le Soufflé p75
Hotel Intercontinental, 1 Hamilton Place, W1 (020 7409 3131)

The Square p76
6-10 Bruton Street, W1 (020 7495 7100)

Windows p76
Hilton Hotel, 22 Park Lane, W1 (020 7208 4021)

Indian

Chor Bizarre p79
16 Albemarle Street, W1 (020 7629 9802/ www.chorbizarre restaurant.com)

Tamarind p79
20 Queen Street, W1 (020 7629 3561/www.tamarind restaurant.com)

Veeraswamy p79
Mezzanine floor, Victory House, 99-101 Regent Street, W1 (020 7734 1401/www.realindian food.com)

Yatra p79
34 Dover Street, W1 (020 7493 0200)

Italian

Alloro p104
19-20 Dover Street, W1 (020 7495 4768)

Diverso p104
85 Piccadilly, W1 (020 7491 2222)

Marquis p104
121A Mount Street, W1 (020 7499 1256)

Sartoria p104
20 Savile Row, W1 (020 7534 7000)

Teca p104
54 Brooks Mews, W1 (020 7495 4774)

Japanese

Benihana p115
37 Sackville Street, W1 (020 7494 2525/ www.benihana.co.uk)

Nobu p115
19 Old Park Lane, W1 (020 7447 4747)

Korean

Kaya p120
42 Albemarle Street, W1 (020 7499 0622/0633)

Middle Eastern

Al Hamra p129
31-33 Shepherd Market, W1 (020 7493 1954)

Al Sultan p129
51-52 Hertford Street, W1 (020 7408 1155/1166)

Fakhreldine p128
85 Piccadilly, W1 (020 7493 3424)

Modern European

Greenhouse p133
27A Hay's Mews, W1 (020 7499 3331/3314)

Langan's Brasserie p133
Stratton Street, W1 (020 7491 8822)

Morton's p133
28 Berkeley Square, W1 (020 7493 7171/020 7499 0363)

Nicole's p133
158 New Bond Street, W1 (020 7499 8408)

noble rot p135
3-5 Mill Street, W1 (020 7629 8877)

Sotheby's Café p135
34-35 New Bond Street, W1 (020 7293 5077)

North African

Mô p145
23 Heddon Street, W1 (020 7434 4040)

Momo p144
25 Heddon Street, W1 (020 7434 4040)

Oriental

Cassia Oriental p147
12 Berkeley Square, W1 (020 7629 8886/ www.cassiaoriental.com)

Pizza & Pasta

Condotti p187
4 Mill Street, W1 (020 7499 1308)

Spanish

El Pirata p153
5-6 Down Street, W1 (020 7491 3810)

Turkish

Sofra Bistro p169
18 Shepherd Market, W1 (020 7493 3320)

Wine Bars

Hanover Square Wine Bar & Grill p219
25 Hanover Square, W1 (020 7408 0935/ www.donhewitsonlondonwine bars.com)

Mill Hill NW7

Branches

TGI Friday's
Watford Way, NW7 (020 8203 9779)

Pizza Express
92-94 The Broadway, NW7 (020 8959 3898)

Chinese

Good Earth p53
143-145 The Broadway, Mill Hill Circus, NW7 (020 8959 7011)

Muswell Hill N10

Branches

Caffè Uno
348 Muswell Hill Broadway, N10 (020 8883 4463)

Pizza Express
290 Muswell Hill Broadway, N10 (020 8883 5845)

Brasseries

Café on the Hill p198
46 Fortis Green Road, N10 (020 8444 4957)

Fish & Chips

Toff's p184
38 Muswell Hill Broadway, N10 (020 8883 8656)

Spanish

Cafe Loco p160
206 Muswell Hill, N10 (020 8444 3370)

Neasden NW9

Indian

New Kabana p85
43 Blackbird Hill, NW9 (020 8200 7094)

New Cross SE14

Thai

Thailand p167
15 Lewisham Way, SE14 (020 8691 4040)

Newington Green N1, N16

Global

Anna's Place p71
90 Mildmay Park, N1 (020 7249 9379/www.annas place.co.uk)

Turkish

Sariyer Balik Lokantasi p171
56 Green Lanes, N16 (020 7275 7681)

New Malden, Surrey

Korean

Chisshine p121
74 Burlington Road, New Malden, Surrey (020 8942 0682)

Norbury SW16

Indian

Mirch Masala p83
1416 London Road, SW16 (020 8679 1828/020 8765 1070)

Shamyana p83
437-439 Streatham High Road, SW16 (020 8679 6162)

Northolt, Middlesex

Indian

Amirthaam p93
200B Alexandra Avenue, Northolt, Middx (020 8423 9666/020 8864 6636)

Notting Hill W2, W8, W11

African & Caribbean

Mandola p18
139-141 Westbourne Grove, W11 (020 7229 4734)

Branches

All Bar One
126-128 Notting Hill, W11 (020 7313 9362)

Ask
145 Notting Hill Gate, W11 (020 7792 9942)

Barley Sugar (branch of The Sugar Club)
33A All Saints Road, W11 (020 7221 4477)

Café Med
184A Kensington Park Road, W11 (020 7221 1150)

Café Rouge
31 Kensington Park Road, W11 (020 7221 4449)

Café Rouge
2 Lancer Square, Kensington Church Street, W8 (020 7938 4200)

Elbow Room
103 Westbourne Grove, W1 (020 7221 5211)

Livebait
175 Westbourne Grove, W11 (020 7727 4321)

The New Culture Revolution
157-159 Notting Hill Gate, W11 (020 7313 9688)

Pizza Express
137 Notting Hill Gate, W11 (020 7229 6000)

Zilli
210 Kensington Park Road, W11, (020 7792 1066)

Brasseries

Portobello Gold p196
95-97 Portobello Road, W11 (020 7460 4918/4913)

Cafés

Buzz Bar p204
95 Portobello Road, W11 (020 7460 4906/ www.buzzbar.co.uk)

Fish & Chips

Costas Fish Restaurant p184
18 Hillgate Street, W8 (020 7727 4310)

Geales p184
2 Farmer Street, W8 (020 7727 7528)

International

The Rotisserie p95
56 Uxbridge Road, W12 (020 8743 3028)

Rotisserie Jules p95
133A Notting Hill Gate, W11 (020 7221 3331)

Italian

The Ark p107
122 Palace Gardens, W8 (020 7229 4024)

Assaggi p105
The Chepstow, 39 Chepstow Place, W2 (020 7792 5501)

Mediterraneo p107
37 Kensington Park Road, W11 (020 7792 3131)

Osteria Basilico p107
29 Kensington Park Road, W11 (020 7727 9372)

Modern European

192 p139
192 Kensington Park Road, W11 (020 7229 0482)

Nosh Brothers p139
12 All Saints Road, W11 (020 7243 2808)

Pharmacy Restaurant & Bar p139
150 Notting Hill Gate, W11 (020 7221 2442)

Oriental

Uli p148
16 All Saints Road, W11 (020 7727 7511)

Pubs

The Chepstow p213
39 Chepstow Place, W2 (020 7229 0323)

The Cow p213
89 Westbourne Park Road, W2 (020 7221 5400)

Prince Bonaparte p213
80 Chepstow Road, W2 (020 7313 9491)

The Westbourne p214
101 Westbourne Park Villas, W2 (020 7221 1332)

Windsor Castle p217
114 Campden Hill Road, W8 (020 7243 9551)

Thai

Churchill Arms p163
119 Kensington Church Street, W8 (020 7792 1246)

Market Thai p163
First floor, The Market Bar, 240 Portobello Road, W11 (020 7460 8320)

Olympia W14

British

Popeseye Steak House p35
108 Blythe Road, W14 (020 7610 4578)

Italian

Cibo p107
3 Russell Gardens, W14 (020 7371 6271/2085)

Middle Eastern

Alounak p129
10 Russell Gardens, W14 (020 7603 7645)

Chez Marcelle p129
34 Blythe Road, W14 (020 7603 3241)

Yas p129
7 Hammersmith Road, W14 (020 7603 9148/3980)

Oxford Street W1

Branches

All Bar One
3-4 Hanover Street, W1 (020 7518 9931)

Geales p184
2 Farmer Street, W8 (020 7727 7528)

All Bar One
289-293 Regent Street, W1 (020 7467 9901)

Break For The Border
8 Argyll Street, W1V (020 7734 5776)

Browns
47 Maddox Street, W1 (020 7491 4565)

Café Rouge
46-48 James Street, W1 (020 7487 4847)

Caffè Uno
28 Binney Street, W1 (020 7499 9312)

Chopper Lump (branch of Davys)
10C Hanover Square, W1 (020 7499 7569)

Cranks
23 Barrett Street, W1 (020 7495 1340)

Don Juan
42 James Street, W1 (020 7224 1544)

EAT
Selfridges, 400 Oxford Street, W1.

The Great American Bagel Factory
40 James Street, W1 (020 7224 4564)

Hanover Square Wine Bar & Grill (branch of Cork & Bottle)
25 Hanover Square, W1 (020 7408 0935)

Pitcher and Piano
10 Pollen Street, W1 (020 7629 9581/9582)

Pizza Express
4-5 Langham Place, W1 (020 7580 3700)

Pizza Express
21 Barrett Street, St Christopher's Place, W1 (020 7629 1001)

Pizza Paridiso
9 St Christopher's Place, W1 (020 7486 3196)

Rasa W1
16 Dering Street, W1 (020 7629 1346)

The Slug and Lettuce
19-20 Hanover Street, W1 (020 7499 0077)

Soup Opera
2 Hanover Street, W1 (020 7629 0174)

Sofra
1 St Christopher's Place, W1 (020 7224 4080)

Spaghetti House
74 Duke Street, W1 (020 7629 6097)

Stockpot
50 James Street, W1 (020 7486 9168)

Thai Pots
5 Princes Street, W1 (020 7499 3333)

Tootsies
35 James Street, W1M (020 7486 1611)

Yo! Sushi
Selfridges, 400 Oxford Street, W1 (020 7318 3885)

Eating & Entertainment

Premier at Selfridges p226
Third floor, Selfridges, Oxford Street, W1 (020 7318 3155)

Paddington W2

Branches

Ask
41-43 Spring Street, W2 (020 7706 0707)

EAT
First floor, Unit R31, Paddington rail station, W2.

Tarboush
143 Edgeware Road, W2
(020 706 9793)

Indian

Indian Connoisseurs p81
8 Norfolk Place, W2 (020
7402 3299)

**Malaysian, Indonesian
& Singaporean**

Satay House p123
13 Sale Place, W2 (020
7723 6763/www.satay
house.com)

Middle Eastern

Isfahan p129
3-4 Bouverie Place, W2 (020
7460 1030)

Spanish

Los Remos p155
38A Southwick Street, W2
(020 7723 5056/020 7706
1870)

Palmers Green N13

French

Café Anjou p68
394 Green Lanes, N13 (020
8886 7267)

Parson's Green SW6

Branches

Newtons on the Green
175 New King's Road, SW6
(020 7731 6404)

Strada
175 New Kings Road, SW6
(020 7731 6404)

Tootsies
177 New King's Road, SW6
(020 7736 4023)

Chinese

Mao Tai p49
58 New King's Road, SW6
(020 7731 2520)

International

Upstairs at the Pen p96
51 Parsons Green Lane,
SW6 (020 7371 8517)

Modern European

The Mission p139
116 Wandsworth Bridge
Road, SW6 (020 7736
3322)

Pubs

White Horse p217
1 Parsons Green, SW6 (020
7736 2115)

Spanish

El Prado p155
764-766 Fulham Road, SW6
(020 7731 7179)

Peckham SE15

Eating & Entertainment

**Elvis Gracelands
Palace** p224
881-883 Old Kent Road,
SE15 (020 7639 3961)

French

Holly p67
38 Holly Grove, SE15 (020
7277 2928)

Piccadilly SW1, W1

The Americas

Cheers p23
72 Regent Street, W1 (020
7494 3322)

Down Mexico Way p30
25 Swallow Street, W1 (020
7437 9895/
www.downmexway.com)

The Gaucho Grill p29
19 Swallow Street, W1 (020
7734 4040)

Bars

Atlantic Bar & Grill p207
20 Glasshouse Street, W1
(020 7734 4888)

**Clipper Bar at China
House** p207
160 Piccadilly, W1 (020
7499 6996)

Branches

Balls Brothers
20 St James's Street, SW1
(020 7321 0882)

EAT
9A Vigo Street, W1.

Ed's Easy Diner
The Trocadero, Shaftesbury
Avenue, W1 (020 7287
1951)

TGI Friday's
25-29 Coventry Street, W1
(020 7839 6262)

Gourmet Pizza Company
7-9 Swallow Street, W1 (020
7734 5182)

ITS
14-16 Quadrant Arcade, 15A
Air Street, W1 (020 7734
4267)

Spaghetti House
16 Jermyn Street, W1 (020
7734 7334)

Stockpot
40 Panton Street, W1 (020
7839 5142)

**West End Kitchen
(branch of Stockpot)**
5 Panton Street, W1 (020
7839 4241)

Brasseries

Café Flo p194
11-12 Haymarket, W1 (020
7976 1313)

Zinc Bar & Grill p195
21 Heddon Street, W1 (020
7255 8899)

British

Fortnum & Mason p34
181 Piccadilly, W1 (020
7734 8040)

Cafés

La Madeleine p200
5 Vigo Street, W1 (020 7734
8353)

Chinese

China House p47
160 Piccadilly, W1 (020
7499 6996/
www.chinahouse.co.uk)

Orient p47
160 Piccadilly, W1 (020
7499 6888/7779/
www.chinahouse.co.uk)

French

Criterion p62
224 Piccadilly, W1 (020
7930 0488)

L'Odéon p62
65 Regent Street, W1 (020
7287 1400)

Hotels & Haute Cuisine

Oak Room p76
Le Meridien Hotel, 21
Piccadilly, W1 (020 7437
0202)

The Ritz p76
Piccadilly, W1 (020 7493
8181 ext 3351)

Japanese

Yoshino p115
3 Piccadilly Place, W1 (020
7287 6622)

Modern European

Atlantic Bar & Grill p135
20 Glasshouse Street, W1
(020 7734 4888)

Red Room p135
Basement, Waterstone's,
203 Piccadilly, W1 (020
7851 2464)

Pimlico SW1

Branches

Pizza Express
46 Moreton Street, SW1
(020 7592 9488)

The Slug and Lettuce
11 Warwick Way, SW1 (020
7834 3313)

British

Chimes of Pimlico p34
26 Churton Street, SW1
(020 7821 7456)

Rhodes in the Square p34
Dolphin Square, Chichester
Street, SW1 (020 7798
6767)

International

**Tate Gallery
Restaurant** p94
Tate Britain, Millbank, SW1
(020 7887
8877/www.tate.org.uk)

Italian

Como Lario p104
22 Holbein Place, SW1 (020
7730 2954/9046)

Spanish

Goya p153
34 Lupus Street, SW1 (020
7976 5309)

Turkish

Marmaris p170
45 Warwick Way, SW1 (020
7828 5940)

Pinner, Middlesex

Branches

Pizza Express
33-35 High Street, Pinner,
Middx (020 8866 9848)

Putney SW15

Branches

K Bar
200B Upper Richmond Road,
SW15 (020 8780 2822)

Café Rouge
200 Putney Bridge Road,
SW15 (020 8788 4257)

**Coat & Badge (branch of
Queens)**
8 Lacy Road, SW15 (020
8788 4900)

Jim Thompson's
408 Upper Richmond Road,
SW15 (020 8788 3737)

Nando's Chicken
148 Upper Richmond Road,
SW15 (020 8780 3215)

Pizza Express
144 Upper Richmond Road,
SW15 (020 8789 1948)

Popeseye
277 Upper Richmond Road,
SW15 (020 8788 7733)

The Slug and Lettuce
14 Putney High Street, SW15
(020 8785 3081)

Brasseries

Frère Jacques p196
136 Upper Richmond Road,
SW15 (020 8780 9000/
www.frerejacques.co.uk)

Chinese

Royal China p49
3 Chelverton Road, SW15
(020 8788 0907)

French

Putney Bridge p67
The Embankment, SW15
(020 8780 1811)

Indian

Ma Goa p81
242-244 Upper Richmond
Road, SW15 (020 8780
1767)

International

Blue Pumpkin p96
147 Upper Richmond Road,
SW15 (020 8780 3553)

Moomba p96
5 Lacy Road, SW15 (020
8785 9151)

Italian

Del Buongustaio p107
283 Putney Bridge Road,
SW15 (020 8780 9361/020
8789 9659)

Enoteca Turi p107
28 Putney High Street, SW15
(020 8785 4449)

Japanese

Chosan p117
292 Upper Richmond Road,
SW15 (020 8788 9626)

Modern European

Phoenix Bar & Grill p139
162-164 Lower Richmond
Road, SW15 (020 8780
3131)

Pubs

Coat & Badge p214
8 Lacy Road, SW15 (020
8788 4900)

Spanish

La Mancha p155
32 Putney High Street, SW15
(020 8780 1022)

Thai

Talad Thai p165
320 Upper Richmond Road,
SW15 (020 8789 8084)

Queens Park NW6

International

Organic Café p99
21-25 Lonsdale Road, NW6
(020 7372 1232)

Penk's p99
79 Salusbury Road, NW6
(020 7604 4484)

Italian

The Park p109
105 Salusbury Road, NW6
(020 7372 8882)

Pubs

The Salusbury p216
50-52 Salusbury Road, NW6
(020 7328 3286)

Rayners Lane, Middlesex

Indian

Balti Hut p87
435 Alexandra Avenue,
Rayners Lane, Middx (020
8868 0007)

Raynes Park SW20

Korean

Kkach'ine p121
34 Durham Road, SW20
(020 8947 1081)

Richmond, Surrey

The Americas

Canyon p27
Riverside, near Richmond
Bridge, Richmond, Surrey
(020 8948 2944/
www.montana.plc.uk)

Branches

All Bar One
11 Hill Street, Richmond,
Surrey (020 8332 7141)

Ask
85 Kew Green, Richmond,
Surrey (020 8940 3766)

Café Flo
149 Kew Road, Richmond,
Surrey (020 8332 2598)

Café Rouge
7A Petersham Lane,
Richmond, Surrey (020 8332
2423)

Caffè Uno
15-17 Hill Rise, Richmond,
Surrey (020 8948 6282)

Dome
26 Hill Street, Richmond,
Surrey (020 8332 2525)

Four Regions
102 Kew Road, Richmond,
Surrey (020 8940 9044)

Good Earth
6 Friars Stile Road, Richmond,
Surrey (020 8948 3399)

Maison Blanc
27B The Quandrant,
Richmond, Surrey (020 8332
7041)

Pitcher and Piano
11 Bridge Street, Surrey
(020 8332 2524)

Pizza Express
20 Hill Street, Richmond,
Surrey (020 8940 8951)

Rani
3 Hill Street, Richmond,
Surrey (020 8332 2322)

The Slug and Lettuce
Riverside House, Water Lane,
Surrey (020 8948 7733)

Tootsies
110 Kew Road, Richmond,
Surrey (020 8948 4343)

Wok Wok
3 Hill Street, Richmond,
Surrey (020 8332 2646)

**Central & East
European**

Kozachok p41
10 Red Lion Street,
Richmond, Surrey (020 8948
2366)

Eating & Entertainment

The Elizabethan p223
The Signal Box, 119-123
Sandycombe Road,
Richmond, Surrey (020 8940
6688)

Fish

Ocean p58
100 Kew Road, Richmond,
Surrey (020 8948 8008)

French

Chez Lindsay p68
11 Hill Rise, Richmond,
Surrey (020 8948 7473)

Italian

Caffè Mamma p109
24 Hill Street, Richmond,
Surrey (020 8940 1625)

Spanish

Don Fernando's p160
27F The Quadrant,
Richmond, Surrey (020 8948
6447)

Roman Road E2, E3

Branches

G Kelly
600 Roman Road E3 (020
8983 3552)

Sheen SW14

Branches

Café Rouge
248 Upper Richmond Road,
SW14 (020 8878 8897)

Pizza Express
305 Upper Richmond Road
West, SW14 (020 8878
6833)

Brasseries

The Depot p196
Tideway Yard, Mortlake High
Street, SW14 (020 8878
9462)

Modern European

Redmond's p140
170 Upper Richmond Road
West, SW14 (020 8878
1922)

Shepherd's Bush W6, W12, W14

Branches

Cafe Rouge
98-100 Shepherds Bush
Road, W6 (0207 602 7732)

Jim Thompson's
243 Goldhawk Road, W12
(020 8748 0229)

Nando's
284-286 Uxbridge Road,
W12 (020 8746 1112)

Pizza Express
7 Rockley Road, W14 (020
8749 8582)

British

Wilson's p36
236 Blythe Road, corner of
Shepherd's Bush Road, W14
(020 7603 7267)

**Central & East
European**

Patio p39
5 Goldhawk Road, W12 (020
8743 5194)

International

Gallery One Twenty p95
120 Goldhawk Road, W12
(020 8749 5505)

Modern European

Blythe Road p139
71 Blythe Road, W14 (020
7371 3635)

Brackenbury p139
129-131 Brackenbury Road,
W6 (020 8748 0107)

Cotto p139
44 Blythe Road, W14 (020
7602 9333)

North African

Adam's Café p145
77 Askew Road, W12 (020
8743 0572)

Pubs

Anglesea Arms p213
35 Wingate Road, W6 (020
8749 1291)

Spanish

La Copita p155
63 Askew Road, W12 (020
8743 1289)

Thai

Esarn Kheaw p163
314 Uxbridge Road, W12
(020 8743 8930)

Vegetarian

Blah Blah Blah p175
78 Goldhawk Road, W12
(020 8746 1337)

Wine Bars

Albertine p221
1 Wood Lane, W12 (020
8743 9593)

Shoreditch N1, EC2, E2

Bars

Cantaloupe p209
35-42 Charlotte Road, EC2
(020 7613 4411)

Dragon Bar p211
5 Leonard Street, EC2 (020
7490 7110)

Home p211
100-106 Leonard Street,
EC1 (020 7684 8618)

**Hoxton Square Bar &
Kitchen** p211
2 Hoxton Square, N1 (020
7613 0709)

The Light p211
233 Shoreditch High Street,
E1 (020 7247 8989)

The Pool p211
104 Curtain Road, EC2 (020
7739 9608)

**Shoreditch Electricity
Showrooms** p211
39A Hoxton Square, N1 (020
7739 6934)

Branches

The Bean
126 Curtain Road, EC2 (020
7739 7829)

Sosho Match
2A Tabernacle Street. EC2
(020 7920 0701)

Budget

Lennie's p180
6 Calvert Avenue, E2 (020
7739 3628)

Eating & Entertainment

**Brick Lane
Music Hall** p225
134-146 Curtain Road, EC2
(020 7739 9997/
www.brick/lane/music/
hall.co.uk)

Comedy Café p222
66-68 Rivington Street, EC2
(020 7739 5706)

Greek

The Real Greek p71
15 Hoxton Market, N1 (020
7739 8212)

Italian

**Great Eastern
Dining Room** p108
54-56 Great Eastern Street,
EC2 (020 7613 4545)

Mediterranean

Cantaloupe p125
35 Charlotte Road, EC2 (020
7613 4411)

Pubs

Wenlock Arms p217
26 Wenlock Road, N1 (020
7608 3406)

Vietnamese

Hanoi Café p177
98 Kingsland Road, E2 (020
7729 5610)

Viet Hoa p177
70-72 Kingsland Road, E2
(020 7729 8293).
Vietnamese.

Sidcup, Kent

Branches

Pizza Express
6 Elm Parade, Sidcup, Kent
(020 8200 5522)

Soho W1

The Americas

Blues Bistro & Bar p23
42-43 Dean Street, W1 (020
7494 1966/
www.bluesbistro.com)

Ed's Easy Diner p23
Old Compton Street, W1
(020 7287 1951)

Sí Señor p30
2 St Anne's Court, off Dean
Street, W1 (020 7494 4632)

Bars

Alphabet p209
61-63 Beak Street, W1 (020
7439 2190)

The Dog House p209
187 Wardour Street, W1
(020 7434 2116/2118)

Freedom p209
60-66 Wardour Street, W1
(020 7734 0071)

Lab p209
12 Old Compton Street, W1
(020 7437 7820)

Rupert Street p209
50 Rupert Street, W1 (020
7292 7141)

Branches

All Bar One
36-38 Dean Street, W1 (020
7479 7921)

Café Flo
103 Wardour Street, W1
(020 7734 0581)

Café Med
22-25 Dean Street, W1 (020
7287 9007)

Cafe Pasta
15 Greek Street, W1 (020
7434 25 45)

Café Rouge
15 Frith Street, W1 (020
7437 4307)

**Chiang Mai (branch of
Thai Bistro)**
48 Frith Street, W1 (020
7437 7444)

Dome
8-10 Charing Cross Road,
WC2 (020 7240 5556)

Dome
57-59 Old Compton Street,
W1 (020 7287 0770)

Freedom
14-16 Ganton Street, W1
(020 7287 5267)

Pitcher and Piano
69-70 Dean Street, W1 (020
7434 3585)

Pizza Express
29 Wardour Street, W1 (020
7437 7215)

Pizza Express
6 Upper James Street,
Golden Square, W1 (020
7437 4550)

Pizza Express
20 Greek Street, W1 (020
7734 7430)

Pizza Express
10 Dean Street, W1 (020
7437 9595)

Royal Dragon
30 Gerrard Street, W1 (020
7734 0935)

The Slug and Lettuce
80-82 Wardour Street, W1
(020 7437 1400)

Sri Siam
16 Old Compton Street, W1
(020 7434 3544)

Wagamama
10A Lexington Street, W1
(020 7292 0990)

Brasseries

Bar du Marché p195
19 Berwick Street, W1 (020
7734 4606)

Café Bohème p195
13 Old Compton Street, W1
(020 7734 0623)

Dôme p195
57-59 Old Compton Street,
WC2 (020 7287 0770)

Hujo's p195
11 Berwick Street, W1 (020
7734 5144)

Randall & Aubin p195
16 Brewer Street, W1 (020
7287 4447)

**Soho Soho
(Rôtisserie)** p195
11-13 Frith Street, W1 (020
7494 3491)

British

Lindsay House p34
21 Romilly Street, W1 (020
7439 0450)

Budget

Café Emm p180
17 Frith Street, W1 (020
7437 0723)

**Carlton Coffee
House** p182
41 Broadwick Street, W1
(020 7437 3807)

Centrale p180
16 Moor Street, W1 (020
7437 5513)

Pierre Victoire p180
5 Dean Street, W1 (020
7287 4582)

Pollo p180
20 Old Compton Street, W1
(020 7734 5456)

Star Café p182
22 Great Chapel Street, W1
(020 7437 8778)

The Stockpot p180
18 Old Compton Street, W1
(020 7287 1066)

Thanks for Franks p182
26 Foubert's Place, W1 (020
7494 2434)

Cafés

Amato p200
14 Old Compton Street, W1
(020 7734 5733/
www.amato.co.uk)

Bar Italia p200
22 Frith Street, W1 (020
7437 4520)

EAT p200
16A Soho Square, W1 (020
7222 7200/
www.eatcafe.co.uk)

The Garden Café p200
4 Newburgh Street, W1 (020
7494 0044)

Global Café p204
15 Golden Square, W1 (020
7287 2242/
www.globalcafe.net)

Maison Bertaux p201
28 Greek Street, W1 (020
7437 6007)

Pâtisserie Valerie p201
44 Old Compton Street, W1
(020 7437 3466)

Pronto p201
26 Rupert Street, W1 (020
7734 5421)

Webshack p204
15 Dean Street, W1 (020
7439 8000/ www.webshack-
cafe.com)

**Central & East
European**

Gay Hussar p38
2 Greek Street, W1 (020
7437 0973/
www.gayhussar.co.uk)

St Moritz p37
161 Wardour Street, W1
(020 7734 3324)

Chinese

YMing p47
35-36 Greek Street, W1 (020
7734 2721)

Eating & Entertainment

**Break for
the Border** p225
5 Goslett Yard, WC2 (020
7437 8595/www.bftb.com)

Garlic & Shots p224
14 Frith Street, W1 (020
7734 9505/
www.garlicandshots.com)

Jazz After Dark p224
9 Greek Street, W1 (020
7734 0545/
www.jazzafterdark.co.uk)

**Joe's Restaurant
Bar** p226
Fenwick, 63 Bond Street, W1
(020 7495 5402)

Mezzo p224
100 Wardour Street, W1
(020 7314 4000)

Old Compton Café p226
34 Old Compton Street, W1
(020 7439 3309)

Pizza Express p225
10 Dean Street, W1 (020
7439 8722)

Rainforest Café p225
20 Shaftesbury Avenue, W1
(020 7434 3111/
www.rainforest.co.uk)

Ronnie Scott's p225
47 Frith Street, W1 (020
7439 0747/
www.ronniescotts.co.uk)

Salsa! p225
96 Charing Cross Road, WC2
(020 7379 3277)

10 p222
10 Air Street, W1 (020 7734
9990)

Fish

Zilli Fish p55
36-40 Brewer Street, W1
(020 7734 8649)

French

L'Escargot p63
48 Greek Street, W1 (020
7437 2679)

Incognico p63
117 Shaftesbury Avenue,
WC2 (020 7836 8866)

Quo Vadis p63
26-29 Dean Street, W1 (020
7437 9585)

Global

Schnecke p68
58-59 Poland Street, W1
(020 7287 6666)

Indian

Cafe Lazeez p81
21 Dean Street, W1 (020
7434 9393)

Soho Spice p81
124-126 Wardour Street, W1
(020 7434
0808/www.sohospice.co.uk)

International

Balans p95
60 Old Compton Street, W1
(020 7437 5212)

Boardwalk p95
18 Greek Street, W1 (020
7287 2051)

Italian

Il Forno p104
63-64 Frith Street, W1 (020
7734 4545)

Little Italy p104
21 Frith Street, W1 (020
7734 4737)

Signor Zilli p104
40 & 41 Dean Street, W1
(restaurant 020 7734
3924/bar 020 7734 1853)

Spiga p104
84-86 Wardour Street, W1
(020 7734 3444)

**Vasco & Piero's
Pavilion** p104
15 Poland Street, W1 (020
7437 8774)

Japanese

Donzoko p115
15 Kingly Street, W1 (020
7734 1974)

Hi Sushi p115
40 Frith Street, W1 (020
7734 9688)

Kulu Kulu p115
76 Brewer Street, W1 (020
7734 7316)

Ramen Seto p115
19 Kingly Street, W1 (020
7434 0309)

Ryo p116
84 Brewer Street, W1 (020
7287 1318)

Satsuma p116
56 Wardour Street, W1 (020
7437 8338)

Ten Ten Tei p116
56 Brewer Street, W1 (020
7287 1738)

**Yo! Sushi/
Yo! Below** p117
52 Poland Street, W1
(Yo! Sushi 020 7287
0443/Yo! Below 020
7439 3660/
www.yosushi.com)

Korean

Arirang p120
31-32 Poland Street, W1
(020 7437 9662/6633)

Jin p120
16 Bateman Street, W1 (020
7734 0908)

Myung Ga p121
1 Kingly Street, W1 (020
7287 9768)

Shilla p121
58-59 Great
Marlborough Street, W1
(020 7434 1650)

**Malaysian, Indonesian
& Singaporean**

Melati p122
21 Great Windmill Street, W1
(020 7437 2745)

Minang p123
11 Greek Street, W1 (020
7287 1408)

Nusa Dua p123
11-12 Dean Street, W1 (020
7437 3559)

Mediterranean

Aurora p125
49 Lexington Street, W1
(020 7494 0514)

Mezzo Café p125
100 Wardour Street, W1
(020 7314 4000)

Middle Eastern

Tarboush p129
11 Wardour Street, W1 (020
7287 1220)

Modern European

Alastair Little p135
49 Frith Street, W1 (020
7734 5183)

Andrew Edmunds p135
46 Lexington Street, W1
(020 7437 5708)

Circus p135
1 Upper James Street, W1
(020 7534 4000)

**French House
Dining Room** p135
First floor, The French House,
49 Dean Street, W1 (020
7437 2477)

The Lexington p137
45 Lexington Street, W1
(020 7434 3401)

Mezzo p137
100 Wardour Street, W1
(020 7314 4000)

The Sugar Club p137
21 Warwick Street, W1 (020
7437 7776)

Sugar Reef p137
41-44 Great Windmill Street,
W1 (020 7851 0800)

Teatro p137
93-107 Shaftesbury Avenue,
W1 (020 7494 3040)

Titanic p137
81 Brewer Street, W1 (020
7437 1912)

Oriental

Busaba Eathai p148
106-110 Wardour Street, W1
(020 7255 8686)

Mezzonine p148
100 Wardour Street, W1
(020 7314 4000)

Wok Wok p148
10 Frith Street, W1 (020
7437 7080)

Pizza & Pasta

Kettners p187
29 Romilly Street, W1 (020
7734 6112)

Pulcinella p187
37 Old Compton Street, W1
(020 7287 3920)

Soho Pizzeria p187
16-18 Beak Street, W1 (020
7434 2480)

Spanish

Café España p153
63 Old Compton Street, W1
(020 7494 1271)

Café Latino p153
25 Frith Street, W1 (020
7287 5676)

Thai

Soho Thai p162
27-28 St Anne's Court, W1
(020 7287 2000)

Thai Pavilion p162
42 Rupert Street, W1 (020
7287 6333)

Vegetarian

Beatroot p175
92 Berwick Street, W1 (020
7437 8591)

Mildred's p175
58 Greek Street, W1 (020
7494 1634)

Wine Bars

Shampers p219
4 Kingly Street, W1 (020
7439 9910)

Southfields SW18

Indian

Sarkhel's p83
199 Replingham Road,
SW18 (020 8870
1483/takeaway 020 8871
0808)

**South Kensington &
Gloucester Road
SW3, SW5, SW7**

Branches

All Bar One
152 Gloucester Road, SW7
(020 7244 5861)

Ask
Unit 23-24, Gloucester
Arcade, SW7 (020 7835
0840)

Balans West
239 Old Brompton Road,
SW5 (020 7244 8838)

La Belle Epoque
151 Draycott Avenue, SW3
(020 7460 5000)

Cafe Flo
25-35 Gloucester Road, SW7
(020 7225 1048)

Cafe Lazeez
93-95 Old Brompton Road,
SW7 (020 7581 9993)

Café Rouge
102 Old Brompton Road,
SW7 (020 7373 2403)

English Garden
10 Lincoln Street, SW3 (020
7584 7272)

**Fileric (branch of La
Madeleine)**
57 Old Brompton Road, SW7
(020 7584 2967)

Good Earth
233 Brompton Road, SW3
(020 7584 3658)

Häagen-Dazs
83 Gloucester Road, SW7
(020 7373 9988)

Langan's Coq d'or
Old Brompton Road, SW5
(020 7259 2599)

LePalais du Jardin
151 Draycott Avenue SW3
(020 7379 5353)

Maison Blanc
11 Elystan Street, SW3 (020 7584 6913)

Mongolian Barbeque
61 Gloucester Road, SW7 (020 7581 8747)

Pâtisserie Valerie
215 Brompton Road, SW3 (020 7823 9971)

Pizza Express
15 Gloucester Road, SW7 (020 7584 9078)

Rotisserie Jules
6-8 Bute Street, SW7 (020 7584 0600)

Tootsies
107 Old Brompton Road, SW7 (020 7581 8942)

Zen Chelsea Cloister
85 Sloane Avenue, SW3 (020 7589 1781)

Brasseries

La Brasserie p196
272 Brompton Road, SW3 (020 7581 3089)

Francofill p196
1 Old Brompton Road, SW7 (020 7584 0087)

The Oratory p196
232 Brompton Road, SW3 (020 7584 3493)

Cafés

Gloriette Pâtisserie p201
128 Brompton Road, SW3 (020 7589 4750)

Central & East European

Daquise p39
20 Thurloe Street, SW7 (020 7589 6117)

Jacob's p38
20 Gloucester Road, SW7 (020 7581 9292)

Ognisko Polskie p39
55 Prince's Gate, Exhibition Road, SW7 (020 7589 4635)

Chinese

Mr Wing p49
242-244 Old Brompton Road, SW5 (020 7370 4450)

Eating & Entertainment

The New Restaurant at the V&A p222
Victoria & Albert Museum, Cromwell Road, SW7 (020 7581 2159)

Fish

Bibendum Oyster Bar p57
Michelin House, 81 Fulham Road, SW3 (020 7581 5817)

Downstairs at One Ninety p57
190 Queens Gate, SW7 (020 7581 5666)

Poissonnerie de l'Avenue p57
82 Sloane Avenue, SW3 (020 7589 2457)

Indian

Bombay Brasserie p83
Courtfield Road, SW7 (020 7370 4040/www.bombay brasserielondon.com)

Star of India p83
154 Old Brompton Road, SW5 (020 7373 2901/www.starofindia.co.uk)

International

The Collection p96
264 Brompton Road, SW3 (020 7225 1212)

Mediterranean

Bistrot 190 p125
190 Queensgate, SW7 (020 7581 5666)

Brompton Bay p125
96 Draycott Avenue, SW3 (020 7225 2500)

Daphne's p125
112 Draycott Avenue, SW3 (020 7589 4257)

Middle Eastern

Soraya p130
36 Gloucester Road, SW7 (020 7589 4060)

Modern European

Bibendum p140
Michelin House, 81 Fulham Road, SW3 (020 7581 5817/www.bibendum.co.uk)

Hilaire p140
68 Old Brompton Road, SW7 (020 7584 8993)

North African

Pasha p145
1 Gloucester Road, SW7 (020 7589 7969/www.pasha-restaurant.co.uk)

Oriental

Itsu p149
118 Draycott Avenue, SW3 (020 7584 5522)

Spanish

Cambio de Tercio p157
163 Old Brompton Road, SW5 (020 7244 8970)

Thai

Bangkok p165
9 Bute Street, SW7 (020 7584 8529)

Exhibition p165
19 Exhibition Road, SW7 (020 7584 8359)

Vietnamese

Red River p177
1 Bray Place, SW3 (020 7584 0765)

Wine Bars

The Crescent p222
99 Fulham Road, SW3 (020 7225 2244)

Thai

Mantanah p168
2 Orton Building, Portland Road, SE25 (020 8771 1148)

Branches

Express Fried Chicken (branch of Tandoori Kebab Centre)
151 The Broadway, Southall, Middx (020 8571 2223)

Tandoori Express on Jalebi Junction (branch of Tandoori Kebab Centre)
93 The Broadway, Southall, Middx (020 8571 6782)

Indian

Balti & Tandoori World p87
185-187 The Broadway, Southall, Middx (020 8867 9991/9993)

Brilliant p87
72-76 Western Road, Southall, Middx (020 8574 1928)

The Genuine Lahore Karahi p89
37 Featherstone Road, Southall, Middx (020 8893 5270)

Gifto's Lahore Karahi p89
162-164 The Broadway, Southall, Middx (020 8813 8669/www.gifto.com)

Madhu's Brilliant p89
39 South Road, Southall, Middx (020 8574 1897/6380)

New Asian Tandoori Centre p89
114-116 The Green, Southall, Middx (020 8574 2597)

Palm Palace p93
80 South Road, Southall, Middx (020 8574 9209)

Tandoori Kebab Centre p89
161-163 The Broadway, Southall, Middx (020 8571 5738)

Indian

Jhopri p91
725 The Broadway, N14 (020 8245 0090)

Spanish

La Paella p160
9 The Broadway, N14 (020 8882 7868)

Branches

EAT
3 Duke of York Street, SW1.

Tapster (branch of Davys)
3 Brewers Green, Buckingham Gate, SW1 (020 7222 0561)

Brasseries

ICA Café p195
The Mall, SW1 (020 7930 8619)

British

Wiltons p34
55 Jermyn Street, SW1 (020 7629 9955)

Eating & Entertainment

The Sports Café p226
80 Haymarket, SW1 (020 7839 8300/www.sportscafe.com)

Fish

Caviar House p55
161 Piccadilly, W1 (020 7409 0445/www.caviarhouse.com)

Greens p55
36 Duke Street St James's, SW1 (020 7930 4566)

Hotels & Haute Cuisine

L'Oranger p76
5 St James's Street, SW1 (020 7839 3774)

Pétrus p76
33 St James's Street, W1 (020 7930 4272)

Indian

Quilon p79
St James's Court Hotel, 41 Buckingham Gate, SW1 (020 7821 1899)

International

Che p94
23 St James's Street, SW1 (020 7747 9380)

Italian

Al Duca p105
4-5 Duke of York Street, SW1 (020 7839 3090)

Japanese

Matsuri p117
15 Bury Street, SW1 (020 7839 1101/www.matsuri-restaurant.com)

Suntory p117
72-73 St James's Street, SW1 (020 7409 0201)

Modern European

The Avenue p135
7-9 St James's Street, SW1 (020 7321 2111)

Le Caprice p135
Arlington House, Arlington Street, SW1 (020 7629 2239)

Quaglino's p135
16 Bury Street, SW1 (020 7930 6767)

Branches

All Bar One
60 St John's Wood High Street, NW8 (020 7483 9931)

Cafe Med
21 Loudon Road, NW8 (020 7625 1222)

Café Rouge
120 St John's Wood Street, NW8 (020 7722 8366)

Caffè Uno
122 St John's Wood High Street, NW8 (020 7722 0400)

Yellow River Cafe
7 St John's Wood High Street, NW8 (020 7586 4455)

Brasseries

The Salt House p198
63 Abbey Road, NW8 (020 7328 6626)

Cafés

Maison Blanc p203
37 St John's Wood High Street, NW8 (020 7586 1982)

Chinese

Royal China p53
68 Queens Grove, NW8 (020 7586 4280)

French

L'Aventure p68
3 Blenheim Terrace, NW8 (020 7624 6232)

Greek

Greek Valley p73
130 Boundary Road, NW8 (020 7624 3217/020 7624 4717/www.greekvalley.co.uk)

International

Gascogne p99
12 Blenheim Terrace, NW8 (020 7625 7034)

Italian

Rosmarino p109
1 Blenheim Terrace, NW8 (020 7328 5014)

Jewish

Harry Morgan's p119
31 St John's Wood High Street, NW8 (020 7722 1869)

Branches

Pizza Express
55 The Broadway, Stanmore, Middx (020 8420 7474)

Branches

Caffè Uno
O2 Centre, 255 Finchley Road, NW3 (020 7431 4499)

Portuguese

O Cantinho de Portugal p151
135-137 Stockwell Road, SW9 (020 7924 0218)

Gira-Sol p151
176A Wandsworth Road, SW8 (020 7622 7526)

Branches

Cafe Pasta
94-98 Upper Richmond Road (020 8780 2224)

Carmelli
145 Stamford Hill, N16 (020 8809 4559)

Mangal Pied
27 Stoke Newington Road, N16 (020 7254 6999)

Ming
98 Northwold Road, E5 (020 8806 3804)

Shemsudeen's
35 Stoke Newington Church Street, N16 (020 7241 4171)

Brasseries

The Fox Reformed p197
176 Stoke Newington Church Street, N16 (020 7254 5975)

Cafés

Blue Legume p203
101 Stoke Newington Church Street, N16 (020 7923 1303)

Eating & Entertainment

Vortex p225
139-141 Stoke Newington Church Street, N16 (020 7254 6516)

Indian

Rasa p90
55 Stoke Newington Church Street, N16 (020 7249 0344)

Mediterranean

Mesclun p126
24 Stoke Newington Church Street, N16 (020 7249 5029)

Oriental

Barracuda p149
125 Stoke Newington Church Street, N16 (020 7923 7488)

Itto p149
226 Stoke Newington High Street, N16 (020 7275 8827)

Pizza & Pasta

Il Bacio p191
61 Stoke Newington Church Street, N16 (020 7249 3833)

Spanish

Bar Lorca p159
175 Stoke Newington High Street, N16 (020 7275 8659)

Thai

Yum Yum p169
30 Stoke Newington Church Street, N16 (020 7254 6751)

The Americas

Smollensky's on the Strand p23
105 Strand, WC2 (020 7497 2101/www.smollenskys.co.uk)

Bars

The American Bar p209
The Savoy, Strand, WC2 (020 7836 4343)

The Lobby Bar at One Aldwych p209
1 Aldwych, WC2 (020 7300 1070)

Branches

Coffee Gallery 2
Courtyard, Somerset House, Strand, WC2 (020 7848 2527)

Pizza Express
450 The Strand, WC2 (020 7930 8205)

Shoeless Joes
Temple Place, Embankment, WC2 (020 7610 9346)

Smollensky's on the Strand
105 The Strand, WC2 (020 7497 2101)

Thai Pot on the Strand
148 Strand, WC2 (020 7497 0904)

British

The Savoy Grill p35
The Savoy Hotel, Strand, WC2 (020 7420 2065)

Simpson's-in-the-Strand p35
100 Strand, WC2 (020 7836 9112)

Eating & Entertainment

Smollensky's on the Strand p225
105 The Strand, WC2 (020 7497 2101/www.smollenskys.co.uk)

Indian

India Club p81
Second floor, Strand Continental Hotel, 143 Strand, WC2 (020 7836 0650)

Wine Bars

Gordon's p219
47 Villiers Street, WC2 (020 7930 1408)

Branches

Pizza Express
Salway Road, E15 (020 8534 1700)

African & Caribbean

Trini's p18
13 High Parade, Streatham High Road, SW16 (020 8696 9669)

Branches

Pizza Express
34 Streatham High Road, SW18 (020 8769 0202)

Eating & Entertainment

La Pergola p224
66 Streatham High Road, SW16 (020 8769 2646)

Modern European

Luca p144
85 Maple Road, Surbiton, Surrey (020 8399 2365)

Branches

Pizza Express
4 High Street, Sutton, Surrey (020 8643 4725)

African & Caribbean

Mekasha p18
75 Fairfax Road, NW6 (020 7625 8964)

Branches

Benihana
100 Avenue Road, NW3 (020 7586 1303)

NW3 Café (branch of Table Café)
Habitat, 191-217 Finchley Road, NW3 (020 7328 3444)

Pizza Express
227 Finchley Road, NW3 (020 7794 5100)

Singapore Garden
83-83A Fairfax Road, NW6 (020 7624 8233)

Laughing Gravy p98
154 Blackfriars Road, SE1
(020 7721 7055)

Modern European

**Oxo Tower
Restaurant, Bar
& Brasserie** p141
Oxo Tower Wharf, Barge
House Street, SE1 (020
7803 3888)

**The People's
Palace** p141
Level 3, Royal Festival Hall,
South Bank, SE1
(020 7928 9999)

Pizza & Pasta

**Gourmet
Pizza Company** p191
Gabriel's Wharf, 56 Upper
Ground, SE1 (020 7928
3188)

Spanish

Mesón Don Felipe p157
53 The Cut, SE1 (020 7928
3237)

Turkish

Tas p170
33 The Cut, SE1 (020 7928
2111)

Wine Bars

The Archduke p221
Concert Hall Approach, SE1
(020 7928 9370)

Wembley, Middlesex

Branches

Pizza Express
456 High Road, Wembley,
Middx (020 8902 4918)
Sakonis
127-129 Ealing Road,
Wembley, Middx (020 8903
9601)
Woodlands
402A High Road, Wembley,
Middx (020 8902 9869)

Indian

Chetna's p91
420 High Road, Wembley,
Middx (020 8900 1466/020
8903 5989)
Jashan p91
1-2 Coronet Parade, Ealing
Road, Wembley, Middx (020
8900 9800)
Karahi King p89
213 East Lane, North
Wembley, Middx (020 8904
2760/4994)
Maru's Bhajia House p91
230 Ealing Road,
Wembley, Middx (020 8903
6771)
Palm Beach p93
17 Ealing Road, Wembley,
Middx (020 8900 8664)
Sakoni p91
127-129 Ealing Road,
Wembley, Middx (020 8903
9601)

Portuguese

O Galinheiro p151
414 High Road, Wembley,
Middx (020 8903 0811)

West Drayton, Middx

Branches

Simply Nico
Crowne Plaza, Stockley
Road, West Drayton, Middx
(01895 437 564)

West Hampstead NW6

The Americas

Babe Ruth's p27
O2 Complex, Finchley Road,
NW3 (020 7433
3388/www.baberuths.com)

Branches

Café Rouge
203 West End Lane, NW6
(020 7328 7177)
The Creative Cafe
172 West End Lane, NW6
(0207 794 0800)
Ed's Easy Diner
The O2 Centre, 255 Finchley
Road, NW3 (020 7431
1958)
Good Earth Express
335 West End Lane, NW6
(020 7433 3111)
**Gung Ho (branch of
Cheng Du)**
332 West End Lane, NW6
(020 7794 1444)
Hafez II
559 Finchley Road, NW3
(020 7431 4546)
Nando's Chicken
252-254 West End Lane,
NW6 (020 7794 1331)
Noho
241-279 Finchley Road, O2
Centre, NW3 (020 7794
5616)
Nando's Chicken
O2 Centre, 255 Finchley
Road, NW3 (020 7435
4644)
Pizza Express
319 West End Lane, NW6
(020 7431 8229)
World Cafe
280 West End Lane, NW3
(020 7431 4188)
Yo! Sushi
O2 Centre, 255 Finchley
Road, NW3 (020 7431 4499)

Central & East
European

**Czech &
Slovak House** p38
74 West End Lane, NW6
(020 7372 5251)

Fish & Chips

Nautilus p184
27-29 Fortune Green Road,
NW6 (020 7435 2532)

Greek

Mario's p73
153 Broadhurst Gardens,
NW6 (020 7625 5827)

Italian

Zuccato p109
Unit 8A, O2 Complex, 225
Finchley Road, NW3 (020
7431 1799)

Pizza & Pasta

La Brocca p191
273 West End Lane, NW6
(020 7433 1989)

Wine Bars

No.77 Wine Bar p222
77 Mill Lane, NW6 (020
7435 7787)

West Norwood SE27

Vegetarian

Hollyhocks p176
10 Knights Hill, SE27 (020
8766 8796)

Westbourne Grove
W2, W11

The Americas

Dakota p24
127 Ledbury Road, W11
(020 7792 9191)
Rodizio Rico p29
111 Westbourne Grove, W2
(020 7792 4035)

Branches

All Bar One
74-76 Westbourne Grove,
W2 (020 7313 9432)

Alounak Kebab
44 Westbourne Grove, W2
(020 7229 4158)
Nando's Chicken
63 Westbourne Grove, W2
(020 7313 9506)
**The Wine Factory
(branch of the Wine
Gallery)**
294 Westbourne Grove, W11
(020 7229 1877)

British

Veronica's p36
3 Hereford Road, W2 (020
7229 5079/1210)

Cafés

Tom's Delicatessen p201
226 Westbourne Grove, W11
(020 7221 8818)

Chinese

Lee Fook p49
98 Westbourne Grove, W2
(020 7727 0099)

International

Bali Sugar p96
33A All Saints Road, W11
(020 7221 4477)

Italian

Zucca p107
188 Westbourne Grove, W11
(020 7727 0060)

Mediterranean

**Beach Blanket
Babylon** p125
45 Ledbury Road, W11 (020
7229 2907)

Middle Eastern

Al Waha p130
75 Westbourne Grove, W2
(020 7229 0806)
Fresco p129
25 Westbourne Grove, W2
(020 7221 2355)
Hafez p130
5 Hereford Road, W2 (020
7221 3167/020 7229
9398)

North African

Kyma p145
84 Westbourne Grove, W2
(020 7792 2207)

Thai

Tawana p163
3 Westbourne Grove, W2
(020 7229 3785)

Westminster SW1

Branches

EAT
37 Tothill Street, SW1.

British

Shepherd's p35
Marsham Court, Marsham
Street, SW1 (020 7834 9552)

International

The Atrium p95
4 Millbank, SW1 (020 7233
0032)

Whetstone N20

Branches

Ask
1257 High Road, N20 (020
8492 0033)

Whitechapel E1

Branches

**Grapeshots
(branch of Davys)**
2-3 Artillery Passage,
E1 (020 7247 8215)
Jamies
Aldgate Barrs, Sedgewick
Centre, 10 Whitechapel High
Street, E1 (020 7265 1977)

**Tayyab (branch of
New Tayyab)**
89 Fieldgate Street, E1 (020
7247 9543)

Indian

Café Spice Namaste p85
16 Prescot Street, E1 (020
7488 9242)
Lahore Kebab House p85
2 Umberston Street, E1 (020
7488 2551)
New Tayyab p85
83 Fieldgate Street, E1
(020 7247 9543/
www.tayybs.co.uk)
Tiffin p85
165 Cannon Street Road, E1
(020 7702 3832)

Thai

Sweet Chilli p169
63-67 Mile End Road, E1
(020 7702 7977)

Willesden NW2, NW10

Branches

**Small Star (branch of
Small and Beautiful)**
26 Station Parade, Willesden
Green, NW2 (020 8830
5221)

Indian

Sabras p91
263 High Road, NW10 (020
8459 0340)

Japanese

Sushi-Say p118
33B Walm Lane, NW2 (020
8459 2971/7512)

Wimbledon SW19

Branches

All Bar One
37-39 Wimbledon Hill Road,
SW19 (020 8971 9871)
K Bar
82 The Broadway, SW19
(020 8544 9944)
Café Pasta
8 High Street, SW19 (020
8944 6893)
Cafe Rouge
26 High Street, Wimbledon,
SW19 (0208 944 5131)
Caffé Uno
21 High Street, SW19 (020
8946 0544)
Dome
91 High Street, SW19 (020
8947 9559)
Gourmet Pizza Company
Merton Abbey Mills,
Watermill Way, SW19 (020
8545 0310)
Jim Thompson's
141 The Broadway, SW19
(020 8540 5540)
Mongolian Barbecue
162 The Broadway, SW19
(020 8545 0021)
Pizza Express
84 High Street, SW19 (020
7946 6027)
San Lorenzo Fuoriporta
Worple Road Mews, SW19
(020 8946 8463)
Tootsies
48 High Street, Wimbledon
Village, SW19 (020 8946
4135)
**Utah (branch of
Coyote Cafe)**
18 High Street, Wimbledon
Village, SW19 (030 8944
1909)

Eating & Entertainment

Wimbledon Stadium p223
Plough Lane, SW17 (020
8946 8000/
www.wimbledondogs.co.uk)

Fish & Chips

Broadway Place p184
8-10 Hartfield Road, SW19
(020 8947 5333)

Indian

Suvai Aruvi p93
96 High Street, SW19 (020
8543 6266/020 8286
6677)

International

Light House p96
75-77 Ridgeway, SW19 (020
8944 6338/020 8946 4440)

Winchmore Hill N21

Branches

Pizza Express
701-703 Green Lanes, N21
(020 8364 2992)

Woodford, E18

Branches

Pizza Express
76 High Road, E18 (020
8924 4488)

Wood Green N22

Branches

Nando's
Hollywood Green, Redvers
Road, N22 (020 8889 2936)

Greek

Vrisaki p73
73 Myddleton Road, N22
(020 8889 8760/020 8881
2920)

Woolwich SE18

Branches

**Tai Cip Mein (branch of
Tai Wan Mein Noodle
House)**
7-9 Woolwich New Road,
SE18 (020 8317
3388/3883)

A-Z index

Bali p122
101 Edgware Road, W2
(020 7262 9100/020
7723 3303). Malaysian,
Indonesian &
Singaporean

Bali Sugar p96
33A All Saints Road, W11
(020 7221 4477).
International

Balls Brothers
20 St James's Street,
SW1 (020 7321 0882).
Branch

Balls Brothers
Mulligans of Mayfair, 13-
14 Cork Street, W1 (020
7409 1370). Branch

Balls Brothers
34 Brook Street, W1 (020
7499 4567). Branch

Balls Brothers p222
Hay's Galleria, Tooley
Street, SE1 (020 7407
4301/www.ballsbrothers.
co.uk). Wine Bars

Balls Brothers
The Hop Cellars, 24
Southwark Street, SE1
(020 7403 6851). Branch

Balls Brothers
Hay's Galleria, Tooley
Street, SE1 (020 7407
4301). Branch

Balls Brothers
158 Bishopsgate, EC2
(020 7426 0567). Branch

Balls Brothers
2 St Mary-at-Hill, EC3
(020 7626 0321). Branch

Balls Brothers
Mark Lane, EC3 (020
7623 2923). Branch

Balls Brothers
52 Lime Street, EC3 (020
7283 0841). Branch

Balls Brothers
King's Arms Yard, EC2
(020 7796 3049). Branch

Balls Brothers
Gow's Restaurant, 81 Old
Broad Street, EC2 (020
7920 9645). Branch

Balls Brothers
6-8 Cheapside, EC2 (020
7248 2708). Branch

Balls Brothers
5-6 Carey Lane (off Gutter
Lane). Branch

**Balti &
Tandoori World** p87
185-187 The Broadway,
Southall, Middx (020
8867 9991/9993).
Indian

Balti Hut p87
435 Alexandra Avenue,
Rayners Lane, Middx (020
8868 0007). Indian

Bam-Bou p177
1 Percy Street, W1 (020
7323 9130). Vietnamese

Bamboula p19
12 Acre Lane, SW2 (020
7737 6633). African &
Caribbean

**Bangers (branch of
Davys)**
2-12 Wilson Street, EC2
(020 7377 6326). Branch

**Bangers Too (branch of
Davys)**
1 St Mary-at-Hill, EC3
(020 7283 4443).
Branch

Bangkok p165
9 Bute Street, SW7 (020
7584 8529). Thai

Bank p132
1 Kingsway, WC2 (020
7234 3344). Modern
European

Banners p198
21 Park Road, N8 (020
8348 2930). Brasseries

K Bar
82 The Broadway, SW19
(020 8544 9944).
Branch

K Bar
200B Upper Richmond
Road, SW15 (020 8780
2822). Branch

K Bar
266A Fulham Road,
SW10 (020 7352 6200).
Branch

Bar Bourse p94
67 Queens Street, EC4
(020 7248 2200/2211).
International

Bar du Marché p195
19 Berwick Street, W1
(020 7734 4606).
Brasseries

Bar Estrela p151
111-115 South Lambeth
Road, SW8 (020 7793
1051). Portuguese

Bar Exellence
25 Victoria Street, SW1
(020 7222 4070). Branch

Bar Exellence
33 Dover Street, W1 (020
7499 2689). Branch

Bar Exellence
2 Old Change Court, EC4
(020 7248 2720). Branch

Bar Gansa p159
2 Inverness Street, NW1
(020 7267 8909).
Spanish

Bar Italia p200
22 Frith Street, W1 (020
7437 4520). Cafés

Bar Latino
144 Upper Street, N1
(020 7704 6868). Branch

Bar Lorca p159
175 Stoke Newington
High Street, N16 (020
7275 8659). Spanish

Bar Lorca
261 Brixton Road, SW9
(020 7274 5537). Branch

Bar Room Bar
48 Rosslyn Hill, NW3
(020 7431 8802). Branch

Bar Room Bar
441 Battersea Park Road,
SW11 (020 7223 7721).
Branch

Baradero p157
Turnberry Quay, off
Pepper Street, E14 (020
7537 1666). Spanish

Baran p172
748 Finchley Road, NW11
(020 8458 0515). Turkish

**Barcelona Tapas Bar
y Restaurante** p152
15 St Botolph Street –
entrance in Middlesex
Street, EC3 (020 7377
5111). Spanish

**Barcelona Tapas
Bar y Restaurate**
481 Lordship Lane, SE22
(020 8693 5111). Branch

**Barcelona Tapas
Bar y Restaurate**
1A Bell Lane, EC3 (020
7247 7014). Branch

**Barley Sugar (branch of
The Sugar Club)**
33A All Saints Road, W11
(020 7221 4477).
Branch

Barracuda p149
125 Stoke Newington
Church Street, N16 (020
7923 7488). Oriental

O Barros p151
168A Old South Lambeth
Road, SW8 (020 7582
0976). Portuguese

Base p126
71 Hampstead High
Street, NW3 (020 7431
2224). Mediterranean

Basilico p189
175 Lavender Hill, SW11
(020 7924 4070). Pizza
& Pasta

Basilico
690 Fulham Road, SW6
(020 7384 2633).
Branch

BB's p19
3 Chignell Place, off
Uxbridge Road, W13 (020
8840 8322). African &
Caribbean

**Beach Blanket
Babylon** p125
45 Ledbury Road, W11
(020 7229 2907).
Mediterranean

The Bean
126 Curtain Road, EC2
(020 7739 7829). Branch

The Bean
70 Compton Street, EC1
(020 7253 5972). Branch

Beatroot p175
92 Berwick Street, W1
(020 7437 8591).
Vegetarian

Bedlington Café p163
24 Fauconberg Road, W4
(020 8994 1965). Thai

Beirut Express
112-114 Edgware Road
W2 (020 7724 2700).
Branch

Bel & the Dragon p228
Bridge Street, Godalming,
Surrey (01483 527333).
Out of Town

Belair House p141
Gallery Road, SE21 (020
8299 9788). Modern
European

Belgo Centraal p68
50 Earlham Street, WC2
(020 7813 2233). Global

Belgo Noord p69
72 Chalk Farm Road,
NW1 (020 7267 0718).
Global

Belgo Zuid p68
124 Ladbroke Grove,
W10 (020 8982 8400).
Global

La Belle Epoque •
151 Draycott Avenue,
SW3 (020 7460 5000).
Branch

Belle Vue p214
1 Clapham Common
Southside, SW4 (020
7498 9473). Pubs

The Belvedere p138
Off Abbotsbury Road,
Holland Park, W8
(020 7602 1238).
Modern European

**Ben's Elephant (branch
Ben's Thai)**
283 Ballards Lane, N12
(020 8492 0201). Branch

Ben's Thai
King's Arms, The Vale,
W3 (020 8740 4210).
Branch

Ben's Thai
48 Red Lion Street, WC1
(020 7404 9991). Branch

Ben's Thai p163
above the Warrington, 93
Warrington Crescent,
W9 (020 7266 3134).
Thai

**Bengal Trader (branch
Bengal Clipper)**
1 Parliament Court, 44
Artillery Lane, E1 (020
7375 0072). Branch

Benihana p115
37 Sackville Street, W1
(020 7494
2525/www.benihana.co.u
k). Japanese

Benihana
100 Avenue Road, NW3
(020 7586 1303). Branch

Benihana
77 King's Road, SW3
(020 7376 7799). Branch

Bertorelli's p100
19-23 Charlotte Street,
W1 (020 7636 4174).
Italian

Bertorelli's
44A Floral Street, WC2
(020 7836 3969).
Branch

**Betjeman's (branch of
Jamies)**
43-44 Cloth Fair, EC1
(020 7600 7778). Branch

**Betjemans (branch of
Jamies)**
43-44 Cloth Fair EC1 (020
7600 7778). Branch

Beyoglu p170
50 Battersea Park Road,
SW11 (020 7627 2052).
Turkish

Bibendum p140
Michelin House, 81
Fulham Road, SW3
(020 7581 5817/
www.bibendum.co.uk).
Modern European

**Bibendum
Oyster Bar** p57
Michelin House, 81
Fulham Road, SW3 (020
7581 5817). Fish

Bierodrome p69
173-174 Upper Street, N1
(020 7226 5835). Global

**Bierodrome (branch of
Belgo)**
44-48 Clapham High
Street, SW4 (020 7720
1118). Branch

Big Easy p24
332-334 King's Road,
SW3 (020 7352 4071).
The Americas

Birdcage p146
110 Whitfield Street, W1
(020 7323 9655).
Oriental

Bistrot 190 p125
190 Queensgate, SW7
(020 7581 5666).
Mediterranean

Black Chapati p227
12 Circus Parade, New
England Road, Brighton,
East Sussex (01273 699
011). Out of Town

Black Truffle p108
40 Chalcot Road, NW1
(020 7483 0077). Italian

Blah Blah Blah
28 Clifton Road, W9 (020
7289 6399). Branch

Blah Blah Blah p175
78 Goldhawk Road, W12
(020 8746 1337).
Vegetarian

Blakes p98
31 Jamestown Road,
NW1 (020 7482 2959).
International

Blakes
2 St John's Square, EC2
(020 7482 5229). Branch

Bleeding Heart p19
Bleeding Heart Yard, off
Greville Street, EC1
(020 7242 8238). Wine
Bars

Bloom's p119
130 Golders Green Road,
NW11 (020 8455 1338).
Jewish

Blue Elephant p165
4-6 Fulham Broadway,
SW6 (020 7385 6595).
Thai

Blue Hawaii p223
2 Richmond Road,
Kingston-upon-Thames,
Surrey (020 8549 6989).
Eating & Entertainment

Blue Jade p162
44 Hugh Street, SW1
(020 7828 0321). Thai

Blue Lagoon p163
284 Kensington High
Street, W8 (020 7603
1231). Thai

Blue Legume p203
101 Stoke Newington
Church Street, N16
(020 7923 1303).
Cafés

Blue Olive p125
56-58 Tooley Street, SE1
(020 7407 6001).
Mediterranean

Blue Orange p203
65 Columbia Road, E2
(020 7366 9272). Cafés

Blue Print Café p142
Design Museum, Butlers
Wharf, SE1 (020 7378
7031). Modern European

Blue Pumpkin p96
147 Upper Richmond
Road, SW15 (020 8780
3553). International

Bluebird p139
350 King's Road, SW3
(020 7559 1000).
Modern European

Blues Bistro & Bar p23
42-43 Dean Street, W1
(020 7494 1966/
www.bluesbistro.com).
The Americas

Bluewater p226
Greenhithe, Kent (08456
021021/
www.bluewater.co.uk).
Eating & Entertainment

Blythe Road p139
71 Blythe Road, W14
(020 7371 3635).
Modern European

Boardwalk p95
18 Greek Street, W1 (020
7287 2051). International

**Boiled Egg
& Soldiers** p202
63 Northcote Road, SW11
(020 7223 4894). Cafés

Boisdale p35
15 Eccleston Street, SW1
(020 7730 6922/
www.boisdale.co.uk).
British

Boisdale p209
15 Eccleston Street, SW1
(020 7730 6922). Bars

Bombay Brasserie p83
Courtfield Road, SW7
(020 7370 4040/www.
bombaybrasserielondon.
com). Indian

**Bonnington
Centre Café** p175
11 Vauxhall Grove, SW8
(no phone). Vegetarian

Borshtch 'n' Tears p41
45-46 Beauchamp Place,
SW3. (020 7589 5003).
Central & East European

La Bota p159
31 Broadway Parade,
Tottenham Lane, N8 (020
8340 3082). Spanish

Brackenbury p139
129-131 Brackenbury
Road, W6 (020 8748
0107). Modern European

M J Bradley's p199
9 King Street, WC2 (020
7240 5178). Cafés

Brady's p184
513 Old York Road, SW18
(020 8877 9599). Fish &
Chips

La Brasserie p196
272 Brompton Road, SW3
(020 7581 3089).
Brasseries

**Brasserie du
Marché** p196
349 Portobello Road,
W10 (020 8968 5828).
Brasseries

Brasserie Metz p196
30 Battersea Rise, SW11
(020 7228 0611).
Brasseries

**Brasserie
St Quentin** p62
243 Brompton Road, SW3
(020 7589 8005). French

Bread & Roses p217
68 Clapham Manor
Street, SW4 (020 7498
1779). Pubs

**Break for the
Border** p225
5 Goslett Yard, WC2 (020
7437 8595/
www.bftb.com). Eating &
Entertainment

Break For The Border
8 Argyll Street, W1V (020
7734 5776). Branch

Brera
Lyric Theatre
Hammersmith, King
Street, W6 (020 8741
9291). Branch

Brew House p205
Kenwood, Hampstead
Lane, NW3 (020 8341
5384). Cafés

**Brick Lane
Music Hall** p225
134-146 Curtain Road,
EC2 (020 7739 9997/
www.brick/lane/music/
hall.co.uk). Eating &
Entertainment

The Bridge p194
1 Paul's Walk, off High
Timber Street, EC4 (020
7236 0000). Brasseries

Brilliant p87
72-76 Western Road,
Southall, Middx (020
8574 1928). Indian

**Brixtonian
Havana Club** p20
11 Beehive Place, SW9
(020 7924 9262). African
& Caribbean

Broadway Place p184
8-10 Hartfield Road,
SW19 (020 8947 5333).
Fish & Chips

La Brocca p191
273 West End Lane, NW6
(020 7433 1989). Pizza
& Pasta

Brompton Bay p125
96 Draycott Avenue, SW3
(020 7225 2500).
Mediterranean

Browns p194
82-84 St Martin's Lane,
WC2 (020 7497 5050).
Brasseries

Browns
3-5 Kew Road, Kew Green
(020 8948 4838). Branch

Browns
Hartsmere Road, E14
(020 7987 9777). Branch

Browns
201 Castlenau Road,
SW13 (020 8748 4486).
Branch

Browns
47 Maddox Street, W1
(020 7491 4565). Branch

Brula p144
43 Crown Road,
Twickenham, Middx (020
8892 0602). Modern
European

Buchan's p36
62-64 Battersea Bridge
Road, SW11 (020 7228
0888). British

The Bug Bar p209
The Crypt, St Matthew's,
Brixton Hill, SW2 (020
7738 3184). Bars

Builders Arms p214
13 Britten Street, SW3
(020 7349 9040). Pubs

Bull & Last p216
168 Highgate Road, NW5
(020 7267 3641). Pubs

**Bung Hole (branch of
Davys)**
Hand Court, 57 High
Holborn, WC1 (020 7831
8365). Branch

**Burgundy Ben's (branch
of Davys)**
102-108 Clerkenwell
Road, EC1 (020 7251
3783). Branch

Busaba Eathai p148
106-110 Wardour Street,
W1 (020 7255 8686).
Oriental

Busabong Too
1A Langton Street, SW10
(020 7352 7414).
Branch

F

O Fado p151
49-50 Beauchamp Place, SW3 (020 7589 3002). Portuguese

Fairuz p127
3 Blandford Street, W1 (020 7486 8108/8182). Middle Eastern

Fakhreldine p128
85 Piccadilly, W1 (020 7493 3424). Middle Eastern

Fakhreldine Express
92 Queensway, W2 (020 7243 3177). Branch

La Famiglia p107
7 Langton Street, SW10 (020 7351 0761/ 020 7352 6095/ www.lafamiglia.sageweb.co.uk). Italian

Farmacia p204
169 Drury Lane, WC2 (020 7831 0830). Cafés

Fat Boy's 2
68 Brentford High Street, Middx (020 8569 8481). Branch

Faulkner's p184
424-426 Kingsland Road, E8 (020 7254 6152). Fish & Chips

feast p199
86 St John Street, EC1 (020 7253 7007). Cafés

Feng Shang p51
Cumberland Basin, Prince Albert Road, NW1 (020 7485 8137). Chinese

Ferrari's p108
225 Balham High Road, SW17 (020 8682 3553). Italian

Fiction p176
60 Crouch End Hill, N8 (020 8340 3403). Vegetarian

The Fifth Floor p132
Harvey Nichols, Knightsbridge, SW1 (020 7235 5250). Modern European

The Fifth Floor Café p194
Harvey Nichols, Knightsbridge, SW1 (020 7823 1839). Brasseries

Fileric (branch of La Madeleine)
57 Old Brompton Road, SW7 (020 7584 2967). Branch

Fina Estampa p32
150 Tooley Street, SE1 (020 7403 1342). The Americas

The Finca p160
96-98 Pentonville Road, N1 (020 7837 5387). Spanish

The Finca
185 Kennington Lane, SE11 (020 7735 1061). Branch

The Fine Line
29-30 Fishman's Wharf, Cabot Square, Canary Wharf, E14 (020 7513 0255).

Gourmet Pizza Company p189
Gabriel's Wharf, 56 Upper Ground, SE1 (020 7928 3188). Pizza & Pasta

Gourmet Pizza Company
18-20 Mackenzie Walk, Canary Wharf, E14 (020 7345 9192). Branch

The Fine Line
182-184 Clapham High Street, SW4 (020 7622 4436). Branch

The Fine Line
236 Fulham Road, SW10 (020 376 5827). Branch

The Fine Line
1 Bow Churchyard, EC4 (020 7248 3262). Branch

The Fine Line
124-127 The Minories, EC3 (020 481 8195). Branch

The Fine Line
Equitable House, 1 Monument Street, EC3 (020 623 5446). Branch

Firebird p41
23 Conduit Street, W1 (020 7493 7000/ 7088). Central & East European

Fish Central p183
149-151 Central Street, EC1 (020 7253 4970). Fish & Chips

Fish in a Tie p180
105 Falcon Road, SW11 (020 7924 1913). Budget

fish! p58
Cathedral Street, SE1 (020 7234 3333). Fish

fish!
Hanover House, 33 Westferry Circus, E14 (020 7234 3333). Branch

fish!
Cathedral Street, SE1 (020 7836 3236). Branch

fish!
3B Belvedere Road, Waterloo, SE1 (020 7234 3333). Branch

Fishmarket p54
Great Eastern Hotel, 40 Liverpool Street, EC2 (020 7618 7200/www.fish-market.co.uk). Fish

Fishnets p56
Chelsea Village, Stamford Bridge, Fulham Road, SW6 (020 7565 1430). Fish

Flamenco p152
54 Pimlico Road, SW1 (020 7730 4484). Spanish

Flask p217
14 Flask Walk, NW3 (020 7435 4580). Pubs

The Floating Boater p223
Prince Regent corner of Warwick Crescent and Westbourne Terrace Road Bridge, W2 (020 7266 1066). Eating & Entertainment

Floriana p100
15 Beauchamp Place, SW3 (020 7838 1500). Italian

Florians p109
4 Topsfield Parade, Middle Lane, N8 (020 8348 8348). Italian

Fluid p204
208 Fulham Road, SW10 (020 7352 4372). Cafés

Foliage p74
Mandarin Oriental Hyde Park Hotel, 66 Knightsbridge, SW1 (020 7235 2000). Hotels & Haute Cuisine

Food for Thought p173
31 Neal Street, WC2 (020 7836 9072/0239). Vegetarian

Fortnum & Mason p34
181 Piccadilly, W1 (020 7734 8040). British

Four Regions p49
County Hall, Riverside Building, Westminster Bridge Road, SE1 (020 7928 0988). Chinese

Four Regions
102 Kew Road, Richmond, Surrey (020 8940 9044). Branch

Four Seasons p49
84 Queensway, W2 (020 7229 4320). Chinese

The Fox Reformed p197
176 Stoke Newington Church Street, N16 (020 7254 5975). Brasseries

Foxtrot Oscar p36
79 Royal Hospital Road, SW3 (020 7352 7179). British

Foxtrot Oscar
Riverside Plaza, SW11 (0207 223 0999). Branch

Foxtrot Oscar
16 Byward Street, EC3 (020 7481 2700). Branch

Franco's (Uffizzi) p191
753-755 Lea Bridge Road, E17 (020 8509 2259). Pizza & Pasta

Francofill p196
1 Old Brompton Road, SW7 (020 7584 0087). Brasseries

Frederick's p99
Camden Passage, N1 (020 7359 2888). International

Freedom p209
60-66 Wardour Street, W1 (020 7734 0071). Bars

Freedom
14-16 Ganton Street, W1 (020 7287 5267). Branch

Freedom Brewing Company p207
41 Earlham Street, WC2 (020 7240 0606). Bars

French House Dining Room p135
First floor, The French House, 49 Dean Street, W1 (020 7437 2477). Modern European

Frère Jacques p196
136 Upper Richmond Road, SW15 (020 8780 9000/www.frerejacques.co.uk). Brasseries

Frère Jacques
10-12 Riverside Walk, Kingston-upon-Thames, Surrey (020 8546 1332). Branch

Fresco p129
25 Westbourne Grove, W2 (020 7221 2355). Middle Eastern

Freuds p207
198 Shaftesbury Avenue, WC2 (020 7240 9933). Bars

TGI Friday's p23
6 Bedford Street, WC2 (020 7379 0585). The Americas

TGI Friday's
702-704 Purley Way, Croydon (020 8681 1313). Branch

TGI Friday's
Watford Way, NW7 (020 8203 9779). Branch

TGI Friday's
69-98 Bishop's Bridge Road, W2 (020 7229 8600). Branch

TGI Friday's
25-29 Coventry Street, W1 (020 7839 6262). Branch

TGI Fridays p225
6 Bedford Street, WC2 (020 7379 0585). Eating & Entertainment

Frocks p98
95 Lauriston Road, E9 (020 8986 3161). International

Fryer's Delight p183
19 Theobald's Road, WC1 (020 7405 4114). Fish & Chips

Fujiyama p149
7 Vining Street, SW9 (020 7737 2369). Oriental

Fulham.ebar p204
42-48 New King's Road, SW6 (020 7384 9746). Cafés

Fung Shing p43
15 Lisle Street, WC2 (020 7437 1539). Chinese

G

Galicia p153
323 Portobello Road, W10 (020 8969 3539). Spanish

O Galinheiro p151
414 High Road, Wembley, Middx (020 8903 0811). Portuguese

O Galinheiro
157 King Street, W6 (020 8741 8563). Branch

The Gallery p151
256A Brixton Hill, SW2 (020 8671 8311). Portuguese

The Gallery Café p176
21 Old Ford Road, E2 (020 8983 3624). Vegetarian

Gallery One Twenty p95
120 Goldhawk Road, W12 (020 8749 5505). International

Gallipoli p172
102 Upper Street, N1 (020 7359 0630). Turkish

Gallipoli II p172
120 Upper Street, N1 (020 7359 1578). Turkish

Garbo's p71
42 Crawford Street, W1 (020 7262 6582). Global

The Garden Café p200
4 Newburgh Street, W1 (020 7494 0044). Cafés

Garlic & Shots p224
14 Frith Street, W1 (020 7734 9505/ www.garlicandshots.com). Eating & Entertainment

The Garratt p96
205 Garratt Lane, SW18 (020 8871 2223). International

Gascogne p99
12 Blenheim Terrace, NW8 (020 7625 7034). International

Gastro p197
67 Venn Street, SW4 (020 7627 0222). Brasseries

The Gate p175
51 Queen Caroline Street, W6 (020 8748 6932). Vegetarian

The Gaucho Grill p29
19 Swallow Street, W1 (020 7734 4040). The Americas

The Gaucho Grill
64 Heath Street, NW3 (020 7431 8222). Branch

Gaucho Grill
12 Gracechurch Street, EC3 (020 7626 5180). Branch

Gaudi p152
63 Clerkenwell Road, EC1 (020 7608 3220). Spanish

Le Gavroche p75
43 Upper Brook Street, W1 (020 7408 0881). Hotels & Haute Cuisine

Gay Hussar p38
2 Greek Street, W1 (020 7437 0973/ www.gayhussar.co.uk). Central & East European

Gazi Antep Lahmacun Salonu t p170
115 Stoke Newington Road, N16 (020 7275 7924/www.londraturk.com). Turkish

Geales p184
2 Farmer Street, W8 (020 7727 7528). Fish & Chips

Geeta p91
57-59 Willesden Lane, NW6 (020 7624 1713). Indian

The Genuine Lahore Karahi p89
37 Featherstone Road, Southall, Middx (020 8893 5270). Indian

Gifto's Lahore Karahi p89
162-164 The Broadway, Southall, Middx (020 8813 8669/ www.gifto.com). Indian

Gilbey's p138
77 The Grove, W5 (020 8840 7568). Modern European

Gingerman p227
21A Norfolk Square, Brighton, East Sussex (01273 326688). Out of Town

Gira-Sol p151
176A Wandsworth Road, SW8 (020 7622 7526). Portuguese

Giraffe p198
46 Rosslyn Hill, NW3 (020 7435 0343). Brasseries

Giraffe
29-31 Essex Road, N1 (020 7359 5999). Branch

Giraffe
6-8 Blandford Street, Marleybourne, W1H (020 7935 2333). Branch

The Glasshouse p144
14 Station Parade, Kew, Surrey (020 8940 6777). Modern European

Global Café p204
15 Golden Square, W1 (020 7287 2242/ www.globalcafe.net). Cafés

Globe p99, p222
100 Avenue Road, NW3 (020 7722 7200). International; Eating & Entertainment

Gloriette Pâtisserie p201
128 Brompton Road, SW3 (020 7589 4750). Cafés

Golborne House p213
36 Golborne Road, W10 (020 8960 6260). Pubs

Golden Dragon p43
28-29 Gerrard Street, W1 (020 7734 2763). Chinese

Golden Harvest p43
17 Lisle Street, WC2 (020 7287 3822). Chinese

Golden Hind p183
73 Marylebone Lane, W1 (020 7486 3644). Fish & Chips

Golden Orient (branch of Indian Connoisseurs)
639 Leytonstone High Road, E11 (020 8539 0747). Branch

Golden Palace p53
146-150 Station Road, Harrow, Middx (020 8863 2333). Chinese

Golders Hill Park Refreshment House p205
North End Road, NW3 (020 8455 8010). Cafés

Good Earth p53
143-145 The Broadway, Mill Hill Circus, NW7 (020 8959 7011). Chinese

Good Earth
6 Friars Stile Road, Richmond, Surrey (020 8948 3399). Branch

Good Earth
233 Brompton Road, SW3 (020 7584 3658). Branch

Good Earth Express
335 West End Lane, NW6 (020 7433 3111). Branch

Goodfellas p181
50 Lamb's Conduit Street, WC1 (020 7405 7088). Budget

Goolies p95
21 Abingdon Road, W8 (020 7938 1122). International

The Goose p228
Britwell Salome, near Watlington, Oxon (01491 612304). Out of Town

Gordon Ramsay p76
68-69 Royal Hospital Road, SW3 (020 7352 4441/3334). Hotels & Haute Cuisine

Gordon's p219
47 Villiers Street, WC2 (020 7930 1408). Wine Bars

The Goring Hotel p35
15 Beeston Place, Grosvenor Gardens, SW1 (020 7396 9000/ www.goringhotel.co.uk). British

Gourmet Pizza Company p191
Gabriel's Wharf, 56 Upper Ground, SE1 (020 7928 3188). Pizza & Pasta

Gourmet Pizza Company
18-20 Mackenzie Walk, Canary Wharf, E14 (020 7345 9192). Branch

Gourmet Pizza Company
Merton Abbey Mills, Watermill Way, SW19 (020 8545 0310). Branch

Gourmet Pizza Company
7-9 Swallow Street, W1 (020 7734 5182). Branch

Goya p153
34 Lupus Street, SW1 (020 7976 5309). Spanish

Goya Belgravia
Eccleston Place, Belgravia, SW1 (020 7730 4299). Branch

Grand Banks p211
156-158 Fortress Road, NW5 (020 7419 9499). Bars

La Grande Marque p218
47 Ludgate Hill, EC4 (020 7329 6709). Wine Bars

La Grande Marque
55 Leadenhall Market, EC3 (020 7929 3536). Branch

Granita p143
127 Upper Street, N1 (020 7226 3222). Modern European

Grano p105
162 Thames Road, W4 (020 8995 0120). Italian

Jones Dairy Café p203
23 Ezra Street, E2 (020 7739 5372). Cafés

Jongleurs
Bar Risa, 221 Grove Road, Victoria Wharf, E3 (020 7564 2500). Branch

Jongleurs Battersea
49 Lavender Gardens, SW11 (020 7564 2500). Branch

Jongleurs Camden Lock p222
Middle Yard, Camden Lock, Chalk Farm Road, NW1 (020 7564 2500/ www.jongleurs.com). Eating & Entertainment

Joy King Lau p44
3 Leicester Street, WC2 (020 7437 1133/1132). Chinese

Judy's p181
249 Holloway Road, N7 (no phone). Budget

Julie's p221
135-137 Portland Road, W11 (020 7229 8331/ www.juliesrestaurant. demon.co.uk). Wine Bars

Just Around the Corner p224
446 Finchley Road, NW2 (020 7431 3300). Eating & Entertainment

K

K-10 p111
20 Copthall Avenue, EC2 (020 7562 8510/ www.k10.net). Japanese

Kai p47
65 South Audley Street, W1 (020 7493 8988/ 1456/www.kaimayfair. co.uk). Chinese

Kaifeng p53
51 Church Road, NW4 (020 8203 7888). Chinese

Kalamis
Truman's Road, N16 (020 7923 4260). Branch

Kandoo p126
458 Edgware Road, W2 (020 7724 2428). Middle Eastern

Karahi King p89
213 East Lane, North Wembley, Middx (020 8904 2760/4994). Indian

Kasbah p145
73 Venn Street, SW4 (020 7498 3622). North African

Kastoori p90
188 Upper Tooting Road, SW17 (020 8767 7027). Indian

Kavanagh's p143
26 Penton Street, N1 (020 7833 1380/ www.kavrestaurant.co.uk). Modern European

Kaya p120
42 Albemarle Street, W1 (020 7499 0622/ 0633). Korean

G Kelly
600 Roman Road E3 (020 8983 3552). Branch

Ken Lo's Memories of China p47
67-69 Ebury Street, SW1 (020 7730 7734). Chinese

Ken Lo's Memories of China
353 Kensington High Street, W8 (020 7603 6951). Branch

Kennington Lane Restaurant & Bar p141
205-209 Kennington Lane, SE11 (020 7793 8313). Modern European

Kensington Place p138
201 Kensington Church Street, W8 (020 7727 3184). Modern European

Kettners p187
29 Romilly Street, W1 (020 7734 6112). Pizza & Pasta

The Kew Greenhouse p204
1 Station Parade, Kew, Surrey (020 8940 0183). Cafés

King's Road Café (branch of Table Café)
Habitat, 208 King's Road, SW3 (020 7351 1211). Branch

Kkach'ine p121
34 Durham Road, SW20 (020 8947 1081). Korean

The Knosherie p118
12-13 Greville Street, EC1 (020 7242 5190/ www.theknosherie. sageweb.co.uk). Jewish

Koi p117
1E Palace Gate, W8 (020 7581 8778). Japanese

Konditor & Cook
22 Cornwall Rd, South Bank, SE1 (020 7261 0456). Branch

Konditor & Cook p203
10 Stoney Street, SE1 (020 7407 5100). Cafés

Kozachok p41
10 Red Lion Street, Richmond, Surrey (020 8948 2366). Central & East European

Kulu Kulu p115
76 Brewer Street, W1 (020 7734 7316). Japanese

Kwan Thai p167
The Riverfront, Hay's Galleria, Tooley Street, SE1 (020 7403 7373). Thai

Kyma p145
84 Westbourne Grove, W2 (020 7792 2207). North African

L

Lab p209
12 Old Compton Street, W1 (020 7437 7820). Bars

Lahore Karahi p83
1 Tooting High Street, SW17 (020 8767 2477). Indian

Lahore Kebab House p85
2 Umberston Street, E1 (020 7488 2551). Indian

Laicram p167
1 Blackheath Grove, SE3 (020 8852 4710). Thai

Lalibela p18
137 Fortress Road, NW5 (020 7284 0600). African & Caribbean

The Lamb p216
94 Lamb's Conduit Street, WC1 (020 7405 0713). Pubs

The Landmark p74
222 Marylebone Road, NW1 (020 7631 8000). Hotels & Haute Cuisine

Langan's Brasserie p133
Stratton Street, W1 (020 7491 8822). Modern European

Langan's Coq d'or
Old Brompton Road, SW5 (020 7259 2599). Branch

The Langley p207
5 Langley Street, WC2 (020 7836 5005). Bars

Lansdowne p215
90 Gloucester Avenue, NW1 (020 7483 0409). Pubs

La Lanterna (branch of Il Bordello)
6 Mill Street, Butlers Wharf, SE1 (020 7252 2420). Branch

Las Brasas p152
63A Clerkenwell Road, EC1 (020 7250 3401). Spanish

Latymers (branch of Churchill Arms)
157 Hammersmith Road, W6 (020 8741 2507). Branch

Laughing Gravy p98
154 Blackfriars Road, SE1 (020 7721 7055). International

Launceston Place p138
1A Launceston Place, W8 (020 7937 6912). Modern European

Laurent p146
428 Finchley Road, NW2 (020 7794 3603). North African

The Lavender p197
171 Lavender Hill, SW11 (020 7978 5242). Brasseries

The Lavender
61 The Cut, SE1 (020 7928 8645). Branch

The Lavender
24 Clapham Road, SW9 (020 7793 0770). Branch

The Lavender Pub & Restaurant
112 Vauxhall Walk, SE11 (020 7735 4440). Branch

Lawn p141
1 Lawn Terrace, SE3 (020 8355 1110). Modern European

Laxeiro p157
93 Columbia Road, E2 (020 7729 1147). Spanish

Leadenhall Wine Bar p152
27 Leadenhall Market, EC3 (020 7623 1818). Spanish

Lebanese Restaurant p126
60 Edgware Road, W2 (020 7723 9130). Middle Eastern

Lee Fook p49
98 Westbourne Grove, W2 (020 7727 0099). Chinese

Lees Bag (branch of Davys)
4 Great Portland Street, W1 (020 7636 5287). Branch

Legless Ladder
339 Battersea Park Road, SW11 (020 7622 2112). Branch

Lehane's p196
100-102 Churchfield Road, W3 (020 8992 6299). Brasseries

The Lemon Tree p228
268 Woodstock Road, Oxford (01865 311936). Out of Town

Lemongrass p150
243 Royal College Street, NW1 (020 7284 1116). Oriental

Lemonia p72
89 Regent's Park Road, NW1 (020 7586 7454). Greek

Lennie's p180
6 Calvert Avenue, E2 (020 7739 3628). Budget

Le Palais du Jardin
151 Draycott Avenue, SW3 (020 7379 5353). Branch

Les Associes p67
172 Park Road, N8 (020 8348 8944). French

Levant p128
Jason Court, 76 Wigmore Street, W1 (020 7224 1111). Middle Eastern

Level 1 Café (branch of Table Café)
Habitat, 1 Drury Crescent, Purley Way, Croydon (020 8681 3818). Branch

Leven is Strijd p223
West India Quay, Hertsmere Road, West India Docks, E14 (020 7987 4002). Eating & Entertainment

The Lexington p137
45 Lexington Street, W1 (020 7434 3401). Modern European

Lezzet Lokanta p172
330 Essex Road, N1 (020 7226 7418/020 7354 1162). Turkish

The Library p205
Lanesborough Hotel, Hyde Park Corner, SW1 (020 7259 5599). Bars

Lickfold Inn p228
Lickfold, nr Lodsworth, Petworth, West Sussex (01798 861285). Out of Town

The Light p211
233 Shoreditch High Street, E1 (020 7247 8989). Bars

Light House p96
75-77 Ridgeway, SW19 (020 8944 6338/020 8946 4440). International

Limani p72
154 Regent's Park Road, NW1 (020 7483 4492). Greek

Lindsay House p34
21 Romilly Street, W1 (020 7439 0450). British

Lisboa Patisserie p150
57 Golborne Road, W10 (020 8968 5242). Portuguese

Lisboa Patisserie
4 Plender Street, NW1 (020 7387 1782). Branch

Lisboa Patisserie
6 World's End Place, off King's Road, SW6 (020 7376 3639). Branch

Little Bay
228 Belsize Road, NW6 (020 7372 4699). Branch

Little Georgia p38
2 Broadway Market, E8 (020 7249 9070). Central & East European

Little Havana (branch of Boardwalk)
1 Leicester Place, WC2 (020 7287 0101). Branch

Little Italy p104
21 Frith Street, W1 (020 7734 4737). Italian

Livebait p58
41-45 The Cut, SE1 (020 7928 7211). Fish

Livebait
175 Westbourne Grove, W11 (020 7727 4321). Branch

Livebait
21 Wellington Street, WC2 (020 7836 7161). Branch

The Lobby Bar at One Aldwych p209
1 Aldwych, WC2 (020 7300 1070). Bars

The Lobster Pot p57
3 Kennington Lane, SE11 (020 7582 5556). Fish

Local Friends p52
28 North End Road, NW11 (020 8455 9258). Chinese

Loch Fyne Restaurant at the Fisherman's Hut p58
175 Hampton Road, Twickenham, Middx (020 8255 6222/ www.loch-fyne.com). Fish

Lococo p81
9A Cullum Street, EC3 (020 7220 7722). Branch

The Loft p96
17 Lavington Street, SE1 (020 7902 0800). International

Lokal p170
107 Sydenham Road, SE26 (020 8659 4361). Turkish

Lola's p143
The Mall Building, Camden Passage, 359 Upper Street, N1 (020 7359 1932). Modern European

Lombok p149
17 Half Moon Lane, SE24 (020 7733 7131). Oriental

Lomo p155
222-224 Fulham Road, SW10 (020 7349 8848). Spanish

Loofs p81
234 Old Brompton Road, SW5 (020 7370 1188/1199). Indian

Lord Palmerston p216
33 Dartmouth Park Hill, NW5 (020 7485 1578). Pubs

Lord Stanley p215
51 Camden Park Road, NW1 (020 7428 9488). Pubs

Los Molinos p153
127 Shepherd's Bush Road, W6 (020 7603 2229). Spanish

Los Remos p155
38A Southwick Street, W2 (020 7723 5056/020 7706 1870). Spanish

Lotus Chinese Floating Restaurant p51
38 Limeharbour, Inner Millwall Dock, E14 (020 7515 6445). Chinese

Lou Pescadou p56
241 Old Brompton Road, SW5 (020 7370 1057). Fish

Louis Pâtisserie p203
32 Heath Street, NW3 (020 7435 9908). Cafés

lounge p202
88 Atlantic Road, SW9 (020 7733 5229). Cafés

Lowiczanka Polish Cultural Centre p39
238-246 King Street, W6 (020 8741 3225). Central & East European

Luba's Place p41
164 Essex Road, N1 (020 7704 2775). Central & East European

Luca p144
85 Maple Road, Surbiton, Surrey (020 8399 2365). Modern European

La Luna p189
380 Walworth Road, SE17 (020 7277 1991). Pizza & Pasta

Luna Nuova p99
Thomas Neal's Centre, 22 Short's Gardens, WC2 (020 7836 4110). Italian

Lunch p199
60 Exmouth Market, EC1 (020 7278 2420/ www.lunch.uk.com). Cafés

Lunch
7 Old Street, EC1 (020 7490 7557). Branch

Lundum's p69
119 Old Brompton Road, SW7 (020 7373 7774). Global

M

Ma Goa p81
242-244 Upper Richmond Road, SW15 (020 8780 1767). Indian

La Madeleine p200
5 Vigo Street, W1 (020 7734 8353). Cafés

Madhu's Brilliant p89
39 South Road, Southall, Middx (020 8574 1897/6380). Indian

Maggie Jones's p35
6 Old Court Place, Kensington Church Street, W8 (020 7937 6462). British

Maghreb p146
189 Upper Street, N1 (020 7226 2305). North African

Magic Wok p47
100 Queensway, W2 (020 7792 9767). Chinese

Maison Bertaux p201
28 Greek Street, W1 (020 7437 6007). Cafés

Maison Blanc p203
37 St John's Wood High Street, NW8 (020 7586 1982). Cafés

Maison Blanc
27B The Quadrant, Richmond, Surrey (020 8332 7041). Branch

Maison Blanc
11 Elystan Street, SW3 (020 7584 6913). Branch

Maison Blanc
303 Fulham Road, SW10 (020 7795 2663). Branch

Maison Blanc
102 Holland Park Avenue, W11 (020 7221 2494). Branch

Maison Blanc
26-28 Turnham Green Terrace, W4 (020 8995 7220). Branch

Makan p123
270 Portobello Road, W10 (020 8960 5169). Malaysian, Indonesian & Singaporean

Malabar Junction p89
107 Great Russell Street, WC1 (020 7580 5230). Indian

Malay House p124
60 Lower Addiscombe Road, Croydon, Surrey (020 8666 0266). Malaysian, Indonesian & Singaporean

Mama Amalfi's p225
45 The Mall, Ealing, W5 (020 8840 5888). Eating & Entertainment

La Mancha p155
32 Putney High Street, SW15 (020 8780 1022). Spanish

Mandalay p69
444 Edgware Road, W2 (020 7258 3696). Global

Mandarin Kitchen p47
14-16 Queensway, W2 (020 7727 9012). Chinese

Mandola p18
139-141 Westbourne Grove, W11 (020 7229 4734). African & Caribbean

New Hoo Wah p44
37-38 Gerrard Street, W1
(020 7434 0521).
Chinese
New Jakarta p122
150 Shaftesbury
Avenue, WC2 (020 7836
2644). Malaysian,
Indonesian &
Singaporean
New Kabana p85
43 Blackbird Hill, NW9
(020 8200 7094).
Indian
New Mayflower p44
68-70 Shaftesbury
Avenue, W1 (020 7734
9207). Chinese
**The New Restaurant
at the V&A** p222
Victoria & Albert
Museum, Cromwell Road,
SW7 (020 7581 2159).
Eating & Entertainment
New Seoul p120
164 Clerkenwell Road,
EC1 (020 7278 8674).
Korean
New Tayyab p85
83 Fieldgate Street, E1
(020 7247 9543/
www.tayybs.co.uk).
Indian
New World p45
1 Gerrard Place, W1 (020
7734 0396). Chinese
Newtons p197
33-35 Abbeville Road,
SW4 (020 8673 0977).
Brasseries
**Newtons on
the Green**
175 New King's Road,
SW6 (020 7731 6404).
Branch
Nicole's p133
158 New Bond Street, W1
(020 7499 8408).
Modern European
Nid Ting p169
533 Holloway Road, N19
(020 7263 0506/ 020
7561 1249). Thai
Nikita's p41
65 Ifield Road, SW10
(020 7352 6326). Central
& East European
1997 p43
19 Wardour Street, W1
(020 7734 2868).
Chinese
**The 19th Hole (branch
of Jamies)**
19 Philpot Lane, EC3
(020 7621 9577).
Branch
Nipa p163
Royal Lancaster Hotel,
Lancaster Terrace, W2
(020 7262 6737).
Thai
No.77 Wine Bar p222
77 Mill Lane, NW6
(020 7435 7787). Wine
Bars
noble rot p135
3-5 Mill Street, W1 (020
7629 8877). Modern
European
Nobu p115
19 Old Park Lane, W1
(020 7447 4747).
Japanese
Noho p147
32 Charlotte Street, W1
(020 7636 4445).
Oriental
Noho
241-279 Finchley Road,
O2 Centre, NW3 (020
7794 5616). Branch
North China p49
305 Uxbridge Road, W3
(020 8992 9183).
Chinese
North Pole p214
131 Greenwich High
Road, SE10 (020 8853
3020). Pubs

North Pole p213
13-15 North Pole Road,
W10 (020 8964 9384).
Pubs
**North Sea Fish
Restaurant** p183
7-8 Leigh Street, WC1
(020 7387 5892). Fish &
Chips
Nosh Brothers p139
12 All Saints Road, W11
(020 7243 2808).
Modern European
**C Notarianni
& Sons** p189
142 Battersea High
Street, SW11 (020 7228
7133). Pizza & Pasta
**Noto Ramen
House** p113
Bow Bells House, 7 Bread
Street, EC4 (020 7329
8056). Japanese
Noto
2-3 Bassishaw Highwalk,
London Wall, EC2 (020
7256 9433). Branch
**Number 25 (branch of
Jamies)**
25 Birchin Lane, EC3
(020 7623 2505).
Branch
Nusa Dua p123
11-12 Dean Street, W1
(020 7437 3559).
Malaysian, Indonesian &
Singaporean
**NW3 Café (branch of
Table Café)**
Habitat, 191-217 Finchley
Road, NW3 (020 7328
3444). Branch

O

**O Cantinho
de Portugal** p151
135-137 Stockwell Road,
SW9 (020 7924 0218).
Portuguese
The O'Conor Don p69
88 Marylebone Lane,
W1 (020 7935 9311).
Global
O'Hanlon p216
8 Tysoe Street, EC1 (020
7837 4112). Pubs
**O's Bar (branch of O's
Thai Cafe)**
115 Park Road, N8 (020
8340 7845). Branch
O's Thai Café p169
10 Topsfield Parade, N8
(020 8348 6898). Thai
Oak Room p76
Le Meridien Hotel, 21
Piccadilly, W1 (020 7437
0202). Hotels &
Haute Cuisine
Ocean p58
100 Kew Road,
Richmond, Surrey (020
8948 8008). Fish
**October Gallery
Café** p181
24 Old Gloucester Street,
WC1 (020 7242 7367).
Budget
L'Odéon p62
65 Regent Street, W1
(020 7287 1400). French
Odette's p143
130 Regent's Park Road,
NW1 (020 7586 5486).
Modern European
**Odette's
Wine Bar** p222
130 Regent's Park Road,
NW1 (020 7722 5388).
Wine Bars
Offshore p56
148 Holland Park Avenue,
W11 (020 7221 6090).
Fish
Ognisko Polskie p39
55 Prince's Gate,
Exhibition Road, SW7
(020 7589 4635). Central
& East European

Oh Boy p167
843 Garratt Lane, SW17
(020 8947 9760). Thai
Old Compton Café p226
34 Old Compton
Street, W1 (020 7439
3309). Eating &
Entertainment
The Old Europeans p38
106 High Road, N2 (020
8883 3964/
www.oldeuropeans.com).
Central & East European
Old Friends p51
659 Commercial Road,
E14 (020 7790 5027).
Chinese
**Oliveto
(branch of Olivo)**
49 Elizabeth Street,
SW1 (020 7730 0074).
Branch
Olivo p99
21 Eccleston Street,
SW1 (020 7730 2505).
Italian
Olley's p184
67-69 Norwood Road,
SE24 (020 8671 8259).
Fish & Chips
1 Blossom Street p131
1 Blossom Street, E1
(020 7247 6530).
Modern European
1 Lombard Street p59
1 Lombard Street, EC3
(020 7929 6611/
www.1lombardstreet.com).
French
192 p139
192 Kensington Park
Road, W11 (020 7229
0482). Modern European
115 at Hodgson's p94
115 Chancery Lane,
WC2 (020 7242
2836/wine bar
020 7404 5027).
International
Oporto Patisserie p150
62A Golborne Road, W10
(020 8968 8839).
Portuguese
L'Oranger p76
5 St James's Street, SW1
(020 7839 3774). Hotels
& Haute Cuisine
The Orangery p205
Kensington Palace,
Kensington Gardens,
W8 (020 7376 0239).
Cafés
The Orangery
Cutlers Gardens, 10
Devonshire Square, EC2
(020 7623 1377).
Branch
The Oratory p196
232 Brompton Road, SW3
(020 7584 3493).
Brasseries
Organic Café p99
21-25 Lonsdale Road,
NW6 (020 7372 1232).
International
Oriel p196
50-51 Sloane Square,
SW3 (020 7730 2804).
Brasseries
Orient p47
160 Piccadilly, W1 (020
7499 6888/7779/
www.chinahouse.co.uk).
Chinese
Oriental p47
The Dorchester Hotel, 55
Park Lane, W1
(020 7317 6328).
Chinese
**Oriental City
Food Court** p118
Oriental City, 399
Edgware Road, NW9
(020 8200 0009).
Japanese
Original Tajines p144
7A Dorset Street, W1
(020 7935 1545). North
African

Orrery p133
55 Marylebone High
Street, W1 (020 7616
8000/www.orrery.co.uk).
Modern European
Orsino p105
119 Portland Road,
W11 (020 7221 3299).
Italian
Orso p100
27 Wellington Street,
WC2 (020 7240 5269).
Italian
Oshobasho Café p205
Highgate Wood,
Muswell Hill Road, N10
(020 8444 1505).
Cafés
**Osteria Antica
Bologna** p108
23 Northcote Road,
SW11 (020 7978 4771).
Italian
Osteria Basilico p107
29 Kensington Park Road,
W11 (020 7727 9372).
Italian
Osteria d'Isola p219
145 Knightsbridge, SW1
(020 7838 1044/1099).
Wine Bars
**Oxo Tower
Restaurant,
Bar & Brasserie** p141
Oxo Tower Wharf,
Barge House Street, SE1
(020 7803 3888).
Modern European
Ozer p169
4-5 Langham Place, W1
(020 7323 0505).
Turkish

P

Pacific Oriental p146
1 Bishopsgate, EC2
(020 7621 9988).
Oriental
**Pacific Spice (branch of
Silks & Spice)**
42 Northampton Road,
EC1 (020 7278 9983).
Branch
La Paella p160
1 The Broadway, N14
(020 8882 7868).
Spanish
**Le Palais
du Jardin** p62
136 Long Acre, WC2
(020 7379 5353).
French
Pallavi p91
Unit 3, Cross Deep
Court, Heath Road,
Twickenham, Middx (020
8892 2345/4466).
Indian
Palm Beach p93
17 Ealing Road, Wembley,
Middx (020 8900 8664).
Indian
Palm Court p222
Waldorf Meridien,
Aldwych, WC2 (020
7836 2400). Eating &
Entertainment
Palm Palace p93
80 South Road, Southall,
Middx (020
8574 9209). Indian
**Palms Pasta
on the Piazza** p185
39 King Street, WC2 (020
7240 2939). Pizza &
Pasta
Palms Kensington
3-5 Campden Hill Road,
W8 (020 7938 1830).
Branch
La Pampa Grill p29
60 Battersea Rise, SW11
(020 7924 4774). The
Americas
Pangaea p189
15 Atlantic Road, SW9
(020 7737 6777). Pizza
& Pasta

**Paolina Café
& Thai
Restaurant** p161
181 King's Cross Road,
WC1 (020 7278 8176).
Thai
Parade p138
18-19 The Mall, W5 (020
8810 0202). Modern
European
**Paradise by Way of
Kensal Green** p213
19 Kilburn Lane, W10
(020 8969 0098).
Pubs
**Paris-London
Café** p181
5 Junction Road, N19
(020 7561 0330).
Budget
The Park p109
105 Salusbury Road,
NW6 (020 7372 8882).
Italian
**Park Café The
Broadwalk** p205
Regent's Park, off
Chester Road, NW1 (020
7224 3872). Cafés
Pasha p172
301 Upper Street, N1
(020 7226 1454).
Turkish
Pasha p145
1 Gloucester Road, SW7
(020 7589 7969/
www.pasha-restaurant.
co.uk). North African
Passione p100
10 Charlotte Street, W1
(020 7636 2833).
Italian
Pasta Browns p185
31-32 Bedford Street,
WC2 (020 7836 7486).
Pizza & Pasta
Pasta Browns
35-36 Bow Street, WC2
(020 7379 5775).
Branch
Pasta Plus p185
62 Eversholt Street, NW1
(020 7383 4943). Pizza
& Pasta
Patara p161
9 Beauchamp Place,
SW3 (020 7581 8820).
Thai
Patara
181 Fulham Road, SW3
(020 7351 5692).
Branch
Patio p39
5 Goldhawk Road, W12
(020 8743 5194). Central
& East European
Pâtisserie Valerie p201
44 Old Compton Street,
W1 (020 7437 3466).
Cafés
**Pâtisserie Valerie
at Sagne** p200
105 Marylebone High
Street, W1 (020 7935
6240). Cafés
Pâtisserie Valerie
215 Brompton Road,
SW3 (020 7823 9971).
Branch
Pâtisserie Valerie
RIBA, 66 Portland Place,
W1 (020 7631 0467).
Branch
Patisserie Valerie
8 Russel Street, WC2
(020 7240 0064).
Branch
Patogh p127
8 Crawford Place, W1
(020 7262 4015). Middle
Eastern
Paulo's p29
30 Greyhound Road, W6
(020 7385 9264). The
Americas
The Pavement p202
21 The Pavement,
SW4 (020 7622 4944).
Cafés

The Pavilion p218
Finsbury Circus Gardens,
EC2 (020 7628 8224).
Wine Bars
**The Pavilion
(branch of Jamies)**
Finsbury Circus Gardens,
EC3 (020 7628 8224).
Branch
Pavillion p123
Holiday Villa Hotel, 37
Leinster Gardens,
W2 (020 7258 0269).
Malaysian, Indonesian &
Singaporean
Peasant p212
240 St John Street, EC1
(020 7336 7726). Pubs
**Penang Satay
House** p124
9 Turnpike Lane, N8 (020
8340 8707). Malaysian,
Indonesian &
Singaporean
Penk's p99
79 Salusbury Road, NW6
(020 7604 4484).
International
**The People's
Palace** p141
Level 3, Royal Festival
Hall, South Bank Centre,
SE1 (020 7928 9999).
Modern European
Pepe Nero p108
133 Lavender Hill,
SW11 (020 7978 4863).
Italian
Pepper Tree p167
19 Clapham Common
Southside, SW4 (020
7622 1758). Thai
Perennial p98
110-112 Columbia Road,
E2 (020 7739 4556).
International
La Pergola p224
66 Streatham High
Road, SW16 (020 8769
2646). Eating &
Entertainment
La Perla p30
28 Maiden Lane, WC2
(020 7240 7400). The
Americas
La Perla
803 Fulham Road,
SW6 (020 7583 8475).
Branch
Pescador p151
33 Pratt Street, NW1
(020 7482 7008).
Portuguese
Le Petit Blanc p228
71-72 Walton Street,
Oxford (01865 510999).
Out of Town
Le Petit Prince p146
5 Holmes Road, NW5
(020 7267 3789). North
African
Pétrus p76
33 St James's Street, W1
(020 7930 4272). Hotels
& Haute Cuisine
**Pharmacy
Restaurant & Bar** p139
150 Notting Hill Gate,
W11 (020 7221 2442).
Modern European
**Philpotts
Mezzaluna** p109
424 Finchley Road, NW2
(020 7794 0455). Italian
Phoenicia p129
11-13 Abingdon Road,
W8 (020 7937 0120).
Middle Eastern
**Phoenix Bar
& Grill** p139
162-164 Lower
Richmond Road, SW15
(020 8780 3131).
Modern European
**Photographers'
Gallery Café** p199
5 Great Newport Street,
WC2 (020 7831 1772).
Cafés

Purple Sage p187
90-92 Wigmore Street, W1 (020 7486 1912). Pizza & Pasta
Putney Bridge p67
The Embankment, SW15 (020 8780 1811). French

Q

Quaglino's p135
16 Bury Street, SW1 (020 7930 6767). Modern European
Quality Chop House p33
94 Farringdon Road, EC1 (020 7837 5093/020 7833 3748). British
The Queens p215
49 Regent's Park Road, NW1 (020 7586 0408). Pubs
The Quiet Revolution p173
49 Old Street, EC1 (020 7253 5556/www. quietrevolution.co.uk). Vegetarian
Quilon p79
St James's Court Hotel, 41 Buckingham Gate, SW1 (020 7821 1899). Indian
Quo Vadis p63
26-29 Dean Street, W1 (020 7437 9585). French
Quod Bar & Grill p228
92-94 High Street, Oxford (01865 202505). Out of Town

R

Radha Krishna Bhavan p90
86 Tooting High Street, SW17 (020 8682 0969). Indian
Rafique's p81
291 King Street, W6 (020 8748 7345). Indian
Ragam (branch of Malabar Junction) p90
57 Cleveland Street, W1 (020 7636 9098). Branch
Rainforest Café p225
20 Shaftesbury Avenue, W1 (020 7434 3111/ www.rainforest.co.uk). Eating & Entertainment
Ramen Seto p115
19 Kingly Street, W1 (020 7434 0309). Japanese
Randall & Aubin p195
16 Brewer Street, W1 (020 7287 4447). Brasseries
Rani p90
7 Long Lane, N3 (020 8349 4386). Indian
Rani
3 Hill Street, Richmond, Surrey (020 8332 2322). Branch
Ranoush Juice Bar p127
43 Edgware Road, W2 (020 7723 5929). Middle Eastern
Ransome's Dock p140
35-37 Parkgate Road, SW11 (020 7223 1611). Modern European
Raoul's p201
13 Clifton Road, W9 (020 7289 7313). Cafés
Raoul's Express p201
10 Clifton Road, W9 (020 7289 6649). Branch
The Rapscallion p98
75 Venn Street, SW4 (020 7787 6555). International

Rasa p90
55 Stoke Newington Church Street, N16 (020 7249 0344). Indian
Rasa Express (branch of Rasa Samundra)
5 Rathbone Street, W1 (020 7637 0222). Branch
Rasa Samudra p90
5 Charlotte Street, W1 (020 7637 0222/www. rasarestaurants.com). Indian
Rasa W1
16 Dering Street, W1 (020 7629 1346). Branch
Rasputin p41
265 High Street, W3 (020 8993 5802). Central & East European
Ravi Shankar (branch of Chutneys)
422 St John Street, EC1 (020 7833 5849). Branch
Raw Deal p173
65 York Street, W1 (020 7262 4841). Vegetarian
The Real Greek p71
15 Hoxton Market, N1 (020 7739 8212). Greek
Rebato's p157
169 South Lambeth Road, SW8 (020 7735 6388). Spanish
Red Lion p216
13 St Mary's Road, W5 (020 8567 2541). Pubs
Red Pepper p189
8 Formosa Street, W9 (020 7266 2708). Pizza & Pasta
Red River p177
1 Bray Place, SW3 (020 7584 0765). Vietnamese
Red Room p135
Basement, Waterstone's, 203 Piccadilly, W1 (020 7851 2464). Modern European
Redmond's p140
170 Upper Richmond Road West, SW14 (020 8878 1922). Modern European
Regent Milk Bar p205
362 Edgware Road, W2 (020 7723 8669). Cafés
Restaurant One-O-One p74
101 William Street, SW1 (020 7290 7101). Hotels & Haute Cuisine
Retsina p72
83 Regent's Park Road, NW1 (020 7722 3194). Greek
Reuben's p119
79 Baker Street, W1 (020 7486 0035). Jewish
Rhodes in the Square p34
Dolphin Square, Chichester Street, SW1 (020 7798 6767). British
Riso p105
76 South Parade, W4 (020 8742 2121). Italian
The Ritz p76
Piccadilly, W1 (020 7493 8181 ext 3351). Hotels & Haute Cuisine
Riva p107
169 Church Road, SW13 (020 8748 0434). Italian
River Café p105
Thames Wharf, Rainville Road, W6 (020 7381 8824). Italian
Roadhouse p225
Jubilee Hall, 35 The Piazza, WC2 (020 7240 6001/www.roadhouse.co. uk). Eating & Entertainment

The Rock p155
619 Fulham Road, SW6 (020 7385 8179). Spanish
Rock & Sole Plaice p183
47 Endell Street, WC2 (020 7836 3785). Fish & Chips
Rodizio Rico p29
111 Westbourne Grove, W2 (020 7792 4035). The Americas
Ronnie Scott's p225
47 Frith Street, W1 (020 7439 0747/ www.ronniescotts.co.uk). Eating & Entertainment
The Room at the Halcyon p76
129 Holland Park Avenue, W11 (020 7221 5411/020 7727 7288). Hotels & Haute Cuisine
Rosmarino p109
1 Bleinham Terrace, NW8 (020 7328 5014). Italian
The Rotisserie p95
56 Uxbridge Road, W12 (020 8743 3028). International
The Rotisserie
134 Upper Street, N1 (020 7226 0122). Branch
Rotisserie Jules p95
133A Notting Hill Gate, W11 (020 7221 3331). International
The Rotisserie (branch of Rotisserie Jules)
316 Uxbridge Road, Middlesex, MA5 (020 8421 2878). Branch
Rotisserie Jules
6-8 Bute Street, SW7 (020 7584 0600). Branch
Rotisserie Jules
338 King's Road, SW3 (020 7351 0041). Branch
Roussillon p59
16 St Barnabas Street, SW1 (020 7730 5550). French
Royal China p47
40 Baker Street, W1 (020 7487 4688). Chinese
Royal China p53
68 Queens Grove, NW8 (020 7586 4280). Chinese
Royal China p49
3 Chelverton Road, SW15 (020 8788 0907). Chinese
Royal China p49
13 Queensway, W2 (020 7221 2535). Chinese
Royal Cous-Cous House p146
316 Holloway Road, N7 (020 7700 2188). North African
Royal Dragon p45
30 Gerrard Street, W1 (0207 734 0935). Chinese
Royal Dragon
30 Gerrard Street, W1 (020 7734 0935). Branch
Royal Oak p217
44 Tabard Street, SE1 (020 7357 7173). Pubs
RSJ p67
13A Coin Street, SE1 (020 7928 4554/020 7401 2455). French
Ruby in the Dust p225
70 Upper Street, N1 (020 7359 1710). Branch
Ruby in the Dust
102 Camden High Street, NW1 (020 7485 2744). Branch

Ruby in the Dust p225
53 Fulham Broadway, SW6 (020 7385 9272). Branch
Rudland & Stubbs p54
35-37 Greenhill Rents, Cowcross Street, EC1 (020 7253 0148). Fish
La Rueda p155
642 King's Road, SW6 (020 7384 2684). Spanish
La Rueda p155
66-68 Clapham High Street, SW4 (020 7627 2173). Branch
La Rueda
102 Wigmore Street, W1 (020 7486 1718). Branch
Rules p34
35 Maiden Lane, WC2 (020 7836 5314/ www.rules.co.uk). British
Rupert Street p209
50 Rupert Street, W1 (020 7292 7141). Bars
Ryo p116
84 Brewer Street, W1 (020 7287 1318). Japanese

S

S&P (branch of Patara)
181 Fulham Road, SW3 (020 7351 5692). Branch
Sabor do Brasil p29
36 Highgate Hill, N19 (020 7263 9066). The Americas
Sabras p91
263 High Road, NW10 (020 8459 0340). Indian
Safa p127
22-23 Nutford Place, W1 (020 7723 8331). Middle Eastern
Saigon Thuy p177
189 Garratt Lane, SW18 (020 8871 9464). Vietnamese
Saint p207
8 Great Newport Street, WC2 (020 7240 1551). Bars
Saints p181
1 Clerkenwell Road, EC1 (020 7490 4199/www.saintsphoto.c o.uk). Budget
Sakoni p91
127-129 Ealing Road, Wembley, Middx (020 8903 9601). Indian
Sakoni
127-129 Ealing Road, Wembley, Middx (020 8903 9601). Branch
Sakoni
6-8 Dominion Parade, Station Road, Harrow, Middx (020 8863 3399). Branch
Sakoni
116 Station Road, Edgware, Middx (020 8951 0058). Branch
Salisbury Tavern p214
21 Sherbrooke Road, SW6 (020 7381 4005). Pubs
Salloos p77
62-64 Kinnerton Street, SW1 (020 7235 4444). Indian
Sally's Diner p27
2 Pancras Road, NW1 (020 7713 8474/ 8462/www.sallysdiner.co. uk). The Americas
Salsa! p225
96 Charing Cross Road, WC2 (020 7379 3277). Eating & Entertainment

The Salt House p198
63 Abbey Road, NW8 (020 7328 6626). Brasseries
The Salusbury p216
50-52 Salusbury Road, NW6 (020 7328 3286). Pubs
San Daniele de Friuli p108
72 Highbury Park, N5 (020 7226 1609). Italian
San Lorenzo p103
22 Beauchamp Place, SW3 (020 7584 1074). Italian
San Lorenzo Fuoriporta
Worple Road Mews, SW19 (020 8946 8463). Branch
San Miguel's on the River p157
Molasses House, Plantation Wharf, Battersea Reach, SW11 (020 7801 9696). Spanish
San Miguel's
256 Edgware Road, Sw (020 7262 1709/020 7706 2063). Branch
Santa Fe p27
75 Upper Street, N1 (020 7288 2288). The Americas
Sarastro p225
126 Drury Lane, WC2 (020 7836 0101). Eating & Entertainment
Sardo p100
45 Grafton Way, W1 (020 7387 2521). Italian
Sariyer Balik Lokantasi p171
56 Green Lanes, N16 (020 7275 7681). Turkish
Sarkhel's p83
199 Replingham Road, SW18 (020 8870 1483/takeaway 020 8871 0808). Indian
Sartoria p104
20 Savile Row, W1 (020 7534 7000). Italian
Sash Oriental Tapas Bar
825 Fulham Road, SW6 (020 7736 9429). Branch
Satay Bar p123
447-450 Coldharbour Lane, SW9 (020 7326 5001). Malaysian, Indonesian & Singaporean
Satay House p123
13 Sale Place, W2 (020 7723 6763/www.satay house.com). Malaysian, Indonesian & Singaporean
Satay Malaysia p123
10 Crouch End Hill, N8 (020 8340 3286). Malaysian, Indonesian & Singaporean
Satay Raya (branch of Satay Malaysia)
10A Crouch End Hill, N8 (020 7624 6030). Branch
Satsuma p116
56 Wardour Street, W1 (020 7437 8338). Japanese
Sauce Organic Diner p198
214 Camden High Street, NW1 (020 7482 0777). Brasseries
Sausage & Mash Café p180
268 Portobello Road, W10 (020 8968 8898). Budget

The Savoy Grill p35
The Savoy Hotel, Strand, WC2 (020 7420 2065). British
Schnecke p68
58-59 Poland Street, W1 (020 7287 6666). Global
Scu-zi p191
360 St John Street, EC1 (020 7833 4393). Pizza & Pasta
Scu-zi
37 Westferry Circus, Canary Riverside, E14 (020 7519 6007). Branch
Scu-zi
2 Creechurch Lane, EC3 (020 7623 3444). Branch
Seabar p113
St Martin's Lane, 45 St Martin's Lane, WC2 (020 7300 5588). Japanese
Seafresh Fish Restaurant p183
80-81 Wilton Road, SW1 (020 7828 0747). Fish & Chips
Searcy's p131
Level 2, Barbican, Silk Street, EC2 (020 7588 3008). Modern European
Searcy's
30 Pavilion Road, SW1 (020 7584 4921). Branch
Searcy's
Covent Gdn. Opera House, WC2 (020 7212 9254). Branch
Searcy's
Lincoln Street, SW3 (020 7581 3986). Branch
Seashell p183
49-51 Lisson Grove, NW1 (020 7224 9000). Fish & Chips
Sedir p172
4 Theberton Street, N1 (020 7226 5489). Turkish
Selasih p122
114 Seymour Place, W1 (020 7724 4454/ www.selasih.co.uk). Malaysian, Indonesian & Singaporean
The Sequel p140
75 Venn Street, SW4 (020 7622 4222). Modern European
Seven p133
1 Leicester Square, WC2 (020 7909 1177). Modern European
Seven Stars p216
53-54 Carey Street, WC2 (020 7242 8521). Pubs
Sevilla Mia p153
22 Hanway Street, W1 (020 7637 3756). Spanish
Shakespeare's Globe p141
New Globe Walk, SE1 (020 7928 9444). Modern European
Shampers p219
4 Kingly Street, W1 (020 7439 9910). Wine Bars
Shamyana p83
437-439 Streatham High Road, SW16 (020 8679 6162/www.shamyana-restaurant.co.uk). Indian
Shanghai p51
41 Kingsland High Street, E8 (020 7254 2878). Chinese
J Sheekey p55
28-32 St Martin's Court, WC2 (020 7240 2565). Fish
Shemsudeen's
35 Stoke Newington Church Street, N16 (020 7241 4171). Branch

Sheng's Tea House p43
68 Millman Street, WC1 (020 7405 3697). Chinese

Shepherd's p35
Marsham Court, Marsham Street, SW1 (020 7834 9552). British

Shilla p121
58-59 Great Marlborough Street, W1 (020 7434 1650). Korean

Shimla Pinks p77
7 Bishopsgate Churchyard, EC2 (020 7628 7888). Indian

Ship p214
41 Jew's Row, SW18 (020 8870 9667). Pubs

Shiraz p219
12 Saint Martin's Lane, WC2 (020 7379 7811). Wine Bars

Shoeless Joe's p226
555 King's Road, SW6 (020 7610 9346/ www.shoelessjoes.co.uk). Eating & Entertainment

Shoeless Joes
Temple Place, Embankment, WC2R (020 7610 9346). Branch

Shoreditch Electricity Showrooms p211
39A Hoxton Square, N1 (020 7739 6934). Bars

Shotberries (branch of Davys)
167 Queen Victoria Street, EC4 (020 7329 4759). Branch

Shree Krishna p90
192-194 Tooting High Street, SW17 (020 8672 4250). Indian

Sí Señor p30
2 St Anne's Court, off Dean Street, W1 (020 7494 4632). The Americas

Sigiri p93
161 Northfield Avenue, W13 (020 8579 8000). Indian

Signor Zilli p104
40 & 41 Dean Street, W1 (020 7734 3924). Italian

Signor Zilli Bar
40 Dean Street, W1 (020 7734 1853). Bars

Silks & Spice p147
23 Foley Street, W1 (020 7636 2718). Oriental

Silks & Spice
28 Chalk Farm Road, NW1 (020 7267 5751). Branch

Silks & Spice
561 King's Road, SW6 (020 7833 5577). Branch

Silks & Spice
95 Chiswick High Road, W4 (020 8995 7991). Branch

Silks & Spice City (branch of Silks and Spice)
11 Queen Victoria Street, EC4 (020 7236 7222). Branch

Silks and Spice
42 Northampton Road, EC1 (020 7278 9983). Branch

Silks and Spice
9-10 Liverpool Street, EC2 (020 7626 1155). Branch

Simply Nico p59
7 Goswell Road, EC1 (020 7336 7677). French

Simply Nico
Crowne Plaza, Stockley Road, West Drayton, Middx (01895 437 564). Branch

Simply Nico
10, London Bridge Street, SE1 (020 7407 4536). Branch

Simply Nico
48A Rochester Row, SW1 (020 7630 8061). Branch

Simpson's-in-the-Strand p35
100 Strand, WC2 (020 7836 9112). British

Singapore Garden p124
83 Fairfax Road, NW6 (020 7624 8233). Malaysian, Indonesian & Singaporean

Singapore Garden
83-83A Fairfax Road, NW6 (020 7624 8233). Branch

Singapura p122
1-2 Limeburner Lane, EC4 (020 7329 1133). Malaysian, Indonesian & Singaporean

Singapura
78-79 Leadenhall Street, EC3 (020 7929 0089). Branch

Singapura EC2 p122
31 Broadgate Circle, EC2 (020 7256 5044). Malaysian, Indonesian & Singaporean

6 Clarendon Road p63
6 Clarendon Road, W11 (020 7727 3330). French

606 Club p224
90 Lots Road, SW10 (020 7352 5953). Eating & Entertainment

Sixty-two p141
62 Southwark Bridge Road, SE1 (020 7633 0831). Modern European

Skinkers (branch of Davys)
42 Tooley Street, SE1 (020 7407 9189). Branch

The Slug and Lettuce p209
14 Upper St Martin's Lane, WC2 (020 7379 4880). Bars

The Slug and Lettuce
Riverside House, Water Lane, Surrey (020 8948 7733). Branch

The Slug and Lettuce
1 Islington Green, N1 (020 7226 3864). Branch

The Slug and Lettuce
30 South Colonnade, E14 (020 7519 1612). Branch

The Slug and Lettuce
4 St John's Hill, SW11 (020 7924 1322). Branch

The Slug and Lettuce
14 Putney High Street, SW15 (020 8785 3081). Branch

The Slug and Lettuce
474 Fulham Road, SW6 (020 7385 3209). Branch

The Slug and Lettuce
96-98 Uxbridge Road, W12 (020 8749 1987). Branch

The Slug and Lettuce
80-82 Wardour Street, W1 (020 7437 1400). Branch

The Slug and Lettuce
11 Warwick Way, SW1 (020 7834 3313). Branch

The Slug and Lettuce
19-20 Hanover Street, W1 (020 7499 0077). Branch

The Slug and Lettuce
9 Stoney Lane, E1 (020 7626 4994). Branch

Small & Beautiful p181
351-353 Kilburn High Road, NW6 (020 7328 2637). Budget

Small Star (branch of Small and Beautiful)
26 Station Parade, Willesden Green, NW2 (020 8830 5221). Branch

Smiths of Smithfield p132
67-77 Charterhouse Street, EC1 (020 7236 6666/www.smithsofsmithfield.co.uk). Modern European

Smollensky's on the Strand p225
105 The Strand, WC2 (020 7497 2101/ www.smollenskys.co.uk). Eating & Entertainment

Smollensky's on the Strand p23
105 Strand, WC2 (020 7497 2101/ www.smollenskys.co.uk). The Americas

Snow's on the Green p125
166 Shepherd's Bush Road, W6 (020 7603 2142). Mediterranean

The Social p207
5 Little Portland Street, W1 (020 7636 4992). Bars

Sofra p169
36 Tavistock Street, WC2 (020 7240 3773). Turkish

Sofra
1 St Christopher's Place, W1 (020 7224 4080). Branch

Sofra
18 Shepherd Street, W1 (020 7495 3320). Branch

Sofra Bistro p169
18 Shepherd Market, W1 (020 7493 3320). Turkish

Soho Pizzeria p187
16-18 Beak Street, W1 (020 7434 2480). Pizza & Pasta

Soho Soho (Rôtisserie) p195
11-13 Frith Street, W1 (020 7494 3491). Brasseries

Soho Spice p81
124-126 Wardour Street, W1 (020 7434 0808/ www.sohospice.co.uk). Indian

Soho Thai p162
27-28 St Anne's Court, W1 (020 7287 2000). Thai

Solly's p119
148A Golders Green Road, NW11 (ground floor and takeaway 020 8455 2121/first floor 020 8455 0004). Jewish

Something Fishy p184
117-119 Lewisham High Street, SE13 (020 8852 7075/020 8318 9577). Fish & Chips

Something Fishy
406 Downham Way, Bromley (020 8461 5114). Branch

Sonny's p139
94 Church Road, SW13 (020 8748 0393). Modern European

Soraya p130
36 Gloucester Road, SW7 (020 7589 4060). Middle Eastern

Sosho Match
2A Tabernacle Street. EC2 (020 7920 0701). Branch

Sotheby's Café p135
34-35 New Bond Street, W1 (020 7293 5077). Modern European

Le Soufflé p75
Hotel Intercontinental, 1 Hamilton Place, W1 (020 7409 3131). Hotels & Haute Cuisine

Souk p144
27 Litchfield Street, WC2 (020 7240 1796). North African

Soulard p67
113 Mortimer Road, N1 (020 7254 1314). French

Sound p224
Leicester Square, W1 (020 7287 1010). Eating & Entertainment

Southampton's 124 (branch of Dover Street)
124 Southampton Row, WC1 (020 7405 1466). Branch

Southeast W9 p148
239 Elgin Avenue, W9 (020 7328 8883). Oriental

Soviet Canteen p41
430 King's Road, SW10 (020 7795 1556). Central & East European

Spaghetti Opera at Trat Est p226
109 Fleet Street, EC4 (020 7353 2680). Eating & Entertainment

Spiga p104
84-86 Wardour Street, W1 (020 7734 3444). Italian

La Spighetta p187
43 Blandford Street, W1 (020 7486 7340). Pizza & Pasta

Spoon+ at Sanderson p94
50 Berners Street, W1 (020 7300 1400/1444). International

The Sports Café p226
80 Haymarket, SW1 (020 7839 8300/ www.sportscafe.com). Eating & Entertainment

Spread Eagle p217
141 Albert Street, NW1 (020 7267 1410). Pubs

Spread Eagle p67
1-2 Stockwell Street, SE10 (020 8853 2333). French

Spread Eagle
71 High Street, SW17 (020 8877 9809). Branch

Springbok Café p71
42 Devonshire Road, W4 (020 8742 3149). Global

The Square p76
6-10 Bruton Street, W1 (020 7495 7100). Hotels & Haute Cuisine

Squeeze p204
27 Kensington High Street, W8 (020 7376 9786). Cafés

Sri Siam
16 Old Compton Street, W1 (020 7434 3544). Branch

Sri Siam City
85 London Wall, EC2 (020 7628 5772). Branch

Sri Thai p160
Bucklersbury House, 3 Queen Victoria Street, EC4 (020 7827 0202). Thai

St John p33
26 St John Street, EC1 (020 7251 0848/ 4998/www.stjohnrestaurant.co.uk). British

St John's p98
91 Junction Road, N19 (020 7272 1587). International

St Moritz p37
161 Wardour Street, W1 (020 7734 3324). Central & East European

St Paul's Steiner Café p176
1 St Paul's Road, N1 (020 7226 4454). Vegetarian

RK Stanleys p34
6 Little Portland Street, W1 (020 7462 0099). British

Star Café p182
22 Great Chapel Street, W1 (020 7437 8778). Budget

Star of India p83
154 Old Brompton Road, SW5 (020 7373 2901/www.starofindia.co.uk). Indian

Stargazer p94
11 Rathbone Place, W1 (020 7636 1057). International

Stefano Cavallini Restaurant at the Halkin p73
5-6 Halkin Street, SW1 (020 7333 1234/ 1000). Hotels & Haute Cuisine

Stephen Bull p133
5-7 Blandford Street, W1 (020 7486 9696). Modern European

Stepping Stone p140
123 Queenstown Road, SW8 (020 7622 0555). Modern European

Sticky Fingers p24
1A Phillimore Gardens, W8 (020 7938 5338). The Americas

The Stockpot p180
18 Old Compton Street, W1 (020 7287 1066). Budget

Stockpot
273 King's Road, SW3 (020 7823 3175). Branch

Stockpot
40 Panton Street, SW1 (020 7839 5142). Branch

Stockpot
50 James Street, W1 (020 7486 9185). Branch

Stockpot
6 Basil Street, SW3 (020 7589 8627). Branch

Stonemason's (branch of Mason's Arms)
54 Cambridge Grove, W6 (020 8748 1397). Branch

The Stonemason's Arms p213
54 Cambridge Grove, W6 (020 8748 1397). Pubs

Strada
11-13 Battersea Rise, SW11 (020 7801 0794). Branch

Strada
175 New Kings Road, SW6 (020 7731 6404). Branch

Strada p185
8-10 Exmouth Market, EC1 (020 7278 0800). Pizza & Pasta

Stratford's (branch of Lou Pescadou)
7 Stratford Road, W8 (020 7937 6388). Branch

Stream Bubble & Shell p54
50-52 Long Lane, Smithfield, EC1 (020 7796 0070). Fish

Street Hawker
166 Randolph Avenue, W9 (020 7286 3869). Branch

The Sugar Club p137
21 Warwick Street, W1 (020 7437 7776). Modern European

Sugar Reef p137
41-44 Great Windmill Street, W1 (020 7851 0800). Modern European

Sun & Doves p214
61-63 Coldharbour Lane, SE5 (020 7733 1525). Pubs

Sunshine Catering @ The Vibe Bar p204
The Truman Brewery, 91 Brick Lane, E1 (020 7247 1685/www.vibe-bar.co.uk). Cafés

Suntory p117
72-73 St James's Street, SW1 (020 7409 0201). Japanese

Surf.Net.Café p204
13 Deptford Church Street, SE8 (020 8488 1200/www.surfnet.co.uk). Cafés

Sushi-Hiro p117
1 Station Parade, Uxbridge Road, W5 (020 8896 3175). Japanese

Sushi-Say p118
33B Walm Lane, NW2 (020 8459 2971/7512). Japanese

Suvai Aruvi p93
96 High Street, SW19 (020 8543 6266/020 8286 6677). Indian

Sweet & Spicy p85
40 Brick Lane, E1 (020 7247 1081). Indian

Sweet Chilli p169
63-67 Mile End Road, E1 (020 7702 7977). Thai

Sweetings p54
39 Queen Victoria Street, EC4 (020 7248 3062). Fish

T

Ta Dilina p71
122 Junction Road, N19 (020 7272 0318). Greek

Tabla p85
West India Dock Gate, Hertsmere Road, E14 (020 7345 0345/ www.tablarestaurant.com). Indian

Table Café p100
Habitat, Tottenham Court Road, W1 (020 7636 8330/020 7255 6043). Italian

Tai Cip Mein (branch of Tai Wan Mein Noodle House)
7-9 Woolwich New Road, SE18 (020 8317 3388/3883). Branch

Tai Pan p51
665 Commercial Road, E14 (020 7791 0118). Chinese

Talad Thai p165
320 Upper Richmond Road, SW15 (020 8789 8084). Thai

Tamarind p79
20 Queen Street, W1 (020 7629 3561/ www.tamarindrestaurant.com). Indian

Tamnag Thai p167
50-52 Westow Hill, SE19 (020 8761 5959). Thai

Tandoori Express on Jalebi Junction (branch of Tandoori Kebab Centre)
93 The Broadway, Southall, Middx (020 8571 6782). Branch

Tandoori Kebab Centre p89
161-163 The Broadway, Southall, Middx (020 8571 5738). Indian

La Tante Claire p74
The Berkeley, Wilton Place, SW1 (020 7823 2003). Hotels & Haute Cuisine

Tao p146
11-11A Bow Lane, EC4 (020 7248 5833). Oriental

Tappit Hen (branch of Davys)
15 William IV Street, WC2 (020 7836 9839). Branch

Tapster (branch of Davys)
3 Brewers Green, Buckingham Gate, SW1 (020 7222 0561). Branch

Tarboush p129
11 Wardour Street, W1 (020 7287 1220). Middle Eastern

Tarboush
143 Edgware Road, W2 (020 706 9793). Branch

Tarboush
143 Edgware Road, W2 (020 7287 1220). Branch

Tartuf p68
88 Upper Street, N1 (020 7288 0954). Global

Tas p170
33 The Cut, SE1 (020 7928 2111). Turkish

Tate Gallery Restaurant p94
Tate Britain, Millbank, SW1 (020 7887 8877/www.tate.org.uk). International

Tate Modern p197
7th floor, Tate Modern, Sumner Street, SE1 (020 7401 5020). Brasseries

Tawana p163
3 Westbourne Grove, W2 (020 7229 3785). Thai

Tayyab (branch of New Tayyab)
89 Fieldgate Street, E1 (020 7247 9543). Branch

Tbilisi p38
91 Holloway Road, N7 (020 7607 2536). Central & East European

Teatro p137
93-107 Shaftesbury Avenue, W1 (020 7494 3040). Modern European

Teca p104
54 Brooks Mews, W1 (020 7495 4774). Italian

10 p222
10 Air Street, W1 (020 7734 9990). Eating & Entertainment

Ten Ten Tei p116
56 Brewer Street, W1 (020 7287 1738). Japanese

Tentazioni p108
2 Mill Street, SE1 (020 7237 1100). Italian

The Tenth p226
Royal Garden Hotel, Kensington High Street, W8 (020 7361 1910). Eating & Entertainment

Terminus Bar & Grill p131
40 Liverpool Street, EC2 (020 7618 7400). Modern European

Terra Brasil p29
36-38 Chalton Street, NW1 (020 7388 6554). The Americas

The Terrace p138
33C Holland Street, W8 (020 7937 3224). Modern European

Terre à Terre p227
71 East Street, Brighton, East Sussex (01273 729051). Out of Town

Terry Neill's Sports Bar & Brasserie p226
Bath House, 53 Holborn Viaduct, EC1 (020 7329 6653/6579). Eating & Entertainment

Texas Embassy Cantina p32
1 Cockspur Street, SW1 (020 7925 0077). The Americas

Thai Bistro p163
99 Chiswick High Road, W4 (020 8995 5774). Thai

Thai Garden p168
249 Globe Road, E2 (020 8981 5748). Thai

Thai Jen p160
10-11 Clerkenwell Road, EC1 (020 7490 4041). Thai

Thai on the River p165
Chelsea Wharf, 15 Lots Road, SW10 (020 7351 1151). Thai

Thai Pavilion p162
42 Rupert Street, W1 (020 7287 6333). Thai

Thai Pot p160
1 Bedfordbury, WC2 (020 7379 4580). Thai

Thai Pot on the Strand
148 Strand, WC2 (020 7497 0904). Branch

Thai Pots
5 Princes Street, W1 (020 7499 3333). Branch

Thai Square p162
21-23 Cockspur Street, SW1 (020 7839 4000). Thai

Thai West p161
10-12 Crawford Street, W1 (020 7224 1367). Thai

Thailand p167
15 Lewisham Way, SE14 (020 8691 4040). Thai

Thanks for Franks p182
26 Foubert's Place, W1 (020 7494 2434). Budget

Thanks for Franks
18 Gate Street. Holborn. WC2 (020 7405 0539). Branch

3 Monkeys p83
136-140 Herne Hill, SE24 (020 7738 5500). Indian

Tiffin p85
165 Cannon Street Road, E1 (020 7702 3832). Indian

Tiger Lil's p223
270 Upper Street, N1 (020 7226 1118). Eating & Entertainment

Tiger Lil's
16A Clapham Common, SW4 (020 7720 5433). Branch

Tiger Lil's
500 King's Road, SW10 (020 7376 5003). Branch

Tiles p221
36 Buckingham Palace Road, SW1 (020 7834 7761). Wine Bars

Time p141
7A College Approach, SE10 (020 8305 9767). Modern European

Tinseltown p226
44-46 St John Street, EC1 (020 7689 2424). Eating & Entertainment

Tiroler Hut p37
27 Westbourne Grove, W2 (020 7727 3981). Central & East European

Titanic p137
81 Brewer Street, W1 (020 7437 1912). Modern European

Toff's p184
38 Muswell Hill Broadway, N10 (020 8883 8656). Fish & Chips

Tokyo Diner p110
2 Newport Place, WC2 (020 7287 8777). Japanese

Tom's Delicatessen p201
226 Westbourne Grove, W11 (020 7221 8818). Cafés

Tootsies p24
120 Holland Park Avenue, W11 (020 7229 8567). The Americas

Tootsies
110 Kew Road, Richmond, Surrey (020 8948 4343). Branch

Tootsies
196-198 Haverstock Hill, NW3 (020 7431 3812). Branch

Tootsies
48 High Street, Wimbledon Village, SW19 (020 8946 4135). Branch

Tootsies
107 Old Brompton Road, SW7 (020 7581 8942). Branch

Tootsies
177 New King's Road, SW6 (020 7736 4023). Branch

Tootsies
147 Church Road SW13 (020 8748 3630). Branch

Tootsies
35 Haven Green, W5 (020 8566 8200). Branch

Tootsies
148 Chiswick High Road, W4 (020 8747 1869). Branch

Tootsies
35 James Street, W1M (020 7486 1611). Branch

Top Floor at Smiths p34
Smiths of Smithfield, 67-77 Charterhouse Street, EC1 (020 7236 6666). British

Topsy Tasty (branch of Bedlington Café)
5 Station Parade Road, off Burlington Lane, W4 (020 8995 3407). Branch

Townhouse Brasserie p94
24 Coptic Street, WC1 (020 7636 2731). International

Trader Vic's p207
Hilton Hotel, Park Lane, W1 (020 7493 8000 ext 420). Bars

The Triangle p198
1 Ferme Park Road, N4 (020 8292 0516). Brasseries

Trini's p18
13 High Parade, Streatham High Road, SW16 (020 8696 9669). African & Caribbean

The Trinity p228
The Crown & Castle, Orford, near Woodbridge, Suffolk (01394 450205). Out of Town

Trojka p42
101 Regent's Park Road, NW1 (020 7483 3765). Central & East European

Troubadour p201
265 Old Brompton Road, SW5 (020 7370 1434). Cafés

Truckles of Pied Bull Yard p218
off Bury Place, WC1 (020 7404 5338). Wine Bars

Tsar's Bar p42
Langham Hilton Hotel, 1C Portland Place, W1 (020 7636 1000). Central & East European

Tuba p108
4 Clapham Common Southside, SW4 (020 7978 3333/ www.tuba.com). Italian

Tuttons p194
11-12 Russell Street, WC2 (020 7836 4141). Brasseries

25 Canonbury Lane p211
25 Canonbury Lane, N1 (020 7226 0955). Bars

Two Brothers Fish Restaurant p184
297-303 Regent's Park Road, N3 (020 8346 0469). Fish & Chips

291 p197
291 Hackney Road, E2 (020 7613 5675). Brasseries

Uli p148
16 All Saints Road, W11 (020 7727 7511). Oriental

Up the Creek p222
302 Creek Road, SE10 (020 8858 4581/ www.up-the-creek.com). Eating & Entertainment

Upstairs at the Pen p96
51 Parsons Green Lane, SW6 (020 7371 8517). International

Utah (branch of Coyote Cafe)
18 High Street, Wimbledon Village, SW19 (030 8944 1909). Branch

Vama p81
438 King's Road, SW10 (020 7351 4118/ www.vama.co.uk). Indian

Vasco & Piero's Pavilion p104
15 Poland Street, W1 (020 7437 8774). Italian

Veeraswamy p79
Mezzanine floor, Victory House, 99-101 Regent Street, W1 (020 7734 1401/ www.realindianfood.com). Indian

Veg Up p45
8 Egerton Garden Mews, SW3 (020 7584 7007). Chinese

Vegia Zena p108
17 Princess Road, NW1 (020 7483 0192/ www.vegiazena.com). Italian

La Ventura p126
28 Crouch Hill, N4 (020 7281 5811). Mediterranean

Veronica's p36
3 Hereford Road, W2 (020 7229 5079/1210). British

Verso 84 p189
84 Clapham Park Road, SW4 (020 7720 1515). Pizza & Pasta

Vertigo 42 p226
Tower 42, Old Broad Street, EC2 (020 7877 7842). Eating & Entertainment

Victory Café p200
Basement, Gray's Antiques Market, South Molton Lane, W1 (020 8960 0086). Cafés

Viet Hoa p117
70-72 Kingsland Road, E2 (020 7729 8293). Vietnamese.

Viet Hoa
222 London Road, West Croydon, 3RO (020 8686 7190). Branch

Vijay p91
49 Willesden Lane, NW6 (020 7328 1087). Indian

Vijay's Chawalla p90
268 Green Street, E7 (020 8470 3535). Indian

Vijaya Krishna p90
114 Mitcham Road, SW17 (020 8767 7688). Indian

Villa p109
38 North End Road, NW11 (020 8458 6344). Italian

The Village p130
34 Queenstown Road, SW8 (020 7720 1161). Middle Eastern

Village Bistro p67
38 Highgate High Street, N6 (020 8340 0257/ www.villagebistro.com). French

Villandry p62
170 Great Portland Street, W1 (020 7631 3131). French

La Viña p159
3 Wightman Road, N4 (020 8340 5400). Spanish

The Vine p216
86 Highgate Road, NW5 (020 7209 0038). Pubs

The Vine
190 North End Road, N1 (020 7388 0254). Branch

The Vineyard p227
Stockcross, Newbury, Berks (01635 528770). Out of Town

Vineyard (branch of Davys)
International House, St Katherine's Way, E1 (020 7480 6680). Branch

Vingt-Quatre p226
325 Fulham Road, SW10 (020 7376 7224). Eating & Entertainment

Vinopolis Wine Wharf p222
Stoney Street, SE1 (020 7940 8335). Wine Bars

Viva p203
236 St Paul's Road, N1 (020 7704 8227). Cafés

Vong p147
The Berkeley, Wilton Place, SW1 (020 7235 1010). Oriental

Vortex p225
139-141 Stoke Newington Church Street, N16 (020 7254 6516). Eating & Entertainment

Vow Thai p160
53 Cleveland Street, W1 (020 7580 7608). Thai

Vrisaki p73
73 Myddleton Road, N22 (020 8889 8760/ 020 8881 2920). Greek

Wagamama p147
101A Wigmore Street, W1 (020 7409 0111). Oriental

Wagamama
11 Jamestown Road, NW1 (020 7428 0800). Branch

Wagamama
26-40 Kensington High Street, W8 (0207 376 1717). Branch

Wagamama
10A Lexington Street, W1 (020 7292 0990). Branch

Wagamama
Lower ground Floor, Harvey Nichols,, SW1 (020 7201 8000). Branch

Wagamama
4A Streatham Street, WC1 (020 7736 2333). Branch

Wakaba p117
122A Finchley Road, NW3 (020 7586 7960). Japanese

Walthamstow Stadium p223
Chingford Road, E4 (020 8531 4255). Eating & Entertainment

The Warrington Hotel p216
93 Warrington Crescent, W9 (020 7286 2929). Pubs

Webshack p204
15 Dean Street, W1 (020 7439 8000/ www.webshack-cafe.com). Cafés

Weng Wah House p52
240 Haverstock Hill, NW3 (020 7794 5123). Chinese

Wenlock Arms p217
26 Wenlock Road, N1 (020 7608 3406). Pubs

West End Kitchen (branch of Stockpot)
5 Panton Street, SW1 (020 7839 4241). Branch

The Westbourne p214
101 Westbourne Park Villas, W2 (020 7221 1332). Pubs

White Horse p217
1 Parsons Green, SW6 (020 7736 2115). Pubs

The White House p119
10 Bell Lane, NW4 (020 8203 2427). Jewish

White Onion p126
297 Upper Street, N1 (020 7359 3533). Mediterranean

Whitstable Oyster Fishery Company p227
Royal Native Oyster Stores, The Horsebridge, Whitstable, Kent (01227 276856). Out of Town

William IV p213
786 Harrow Road, NW10 (020 8969 5944). Pubs

Willie Gunn p221
422 Garratt Lane, SW18 (020 8946 7773). Wine Bars

Wilson's p36
236 Blythe Road, corner of Shepherd's Bush Road, W14 (020 7603 7267). British

Wiltons p34
55 Jermyn Street, SW1 (020 7629 9955). British

Wimbledon Stadium p223
Plough Lane, SW17 (020 8946 8000/www. wimbledondogs.co.uk). Eating & Entertainment

Advertisers' Index

Eating & Drinking Guide 2001

Maps

The following maps highlight London's key restaurants areas – the districts with the highest density of good places to eat and drink. The map shows precisely where each restaurant is located, as well as underground stations and major landmarks. For an overview of every area, see **Key to maps** below; this shows which areas are covered, and places them in context.

In association with

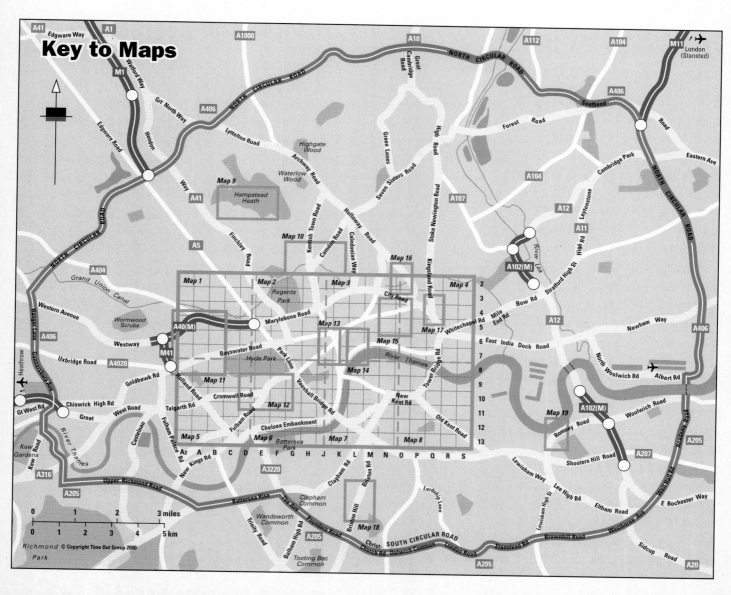

Pure Perrier!

As well as its unique, naturally bubbly water, it is the *personality* of Perrier that has made it the No.1 sparkling mineral water in the world and this is apparent in all its activities.

Perrier is present at all the best parties. It brings added sparkle to thousands of social and sporting occasions throughout the year and every time it contributes to the enjoyment of the occasion.

The natural partner for good food and wine, Perrier is also an excellent mixer bringing extra 'zip' to such events as the Wimbledon Tennis Championships, Ascot, Henley, Cartier Polo and Oxbridge Balls.

In 1981 it created the Perrier Pick of the Fringe, now established as the 'Oscar' of alternative comedy. Winners see the 'Perrier' as a passport to fame and fortune. The winner at Edinburgh in 2000 was American comedian Rich Hall, whose creative wit even has fellow comics laughing! Previous winners have included stars such as Frank Skinner, Lee Evans and Al Murray.

In 1998, the Perrier Young Jazz Awards were launched. Already they have given an enormous boost to the careers of young musicians among whom, it is predicted, will be some of tomorrows' great jazz names. The Perrier Young Jazz Winners CD was launched with great applause from Jazz critics all over the country including Jack Massarik of the Evening Standard and Humphrey Lyttelton who played excerpts from it on his BBC2 Radio Jazz programme.

Always stylish and witty, Perrier's advertising never takes itself seriously. It is fun. Last year the official bubble of Wimbubbledon was a chuckle. This year 'Out of the H2Ordinary' is an inspiration.

PERRIER WINNERS 2000
Pictured clockwise from the top: Dunstan Coulber - Perrier Young Jazz Musician, Rich Hall winner of the Perrier Pick of the Fringe, Douglas Ankrah and Richard Hargroves of The Lab Bar, London, celebrate the Perrier Time Out Best Bar Award, the winners of the Perrier Young Jazz Awards, Tom Caris, Tom Herbert, Dunstan Coulber, Chris Higginbottom, Sam Mayne and Julia Biel.

Perrier is one of the few naturally bubbling mineral waters in the world. It was discovered by an Englishman, St John Harmsworth. He was so impressed with its quality and natural bubbles that he bought the Spring and named it Perrier after his doctor. He based the design of the famous French green Perrier bottle on Indian Clubs he used for exercising. Now Perrier is introducing a new bottle size especially for Restaurants and Bars. This elegant 50cl bottle is based on the original 1903 design.

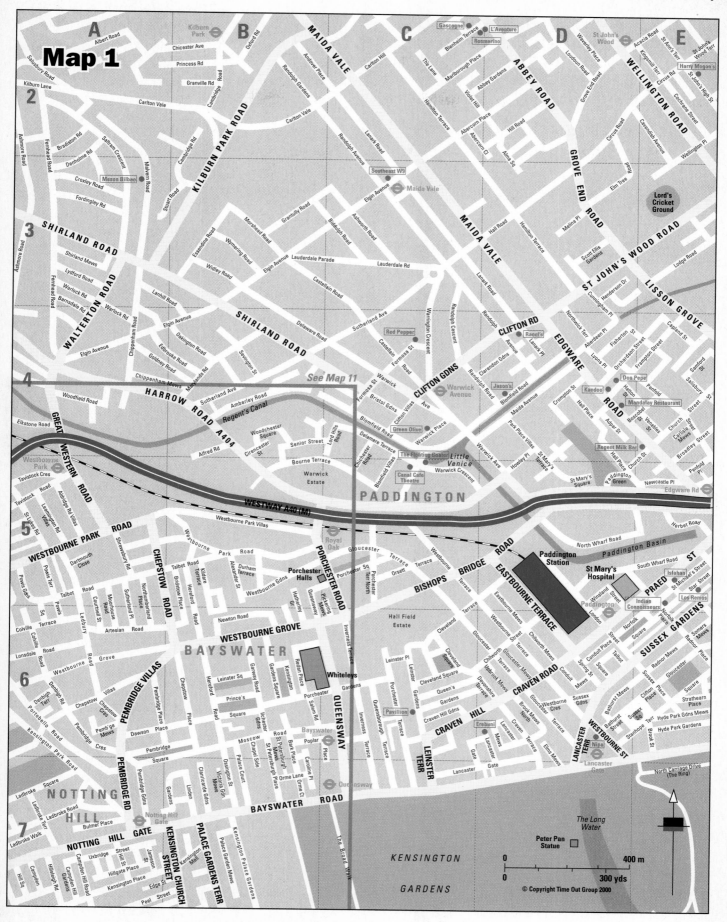

Map 1

Map 1

A **B** **C** **D** **E**

Kilburn Park

Albert Road

Chicester Ave

Salisbury Road

Oxford Rd

Kilburn Lane

Princess Rd

Granville Rd

MAIDA VALE

Gascogne

L'Aventure

Rosmarino

Carlton Hill

Blenheim Terrace

St John's Wood

Acacia Rd

St Ann's Terr

2

Cambridge Rd

Andover Place

The Lane

Marlborough Place

Waverley Place

Kingswell Terr

Circus Rd

St John's High St

Harry Mogan's

Carlton Vale

Randolph Gardens

Carlton Hill

Loudoun Road

Grove End Road

Circus Rd

Cochrane Street

St John's Wood Terr

Kilburn Lane

Carlton Vale

Hamilton Terrace

Violet Hill

Abbey Gardens

WELLINGTON ROAD

Cavendish Avenue

Ashmore Road

Bradiston Rd

Saltram Crescent

Cambridge Rd

Carlton Vale

ABBEY ROAD

Abercorn Place

Hill Road

Cavendish Avenue

Wellington Pl

Fernhead Road

Denholme Rd

Randolph Avenue

Morshead Road

Abercorn Cl

Hall Rd

Hamilton Terrace

Alma Sq

Wellington

Lord's Cricket Ground

Croxley Road

Malvern Road

Stuart Road

Lanark Road

Melina Pl

Elm Tree

Meson Bilbao

Fordingley Rd

SHIRLAND ROAD

Shirland Mews

Grantully Road

Biddulph Road

Ashworth Road

Southeast W9

Elgin Avenue

Maida Vale

MAIDA VALE

Hall Road

Scott Ellis Gardens

ST JOHN'S WOOD ROAD

Lodge Road

3

Ashmore Road

WALTERTON ROAD

Lydford Road

Essendine Road

Wirnering Road

Elgin Avenue

Lauderdale Parade

Lauderdale Rd

Randolph Avenue

Henderson Dr

Cunningham Pl

LISSON GROVE

Warlock Rd

Fernhead Rd

Barnsdale Rd

Warlock Rd

Widley Road

Castellain Road

Randolph

CLIFTON RD

Raoul's

Northwick Terr

Aberdeen Pl

Fisherton Street

Capland St

Chippenham Road

Oakington Road

Lanhill Road

SHIRLAND ROAD

Delaware Road

Sutherland Ave

Red Pepper

Warrington Crescent

Randolph Crescent

Edgware

Lyons Pl

Orchardson Street

Frampton Street

Samford St

Salisbury St

Elgin Avenue

Edbrooke Road

Goldney Road

Sevington St

Maylands Rd

Castellain

Formosa St

CLIFTON GDNS

Clarendon Gdns

Blomfield Road

Crompton St

Don Pepe

Hatton

Boscobel

Venables

Chippenham Mews

Warwick

Bristol Gdns

Clifton Villas

Warwick Ave

Jason's

Maida Avenue

Hall Place

Kandoo

Mandalay Restaurant

Church Street

Carlisle Mews

Broadley Street

4

Woodfield Road

HARROW ROAD A404

Sutherland Ave

Amberley Road

Formosa St

Clifton

Ave

Warwick Avenue

Warwick

Randolph Ave

Blomfield Road

Park Place Villas

Adpar St

St Mary's Terrace

Hall Place

Regent Milk Bar

Penfold

Elkstone Road

Regent's Canal

Woodchester Square

Alfred Rd

Senior Street

Cirencester St

Lord Hills Road

Delamere Terrace

Chichester Road

Blomfield Villas

Green Olive

Warwick Place

The Floating Boater

Little Venice

Warwick Ave

Howley Pl

St Mary's Terrace

St Mary's Square

Paddington Green

Penfold St

Newcastle Pl

GREAT WESTERN ROAD

Tavistock Cres

Bourne Terrace

Warwick Estate

Canal Cafe Theatre

Warwick Crescent

PADDINGTON

Edgware Rd

Westbourne Park

Tavistock

St Luke's Rd

Aldridge Rd Villas

Leamington Villas

WESTWAY A40 (M)

Westbourne Park Villas

5

Powis Gdns

Powis Terr

WESTBOURNE PARK ROAD

Dartmouth Close

Shrewsbury Rd

Westbourne

Park Road

Royal Oak

Gloucester

Terrace

Westbourne

Terrace

ROAD

North Wharf Road

Paddington Basin

PRAED ST

Herbet Road

Powis Gdns

Talbot

Road

Colville

Terrace

CHEPSTOW ROAD

Courtnall St

Moorhouse

Road

Kildare

Terrace

Alexander St

Porchester Gdns

Westbourne Gdns

Porchester Sq

Porchester

Terr North

Orsett

Terrace

Bishop's

Bridge

EASTBOURNE TERRACE

Paddington Station

St Mary's Hospital

South Wharf Road

Isfahan

St Michael's Street

Star Street

Los Remos

Powis

Sq

Ledbury

Road

Sutherland

Place

Northumberland

Place

Bridstow Place

Hereford

Road

Newton Road

Porchester

Mews

Westbourne

Street

Eastbourne Mews

Chilworth Mews

Gloucester Mews

Indian Connoisseurs

Paddington

London

Norfolk

Square

SUSSEX GARDENS

Colville

Road

Lonsdale

Road

Westbourne

Grove

Pickering

Grove

Hatherley

Gr

WESTBOURNE GROVE

Queensway

Inverness Terrace

Leinster Pl

Leinster

Gdns

Cleveland

Square

Westbourne

Terrace

Chilworth

Street

Gloucester

Terrace

Devonshire

Terrace

Upbrook Mews

Gloucester

Terrace

Conduit

Mews

Conduit

Spring St

Norfolk

Place

Talbot

Square

Radnor Mews

Gloucester

Square

Bathurst Mews

Clifton

Place

Sussex

Square

Sussex

Mews

Gloucester

Square

6

Denbigh

Terr

Denbigh Rd

Portobello

Road

PEMBRIDGE VILLAS

Chepstow

Cres

Pemb'ge

Mews

Chepstow

Place

BAYSWATER

Leinster Sq

Prince's

Square

Garway Road

Kensington

Gardens Square

Redan

Place

Whiteleys

Porchester

Gardens

Queen's

Gardens

Porchester

Gardens

Cleveland

Square

Craven Hill Gdns

Devonshire

Terrace

Craven

Terrace

Westbourne

Cres

Sussex

Gdns

Brook Mews

North

Lancaster

Mews

Sussex

Square

Gloucester

Square

Strathearn

Place

Hyde Park Gdns Mews

Kensington Park Road

Portobello

Road

Pembridge Cres

Pembridge

Square

Chepstow

Place

Dawson

Place

Moscow

Road

Poplar

Place

Bark Place

Caroline Pl

St Petersburgh

Mews

St Petersburgh Pl

Inverness

Terrace

Queensborough

Terrace

CRAVEN ROAD

Pavillion

Craven Hill

CRAVEN HILL

Brook Mews

Westbourne

Terrace

Lancaster

Mews

Elms Mews

Radnor

Place

Stanhope

Terr

Bathurst

St

Brook St

Hyde Park Gardens

7

Ladbroke

Square

Ladbroke Road

NOTTING HILL

PEMBRIDGE RD

Pembridge

Square

Bulmer

Place

Notting Hill

Gate

NOTTING HILL GATE

Pembridge Villas

PALACE GARDENS TERR

KENSINGTON CHURCH STREET

Linden

Gardens

Victoria Gdn

Palace Court

Orme Lane

Orme Ct

Palace Garden Mews

Kensington Palace Gardens

Kensington Mall

Kensington

Palace Gdns

Chepstow

Place

Salem Rd

Erebuni

Queensway

Lancaster

Gate

Nipa

Lancaster Gate

LANCASTER TERR

WESTBOURNE ST

Bayswater

Queensway

BAYSWATER ROAD

The Broad Walk

LEINSTER TERR

Lancaster

Mews

North Carriage Drive (The Ring)

Ladbroke Walk

Campden Hill Rd

Uxbridge Street

Jameson

Street

Hillgate

Street

Hill St

Hillgate Pl

Kensington Place

Edge St

Peel Street

Camden Hill Gdns

Camden Hill

Hill Sq

KENSINGTON

GARDENS

The Long Water

Peter Pan Statue

0   400 m

0   300 yds

© Copyright Time Out Group 2000

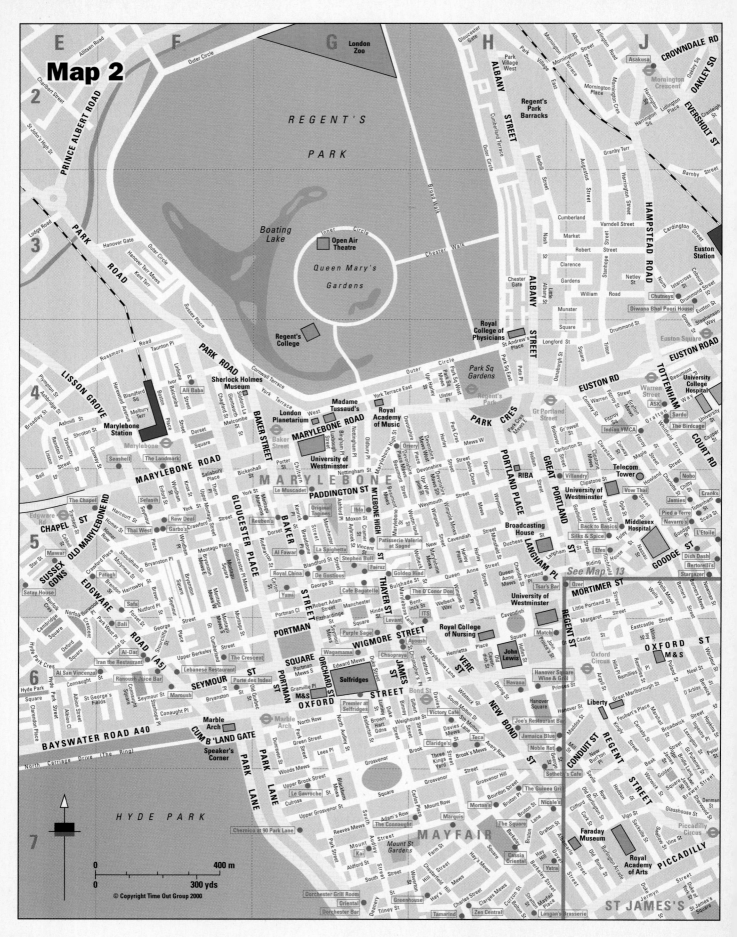

Map 2

E Cheribert Street

Allitsen Road

F Outer Circle

G London Zoo

Gloucester Gate

H Park Village West

Park Village East

Mornington Crescent

J CROWNDALE RD

Oakley Sq

OAKLEY SQ

Asakusa

Mornington Crescent

Cranleigh St

EVERSHOLT ST

St John's High St

PRINCE ALBERT ROAD

REGENT'S PARK

ALBANY STREET

Regent's Park Barracks

Mornington Place

Mornington Cres

Harrington Sq

Lillington St

Harrington St

Granby Terr

Barnby Street

Lodge Road

PARK ROAD

Hanover Gate

Hanover Terr Mews

Outer Circle

Kent Terr

Cumberland Terrace

Redhill Street

Augustus Street

Cardington Street

Euston Station

Rossmore Road

Taunton Pl

Sussex Place

Boating Lake

Inner Circle

Open Air Theatre

Queen Mary's Gardens

Chester Walk

Broad Walk

Chester Gate

ALBANY STREET

Cumberland Market

Varndell Street

Robert Street

Clarence Gardens

Netley St

Munster Square

William Road

Longford St

Triton St

Drummond Street

Chutneys

Diwana Bhal Poori House

Euston Square

Stephenson Way

Euston Square

EUSTON ROAD

LISSON GROVE

Plympton St

Ashbridge St

Ali Baba

Lilhope Pl

Ivor Pl

Balcombe Street

Boston Pl

Melcombe St

Chagford St

Ginmott St

Sherlock Holmes Museum

York Terrace

Cornwall Terrace

Regent's College

York Terrace East

York Terrace West

Ulster Pl

Upr Harley St

Park Sq West

Park Sq East

Peto Pl

Outer Circle

Park Sq Gdns

Regent's Park

PARK CRES

Park Cres Mews W

Gt Portland Street

EUSTON RD

TOTTENHAM COURT RD

Beaumont Pl

University College Hospital

Warren Street

ASK

University

Bradley's Ashmill St

Shroton St

Lisson Street

Bell Street

MARYLEBONE ROAD

Blandford Sq

Melbury Terr

Marylebone Station

Marylebone

Dorset Square

Salisbury Place

Madame Tussaud's

London Planetarium

Luxborough St

BAKER STREET

Nottingham Pl

Royal Academy of Music

Devonshire Mews West

Devonshire Place Mews

Beaumont St

Weymouth St

Devonshire St

Weymouth

New Cavendish

Hallam St

PORTLAND PLACE

Carburton St

Cleveland St

Greenwell St

Fitzroy St

Conway St

Maple St

Howland St

Grafton Way

Whitfield Street

Capper

Warren St

Sardo

The Birdcage

COURT RD

University

The Landmark

Seashell

MARYLEBONE ROAD

The Chapel

CHAPEL ST

OLD MARYLEBONE RD

Selasih

Raw Deal

Thai West

Harcourt St

Homer St

Crawford Street

Seymour Place

York St

Upper Montagu St

Montagu Mansions

Le Muscadet

MARYLEBONE

Nottingham St

PADDINGTON ST

Baker

Broadstone

Ibla

Ashford St

Manchester St

Marylebone High St

Aybrook St

Cramer St

Vincent

Moxon St

New Cavendish

St Vincent

Harley Place

Harley St

Wimpole St

Broadcasting House

Mansfield St

Duchess

Langham St

Riding House

Foley St

Langham

Efes

Nassau

Goodge St

Middlesex Hospital

L'Etoile

Cranks

Noho

Chitty St

Scala St

Pied a Terre

Navarro's

GOODGE ST

Dish Dash

Bertorelli's

Stargazer

Orrery

RIBA

Villandry

University of Westminster

Telecom Tower

Vow Thai

University of Westminster

Back to Basics

Silks & Spice

Jamies

Tottenham

Indian YMCA

Garbo's

Reuben's

Original Tagines

La Spighetta

Stephen Bull

Patisserie Valerie at Sagne

Golden Hind

The O'Conor Don

Tsar's Bar

See Map 13

Mawar

Star St

Sussex Gdns

Patogh

Edgware Rd

Transept St

Homer Row

Shouldham St

Brendon St

Harrowby St

Crawford Place

Montagu Place

Montagu Sq

Bryanston Pl

Gloucester Pl Mews

Al Fawar

Royal China

De Gustibus

Yumi

GLOUCESTER PLACE

BAKER STREET

Blandford St

George St

Dorset St

Fairuz

THAYER ST

Bulshade St

Bentinck St

Welbeck Way

Levant

ITS

Queen Anne Mews

Chandos St

Portland Mews

Mortimer St

REGENT ST

Margaret

John Prince's St

Ozer

Little Portland St

Wells St

Eastcastle St

Berners St

Newman St

OXFORD ST

Poland St

M&S

SATAY HOUSE

Mawar

SUSSEX GDNS

EDGWARE ROAD (A5)

Bali

Safa

George Street

Nutford Pl

Brown St

Seymour Pl

Great Cumberland Pl

Montagu Mews W

Montagu Square

PORTMAN SQUARE

Bryanston Square

Gloucester Place

Robert Adam Street

Fitzhardinge St

Manchester Square

Hinde St

Purple Sage

Wigmore Pl

Mandeville Pl

Stratford Pl

Henrietta Place

Cavendish

Queen Anne St

Cavendish Sq

John Lewis

Hanover Square

Oxford Circus

Havana

Hanover St

Oxford Circus

M&S

Liberty

Great Marlborough St

Foubert's Pl

Argyll St

Ramillies Pl

Kingly St

Beak St

Carnaby St

Broadwick St

Marshall St

Lexington St

D'Arblay St

Berwick St

Noel St

Iran the Restaurant

Al-Dar

Al San Vincenzo

Ranoush Juice Bar

Lebanese Restaurant

The Crescent

Upper Berkeley St

Hyde Park Cres

Oxford Square

Cambridge Square

Norfolk Cres

Norfolk Square

Park West Pl

Connaught Square

St George's Fields

Porte des Indes

Maroush

SEYMOUR ST

Granville Pl

Old Quebec St

Wagamama

Chaoraya

Ayoush

WIGMORE STREET

St Christopher's Pl

James St

JAMES ST

Duke St

Barrett St

VERE ST

Royal College of Nursing

Match

University of Westminster

Hanover Square Wine & Grill

Conduit St

CONDUIT ST

Mill St

New Burton St

Clifford St

Cork St

Old Burlington St

Savile Row

Vigo St

Sackville St

REGENT STREET

Glasshouse St

Piccadilly Circus

Clarence

Hyde Park Sq

Clarendon Place

Albion Street

Seymour St

Connaught St

Bryanston

Portman St

ORCHARD ST

Selfridges

M&S

OXFORD STREET

Bond St

Duke St

Binney St

Weighhouse St

Gilbert St

Davies Mews

South Molton Lane

NEW BOND ST

Bourdon St

Maddox St

Princes St

Mill St

Victory Café

Teca

Joe's Restaurant Bar

Jamaica Blue

Noble Rot

Sotheby's Café

The Guinea Grill

Havana

Nicole's

Morton's

BAYSWATER ROAD A40

CUMB'LAND GATE

Marble Arch

Speaker's Corner

PARK LANE

Premier at Selfridges

Marble Arch

North Row

Green Street

Lees Pl

Dunraven St

Balderton St

Woods Mews

Brook

Brook's Mews

Davies

Avery Row

Grosvenor

Three Kings Yard

Claridge's

Adam's Row

Brook St

Grosvenor Hill

Bruton Lane

Berkeley Square

Bruton St

Grafton St

Bourdon St

Cassia Oriental

Yatra

Dover St

Hay Hill

Berkeley St

Stratton St

Faraday Museum

Royal Academy of Arts

Old Bond St

Albemarle St

North Carriage Drive (the Ring)

HYDE PARK

Cheznico at 90 Park Lane

PARK LANE

Upper Brook Street

Blackburn Mews

Culross St

Upper Grosvenor St

Reeves Mews

Le Gavroche

The Connaught

Mount Row

Mount Street

Adams Row

Carlos Place

Grosvenor Square

Grosvenor St

South Audley St

Mount St Gdns

Mount St

Aldford St

South St

Farm St

Hay's Mews

Charles Street

Chesterfield St

Waverton St

Chesterfield Hill

Hill St

Charles St

Curzon St

Clarges St

Bolton St

Half Moon St

The Square

Marquis

Kai

Greenhouse

Tamarind

Zen Central

Langan's Brasserie

Mayfair Place

Vine St

Swallow St

Jermyn St

Duke of York St

MAYFAIR

Dorchester Grill Room

Oriental

Dorchester Bar

Deanery St

Tilney St

Hay's

Clarges Mews

PICCADILLY

Piccadilly Arcade

ST JAMES'S

St James's Square

Map 2 & 3

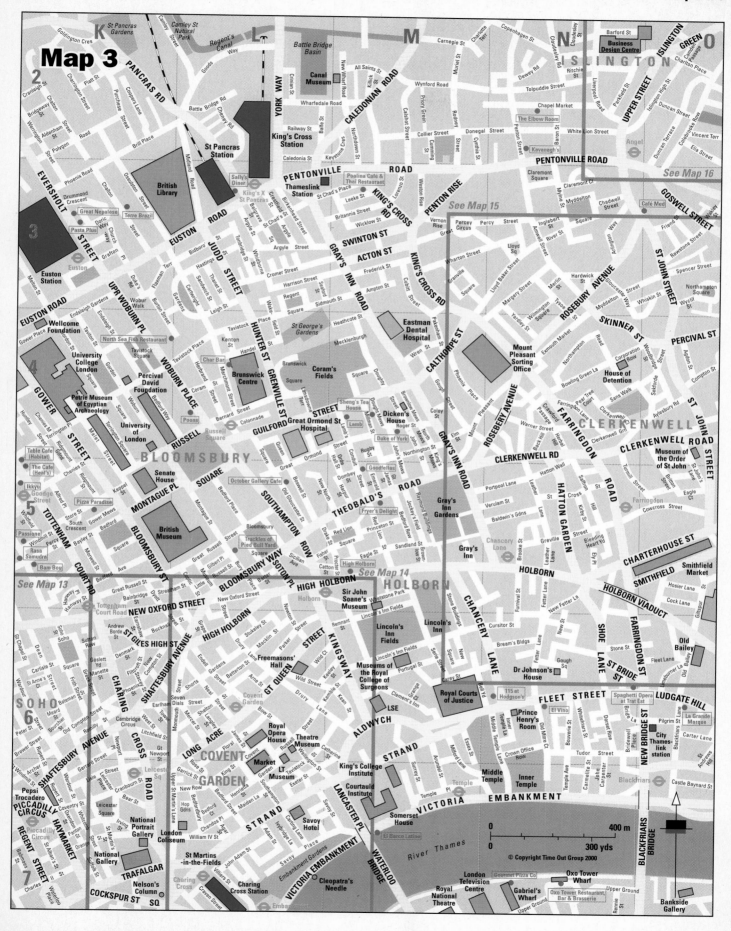

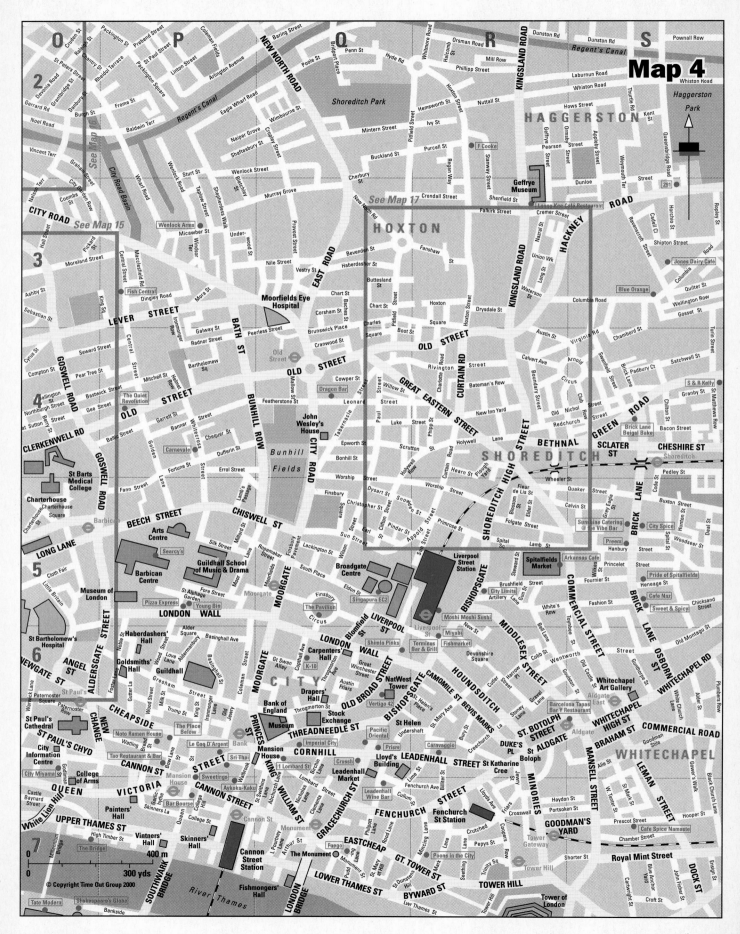

Map 4

Map 4 & 5

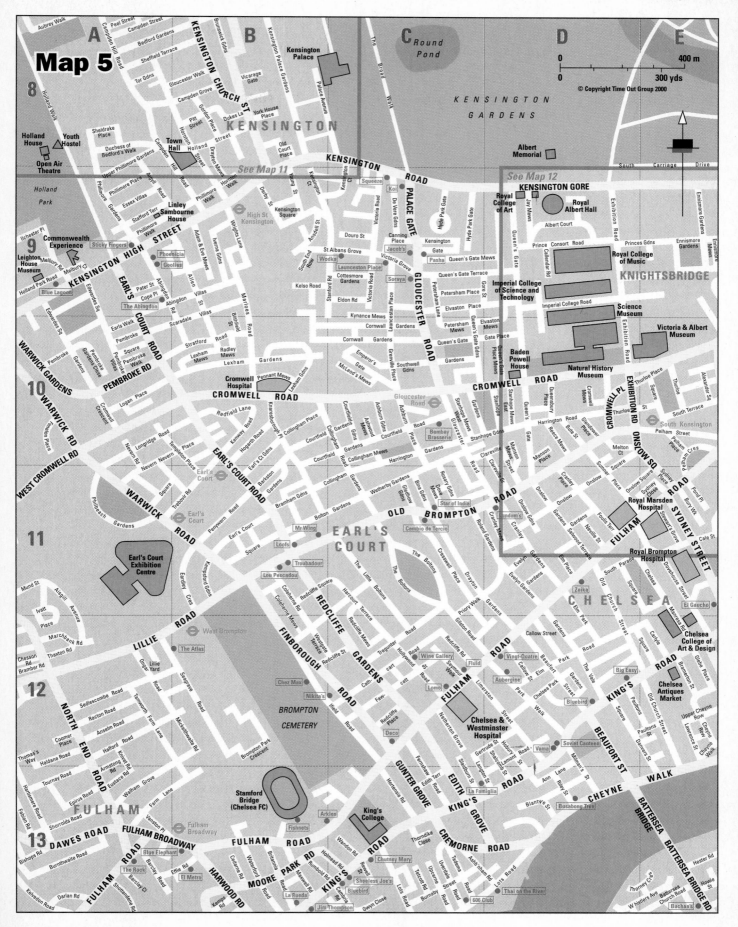

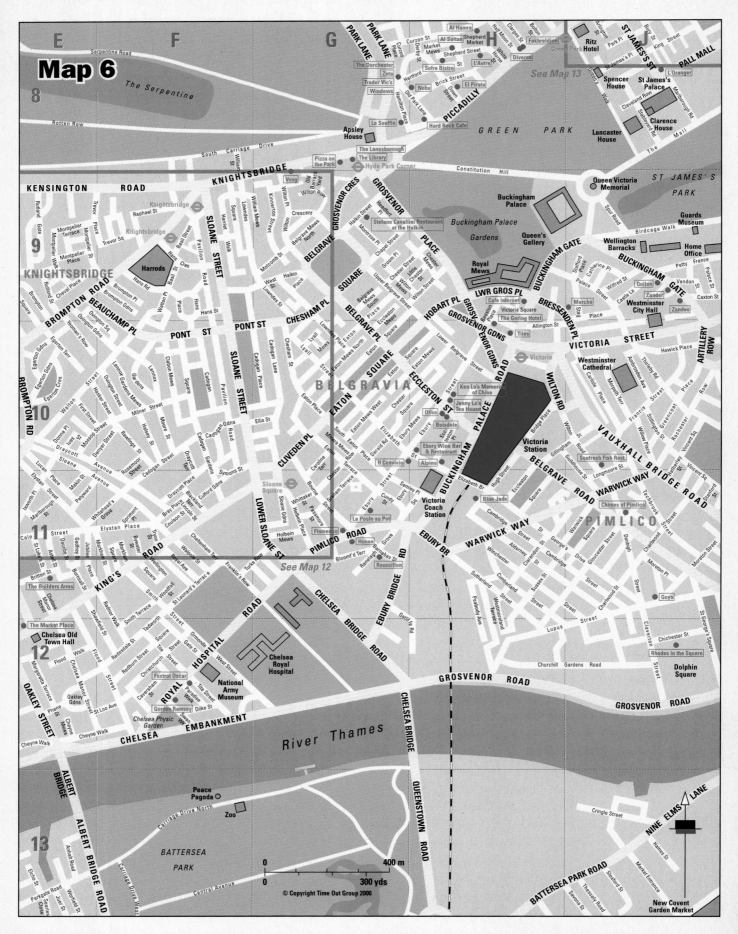

Map 6

The Serpentine

Serpentine Road

Rotten Row

KENSINGTON ROAD

South Carriage Drive

Williams

KNIGHTSBRIDGE

PARK LANE

PARK LANE

PICCADILLY

Al Hamra
Al Sultan
Shepherd Market
Curzon St
Derby St
Market Mews
Shepherd Street
Curzon Place
Hertford
Sofra Bistro
St
L'Autre
Half Moon St
White Horse St
Charges St
Bolton St
Fakhreldine
Diverse

The Dorchester
Zeta
Trader Vic's
Windows
Nobu
Brick Street
Down St
El Pirata
Old Park Lane
Hamilton Place

Ritz Hotel
ST JAMES'S ST
St James's Place
Arlington
St
King
St
PALL MALL
L'Oranger
Spencer House
St James's Palace
Cleveland Row
Stubbard Rd
Clarence House
Marlborough Rd
Lancaster House

See Map 13

Le Soufflé
Hard Rock Cafe

Apsley House

GREEN PARK

Constitution Hill

The Lanesborough
Pizza on the Park
The Library
Hyde Park Corner

Queen Victoria Memorial

ST JAMES'S PARK

Vong
Old Barrack Yard
Wilton Row

KNIGHTSBRIDGE

Buckingham Palace

Guards Museum

KENSINGTON ROAD

Knightsbridge
Rutland Gate
Trevor Place
Montpelier Terrace
Montpelier Place
Montpelier Walk
Trevor Sq
Raphael St
Harriet St
Basil Street
Sloane Street
William Mews
Lowndes Square
Crescent
Kinnerton Street
Wilton Pl

GROSVENOR CRES
GROSVENOR PLACE
Halkin St
Headfort Pl
Montrose Pl
Stefano Cavallini Restaurant at the Halkin

Buckingham Palace Gardens
Queen's Gallery
Royal Mews
BUCKINGHAM GATE

Birdcage Walk
Wellington Barracks
BUCKINGHAM
Spur Road

Guards Museum
Home Office
BUCKINGHAM GATE
Petty France
Palace St
Vandon
Caxton St
Quilon
Zander
Westminster City Hall
Zandes

Harrods
KNIGHTSBRIDGE
Hans Cres
Hans Rd
Basil St
Pavilion Rd
Walton Pl
Hans St
CHESHAM PL
BELGRAVE SQUARE
BELGRAVE PL

BELGRAVIA
Chester Street
Chester Mews
Little Chester St
Wilton St
Groom Pl
Chapel St
Upper Belgrave Street
HOBART PL
GROSVENOR GDNS
GROSVENOR GDNS
Cafe Internet
The Goring Hotel
Tiles
Victoria Square
Bressan Place
BRESSENDEN PL
Marché
Stag Place
LWR GROS PL

VICTORIA STREET
Westminster Cathedral
Ambrosine
Thirleby Rd
Morpeth Ter
Carlisle Place
ARTILLERY ROW
Howick Place
Francis St

BROMPTON ROAD
BEAUCHAMP PL
Cheval Place
Brompton Square
Brompton Gdns
Brompton Pl
Egerton Gdns
Egerton Terr
Egerton Cres
Yeoman's Row
Ovington Sq
Ovington Gdns
Lennox Gardens
First Street
Walton Street
Hasker Street
Mossop Street
Milner Street
Moore Street
Cadogan Street
PONT ST
PONT ST
SLOANE STREET
Cadogan Place
Cadogan Lane
Lowndes Street
West Halkin Street
Lyall Street
Lyall Mews
Eaton Place
Eaton Mews North
EATON SQUARE
Belgrave Mews North
Belgrave Mews South
Eccleston Mews
Eccleston Street
Lower Belgrave Street
ECCLESTON ST
Eaton Mews
Eaton Lane
GROSVENOR GARDENS
PALACE ROAD
Ken Lo's Memories of China
Jenny Lo's Tea House
Olivo
Boisdale
Victoria
WILTON RD
Bridge Place
Gillingham
Wilton St
Willow Place
Vincent St
Greencoat Pl
Rochester Row
VAUXHALL BRIDGE ROAD
Vincent Square
Sillington St
Maunsel St

BROMPTON RD
Egerton Gdns
Walton Street
Donne Pl
Ives St
Draycott Pl
Lucan Place
Elystan Place
Elystan Street
Inworth Pl
Marlborough St
Cale Street
St Luke's St
Astell St
Britten St
KING'S ROAD

Draycott Avenue
Denyer Street
Rosemoor Street
Sloane Avenue
Cadogan Gardens
Blackland
Coulson St
Bray Pl
Culford Gdns
Lincoln St
Symons St
SLOANE SQUARE
Cheltenham Terrace
Holbein Pl
Holbein Mews
LOWER SLOANE ST
Whittaker St
Bourne St
Graham Terrace
Graham Street
Passmore St
Ebury St
Cundy St
Semley Pl
Ebury Mews
Elizabeth St
Ebury Square
Gerald Rd
Chester Sq
Chester Row
Chester St
Eaton Terrace
Caroline Terrace
Minera Mews
Eaton Mews West
South Eaton Pl
Eaton Terrace
CLIVEDEN PL
Mozart Terrace
Il Convivio
Ebury Wine Bar & Restaurant
Alpino
Alpha Pl
Pimlico Road
Flamenco
La Poule au Pot
Hunan
Bloomf'd Terr
Randall
Grove
St Barnabas St
Roussillon
PIMLICO ROAD
EBURY BR
EBURY BRIDGE ROAD
Gatliff Rd
Sutherland Street
Cumberland Street
Alderney
Winchester
Gloucester
Cambridge Street
Clarendon
Sussex Street
Denbigh
Charlwood
Moreton Pl
WARWICK WAY
WARWICK WAY
PIMLICO
Seafresh Fish Rest.
BELGRAVE ROAD
Guildhouse St
Longmoore St
Warwick Square
Warwick Way
St George's Drive
Chimes of Pimlico
Cambridge St
Gloucester St
Charlwood
Goya
Claverton St
Chichester St
Rhodes in the Square
Dolphin Square

See Map 12

Victoria Coach Station
Victoria Station
Blue Jade

Churchill Gardens Road
Lupus
Westmoreland Terrace
Peabody Ave
Sutherland
Grosvenor Road
Claverton St

KING'S ROAD
The Builders Arms
The Market Place
Chelsea Old Town Hall
HOSPITAL ROAD
West Road
Foxtrot Oscar
ROYAL HOSPITAL ROAD
Gordon Ramsey
Chelsea Royal Hospital
National Army Museum
Tite Street
Dilke St
Swan Walk
Paradise
Chelsea Physic Garden
CHELSEA EMBANKMENT
Cheyne Walk
OAKLEY STREET
Oakley Gdns
Margaretta Terrace
Phene St
Cheyne Mews
Flood Street
Christchurch Street
Smith Terrace
Radnor Walk
Tedworth Square
Ormonde Gate
Franklin's Row
St Leonard's Terrace
Turks Row
Royal Ave
Redcliffe St
Caversham St

ALBERT BRIDGE
ALBERT BRIDGE ROAD
Anhalt Road
Parkgate Road

CHELSEA BRIDGE ROAD
CHELSEA BRIDGE

GROSVENOR ROAD
GROSVENOR ROAD

Peace Pagoda
Zoo
Carriage Drive North

River Thames

QUEENSTOWN ROAD

NINE ELMS LANE
Cringle Street
Thames St
BATTERSEA PARK ROAD
Sleaford St
Market Entrance
Savona St
Thessaly Rd

New Covent Garden Market

BATTERSEA PARK
Central Avenue
Carriage Drive West
Carriage Drive

0   400 m
0   300 yds

© Copyright Time Out Group 2000

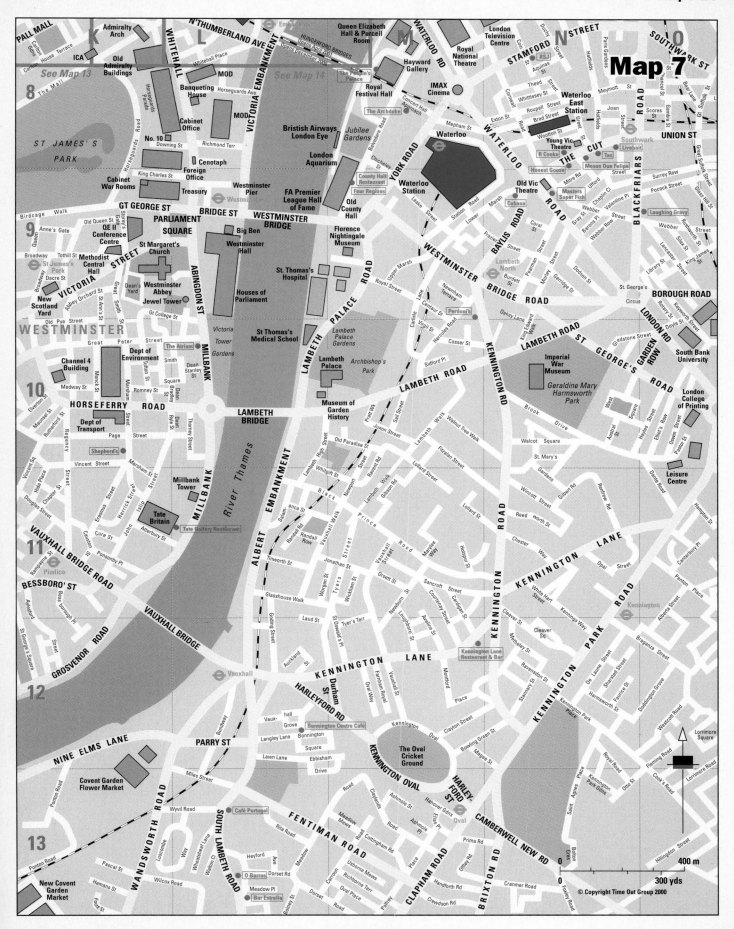

Map 6 & 7

Map 7

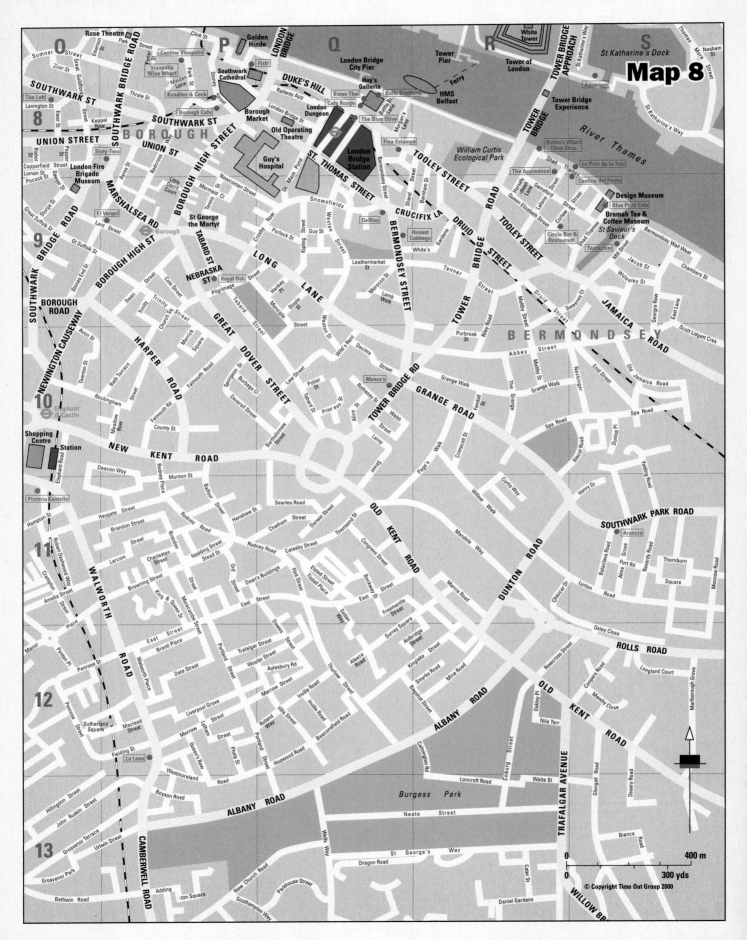

Map 8

River Thames

St Katharine's Dock

O
P
Q
R
S

8
9
10
11
12
13

BOROUGH

BERMONDSEY

SOUTHWARK ST

UNION STREET

SOUTHWARK ST

UNION ST

BOROUGH HIGH STREET

MARSHALSEA RD

SOUTHWARK BRIDGE ROAD

SOUTHWARK BRIDGE ROAD

BOROUGH HIGH ST

TABARD ST

GREAT DOVER STREET

ST. THOMAS STREET

CRUCIFIX LA

TOOLEY STREET

DRUID STREET

TOWER BRIDGE ROAD

TOWER BRIDGE APPROACH

TOOLEY STREET

BERMONDSEY STREET

DUKE'S HILL

LONG LANE

GRANGE ROAD

JAMAICA ROAD

NEWINGTON CAUSEWAY

BOROUGH ROAD

HARPER ROAD

WALWORTH ROAD

NEW KENT ROAD

OLD KENT ROAD

DUNTON ROAD

SOUTHWARK PARK ROAD

ALBANY ROAD

OLD KENT ROAD

TRAFALGAR AVENUE

ROLLS ROAD

CAMBERWELL ROAD

ALBANY ROAD

Burgess Park

WILLOW BR

Rose Theatre
Golden Hinde
London Bridge
Tower Pier
White Tower
Tower Bridge
Cantina Vinopolis
Fish!
London Bridge City Pier
Tower of London
St Katharine's Way
Clink St
Vinopolis Wine Wharf
Southwark Cathedral
Hay's Galleria
Ferry
HMS Belfast
Tower Bridge Experience
Aquarium
The Loft
Konditor & Cook
Kwan Thai
Balls Brothers
Cafe Rouge
Borough Cafe
Railway App
Battle Br
Morgan's Lane
Butler's Wharf Chop Shop
Le Pont de la Tour
Borough Market
London Dungeon
The Blue Olive
Shad Thames
Old Operating Theatre
Fina Estampa
The Apprentice
Cantina del Ponte
Sixty-Two
Guy's Hospital
London Bridge Station
William Curtis Ecological Park
Shad
Design Museum
London Fire Brigade Museum
Delfina
Queen Elizabeth Street
Blue Print Cafe
Bramah Tea & Coffee Museum
St George the Martyr
Honest Cabbage
Circle Bar & Restaurant
St Saviour's Dock
El Vergel
White's
Tentazioni
Royal Oak
Leathermarket St
Morocco St
Lamb Walk
Manze's
Grange Walk
The Grange
Grange Walk
Pizzeria Castello
Arancia
La Luna
Bianca

400 m
300 yds
© Copyright Time Out Group 2000

Map 8 & 9/10

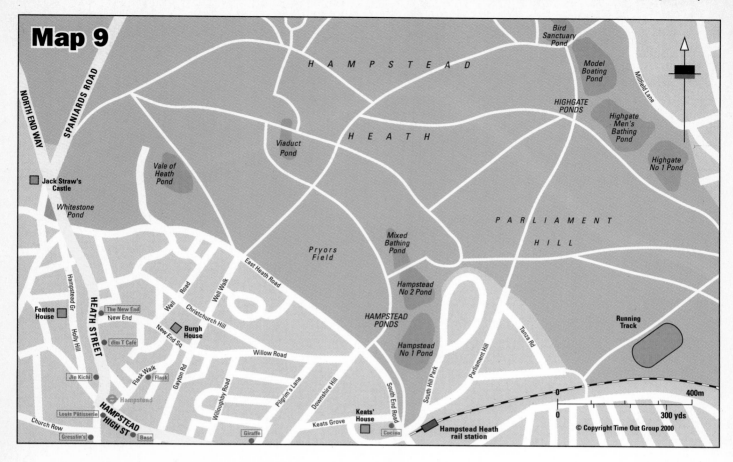

Map 9

HAMPSTEAD

HEATH

Bird Sanctuary Pond

Model Boating Pond

HIGHGATE PONDS

Highgate Men's Bathing Pond

Highgate No 1 Pond

Millfield Lane

NORTH END WAY

SPANIARDS ROAD

Viaduct Pond

Vale of Heath Pond

Jack Straw's Castle

Whitestone Pond

PARLIAMENT HILL

Pryors Field

Mixed Bathing Pond

East Heath Road

Hampstead Gr

HEATH STREET

The New End

New End

Fenton House

Holly Hill

dim T Café

Well Walk

Well Road

Road

Christchurch Hill

Burgh House

New End Sq

Hampstead No 2 Pond

Running Track

Jin Kichi

Flask Walk

Flask

Gayton Rd

Willow Road

Willoughby Road

HAMPSTEAD PONDS

Hampstead No 1 Pond

South Hill Park

Parliament Hill

Tanza Rd

Hampstead

Louis Pâtisserie

HAMPSTEAD HIGH ST

Pilgrim's Lane

Downshire Hill

South End Road

Church Row

Gresslin's

Base

Giraffe

Keats Grove

Keats' House

Cucina

Hampstead Heath rail station

0   400m

0   300yds

© Copyright Time Out Group 2000

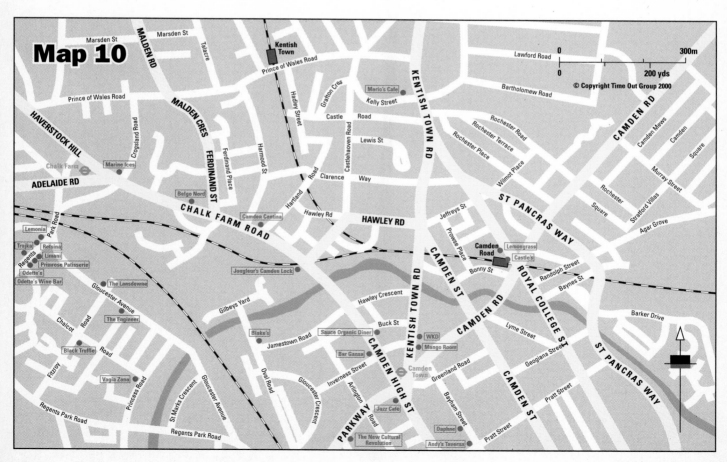

Map 10

Marsden St

Marsden St

MALDEN RD

Talacre

Kentish Town

Prince of Wales Road

Grafton Cres

Mario's Cafe

KENTISH TOWN RD

Lawford Road

0   300m

0   200 yds

© Copyright Time Out Group 2000

Bartholomew Road

CAMDEN RD

Prince of Wales Road

MALDEN CRES

Crogsland Road

Hadley Street

Kelly Street

Castle   Road

Rochester Road

Rochester Terrace

Camden Mews

Camden

HAVERSTOCK HILL

Marine Ices

FERDINAND ST

Ferdinand Place

Harmood St

Castlehaoven Road

Lewis St

Rochester Place

Wilmot Place

Camden Square

Murray Street

Chalk Farm

ADELAIDE RD

Belgo Nord

CHALK FARM ROAD

Clarence   Way

ST PANCRAS WAY

Rochester

Stratford Villas

Camden Cantina

Hartland   Road

Hawley Rd

HAWLEY RD

Jeffreys St

Square

Agar Grove

Lemonia

Park Road

Trojka

Retsina

Regents

Limani

Primrose Patisserie

Odette's

Odette's Wine Bar

Jongleur's Camden Lock

Prowse Place

Camden Road

Lemongrass

Castle's

Bonny St

Randolph Street

ROYAL COLLEGE ST

Baynes St

KENTISH TOWN RD

CAMDEN ST

CAMDEN RD

The Lansdowne

Gloucester Avenue

Gilbeys Yard

Hawley Crescent

Barker Drive

The Engineer

Black Truffle

Chalcot   Road

Fitzroy   Road

Vagia Zana

Jamestown Road

Blake's

Buck St

Sauce Organic Diner

WKD

Mango Room

Lyme Street

Greenland Road

Geogiana Street

ST PANCRAS WAY

Bar Gansa

CAMDEN HIGH ST

Camden Town

Princess Road

St Marks Crescent

Gloucester Avenue

Regents Park Road

Regents Park Road

Gloucester Crescent

Inverness Street

Arlington

Oval Road

PARKWAY

Jazz Cafe

Bayham Street

Pratt Street

CAMDEN ST

Daphne

The New Cultural Revolution

Andy's Taverna

Pratt Street

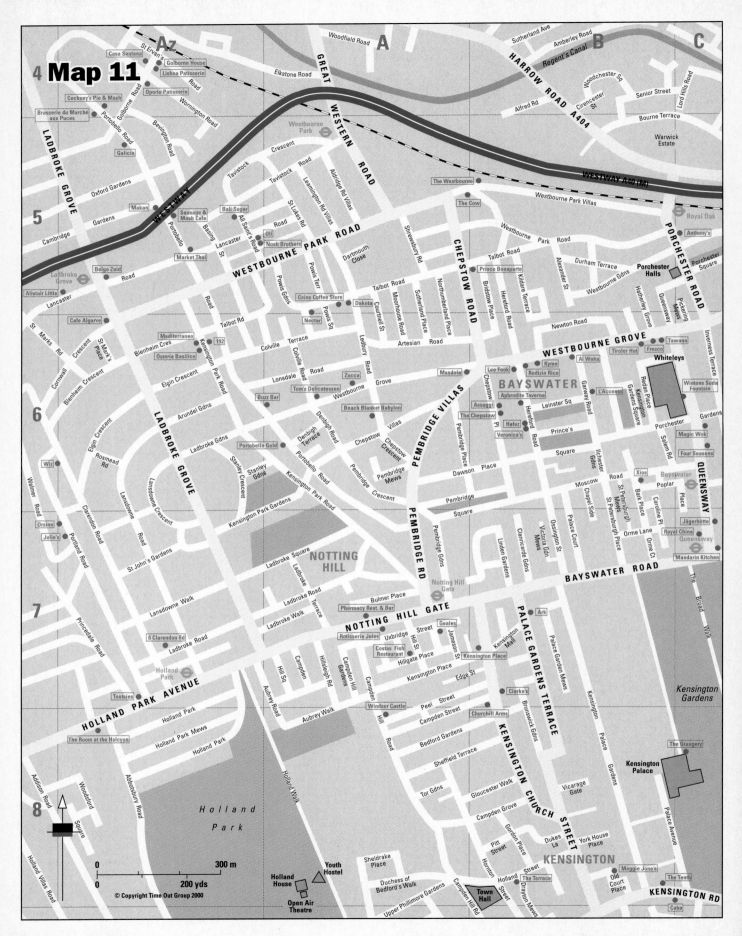

Map 11

Map 11 & 12

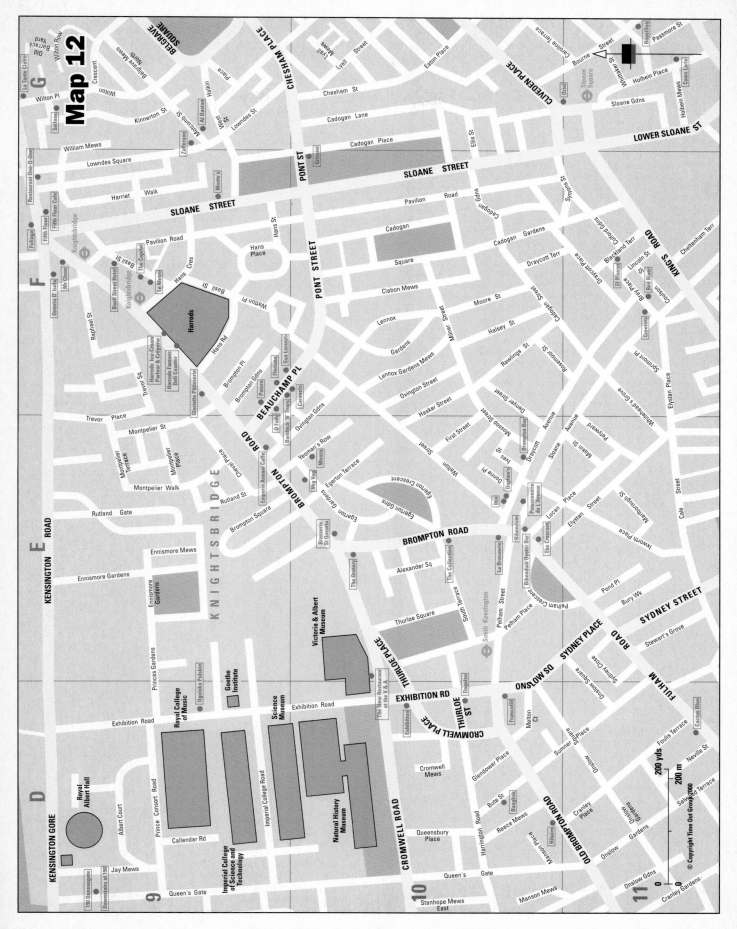

Map 12

Old Barrack Yard
Wilton Row
Wilton Pl
La Tante Claire
Salloos
Crescent
Belgrave Mews North
Wilton Cres
BELGRAVE SQUARE
William Mews
Kinnerton St
Motcomb St
West Halkin St
Place
Al Bustani
Zafferano
Lowndes Square
Harriet Walk
Monte's
Lowndes St
Chesham St
CHESHAM PLACE
Lyall Mews
Lyall Street
Eaton Place
CLIVEDEN PLACE
Caroline Terrace
Bourne Street
Whittaker St
Raeusti Hael
Passmore St
Holbein Place
Como Lario
Grissini
Cadogan Lane
Cadogan Place
Oriel
Sloane Square
Holbein Mews
Sloane Gdns
LOWER SLOANE ST
Fifth Floor
Fifth Floor Cafe
Foliage
Restaurant One-O-One
SLOANE STREET
SLOANE STREET
Pavilion Road
Hans St
Hans Place
Pavilion Road
Cadogan
Square
Cadogan Gardens
Symons St
Cadogan Gdns
Clifford Gdns
Cheltenham Terr
Blackland Terr
Lincoln St
KING'S ROAD
Knightsbridge
Mr Chow
Osteria D' Isola
The Capital
Basil St Hotel
Basil St
Le Metro
Knightsbridge
Raphael St
Harrods
Hans Cres
Basil St
Hans Pl
Hans Rd
Watton Pl
Clabon Mews
Lennox
Gardens
Lennox Gardens Mews
Ovington Street
Moore St
Halsey St
Milner Street
Rawlings St
Draycott Terr
Draycott Place
Rosemoor St
Whitehead's Grove
Elystan Place
Bray Place
Red River
El Blason
Sprimont Pl
Creelers
Harrods Ice-Cream Parlour & Crêperie
Harrods Famous Deli Counter
Gloriette Patisserie
Brompton Pl
Brompton Gdns
San Lorenzo
Floriana
Patara
BEAUCHAMP PL
Caraffini
O Fado
Borshtch 'N' Tears
Hasker Street
Ovington Gdns
First Street
Mossop Street
Denyer Street
Sloane Avenue
Makin St
Ixworth St
Trevor Sq
Montpelier St
Trevor Place
Montpelier Terrace
Montpelier Place
Montpelier Walk
Cheval Place
Rutland St
Emporio Armani Caffe
BROMPTON
Yeoman's Row
Monza
Veg Veg
Egerton Terrace
Walton Street
Brompton Bay
Donne Pl
Ives St
Isul
Daphne's
Pelham Place
Petyward
Elystan Street
Lucan Place
Poissonnerie de L'Avenue
The Crescent
Bibendum
Marlborough St
Cale Street
KNIGHTSBRIDGE ROAD
Rutland Gate
Ennismore Mews
Ennismore Gardens
Ennismore Gardens
Brompton Square
Egerton Gardens
Brasserie St Quentin
Egerton Gdns
Egerton Crescent
BROMPTON ROAD
Alexander Sq
The Oratory
The Collection
South Terrace
La Brasserie
Pelham Street
Bibendum Oyster Bar
Pelham Crescent
Pond Pl
Bury Wk
SYDNEY STREET
KENSINGTON
ROAD
Princes Gardens
Gnietsko Polskie
Goethe Institute
Victoria & Albert Museum
Thurloe Square
THURLOE PLACE
South Kensington
South Terrace
SYDNEY PLACE
ONSLOW SQ
SYDNEY PLACE
Stewart's Grove
FULHAM ROAD
Exhibition Road
Royal College of Music
Science Museum
Exhibition Road
The New Restaurant at the V. & A.
EXHIBITION RD
THURLOE ST
Daquise
Melton Ct
Francofill
Onslow Square
Sydney Close
Sydney Place
Foulis Terrace
Cactus Blue
Exhibition Road
Exhibiting
CROMWELL PLACE
THURLOE PLACE
Glendower Place
Sumner Place
Neville St
KENSINGTON GORE
Royal Albert Hall
Albert Court
Prince Consort Road
Imperial College Road
Natural History Museum
Cromwell Mews
Bute St
Bangkok
OLD BROMPTON ROAD
Cranley Place
Onslow Gardens
Selwood Terrace
Selwood Gardens
190 Queensgate
Downstairs at 190
Jay Mews
Callendar Rd
Imperial College of Science and Technology
CROMWELL ROAD
Queensbury Place
Reece Mews
Harrington Road
Hilaire
Manson Place
Onslow Gdns
Queen's Gate
Stanhope Mews East
Manson Mews
Cranley Gardens

200 yds
200 m
© Copyright Time Out Group 2000

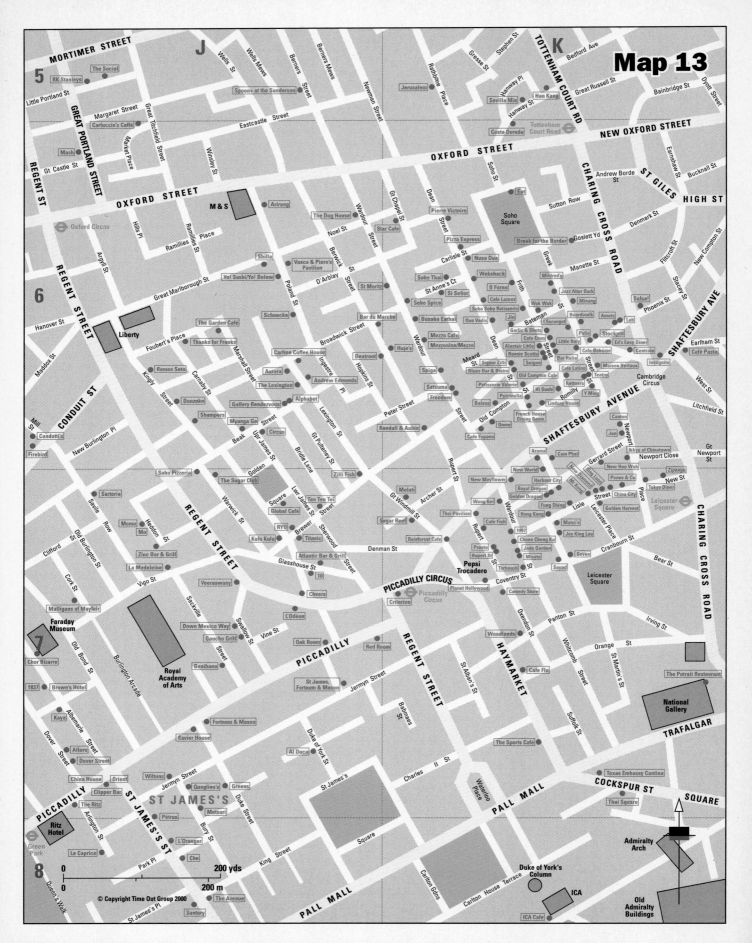

Map 13 & 14

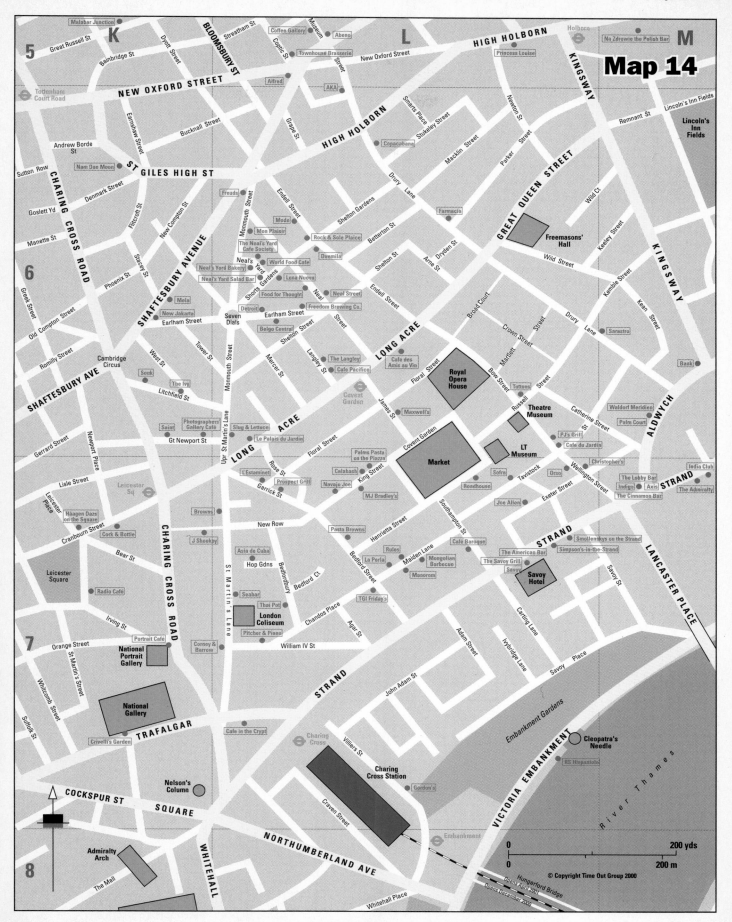

Map 14

5

K L M

Malabar Junction

Great Russell St

Bainbridge St

Streatham St

Coffee Gallery

Museum

Abeno

Townhouse Brasserie

New Oxford Street

Na Zdrowie the Polish Bar

Holborn

HIGH HOLBORN

Princess Louise

KINGSWAY

Lincoln's Inn Fields

Remnant St

Lincoln's Inn Fields

Dyott Street

BLOOMSBURY ST

NEW OXFORD STREET

Coptic St

Alfred

AKA

Grape St

HIGH HOLBORN

Smarts Place

Stukeley Street

Macklin Street

Newton St

Parker Street

Tottenham Court Road

Bucknall Street

Andrew Borde St

Earnshaw Street

Copacabana

Drury Lane

Farmacía

GREAT QUEEN STREET

Freemasons' Hall

Wild Ct

Keeley Street

Kemble Street

Kean Street

KINGSWAY

ALDWYCH

Nam Dae Moon

ST GILES HIGH ST

Sutton Row

Denmark Street

Fitzroft St

New Compton St

Freuds

Mercer Monmouth Street

Endell Street

Shelton Gardens

Betterton St

Dryden St

Arne St

Wild Street

Broad Court

Crown Street

Bow Street

Drury Lane

Sarestro

Bank

CHARING CROSS ROAD

Goslett Yd

Manette St

Stacey St

Mela

New Jakarta

Modo

Mon Plaisir

The Neal's Yard Cafe Society

Rock & Sole Plaice

Duemila

World Food Cafe

Neal's Yard

Neal's Yard Bakery

Luna Nuova

Neal's Yard Salad Bar

Shorts Gardens

Food for Thought

Neal Street

Freedom Brewing Co.

Shelton St

Endell Street

LONG ACRE

Royal Opera House

Marklett

Russell St

Tuttons

Theatre Museum

Catherine Street

PJ's Grill

Cafe du Jardin

Waldorf Meridien

Palm Court

6

Greek Street

Old Compton Street

Phoenix St

SHAFTESBURY AVENUE

Earlham Street

Detroit

Earlham Street

Belgo Central

Shelton Street

Neal Street

Langley St

The Langley

Cafe Pacifico

Cafe des Amis au Vin

Floral Street

James St

Maxwell's

Covent Garden

Christopher's

India Club

Romilly Street

Cambridge Circus

West St

Tower St

Monmouth Street

Mercer St

SHAFTESBURY AVE

Souk

The Ivy

Litchfield St

Seven Dials

LONG ACRE

Floral Street

Palms Pasta on the Piazza

Calabash

King Street

Market

Covent Garden

LT Museum

Sofra

Orso

Tavistock

Wellington Street

Exeter Street

The Lobby Bar

Indigo

Axis

The Cinnamon Bar

STRAND

The Admiralty

Gerrard Street

Newport Place

Lisle Street

Leicester Sq

Saint

Photographers' Gallery Café

Gt Newport St

Upr St Martin's Lane

Slug & Lettuce

Le Palais du Jardin

Rose St

L'Estaminet

Prospect Grill

Navajo Joe

MJ Bradley's

Roadhouse

Joe Allen

Smollenskys on the Strand

Simpson's-in-the-Strand

LANCASTER PLACE

Leicester Place

Häagen Dazs on the Square

Cranbourn Street

Browns

New Row

Garrick St

Pasta Browns

Henrietta Street

Rules

Maiden Lane

Café Baroque

STRAND

The American Bar

Savoy

The Savoy Grill

Savoy Hotel

Savoy St

Leicester Square

Radio Café

Bear St

CHARING CROSS ROAD

J Sheekey

Asia de Cuba

Hop Gdns

St Martin's Lane

Bedfordbury

Bedford St

La Perla

Mongolian Barbecue

Manorom

Carting Lane

Ivybridge Lane

Savoy Place

Cork & Bottle

Irving St

Seabar

Thai Pot

London Coliseum

Pitcher & Piano

Chandos Place

Agar St

TGI Friday's

Chandos Place

7

Orange Street

St Martin's Street

Portrait Café

National Portrait Gallery

Corney & Barrow

William IV St

William IV St

John Adam St

Adam Street

Whitcomb Street

National Gallery

Crivelli's Garden

TRAFALGAR

Cafe in the Crypt

Charing Cross

Villiers St

STRAND

Embankment Gardens

Cleopatra's Needle

RS Hispaniola

Suffolk St

Nelson's Column

Charing Cross Station

Gordon's

VICTORIA EMBANKMENT

River Thames

COCKSPUR ST

SQUARE

WHITEHALL

Craven Street

Embankment

0   200 yds

0   200 m

8

Admiralty Arch

The Mall

NORTHUMBERLAND AVE

Whitehall Place

Hungerford Bridge

Opens December 2000

Opens April 2001

© Copyright Time Out Group 2000

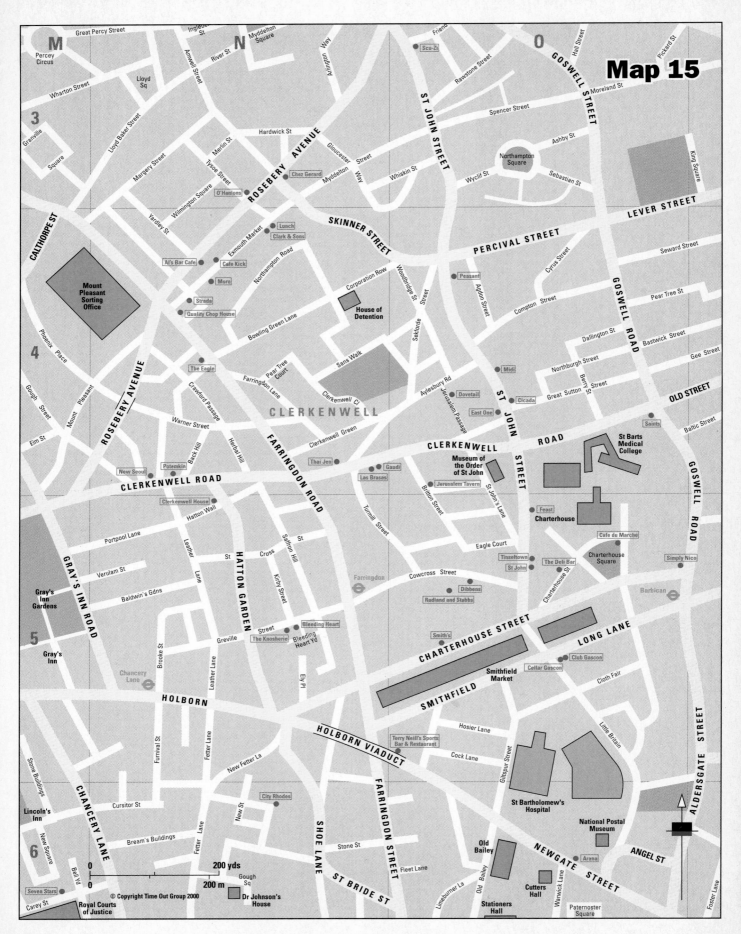

Map 15 & 16/17

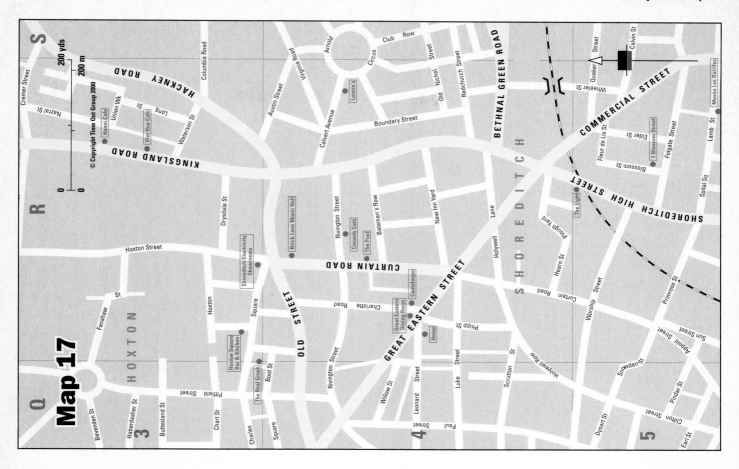

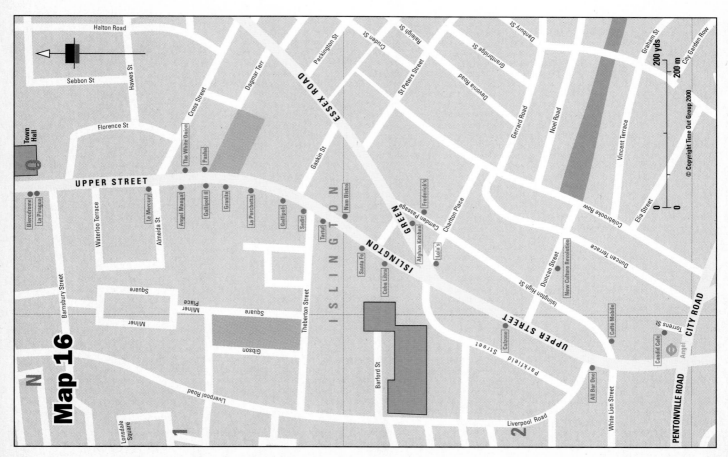

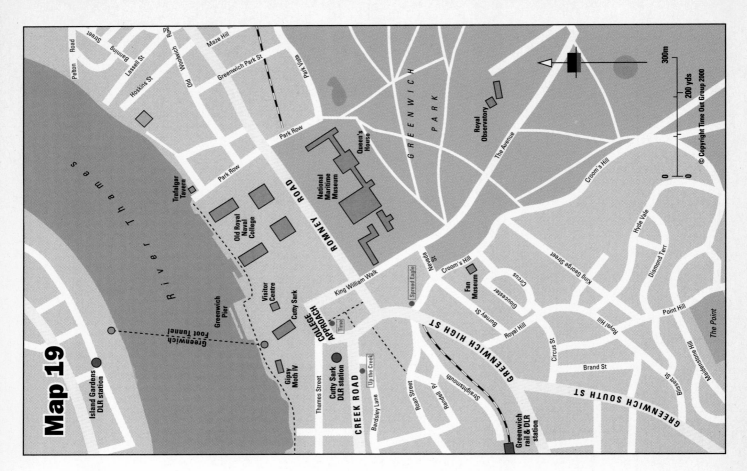

Map 19

Island Gardens
DLR station

River Thames

Greenwich Foot Tunnel

Greenwich Pier

Visitor Centre

Cutty Sark

Gipsy Moth IV

Trafalgar Tavern

Park Row

Old Royal Naval College

Maze Hill

Greenwich Park St

Pelton Road

Banning Street

Lassell St.

Hoskins St

Old Woolwich

Park Row

Park Vista

ROMNEY ROAD

National Maritime Museum

Queen's House

GREENWICH PARK

Royal Observatory

The Avenue

Croom's Hill

Hyde Vale

Diamond Terr

King George Street

Nevada St

Croom's Hill

Fan Museum

Croom's Hill

Gloucester Circus

Burney St

Royal Hill

Circus St

Point Hill

Royal Hill

Brand St

Maidenstone Hill

Blissett St

The Point

GREENWICH SOUTH ST

King William Walk

Spread Eagle

Time

COLLEGE APPROACH

Thames Street

Cutty Sark DLR station

Up the Creek

CREEK ROAD

Bardsley Lane

Roan Street

Randell Pl

Straightsmouth

GREENWICH HIGH ST

Greenwich rail & DLR station

300m

200 yds

© Copyright Time Out Group 2000

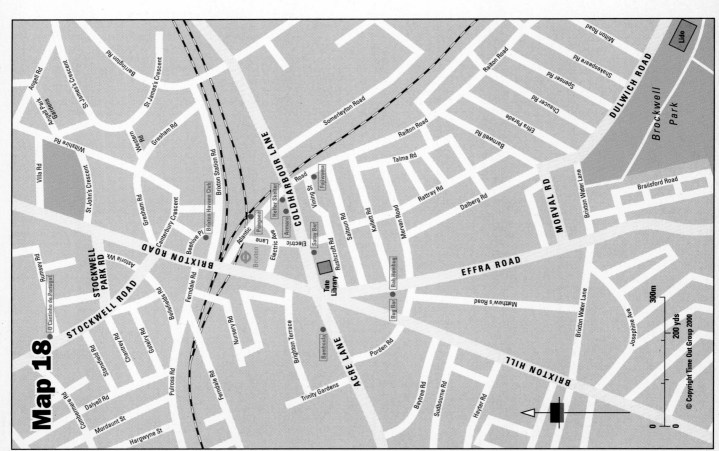

Map 18

Cantinho de Portugal

Rumsey Rd

Villa Rd

Aingell Rd

Angell Park Gardens

St James's Crescent

St James's Crescent

Barrington Rd

Wiltshire Rd

Western Rd

Gresham Rd

St John's Crescent

Gresham Rd

Canterbury Crescent

Combermere Rd

Dalyell Rd

Stansfield Rd

Chantrey Rd

Gateley Rd

Bellefields Rd

Pulross Rd

Astoria Wk

STOCKWELL PARK RD

STOCKWELL ROAD

Mordaunt St

Hargwyne St

Fernlale Rd

Nursery Rd

Brighton Terrace

Trinity Gardens

ACRE LANE

Porden Rd

Bamboula

Brighton Pl

Beehive Pl

Brixton Havana Club

Brixton Station Rd

BRIXTON ROAD

Brixton

Atlantic

Pangaea

Helter Skelter

Asmara

Lane

Electric Ave

Electric

COLDHARBOUR LANE

Vining St

Fujiyama

Road

Satay Bar

Rushcroft Rd

Saltoun Rd

Kellett Rd

Tate Library

Bug Bar

Bah Humbug

EFFRA ROAD

Matthew's Road

Somerleyton Road

Railton Road

Talma Rd

Mervan Road

Rattray Rd

Dalberg Rd

Railton Road

Barnwell Rd

Effra Parade

Chaucer Rd

Spenser Rd

Shakespeare Rd

Railton Road

Milton Road

Lido

DULWICH ROAD

MORVAL RD

Brixton Water Lane

Brixton Water Lane

Brixton Water Lane

Josephine Ave

BRIXTON HILL

Baytree Rd

Sudbourne Rd

Harter Rd

Brockwell Park

Brailsford Road

300m

200 yds

© Copyright Time Out Group 2000

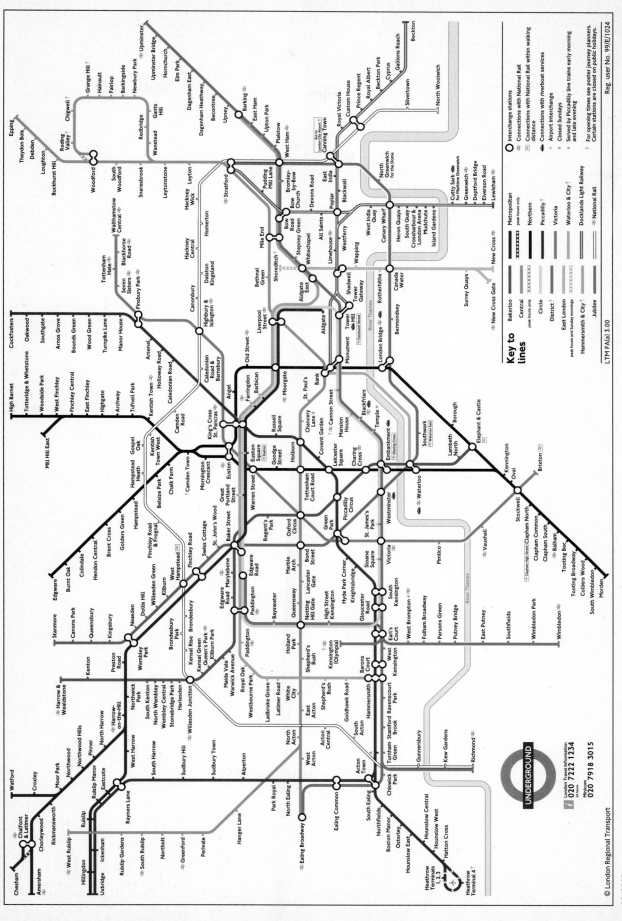

Street Index

See page 265 for an overview of the maps and grid references

a

Abbey Gardens - C2/D2
Abbey Orchard Street - K9
Abbey Road - D2
Abbey Street - R10/S10
Abbotsbury Road - Az8
Abchurch Lane - Q7
Abercorn Close - C2/D2
Abercorn Place - C2/D2
Aberdeen Place - D4
Abingdon Road - A9/B10
Abingdon Street - L9
Abingdon Villas - A9/B9
Acacia Road - D2/E2
Acre Lane - Map 18
Acton Mews - R1
Acton Street - M3
Adam & Eve Mews - B9
Adam Street - L7
Adam's Row - G7
Addington Square - P13
Addison Road - Az8
Adelaide Road - Map 10
Adpar Street - D4
Agar Grove - Map 10
Agar Street - L7
Agdon Street - O4
Aisgill Avenue - A11/12
Albany Road -
   P13/Q12/13/R12
Albany Street - H2/3
Albemarle Street - H7/J7
Albert Bridge - E12/13
Albert Bridge Road - E13
Albert Court - D9
Albert Embankment -
   L10/11
Albert Road - A2
Albert Street - J2
Alberta Street - O11/12
Albion Close - E6
Albion Drive - S1
Albion Square - S1
Albion Street - E6
Aldbridge Street - Q12/R12
Aldenham Street - K2
Alder Square - P6
Alder Street - S6
Aldermanb'y - P6
Alderney Street - H11
Aldersgate Street -
   O6/P5/6
Aldford Street - G7
Aldgate - R6
Aldridge Road Villas - A5
Aldwych - M6
Alexander Square - E10
Alexander Street - B5
Alfred Place - K5
Alfred Road - B4
Alice Street - Q10
Alie Street - S6
All Saint's Road - Az5
All Saints Street - M2
Allen Street - B9/10
Allington Street - H10
Alma Grove - S11
Alma Square - D2/3
Almeide Street - O1
Almorah Road - Q1

Alsace Road - Q12
Alscot Road - R10/S10
Amberley Road - B4
Ambrosden Avenue - J10
Amelia Street - O11
Ampton Street - M3
Amwell Street - N3
Andover Place - B2
Andrew Borde Street - K6
Angel Street - O6
Angell Park Gardens -
   Map 18
Angell Road - Map 18
Anhalt Road - E13
Ann Lane - D13
Ansdell Street - B9
Anselm Road - A12
Appleby Street - S2
Appold Street - Q5/R5
Aquinas S - N8
Archer Street - K7
Argyle Square - L3
Argyle Street - L3
Argyll Road - A9/3 A9/B9
Arlington Avenue - P2
Arlington Road - J2
Arlington Road - Map 10
Arlington Street - J8
Armstong Road - A12
Arne Street - L6
Arnold Circus - R4/S4
Artesian Road - A6
Arthur Street - Q7
Artillery Lane - R5
Artington Way - N3
Arundel Gardens - Az6
Arundel Street - M6/7
Aryll Street - J6
Ashbridge Street - E4
Ashburn Gardens - C10
Ashburn Place - C10
Ashburnham Road - C13/4
   D13
Ashby Street - O3
Ashmill Street - E4
Ashmole Place - M13
Ashmole Street - M13
Ashmore Road - A2/3
Ashwood Mews - C10
Ashworth Road -C3
Astell Street - E11
Astoria Walk - Map 18
Atlantic Road - Map 18
Atterbury Street - K11
Aubrey Road - A7/8
Aubrey Walk - A7/8
Auckland Street - L12
Augustus Street - J2/3
Austin Friars - Q6
Aveline Street - M11/12
Avery Row - H6
Aybrook Street - G5
Ayers Street - P8/9
Aylesbury Road - O4
Aylesbury Road - Q12
Aylesford Street - K11/12

Babmaes Street - K7
Baches Street - Q3

Back Church Lane - S6/7
Back Hill - N4
Bacon Street - S4
Bagshot Street - Q12/R12
Bainbridge Street - K5
Baker Street - G4/5
Balaclava Road - S11
Balcombe Street - F4
Balderton Street - G6
Baldwin Terrace - P2
Baldwin's Gardens - N5
Balfe Street - L2
Balfour Street - P11
Balmes Road - Q1
Baltic Street - P4
Bankside - P7
Banner Street - P4
Banning Street - Map 19
Barclay Close - A13
Barclay Road - A13
Bardsley Lane - Map 19
Barford Street - N2
Baring Street - Q1/2
Bark Place - B6/7
Barker Drive - Map 10
Barkston Gardens - B11
Barnabas Street - G11
Barnby Street - J3
Barnham Street - Q9
Barnsbury Road - N1/2
Barnsbury Street - N1/O1
Barnsdale Road - A3/4
Barnwell Road - Map 18
Baron Street - N2
Barons Place - N9
Barrington Road - Map 18
Barter Street - L5
Bartholomew Road -
   Map 10
Bartholomew Square - P4
Basil Street - F9
Basing Street - Az5
Basinghall Avenue - P6
Basinghall Street - P6
Basire Street - P1
Bastwick Street - O4/P4
Bateman Street - K6
Bateman's Row - R4
Bath Street - P3/4
Bath Terrace - P10
Bathurst Mews - D6
Bathurst Street - D6
Battersea Bridge - E13
Battersea Bridge Road -
   E13
Battersea Church Road -
   E13
Battersea Park Road -
   H13/J13
Battle Bridge Lane - Q8
Battle Bridge Road - L2
Bayham Street - Map 10
Bayley Street - K5
Baylis Road- N9
Baynes Street - Map 10
Bayswater Road - B7/C7/
   2 E6/F6
Baytree Road - Map 18
Beaconsfield Road - Q12
Beak Street - J6
Bear Gardens - P7/8

Bear Lane - O8
Bear Street - K7
Beauchamp Place - F9/10
Beaufort Street - D12
Beaumont Mews - G5
Beaumont Place - J4
Beaumont Street - G5
Beckway Street - Q11
Bedford Avenue - K5
Bedford Court - L7
Bedford Gardens - A8/B8
Bedford Place - L5
Bedford Row - M5
Bedford Square - K5
Bedford Street - L7
Bedford Way - K4
Bedfordbury - L7
Beech Street - P5
Beehive Place - Map 18
Beeston Place - H9
Belgrave Mews North - G9
Belgrave Mews South - G9
Belgrave Place - G10
Belgrave Road - H10/J11
Belgrave Square - G9
Belgrave Street - L3
Bell Lane - R6
Bell Street - E4/5
Bell Yard - M6
Bellefields Road - Map 18
Belvedere Road - M8/9
Bentinck Street - H5
Berkeley Square - H7
Berkeley Street - H7
Bermondsey Street -
   Q8/9/10
Bermondsey Wall West - S9
Bernard Street - L4
Berners Mews - J5
Berners Street - J5/6
Berry Street - O4
Berwick Street - J6/6 K6
Bessborough Place -
   K11/12
Bessborough Street - K11
Bethnal Green Road -
   R4/S4
Bethwin Road - O13
Betterton Street - L6
Bevenden Street - Q3
Bevington Road - Az5
Bevis Marks - R6
Bianca Road - S13
Bickenhall Street - F5
Bidborough Street - L3
Biddulph Road - B3/C3
Billiter Street - R6/7
Bina Gardens - C11
Bingham Place - G4
Binney Street - G6
Birchin Lane - Q6
Birdcage Walk - K9
Birkenhead Street - L3
Bishops Bridge Road -
   C5/D5
Bishops Road - A13
Bishopsgate - Q6/R5/6
Black Prince Street -
   L11/M11
Blackfriars Bridge - O7
Blackfriars Lane - O6
Blackfriars Road - N8/9/O8
Blackland Terrace - F11
Blandford Square - F4
Blandford Street - G5
Blantyre Street - D13
Bleeding Heart Yd - N5
Blenheim Crescent - Az6
Blenheim Terrace - C2
Bletchley Street - P3
Blissett Street - Map 19
Blithfield Street - B10
Blkbrne's Mews - G7

Blomfield Road - C4/D4
Blomfield Street - Q5/6
Blomfield Villas - C5
Bloomfield Terrace - G11
Bloomsbury Square - L5
Bloomsbury Street - K5
Bloomsbury Way - L5
Blossom Street - R5
Blue Anchor Yard - S7
Bolney Street - L13
Bolsover Street - H4/J5
Bolton Gardens - B11/C11
Bolton Street - H7/8
Bondway - L12
Bonhill Street - Q4
Bonnington Square - L12
Bonny Street - Map 10
Borough High Street - P8/9
Borough Road - O9
Boscobel Street - E4
Boston Place - F4
Boswell Street - L5
Boundary Street - R4
Bourchier Street - K6
Bourdon Street - H7
Bourne Street - G11
Bourne Terrace - B5/C5
Bouverie Street - N6
Bow Lane - P6
Bow Street - L6
Bowling Green Lane - N4
Bowling Green Street -
   M12/N12
Boyson Road - P13
Brad Street - N8
Bradiston Road - A2
Braes Street - O1
Braganza Street - N12/O12
Braham Street - S6
Brailsford Road - Map 18
Bramber Road - A12
Bramerton Street - E12
Bramham Gdns - B11
Brand Street - Map 19
Brandon Street - P11
Bray Place -F11
Bread Street - P6
Bream's Building- N6
Brendon Street - F5
Bressenden Place - H9/J10
Brewer Street - J7/K7
Brick Lane - S4-6
Brick Street - H8
Bride Lane - N6
Bridewell Place - N6
Bridge Place - H11
Bridge Street - L9
Bridgeway Street - K2
Bridle Lane - 6/7
Bridstow Place - B5
Brighton Terrace - Map 18
Brill Place - K2
Bristol Gardens - C4
Britannia Road - B13
Britannia Row - P1
Britannia Street - M3
Britten Street - E11
Britton Street - O4/5
Brixton Hill - Map 18
Brixton Road - M13/N13
Brixton Road - Map 18
Brixton Station Road -
   Map 18
Brixton Water Lane -
   Map 18
Broad Street - E4
Broad Walk - H2/3
Broadley Street - E4
Broadstone Place - G5
Broadway - K9
Broadwell - N7/8
Broadwick Street - J6
Brompton Gardens - F9

Brompton Park Crescent -
   B12
Brompton Place - F9
Brompton Road - E9/10/F9
Brompton Square - E9
Bronti Place - P12
Brook Drive - N10
Brook Mews North - D6
Brook Street W1- H6/7
Brook Street W2- E6
Brooke Street - N5
Brook's Mews - H6
Brown Hart Gardens - G6
Brown Street - F5
Browning Street - P11
Brownlow Mews - M4
Brownlow Road - S1
Brownlow Street - M5
Brunswick Gardens - B7/8
Brunswick Place - Q3/4
Brunswick Square - L4
Brushfield Street - R5
Bruton Lane - H7
Bruton Place - H7
Bruton Street - H7
Bryanston Mews E - F5
Bryanston Place - F5
Bryanston Square - F5
Bryanston Street - F6
Buck Street - Map 10
Buckingham Gate - H9/J9
Buckingham Palace Road -
   H10/11
Buckland Street - Q2
Bucknall Street - K6/L6
Bulinga Street - K11
Bulmer Place - A7
Bunhill Row - P4/Q4
Burbage Close - P10
Burdett Street - N9
Burgh Street - O2
Burlington Arcade - J7
Burnaby Street - C13
Burney Street - Map 19
Burnsall Street - E11
Burnthwaite Road - A13
Burrell Street - O8
Burton Street - K3/4
Burwood Place - E5
Bury Place - L5
Bury Street EC3- R6
Bury Street SW1- J7/8
Bury Walk - E11
Bute Street - D10
Buttesland Street - Q3
Buxton Street - S5
Byward Street - Q7/R7
Bywater Street - F11

Cabbell Street - E5
Cadell Close - S3
Cadogan Gardens - F10/11
Cadogan Lane - G10
Cadogan Place - G10
Cadogan Square - F10
Cadogan Street - F10/11
Cale Street - E11
Caledonia Street - L2
Caledonian Road - L2/M2
Callendar Road - D9
Callow Street - D12
Calmington Road - R12
Calshot Street - M2
Calthorpe Street - M4
Calvert Avenue - R4
Calvin Street - R5/S5
Camberwell New Road -
   M13/N13
Camberwell Road - P13
Cambria Road - C13
Cambridge Circus - K6

Eagle Court - O4/5
Eagle Street - M5
Eagle Wharf Road - P2/Q2
Eardley Crescent - B11
Earl Street - Q5
Earlham Street - K6/L6
Earl's Court Gardens - B10
Earl's Court Road - A9/10/B10/11
Earl's Court Square - B11
Earls Walk - E10
Earnshaw Street - K6
East Heath Road - Map 9
East Lane - S9
East Road - Q3
East Smithfield - S7
East Street - P11/12/Q11
Eastbourne Mews - D5/6
Eastbourne Terrace - D5/6
Eastcastle Street - J5/6
Eastcheap - Q7
Eaton Mews - H10
Eaton Place - G9/10
Eaton Square - G10/H10
Eaton Terrace - G10/12
Ebbisham Drive - L12/13
Ebury Bridge - H11
Ebury Bridge Road - G11/12
Ebury Mews - H10
Ebury Square - G11
Ebury Street - G10/11H10
Ecclesbourne Road - P1
Eccleston Mews - G9
Eccleston Place - H10
Eccleston Square - H11
Eccleston Street - G10/H10
Edbrooke Road - A4/B4
Edge Street - A7
Edgware Road - D4/E4/5
Edith Grove - C12/13
Edith Terrace - C13
Edward Mews - G6
Edwardes Square - A9/10
Effie Road - A13/B13
Effra Parade - Map 18
Effra Road - Map 18
Egerton Crescent - E10
Egerton Gardens - E10
Egerton Terrace - E10
Elcho Street - E13
Elder Street - R5
Eldon Road - C9
Eldon Street - Q5
Electric Avenue - Map 18
Electric Lane - Map 18
Elephant Road - O10/11
Elgin Avenue - A4/B3/4/C2
Elgin Crescent - Az6
Elia Street - O2
Elias Place - M13
Elizabeth Avenue - P1/10 Q1
Elizabeth Bridge - H11
Elizabeth Street - G10/H10
Elkstone Road - A4
Elliot's Row - O10
Elm Park Gardens - D11/12
Elm Park Lane - D12
Elm Park Road - D12
Elm Place - D11
Elm Street - M4
Elm Tree Road - D2/3
Elms Mews - D6
Elsted Street - Q11
Elvaston Place - C9/D9
Elverton Street - K10
Ely Place - N5
Elystan Place - F11

Elystan Street - E11
Emerald Street - M5
Emerson Street - O8
Emperor's Gate - C10
Endell Street - L6
Endsleigh Gardens - K3/4
Endsleigh Street - K4
Enford Street - F5
Enid Street - S10
Ennismore Gardens - E9
Ennismore Mews - E9
Ensign Street - S7
Epirus Road - A13
Epworth Street - Q4
Erasmus Street - K11
Errol Street - P4
Essendine Road - B3
Essex Road - O1/P1
Essex Street - M6
Essex Villas - A9
Eustace Road - A13
Euston Road - J4/K3/L3/4
Euston Street - J3
Evelyn Gardens - D11
Eversholtstreet - J2/6 K3
Ewer Street - O8
Exeter Street - L7
Exhibition Road - D9/10
Exmouth Market - N4
Exton Street - N8

Fabian Road - A13
Falkirk Street - R3
Falmouth Road - P10
Fann Street - P5
Fanshaw Street - R3
Farm Lane - A13/B13
Farm Street - H7
Farnham Royal - M12
Farringdon Lane - N4
Farringdon Road - N4/5
Farringdon Street- N6/O6
Fashion Street - S5
Faurice Street -N12
Fawcett Street - C12
Featherstone Street - Q4
Fenchurch Avenue - R7
Fenchurch Street - Q7/R7
Fendall Street - R10
Fenelon Place - A10
Fentiman Road - L13/M13
Ferdinand Place - Map 10
Ferdinand Street - Map 10
Ferndale Road - Map 18
Fernhead Road - A2-4
Fernshaw Road - C12/13
Fetter Lane - N6
Fielding Street - P12
Finborough Road - B12/C12
Finsbury Circus - Q5
Finsbury Pavement - Q5
Finsbury Square - Q5
First Street - E10
Fisher Street - L5
Fisherton Street - D4/E4
Fitzalan Street - M10
Fitzhardinge Street - G6
Fitzroy Road - Map 10
Fitzroy Square - J4
Fitzroy Street - J4
Flask Walk - Map 9
Flaxman Terrace - K3
Fleet Lane - O6
Fleet Street- N6
Fleming Road - O12
Fleur de Lis Street - R5
Flint Street - Q11
Flitcroft Street - K6

Flood Street - E12/F12
Flood Walk - E12
Floral Street - L6
Florence Street - O1
Foley Street - J5
Folgate Street - R5
Fordingley Road - A3
Fore Street - P5
Formosa Street - C4
Forset Street - F5/6
Fort Road - S11
Fortune Street - P4
Foster Lane - P6
Foubert's Place - J6
Foulis Terrace - D11
Fount Street - K13
Fournier Street - S5
Foxley Road - N13
Frampton Street - D4/E4
Francis Street - J10
Franklin's Row - F11
Frazier Street - N9
Frederick Street - M3
Freemantle Street - Q11
Friend Street - O3
Frith Street - K6
Frome Street - P2
Fulham Broadway - A13/B13
Fulham Road - A13/B13/C12/13/D11/12/E11
Furnival Street - N5

Gainsford Street - R9/S9
Galway Street - P3/4
Gambia Street - O8
Garden Row - O10
Garlichythe - P7
Garrick Street - L7
Garway Road - B6
Gaskin Street - O1
Gate Place - D10
Gate Street - F12
Gatelry Road - Map 18
Gatliffe Road - G11/H12
Gaunt Street - O10
Gayton Road - Map 9
Gee Street - O4/P4
Geffrye Street - R2
Geogiana Street - Map 10
George Street - F5/6/G5
Georgre Row - S9
Gerald Road - G10
Gerrard Road - O2
Gerrard Street - K6/7
Gerridge Street - N9
Gertrude Street - D12
Gibson Road - M11
Gidson Square - N1
Gilbert Place - L5
Gilbert Street - H6
Gilbeys Yard - Map 10
Gillingham Street - H10/J10
Gilston Road - C12
Giltspur Street - O5
Gladstone Street - N10/O10
Glasshill Street - O9
Glasshouse Street - J7
Glasshouse Walk - L11
Glebe Place - E12
Gledhow Gardens - C11
Glendower Place - D10
Glengall Road - S12/13
Glentworth Street - F4
Gloucester Avenue - Map 10
Gloucester Circus - Map 19

Gloucester Crescent - Map 10
Gloucester Gate - H2
Gloucester Mews - D6
Gloucester Place - F5/G5/6
Gloucester Place Mews - F5
Gloucester Road - C9/10
Gloucester Square - E6
Gloucester Street - J11
Gloucester Terrace - C5/D6
Gloucester Walk - B8
Gloucester Way - N3
Godfrey Street - E11
Goding Street - L11/12
Godliman Street - O6
Golborne Road - Az4/5
Golden Lane - P4/5
Golden Square - J7
Goldington Crescent - K2
Goldington Street - K2
Goldney Road - A4/B4
Goodge Place - J5
Goodge Street - J5/6 K6
Goodman's Yard - R7/S7
Goods Way - L2
Gordon Place - B8
Gordon Square - K4
Gordon Street - K4
Gore Street - D9
Gosfield Street - J5
Goslett Yard - K6
Gosset Street - S3
Goswell Road - O3-5/P5
Gough Square- N6
Gough Street - M4
Goulston Street - R6/S6
Gower Mews - K5
Gower Place - K4
Gower Street - K4/5
Gower's Walk - S6/7
Gracechurch Street - Q6/7
Grafton Crescent - Map 10
Grafton Mews - J4
Grafton Place - K3
Grafton Street - H7
Grafton Way - J4
Graham Street - O2/P3
Graham Terrace - G11
Granby Street - S4
Granby Terrace - J2
Grange Court - M6
Grange Road - R10
Grange Walk - R10
Grantbridge Street - O2
Grantully Road - B3
Granville Place - G6
Granville Road - B2
Granville Square - M3
Gravel Lane - R6
Gray Street - N9
Gray's Inn Road - L3/M3-5
Great Castle Street - J6
Great Chapel Street - K6
Great College Street - K9/10
Great Cumberland Place - F6
Great Dover Street - P9/10/Q10
Great Eastern Street - Q4/R4
Great George Street - K9
Great Guildford Street - O8
Great James Street - M5
Great Marlborough Street - J6
Great Maze Pond - Q8/9
Great Newport Street - K6
Great Ormond Street - L5/M4
Great Percy Street - M3/N3
Great Peter Street - K10

Great Portland Street - H5/J5
Great Pulteney Street - J6
Great Queen Street - L6
Great Russell Street - K5/L5
Great Smith Street - K9/10
Great Suffolk Street - O8/9
Great Sutton Street - O4
Great Swan Alley - Q6
Great Titchfield Street - J5/6
Great Western Road - A4/5
Great Winchester Street - Q6
Great Windmill Street - K7
Great. Tower Street - Q7/R7
Greek Street - K6
Green Street - G6
Greencoat Place - J10
Greenland Road - Map 10
Greenman Street - P1
Greenwell Street - H4/J4
Greenwich High Street - Map 19
Greenwich Park Street - Map 19
Greenwich South Street - Map 19
Greet Street - N8
Grenville Place - C10
Grenville Street - L4
Gresham Road - Map 18
Gresham Street - P6
Gresse Street - K5
Greville Street - N5
Grey Eagle Street - S5
Greycoat Street - J10/8 K10
Groom Place - G9
Grosvenor Crescent - G9
Grosvenor Gardens - H9/10
Grosvenor Hill - H7
Grosvenor Park - O13
Grosvenor Place - G9/H9
Grosvenor Road - H12/J12/K12
Grosvenor Square - G6/7
Grosvenor Street - H6/7
Grosvenor Terrace - O13/P13
Grove End Road - D2/3
Guildhouse Street - J10/11
Guilford Street - L4/M4
Gun Street - R5
Gunter Grove - C13
Gunthorpe Street - S6
Gutter Lane - P6
Guy Street - Q9
Gwyn Close - C13

Haberdasher Street - Q3
Hackney Road - R3/S3
Hadley Street - Map 10
Haggerston Road - R1/S1
Haines Street - J13
Haldane Road - A12
Half Moon Street - H8
Halford Road - A12
Halkin Place - G9
Halkin Street - G9
Hall Place - D4/5
Hall Road - D3
Hall Street - O3
Hallam Street - H4/5
Halliford Street - P1/Q1
Halsey Street - F10
Halton Road - O1

Hamilton Park Road - O1
Hamilton Place - G8
Hamilton Terrace - C2/D3
Hampstead Green - Map 9
Hampstead High Street - Map 9
Hampstead Road - J3
Hampton Street - O11
Hanbury Street - S5
Handel Street - L4
Handforth Road - M13
Hankey Place - Q9
Hanover Gardens - M13
Hanover Square - H6
Hanover Street - H6/J6
Hans Crescent - F9
Hans Place - F9
Hans Road - F9
Hans Street - F9
Hanson Street - J5
Hanway Place - K5
Hanway Street - K5
Harbet Road - E5
Harcourt Street - F5
Harcourt Terrace - C11/12
Hardwick Street - N3
Harewood Avenue - F4
Hargwyne Street - Map 18
Harley Place - H5
Harley Street - H4/5
Harleyford Rd - L12/M12
Harleyford Street - M13
Harmood Street - Map 10
Harmsworth Street - N12
Harper Street - P10
Harpur Street - M5
Harriet Walk - F9
Harrington Gardens - C10
Harrington Road - D10
Harrington Square - J2
Harrington Street - J2/3
Harrison Street - L3
Harrow Place - R6
Harrow Road - A4/B4/5
Harrowby Street - F5
Hartismere Road - A13
Hartland Road - Map 10
Harwood Road - B13
Hasker Street - F10
Hastings Street - L3
Hatfields - N8
Hatherley - B5/6
Hatherley Street - H10
Hatton Garden - N5
Hatton Street - D4/E4
Hatton Wall - N5
Haverstock Hill - Map 10
Hawes Street - O1
Hawley Crescent - Map 10
Hawley Road - Map 10
Hay Hill - H7
Haydon Street - R7/S7
Hayles Street - O10
Haymarket - K7
Hay's Mews - H7
Hayter Road - Map 18
Headfort Place - G9
Hearn Street - R4
Heath Street - Map 9
Heathcote Street - M4
Heddon Street - J7
Helmet Row - P4
Hemans Street - K13
Hemsworth Street - R2
Henderson Drive - D3
Heneage Street - S5
Henrietta Place - H6
Henrietta Street - L7
Henry Drive - S11
Henshaw Street - P11
Herbal Hill - N4
Herbrand Street - L4
Hercules Road - M9/10

Middleton Road - S1
Midland Road - L2/3
Miles Street - L13
Milford Lane - M6/7
Milford Street - P5
Milk Street - P6
Mill Street SE1 - S9
Mill Street W1 - H6/J6
Millbank - L10/11
Millfield Lane - Map 9
Millman Street - M4
Milman's Street - D12/13
Milner Place - N1/O1
Milner Square - N1/O1
Milner Street - F10
Milton Road - Map 18
Mina Road - R12
Mincing Lane - R7
Minera Mews - G10
Minories - R6/7
Mintern Street - Q2
Mitchell Street - P4
Mitre Road - N9
Molyneux Street - F5
Monck Street - K10
Monmouth Street - L6
Monnow Road - S11
Montagu Mansions - G5
Montagu Mews S - F6
Montagu Place - F5
Montagu Square - F5
Montagu Street - F6
Montague Place - K5
Montague Street - L5
Montford Place - M12
Montpelier Place - E9
Montpelier Street - E9
Montpelier Terrace - E9
Montpelier Walk - E9
Montrose Place - G9
Monument Street - Q7
Moor Lane - P5
Moore Park Road - B13
Moore Street - F10
Moorfields - Q5
Moorgate - Q5/6
Moorhouse Road - A5/6
Mora Street - P3
Mordaunt Street - Map 18
Morecambe Street - P11/12
Moreland Street - O3/P3
Moreton Place - J11
Moreton Road - P1
Moreton Street - J11
Morgan's Lane - Q8
Morley Street - N9
Mornington Crescent - J2
Mornington Place - J2
Mornington SE1 - H2/J2
Mornington Terrace - H2/J2
Morocco Street - Q9
Morpeth Terrace - J10
Morshead Road - B3
Mortimer Road - R1
Mortimer Street - J5
Morval Road - Map 18
Morwell Street - K5
Moscow Road - B6
Mossop Street - E10
Motcomb Street - G9
Mount Pleasant - M4
Mount Row - H7
Mount Street - G7
Moxon Street - G5
Mund Street - A11
Munster Square - H3/4/J3/4
Munton Street - P10/11
Muriel Street - M2
Murray Grove - P3/10 Q3
Murray Street - Map 10

Museum Street - L5/6
Musgrave Crescent - B13
Myddelton Square - N3
Myddelton Street - N3/O3
Mylne Street - N3

 n

Nadding Street - P11
Napier Grove - P2
Nash Street - H3
Nassau Street - J5
Nazral Street - R3
Neal Street - L6
Neal's Yard - L6
Neate Street - Q13/R13
Nebraska Street - P9
Neckinger - S10
Nelson Terrace - O3
Nesham Street - S8
Netherton Grove - C12
Netley Street - J3
Nevada Street - Map 19
Nevern Place - A10/B10
Nevern Square - A11
Neville Street - D11
New Bond Street - H6/7
New Bridge Street - O6
New Burlington Place - J6
New Cavendish Street - G5/H5/J5
New Change - O6
New Church Road - P13/Q13
New Compton Street - K6
New End - Map 9
New End Square - Map 9
New Fetter Lane - N5
New Globe Walk - O8/P7
New Inn Yard - R4
New Kent Road - P10/Q10
New North Road - P1/10 Q2/3
New North Street - L5
New Oxford Street - K6/L5
New Row - L7
New Square - M6
New Street - K7
New Street- N5/6
New Wharf Road - M2
Newburn Street - M11
Newcastle Place - E5
Newcomen Street - P9/Q9
Newgate Street - O6
Newington Causeway - O9/10
Newman Street - J5
Newnham Terrace - M9
Newport Close - K6
Newport Place - K6/7
Newport Street - L11/M10/11
Newton Road - B6
Newton Street - L5/6
Nicholas Lane - Q7
Nile Street - P3/Q3
Nile Terrace - R12
Nine Elms Lane - J13/K12
Noble Street - P5/6
Noel Road - O2
Noel Street - J6
Norfolk Crescent - E5/6
Norfolk Place - E5/6
Norfolk Square - D6/E6
North Audley Street - G6
North Carriage Drive - E6/F6
North End Road - A12/13
North End Way - Map 9
North Gower Street - J3/4
North Mews - M4

North Row - G6
North Wharf Road - D5
Northampton Road - N4
Northampton Square - O3
Northburgh Street - O4
Northchurch Road - Q1/R1
Northdown Street - M2
Northington Street - M4
Northumberland Avenue - L8
Northumberland Place - A5/6
Northwick Terrace - D4
Notting Hill Gate - A7
Nottingham Place - G4
Nottingham Street - G4/5
Nursery Road - Map 18
Nutford Place - F5
Nuttal Street - R2

 o

Oakey Lane - N9/10
Oakington Road - B4
Oakley Gardens - E12
Oakley Place - R12
Oakley Square - J2
Oakley Street - E12
Offley Road - M13
Ogle Street - J5
Old Bailey - O6
Old Barrack Yard - G9
Old Bond Street - J7
Old Broad Street - Q6
Old Brompton Road - C11/D11
Old Burlington Street - J7
Old Castle Street - S6
Old Cavendish Street - H6
Old Church Street - D11/12/E12
Old Compton Street - K6
Old Court Place - B8
Old Gloucester Street - L5
Old Jamaica Road - S10
Old Jewry - P6
Old Kent Road - Q11/R11/12/S/12
Old Marylebone Road - E5/F5
Old Mitre Court- N6
Old Montagu Street - S5/6
Old Nichol Street - R4/S4
Old Paradise Street - M10
Old Park Lane - G8
Old Pye Street - K10
Old Quebec Street - G6
Old Queen Street - K9
Old Street - P4/Q4/R4
Old Woolwich Road - Map 19
Oldbury Place - G4
Ongar Road - A12/B12
Onslow Gardens - D11
Onslow Square - D10/11/E10/11
Opal Street - N11
Orange Street - K7
Orchard Street - G6
Orchardson Street - D4/E4
Ord Street - P11
Orde Hall Street - M5
Orme Court - B7
Orme Lane - B7
Ormonde West Road - F12
Ormonde West Street - F12
Ormsby Street - R2
Orsett Street - M11
Orsett Terrace - C5
Osborn Street - S6
Osnaburgh Street - H4
Ossery Road - S12/13

Ossington Street - B7
Ossulston Street - K3
Otto Street - N13
Outer Circle - G4/H2/3/4
Oval Place - M13
Oval Road - Map 10
Oval Way - M12
Ovington Gardens - E9/10
Ovington Street - F10
Oxendon Street - K7
Oxford Gardens - Az5
Oxford Road - B2
Oxford Square - E6
Oxford Street - G6/J6/K6/H6
Oxley Close - S12

 p

Packington Square - P2
Packington Street - O1/P1
Paddington Green - D5
Paddington Street - G5
Page Street - K10
Page's Walk - R10/Q11
Pakenham Street - M4
Palace Avenue - B8/C8
Palace Court - B7/8
Palace Garden Mews - B7
Palace Gardens Terrace - B7/8
Palace Gate - C9
Palace Street - J9
Palfrey Place - M13
Pall Mall - J8/7 K8
Pancras Road -K2
Panton Street - K7
Paradise Walk - F12
Paris Garden- N8
Park Crescent - H4
Park Crescent Mews E - H4
Park Crescent Mews W - H4
Park Lane - F6/G6-8
Park Place - J8
Park Place Villas - D4
Park Row - Map 19
Park Square East - H4
Park Square Mews - H4
Park Square West - H4
Park Street SE1- P8
Park Street W1 - G7
Park Village East - H2
Park Village West - H2
Park Vista - Map 19
Park Walk - D12
Park West Place - F6
Parker Street - L6
Parkfield Street - N2
Parkgate Road - E13
Parkhouse Street - Q13
Parkway - Map 10
Parliament Hill - Map 9
Parliament Square - K9
Parry Street - L12
Pascal Street - K13
Passmore Street - G11
Pater Street - A9
Paternoster Row - O6
Paternoster Square - O6
Paul Street - Q4
Paultons Square - D12
Paultons Street - E12
Pavilion Road - F9/10
Peabody Avenue - H11/12
Pear Tree Court - N4
Pear Tree Street - O4/P4
Pearman Street - N9
Pearson Street - R2
Pedley Street - S4
Peel Street - A7/8
Pelham Crescent - E10
Pelham Place - E10

Pelham Street - E10
Pelton Road - Map 19
Pembridge Mews - A6
Pembridge Crescent - A6
Pembridge Gardens - A7
Pembridge Place - A6
Pembridge Road - A7
Pembridge Square - A5/B6
Pembridge Villas - A6
Pembroke Gardens - A10
Pembroke Gardens Close - A10
Pembroke Road - A10
Pembroke Villas - A10
Pembroke Walk - A10
Penfold Place - E4/5
Penfold Street - E4
Penn Street - Q2
Pennant Mews - B10
Penrose Street - O12
Penton Place - O11/12
Penton Rise - M3
Penton Street - N2
Pentonville Road - L3/M3/N2
Penywern Road - B11
Pepper Street - O8
Pepys Street - R7
Percey Circus - M3
Percival Street - O4
Percy Street - K5
Peter Street - K6
Petersham Lane - C9
Petersham Place - C9
Peto Place - H4
Petty France - J9
Phelp Street - P12
Phene Street - E12
Philbeach Gardens - A11
Phillimore Gardens - A8/9
Phillimore Place - A9
Phillimore Walk - B9/3 A9
Phillip Street - R2
Philpott Lane - Q7
Phoenix Place - M4
Phoenix Road - K2/3
Phoenix Street - K6
Piccadilly - H8/J7
Piccadilly Circus - K7
Pickard Street - O3
Pickering Mews - C5/6
Pilgrim Street - O6
Pilgrimage Street - P9/Q9
Pilgrim's Lane - Map 9
Pimlico Road - G11
Pimlico Road - G11
Pindar Street - Q5
Pinder Street - Q5/R5
Pitfield Street - Q2-4/R2
Pitt Street - B8
Platt Street - K2
Plough Yard - R4
Plumbers Row - S6
Plympton Street - E4
Pocock Street - O8/9
Point Hill - Map 19
Poland Street - J6
Polygon Road - K2
Pond Place - E11
Ponsonby Place - K11
Pont Street - F10/G10
Ponton Road - K13
Poole Street - Q2
Popham Road - P1
Popham Street - P1
Poplar Place - B6/C6
Porchester Gardens - B6/C6
Porchester Road - C5
Porchester Square - C5
Porchester Terrace - C6/7
Porchester Terrace North - C5

Porden Road - Map 18
Pelton Road - Map 19
Porter Street - G4
Porter Street - P8
Portland Place - H4/5
Portland Road - Az7
Portland Street - P12/Q12
Portman Close - G5
Portman Mews S - G6
Portman Square - G6
Portman Street - G6
Portobello Road - Az4-6/A6
Portpool Lane - N5
Portsoken Street - R7/S7
Portugal Street - M6
Potier Street - Q10
Powis Gardens - A5
Powis Square - A6
Powis Terrace - A5
Pownall Row - S2
Praed Street - D6/E5
Pratt Street - Map 10
Pratt Walk - M10
Prebend Street - P1/2
Prescot Street - S7
Prima Road - M13/N13
Primrose Street - Q5/R5
Prince Consort Road - D9
Prince of Wales Road - Map 10
Princedale Road - Az7
Princelet Street - S5
Princes Gardens - D9/E9
Prince's Square - B6
Princes Street EC2 - P6/Q6
Princes Street W1 - H6
Princess Road - A2/B2
Princess Road - Map 10
Princeton Street - M5
Prior Ess Street - Q10
Priory Green - M2
Priory Walk - C11
Procter Street - M5
Provost Street - Q3
Prowse Place - Map 10
Pudding Lane - Q7
Pulross Road - Map 18
Purbrook Street - R10
Purcell Street - R2
Purchese Street - K2

q

Quaker Street - S5
Queen Anne Mews - H5
Queen Anne Street - H5
Queen Anne's Gate - K9
Queen Elizabeth Street - R9
Queen Square - L4
Queen Street EC4 - P6/7
Queen Street W1 - H7
Queen Victoria Street - O7/P6/7
Queen's Row - P12
Queen's Gardens - C6
Queens Gate - D9/10
Queen's Gate Gardens - C10
Queen's Gate Mews - C9
Queen's Gate Place Mews - D10
Queen's Gate Terrace - C9/D9
Queen's Walk - J8
Queensborough Terrace - C6/7
Queensbridge Road - S1/2
Queensbury Place - D10
Queenstown Road - H13
Queensway - B5/6/C6/7
Quilter Street - S3

288 Eating & Drinking in London

Racton Road - A12
Radley Mews - B10
Radnor Mews - E6
Radnor Place - E6
Radnor Street - P4
Radnor Walk - F11/12
Railton Road - Map 18
Railway Approach - Q8
Railway Street - L2
Raleigh Street - O2
Ramillies Place - J6
Ramillies Street - J6
Rampayne Street - K11
Randall Road - L11
Randall Row - L11
Randell Place - Map 19
Randolph Avenue - C2/3/D4
Randolph Crescent - C3/4
Randolph Gardens - B2
Randolph Road - C4/D4
Randolph Street - Map 10
Ranelagh Grove - G11
Ranston Street - E4
Raphael Street - F9
Rathbone Place - K5
Rathbone Street - J5
Rattray Road - Map 18
Ravenscroft Street - S3
Ravensdon Street - N12
Ravent Road - M10/11
Rawlings Street - F10
Rawstone Street - O3
Raymond Buildings - M5
Red Lion Square - M5
Red Lion Street - M5
Redan Place - B6
Redburn Street - F12
Redchurch Street - R4/S4
Redcliffe Gardens - B11/C12
Redcliffe Mews - C12
Redcliffe Place - C12
Redcliffe Road - C12
Redcliffe Square - B11/C11
Redcliffe Street - C12
Redcross Way - P8/9
Redesdale Street - F12
Redfield Lane - B10
Redhill Street - H2/3
Reece Mews - D10
Reeves Mews - G7
Regan Way - R2/3
Regency Street - K10/11
Regent Square - L3
Regent Street - J6-8/K7
Regents Park Road - Map 10
Remnant Street - M6
Rennie Street - N7
Reverdy Road - S11
Rewell Street - C13
Rheidol Terrace - P2
Richborne Terrace - M13
Richmond Avenue - N1
Richmond Crescent - N1
Richmond Terrace - L8
Ridgmount Gardens - K4/5
Ridgmount Street - K5
Riding House Street - J5
Riley Road - R9/10
Riley Street - D13
Ripplevale Grove - N1
Risbor Street - O8
Rita Road - L13
Ritchie Street - N2
River Street - N3
Rivington Street - R4
Roan Street - Map 19
Robert Adam Street - G5
Robert Dashwood Way - O11

Robert Street - H3/J3
Rochester Place - Map 10
Rochester Road - Map 10
Rochester Row - J10
Rochester Square - Map 10
Rochester Terrace - Map 10
Rockingham Street - O10/P10
Rodmarton Street - G5
Rodney Place - P10/11
Rodney Road - P11/Q11
Rodney Street - M2
Roger Street - M4
Roland Gardens - C11/D11
Roland Way - Q12
Rolls Road - S12
Romilly Street - K6
Romney Road - Map 19
Romney Street - K10
Rood Lane - Q7
Ropemaker Street - Q5
Ropley Street - S3
Rosary Gardens - C11
Rose Street - L7
Rosebury Avenue - N3/4
Rosemoor Street - F10
Rosmead Road - Az6
Rotary Street - O9
Rotherfield Street - P1/Q1
Rothesay Street - Q10
Rotten Row - E8/F8
Roupell Street - N8
Rowcross Street - R12
Royal Avenue - F11
Royal College Street - Map 10
Royal Hill - Map 19
Royal Hospital Road - F11/12/G11
Royal Mint Street - S7
Royal Road - N12/13
Royal Street - M9
Rugby Street - M4
Rumbold Road - B13
Rumsey Road - Map 18
Rupert Street - K6/7
Rushcroft Road - Map 18
Rushworth Street - O9
Russell Square - L4/5
Russell Street - L6/8 L6
Russia Row - P6
Rutherford Street - K10
Rutland Gate - E9
Rutland Street - E9

Sackville Street - J7
Saffron Hill - N5
Sail Street - M10
Salamanca Street - L11
Sale Place - E5
Salem Road - B6
Salisbury Place - F5
Salisbury Street - E4
Saltoun Road - Map 18
Saltram Crescent - A2/3
Salusbury Road - A2
Sancroft Street - M11
Sandland Street - M5
Sandwich Street - L3
Sans Walk - N4
Savile Row - J7
Savona Street - J13
Savoy Place - L7/M7
Savoy Street - M7
Sawyer Street - O8/9
Scala Street - J5
Scarsdale Villas - A10/B9
Sclater Street - S4
Scores Street - O8
Scott Ellis Gardens - D3

Scott Lidgett Crescent - S10
Scriven Street - S1
Scrutton Street - Q4/R4
Seacoal Lane - O6
Seaford Street - L3
Seagrave Road - B12
Searles Close - E13
Searles Road - Q11
Sebastian Street - O3
Sebbon Street - O1
Sedan Way - Q11
Sedlescombe Road - A12
Seething Lane - R7
Sekforde Street - O4
Selwood Terrace - D11
Semley Place - G11/H11
Senior Street - B4
Serle Street - M6
Serpentine Road - E8/F8
Seven Dials - L6
Sevington Street - B4
Seward Street - O4/P4
Seymour Street - F6
Seymour Walk - C12
Shorter Street - R7/S7
Shad Thames - R8/S9
Shaftesbury Street - P2
Shakespeare Road - Map 18
Shalcomb Street - D12
Shand Street - Q9/R8
Sharsted Street -N12
Shawfield Street - E11/F12
Sheffield Terrace - A8/B8
Sheldrake Place - A8
Shelton Street - L6
Shenfield Street - R3
Shepherd Street - H8
Shepherds Market - H8
Shepperton Road - P1/Q1
Sherbourne Street - Q1
Sherwood Street - J7
Shipton Street - S3
Shirland Mews - A3
Shorrolds Road - A13
Shorts Gardens - L6
Shottendone Road - A13
Shouldham Street - F5
Shrewsbury Road - A5
Shroton Street - E4
Shepherdess Walk - P2/3
Shirland Road - A3/B3/4/C4
Shoreditch High Street - R4/5
Seymour Place - F5/6
Shoe Lane- N5/6
Shaftesbury Avenue - K6/7/L6
Shrubland Road - S1
Sicilian Avenue - L5
Siddons Lane - F4
Sidford Place - M10
Sidmouth Street - L3/M3
Silex Street - O9
Silk Street - P5
Skinner Street - N4/O4
Skinners Lane - P7
Slaidburn Street - C12/13
Sleaford Street - J13
Sloane Avenue - E10/F11
Sloane Gardens - G11
Sloane Street - F9/10
Smith Square - K10/L10
Smith Street - F11/12
Smith Terrace - F11/12
Smyrks Road - R12
Snowden Street - R5
Snowsfields - Q9
Soho Square - K6
Soho Street - K6

Somerleyton Road - Map 18
Somers Crescent - E6
Soton Street - S1
South Audley Street - G7
South Carriage Drive - E8/F8/G8
South Crescent - K5
South Eaton Place - G10
South End Road - Map 9
South End Row - B9
South Hill Park - Map 9
South Lambeth Road - L13
South Molton Lane - H6
South Molton Street - H6
South Parade - D11
South Place - Q5
South Street - G7
South Terrace - E10
South Wharf Road - D5/E5
Southampton Row - L5
Southampton Street - L7
Southampton Way - P13/Q13
Southgate Grove - Q1
Southgate Road - Q1
Southwark Bridge - P7
Southwark Bridge Road - P7/8
Southwark Park Road - S11
Southwark Street - O8/P8
Southwick Street - E5/6
Spa Road - R10/S10
Spaniards Road - Map 9
Spencer Street - O3
Spenser Road - Map 18
Spital Square - R5
Spital Street - S5
Sprimont Place - F11
Spring Street - D6
Spur Road - J9
Spurgeon Street - P10
St Agnes Place - N12/13
St Albans Grove - B9/C9
St Alban's Street - K7
St Alphage Gardens - P9
St Andrews Hill - O6
St Andrew's Place - H4
St Ann's Terrace - E2
St Anne's Court - K6
St Anne's Street - K9/10
St Botolph Street - R6
St Bride Street - N6
St Chad's Place - L3/M3
St Chad's Street - L3
St Christopher's Place - H6
St Clement's Lane - M6
St Cross Street - N5
St Dunstens Hill - Q7
St Ervan's Road - Az4
St George Street - H6/7 H6
St George's Circus - N9
St George's Drive - H11/J11
St George's Fields - E6/F6
St George's Road- N10/O10
St George's Square - J11/12
St George's Square - K12
St George's Way - Q13/R13
St Giles High Street - K6
St Helen's Place - R6
St James's Crescent - Map 18
St James's Place - J8
St James's Square - J7/8
St James's Street - J8
St John Street - O3/4/5
St John's Crescent - Map 18
St John's High Street - E2

St John's Wood Road - D3/E3
St John's Wood Terrace - E2
St John's Gardens - Az7
St John's Lane - O4/5
St Katherine's Way - S8
St Leonard's Terrace - F11
St Loo Avenue - E12/F12
St Lukes Road - A5
St Luke's Street - E11
St Mark Street - S7
St Marks Crescent - Map 10
St Mark's Place - Az6
St Marks Road - Az6
St Martin's Lane - L7
St Mary At Hill - Q7
St Mary Axe - R6
St Mary's Square - D5
St Mary's Terrace - D4
St Matthews Row - S4
St Michael's Street - E5
St Oswald's Place - M11/12
St Pancras Way - Map 10
St Paul Street -P1/2
St Paul's Chyd - O6
St Peters Street - O2
St Petersburgh Mews - B6/7
St Petersburgh Place - B6/7
St Swithins Lane - Q6/7
St Thomas Street - Q8/9
St Vincent Street - G5
Stableyard Road - J8
Stacey Street - K6
Stafford Place - J9
Stafford Street - J11
Stafford Terrace - A9
Stag Place - J9
Stamford Street- N8
Stanford Road - B9
Stanford Street - J11
Stanhope Gardens - C10/D10
Stanhope Mews East - D10
Stanhope Mews West - C10
Stanhope Place - F6
Stanhope Street - J3
Stanhope Terrace - E6
Stanley Crescent - Az6
Stanley Gardens - Az6
Stannary Street - N12
Stansfield Road - Map 18
Stanway Street - R2/3
Staple Street - Q9
Star Street - E5
Station Road - M9
Stead Street - P11
Stean Street - R1
Stephen Street - K5
Stephenson Way - J3/4
Steward Street - R5
Stewart's Grove - E11
Stillington Street - J10
Stockwell Park Road - Map 18
Stockwell Road - Map 18
Stone Buildings - M6
Stone Street - N6
Stones End Street - O9
Stoney Lane - R6
Stoney Street - P8
Store Street - K5
Storey's Gate - K9
Stourcliffe Street - F6
Straightsmouth - Map 19
Strand - L7/M6/7
Stratford Place - H6
Stratford Road - B10
Stratford Villas - Map 10
Strathearn Place - E6

Stratton Street - H7/8
Streatham Street - K5/L5
Stuart Road - A3/B3
Stukeley Street - L6
Sturge Street - O9
Sturt Street - P2
Sudbourne Road - Map 18
Suffolk Street - K7
Sumner Place - D10/11
Sumner Street - O8/P8
Sun Street - Q5
Surrey Row - O8/9
Surrey Square - R11/12
Surrey Street - M6/7
Sussex Gardens - E5/6
Sussex Place - E6
Sussex Square - D6/E6
Sussex Street - H11
Sutherland Avenue - B4/C3/4
Sutherland Place - A5/6
Sutherland Square - O12
Sutherland Street - H11
Sutton Row - K6
Swallow Street - J7
Swan Street - P9
Swan Walk - F12
Swanfield Street - S4
Sweeney Court - S10
Swinton Street - M3
Sydney Close - E11
Sydney Place - E11
Sydney Street - E11
Symons Street - F11

Tabard Street - P9/Q10
Tabernacle Street - Q4
Tachbrook Street - J11
Tadema Road - C13
Talacre - Map 10
Talbot Road - A5/B5
Talbot Road - Az6
Talbot Square - D6
Talma Road - Map 18
Tamworth Farm Lane - A12
Tanner Street - R9
Tanza Road - Map 9
Taplow Street - P3
Tavistock Crescent - Az5/A5
Tavistock Place - L4
Tavistock Road - A5
Tavistock Square - K4
Tavistock Street - L6/7
Taviton Street - K4
Tedworth Square - F12
Temple Avenue - N7
Temple Place - M7
Tennis Street - P9
Tetcott Road - C13
Thames Street - Map 19
Thanet Street - L3
Thaxton Road - A12
Thayer Street - G5
The Avenue - Map 19
The Boltons - C11
The Broad Walk - C7/8
The Cut- N8
The Grange - R10
The Lane - C2
The Little Boltons - C11
The Mall - J8/K8
The Vale - D12
Theberton Street - N1/O1
Theed Street - N8
Theobald's Road - L5/M5
Thessaly Road - J13
Thirleby Road - J10
Thomas More Street - S8
Thorn Place - F5

Thornburn Square - S11
Thorndike Close - C13
Thorney Crescent - E13
Thorney Street - L10
Thornhill Road - N1
Thrale Street - P8
Threadneedle Street - Q6
Three Kings Yard - H6
Throgmorton Avenue - Q6
Throgmorton Street - Q6
Thurloe Place - E10
Thurloe Square - E10
Thurlow Street - Q12
Thurtle Road - S2
Tilney Street - G7
Tinworth Street - L11
Tisdall Place - Q11
Tite Street - F12
Tiverton Street - O10
Tolpuddle Street - N2
Tonbridge Street - L3
Tooley Street - Q8/R8/9
Tor Gardens - A8
Torrington Place - K4
Torrington Square - K4
Tothill Street - K9
Tottenham Court Road - J4/K5
Tottenham Street - J5
Tournay Road - A13
Tower Bridge - R8
Tower Bridge Approach - R8/S7
Tower Bridge Road - Q10/R8-10
Tower Hill - R7
Tower Street - K6
Townsend Street - Q11
Toynbee Street - S5/6
Trafalgar Avenue - R12/13
Trafalgar Square - K7
Trafalgar Street - P12/Q12
Transept Street - E5
Trebovir Road - B11
Tregunter Road - C12
Trevor Place - E9
Trinity Gardens - Map 18
Trinity Square - R7
Trinity Street - P9/10
Triton Square - J4
Trump Street - P6
Tryon Street - F11
Tudor Street - N6
Tufton Street - K10
Turks Row - F11/G11
Turnmill Street - N5/O5
Turrens Street - N2
Tyers Street - M10
Tyer's Terrace - M11/12
Tysoe Street - N3

Ufford Street - N9
Ufton Road - Q1
Ulster Place - H4
Undershaft - Q6/R6
Underwood Street - P3
Union Street - O8/P8
Union Walk - R3
University Street - J4/K4
Upcerne Road - C13
Upper Belgrave Street - G9
Upper Berkeley Street - F6
Upper Brook Street - G7
Upper Cheyne Row - E12
Upper Ground - N7/8
Upper Harley Street - H4
Upper James Street - J6
Upper Marsh - M9
Upper Montagu Street - F5
Upper Phillimore Gardens - A8/9
Upper Street - N2/O1/2
Upper Thames Street - O7/P7
Upper Wimpole Street - H5
Upper Woburn Place - K3/4
Urlwin Street - O13/P13
Usborne Mews - M13
Uverdale Road - C13
Uxbridge Street - A7

Valentine Place - N9
Vandon Street - J9
Vanston Place - A13
Varndell Street - J3
Vaughan Way - S7
Vauxhall Bridge - K12/L12
Vauxhall Bridge Road - J10/11/K11
Vauxhall Grove - L12
Vauxhall Street - M11/12
Vauxhall Walk - L11/M11
Venables Street - E4
Vere Street - H6
Vernon Rise - M3
Verulam Street - N5
Vicarage Gate - B8
Victoria Embankment - L7/8/M7/N7
Victoria Garden Mews - B7
Victoria Grove - C9
Victoria Road - C9/3 C9
Victoria Square - H9
Victoria Street - H10/J10/K9
Vigo Street - J7
Villa Road - Map 18
Villa Street - Q12

Villiers Street - L7/8
Vincent Square - J10/11/K10/11
Vincent Street - K10
Vincent Terrace - O2
Vine Street - J7
Vining Road - Map 18
Violet Hill - C2/D2
Virgil Street - M10
Virginia Road - R4/S3/4

Waite Street - R13
Wakefield Street - L3/4
Wakley Street - O3
Walbrook - P6/7
Walham Grove - A13/B12
Walmer Road - Ay6/7
Walnut Tree Walk - M10
Walpole Street - F11
Walterton Road - A3/4
Walton Close - L13
Walton Street - E10/F10
Walworth Place - P12
Walworth Road - O11/P11/12
Wandon Road - C13
Wandsworth Road - K13
Wardour Street - J6/K6/7
Warlock Road - A3/4
Warner Street - N4
Warren Street - J4
Warrington Crescent - C3/4
Warwick Avenue - C4/D4/5
Warwick Crescent - C5
Warwick Gardens - A10
Warwick Lane - O6
Warwick Place - C4
Warwick Road - A10/11/B11
Warwick Square - J11
Warwick Street - J7
Warwick Way - H11/J11
Waterford Road - B13
Waterloo Bridge - M7
Waterloo Place - K7/8
Waterloo Road - M8/N8/9
Waterloo Terrace - O1
Watling Street - P6
Watton Place - F9
Waverley Place - D2
Waverton Street - H7
Webb Street - Q10
Webber Row - N9
Webber Street - N9/O9
Weighhouse Street - G6/H6
Welbeck Street - H5
Welbeck Way - H5
Well Road - Map 9
Well Walk - Map 9
Wellington Place - E2

Wellington Road - D2/E2
Wellington Row - S3
Wellington Square - F11
Wellington Street - L6/7
Wells Street - J5/6
Wells Way - Q13
Wenlock Road - P2/3
Wenlock Street - P2/Q2
Wentworth Street - R6/S6
Werrington Street - K2/3
West Carriage Drive - E7
West Cromwell Road - A11
West Smithfield - O5
West Square - N10
West Street - G9
West Street - K6
West Tenter Street - S7
Westborne Crescent - D6
Westbourne Park Road - A5/B5
Westbourne Gardens - B5
Westbourne Grove - A6/B6
Westbourne Park Road - Az5/A5
Westbourne Park Villas - B5
Westbourne Street - D6
Westbourne Terrace - C5/2 D6
Westcott Road - O12
Western Road - Map 18
Westgate Terrace - B12
Westminster Bridge - L9
Westminster Bridge Road - M9/N9
Westmoreland Road - P12/13
Westmoreland Street - H5
Westmoreland Terrace - H11/12
Weston Rise - M3
Weston Street - Q9/10
Westway A40 (M) - Az6/A4/B5/C5
Wetherby Gardens - C11
Weymouth Mews - H5
Weymouth Street - G5/H5
Weymouth Terrace - S2/3
Wharf Road - P2/3
Wharfedale Road - L2/M2
Wharton Street - M3
Wheatsheaf Lane - L13
Wheeler Street - R4/5
Whetstone Park - M5
Whidborne Street - L3
Whiskin Street - O3
Whistlers Avenue - D13/E13
Whiston Road - R2/S2
Whitcomb Street - K7
White Church Lane - S6
White Hart Street - N11

White Horse Street - H8
White Lion Hill - O7
White Lion Street - N2
Whitechapel High Street - S6
Whitechapel Road - S6
Whitecross Street - P4/5
Whitefriars Street - N6
Whitehall - L8/9
Whitehall Place - L8
Whiteheads Grove - F11
White's Gardens - Q9/R9
White's Row - R5
Whitfield Street - J4-6 K5
Whitgift Street - L11/M11
Whitmore Road - R2
Whittlesey Street - N8
Wickham Street - M11
Wicklow Street - M3
Widley Road - B3
Wigmore Place - H5
Wigmore Street - G6
Wilcox Road - K13/L13
Wild Court - L6
Wild Street - L6
Wild's Rent - Q10
Wilfred Street - J9
Wilkes Street - S5
William IV Street - L7
William Mews - G9
William Road - J3
William Street - F8/9
Willoughby Road - Map 9
Willow Brook Rd - S13
Willow Place - J10
Willow Road - Map 9
Willow Street - Q4
Willow Walk - R11
Wilmington Square - N3/4
Wilmot Place - Map 10
Wilson Street - Q5
Wilton Crescent - G9
Wilton Mews - G9
Wilton Place - G9
Wilton Road - H10/J10
Wilton Row - G9
Wilton Street - H9
Wilton Street - Q1
Wiltshire Road - Map 18
Wimbourne Street - Q2
Wimpole Mews - H5
Wimpole Street - H5
Winchester Street - H11/J12
Windmill Street - K5
Windsor Terrace - P3
Winsland Street - D5
Winsley Street - J6
Woburn Place - L4
Woburn Square - K4
Woburn Walk - K3

Wolseley Street - S9
Wood Street - P6
Woodbridge Street - O4
Woodchester Square - B4
Woodfall Street - F11
Woodfall Street - F11
Woods Mews - G6/7
Woodseer Street - S5
Woodsford Square - Az8
Woodstock Street - H6
Wooler Street - P12/Q12
Wootton Street - N8
Worfield Street - E13
Worfield Street - E13
Worgan Street - L11
Wornington Road - Az4
Worship Street - Q4/5/R5
Wren Street - M4
Wrights Lane - B9
Wyclif Street - O3
Wymering Road - B3
Wyndham Place - F5
Wyndham Street - F5
Wynford Road - M2
Wyvil Road - L13

Yalding Road - S10/11
Yardley Street - N4
Yeoman's Row - E10
York House Place - B8
York Road - M8/9
York Street - F5/5 G5
York Terrace East - G4/H4
York Terrace West - G4
York Way - L2
Young Street - B9/3 B9

Zoar Street - O8